RELIGIONS IN THE UK
2001–03

edited by

Paul Weller

researched by

Eileen Fry, Michele Wolfe
and Paul Weller

Published by the Multi-Faith Centre at the University of Derby
in association with
the Inter Faith Network for the United Kingdom

ISBN 0 901437 96 4

Published by the Multi-Faith Centre at the University of Derby
in association with
the Inter Faith Network for the United Kingdom
(Registered Charity number 296773).

The Multi-Faith Centre at the University of Derby,
Kedleston Road, Derby, DE22 1GB.

In association with
The Inter Faith Network for the United Kingdom,
5-7 Tavistock Place, London, WC1H 9SN.

Typeset by Debbie Martin and Indexed by David Bush,
University of Derby

Printed by MWL Print Group Limited, Pontypool, South Wales

SYMBOLS TABLE

SYMBOL	RELIGION	DESCRIPTION
	BAHÁ'Í	**Nine Pointed Star –** the number nine has particular significance for Bahá'ís, being known as "the number of Bah" . The Arabic letters of the word "Bah", the first part of the title of the founder of the Bahá'í faith, Bahá'u'lláh, add up to nine in the Abjad notation.
	BUDDHISM	**Wheel of Law and Truth –** An eight spoked wheel with the spokes symbolising the eight-fold path, the Middle Way, propounded by the Buddha. By following the Middle Way a Buddhist may obtain Moksha and thus escape the cyclical nature of rebirth.
	CHRISTIANITY	**Cross –** Of prime significance to the Christian Church because of the belief that the crucifixion of Jesus was the ultimate expression of God's love for humanity. Crosses can be found in a variety of forms and may depict the Crucified Christ or may be plain - symbolising the resurrection.
	HINDUISM	**Om (Aum) –** The utmost sacred symbol in Hinduism. Regarded as bija (seed) of all mantras. The three phonetic elements (AUM), connected but remaining distinct are said to represent Shiva, Vishnu and Brahma, respectively the destroyer, the creator and the sustainer.
	ISLAM	**Crescent moon and star –** Introduced as an emblem of the Islamic faith by the Ottomans, the constantly regenerating moon is a reflection of God's everlasting purpose and control. Portrayed with the star the symbol represents divine authority and paradise. Just as the moon and stars are guiding lights so too is Islam.
	JAINISM	**Palm –** The raised hand is a symbol of protection and blessing. In Jain belief there have been twenty-four great teachers called Tirthankaras. Thus the wheel is divided into twenty-four segments. Central to the wheel is the word ahimsa, meaning non-violence and reverence for life, one of the five principles of Jainism.
	JUDAISM	**Menorah –** Mosaic seven-branched candelabrum which indicates divine presence. According to Josephus the seven branches represent the sun, the moon and the planets and also the seven days of the week. The Star of David, an equilateral hexagram, originally known as the Seal of Solomon, is found on the base of the branches.
	SIKHISM	**Khanda –** The double edged sword in the centre signifies truth, strength, freedom and justice. The circle or chakkar represents the eternal and the two swords (Miri and Piri) represent political and spiritual sovereignty.
	ZOROASTRIANISM	**The Winged Figure –** The winged disc, representing divine protection is the symbol of Ahura Mazda. Some argue that the figure is not of Ahura Mazda but symbolises the divine grace people seek. In the left hand of the figure is a ring, representing cosmic sovereignty whilst the right hand is raised in a gesture of blessing.

Symbols take on different meanings for different people. What may be seen as being a "pretty picture" or object for one person may be seen as being something which invokes a feeling of reverence in another, in that it is a symbol which serves a religious purpose to people of a particular community. Religious symbols can be found across all religious communities in their beliefs and practices and their arts and cultures. Indeed some religious communities may share particular symbols but will probably attach a slightly differing meaning to them. Therefore symbols are not and cannot be definitive, in that many symbols have a slight variation of form depending on context in which they appear. In many cases, however, the basic form of certain symbols have become synonymous with particular religions. The religious symbols found on the front cover of the directory come from a wide range of religious symbols and are some of the most common religious representations found among the world religions.

BIBLIOGRAPHY

Bowker, J (ed) *The Oxford Dictionary of World Religions*, Oxford University Press, Oxford and New York, 1997.

Cooper, J C, *An Illustrated Encyclopaedia of Traditional Symbols*, Thames and Hudson Limited, London, 1978.

Giddens, A, *Sociology* (2nd edition), Polity Press, Cambridge, 1993.

Tressider, J, *The Hutchinson Dictionary of Symbols*, Helicon Publishing Ltd, 1997.

CONTENTS

Page references for the more detailed sections within each chapter can be found in the left hand column at the start of each major chapter and in the same column at the start of the Regional and Local organisation listings. More detailed page references for sub-sections can be found in the Topic Index (in the case of the textual material) and in the Local Guide Index (in the case of the listings).

PREFACE 7

USER'S GUIDE 15

RELIGIOUS LANDSCAPE OF THE UK

The Variety of Religions 23
The Historical Development of a
    Religiously Plural Country 25
Places of Worship 29
Size of the Religious Communities 30
Statistics On Places of Worship 35
Religions in Public Life: The Christian
    Inheritance 40
Religions in Public Life: An Evolving
    Diversity 42
Religion and the Law 46
Religious Communities and Education 49
The Challenge of the Future 54
Further Information 55
Further Reading 56

MAKING CONTACTS, ORGANISING EVENTS AND CONSULTATIONS

Introduction 63
Making Contact 63
Arranging a Multi-Faith Event 64
Arranging Multi-Faith Consultations
    or Panels 68
Producing Guidelines 69
Further Help 69

VISITING PLACES OF WORSHIP AND HOSTING VISITS

Introduction 71
Visiting Places of Worship 71
Hosting Visits To Places of Worship 77
Further Help 77

INTER-FAITH ACTIVITY IN THE UK

Introduction 79
Types of Inter-Faith Initiative 79
Multi-Lateral Initiatives:
    UK and International 80
Bilateral Initiatives 83
Trilateral Initiatives 84
Northern Ireland, Scotland and Wales 84
Local Inter-Faith Activity 84
Faith Communities and Inter-Faith
    Relations 85
Pattern of Involvement in Inter-Faith
    Activities 86
Special Issues 87
The New Millennium as a Time for
    Focus On Shared Values 89
Towards the Future 90
Building Good Relations with
People of Different Faiths and Beliefs 91
Further Reading 92
Inter Faith United Kingdom
    Organisations 95
Inter-Faith Regional and Local
    Organisations 101

THE BAHÁ'Í COMMUNITY

Introducing Bahá'ís in the UK 111
Bahá'í United Kingdom Organisations 120
Bahá'í Local Spiritual Assemblies 126

THE BUDDHIST COMMUNITY

Introducing Buddhists in the UK 139
Buddhist United Kingdom
    Organisations 158
Buddhist Regional and Local Centres
    and Organisations 169

THE CHRISTIAN COMMUNITY

Introducing Christians in the UK   203
Christian United Kingdom Organisations   237
Christian National and Regional
    Organisations   251

THE HINDU COMMUNITY

Introducing Hindus in the UK   297
Hindu United Kingdom Organisations   317
Hindu Regional and Local Organisations
    and Mandirs   323

THE JAIN COMMUNITY

Introducing Jains in the UK   357
Jain United Kingdom
Organisations   366
Jain Regional and Local
    Organisations and Temples   369

THE JEWISH COMMUNITY

Introducing Jews in the UK   375
Jewish United Kingdom Organisations   391
Jewish Regional and Local Organisations
    and Synagogues   402

THE MUSLIM COMMUNITY

Introducing Muslims in the UK   433
Muslim United Kingdom Organisations   449
Muslim Regional and Local Organisations
    and Mosques   467

THE SIKH COMMUNITY

Introducing Sikhs in the UK   549
Sikh United Kingdom Organisations   562
Sikh Regional and Local Organisations
    and Gurdwaras   566

THE ZOROASTRIAN COMMUNITY

Introducing Zoroastrians in the UK   587
Zoroastrian United Kingdom
    Organisations   598
Zoroastrian Regional and Local
    Organisations And Communities   599

SOME OTHER RELIGIOUS COMMUNITIES AND GROUPS

Introduction   601
Brahma Kumaris   603
Christian Scientists   605
Church of Jesus Christ of Latter-Day
    Saints   606
Jehovah's Witnesses   608
Namdhari Sikh Community   610
Pagans   613
Rastafarians   615
Ravidassia   616
Sant Nirankaris   618
Sathya Sai Service Organisation   619
Valmikis   620

FINDING OUT MORE: SOME OTHER RELEVANT PUBLICATIONS AND RESOURCES

Finding Out More   623
General Texts On Religions   625
Directories of Religious Organisations   628
Directories of Ethnic Minority
    Organisations   631
Some Relevant Resource Organisations   633
Some Relevant Publications   638

ACKNOWLEDGEMENTS   643

INDEXES

Topic Index   651
Significant Word Index   661
UK and National Organisation Index   679
Local Guide Index   689

PREFACE

Religions in the UK: A Ground-Breaking Project

The initial 1993 edition of *Religions in the UK* was the first comprehensive directory of national and local religious organisations and places of worship covering the United Kingdom's major faith communities. It was widely welcomed as a new resource for a multi-faith society and was followed by an updated and extended 1997 edition. Religious organisation representatives, journalists, academics and educators, as well as those working in community relations and service provision, are among the many for whom it has already become a standard reference book.

The 2001 Edition

This new edition of the directory, like the first and second editions, is designed to assist and encourage the development of inter-faith contacts and dialogue in the UK and to facilitate the participation in public life of the religious communities of this country. It develops and updates the previous editions in ways suggested by users of these editions who participated in a user survey.

The 2001 edition contains listings for over three and a half thousand organisations. This is fewer than the previous edition, because for this edition an editorial decision was taken to include listings only if organisations had themselves confirmed their contact details directly with the project, or else if their details could be positively verified from other reliable sources. However, whilst fewer organisations are listed this approach has enhanced the accuracy of the present edition. It also means that there is greater detail about many of those which are listed.

Finally, the preparation of a new edition has given an opportunity to update the descriptions of each religion in the UK to ensure accuracy at the time of writing. The chapters on "The Religious Landscape of the UK" and also on "Inter-Faith Activity in the UK" have been substantially rewritten to reflect developments in the four years since the publication of the last edition.

Religions in the UK is now also available by subscription over the Internet in a regularly updated electronic version as *Religions in the UK: On-Line*. Further details and a free sample tour of the electronic version can be accessed via the University of Derby's *MultiFaithNet* Internet site, at http://www.multifaithnet.org. Data from *Religions in the UK* is also available as part of the *KnowUK* Internet information service at http://www.knowuk.co.uk, which was developed for libraries and public authorities by the electronic publishers Bell and Howell. In these and other ways, the original Multi-Faith Directory Research Project that lies behind this publication has extended and developed the ways in which information in the directory is being made available.

The Partnership Behind the Directory

Religions in the UK is a product of ten years co-operation between the Religious Resource and Research Centre of the University of Derby and the Inter Faith Network for the UK.

The Religious Resource and Research Centre is a designated research centre of the University of Derby located in the School of Education, Human Sciences and Law. Its research focuses on personal, social, and values issues relating to religious diversity. It has undertaken a range of policy-related research projects concerned with religion. These include the Home Office commissioned research project on Religious Discrimination in England and Wales. The publication of the present edition is under the auspices of the new Multi-Faith Centre at the University of Derby (see page 9).

The Inter Faith Network was founded in 1987. It works alongside over ninety member organisations to increase mutual understanding and respect between the faith communities of the world religions represented in the UK today. It also works more widely within society to promote an appreciation of the importance of religious identity and inter-faith understanding.

The Consultative Process

The materials about each religion in the UK are the product of a lengthy, extensive and careful process of consultation and debate that has taken place over the ten years of the project's life. This process has involved a wide range of consultants who are listed in the "Acknowledgements" chapter.

An important principle of effective inter-faith dialogue is that partners in dialogue should be free to define themselves. The editorial process for this directory has tried to take into account as fully as possible the perspectives and sensitivities of all the adherents of the religions included. At the same time, the drafting process has benefited from the expertise and advice of religious practitioners and other academic experts working in the relevant fields.

The Challenge of the Task

Describing such a range of religions and traditions within a single volume is a challenging and sensitive task. Similarly, it is a complex and extensive operation to gather data on thousands of their organisations. We have aimed for the highest degree of accuracy possible, but if there are omissions and accidental inaccuracies, we apologise and ask readers to let us know. We believe, however, that a high level of comprehensiveness and accuracy has been achieved and that *Religions in the UK* will continue to be a standard reference work and resource for building a society that is characterised by mutual understanding and respect. As the significance of religion in public life becomes increasingly recognised at local, national and European levels, it is our hope that this edition of the directory will prove to be of particular value in all sectors of society where the resources of religious organisations might, in partnership with others, be able to make a contribution of distinctive value to the wider common good.

Paul Weller
Professor of Inter-Religious Relations
Editor and Director, Multi-Faith
Directory Research Project
Religious Resource and Research
Centre, School of Education, Human
Sciences and Law, University of Derby

THE MULTI-FAITH CENTRE AT THE UNIVERSITY OF DERBY

■ The gestation of the concept of the Multi-Faith Centre, based at the University of Derby, is almost coextensive with the history of the *Directory* project. The group within which the idea germinated was a liaison committee between the University and a range of different faith communities, established to provide advice to the University on its policies and procedures, and its teaching and research in Religious Studies (including the *Directory* project itself). The development of the Multi-Faith Centre thus exemplifies the values which lie at the heart of the *Directory*.

■ It is hoped to complete the building by the end of 2002, following a fund-raising campaign which has been running for two years. The Centre exists to promote understanding and mutual respect between members of different faith communities through dialogue, courses, conferences, workshops, exhibitions, open festivals, and dramatic performance. It is intended as a national focus for dialogue, as well as a local and regional centre.

■ The project has been overseen by members of the local Bahá'í, Buddhist, Christian (Anglican, Roman Catholic, and Free Church), Hindu, Jewish, Muslim and Sikh communities, working together with representatives of the University. (To this grouping are now added Russian Orthodox Christian, Unitarian, and Brahma Kumari representatives.) The design brief was drawn up and an architectural competition adjudicated by members of these different communities. The winning design is conceived as a village of organically formed spaces, to be operated on a "time-sharing" basis.

■ The Centre has been established as a charitable company, limited by guarantee, in a way which ensures that the different communities are genuine stakeholders in the project. The Centre is being constructed on land gifted for 125 years, close to the main entrance to the buildings on the main campus of the University.

■ The planned mode of operation of the Multi-Faith Centre makes it an ideal location for the future development of the *Directory* and the maintenance of the *MultiFaithNet Internet Service* (giving access to the electronic version *Religions in the UK: On-Line*). The Multi-Faith Centre looks forward to the challenge of taking these projects forward.

Contact: The Centre Manager, The Multi-Faith Centre, c/o The University of Derby, Kedleston Road, Derby DE22 1GB

THE STUDY OF RELIGIONS
AT THE UNIVERSITY OF DERBY

Religious and Philosophical Studies Subject Area - Division of Humanities and Social Sciences

The Religious and Philosophical Studies Subject Area is a part of the Division of Humanities and Social Sciences within the University's School of Education, Human Sciences and Law. Religious and Philosophical Studies in the University is offered by the University from Foundation/Access level through undergraduate and taught postgraduate study to doctoral research. The School also offers Religious Education within the BEd and PGCE primary teacher training programme of the Division of Education.

- **Religious Studies in the University's Foundation/Access Programme**
  Religious Studies is available as one of the subjects on offer within the University's Foundation/Access programme for students with non-standard academic backgrounds.

- **Religions: Culture and Belief, Major, Joint and Minor pathways in the BA/BSc (Hons) Combined Subject programme**
  At undergraduate level/Religions: Culture and Belief is available within the University's Combined Subject BA/BSc degrees, as a major, joint or minor programme that can be taken in combination with other subjects.

- **BA (Hons) Study of Religions**
  A specialist undergraduate degree which combines phenomenological, sociological, and philosophical approaches to the study of religion, allowing both study of particular religions and cross-religious themes, as well as opportunities for fieldwork.

- **MA in Religion Within a Plural Society**
  The programme has been offered since 1992 under its original name of the MA in Religious Pluralism. It provides an opportunity to engage critically with both the social and the religious issues posed by religious plurality within the context of secularity.

- **MA in Pastoral Studies**
  A programme of study for those involved with, and interested in, pastoral care, including those in religious leadership roles and those in secular care organisations who wish to take account of the religious needs of the individuals and communities with whom they work.

- **Doctor of Religious Care/Ministry**
  A professional/doctorate of practice, offering those engaged in religious care and ministry, of all religions and none, the opportunity to undertake doctoral level study rooted in advanced reflection on practice.

- **MPhil and PhD Research**
  Supervision is offered within the Religious Resource and Research Centre, a designated Research Centre of the University of Derby, for full and part-time research in religion. Centre staff have particular research interests and specialisms which include: inter-faith dialogue; missiology; religions and ethnicity; religions, state and society; religion and the social sciences; Islam in Britain; religions and education; the Hindu tradition; Sikhism in the modern world; religion in India; Parsees and Zoroastrianism.

Further information available from: Professor Richard King by phone on 01332-592119 and by Email: r.king@derby.ac.uk or from the School of Education, Human Sciences and Law, University of Derby, Mickleover, Derby DE3 5GX. Tel: 01332-622231, Fax: 01332-622746, http://www.derby.ac.uk

RESEARCH IN RELIGION AT THE UNIVERSITY OF DERBY

The Religious Resource and Research Centre is a designated Research Centre of the University of Derby. The Centre researches into the religious dimensions of social and individual life with a special focus upon religious and social issues related to religious plurality; pastoral care in a plural context; and issues of values. The spirit and practice of dialogue are fundamental to the Centre's activities which it conducts in co-operation with a wide range of academic disciplines, religious communities and other insitutions.

- **Multi-Faith Directory Research Project**
  The project which lies behind this directory commenced in 1991 and is a joint project between the Centre and the Inter Faith Network for the United Kingdom, of which the Centre is an affiliated organisation.

- **Religious Discrimination in England and Wales Research Project**
  This project was commissioned by the Home Office in order to: assess the evidence of the nature and extent of discrimination on the basis of religion; describe the patterns shown by this evidence, including its overall scale, the main victims, the main perpetrators, and the main ways in which discrimination manifests; indicate the extent to which religious discrimination overlaps with racial discrimination; and identify the broad range of policy options available for dealing with religious discrimination.

- *MultiFaithNet*
  MultiFaithNet (http://www.multifaithnet.org) is a web site developed by the Religious Resource and Research Centre which is a self-access tool providing information and resources on religions and the relationships between them, and provides a virtual space for inter-faith dialogue. It includes, on a subscription basis, access to the electronic version of the directory, *Religions in the UK: On-Line.*

Further information available from: Professor John Hinnells by phone on 01332-592131and by Email: j.hinnells@derby.ac.uk or from the School of Education, Human Sciences and Law, University of Derby, Mickleover, Derby DE3 5GX. Tel: 01332-622231, Fax: 01332-622746, http://www.derby.ac.uk

THE INTER FAITH NETWORK FOR THE UK

The Inter Faith Network was established in 1987. It works with its member bodies to combat inter religious prejudice and intolerance and to help make Britain a country marked by mutual understanding and respect between religions where all can practise their faith with integrity.

The Network:

- Provides information on faith communities and on inter faith affairs
- Advises the public and private sectors on multi faith projects and inter faith issues
- Publishes materials designed to help people working in the religious and inter faith sectors
- Fosters inter faith co-operation on social issues
- Holds regular national meetings of its member bodies where social and religious questions of concern to the different faith communities can be examined together and sets up multi faith working groups, seminars and conferences to pursue these where appropriate
- Links over ninety member organisations including representative bodies from the different faith communities; national inter faith organisations; local inter faith groups; academic institutions and bodies concerned with multi faith education.

The Network has also worked with other organisations on a number of projects, including in the recent past the Inner Cities Religious Council, the Local Government Association, the National Association of SACREs and the Religious Education Council for England and Wales. Its partnership with the Religious Resource and Research Centre at the University of Derby lies behind *Religions in the UK*.

Further information available from: The Inter Faith Network for the UK,
5-7 Tavistock Place,
London, WC1H 9SN
Tel (020) 7388 0008
Fax (020) 7387 7968
Email: ifnet@interfaith.org.uk
Internet: http://www.interfaith.org.uk

MEMBER ORGANISATIONS OF
THE INTER FAITH NETWORK FOR THE UK

FAITH COMMUNITY
REPRESENTATIVE BODIES

Afro West Indian United Council of Churches
Arya Pratinidhi Sabha (UK)
Bahá'í Community of the United Kingdom
Board of Deputies of British Jews
Buddhist Society
Churches' Agency for Inter Faith Relations in Scotland
Churches' Commission for Inter-Faith Relations (Council
　of Churches for Britain and Ireland)
Council of African and Afro-Caribbean Churches (UK)
Friends of the Western Buddhist Order
Hindu Council (UK)
Imams and Mosques Council (UK)
Islamic Cultural Centre, Regent's Park, London
Jain Samaj Europe
Jamiat-e-Ulama Britain (Association of Muslim Scholars)
Muslim Council of Britain
National Council of Hindu Temples
Network of Buddhist Organisations (UK)
Network of Sikh Organisations (UK)
Quaker Committee for Christian and Inter Faith Relations
Roman Catholic Committee for Other Faiths of the
　Bishops' Conference of England and Wales
Sikh Missionary Society (UK)
Sri Lankan Sangha Sabha of Great Britain
Swaminaryan Hindu Mission
Unitarian and Free Christian Churches Interfaith
　Subcommittee
Vishwa Hindu Parishad (UK)
World Ahl ul-Bayt Islamic League
World Islamic Mission (UK)
Zoroastrian Trust Funds of Europe

INTER FAITH ORGANISATIONS

Calamus Foundation
Christians Aware Interfaith Programme
Council of Christians and Jews
Interfaith Foundation
International Interfaith Centre
London Society of Jews and Christians
Maimonides Foundation
Northern Ireland Inter Faith Forum
Scottish Interfaith Council
Three Faiths Forum
United Religions Initiative (Britain & Ireland)
Westminster Interfaith
World Conference on Religion and Peace
　(UK Chapter)
World Congress of Faiths

LOCAL INTER FAITH GROUPS:

Bedford Council of Faiths
Birmingham Council of Faiths
Bolton Interfaith Council
Bradford Concord Inter Faith Society
Brent Interfaith
Brighton and Hove Interfaith Contact Group
Bristol Interfaith Group
Cambridge Inter-Faith Group
Cardiff Interfaith Association
Cleveland Interfaith Group
Coventry Inter Faith Group
Derby Open Centre Multi-Faith Group
Dudley Council of Faiths
Glasgow Sharing of Faiths Group
Gloucestershire Inter Faith Action
Harrow Inter-Faith Council
Kirklees and Calderdale Inter-Faith Fellowship
Leeds Concord Inter Faith Fellowship
Leicester Council of Faiths
Loughborough Council of Faiths
Luton Council of Faiths
Manchester Inter Faith Group
Medway and Maidstone Inter-Faith Group
Merseyside Inter Faith Group
Newham Association of Faiths
Nottingham Inter-Faith Council
Oxford Round Table of Religions
Peterborough Inter-Faith Council
Reading Inter-Faith Group
Redbridge Council of Faiths
Richmond Inter-Faith Group
Rochdale Interfaith Action
Sheffield Interfaith
South London Inter Faith Group
Tyne and Wear Racial Equality Council Inter Faith Panel
Watford Inter Faith Association

EDUCATIONAL AND ACADEMIC
BODIES

Bharatiya Vidya Bhavan
Centre for the Study of Islam and Christian-Muslim
　Relations, Selly Oak, Birmingham
Community Religions Project, University of Leeds
Institute of Jainology
Islamic Foundation, Leicester
National Association of SACREs
Religious Education Council forEngland and Wales
Shap Working Party on World Religions in Education
Study Centre for Christian-Jewish Relations (Sisters of Sion)
University of Derby Religious Resource and Research
　Centre

STOP PRESS

BUDDHIST LISTINGS
Scotland

Samye Dzong Edinburgh
15 Rosebery Crescent, Edinburgh EH15 5JY
Tel: (0131) 3130304
Contact: Mr Ian Tullis
Position: Chairman
Activities: Worship/meditation, resource, visits, newsletter, inter-faith
Traditions: Tibetan
Movements: Kagyupa
Affiliations: Samye Ling Tibetan Centre

JEWISH LISTINGS
North West

Blackpool United Hebrew Congregation
The Synagogue, Leamington Road, Blackpool FY3 9DX
Tel: (01253) 392382
Contact: Revd David Braunold
Position: Rabbi
Activities: Worship, resource, media, visits, youth, inter-faith
Traditions: Orthodox
Other Languages: Hebrew
Affiliations: Manchester Jewish Representative Council

MUSLIM LISTINGS
North West

Werneth Mosque and Urdu School
116 Manchester Road, Werneth, Oldham OL9 7AX
Tel: (0161) 6245448
Contact: Mr A Khan
Position: President
Contact Tel: (07971) 307196
Activities: Worship/practice/meditation
Other Languages: Urdu, Punjabi

USER'S GUIDE

INTRODUCTION 15

RELIGIONS COVERED BY THE DIRECTORY 15

INTRODUCTIONS TO THE RELIGIONS IN THE UK 15

CALENDARS AND FESTIVALS 16

TRANSLITERATION, TRANSLATION AND DIACRITICAL MARKINGS 16

USING THE ORGANISATION LISTINGS 17

UNDERSTANDING THE ORGANISATION LISTINGS 19

HOW THE ORGANISATION LISTINGS WERE COMPILED 21

FINDING OUT MORE: SOME OTHER RELEVANT PUBLICATIONS AND RESOURCES 22

INDEXES 22

FURTHER READING AND HELP 22

INTRODUCTION

This chapter explains the layout of the directory and what the reader will find in its texts and listings.

RELIGIONS COVERED BY THE DIRECTORY

The directory contains basic information about Bahá'ís, Buddhists, Christians, Hindus, Jains, Jews, Muslims, Sikhs and Zoroastrians in the UK. It also covers inter-faith activities, organisations, groups and resources.

There are many other kinds of formal and informal religious belief and practice in the UK, but it is not possible to be totally comprehensive within the constraints of a single volume. However, the chapter on "Some Other Religious Communities and Groups" provides information on some of these and gives signposts for further information. For information on New Religious Movements, readers are referred to the specialist information service, INFORM, at Houghton Street, London, WC2A 2AE, Tel: (020) 7955 7654 (and see display page 621 at the end of "Some Other Religious Communities and Groups" chapter).

INTRODUCTIONS TO THE RELIGIONS IN THE UK

The materials about each tradition have been prepared with the help of religious practitioners and academic specialists to provide a starting place for the interested enquirer. More detailed information about each religion can be found in the books and articles suggested in the sections on "Further Reading"; from religious organisations themselves; and from the education and information organisations listed in the chapter on "Finding Out More: Some Other Relevant Publications and Resources".

The introductory chapters to the religions generally follow a standard format for ease of reference. Slight variations in approach and internal balance reflect some differences concerning how a specific religion and its tradition can best be presented to the general reader. However, normally, the main sections in each chapter are:

In the UK

Basic historical, ethnic, linguistic and statistical information.

Origins and Development

The historical origins of the religion in terms of its significant or founding figure or figures and an outline of some of the principal features of its global and historical development.

Sources of Beliefs and Practices

The teachings, scriptures and religious structures which are seen as authoritative within the religion.

Key Beliefs

The religion's central understandings of the nature of the human and the divine or the ultimate, as well as its basic understandings of the purpose of existence.

Traditions

The principal traditions of interpretation within the religion.

Life

How adherents are initiated into the religion and something of the way in which the religion shapes their everyday life in terms of ethics, family, food and similar matters.

Worship

Information on the buildings in which the religion's worship takes place and outlines of some of the forms of worship which occur within them.

Calendar and Festivals

The dating system of the religion, the rhythm of its year, and its major days of religious observance.

Organisation

Organisational patterns of the religion in the UK and descriptions of the roles of its religious personnel.

Further Reading

Details of a number of useful general introductions to the religion, together with a number of books and articles which particularly focus on the life of that religion in the UK.

CALENDARS AND FESTIVALS

The directory cannot list specific dates for every festival since many religious traditions operate according to calendars which differ from that used in public life in the UK and some do not determine the dates of their festivals far in advance. A calendar of festivals is produced annually by the Shap Working Party on World Religions in Education (available from the National Society's RE Centre, 36 Causton Street, London, SW1P 4AU, Tel: (020) 7932 1190 and see the display page 642 at the end of the chapter "Finding Out More: Some Other Relevant Publications and Resources"). Many religions also publish their own calendars.

In this directory, dates are given as CE (Common Era) rather than AD (Anno Domini), and BCE (Before Common Era) rather than BC (Before Christ), reflecting the increase in this usage. Thus, instead of 2001AD, one will find 2001CE.

TRANSLITERATION, TRANSLATION AND DIACRITICAL MARKINGS

The religious traditions covered in this directory all have scriptures and other important texts which were not originally written in English. For some religions, languages other than English remain the main medium for their religious discourse and practice. In the directory, such terms are given in italics in the original language in a transliterated form, together with an English approximation of their meaning as a translation.

Italics have also been used for English language terms which, although perhaps in more general usage, may have a specific religious meaning or overtone which might not be clear to English speakers from outside the tradition concerned. Personal names are not italicised, but the names of religious titles, of scriptures and of particular books within them are.

Apostrophes, inverted apostrophes, acute, grave and circumflex accents and a number of other markings are used in the transliterations, but other less well known diacritical markings of the kind often used in scholarly texts are not used. In the descriptions of the religions an attempt has been made to ensure consistency of transliteration and translation. In the organisational listings, however, there is variety since the directory has largely followed the spellings and transliterations supplied by the organisations rather than attempting to improve an editorial conformity.

USING THE ORGANISATION LISTINGS

After the introduction to each religion a listing is given of its organisations and places of worship, together with their contact details and other information. With the exception of the Christian listings, these are laid out in alphabetical order, in the following sequence:

UK-Wide Organisations

UK-wide organisations within each religion are listed in alphabetical order.

National, Regional and Local Organisations and Places of Worship

Local organisations and places of worship are listed within the chapter on each religion, sequentially by nation of the UK. Listings for England nationally, and then region by region come first, followed by listings for Northern Ireland, Scotland and Wales. In each case any bodies covering the whole of one of these nations are listed first, followed by bodies covering the whole of a region or of a county within it, and then by bodies operating at a city,

town or local level. These are listed in alphabetical order of town or city. Within each town or city organisations are then listed in alphabetical order by name.

Listings for **London** are, however, divided by borough and are then ordered alphabetically by their organisation names. The regional boundaries which are used for England correspond to those used used by the Government, for example, the areas covered by the Regional Development Agencies. The map on the following page indicates which counties and unitary authorities are located in each of the English regions.

England
North East
Yorkshire and the Humber
North West
East Midlands
West Midlands
East of England
London
South East
South West
Northern Ireland
Scotland
Wales

Local Inter Faith Listings

The local inter faith listings differ from those in other chapters. Where the place name of the contact address is not the same as that in their organisational title, they are listed in alphabetical order according to their area of operation. The London inter faith listings are also not subdivided into London boroughs.

Christian Listings .

The Christian listings differ from those in other chapters due to the sheer number of Christian organisations and places of worship in this country. UK-wide Christian organisations are laid out in alphabetical order within the following sections:

● Organisations known as *ecumenical instruments* and other groupings of *Churches* operating at a UK-wide level.

REGIONAL BOUNDARIES IN ENGLAND USED BY THE DIRECTORY

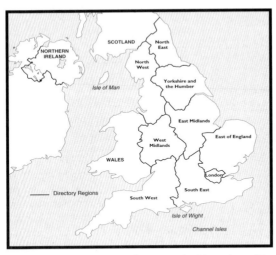

The following shows which counties and unitary authorities are located in each of the English regions.

★ For convenience, any listings for the Channel Islands will be found under the section on the South West region and for the Isle of Man under the North West region.

NORTH EAST
Darlington
Durham
Gateshead
Hartlepool
Middlesborough
Newcastle upon Tyne
North Tyneside
Nothumberland
Redcar and Cleveland
South Tyneside
Stockton on Tees
Sunderland

WEST MIDLANDS
Birmingham
Coventry
Dudley
Herefordshire
Sandwell
Shropshire
Solihull
Staffordshire
Stoke on Trent
Telford and Wrekin
Walsall
Warwickshire
Wolverhampton
Worcestershire

YORKSHIRE AND THE HUMBER
Barnsley
Bradford
Calderdale
Doncaster
East Riding of Yorkshire
Kingston upon Hull
Kirklees
Leeds
North East Lincolnshire
North Lincolnshire
North Yorkshire
Rotherham
Sheffield
Wakefield
York

EAST MIDLANDS
Derby city
Derbyshire
Leicester
Leicestershire
Lincolnshire
Northamptonshire
Nottingham
Nottinghamshire
Rutland

NORTH WEST★
Blackburn with Darwen
Blackpool
Bolton
Bury
Cheshire
Cumbria
Halton
Knowsley
Lancashire
Liverpool
Manchester
Oldham
Rochdale
Salford
Sefton
St Helens
Stockport
Tameside
Trafford
Warrington
Wigan
Wirral

EAST OF ENGLAND
Bedfordshire
Cambridgeshire
Essex
Hertfordshire
Luton
Norfolk
Peterborough
Southend on Sea
Suffolk
Thurrock

LONDON

SOUTH EAST
Bracknell Forest
Brighton and Hove
Buckinghamshire
East Sussex
Hampshire
Isle of Wight
Kent
Medway
Milton Keynes
Oxfordshire
Portsmouth
Reading
Slough
Southampton
Surrey
West Berkshire
West Sussex
Royal Windsor and
Maidenhead
Wokingham

SOUTH WEST★
Bath and North East
Somerset
Bournemouth
Bristol
Cornwall
Devon
Dorset
Gloucestershire
North Somerset
Plymouth
Poole
Somerset
South Gloucestershire
Swindon
Torbay
Wiltshire

- *Churches* operating at the level of the UK which are either directly or indirectly (through their affiliation to a full member organisation) part of an *ecumenical instrument* and some other Christian *Churches*.

- Networks, agencies and other bodies which are either directly or indirectly part of an ecumenical instrument.

There are no listings for local Christian organisations. Rather, regional level organisations are listed. These appear by nation of the UK and then by region. Within each region, regional *ecumenical instruments* appear in alphabetical order of their name, followed by regional *Church* structures also in alphabetical order of names. Finally, information is given on local Evangelical Fellowships and some other bodies, also in alphabetical order. Christian listings for London are not broken down by borough because most *Church* regional bodies cover more than one London borough.

The national and regional *Church* and ecumenical bodies can give more information about local Christian organisations and places of worship. The vast majority of Christian *Churches* produce their own national hand-books and directories. Many also have publications covering regional and local areas, as do a number of regional and local *ecumenical instruments*.

In addition to *Churches* and places of worship, there are many hundreds of Christian voluntary organisations. The *UK Christian Handbook* and the *Irish Christian Handbook* (see section on "Directories of Religious Organisations" in the chapter on "Finding Out More: Some Other Relevant Publications and Resources") give information on many that are active in the UK and in Ireland.

In addition, details of English and Welsh Christian and other religious buildings certified as places of worship and/or for the solemnisation of marriage can be obtained from the General Register Office of the Office for National Statistics' *Official List of Certified Places of Worship, parts I-IV*. There are no comparable lists for Scotland and Northern Ireland.

UNDERSTANDING THE ORGANISATION LISTINGS

Every organisation listing includes a name and an address or telephone number for the organisation or place of worship. For most organisations and places of worship there is also additional contact information. Further information given about such matters as activities and the particular traditions, movements, or social groupings within a religion varies according to the detail provided by the organisations.

It is important to note that the information, or lack of it, in these fields reflects the choices made by listed organisations. The directory has not imposed information editorially, even where this is widely known or could be deduced from other information supplied. In particular, with regard to the affiliations field, organisations may have more affiliations than are listed here, but what appears reflects the information prioritised by the organisations themselves.

National organisations have also had the option to add a note on matters which they feel it is particularly important for the directory user to know. Where this opportunity has been taken up, then self-descriptions of around thirty words follow.

The fields of information used are as follows:

Name:

Name of the organisation or place of worship.

Address:

Normally that of the organisation's offices in a public building or of the place of worship.

Telephone:

Normally that of an organisation's offices in a public building or the place of worship. Some places of worship and organisations do not have an office telephone, or the regular contact person for that organisation is not generally present at the place of worship. In such cases, the entry may well be the home or mobile telephone number of the contact person. If we have been informed of the home or mobile telephone number then this appears after the name and position of the contact person.

Fax:

Normally that of an organisation's office or of a place of worship.

Email:

An email address is given if one is available. Some places of worship and organisations do not have an email address, or the regular contact person for that organisation is not generally present at the place of worship. In such cases, the entry may well be the home email address of the contact person. If we have been informed of the home email address, then this appears after the name and position of the contact person.

Internet:

Where the organisation has a Web site on the Internet, then this Internet address is given.

Contact:

The person or office holder designated as the principal contact to handle incoming enquiries. This may be an individually named person or an office-holder such as a Chairperson, President or Secretary. Office holders may change (sometimes annually) but former officers will usually refer callers to the relevant new person.

Position:

A description of the position which the contact person holds in the organisation eg President, Secretary.

Contact Person's Telephone:

Home or mobile telephone number of the contact person if they are willing for this to be published.

Contact Person's Email:

Email address of the contact person if one is available.

Activities:

The following range of standard entries indicate what the nature and main activities of organisations and places of worship are: **worship/practice/meditation** (place of worship); **community centre** (activities open to the wider community); **central body** (of which branches are members); **umbrella body** (to which other organisations are affiliated); **youth** (activities organised for young people); **elderly** (activities organised for the elderly); **women** (activities organised for women); **newsletter/journal** (publication of regular newsletter or journal); **books** (the publication of books); **newspapers** (publication of newspapers); **radio** (broadcast of radio programmes); **television** (broadcast of television programmes); **visits** (welcomes pre-arranged visits by groups of visitors); **inter-faith** (participation in inter-faith activities); **resources** (academic/educational resources).

Community Audience:

For a resource organisation that is a media outlet, up to three religious community audiences served by the publication are given.

For most religions, there is also the heading:

Traditions:

The major broad grouping within the religion with which the organisation or place of worship identifies.

For a number of religions, there are also the headings:

Social Groups:

Any particular social group(s) with which the organisation or place of worship most closely identifies.

Movements:

Any specific movements with which the organisation or place of worship most closely identifies.

Other Languages:

Up to four languages other than English are

listed, if spoken by significant numbers within the organisation or at the place of worship. They appear in the order of most widespread use.

Affiliations:

The name of one local or regional body, one national body, and one international body within its own religious tradition to which the organisation or place of worship is affiliated. Where it is applicable, affiliations to the Inter Faith Network for the UK is also indicated.

Organisation Self-description:

For national organisations up to thirty words of self-description about the organisation. Any local organisation self-descriptions appear only in the Internet version of the directory, *Religions in the UK: On-Line*.

HOW THE ORGANISATION LISTINGS WERE COMPILED

We offered free inclusion in the directory, thus ensuring that its coverage is as wide as possible. The variety of information contained in each organisation's entry reflects both the questions asked of organisations in different religious traditions and the choices made by particular organisations about the kind of information which they wished to have published.

To understand the range of information provided in different entries on organisations and places of worship, it is important to explain something of the process by which they came to be included in their present form. The assistance of all those listed in the "Acknowledgements" chapter at the end of the directory helped the project in its aim of constructing a grid of interlocking information sources in order to ensure that as many organisations as possible would be identified and checked. Information was gathered and checked in the following ways:

- On the basis of the project's past use of questionnaires, a draft questionnaire for the 2001 edition was drawn up, including variations, where necessary, to tailor it to different religious traditions.

- The draft questionnaires were piloted with a sample of organisations and the results of the pilot were used to modify the original designs.

- Postal contact was made with each organisation about which the project had any contact information, with a request to complete and return the questionnaire form in a Freepost envelope provided or to reply stating that it did not wish to be included in the directory.

- Follow-up postcards were sent to the organisations and places of worship which did not respond to the original request to complete the questionnaire.

- A range of local inter-faith groups in various localities, project consultants from within the religious communities and from higher education institutions and religious organisations assisted in cross-checking the draft organisation entries.

- Additional forms were sent out during the course of the project as new information on additional organisations and places of worship came to light.

- In spring 2001, a draft entry was sent to every listed organisation that had returned a questionnaire, giving an opportunity to update and correct its draft entry or to ask for it to be omitted.

- In a further mailing in the summer of the 2001, a final opportunity was given to organisations that had not originally responded.

- Prior to publication, where possible, final telephone checks were made in respect of organisations which had not returned a questionnaire, but where the project had telephone contact information.

- Finally, other reliable published directories and other sources of reliable information were used to check the details of organisations which had not responded to the project, or with which the project could not, other than by post, make contact.

Level of Accuracy

Users will appreciate that not all organisations reply to correspondence and questionnaires, not all are contactable by telephone, and that contact details can and do change with the passage of time.

As a result, the absolute accuracy of all entries cannot be guaranteed. But as will be seen, the project has gone to considerable lengths to ensure that the entries are as accurate as possible. Those entries which have received a positive confirmation of their details by the project in 2001 are marked by an asterisk after the name of the organisation. Those without an asterisk have not been confirmed directly by the organisation but are included on the basis of verification from other reliable sources or on the basis of the best judgement of the project.

Apparent Omissions

We have also sought to respect the wishes of organisations that have requested that we do not include details about their existence, even where this information might be available elsewhere in the public domain. The small number of such requests may be the reason why some organisations known to directory users do not appear in the directory. Organisations were also given the opportunity to affirm their wish to be included in the paper-based version of the directory, but to decline to be included in the Internet version, *Religions in the UK: On-Line*.

FINDING OUT MORE: SOME OTHER RELEVANT PUBLICATIONS AND RESOURCES

The final chapter "Finding Out More: Some Other Relevant Publications and Resources", points the directory user to additional sources of published information as well as to organisations which provide information on religious life in the UK and that can give further information on particular religions as they exist in the UK. Within this chapter is also a section that includes details of some newspapers and magazines that provide coverage of a variety of religions in the UK.

INDEXES

There are four indexes:

The "Topic Index" gives page references for each major section and sub-section of the introductions to each religion and the other descriptive material in the directory. It enables the directory user to find broad topic areas.

The "Significant Word Index" indexes italicised words throughout the directory.

The "UK and National Organisation Index" is an alphabetical listing of all the religious organisations listed in the directory and operating at a UK and/or national level together with national inter-faith organisations and groups and resource organisations.

The "Local Guide Index" lists all the towns and cities in the directory and indicates the page ranges where organisations and places of worship located in these towns and cities can be found.

FURTHER READING AND HELP

At the end of most chapters there is a section on "Further Reading" to assist directory users in following up additional relevant information. Questions about the directory can be directed to the Multi-Faith Directory Research Project at the University of Derby, Kedleston Road Campus, Derby DE22 1GB, Tel: (01332) 591179; Email: P.G.Weller@derby.ac.uk. (More details on the Multi-Faith Centre and the University can be found in the display panels on pages 9-11).

Further advice and information about inter-faith relations and making contact with religious communities and their organisations can be obtained from The Inter Faith Network for the UK at 5-7 Tavistock Place, London WC1H 9SN, Tel: (020) 7388 0008; Fax: (020) 7387 7968; Email: ifnet@interfaith.org.uk. (More details on the Network can be found in the display panels on pages 12-13).

RELIGIOUS LANDSCAPE OF THE UK

THE VARIETY OF RELIGIONS   23

THE HISTORICAL DEVELOPMENT
OF A RELIGIOUSLY PLURAL
COUNTRY   25

PLACES OF WORSHIP   29

SIZE OF THE RELIGIOUS
COMMUNITIES   30

STATISTICS ON PLACES OF
WORSHIP   35

RELIGIONS IN PUBLIC LIFE:
THE CHRISTIAN INHERITANCE   40

RELIGIONS IN PUBLIC LIFE:
AN EVOLVING DIVERSITY   42

RELIGION AND THE LAW   46

RELIGIOUS COMMUNITIES
AND EDUCATION   49

THE CHALLENGE OF THE
FUTURE   54

FURTHER INFORMATION   55

FURTHER READING   56

THE VARIETY OF RELIGIONS

The United Kingdom has a strong heritage from Christianity and this remains the predominant religious tradition, particularly in Northern Ireland, Scotland and Wales, but also in England. At the same time, it is now more religiously diverse than any other country of the European Union and the religions found within it continue to exhibit a considerable degree of vigour and diversity despite the effects of secularisation on personal and social life.

A question on religious affiliation has, for the first time, been included in the 2001 Censuses of England and Wales, and Scotland, alongside that in Northern Ireland where a question on religion has been asked in previous Censuses. Until the results of the 2001 Census are available, there are no precise statistics available for most communities. However, in general terms it seems clear that, of the world religious traditions with a following in the UK, Christians are by far the largest group, followed by Muslims; then Hindus and Sikhs; then Jews; then Buddhists; and then Jains, Bahá'ís and Zoroastrians.

Members within each of these religious communities share in common many beliefs and practices, but within most communities there are also significant variations of tradition, organisation, ethnicity and language. Over the centuries, Christianity in these islands has developed into richly diverse forms. This diversity reflects both doctrinal differences and the varied national and religious histories of the different parts of the UK.

In addition to diversity within traditions, in some cases the boundaries between different religious traditions can be somewhat fluid. For example, within the religious practice of many ethnically Chinese people, traditions of Taoism, Confucianism and also Buddhism can often be found in intermingled forms.

Alongside those who belong to the major world religions in the UK, there are those who follow other forms of religious expression. The following categories and groupings of these are contested and there can be overlap between them. Among these are groups often popularly referred to as "sects" or "cults" but which, in academic usage, have normally come to be described as "New Religious Movements" (NRMs), as well as those who understand themselves as Pagans. Another area of religious life, often described as "New Age" spirituality, is characterised by a concern for ecology and personal growth and draws upon spiritual practices and traditions from a variety of sources.

Drawing upon elements both from Pagan traditions and from Christianity, there has been a recent growth, especially in Scotland, of interest in "Celtic Spirituality" that has become an important way of thinking and worshipping in terms of distinctively Celtic features which include, for example, an emphasis on the divine in the world of nature.

As well as people who have an active involvement in the corporate life of their religious communities, the UK also has a significant proportion of people whose religious belief and practice is often described as "folk religion" or "residual Christianity". Such people may turn to an active involvement in Christian religious life only, or mainly, at times of crisis or personal significance such as birth, marriage and death, or at festivals such as *Christmas*. Other faith communities also have followers whose religious observances are relatively limited.

In relation to all communities there are in addition some individuals and groups who acknowledge their connection with a particular tradition but find themselves in conflict with its official representatives over one or other single issue or across a whole range of ways of understanding the significance of their inherited or adopted tradition. There are also those who identify with "spirituality" but not with a particular religion.

Not everyone, of course, is religious. The British Social Attitudes Survey, 1998 recorded the following percentages for respondents' identification with statements concerning belief in God: 21% said that "I know God exists and I have no doubt about it"; 23% that "While I have doubts, I feel that I do believe in God", 15% of respondents said that "I don't believe in a personal God, but I do believe in a Higher Power of some kind".

However, belief in God and identification with a religion are not identical. There are, for example, religions such as Buddhism and Jainism which are not *theistic*. As Grace Davie, a sociologist of religion, has argued, there is a phenomenon of "believing without belonging" which means that religious belief is likely to be considerably wider than either active involvement in, or even passive identification with, a religious tradition or community. In addition, in all religious communities there are numbers of people who could be described as "belonging without believing".

Finally, there are also many, such as humanists, who uphold strong ethical and moral values but do not profess any form of religious belief. There are also atheists who specifically reject belief in the divine. In the 1998 British Social Attitudes Survey, 14% of respondents stated that "I find myself believing in God some of the time, but not at others"; 15% that "I don't know whether there is a God and I don't believe there is any way to find out"; and 10% that "I don't believe in God". 3% did not respond.

Those who are non-religious are usually indifferent rather than antagonistic towards religion, but some do have deeply felt concerns about allowing too prominent a role for religion in public life and certainly about any official privileging of religion in general or any one religion in particular.

As the following brief summary shows, whilst Christianity remains the UK's principal religious tradition in terms of the size of its following and of its historical and contemporary significance, there is a very wide spectrum of belief and practice in the UK.

THE HISTORICAL DEVELOPMENT OF A RELIGIOUSLY PLURAL COUNTRY

For much of the history of these islands (as elsewhere in the world) it has been difficult to distinguish between political and religious loyalties. There have, in the past, often been attempts to impose varying degrees of uniformity in the public profession of belief and in religious worship, sometimes through physical force and sometimes through the use of the law.

Despite this, religious diversity has always been present. Pagan traditions were present here from before the arrival of Christianity. Some aspects of Pagan traditions were incorporated into local Christian practice (as, for example, in the way in which some festivals were celebrated), whilst other aspects were driven underground until the modern era when there has been a serious attempt to revive Pagan religion. From the time of the Roman conquest onwards, alongside varieties of Christian belief and practice, individuals and groups of people belonging to other religious traditions have come as visitors, or to live here, with much more extensive settlement taking place during the last half century.

A small Jewish presence was established after the Norman conquest in 1066, but Jews were expelled in 1290 and only re-admitted during the period of the Commonwealth, following the 17th Century English Civil War. In the following centuries, Britain's international role expanded through trade, with the development of colonialism and imperialism. In the earlier part of this period, numbers of individual Hindus, Muslims and others came as servants or *ayahs*.

The Nineteenth and Early Twentieth Centuries

Prior to the nineteenth century, religious minorities both within and beyond the Christian tradition experienced a variety of civil disabilities, including exclusion from higher education and from local government and a number of offices of state. During the nineteenth century, there were rapid advances in religious toleration and the abolition of many civil disabilities related to religion. This facilitated both the development and the public visibility of diverse forms of religious life, including an expansion of the influence of *Nonconformist* Christian denominations and the re-emergence of *Roman Catholic* Christianity as a public religion after centuries of restricted existence. *Catholic* Christianity was also strengthened in Great Britain by the migration from Ireland of many *Catholic* workers to fill jobs, especially in the construction industries.

Also in the nineteenth century many civil disabilities were removed from Jews. Between 1881 and 1914, the Jewish population was strengthened by a combination of economic migration in the face of restricted social and economic possibilities and escape from the anti-Jewish pogroms occurring within the Russian Empire.

Zoroastrians began to settle in some numbers in England during the nineteenth century. The majority were of Indian origin and known as *Parsis*. The *Parsi* Zoroastrians were the first group with South Asian origins to make an impact, as a community, on the social and political life of the UK. The first three Asian Members of Parliament, who were elected in the latter part of the nineteenth century, were all *Parsis*. The first of these was the Liberal, Dadabhai Naoroji, who became an MP in 1892.

Also in the nineteenth century a Muslim presence developed in particular geographical areas, such as the Yemeni Muslims who settled in South Shields and other communities centred on seaports such as Cardiff and Liverpool. Individual Hindu and Sikh traders and settlers were also to be found.

As with the Muslim and Hindu communities, the origins of the Sikh presence in the UK can also be traced to individuals and small groups of settlers in the nineteenth and early twentieth centuries.

In the opening years of the twentieth century a Buddhist community began to emerge. Initially, it was mainly composed of individual indigenous followers who had become interested in the tenets of Buddhism through reading the texts translated and prepared by 19th century Western academics.

Following the First World War there was further settlement by Muslims and people of other religions from all over the Empire who had been demobilised from the British forces. Together with the movement of families from the original seaport areas of settlement this led to the establishment of small Muslim communities in a larger number of localities.

Bahá'ís have been present in England since 1898. An organised Bahá'í community began to develop in the early twentieth century under the guidance of *Abdul'Baha*, the eldest son of the founder of the Bahá'í faith and, after him, from 1921, of Shoghi Effendi (*Guardian of the Bahá'í Faith*).

From 1933 onwards, the arrival of escapees from Nazi persecution and the Holocaust in Germany and other Nazi-occupied European countries led to a further strengthening of the Jewish community in the UK.

During the nineteenth century, some people from China settled in Britain. Most were seafarers from the southern provinces of China, particularly from Guangdong. However, there was only a small Chinese population in Britain until after the Second World War.

Post–Second World War

The religious diversity of the UK increased rapidly after the Second World War, with the settlement of some groups of demobilised members of the armed forces of the Empire, among whom were Hindus, Muslims, Sikhs and African-Caribbean Christians. There was also migration to the UK of significant numbers of people from Poland and Italy which led to a further strengthening of the *Roman Catholic* Christian community as well as to its ethnic diversification. In addition some *Orthodox* Christians arrived here, including groups of people with Serbian, Bulgarian and Romanian backgrounds.

In the 1950s, new settlers included people from the Caribbean islands. Some of these, in response to what they often felt was at best a frosty reception, and at worst discrimination from indigenous Christians, developed new forms of Christian *Church* life.

But it was the migration of significant numbers of people from India, Pakistan, Bangladesh and Hong Kong and, later, in the 1960s and 1970s, of South Asians from Tanzania, Uganda and Kenya, that led to the present breadth of religious diversity in the UK, bringing about the existence here of significant communities of Hindus, Jains, Muslims and Sikhs.

The Muslim population is the largest of those minority religious groups which became established here primarily based on the immigration from the New Commonwealth in the years immediately following the Second World War. Also the Hindu population became more fully established here when significant numbers settled from East Africa in the years following 1968 and the outlines of an organised community began to emerge.

The Chinese population in the UK grew during the nineteen sixties onwards, with the migration of ethnic Chinese from Singapore, Malaysia and the rural Territories of Hong Kong.

During the 1960s to 1980s refugee settlement further strengthened, in particular: the Buddhist population, following the Chinese take-over of Tibet; the *Orthodox* tradition of Christianity following conflict in Cyprus; the Hindu, Jain and Sikh populations by South Asian Hindus, Jains and Sikhs migrating from East African states as a consequence of the Africanisation policies introduced during the early nineteen sixties; the Bahá'í and Zoroastrian communities following the Iranian Revolution; and the Muslim population in the wake of conflicts in Somalia, Bosnia and the Middle East.

Those who migrated in the early post-war period focused first on the basic need to find somewhere to live, and on getting a job so that they could send remittances back to their families in their home countries. In this phase of settlement, ethnic associations flourished rather than groups organised on a distinctively religious basis, resulting in forms of organisation centred around groupings based on the country of origin.

As immigration restrictions began to tighten throughout the 1960s to 1980s, an acceleration took place in the number of spouses and children joining the original migrants due to a growing concern that it would become increasingly difficult or impossible to do so later. This phase of migration laid the basis for the development of a range of social, cultural and religious communities and institutions which would maintain and transmit their religious traditions. *Mandirs*, *gurdwaras* and *mosques* were founded and became an increasingly established part of community life.

The twentieth century also saw the growth of a plethora of New Religious Movements. Some of these see their role in unique or original terms, while others understand themselves as related to one or more of the world religious traditions. Some movements related to the Christian tradition developed in the late nineteenth and early twentieth centuries, such as the Jehovah's Witnesses, the Christian Scientists, the Church of Jesus Christ of Latter-day Saints (popularly known as the Mormon Church). Others are newer groupings such as the Church of Scientology and the Family Federation for World Peace and Unification (often known as the *Unificationists*, or sometimes more popularly referred to as the "Moonies", in a reference to their Korean founder, Revd Sun Myung Moon).

In addition, a growing number of people identify themselves with Pagan religious traditions. Many of these also understand themselves as, in some sense, heirs to early Pagan traditions. Some have been drawn to contemporary Paganism predominantly by ecological concerns and commitments.

Religion, Ethnicity and Language

Religion is an important aspect of the identity of a significant number of individuals and groups. For some it is the most important. Other aspects of identity are represented by ethnicity and language. These are often linked with religious identity because of the history of when and where religious traditions developed. Thus, for example, the majority of people in the UK with Pakistani antecedents are also Muslim, and nearly all Sikhs have some antecedents in the Punjab.

However, the patterns of overlap between religion and ethnicity are not always straightforward and the majority of the UK's religious communities are ethnically diverse, having origins in various parts of the world. So, for example, the Christian population includes, among others, people of African, African-Caribbean, Chinese, East and Central European and South Asian backgrounds. Similarly, there are Muslims with South Asian, Middle Eastern, Far Eastern and British or other European indigenous roots, just as there are Hindus with a recent history of living in the Caribbean region, Fiji and East Africa. Also, just as one religious tradition may embrace many ethnicities, so one national or regional origin can be shared by several religions. Someone with roots in Gujarat, for example, might be Christian, Hindu, Jain or Muslim.

Shared language can also be an important factor in the relationship between religion and ethnicity. For example, in Wales there are local Christian communities for whom Welsh is the first language of both worship and everyday life. This is also true of Gaelic for smaller numbers of Christians in Scotland. Punjabi is the common language among most Sikhs.

Geographical Distribution of Religions

In particular local areas in the UK, members of faith communities may share ethnic, cultural and linguistic backgrounds. In some cases the bulk of those adhering to a religion may, for example, be Muslims from Pakistan or, in others, Muslims from Bangladesh, or Muslims from particular regions and even villages within these regions. For example, in Preston the Muslim population is largely Gujarati as are the local Hindus.

Both longer-term religious and national history and more recent patterns of migration and settlement have affected the religious composition of each local and regional area. Therefore some areas have a more multi-faith character, and others have concentrations of people of particular religions or traditions within these religions.

In England, the largest single Christian *Church* is the Church of England, whilst in Scotland it is the Church of Scotland (which is *Presbyterian* in tradition). In Wales, the *Free Churches* collectively are larger than any other Christian tradition, as are the *Protestant* Churches in Northern Ireland, although the

Roman Catholic Church is the largest single *Church* there.

Even within the four nations, however, a range of groups and denominations within Christianity can be found in varying strengths in different regional and local areas. Throughout England, Scotland and Wales, *Roman Catholic* Christians are predominantly concentrated in urban areas whilst, in rural areas of England, the Church of England has a more widespread presence than any other Christian *Church*.

England has the widest and proportionately greatest variety of religious communities, followed by Scotland and Wales, and then Northern Ireland. Throughout the UK the greatest diversity is to be found in cities, metropolitan boroughs and some towns, and religious, ethnic and linguistic diversity is, not surprisingly, at its greatest in the cosmopolitan capital city of London.

Seaports such as Liverpool and Cardiff often have the oldest local minority religious communities because international trade led to the settlement there of seafarers from other countries. Many old industrial towns and cities of the English Midlands and North, such as Leicester and Bradford, have communities which were established as a result of migration from particular areas of Commonwealth countries in response to the invitation to work in British industries during post-World War II labour shortages.

Bahá'í and Buddhist groups can be found scattered throughout the UK. Other communities, however, are often more geographically concentrated. The largest Hindu communities are in Greater London (especially Wembley and Harrow), Birmingham and Leicester. Many Jains live in and around Greater London and in Leicester where the largest Jain Temple in Europe is located. Zoroastrians are found mainly in the Greater London area, but also in the North West of England.

The most concentrated Jewish population is in the Greater London area and the largest provincial Jewish populations are in Glasgow, Leeds and Manchester. There are also other sizeable Jewish communities in Birmingham, Bournemouth, Brighton, Liverpool and Southend. The largest Muslim communities are to be found in Lancashire, Greater London, the West Midlands, West Yorkshire and in Scotland's central belt. The most substantial Sikh communities are to be found in Greater London (especially Southall), Birmingham, Bradford, Cardiff, Coventry, Glasgow, Leeds, Leicester, and Wolverhampton. There is little detailed information currently available on the geographical distribution of Pagans and the adherents of New Religious Movements and New Age groups.

PLACES OF WORSHIP

The historical development and present diversity of the religious profile of the UK is mirrored in its religious architecture. One way in which the religious landscape has quite literally changed is in the presence and range of a variety of different religious buildings. *Church* steeples and towers are a familiar part of both the urban and rural landscape of the UK. *Synagogues* have had a long historical presence, but increasingly *gurdwaras*, *mandirs*, *mosques* and *viharas* are also becoming part of the skyline in a significant number of areas.

Places of worship can have an important role as community resources within local neighbour-hoods, although some places of worship are not frequented as much by women and young people as they are by men within their communities. Places of worship incorporate the sources and goals of their religious traditions, thus signifying the established presence and the geographical belonging of these traditions of faith to both national and local society.

Apart from those among the pre-Christian Pagan traditions and also Christians, Jews were the first to establish places of worship in Britain. The oldest *synagogue* in current use is the Bevis Marks Synagogue in London, which was built in 1701. As other communities began to emerge, places of worship within their traditions also began to be established. For example, the first purpose-built *mosque* was established in Woking in 1899 and the first Sikh *gurdwara* in Putney, London, in 1911.

It was in the wake of the major post-Second World War migrations that the pattern and distribution of places of worship began to change significantly. Gradually, during the 1960s, as migrants decided to settle in the UK and to bring their families rather than just working here, the provision of worship facilities began to emerge as a community concern. People began to look for premises in which to meet. Often lacking the economic means to buy or build new facilities, they either adapted existing private dwellings for religious purposes or, faced with prejudice and misunderstanding from the general population, initially turned to those Christian places of worship which were sympathetic in order to seek hospitality for their gatherings for worship.

This phase coincided with the continuing numerical decline in attendance at the traditional Christian *Churches* which was resulting in the closure of many Christian buildings, particularly in those inner city areas where traditional Christianity had become weak. As a result, minority religious organisations quite often sought to purchase formerly Christian places of worship. This gave rise to considerable debate among Christians. For some Christians it seemed tangible evidence of Christianity's lessening significance in British life. In addition, for many minority ethnic groups within the Christian *Church*, such sales were met with puzzlement. The *Churches* that have predominantly black Christian membership and leadership often could not understand why such redundant buildings were not either given or sold on favourable terms to them as fellow Christians, since they also needed places of worship and often lacked the economic means to build new ones.

In addition to purchasing redundant *church* buildings, minority religious groups began to convert dwelling-houses and to purchase old warehouses, cinemas and other public buildings and, in a few cases, to construct their own buildings. At this stage, it was often the case that groups which would normally have remained separate on grounds of ethnicity, *caste* or sect found that, in the new situation, and under pressure of smaller total numbers and the consequent limitations of economic resources, they needed to join together to create premises for common use within the community.

Rediversification into sectarian and ethnically based groups has sometimes occurred with increasing relative security and prosperity in those areas with the greatest numerical concentrations. Conversely, pressing economic factors have also been influential in bringing about rationalisation and *ecumenical* sharing of buildings among the Christian traditions, especially in the inner urban areas.

There has been a recent growth in the numbers of purpose-built places of worship for minority religious traditions which has led to the need for flexibility on the part of planning authorities in relation to architectural styles which are traditional in the religions concerned.

SIZE OF THE RELIGIOUS COMMUNITIES

Statistical Problems

Readers will naturally expect a directory entitled *Religions in the UK* to offer figures on the size of religious communities in the UK. However, whilst Census data on religious identity has been collected in Northern Ireland, it has not in recent years been collected in England, Wales and Scotland. In England and Wales, until 2001, there had been no official Census dealing with religion since the 1851 Census of Public Worship. Internal data on religious affiliation and practice has only been collected in particular contexts for a variety of specific purposes, such as in prisons, the armed forces and the health service.

In the course of considering the range of questions to be included in the 2001 decennial Census, the Office for National Statistics consulted both data users and religious communities on the desirability of including a question on religious identity. In the light of this consultation a question on religious affiliation was included in the 2001 Census for England and Wales. The necessary amending legislation to permit this was passed by the Westminster Parliament. A religion question was also included in the Census in Scotland and the Scottish Parliament passed the relevant legislation for this. Therefore, in the 2001 Census a question on religious identity was asked on a voluntary basis in each of the four nations of the UK. This means that, although the results of the Censuses are not available at the time of publication, in future, at least in respect of the figures on community belonging, there should be a more solid basis for comparison than is currently possible.

At the same time, the way that the question was posed in England and Wales, in Scotland, and in Northern Ireland has been different. The question in England and Wales asked "What is your religion?". That in Scotland asked "What religion, religious denomination or body do you belong to?" as well as one on "What religion, religious denomination or body were you brought up in?" For England and Wales, as well as for Scotland, there were pre-defined options for response. These included the option of "none", as well as those of Buddhist, Christian, Hindu, Jewish, Muslim and Sikh. In both England and Wales, and in Scotland, there was also an option in which respondents could write their own, alternative self-description of another religion.

For the question in England and Wales, the overall Christian option was one that was signalled to be inclusive of all Christian traditions by a bracket within which was stated "including Church of England, Catholic, Protestant and all other Christian Denominations". In Scotland an overall Christian option was not offered, but rather the sub-options of Church of Scotland, Roman Catholic, and Other Christian.

In Northern Ireland, the question was asked "Do you regard yourself as belonging to any particular religion?", with the options "Yes" and "No". Those who answered "Yes" were invited to choose between the options of "Roman Catholic, Presbyterian Church in Ireland, Church of Ireland, Methodist Church in Ireland, and Other". There was also a parallel set of options for responding to the question, "What religion, religious denomination or body were you brought up in?"

In the absence until after 2001 of Census data relating to religious affiliation (except for Northern Ireland), there are very great problems in estimating statistics on UK religious communities. For the UK as a whole and for England, Wales and Scotland separately, the only figures which are at the time of publication available remain estimates based upon extrapolations from data on ethnic background gathered by the 1991 Census; data based upon the collection of information on the religious affiliation of schoolchildren; data from other sample studies; or figures supplied by organisations from within the religious communities themselves. All of these are subject to limitations.

Figures for religious affiliation extrapolated from the limited categories of ethnicity offered in the currently available Census ethnicity data are open to some question because there is no complete match between the categories of ethnic groups and religious communities. For example, as already noted, whilst the majority of people in the UK with Pakistani antecedents might reasonably be expected to be Muslims some, at least, will be members of other religious traditions.

At local level in England and Wales, some profiles have been built up of the religious affiliation of schoolchildren within local authority areas, based upon data collected in response to the then Department of Education and Science's introduction of the requirements of July 1989 Circular on "Ethnically-Based Statistics on School Pupils". This Circular required the recording of information on the religious affiliation of schoolchildren alongside data on ethnicity, gender and language, using the classifications of Christian, Hindu, Jewish, Muslim, Sikh, Other (please specify), No religion and Unclassified for recording this data.

From this data, in some local authority areas, extrapolations have been made to estimate the proportion of religious communities in the population as a whole. However, the results that are derived from this exercise need to be treated with caution. This is because answering the question has been voluntary; answers have been supplied by parents rather than by the children themselves; and the data thus far collected has been patchy in its coverage, with a comparatively high non-response rate particularly, it appears, from among the white population.

Data from this and other sample studies are always open to question, especially when attempts are made to extrapolate from them to the wider population. The smaller the sample, the more difficult it is to take account of varied factors related to the geographical, occupational and other spreads and concentrations of groups. This, in turn, makes more open to question any national projections based upon sample surveys.

There can also be difficulty when religious communities supply their own statistical data. It is not always clear how such data are arrived at, or whether the data encompass all members of a community or only active participants. The criteria for establishing what are "active" and "community" memberships can vary, both within and between different religious communities. Some communities count all family members associated in any way with that faith, whilst others only count committed adults. This makes comparison of communities, using internally generated figures, a complex and problematic matter. There are particular difficulties in estimating the membership of New Religious Movements.

Indeed, regardless of sources, where figures for faith communities are quoted, it is very important to establish whether these relate to active or community membership. For example, the Christian Research Association's *Religious Trends No. 2, 2000/01 Millennium Edition* offers a year 2000 estimate of 5,861,796 for the total membership of Christian *Churches* in the UK. At the same time, in relation to those people who see themselves as, at least in some sense, broadly identified with Christianity, it offers a year 2000 estimate of approximately 38,100,000.

The approximate estimates given in the next section are generally figures for *community* membership rather than *active* membership. In other words, they reflect figures for those who in some way identify with a particular religious tradition, including children and adults, *whether or not* they are actively involved in any organisation within the religion concerned.

UK Figures

As stressed above, in the current state of knowledge and research, and until the results of the 2001 Censuses are available, there are inevitably speculative elements involved in all estimates in this field.

The matter of statistics is very sensitive as communities will naturally be concerned if they believe that their numbers have been underestimated. The directory project has been carried out in consultation with individuals from within the religious communities, as well as with external academic researchers, and some internal religious community assessments suggest the possibility of a significantly higher figure than the numerical estimates which are offered by the directory.

The UK *community* membership figures offered below are in many, though not all cases, related to derivations from ethnicity data in the 1991 Census and to figures included in the 1997 edition of the directory. They represent the product of a survey of such research as has been conducted on religious statistics in the UK. Consultation has also taken place with a range of academics and directory consultants from within the various faith communities, as listed in the "Acknowledgements" chapter. However, and especially in the case of those derived from ethnicity data, these figures do not reflect the most likely recent demographic developments since the last Census. In the absence of Census data on the size of different communities until the results of the 2001 Census are available, new estimates, especially for Hindus, Jains, Muslims and Sikhs are inevitably based as much on judgement as upon detailed and uncontestable evidence. The figures for such groups have therefore not varied from the estimates given in the previous edition of the directory. These *community* (as distinct from *active membership*) estimates offered by the directory are, in alphabetical order, as follows:

Bahá'ís	6,000
Buddhists	30,000 – 130,000
Christians	38,100,000
Hindus	400,000 – 550,000
Jains	25,000 – 30,000
Jews	283,000
Muslims	1,000,000 – 1,500,000
Sikhs	350,000 – 500,000
Zoroastrians	5,000 – 10,000

These figures for the size of *communities* in the UK should be read in the light of the following notes:

Bahá'ís

The figure for Bahá'ís reflects detailed records of Bahá'í membership kept at national level.

Buddhists

The higher of the Buddhist figures offered is based on the inclusion under the classification, for this purpose, as Buddhist, of a significant proportion of the 156,938 ethnically Chinese people recorded in the 1991 decennial Census. Given the often overlapping and intermingling complexity of Buddhist, Taoist and Confucian belief and practice found among many ethnic Chinese families and individuals estimating the Chinese population who might appropriately be described as Buddhist is problematic. It is also the case that a recent Policy Studies Institute survey suggests very low rates of "religiosity" among Chinese people in the UK. Nevertheless, it would also be misleading not to acknowledge in any way the role and significance of Buddhism among Chinese people. At the same time, there are very real difficulties in estimating the number of indigenous Buddhists since these cannot be estimated on the basis of any kind of abstraction from ethnicity figures. Thus, the ethnic diversity

among Buddhists makes all estimates of the size of the Buddhist population problematic until firmer figures are produced in the Census.

Christians

The figure for Christians is based upon work by the Christian Research Association and depends upon a very broad interpretation of the identification with the Christian tradition of many indigenous people in the overall population.

Hindus

The range of figures for Hindus reflects, in part, differences of judgement concerning the balance between the Hindu and non-Hindu components of the population group classified as Indian in the 1991 Census. But, in addition, for some Hindus, the drawing of sharp boundaries in relation to religious traditions originating in the Indian subcontinent is not thought to be appropriate. Such Hindus tend to classify the Buddhist, Jain and Sikh traditions (which this directory covers in separate chapters) as expressions of the *Sanatana Dharma* (see the chapter on "Introducing Hindus in the UK") and because of this might suggest a figure significantly higher than even the top of the range offered here. Some would also wish to include the members of a range of more recent groupings which are, to various degrees, influenced or shaped by Hindu or Hindu-related perspectives.

Jains

The range of figures for Jains reflects differing internal and external estimations of the size of the Jain community in the UK.

Jews

The figures for Jews are produced by the Community Research Unit of the Board of Deputies of British Jews. They are based upon formal research work of considerable detail and scope, in which both the process and the results are open to methodological scrutiny.

Muslims

The range of figures for Muslims reflects different evaluations of the proportion of Indian-origin people listed by the 1991 Census who might be expected to be Muslims on the basis of projections made from the distribution of Muslims in the population of India, as well as debate about the likely numbers of Muslims in other, smaller, ethnic and national groupings.

Sikhs

The range of figures for Sikhs also reflects different evaluations of the likely relative proportion of different religious groups among those ethnically categorised as Indian in the 1991 Census.

Zoroastrians

The range of figures for Zoroastrians reflects the range of estimations proposed by different researchers into Zoroastrianism in the UK.

Statistics for Northern Ireland

More precise figures can be given for religious affiliation in Northern Ireland, since these can be based upon data derived from the religious question in the 1991 Census for Northern Ireland. The following cumulative totals can be derived from the published Census tables: Bahá'ís 319; Buddhists 270; Christians 1,397,006; Hindus 742; Jains are not listed (and are therefore presumably fewer than 10, at least 10 adherents being the criteria for separate listing); Jews 410; Muslims 972; Sikhs 157; Zoroastrians 10.

However, once again, it should noted that the ten years that have now elapsed since the 1991 Census may have resulted in some significant demographic changes with respect to religious affiliation and this will not, therefore, be reflected in the data set out above.

Figures for Christian Traditions in the UK

The following figures are year 2000 estimates of membership of the various *Churches* of the Christian tradition in the UK, as taken from the Christian Research Association's *Religious Trends No. 2, 2000/01 Millennium Edition*. These are, in alphabetical order, as follows:

Anglicans	1,657,150
Baptists	209,234
Independent	195,498
Methodists	386,590
New Churches	137,225
Orthodox	207,930
Pentecostalists	233,234
Presbyterians	979,072
Roman Catholics	1,721,500
Others	134,363

Of course, in relation to the above figures, it needs to be recognised that the basis for membership varies between the broad traditions that are listed and sometimes even within them. For example, in the case of *Roman Catholic* membership, the above figures are based on Mass attendance. The Roman Catholic Church itself defines membership in terms of its community figures. The "Others" category includes, for example, such smaller groupings as *Christian Brethren, Congregationalists, Lutherans, Moravians, Salvationists,* members of the Society of Friends (*Quakers*) and *Unitarian and Free Christians.*

Some Other Widely Used UK Figures

Despite the problems associated with religious statistics, a number of figures are given in official publications and thus are widely used. Many of these themselves draw upon figures produced by the Christian Research Association. This is a non-governmental and widely used source of figures. However, the Association itself acknowledges that these figures are largely estimates.

In *Britain 2001: The Official Yearbook of the United Kingdom*, written by the Office for National Statistics and published by the Stationery Office, *community membership* figures are given as follows, and are set out here in alphabetical order: Bahá'ís 6,000; Hindus 400,000-550,000 (although the handbook notes that "some community representatives suggest a considerably higher figure [of close to 1 million]); Jains 25-30,000; Jews 283,000; Muslims 1,500,000 – 2,000,000); Sikhs 400,000-500,000; and Zoroastrians 5-10,000. *Britain 2000* gives no community membership figures for Buddhists or Christians.

Social Trends 30: 2000 Edition, written by the Office for National Statistics and published by the Stationery Office, uses figures for what it describes as *"adult active members"* which are based upon 1990 data published by the Christian Research Association. These figures are, in alphabetical order: Christians (including non-Trinitarian Christian) 7,083,000; Hindus 140,000; Jews 101,000; Muslims 495,000; Sikhs 250,000; and Others 87,000 (it is again probable that this category includes the Bahá'ís, Buddhists, Jains and Zoroastrians who are treated separately within this directory). *Social Trends 31: 2001 Edition* does not include any statistics of this kind.

Global Figures

The conditions and qualifications which apply to community figures for religions in the UK apply even more so in the case of global estimates of the size of the religious traditions contained within this directory's individual chapters on these religions. Global figures can only give a very rough indication of relative size and they inevitably lack any real precision.

Those included here draw upon the work of David Barrett, who has done research over a

number of years on this topic. His most recent estimates for 2000 covering the religions included in this directory were published in the second (2000) edition of the *World Christian Encyclopaedia*, and are, in alphabetical order:

Bahá'ís	7,106,000
Buddhists	359,982,000
Christians	1,999,564,000
Hindus	811,336,000
Jains	4,218,000
Jews	14,434,000
Muslims	1,188,243,000
Sikhs	23,258,000
Zoroastrians	2,544,000

STATISTICS ON PLACES OF WORSHIP

"Certified Buildings" in England and Wales

Statistics on the size of religious communities remain controversial and sensitive. Somewhat less controversial are statistics on places of worship although, even here, matters are not straightforward. While no parallel figures are kept for Scotland and Northern Ireland, an indication of some kind of the numbers of places of worship in England and Wales can be derived from tables found in the Annual Register of Statistics of the Registrar General in the Office for National Statistics. The list is unpublished, but is available for consultation, and contains cumulative totals relating to three kinds of buildings:

- Buildings of all religious bodies that are "certified" as places of worship (excluding buildings of the Church of England or the Church in Wales which are technically not "certified" buildings, but "recorded").

- "Recorded" churches and chapels of the Church of England and the Church in Wales.

- Buildings of religious bodies that are registered for the lawful solemnisation of marriages (with all such registered buildings also being "certified" or being buildings of the Church of England or the Church in Wales).

The categories in which running totals are kept in the Annual Register of Statistics do not exactly match the nine world religious traditions with which this directory is principally concerned, for example, there are no separate data for Bahá'í, Buddhist, Hindu, Jain and Zoroastrian places of worship, although there is a collective category of "other bodies" and the Christian, Jewish, Muslin and Sikh categories for which separate data is recorded.

However, the following tables give the total number of "certified" and "recorded" buildings that can be derived from the Office for National Statistics' *Classification of Denominations and Production of Annual Statistics*, as at 30th June 1999 which were the last figures available at the time of publication.

TABLE 1

Certified and Recorded Christian (Trinitarian[1], non–Trinitarian[2] and Christian "other"[3]), Jewish, Muslim, Sikh and "Other"[4] Places of Worship in England and Wales

on 30th June in the specified Years

	1972	1975	1980	1985	1990	1995	1999
Christian Churches	47638	47139	45378	45129	44922	44722	44648
Jewish Synagogues	320	348	335	351	355	357	349
Muslim Mosques	79	90	193	314	452	535	584
Sikh Gurdwaras	40	59	90	129	149	174	180
Other Bodies	222	217	219	264	305	342	385

[1] In relation to these totals, Trinitarian" Christian figures are derived from the Register's categories of Baptist, Brethren, Methodists, Church in Wales, Church of England, Congregationalist, Methodist, Roman Catholic, Salvation Army and United Reformed Church.

[2] In relation to these totals, the "non–Trinitarian" Christian figures are derived from the Register's categories of Jehovah's Witnesses, Society of Friends and Unitarians.

[3] "Christian other" is a category used by the Register for all other Christian organisations.

[4] The Register does not give separate figures for Bahá'ís, Hindus, Jains and Zoroastrians whose places of worship will be included in this overall category of "Other".

TABLE 2

Approximate Numbers of Places of Worship in the UK in the Buddhist, Hindu, Jain, Jewish, Muslim and Sikh Traditions recorded in *Religions in the UK*, The Multi-Faith Centre at the University of Derby, 2001.

	UK	England	Scotland	Wales	Northern Ireland
Buddhist	148	129	8	10	1
Hindu	131	121	3	5	2
Jain	4	4	0	0	0
Jewish	184	176	5	2	1
Muslim	486	443	21	21	1
Sikh	170	159	6	4	1

The number of places worship listed in the directory is fewer than the total number indicated by the ONS' Annual Register of Statistics due to the editorial policy of the current edition to include only those organisations that directly confirmed their details with the project or could be verified from other reliable sources. In addition, it should be noted that the numbers of places of worship in the directory cannot be known with certainty since not all organisations have made it clear if they are a place of worship. However, these figures represent an informed judgement of the numbers of places of worship recorded.

The Buddhist figure includes details of centres, *viharas*, monasteries and other publicly accessible Buddhist buildings. The Bahá'ís do not have one of their *Houses of Worship* in the UK, but *Religions in the UK* contains details of a number of Bahá'í centres which are publicly accessible buildings. The Zoroastrians do not have any *Fire Temples* in the UK, but Zoroastrian House in London has a room which is used for worship.

TABLE 3

Recorded (Church of England and Church in Wales) and Certified (all others) Christian Trinitarian, non-Trinitarian and "other Christian" Places of Worship in England and Wales on 30th June in Relevant Years

	1972	1975	1980	1985	1990	1995	1999
Christian	47683	47139	45378	45129	44922	44722	44648
Trinitarian (composed of:)							
Anglican	17046	16901	16721	16614	16563	16529	16464
Roman Catholic	3502	3585	3630	3673	3693	3699	3708
Traditional Free Church	21059	20237	18655	18117	17668	17235	17112
Non-Trinitarian							
Jehovah's Witnesses	652	723	759	809	872	907	918
Society of Friends	368	368	355	358	365	363	365
Unitarian	192	199	186	186	178	178	180
Other							
"Other Christian"	4864	5126	5072	5372	5583	5811	5901

TABLE 4

Recorded and Certified Places of Worship by Region in England and Wales
on 30th June in the year 1999

	Trinitarian Christian	Non-Trinitarian	"Other Christian"	Jewish Synagogues	Muslim Mosques	Sikh Gurdwaras	Other
North East	2209	73	273	10	14	5	11
Yorks and Humb[1]	3327	164	491	15	122	25	28
North West	4084	206	852	60	127	10	55
East Midlands	3424	113	428	5	32	15	37
West Midlands	3138	135	634	9	134	49	45
Eastern[2]	4736	134	508	6	5	12	20
London[3]	2495	124	875	199	91	31	86
South East[4]	3569	221	770	29	36	23	70
South West	5091	179	577	10	6	7	23
Wales	5321	114	493	6	17	3	10
TOTALS	37284	1463	5901	349	584	180	385

Please note the basis for the classification and presentation of figures in 1999 has changed with respect to the Eastern, London and South East areas according to the notes below.

[1] Yorkshire and Humberside was abolished as a specific area during a local government review some time ago. However, this area is still used by the Office for National Statistics to classify cumulative totals
[2] For the 1999 figures, includes both non-metropolitan counties and unitary authorities
[3] For the 1999 figures, includes metropolitan counties
[4] For the 1999 figures, includes both non-metropolitan counties and unitary authorities.

The legislative framework for "certification" is the *Places of Worship Registration Act* passed in 1855. "Certification" is not compulsory, but has benefits. Provided the worship held in the building is accessible to the general public it can bring exemption from local taxation – an exemption which extends to associated and attached buildings of the place of worship even if used for purposes other than religious worship. It is also the basis for an application to become a registered for the solemnisation of marriages. In addition, certification frees a place of worship from the need to register itself under the 1960 *Charities Act*.

For a place of worship to become "certified", the Registrar needs to be satisfied that the organisation is religious and that its buildings are being used for "religious worship." This is done by submitting to the local Superintendent Registrar of Births, Marriages and Deaths two copies of a document signed by an owner, occupier, minister or member of a building's congregation, declaring an intention to use this building for the purposes of worship and naming the religious tradition concerned.

The Superintendent Registrar forwards this to the Registrar General who grants certification through the Superintendent Registrar if satisfied that the certified place is to be used "wholly or predominantly" for worship by an identifiable and settled group. *Churches* of the *established* Church of England and the *Anglican* Church in Wales do not need to apply to be "certified", they are automatically "recorded".

Since places of worship are not required to be certified and, because house-based places of worship are rarely certified, the total numbers of those which are certified does not give a completely accurate picture of the actual numbers of places of worship for each tradition.

In addition, and especially for the earlier years in which records were kept, the number of classified buildings is likely to have reflected an under-reporting. Not all the minority traditions knew the procedures for certification and since many of their early places of worship were house-based they were therefore less likely to apply for certification.

In recent years the relationship between the actual numbers of places of worship and the numbers certified and recorded has undoubtedly become closer as increasing numbers of buildings in minority religious traditions have sought certification.

However, since there is no complete correspondence between the numbers of certified and recorded places of worship (see Table 1) and the actual numbers of places of worship, the directory also presents its own figures for the numbers of places of worship in other than Christian traditions (see Table 2).

The figures in Table 2 set out the number of places of worship listed in this directory which covers Scotland and Northern Ireland as well as England and Wales. It is important to make clear that these figures reflect the present edition's editorial policy of including listings only for organisations directly confirming their details with the project or else which can be confirmed from other reliable sources. They also reflect a degree of ambiguity where organisations have not made clear whether it would be appropriate to classify them as places of worship. The directory's figures also exclude a number of places of worship in each group which did not wish to have their details included in this edition.

Trends

Table 1 contains figures derived from the General Register Office's annual statistics. Table 2 contains data on the approximate number of places of worship listed in the present directory.

The columns of figures in Table 1 begin with the earliest cumulative figures held by its office in Southport – namely, those for 1972, and then records figures at five yearly intervals between 1975 and 1995, and finally the latest figures available at the time of publication, which are those for 1999.

The General Register Office's figures conflate all religions other than Christian (and a number of Christian-related bodies appear separately), Jewish, Muslim and Sikh, into a cumulative category of "Other (Eastern) Bodies". The *Religions in the UK* figures, however, distinguish between Bahá'í, Buddhist, Hindu, Jain and Zoroastrian places of worship, according to notes set out at the foot of Table 2.

From the General Register Office's cumulative totals over a period of years it is possible to discern certain trends in the provision of places of worship. The overall number of certified and recorded Christian *Trinitarian*, non-*Trinitarian* and Christian-related *churches* has shown a pattern of decline over the period surveyed.

Over the same period, Muslim *mosques*, Sikh *gurdwaras*, and places of worship of "Other Bodies" have more or less consistently increased. This is also true of Jewish *synagogues*, perhaps surprisingly in view of the overall slight demographic decline of the Jewish population.

However, these bald national figures hide a number of variations which are more clearly visible in Table 3. For example, the main decline in the numbers of certified and recorded Christian places of worship has been among the *Trinitarian* Christian traditions, with the exception of the *Roman Catholic* tradition which has seen some small increase over the same period.

The more traditional *non-Trinitarian Unitarians* have, until the most recent figures, also reflected the pattern of decline found among the *Anglican* and traditional *Free Churches*. The Society of Friends have remained broadly stable, with only some slight downward and upward movements recorded over the period. However, the number of certified places of worship in the Jehovah's Witnesses tradition has grown significantly, making the total trend among the *non-Trinitarian* Churches one of growth.

The "Other Christian" category has also seen a significant expansion of the number of its certified places of worship. This sector includes the *Pentecostalist* and *Independent* traditions, as well as the other burgeoning "black-led" or "black-majority" *Churches*.

At the same time, it should be noted that there will be many places of worship within the *New Church* movement (networks of Christians not in the traditional denominations, often meeting in private homes or hired public buildings rather than in specially constructed and/or specifically dedicated *church* buildings) which are not certified.

Table 4 illustrates regional variations in the distribution of "recorded" and "certified" places of worship which are of considerable significance because they reflect the geographical concentrations of people within the minority religious traditions. However, in relation to comparison over time it should be noted, as set out in notes below the table concerned that the basis for classifying and presenting figures has changed in 1999 with respect to the Eastern, London and South Eastern regions.

Thus the 1999 figures of over 100 *mosques* in each of Yorkshire and Humberside, the North West and the West Midlands, reflect the main areas of Muslim settlement. The dominant concentration of 199 *synagogues* in the London area underlines the importance of London for the Jewish community in England, while the 60 and 29 *synagogues* in the North West and the South East, respectively, demonstrate the clear provincial centres of the Anglo-Jewry. The 49 *gurdwaras* in the West Midlands testify to the large Sikh settlement in that area.

As has been noted, however, the "Other (Eastern) Bodies" category includes all those other traditions that are separately featured in *Religions in the UK* - namely, Bahá'ís, Buddhists, Hindus, Jains and Zoroastrians, and it is therefore difficult to read much of significance from the regional variations in this category.

RELIGIONS IN PUBLIC LIFE: THE CHRISTIAN INHERITANCE

Religion, State and Society in the UK

Christianity, especially in its *established* forms, still plays a pre-eminent role in the public religious life of the UK. The Church of England has a special constitutional position with regard to the UK state as a whole which marks it out from other *Churches*. As an expression of the current relationship between the state and this *Church*, at the time of writing, twenty-four of its *bishops* and its two *archbishops* sit in the House of Lords as of right and the Prime Minister's Office and the monarch are involved in their appointment.

In its report published in January 2000, The Royal Commission on the Reform of the House of Lords made proposals to widen the basis of representation for "organised religions" in the second chamber as part of an overall process of reform. At the time of writing these suggestions are still being considered.

The Church of England continues to have a special role in public ceremonial on both ordinary occasions (such as the daily prayers offered by an *Anglican Chaplain* in the House of Commons) and special ones (such as the prayers at the Cenotaph on Remembrance Day). Its *ecclesiastical* law is treated as a part of the public law of England, being passed through parliamentary processes and receiving the Royal Assent. In addition, its ecclesiastical courts currently have the legal power to call as witnesses individuals of any faith or none.

However, despite this special relationship with the state, in contrast with the national *Churches* of some other European countries, the Church of England is not funded by the state in any direct way. Also, within the various parts of the UK there is a range of different arrangements for defining the relationships between religious bodies, the state and society.

England

In England, the Church of England is the form of religion "by law established" and other Christian denominations do not have any formal link with the state. The reigning monarch is its *Supreme Governor* (not, as is sometimes popularly, but incorrectly stated, its "Head").

The monarch has the title *Defender of The Faith* which, although its origins pre-date the *Reformation*, has since been understood in terms of upholding the particular character and role of the Church of England. Nevertheless some years ago the Prince of Wales made a suggestion that the more general term *Defender of Faith* might be more appropriate given the religiously plural nature of contemporary society.

Scotland

Since the 1603 accession of James VI of Scotland to the English Crown as James I and the union of the Parliaments in 1707, Scotland has had close links with England. But in many ways Scotland remains distinct, especially in its systems of law and education, as well as in relation to matters of religion. The re-establishment of the Scottish Parliament in 1999 has reinforced this distinctiveness.

The *Presbyterian* Church of Scotland (rather than the *Anglican* tradition's Episcopal Church of Scotland) is the *established* Church in Scotland and among *Presbyterians* in Scotland is often understood as the national Church. Prior to the recent devolution of powers from Westminster to the Scottish Parliament, the *Kirk* (as it is known in Scotland), which is governed by a hierarchy of elected clerical and lay *Kirk* Sessions, *Presbyteries* and the *General Assembly*, was frequently seen as a surrogate Scottish parliament.

The Scottish form of *establishment* differs from that of the Church of England in that it does not place legal restrictions upon the Church of Scotland's self-government, nor does the British Prime Minister, the Secretary of State for Scotland nor the Scottish Executive's First Minister, have any role in the appointment of its leadership. Similarly, despite its legal status and prominent role within Scottish history, the Church of Scotland has no right, corresponding to that of the Church of England, for its leaders to have seats in the House of Lords. The Church of Scotland does, however, maintain a formal link with the Crown which is symbolised by the Lord High Commissioner's presence at the Church's *General Assembly*, which meets each May in Edinburgh.

The re-establishment of the Scottish Parliament has led to the consideration of new and important questions concerning the role of religion in such institutions of state, and the implications of the contemporary religious plurality for such a role. So, for example, in the

Westminster Parliament there has been a long tradition of beginning the day with prayers that have traditionally been led by a member of the clergy of the Church of England. By contrast, the new Scottish Parliament debated whether or not prayers or a time of reflection would be appropriate at all and, if so, which people of what religions should lead such prayers. It concluded that a time of non-denominational reflection should be held each week, and that those leading this should be selected on the basis of broadly reflecting the relative size of the various religious communities in Scotland.

In 1988 the Scottish Churches Parliamentary Office was set up with a Parliamentary Officer who provides information and facilitates working relationships between the Scottish Parliament and member *Churches* of Action of Churches Together in Scotland. The *Catholic* and Jewish communities in Scotland have appointed their own Parliamentary Officers who provide a similar service for their communities.

Wales

Following the 1920 *disestablishment* of the Anglican Church in Wales, there is now no established form of religion. Wales does not have a single denominational focus for national identity, but the *Nonconformist Free Churches* have played a particular and significant role in Wales' social, political and cultural life, especially in preserving and promoting the use of the Welsh language. In recent decades, the Church in Wales has also been promoting its Welsh identity and the use of the Welsh language in its liturgical life.

Ireland (Northern Ireland and the Republic of Ireland)

Northern Ireland has a much higher level of professed religious belief and participation than England, Wales and Scotland as does the Republic of Ireland. There is no officially *established* form of religion in either the North

or the Republic. The *episcopal* Church of Ireland (which is part of the global *Anglican* Communion) was *disestablished* in 1871. In Northern Ireland, although the *Roman Catholic* population is the largest single denomination, it is outnumbered two to one by the combined *Protestant* groupings of which the *Presbyterians* (organised in a number of different denominations) are the largest.

In the Republic of Ireland, the Roman Catholic Church originally had a special position within the 1937 constitution of the Republic which meant that its teachings had a significant formative effect upon legislation in the Republic, particularly in areas of personal, social and sexual morality. However, in 1972 its "special position" clause in the Irish Republic's constitution was abolished.

Despite the existence of the political border between Northern Ireland and the Republic of Ireland, the *Churches* of the island of Ireland are organised on an all-Ireland basis with regional and local bodies existing within a common organisational framework both north and south of the border.

At the same time, religion has been a dimension of the conflict which became known as "The Troubles" and which has resulted in a substantial level of violence, loss of life, injuries and death until the cease-fire of paramilitary organisations and the Good Friday agreement of 1998. The *Roman Catholic* community in the North has been closely identified with broad nationalist aspirations, whilst the continuing demographic decline of Southern *Protestants* has reinforced Northern *Protestants'* concerns about their minority position in the island of Ireland as a whole.

RELIGIONS IN PUBLIC LIFE: AN EVOLVING DIVERSITY

The Christian *Churches* continue to play a significant role in public life in the UK and in its constituent nations. But the public role of religions is evolving alongside the changes in the composition of society and also in its social and political structures. In response to these changes, Government and public bodies have also been evolving their relationship with religions with regard to a range of activities and events, including the areas outlined below.

Patterns of Consultation

Over the years many governmental, public and voluntary bodies have developed arrangements for consultation with both the Christian and Jewish communities. Because of their presence over a long period of time, these communities have been able to develop the kind of broadly representative bodies which can facilitate this consultation at a variety of local, regional and national levels. These bodies are professionally staffed and funded by their congregations and by donors from within their traditions.

Other religious communities which have only recently settled in the UK have had to engage with the difficult task of developing representative bodies that can find a general acceptance within their own communities. This has been particularly difficult to achieve at national level, since many of these communities have had to put their initial energies into establishing and building up local organisational capacity.

In the past, the Churches' Main Committee has been used as a mechanism for Government consultation of the Christian *Churches* and the Office of the United Synagogue. With regard to Religious Education there has also been a Joint Churches Education Policy Group and Government has consulted with the Religious Education Council for England and Wales.

In more recent times the Inner Cities Religious Council, founded in 1992 within what is now the Department for Transport, Local Government and the Regions, has offered advice on issues affecting the inner cities from the perspective of the Christian (including black-majority Churches), Hindu, Jewish, Muslim, and Sikh communities.

In addition, use is also being made by the Government of external and autonomous sources of advice such as the Inter Faith Network for the UK. The Scottish Parliament has also moved in this direction by seeking faith community input on particular policy areas, for example, through the Scottish Inter Faith Council.

The Government has announced its intention to initiate a review of the arrangements for consultation of faith communities and their representation at national levels.

A similar evolution can also be seen in the consultative patterns of local government. For example, it is now not uncommon for a local authority to seek input from a local council of faiths about local policies and services. Some local authorities, such as Blackburn with Darwen, have also played an active role in seeking to establish new local inter-faith initiatives for conversation with local religious communities. The new Regional Development Agencies for England have established Regional Assemblies, but so far in only one case (the East Midlands) has representation been from more than one religion.

Media and Advertising

UK regulation of television and radio broadcasting on religion differs from that found in the USA and in many other European countries, by requiring the BBC and the ITV to broadcast a specific number of hours of religious programming, though with stricter controls on their content. Up to the mid 1990s, much religious broadcasting, broadsheet and tabloid coverage of religion (with the notable exception of New Religious Movements) gave relatively scant coverage to religions other than Christianity. The last few years have, however, seen significant change, with coverage beginning to reflect more proportionately the religious mix of the UK population. The British Broadcasting Corporation and the Independent Television Commission continue to make use of the Central Religious Advisory Committee which has members drawn from a number of different religious traditions.

At the same time, increasing concern has also been expressed by people within a range of religious traditions about what is felt to be the misuse of religious images and symbols in advertising. During the year 2000, this became a pressing concern for some Buddhists who were troubled by the use of images of Buddhist *monks* to sell a range of products. Hindus have also recently successfully complained about the use of Hindu related imagery in advertising a chicken sauce. Possible changes in broadcasting regulations in the near future may mean it will be more possible for religious groups to advertise on radio and television.

Chaplaincy and Pastoral Care

The particular relationship of the Church of England and the Church of Scotland to the state is reflected in their pastoral access to, and influence within, social institutions such as hospitals, prisons, schools, and institutions of higher education. This access is sometimes rooted in particular legal aspects of *establishment* and at other times is a matter of long-rooted tradition. The increase in religious diversity has led to a fresh assessment of what arrangements are now appropriate. For example, a research project carried out at the University of Warwick during 1994-96 looked at the pattern of publicly-funded chaplaincy provision in the health and prison services and the role of civic religion. Its focus was on the Church of England and its relationship with other religions in these contexts.

Chaplaincy in public institutions is a rapidly changing area and, in a number of contexts, chaplaincy provision is gradually opening up to include the participation of other than Christian religious traditions. A number of hospitals and prisons now have multi-faith chaplaincy teams and the then Department of Health and Social Security initiated a Multi Faith Joint National Consultation, which has been working since 1997 to draft a guidance document on developing such as approach. In respect of the prisons, at national level there is now a Muslim adviser to Her Majesty's Prison Service, although it should be noted that this post does not exist on the same legal basis within the Prison Service as that of the Church of England's chaplaincy provision.

State Occasions and Religious Observances

The issue of how religions other than Christianity can be represented in events to mark key points in national and local life is a complex one. Because of the particular relationship between the State and the Church of England, this *Church* has had, and continues to have, a special role in many public events at both local and national levels. During the latter part of the 20th century, other Christian denominations were also given an opportunity to participate in many such events and activities.

Increasingly, religious groupings other than the Christian *Churches* have also been invited to take part in various ways. For example, for some years there has been a tradition, at the annual Commonwealth Day Observance, held at Westminster Abbey, to include contributions from representatives of other than Christian religions. In the year 2000 representation at the Remembrance Sunday event in London was widened to include people from a variety of faith communities.

The Government asks the *Churches* to organise "national services" to mark particularly significant events. In England and Scotland, the lead in the organisation of these events is taken by the *established Churches* of these countries with significant involvement from the other major Christian denominations through the ecumenical structures of Churches Together in England and Action of Churches Together (in Scotland). In Wales and Northern Ireland, the Christian *ecumenical* structures are invited to take the lead. Churches Together in Britain and Ireland is also involved in discussions about any UK-wide state religious observance.

At the local level civic services are generally arranged by the *Churches* just as are "national services". They therefore usually take place in *cathedrals* or *churches* and operate within clearly Christian parameters. In the case of the Church of England *canon law* dictates this. *Canon law* is ecclesiastical law of the Church of England that, because of its established status, is also part of the law of the land. This makes difficult anything more than short readings or prayers from other traditions and also rules out any readings not compatible with Christian doctrine. In consequence the readers are most often Christian. While representatives of other faiths may well be seated prominently as "honoured guests" they are unlikely to be active participants in the liturgy.

In some contexts, new forms of civic religious events are emerging and it is a challenge to develop ones with a structure and content with which all participants are at ease. January 2000 saw the first example of a Government hosted event bringing together leaders and members of the principal faith communities in the UK. This was the Shared Act of Reflection and Commitment held at the Houses of Parliament as part of the official celebrations during the First Weekend of the new Millennium and was arranged with the assistance of the Inter Faith Network for the UK. The event was opened by the Secretary of State for Culture, Media and Sport (the lead agency on the Millennium) and the Archbishop of Canterbury included speakers from all the major faith communities, and closed with a speech from the Prime Minister. It complemented the "national services" which were held by the Christian *Churches* earlier in the weekend but was not, itself, a service of worship. As a consequence, no participants needed to feel compromised by being invited to join in prayers or actions with which they might not feel comfortable.

Comparable gatherings are beginning to happen in different areas of the UK, and which mirror the move towards more devolved government in the UK. So, at the beginning of the new Millennium, for example, special services took place in Belfast, Cardiff, Edinburgh, and London.

In a whole range of areas there are increasing signs that organisations and bodies which have previously only liaised with the Christian and Jewish communities are now beginning to make efforts to consult more widely. At the same time, though, there remains some concern among more recently settled religious communities that these developments in the direction of consultation are not fast enough or sufficiently widespread. Religious leaders and other representatives of these religious communities can still find it hard to gain access to many public and social institutions on the same basis that is available to most Christian leaders and representatives. This problem is also shared by representatives of smaller Christian denominations that can feel overlooked by local and national government.

RELIGION AND THE LAW

Religions and the Legal Systems of the UK

The legal framework for the practice of religion in the UK is clearly of importance to all religious communities since it has a bearing on the degree to which religions can operate in accordance with their own traditions. In general terms, the legal system for England and Wales differs from that of Scotland, and these differences could well develop still further in the light of political devolution from Westminster. Northern Ireland, in turn, has many provisions which are different from those which exist in the rest of the UK. These differences affect the relationship between religion and the law in the various parts of the UK.

Unlike some other European countries, the UK has no formal list of religions officially recognised by the state. From time to time, however, although there are no clear criteria, the courts have to decide whether a particular organisation or movement is a "religion" in order, for example, to interpret a legal provision in relation to charity law. In the past, indicators of religious status have been taken to include monotheistic belief, but even this is not a firm requirement since, for instance, it is clearly problematic with regard to Buddhism.

Recognition and the Legal Protection of Religious Identity: History

The status of religious belief and practice is a complex matter. At times in the UK's history, the law has been used to uphold certain forms of belief and suppress others. For example, the position of the Church of England as the *established* church in England has been buttressed, not only by custom, but also at times by laws such as the *Corporation* and *Test Acts* of 1661 and 1673, which limited the holding of office under the Crown to communicant members of the Church of England.

Most of the provisions of the *Corporation* and *Test Acts* were repealed in 1828 and 1829, removing important legal restrictions on the participation of *Roman Catholic* and *Non-Conformist* Christians in public life. Many of the legal restrictions on the full participation of Jewish people in wider social and political life were, however, not fully removed until 1858.

A number of restrictions still remain with respect to people within traditions other than *Anglican* Christianity. For example, an heir to the Throne is specifically precluded from marrying a *Roman Catholic*. In addition, there is legal uncertainty over whether the office of Lord Chancellor can be held by someone who is not a Christian. Although most forms of overt legal religious discrimination have now been lifted, the degree to which the present law accommodates the full practice of all religious traditions is being continually tested.

For example, Sikhs had to engage in a lengthy struggle before being allowed exemption from a 1972 *Road Traffic Act* requirement for motorcyclists to wear safety helmets. The *Road Traffic Act* 1988, re-enacting the *Motor-Cycle Crash Helmets (Religious Exemption) Act* 1976, now exempts a follower of the Sikh religion "while he is wearing a turban" from the crash helmet requirements applicable to others. A similar exemption was granted by the *Employment Act* 1989 to allow turbaned Sikhs to work on construction sites without a helmet or hard hat as required by new safety regulations.

Another example is the exemption for Jewish and Muslim methods of animal slaughter from the general legislation governing the protection of animals at the time of slaughter. A Statutory Instrument of 1995, implementing the European Community's Directive on this matter, contains provision to allow Jews and Muslims to follow the requirements of their religious traditions with regard to the slaughter of animals for Jewish and Muslim consumption, waiving, for example, the general requirement for pre-stunning an animal prior to slaughter.

Family, marriage and burial law have also been the subject of some legal and social debate involving the religious communities, raising questions about the relationship to religious law and practice of social legislation on matters such as marriage, divorce and inheritance. There has also been debate about the extent to which employers can or should provide time and facilities at work for the performance of obligatory prayers and days off for the observance of religious festivals.

Until now, the response of the legal system to increased religious diversity has generally been of an *ad hoc* and pragmatic nature rather than seeking to provide generally applicable new frameworks for law. It has therefore often been concerned with defining permissible exceptions to generally applicable laws.

There has been continuing and recently intensified debate about the extent to which the law should protect people against forms of direct discrimination connected with religious identity. Much of the legislation and social policy that is designed to deal with social identities based upon race and ethnicity does not sit easily with the rise of religious self-definition. The possible avenues of redress which are at present available in England where discrimination has a religious dimension are summarised in the Inner Cities Religious Council's pamphlet on *Challenging Religious Discrimination: A Guide for Faith Communities and their Advisers.*

Recognition and the Legal Protection of Religious Identity: The Present Position

In Northern Ireland, the *Prevention of Incitement to Hatred Act (Northern Ireland) 1970* makes it an offence intentionally to stir up hatred against, or rouse the fear of, any section of the public on the grounds of religious belief, colour, race or ethnic or national origins. This covers the publication or distribution of written or any other matter which is threatening, abusive or insulting as well as the use of words of a similar nature in a public place or in a public meeting. Although its provisions have only rarely been used, the scope of this law is not only concerned with incitement directed to, or against religious groups, but is also concerned with incitement against any group when such incitement is carried out on religious grounds.

Therefore, at the time of writing there are specific legal provisions in Northern Ireland against religious discrimination in employment and for the prosecution of incitement to religious hatred, but not in the rest of the UK. At the same time, on the basis of the *Amsterdam Treaty* of the European Union, which extended, in principle, the competence of the European Commission to make Directives in relation to a number of grounds of discrimination, a Directive on discrimination in employment (which includes religious discrimination) has been agreed by the Council of Ministers. The Government will need to legislate to give the Directive appropriate UK-wide effect before the end of 2003.

There are some provisions in the common law of England and Wales against *blasphemy* and *blasphemous libel.* However, as the testing of these provisions in the courts during the controversy over the book *The Satanic Verses* in the late 1980s and early 1990s demonstrated, these laws only give protection to the Christian religion and, sometimes, more particularly only to the doctrines and practices of the Church of England.

In England, Scotland and Wales there are provisions against discrimination occurring in relation to a member of an "ethnic group". In terms of the law, one of the factors which is taken as indicative of the existence of an ethnic group is that of a long, shared group history of which religion may be a dimension. Jews have therefore been judged to be an "ethnic group", as also have Sikhs following the case of *Mandla v. Dowell Lee* in 1983.

Muslims, as such, however, fall outside the scope of the *Race Relations Act* because they are correctly viewed as being a religious, and not a racial or ethnic group. As members of a community which defines itself in terms of faith and includes a wide variety of different ethnic groups, they are not viewed as having a shared history linked to a shared ethnicity in the same sense as Jewish or Sikh people.

"Indirect" discrimination is the most that Muslims can claim under the present law (by pursuing a case as an Asian or an Arab or as a Yemeni or Pakistani, relying on a racial or national identity, and complaining that certain practices or procedures may have had a disproportionately adverse effect because they unjustifiably interfere with their religious observance). A white Muslim does not, therefore, have any protection under the present law.

Religious Discrimination: Evidence and Policy Options

It is the lack, other than in Northern Ireland, of legal protection against discrimination on religious grounds which has led to increasing calls for specific legislation to be enacted. In its *Second Review of the Race Relations Act 1976*, published in 1992, the Commission for Racial Equality stated that it considered the present *blasphemy* laws to be unsatisfactory and recommended that consideration be given to making incitement to religious hatred an offence under English law, as well as to incorporating international obligations against religious discrimination into domestic law. This would bring the law in the rest of the UK into line with that of Northern Ireland.

In the early 1990s, the Commission for Racial Equality conducted a survey of advice agencies to collect evidence of religious discrimination. Although advice agencies had not generally reported such discrimination, the overwhelming majority of religious organisations that were consulted believed there was a need for legislation to outlaw

religious discrimination. However, the Government of the day felt that there was insufficient hard evidence to act in terms of legislation.

In April 1999, the Home Office commissioned research on religious discrimination in England and Wales from the University of Derby's Religious Resource and Research Centre. The project team conducted questionnaire and fieldwork research into evidence of religious discrimination, both actual and perceived; the patterns shown by this evidence, including its overall scale, the main victims, the main perpetrators, and the main ways in which discrimination manifests; and the extent to which religious discrimination overlaps with racial discrimination. The aim of this research was to identify the broad range of policy options available for dealing with religious discrimination. In January 2000, the project issued *Religious Discrimination in England and Wales: An Interim Report* and, in February 2001, the Home Office Research, Development and Statistics Directorate published its Research Study No. 220 on *Religious Discrimination in England and Wales*.

The report found that ignorance and indifference towards religion were of generally widespread concern amongst research participants from all faith groups. It also found that in institutional settings such ignorance and indifference can contribute towards an environment in which discrimination of all kinds, including institutional discrimination, is able to thrive. Education, employment and the media were the areas most often highlighted as contexts for unfair treatment and for discrimination on the basis of religion.

A consistently higher level of unfair treatment was reported by Muslim organisations than by most other religious groups. Such unfair treatment was also consistently reported to be frequent rather than occasional. Hindu, and especially Sikh, organisations also reported a relatively high level of unfair treatment. Pagans and people from New Religious Movements frequently complained of open hostility and discrimination.

In terms of policy options for tackling religious discrimination, research participants generally advocated a comprehensive approach in which education, training and a bigger effort in teaching comparative religion in schools would all play an important part. The strengths and limitations of the law were recognised and many participants thought the law could help if used judiciously and in conjunction with other approaches.

The Home Office Research, Development and Statistics Directorate also published a parallel report (Research Study No. 221) from the University of Cambridge's Faculty of Public Law on *Tackling Religious Discrimination: Practical Implications for Policy Makers and Legislators* which explored the strengths and weaknesses of the various legal options.

Religion and Human Rights: New Developments

Potentially significant developments have already started with the implementation in the year 2000 of the *Human Rights Act* 1998. This Act introduces into domestic law the provisions of the *European Convention on Human Rights*, including those of Article 9 which states that: "Everyone has the right to freedom of thought, conscience and religion: this right includes freedom to change his belief and freedom, either alone or in community with others and in public or private, to manifest his religion or belief, in worship, teaching, practice and observance" and that "Freedom to manifest one's religion or beliefs shall be subject only to such limitations as are prescribed by law and are necessary in a democratic society in the interests of public safety, for the protection of public order, health or morals, or for the protection of the rights or freedom of others."

Under the *Human Rights Act,* Government and all bodies acting as "public authorities" must examine how far their policies, practices and proposals conform with the *Convention*, since individuals will now be able directly to appeal to its protection within the UK courts. The precise implications of this are, however, still subject to interpretation and are likely to remain contentious until the courts build up a body of case law deriving from the Act.

RELIGIOUS COMMUNITIES AND EDUCATION

As in other aspects of life in the UK, there are both commonalities and important differences with respect to the relationship between religion and education in the various nations. Schools in both England and Wales share much of the same legislative framework, although education administration in Wales is now the responsibility of the devolved National Assembly.

Religiously Based Schools in England and Wales

Religious communities have always had a natural interest in education. The Church of England became a provider of education before either national or local Government. When, early in this century, educational provision came under Government administration, the Church of England's denominational schools became part of a national education framework as a result of an agreement between it and the state embodied in the 1902 *Education Act*.

The continuing *Anglican* denominational schools preserved some degree of autonomy as "voluntary aided" or "voluntary controlled" schools. Both categories of school receive public funding, but a proportion of the financial responsibility for "voluntary aided" schools rests with the sponsoring religious body. These schools also have more autonomy with respect both to admissions policies as well as arrangements for Religious Education and Collective Worship. "Voluntary controlled" schools are much more fully integrated into the local authority system.

The *Anglican* and *Roman Catholic* (and to a much lesser extent the *Methodist*) *Churches* now have "voluntary aided" and "voluntary controlled" schools in England and Wales, as has the Jewish community, and as do some of the Christian *Churches* in Northern Ireland.

Within the independent, fee-paying sector, there are a significant number of institutions based on a religious foundation or ethos, including around sixty Muslim schools. During the 1980s and 1990s, a significant body of opinion among Muslims pressed the Government to grant public funding, as voluntary aided schools, to a number of Muslim schools which applied under Government criteria for recognition. During this period it was frequently pointed out that, although the Government affirmed that in principle that there could be Muslim schools alongside Jewish and Christian ones, no applications had been successful, leading to a significant concern that discrimination may have been at work.

However, the Government's decision to fund two Muslim primary schools (and, subsequently a Muslim secondary school and a Sikh school) represented a new development which is now being followed by some groups in other religious communities. Under the provisions for "Foundation Schools" made in the 1998 *School Standards and Framework Act*, such schools receive funding direct from national Government rather than through the Local Education Authority. There remains a body of opinion, however, that the designation of Voluntary School status for Muslim and other faith-based schools is necessary as a signal of parity of esteem with the Christian and Jewish Voluntary Schools.

The majority of children attend "Community" schools (often, in the past, referred to as "county" schools) rather than religiously-based (or "denominational") schools whether Foundation Schools, Voluntary Schools or Private Schools. Educators in these schools have therefore had to confront issues arising from the growth of religious diversity in their catchment areas.

Religious Education in England and Wales

Unlike in many other countries, in UK schools there are legal requirements for Religious Education and Collective Worship, although parents may withdraw their children from these if they so wish. In England and Wales the 1944 *Education Act* made "Religious Instruction" mandatory and required that syllabuses should be drawn up ("agreed") at a local level. By way of guidance, the Act merely specified that the content of the "instruction" should not be of a "denominational" character, although the unwritten assumption of that time was that the content would be Christian.

However, a gradual shift of approach took place and was reflected in a change of subject name to "Religious Education." The task of Religious Education was increasingly no longer seen as "instructing" or "nurturing" pupils in a particular religious tradition but as educating them *about* religion. Its scope also broadened to include learning about religions other than Christianity. With changes in the composition of society and the development of new faith communities, "multi-faith syllabi" were developed which were designed to help children understand the diversity of religious traditions. By the late 1970s those maintained schools which employed Religious Education specialists were teaching this kind of broader-based Religious Education but many schools used only Christian content or failed to provide the subject at all. Many "denominational" schools had also introduced learning about a variety of religions.

The 1988 *Education Reform Act* (which applies to England and Wales but not to Scotland and Northern Ireland) introduced a requirement that any new Religious Education syllabus must "reflect the fact that the religious traditions in Great Britain are in the main Christian whilst taking account of the teaching and practices of the other principal religions represented in Great Britain." The precise meaning and implications of these new statutory provisions have been widely debated since the 1988 legislation was enacted.

In July 1994 "model syllabi" were published by the Schools Curriculum and Assessment Authority (SCAA) which advised the Government on the content of the school curriculum. SCAA worked with both the teaching professions and representatives of the principal religions represented in Great Britain in producing syllabi, which do not have statutory force, but which are intended as advisory guidance to local authority Agreed Syllabus Conferences. The SCAA model syllabi do not, however, have any standing in Wales since SCAA had only a remit for England.

A variety of religious traditions are represented on every local authority's Agreed Syllabus Conference which has responsibility for drawing up the syllabus of Religious Education to be used by publicly funded schools in the relevant area. Voluntary aided schools do not have to include other religious traditions within their Religious Education syllabi, although they often mirror the local agreed syllabus to a greater or lesser extent.

In early 2000, the Qualifications and Curriculum Authority (QCA) which has taken over the functions of the SCAA, published non-statutory guidance designed to supplement the model syllabi and also released schemes of work. These are not intended to displace existing local syllabi but to exemplify work in schools which can fulfil locally determined requirements. The QCA also has only a remit for England, however.

The QCA has published guidance for schools on the new requirements for citizenship education and, in its Religious Education document, noted the role which Religious

Education can play in preparing pupils "for life as citizens in a plural society". It pointed out that Religious Education promotes the values and attitudes needed for citizenship in a democratic society and suggested that "pupils can understand how believers in different religious traditions may interact with each other, not just historically, but in contemporary ways, nationally and locally." The schemes of work include units dealing with inter-faith issues.

All Agreed Syllabi now have to be reviewed on a five yearly basis. Local religious groups (including, in England, the Church of England and representation from other Christian *Churches* and other religions) are also represented, alongside teacher and local authority representatives, on SACREs (Standing Advisory Councils for Religious Education). These have a statutory role in monitoring the delivery of Religious Education and collective worship within the publicly funded sector of education in their area. Often Agreed Syllabus Conferences are constituted from the membership of the local SACRE.

In Wales SACREs have only three constituent Committees, with the Church in Wales being part of a single Committee along with other Christian denominations and other religious groups, as compared with the position in England where the Church of England has its own Committee. In both England and in Wales there are National Associations of SACREs.

Whilst parents have a statutory right to withdraw their children, many within the minority religious communities have been concerned that the emphasis given to Christianity in Religious Education and collective worship in recent legislation and non-statutory guidance has shifted the balance back from the broader approaches which had been developing during the 1970s and 1980s. At the same time the evidence of OFSTED (Office for Standards in Education and Training) inspections in England suggests that breadth and rigour are growing in Religious Education, with the possible exception of the earlier years in secondary school. However, Religious Education may be negatively affected by the general weakness of educational provision in some urban areas.

Collective Worship in England and Wales

The 1988 *Education Reform Act* included complex provisions on school collective worship in England and Wales. In recent years many schools had moved away from exclusively Christian acts of worship seeing these as inappropriate for a plural school community containing children with different religious commitments and with none.

The 1988 legislation provides that the majority of acts of "collective worship" should be "wholly or mainly of a broadly Christian character". As in the case of Religious Education, the existing right of parents to withdraw their children from collective worship was maintained and fresh provisions were introduced under which what is known as a "determination" might be issued by a local authority to allow alternative arrangements for whole school collective worship to take place.

In January 1994 the then Department for Education issued a circular on *Religious Education and Collective Worship* setting out the provisions of the 1988 Act (and supplementary provisions enacted in 1993) and giving guidance on their application. Considerable concern was expressed by many educators and religious community leaders that the circular went beyond legislative requirements with regard to collective worship.

This continuing concern relates to whether the present requirements provide for an appropriate balance between the need to respect the integrity of pupils from different faith backgrounds and those without any religious faith commitment. It is also related to the need to encourage the development, in an inclusive way, of the whole school as a community, as well as to the practicalities of the capacity of schools to meet the current requirements for collective worship. Debates on the issues involved have continued. The Religious Education Council for England and Wales, the National Association of SACREs and the Inter Faith Network co-sponsored a consultative process during 1997 which explored the degree to which any consensus might exist or emerge concerning educationally appropriate provision for collective worship in schools in contemporary society. The consultation did not, however, reach agreed conclusions and neither did the Government accept its recommendation that the existing provisions needed review.

Religion and Education in Scotland

From the years of the *Reformation* in Scotland until 1872, the *established* Church of Scotland shared responsibility for education with the civic authorities. It is this partnership which undergirded the 1696 *Education Act's* requirement that there should be a school established, and a school-master appointed, in every parish "by advice of the Heritor and Minister of the Parish". These schools were, in effect, *Presbyterian* in outlook. But eventually, during the first half of the 19th century, the Scottish Episcopal Church and the Roman Catholic Church established their own denominational schools.

In 1872, another *Education Act* transferred responsibility for education in Scotland wholly to the state. However, the right to continue religious instruction was secured in a Preamble to this Act, subject to the operation of a conscience clause which gave "liberty to parents, without forfeiting any other of the advantages of the schools, to elect that their children should not receive such instruction." Under the 1918 *Education Act*, *Roman Catholic* schools, which had not been transferred in 1872, became part of the state system, thus establishing in Scotland a system of denominational schools which continues to be publicly funded.

Historically, therefore, it has been the custom for religious observance to be practised and instruction in religion provided in Scottish schools. This tradition has been reflected in recent *Education Acts* which allow education authorities to continue this provision. Indeed, it is unlawful for an education authority to discontinue religious observance or instruction unless the proposal to do so has been the subject of a poll of the local government electors in the area concerned and has been approved by the majority of those voters.

Every school run by the education authority must be open to pupils of all denominations and faiths, and the law continues to provide a "conscience clause" whereby parents may withdraw their children from any instruction in religious subjects and from any religious observance in the school. It also continues to be laid down that no pupils must be placed at a disadvantage as regards their secular education at the school, either because they have been withdrawn from such classes or because of the denomination to which they or their parents belong.

Guidance on the provision of Religious and Moral Education and Religious Observance in both primary and secondary schools was issued by the Education and Industry Department of the Scottish Office and local authorities formulate their own policies based on these guidelines. The guidelines stated that Religious Education in all schools should be based on Christianity, this being the main religious tradition in Scotland. But the syllabus should also take account of the teaching and practices of other religions. Religious Education should enable the individual to explore questions concerning the meaning of life. It should aim to promote understanding and respect for the belief of others, which is recognised as being particularly important in schools where there are significant numbers of children from faiths other than Christianity.

Government guidelines indicate that religious observance in non-denominational schools should be of a broadly Christian nature, but the form it takes varies very much from school to school, and takes account of the presence of the pupils of different faiths and of none. There is one publicly-funded Jewish primary school in Scotland, but denominational schools are mainly *Roman Catholic* and provide their own particular form of worship. The devolved Scottish Executive has not so far made any change to guidance on these matters.

Religion and Education in Northern Ireland

In the wake of the *Education Reform Act (England and Wales)*, 1988, a new statutory Core Syllabus for Religious Education in Northern Ireland was drawn up by the four largest Christian *Churches* in the Province (*Roman Catholic*, *Presbyterian*, Church of Ireland and *Methodist*). This historic achievement provided a commonly agreed programme of Religious Education from both sides of the traditional *Catholic-Protestant* divide. However, it is characterised by an exclusively Christian content. Beyond this Christian content, schools are free to include teaching relating to religions other than Christianity within their total Religious Education programme.

A formal set of non-statutory guidelines (which include a limited amount of material relating to Judaism and Islam) has been produced to assist teachers both in implementing the Core Syllabus, and in moving beyond it. However, this guidance package, being entirely optional, is unlikely to make a significant difference to the traditional styles and content of the Religious Education generally available in Northern Ireland's schools. A World Religions paper is available as an option in the Northern Ireland GCE A Level examination in Religious Studies, but this has not proved to be a particularly popular choice on the part of Northern Ireland schools.

Proposals for a revision of the Northern Ireland curriculum were supported by the Council for Curriculum Examinations and Assessment (CCEA) in its published advice to the Minister of Education (April 1999) suggesting that in the new schools' curriculum there should be "a shift in the emphasis of religious education towards understanding of major world religions, in particular Islam, as well as other Christian denominations within Northern Ireland."

Higher Education and Religious Identity

There has been a steady growth in the religious diversity of the student population of the United Kingdom. A project carried out during 1998 by Dr Sophie Gilliat-Ray gathered information on university/college policies on student religious identity. It also examined how institutions are developing structures for relating to the various religious groups on campus; the provision of worship facilities; how chaplaincy arrangements are being developed in multi-faith contexts to respond to the pastoral needs of students of the various faiths; the emergence of inter-faith organisations on campus; and how faith communities are developing national structures to respond to the religious needs of their students. A short report, *Higher Education and Student Religious Identity* was published in 1999 and circulated to all institutions of higher education to enable sharing of good practice and a chance for developing strategies appropriate to multi-faith campuses.

THE CHALLENGE OF THE FUTURE

Alongside difficulties related to their minority religious status, the ethnic profile of many religious minorities means they have also had to contend with discrimination and disadvantage on the basis of their racial or ethnic origins. At the same time, in contrast to many other European Union countries, the majority of the religious minorities with roots in recent migrations who settled in the UK either had, or were entitled to take up, British citizenship.

There does, however, remain a gap between this formal, legal position and the personal and social experiences of discrimination and disadvantage found among the minority communities. Nevertheless, the formal and legal position of the minority religious communities in the UK offers a stronger basis for organisational and community development than in some other European countries where their second or third generation counterparts still retain the status of migrant rather than citizen, with all of its accompanying legal and psychological consequences.

Although the UK's legal and constitutional structure is a key factor in how newer communities develop their structures, the political significance of the European Union, of which the UK is now inextricably a part, is becoming increasingly important for the future development of both law and social policy in the UK, including the dimensions of these that relate to religion.

In the past, there have been attempts in the European Parliament to legislate in a controversial way in relation to the activities of New Religious Movements without taking full account of the complex issues involved. At the same time, the European Union is also becoming a setting for positive policy and legislation against discrimination on the basis of religion. Under Article 13 of the *Amsterdam Treaty*, European Union competence is now extended beyond the basis of gender, to take appropriate action against discrimination on the basis of "racial or ethnic origin, religion or belief, disability, age or sexual orientation". It is able to do so when there is unanimity in the European Council of Ministers, acting on a proposal of the European Commission, and after consulting the European Parliament.

As mentioned earlier, the Council of Ministers adopted a draft Directive dealing with direct and indirect discrimination in employment, including on the grounds of religion. This use of the *Amsterdam Treaty* is a sign of the European Union's increasing importance in respect of matters of religion and social policy.

In the UK, since the mid-1960s, the ideal of multi-culturalism has been the basis of a general political consensus underlying the equal opportunity policies of central and local government and other significant social institutions. On the basis of this policy, significant social institutions have engaged in concerted attempts at positive action to address the needs of those citizens widely referred to as the "ethnic minorities".

However, religion was initially only rarely considered in terms of the implications of the new plurality. As this chapter has indicated, there has been recent change in this regard, reflecting a greater recognition of the increasing differentiation of personal and social identities on the basis of religion. In a cultural milieu in which ethnicity, nationality, class and lifestyle have been seen as the major determining factors of individual and corporate identity, for people and organisations to define themselves primarily in terms of their religious identity and values represents a significant challenge to the prevailing social ethos.

The increasing religious diversity of UK society continues to raise new questions and possibilities. These questions need increasingly to be considered within a wider international context. In terms of the European Union, the role of religion will increasingly need consideration as part of the widening agenda of political as well as economic integration. In the wider Europe, from the Atlantic to the Urals, the context of the Council of Europe will also be important as an arena for questions related to religion in the maintenance and promotion of international standards of human rights. At the same time, in the context of devolution of power within the UK itself to its constituent nations and regions, the profile of these European-wide issues is likely to take on increasingly distinctive national and regional dimensions.

Religious communities and individuals stand at the intersection between the global and the local in a world that is both increasingly globalising and localising. Religious individuals and committees are simultaneously part of transnational communities of information and solidarity, whilst sharing in the civic society of the state of which they are citizens and being rooted firmly within their wider local communities.

In the UK, as elsewhere in the world, religious communities have great potential to contribute to the common good, but can also become a source of fragmentation and conflict. The challenge facing both religious communities and the wider societies in which they are set is that of encouraging the common visions and structures necessary for sustaining an integrated but richly diverse community, but avoiding both assimilation or fragmentation. As well as expecting the wider society and the state to respond in positive ways, religious communities themselves will need to develop still further their commitment to positive inter-faith relations.

The shape of our common future will depend on whether the religious communities, social organisations and the state can rise to this challenge and draw upon the distinctiveness and resources of all sectors of society for the benefit of the common good.

FURTHER INFORMATION

The following list is of public bodies relevant to matters covered in this chapter. These do not include the full spectrum of bodies involved in multi-faith aspects of life in the UK. The reader will therefore also find it helpful to look in the listings for the chapter on "Inter-Faith Activity" in the UK.

Central Religious Advisory Committee
Religious Broadcasting Officer, Independent
Television Commission, 33 Foley Street, London
W1W 7TL
Tel: (020) 7255 3000
Internet: http://www.itc.org.uk

Commission for Racial Equality
10-12 Allington Street, London SW1E 5EH
Tel: (020) 7828 7002
Internet: http://www.cre.gov.uk

Inner Cities Religious Council
Department of Transport, Local Government and
the Regions, Floor 4, H10, Eland House,
Bressenden Place, London SW1E 5DU
Tel: (020) 7890 3704
Internet: http://www.dtlr.gov.uk

**General Register Office for England and
Wales**
PO Box 2, Southport PR8 2JD
Tel: (0870) 243 7788

General Register Office for Scotland
New Register House, 3 West Register Street,
Edinburgh EH1 3YP.
Tel: (0131) 334 0380

**General Register Office for Northern
Ireland**
Oxford House, 49-55 Chichester Street, Belfast
BT1 4HL.
Tel: (028) 9025 2000

Department for Education and Skills
Sanctuary Buildings, Great Smith Street, London
SW1P 3BT
Tel: (020) 7925 5000
Internet: http://www.dfes.gov.uk

**Department of Education for Northern
Ireland**
Rathgael House, Balloo Road, Bangor, County
Down BT19 7PR

Tel: (028) 9127 9279
Internet: http://www.deni.gov.uk

Scottish Executive Education Department
Victoria Quay, Edinburgh EH6 6QQ
Tel: (0131) 556 8400

**Training and Education Department
National Assembly for Wales**
National Assembly for Wales, Cathays Park,
Cardiff CF10 3NQ
Tel: (029) 2082 5111

FURTHER READING

Abrams, M, Gerard, D and Timms, N (eds),
Values and Social Change in Britain, MacMillan,
London, 1985.

Archbishops' Commission, *Church and State
1970*, (reprinted), Church Information Office,
London, 1985.

Badham, P, "Religious Pluralism in Modern
Britain", in Gilley, S and Sheils, W (eds), *A
History of Religion in Britain: Practice and Belief
from Pre-Roman Times to the Present*, Blackwell,
Oxford, 1984, pp 488-502.

Badham, P (ed), *Religion, State and Society in
Modern Britain*, Edwin Mellen Press, Lampeter,
1989.

Badham, P, "The contribution of religion to
the conflict in Northern Ireland", in Cohn-
Sherbok, D (ed), *The Canterbury Papers: Essays
on Religion and Society*, Bellew, London, 1990, pp
119-128.

Ballard, R (ed), *Desh Pardesh: The South Asian
Presence in Britain*, Hurst and Co, London, 1994.

Ballard, R and Kalra, V, *The Ethnic Dimensions of
the 1991 Census*, Manchester University Press,
Manchester, 1994.

Barker, D, Holman, L and Vloet, A, *The European
Values Study, 1981-1990: Summary Report*,
Gordon Cook Foundation, Aberdeen, 1992.

Barker, E, *New Religious Movements: A Practical Introduction*, HMSO, London, 1989.

Barley, C, Field, C, Kosmin, B and Nielsen, J, *Religion: Reviews of United Kingdom Statistical Sources, Volume XX*, Pergamon Press, Oxford, 1987.

Barot, R (ed), *Religion and Ethnicity: Minorities and Social Change in the Metropolis*, Kok Pharos, Kampen, 1993.

Barrett, D, *World Christian Encyclopaedia: A Comparative Survey of Churches and Religions*, 2nd edition, Oxford University Press, Oxford, 2000.

Bauman, G, "Religious Migrants in Secular Britain: The State as an Agent of Religious Encorporation", in *Etnofoor*, Volume VIII, No. 2, pp 31-46.

Bauman, G, *Contesting Cultures: Discourses of Identity in Multi-Ethnic Britain*, Cambridge University Press, Cambridge, 1996.

Bauman, G, *The Multicultural Riddle: Rethinking National, Ethnic and Religious Identities*, Routledge, London, 1999.

Beckford, J and Gilliat, S, *The Church of England and Other Faiths in a Multi-Faith Society*, Warwick Working Papers in Sociology, University of Warwick, Coventry, 1996.

Beckford, J and Gilliat, S, *The Church of England and Other Faiths in a Multi-Faith Society, Volume I & Volume II*, Department of Sociology, University of Warwick, Coventry, 1996.

Beckford, J and Gilliat, S, *The Church of England and Other Faiths in a Multi-Faith Society: Summary Report*, Department of Sociology, University of Warwick, Coventry, 1996.

Beckford, J and Gilliat, S, *Religion in Prison: Equal Rites in a Multi-Faith Society*, Cambridge University Press, Cambridge, 1998.

Berman, D, *A History of Atheism in Britain: From Hobbes to Russell*, Croom Helm, London, 1988.

Bishop, P, "Victorian Values? Some Antecedents of a Religiously Plural Society", in Hooker, R and Sargant, J (ed), *Belonging to Britain: Christian Perspectives on a Plural Society*, Council of Churches for Britain and Ireland, London, nd, pp 31-52.

Bradney, A, "Separate schools, ethnic minorities and the law", in *New Community*, Volume XIII, No 3, Spring 1987, pp 412-420.

Bradney, A, *Religions, Rights and Laws*, Leicester University Press, Leicester, 1993.

Brierley, P, *'Christian' England: What the English Church Census Reveals*, MARC Europe, London, 1991.

Brierley, P, *Religious Trends No. 2, 2000/01 Millennium Edition*, Christian Research Association, London, 2000.

Brierley, P, "Religion", in Halsey, A and Webb, J, *British Social Trends 2000*, Macmillan, Basingstoke, 2000.

Brown, A, *Festivals in World Religions*, Longmans, Essex, 1986.

Bruce, S, *Religion in Modern Britain*, Oxford University Press, Oxford, 1995.

Buchanan, C, *Cut the Connection: Disestablishment and the Church of England*, Darton, Longman and Todd, London, 1994.

Chalke, S, *Faithworks: Actions Speak Louder than Words*, Kingsway Publications, Eastbourne, 2001.

Charlton, R and Kay, R, "The politics of religious slaughter: an ethno-religious case study", in *New Community*, Volume XII, No 3, Winter 1985-86, pp 409-503.

Cohen, J, Howard, M and Nussbaun (eds), *Is Multiculturalism Bad for Women?*, Princeton University Press, New Jersey, 1999.

Cohn-Sherbok, D and McClellan, D (eds), *Religion in Public Life*, Macmillan, London, 1992.

Comerford, R, Cullen, M and Hill, J, *Religion, Conflict and Coexistence in Ireland*, Gill and Macmillan, London, 1990.

Commission for Racial Equality, *Britain a Plural Society: Report of a Seminar*, Commission for Racial Equality, London, 1990.

Commission for Racial Equality, *Schools of Faith: Religious Schools in a Multi-Cultural Society*, Commission for Racial Equality, London, 1990.

Commission for Racial Equality, *Religious Discrimination: Your Rights*, Commission for Racial Equality, London, 1997.

Commission on the Future of Multi-Ethnic Britain, *The Future of Multi-Ethnic Britain*, Profile Books, London, 2000.

Copley, T, *Teaching Religion: Fifty Years of Religious Education in England and Wales*, Exeter University Press, Exeter, 1997.

Council of Europe, *Religion and the Integration of Migrants*, Council of Europe, Strasbourg, 1999.

Coward, H, Hinnells, J and Williams, R, *The South Asian Religious Diaspora in Britain, Canada and the United States*, State University of New York Press, Albany, 2000.

Davie, G, *Religion in Britain Since 1945: Believing Without Belonging*, Blackwell, Oxford, 1994.

Davie, G, *Religion in Modern Europe: A Memory Mutates*, Oxford University Press, Oxford, 2000.

Department for the Environment, Transport and the Regions, *Challenging Religious Discrimination: A Guide for Faith Communities and their Advisers*, Department for the Environment, Transport and the Regions, London, 1996.

Edwards, D, "A Brief History of the Concept of Toleration in Britain", in Horton, J and Crabtree, H (eds), *Toleration and Integrity in a Multi-Faith Society*, University of York Department of Politics, York, 1992, pp 41–49.

Edge, P and Harvey, G, *Law and Religion in Contemporary Society: Communities, Individualism and the State*, Ashgate, Aldershot, 2000.

Forrester, D, *Beliefs, Values and Policies*, Oxford University Press, Oxford, 1990.

Froh, M, *Roots of the Future: Ethnic Diversity in the Making of Britain*, Commission for Racial Equality, London, 1996.

Fryer, P, *Staying Power: The History of Black People in Britain*, Pluto, London, 1984.

Gilbert, A D, *The Making of Post-Christian Britain: A History of the Secularization of Modern Society*, Longman, Essex, 1980.

Gill, S, D'Costa, G and King, U (eds), *Religion in Europe: Contemporary Perspectives*, Kok Pharos, Kampen, 1994.

Gilley, S and Sheils, W (eds), *A History of Religion in Britain: Practice and Belief from Pre-Roman Times to the Present*, Blackwell, Oxford, 1994.

Gilliat-Ray, S, *Higher Education and Student Religious Identity*, Department of Sociology, University of Exeter, Exeter, in association with the Inter Faith Network for the United Kingdom, London, 1999.

Gilliat-Ray, S, *Religion in Higher Education: The Politics of the Multi-Faith Campus*, Ashgate, Aldershot, 2000.

Gunter, B and Viney, R, *Seeing Is Believing: Religion and Television in the 1990s*, John Libbey and Co, London, 1994.

Halstead, M, *The Case for Muslim Voluntary-Aided Schools: Some Philosophical Reflections*, Islamic Academy, Cambridge, 1986.

Harding, S, Phillips, D and Fogarty, M, *Contrasting Values in Western Europe*, Macmillan, Basingstoke, 1986.

Harrison, P, *'Religion' and the Religions in the English Enlightenment* Cambridge University Press, Cambridge, 1990.

Hastings, A, *Church and State: The English Experience*, University of Exeter Press, Exeter, 1991.

Hepple, B and Choudhary, T, *Tackling Religious Discrimination: Practical Implications for Policy Makers and Legislators*, Home Office Research Study 221, Home Office Research, Development and Statistics Directorate, London, 2001.

Hooker, R, and Sargant, J (eds), *Belonging to Britain: Christian Perspectives on a Plural Society*, Council of Churches for Britain and Ireland, London, nd.

Horton, J, "Religion and Toleration: Some Problems and Possibilities", in Horton, J and Crabtree, H (eds), *Toleration and Integrity in a Multi-Faith Society*, University of York Department of Politics, York, 1992, pp 62-70.

Horton, J (ed), *Liberalism, Multiculturalism and Toleration*, Macmillan, London, 1993.

Horton, J and Crabtree, H (eds), *Toleration and Integrity in a Multi-Faith Society*, University of York Department of Politics, York, 1992.

Hulmes, E, *Education and Cultural Diversity*, Longman, Harlow, 1989.

Inner Cities Religious Council, *Challenging Religious Discrimination: A Guide for Faith Communities and their Advisers*.

Inter Faith Network for the UK and Commission for Racial Equality, *Law, Blasphemy and the Multi-Faith Society*, Commission for Racial Equality, London, 1990.

Inter Faith Network for the UK, *Places of Worship: The Practicalities and Politics of Sacred Space in Multi-Faith Britain*, Inter Faith Network for the UK, London, 1995.

Inter Faith Network for the UK, *Britain's Faith Communities: Equal Citizens?*, Inter Faith Network for the UK, London, 1996.

Jones, T, *Britain's Ethnic Minorities*, Policy Studies Institute, London, 1993.

Kerr, D (ed), *Religion, State and Ethnic Groups*, Dartmouth Publishing Company, Aldershot, 1992.

Kerr, D, "Religion, State and Ethnic Identity", in *Religion, State and Ethnic Groups*, Dartmouth Publishing Company, Aldershot, 1992, pp 1-26.

Lamont, S, *Church and State: Uneasy Alliances*, Bodley Head, London, 1989.

Larsen, T, *Friends of Religious Equality: Nonconformist Politics in Mid-Victorian England*, The Boydell Press, Woodbridge, 1999.

Lynch, J, "Cultural Pluralism, Structural Pluralism and the United Kingdom", in Commission for Racial Equality, *Britain a Plural Society: Report of a Seminar*, Commission for Racial Equality, London, 1990, pp 29-43.

Modood, T, "Religious anger and minority rights", in *Political Quarterly*, Volume LX, July-September, 1989, pp 280-285.

Modood, T, *Not Easy Being British: Colour, Culture and Citizenship*, Trentham Books, Stoke-on-Trent, 1992.

Modood, T, "Minorities, faith and citizenship", in *Discernment: A Christian Journal for Inter-Religious Encounter*, Volume VI, No. 2, 1992, pp 58-60.

Modood, T, "Establishment, multiculturalism and British citizenship", in *Political Quarterly*, Volume LXV, No. 1, January-March, 1993, pp 53-73.

Modood, T, "Establishment, multiculturalism and British citizenship", in *Political Quarterly*, Volume LXV, January 1994, pp 53-59.

Modood, T, "Ethno-religious minorities, secularism and the British state", in *British Political Quarterly*, Volume LXV, 1994, pp 53-73.

Modood, T, (ed) *Church, State and Religious Minorities*, Policy Studies Institute, London, 1997.

Modood, T, "Introduction: Establishment, Reform and Multiculturalism", in Modood, T (ed), *Church, State and Religious Minorities*, Policy Studies Institute, London, 1997, pp 3-15.

Modood, T, "Anti-Essentialism, Multiculturalism and the 'Recognition' of Religious Groups", in *Journal of Political Philosophy*, Volume 6, no 4, 1998, pp 378-399.

Modood, T, Beishon, S and Virdee, S, *Changing Ethnic Identities*, Policy Studies Institute, London, 1994.

Modood, T, Berthoud, R, et al, *Ethnic Minorities in Britain: Diversity and Disadvantage*, Policy Studies Institute, London, 1997.

Modood, T and Werbner, P (eds), *The Politics of Multiculturalism in the New Europe: Racism, Identity and Community*, Zed Books, London, 1997.

Modood, T and Werbner, P (eds), *Debating Cultural Hybridity: Multi-Cultural Identities and the Politics of Anti-Racism*, Zed Books, London, 1997.

Murphy, T, "Toleration and the Law", in Horton, J and Crabtree, H (eds), *Toleration and Integrity in a Multi-Faith Society*, University of York Department of Politics, York, 1992, pp 50-61.

Nielsen, J, *Islamic Law: Its Significance for the Situation of Muslim Minorities in Europe*, Research Papers on Muslims in Europe, No 35, September 1987.

Office for National Statistics, *Britain 2001: The Official Yearbook of the United Kingdom*, The Stationery Office, London, 2001.

Office for National Statistics, *Social Trends 31: 2001 Edition*, The Stationery Office, London, 2001.

Pan, L, *The Encylopaedia of the Chinese Overseas*, Curzon Press, Richmond, 1998.

Parekh, B, "Britain and the Social Logic of Pluralism", in Commission for Racial Equality, *Britain a Plural Society: Report of a Seminar*, Commission for Racial Equality, London, 1990, pp 58-78.

Parekh, B, *Rethinking Multiculturalism: Cultural Diversity and Political Theory*, Macmillan, Basingstoke, 2000.

Parsons, G (ed), *The Growth of Religious Diversity: Britain From 1945, Volume I: Traditions*, Routledge/Open University, London, 1993.

Parsons, G (ed), *The Growth of Religious Diversity: Britain From 1945, Volume II: Issues*, Routledge/Open University, London, 1994.

Patel, N, Naik, D and Humphries, B (eds), *Visions of Reality: Religion and Ethnicity in Social Work*, Central Council for Education and Training in Social Work, London, 1998.

Pearl, D, *Family Law and the Immigrant Communities*, Jordan's, London, 1986.

Poulter, S, *English Law and Ethnic Minority Customs*, Butterworth's, London, 1986.

Poulter, S, *Asian Traditions and English Law: A Handbook*, Trentham Books, Stoke-on-Trent, 1990.

Poulter, S, "Cultural Pluralism and its Limits: a Legal Perspective", in Commission for Racial Equality, *Britain a Plural Society: Report of a Seminar*, Commission for Racial Equality, London, 1990, pp 3-28.

Ratcliffe, P (ed), *Ethnicity in the 1991 Census: Social Geography and Ethnicity in Britain*, Vol 3. HMSO, London, 1996.

Rex, J, *The Concept of a Multi-Cultural Society*, University of Warwick Centre for Research in Ethnic Relations, Coventry, 1985.

Rex, J, "Religion and Ethnicity in the Metropolis", in Barot, R (ed), *Religion and Ethnicity: Minorities and Social Change in the Metropolis*, Kok Pharos, Kampen, 1993, pp 17-26.

Rex, J, *Ethnic Minorities in the Modern Nation State: Working Papers in the Theory of Multi-Culturalism and Political Integration*, Macmillan Press, Basingstoke, 1996.

Rhys, G, "The Divine Economy and the Political Economy: the Theology of Welsh Nationalism", in Hooker, R and Sargant, R, *Belonging to Britain: Christian Perspectives on a Plural Society*, Council of Churches for Britain and Ireland, London, 1991, pp 55-74.

Richardson, N, *A Tapestry of Beliefs: Christian Traditions in Northern Ireland*, Blankstaff Press, Belfast, 1999.

Robbins, K, "Religion and community in Scotland and Wales", in Gilley, S and Sheils, W (eds), *A History of Religion in Britain: Belief and Practice from Pre-Roman Times to the Present*, Blackwell, Oxford, 1994, pp 363-380.

Royal Commission on Reform of the House of Lords, *Reform of A House for the Future: A Summary*, Royal Commission on Reform of the House of Lords, London, 1999.

Ryan, M, *Another Ireland: An Introduction to Ireland's Ethnic-Religious Minority Communities*, Stranmillis University College, Belfast, 1996.

Sacks, J, *The Persistence of Faith*, Weidenfeld and Nicholson, London, 1991.

Saghal, G and Yuval-Davis, N (eds), *Refocusing Holy Orders: Women and Fundamentalism in Britain*, Virago Press, London, 1992.

Schmool, M and Cohen, F, *A Profile of British Jewry*, Board of Deputies of British Jews, London, 1998.

Scottish Office, The, *Ethnic Minorities in Scotland*, HMSO, London, 1991.

Smart, N, "Church, Party and State" in, Badham, P (ed), *Religion, State and Society in Modern Britain*, Edwin Mellen Press, Lampeter, 1989, pp 381-395.

Smith, P, *Ethnic Minorities in Scotland*, Social and Community Planning Research, 1991.

Social Policy Group of the British Council of Churches Committee on Relations with People of Other Faiths and the Race Relations Unit, "Religiously-based voluntary schools", in *Discernment: A Christian Journal of Inter-Religious Encounter*, Volume VI, No 2, 1992, pp 32-40.

Thomas, T (ed), *The British: Their Religious Beliefs and Practices*, Routledge, London, 1988.

Taylor, C, *Multiculturalism and the Politics of Recognition*, Princeton University Press, Princeton, 1992.

Verma, G, "Pluralism: Some Theoretical and Practical Considerations", in Commission for Racial Equality, *Britain a Plural Society: Report of a Seminar*, Commission for Racial Equality, London, 1990, pp 44-57.

Vertovec, S (ed), *Aspects of the South Asian Diaspora, Volume II, part 2: Papers on India*, Oxford University Press, Delhi, 1991.

Viney, R, "Religious Broadcasting on UK Television: policy, public perception and programmes", in *Cultural Trends 36*, 1999.

Visram, R, *Ayahs, Lascars and Princes: The Story of Indians in Britain 1700-1947*, Pluto Press, London, 1986.

Watson, B, "Integrity and Affirmation: an Inclusivist Approach to National Identity", in Hooker, R, and Sargant, J (ed), *Belonging to Britain: Christian Perspectives on a Plural Society*, Council of Churches for Britain and Ireland, London, nd, pp 135-148.

Weller, P, "Integrating religious, social and political values in a multi-cultural society", in *Current Dialogue*, June, 1990, pp 39-44.

Weller, P, "The Rushdie affair, plurality of values and the ideal of a multi-cultural society", in *National Association for Values in Education and Training Working Papers*, Volume II, October 1990, pp 1-9.

Weller, P, "Religion and equal opportunities in Higher Education", in *Cutting Edge*, No 2, 1991, pp 26-36.

Weller, P, "Religion and equal opportunities in Higher Education", in *The Journal of International Education*, Volume III, November, 1992, pp 53-64.

Weller, P, "Values, visions and religions: pluralist problematics in a secular and multi-faith context", in *Cutting Edge*, No 9, February 1994, pp 15-17.

Weller, P, "A Christian perspective on integrating religious, social and political values in a multi-cultural society", in *World Faiths Encounter*, November 1995, pp 28-37.

Weller, P and Andrews, A, *Religions and Statistics Research Project: Report of a Pilot Phase (March 1994-March 1995)*, 1996, University of Derby, Derby.

Weller, P and Andrews, A, "Counting Religion: Religion, Statistics and the 2001 Census", in *World Faiths Encounter*, No. 21, November, 1998, pp 23-34.

Weller, P and Purdam, K, et al, *Religious Discrimination in England and Wales: Interim Report*, University of Derby, Derby, 2000.

Weller, P and Purdam, K, et al, *Religious Discrimination in England and Wales: Executive Summary of an Interim Report*, University of Derby, Derby, 2000.

Weller, P, Feldman, A and Purdam, K, *Religious Discrimination in England and Wales*, Home Office Research Study 220, Home Office Research, Development and Statistics Directorate, London, 2001.

Williams, G, *The Welsh and Their Religion*, University of Wales Press, Cardiff, 1991.

Wilson, B, "Old Laws and New Religions", in Cohn-Sherbok, D (ed), *The Canterbury Papers; Essays on Religion and Society*, Bellew Publishing, London, 1990, pp 210-224.

Wolffe, J (ed), *The Growth of Religious Diversity: Britain From 1945. A Reader*, Hodder and Stoughton, Sevenoaks, 1993.

Wolffe, J, "Religions of the silent majority", in Parsons, G (ed) (1993), *The Growth of Religious Diversity: Britain from 1945. Volume I: Traditions*, Routledge, London, 1993, pp 305-346.

Wolffe, J, *God and Greater Britain: Religion and National Life in Britain and Ireland, 1843-1945*, Routledge, London, 1994.

Wolffe, J, "And there's another country....': religion, the state and British identities", in Parsons, G (ed), *The Growth of Religious Diversity: Britain From 1945. Volume II, Issues*, Routledge, London, 1994, pp 85-159.

Yarrow, S, *Religious and Political Discrimination in the Workplace*, Policy Studies Institute, London, 1997.

York, M, *The Emerging Network: A Sociology of New Age and Neo-Pagan Movements*, Rowman and Littlewood, London, 1995.

Yuval-Davis, N, "Fundamentalism, Multiculturalism and Women in Britain", in Donald, J and Rattansi, A, (eds) *'Race' Culture and Difference*, Sage, London, pp 278-291, 1992.

MAKING CONTACTS, ORGANISING EVENTS AND CONSULTATIONS

INTRODUCTION   63

MAKING CONTACT   63

ARRANGING A MULTI-FAITH
EVENT   64

ARRANGING MULTI-FAITH
CONSULTATIONS OR PANELS   68

PRODUCING GUIDELINES   69

FURTHER HELP   69

INTRODUCTION

This chapter offers some pointers to organising events, projects or consultations which draw together members of different religious communities. There are no hard and fast guidelines as to how to do this successfully but this chapter may offer some useful ideas.

MAKING CONTACT

The Importance of the Introductory Materials

The directory lists most of the key religious organisations and groups in the United Kingdom and includes material about the basic aspects of each religion, especially as it is represented in the UK.

Although much is held in common within individual religious communities, within most there are also a number of different traditions of interpretation and it is helpful to have a sense of these when planning to contact particular groups. The introductory chapters on each of the religions in the UK contained in the directory are therefore designed to convey something of the diversity within each community, as well as an appreciation of its common beliefs and practices.

Understanding the context is particularly helpful when planning a multi-faith event or consultation which it is intended will be representative of the religions involved. Knowing from which part of a religion a possible speaker or participant comes can help ensure balance and avoid later difficulties. For consultation purposes it can also be worth bearing in mind that within any given religious community, many ethnic and national backgrounds are likely to be represented.

Some Things to be Aware of When Making Contact

Contacts for the various religious organisations are generally happy to explain more about their community and to help with enquiries. However, this partly depends on the time they have available. If seeking information or organising an event, it is important to allow ample time for getting hold of the contact people and arranging a time to speak with them.

It is often helpful, when inviting a speaker, to write to them first, in order to give them some time to consider the invitation, and then to follow this up with a telephone call. Sometimes people who are not fluent in the enquirer's first language, and in whose first language the enquirer may not be fluent, will answer the telephone and it will be necessary to ring back later or ask for an alternative contact number.

It may be necessary to ring an organisation several times because contact people for the various religious communities are usually extremely busy and often work on a voluntary basis. *Imams*, *vicars*, temple secretaries, women's group leaders and others have hectic schedules and may have full-time employment in addition to voluntary work on behalf of their community. Having made an arrangement for someone to speak or contribute to a consultation it is wise to check on the day before the event that the person is still planning to come or has found a suitable substitute (if necessary).

Possible Areas of Sensitivity

Many people will be keen to respond positively to invitations. However, there are certain areas of sensitivity of which it is helpful to be aware when making contact. Sometimes, the previous experiences or the beliefs of the person being contacted may make them suspicious of, or even hostile towards inter-faith encounter or multi-faith initiatives. Where communities or their members have been the target of conversion campaigns by other religious groups, or have in the past found themselves drawn into some kind of syncretistic inter faith encounter which has not honoured the

integrity of the participating traditions, there may be particular wariness about inter-religious encounter. It is very important to explain the context of an enquiry or approach.

Avoiding Stereotypes

It is important, in sensitive ways, to ask faith community groups or individuals what they believe and consider important. Religion is not monolithic and it can be unhelpful and dangerous to operate with a stereotypical concept of, for example, a Bahá'í, a Christian or a Jew (even where this is based on much research). Some people born into religious communities may not consider themselves any longer to be members of that community. There are some atheists, agnostics and humanists who would find it unacceptable to be asked to say what their religious background is. Likewise, there may be people who belong to a tradition by birth, and for whom religion is still important, but who do not set particular store by ceremonial or ritual observance and may also not observe the usual dietary regulations. In all cases, it is best to allow people to define their own religious identity.

ARRANGING A MULTI-FAITH EVENT

The following checklist may be helpful for organisers of events involving a number of religious traditions.

Avoid Clashes with Religious Festivals

Double check the date for the event so that it does not clash with one of the key festivals or special days of a group that is likely to be involved. The annual Shap Calendar of Festivals (available from the Shap Working Party, c/o The National Society's Religious Education Centre, 36 Causton Street, London, SW1P 4AU, Tel: 020-7932-1190) is a vital resource for this. Many commercial diaries now also include the main festival dates from a range of religions. If in any doubt about the significance of the festival (in other words, whether it is one that means those observing it are unlikely to be able to attend other events), then contact the relevant community to double-check details.

Fridays are difficult for observant Muslims, and especially for *imams*, because of the importance of the Friday midday prayer. If possible, avoid scheduling afternoon events during the period of *Ramadan* when practising Muslims *fast* from before dawn until sunset. From midday on Friday until sunset on Saturday can be problematic for observant Jews in relation to events involving travel and what could be construed as "work" (although interpretations of this vary within different parts of the community).

For *church*-going Christians, and for members of other faiths who meet regularly on Sundays, that day can be difficult. However, because of the practical difficulty for many people of not being able to take time off during the working week, weekend events may prove necessary. If planning a weekend event, it is important to check with members of these religions how they personally feel about attending on these days or about their participation during particular parts of the event's timetable.

Allow Plenty of Planning And Organising Time

Planning time of at least two to three months is advisable for local events and, for national events, a lead time of at least six, and preferably nine to twelve months will probably be needed. Good speakers and participants are obtainable from all religious communities, but are likely to have quite full diaries and need to be booked well in advance (except for response to political or social emergencies). Participant lists also take time to draw up and, if the event involves people needing to take time off work or to arrange child care, adequate notice is needed.

Choose an Appropriate Venue

It is important to use a venue in which participants feel at ease. For example, for a local inter-faith group just starting up and without a strong sense of each other's views and sensitivities, a meeting at a member's house or on "neutral" ground such as a local school or village hall might be the best way to begin, rather than meeting at one community's place of worship (even if such venues are later used).

If a meeting is to be held at the premises of a faith community it is important to discover where the "sacred" area of the religious building is. There may be other parts, such as a social meeting hall, which are not so imbued with religious and symbolic significance and which might therefore be more appropriate for inter-faith meetings. This is because participants of different religions may feel more comfortable about meeting in these other areas (for example in the community centre attached to a *mandir*). They may not, however, feel comfortable about any visit which would involve them in entering the sacred space where they might feel obliged to offer gestures of respect to another's sacred symbols (or might be worried about causing offence in declining to do so for religious reasons).

In a *gurdwara*, *mandir* or a *mosque*, for example, the sacred area is clearly definable by the point beyond which visitors should not go without removing their shoes. In Christian *churches*, the matter may be less clear-cut because, particularly in modern and adapted buildings, meetings without a specifically religious purpose sometimes take place even in what is the *church* itself, as distinct from its *church* hall. The introductory materials on each religious community and the chapter on "Visiting Places of Worship and Hosting Visits" provide further background on sacred buildings, their contents and significance.

Religious Observance During an Event

Members of all the different religious traditions may wish to retire for prayer or meditation at certain points during the day and time should be left within the schedule for this after consultation with members of the religious traditions involved. However, practising Muslims pray five times a day at specific times. For Muslims, it is important also to offer a room for prayer, showing the direction of Mecca, and to provide a sheet for covering the floor for prayer, as well as a bowl and jug of water and a towel for ablutions before prayer. If there is a toilet or bathroom nearby with washing facilities this is usually sufficient.

Shared Religious Observance During an Event

Any shared religious observance should be approached with great care. The least controversial option is a shared silent meditation or wordless prayer. If there is any doubt about the feelings of the participants it is wise to go for this choice. When spoken prayers or readings are used there is always the danger that people find themselves voluntarily or involuntarily joining in what appears to be a lowest common denominator activity, or which presupposes a particular view of the basic unity of all religions. For example, participants may not be able to recognise in it worship of the deity to which they are themselves committed. Similarly, non-*theists* (such as Buddhists or Jains) can be put into an awkward situation by assumptions that all religions acknowledge a deity. For traditions where the divine is understood wholly or partly in feminine or impersonal terms, the exclusive use of masculine or personal terms may prove alienating. Given these possibilities of misunderstanding and offence, it is necessary to proceed with caution.

However, there are occasions when people may very much wish to meet together for prayer, or when civic life calls for communal celebration or mourning. In such contexts a widely used option is what is sometimes called "serial worship". In serial worship, members of different religions pray or offer a reading relevant to the theme to which others listen but in which they do not join. Rather, prayer is offered individually by members of the gathering in a way which respects the integrity of their own tradition.

Because the Church of England is the established Church in England, its *churches* and especially *cathedrals* have often been the venue for this kind of civic or communal worship. There are both opportunities and difficulties associated with this which are discussed in the booklet *Multi-Faith Worship?*, Church House Publishing, London, 1992 and in *All in Good Faith*, published by the World Congress of Faiths.

Catering for Multi-Faith Events

Many religious traditions have certain dietary requirements as a result of their beliefs. These are explained in more detail in the appropriate introductory material on each religion. Generally speaking, the easiest way to cater for a multi-faith event is to make it absolutely vegetarian. It is helpful to label food where its contents are not immediately apparent.

No animal fat should be used in any vegetarian cooking and when cheese is used it should be marked "vegetarian" on the packet indicating that it has not been made with rennet which is a meat product of cows. Puddings should not include gelatine (unless it is of a vegetarian variety). Cakes and biscuits should include no animal fat or gelatine. Some butter substitutes contain rendered beef fat, so labels need careful checking.

Within the vegetarian dishes, make sure that at least some contain no eggs or milk products like cheese, and that some of these non-egg dishes also contain no garlic or onions (since all these may be unacceptable to some Hindus, observant Jains and also some other groupings). Observant Jains avoid eating all root vegetables that produce numerous sprouts from the skin (such as potatoes).

Within Judaism, the *kosher* rules are widely observed but with differing interpretations.

Check in advance how any Jewish participants in the event interpret them. Normally, it is sufficient to provide vegetarian food and disposable plates, cups and cutlery. However, for the very *Orthodox*, it is necessary to provide separate meals which have been prepared in a *kosher* kitchen. *Kosher* foods include *kosher* wine, bread and cheese as well as meats. Such food and drink is marked with a *hechsher* (seal) which certifies it to be *kosher*. A local *synagogue* can be asked for advice on vendors and also on any meals to be served during the festival of *Pesach/Passover* when special requirements apply.

Muslims will wish that, if possible, their food be prepared in a kitchen where the utensils (including knives) and contents have not been in contact with *haram* (forbidden) food. However, most Muslims are primarily concerned to ensure that any meat served is *halal* (permitted and slaughtered according to the *Shari'ah*), and are generally happy to eat vegetarian food that has no animal fat used in its production.

Buddhist *monks* frequently do not eat after midday. In an all day event it may therefore be important to provide substantial refreshments for them earlier in the morning. Some Christians fast on *Ash Wednesday* and limit the range of foods consumed during *Lent*. Some Jains do not eat after sunset. During *Ramadan*, most Muslims do not eat between dawn and sunset. Many Sikhs are vegetarian, but Sikhs who do eat meat are not permitted to eat *halal* or *kosher* meat.

Different traditions have varying approaches to the consumption of alcohol. In Islam it is considered *haram* (forbidden) to consume alcohol, even as an ingredient in cooked foods or sauces. Some Muslims may also consider socialising with those who are drinking alcohol to be prohibited. For Hindus and Jains it is considered undesirable. *Amritdhari* (initiated) Sikhs are also required to avoid alcohol. For most Christians alcohol is not prohibited, although some groups advocate abstinence. Within Judaism there is likewise no prohibition and responsible use of alcohol is not frowned upon. Practice varies among Buddhists although alcohol is viewed as dangerous in so far as it can hinder *mindfulness*. Bahá'ís are not allowed to consume alcohol, even as an ingredient in cooked foods or sauces.

Because of the diversity of practice within religions, alcohol is often not served at a specifically inter-faith event. If you do provide alcohol at a function, it is wise to provide only wine and to set it at some distance from the non-alcoholic drinks. Fruit juices and mineral water should always be provided as an alternative. Coffee and tea, as stimulants, are avoided by observant members of certain traditions. It is therefore important to provide fruit juice, water or herbal tea as alternatives to morning and afternoon coffee and tea.

Gender Relations

It is important to be aware of differing attitudes to the roles and relationships of men and women. These may vary even within one religious tradition according to how a group interprets that tradition and according to the cultural background in which their tradition has been practised.

For example, a *Chasidic* Jewish family will have a somewhat different dynamic from a *Reform* Jewish one, and Christians within various traditions may differ radically one from another concerning what they believe the *Bible* and tradition teaches about the roles of Christian men and women. Within Islam, interpretations of the *Qur'an* and *Shari'ah* by the different legal schools mean that there is a legitimate diversity of interpretation. However, modesty is an important concept in Islam for both women and men. Some interpret this to mean that single sex events should be the norm. Others interpret it to mean that a careful, formal and modest manner should characterise meetings between people of different sexes in public contexts.

Within almost every religious tradition there are those who believe that women should not exercise a public leadership role and there are those who believe they can do so. This can occasionally lead to some awkwardness when seeking women to participate in multi-faith events and panels.

Generally speaking the best rule is to proceed with courtesy and care in requests for speakers and to try to accommodate requests for such things as hotel rooms in separate parts of the building for men and women, or perhaps to consider offering additional travel expenses to allow a person's husband, wife or family member to travel with them for reasons of propriety.

Consider Arranging a Crèche

The provision of a crèche will support family participation.

ARRANGING MULTI-FAITH CONSULTATIONS OR PANELS

When people are looking for contributions from different faith communities on particular issues, such as disability, inner city regeneration or sex education, there are some questions worth asking prior to setting up the consultation:

What Kind of Input is Actually Wanted?

Depending on the project, it might be most appropriate to bring together some or all of the following:

- Religious experts (including scholars or knowledgeable *clergy* or *laity*).
- Religious community leaders (who are not necessarily scholars or religious teachers themselves but can be official representatives).

- "Ordinary" members of particular faith communities (including women and young people).
- Members of religious communities with expertise on a particular topic.

Often a mixture of different kinds of participants is needed. For example, suppose a project is being set up to determine what different religions have to say about the care of the elderly. It might be good to include an expert who can give an overview of what the sacred texts and historical traditions have said. At the same time it could also be important to include members of faith communities who are older citizens and have thought about what their religion means in the context of their own ageing, as well as carers who are putting their faith into practice in caring for the elderly. There are many options and it is important to decide what it is hoped to gain from the encounter.

What Should the Composition of a Panel/Consultants be?

The scope, timetable and financing of any project will clearly define some of the constraints. However, there are certain questions which it is important to ask at the outset:

- From which religions is an input sought?
- Should all the religions represented in the UK be represented, or just the larger faith communities?
- Are there occasions on which it is important to include smaller traditions within religions which are often perceived as being less mainstream? (particularly, for example, Jehovah's Witnesses or Christian Scientists, when health issues are being discussed)
- Should the panel or consultants reflect the national religious composition of the UK, or of the geographical areas in which particular religions are most involved? (Jains, for

example, might be a small grouping nationally but are particularly important in a city such as Leicester).

- Is input needed from: both men and women; people of varying ages; and lay people as well as *clergy*?

Such questions can only be answered in the context of a particular project. People often overlook the smaller religious communities, but if a project is working on an issue such as medical ethics its organisers may, for example, want to make a special effort to include a tradition which has a particular contribution to make to the discussion, even if that tradition is numerically not a large one in the UK.

For some purposes a "representative group" is sought. The diversity within and between most religious communities makes this difficult to achieve. It takes a while to establish who are the key figures in a religious tradition in a particular area of the country. It is also not always easy to find out who is genuinely representative and what their capacity is to relay information back to that community or to provide accurate information about what that community itself needs.

If seeking to involve religious "leaders", it will become apparent that the nature of these may vary very widely between traditions, as will the understanding of who or what is a religious leader. The role of an *imam*, for example, is not strictly comparable to that of a *vicar*. The job of a Sikh *granthi* is likewise very different.

Different community structures have given rise to different types of religious personnel functions and roles. Information on some of these roles can be found in the directory's introduction to the various communities. Care should be taken not to assume that religious leaders in other communities will conform to the pattern of the Christian *Churches*. With regard to all religious traditions, women and men under forty rarely appear in consultations where the membership draws solely upon religious leaderships.

PRODUCING GUIDELINES

Producing Information Packs

This will depend on what kind of information is needed. If it is basic information about different religions, many good resources already exist. It may not be necessary to arrange for consultants from different religions to produce an entirely new pack. At the same time, putting together such material can, in itself, be an important learning experience.

Some national religious organisations may have staff available to respond to written requests for information or invitations to participate in various events. Many do not, and this is also true at local level. If no reply is received to a request for help within a couple of weeks, it may be necessary to follow up the letter with a phone call.

If producing pamphlets or guidance for service providers working with people of a variety of religions, as noted earlier in this chapter, it is important to avoid stereotypes and in producing accessible materials, also to make clear that there can be a wide variety of interpretation, and degrees of strictness in observance.

FURTHER HELP

For further advice and information on the points discussed in this chapter or to be put in touch with individuals and organisations who can advise or assist, contact the Inter Faith Network (5-7 Tavistock Place, London, WC1H 9SN, Tel: (020) 7388 0008 or Email: ifnet@interfaith.org.uk). Information and advice can also be obtained from the other organisations listed in the chapter on "Inter-Faith Activity in the UK" and from the chapter on "Finding Out More: Some Other Relevant Publications and Resources".

VISITING PLACES OF WORSHIP AND HOSTING VISITS

INTRODUCTION   71

VISITING PLACES OF WORSHIP   71

VISITING A BAHÁ'Í PLACE OF
WORSHIP   72

VISITING A BUDDHIST TEMPLE   72

VISITING A CHRISTIAN
CHURCH   72

VISITING A HINDU MANDIR   73

VISITING A JAIN TEMPLE   74

VISITING A JEWISH
SYNAGOGUE   74

VISITING A MUSLIM MOSQUE   75

VISITING A SIKH GURDWARA   75

VISITING A ZOROASTRIAN
PLACE OF WORSHIP   76

HOSTING VISITS TO PLACES
OF WORSHIP   77

FURTHER HELP   77

INTRODUCTION

In the introductory materials on each religious community a description is given of what a visitor may see if visiting the places of worship of that religious tradition. Also included is a description of the personnel the visitor is likely to meet and explanations of some of the key concepts found in the religious tradition concerned.

Usually people are delighted to show others their place of worship. It is a sharing of what they hold very dear. They will, however, hope that the visitor observes certain basic rules of conduct.

VISITING PLACES OF WORSHIP

Before going to another's place of worship it is important that visitors give some thought to how they feel about such matters as joining in a service, or receiving food that has been offered to the deities of other religions and has been blessed. It is quite possible to visit others' places of worship without this kind of participation as long as reservations are explained courteously in advance.

The religious community being visited would not want visitors to feel ill at ease. Likewise, they would not wish to be made ill at ease themselves by criticisms of their ways of worship or of their religion. Questions are always welcomed but negative comparisons with the visitor's own customs are unlikely to promote a friendly relationship!

Whether visiting alone, or as a group, it is important to follow the guidelines for clothing and behaviour so as not to cause offence. For groups, it is important not to talk loudly, thus disturbing any who may be at prayer. If any group members have special needs, let the members of the place/centre that is being visited know about this in advance so that they can prepare to help. For example, although the normal custom of the place of worship in question may be to sit on the floor or to stand for worship, chairs can often be provided for elderly, infirm or disabled visitors.

Ask before taking any photographs as this is not always allowed.

VISITING A BAHÁ'Í PLACE OF WORSHIP

There are no formal buildings for Bahá'í worship in the UK. Gatherings are held at the Bahá'í Centre in London and various regional Bahá'í centres, as well as in members' homes or meeting rooms. Interested members of other religious traditions are welcome to attend *Unity Feasts* and other meetings for worship and prayer, as well as *Holy Day* celebrations. Those wishing to attend a Bahá'í meeting should contact the secretary of the *Local Assembly* to make suitable arrangements.

Clothing in Bahá'í Places of Worship

There are no special requirements, although it is appropriate to dress tidily and modestly.

Entering the Bahá'í Meeting

Visitors may find a place wherever they feel comfortable.

Bahá'í Worship

A *Unity Feast* begins with devotional readings, prayers or songs. Visitors may join in or not, according to their wish. During prayers, a reverent silence is requested. There is no sacred food or sacrament. The *Feast* closes with a period during which people meet each other and share refreshments.

VISITING A BUDDHIST TEMPLE

Buddhist places of devotion vary considerably in style and practice. Such places may be a part of a *vihara* (a place where *monks* live), or may be found in a centre. In either case, the actual place of devotion is the *shrine room*. The *shrine room* may contain a statue or image of a *Buddha* or, in some Buddhist traditions, of a *Bodhisattva*.

This will be a central position, commonly with an incense holder, flowers and candles by its side.

Clothing in a Buddhist Temple

There are no particular requirements with regard to clothing except that it should be modest. For reasons of practicality it is best if clothing is loose fitting because of the normal practice of sitting on the floor. Because of the need to remove shoes, clean and presentable socks, stockings or tights are a good idea.

Entering a Buddhist Shrine Room

Before entering the *shrine room*, one should remove one's shoes as a mark of respect. Inside the room, seating is generally on the floor and it is appropriate to adopt a quiet and meditative demeanour. One may see Buddhists, on entering a temple or *shrine room*, prostrating themselves three times before the shrine, but visitors would not be expected to do this. In some traditions it is considered disrespectful to sit with one's legs or feet pointed in the direction of the shrine, or with one's back turned to the *Buddha*.

Buddhist Worship

The *shrine room* is primarily a place for meditation and teaching. It is also the place for the performance of *puja*, which is a way of expressing one's devotion by means of offering flowers, lights, incense, food or other gifts. There is no expectation that visitors will participate in this although they may do so, if they wish.

VISITING A CHRISTIAN CHURCH

Clothing in a Christian church

There is a wide variation in practice between different types of *churches*, but as a general rule it is wise to dress tidily and avoid particularly revealing clothing. This is perhaps most strongly true in *Orthodox* as well as conservative *Catholic* and *Protestant churches*. Men traditionally remove their hats when entering *church*. It is a courtesy for any male visitors of other religious traditions who normally keep their head covered for religious reasons, to explain this fact to their hosts. In some very conservative Christian *churches* women are expected to cover their heads.

Entering a church

Most *churches* have *pews* (benches with raised backs) or rows of seats, although in *Orthodox churches* people generally stand for worship. Where there are *pews* or seats, find a seat and sit quietly. Christians will not generally expect visitors to bow or show other forms of special outward respect to the *altar* (or to any of the statues or *icons* that may be found respectively in *Catholic* or *Orthodox churches*). In some *Orthodox* and *Eastern Catholic churches*, women sit on the left and men on the right.

Christian Worship and Sacred Food

Visitors are generally welcome to join in the prayers and hymns of the service if they wish. During services, the congregation may kneel, stand or sit depending on the part of the service. Visitors who are not Christians usually sit and stand with the rest of the congregation and kneel if they feel comfortable doing so.

Visitors attending a *Eucharist/Mass/Communion* service who are not *communicant* Christians will not be expected to take bread or wine (and in many *churches*, may not be allowed to do so). In certain *Protestant churches* the bread and wine of the *Communion* service is passed around the seated congregation. In this case, visitors of other faiths would let the plate and cup pass by to the person next to them.

Visitors to a *church* where people are going up to the *altar* to take *Communion* should simply remain in their seats at this time unless non-*Communion* takers are invited to come forward and receive a *blessing* from the *priest*, when it is optional to do so. If a visitor chooses to go forward to receive a blessing, rather than remain seated, they should stand or kneel with head

bowed, and hands kept folded together or holding a book or service paper so that the priest can see a *blessing* is sought rather than *Communion*. It is important to be aware that the form of any *blessing* will be specifically Christian, including the invocation of the name of Jesus, or of God the Son.

VISITING A HINDU MANDIR

Clothing in a Hindu Mandir

Clothing should be modest for both men and women. Shoes are removed before going into the *mandir* and put on the racks provided. Clean and presentable socks, stockings, or tights are therefore a good idea. Sometimes women are requested to cover their heads and they should also keep in mind that, since they will be sitting on the floor, short dresses and skirts are unsuitable.

Entering a Hindu Mandir

Walk in quietly and find a place to sit on the floor (usually carpeted). In some *mandirs* men and boys sit on one side of the room and women and girls on the other. Sit with crossed legs or with legs pointing to one side. It is considered disrespectful to sit with legs forward with the feet pointing towards the sacred area at the front of the *mandir*. In some *mandirs* guests may be expected to stand as a sign of respect during *arti*.

Hindu Worship and Sacred Food

There is no expectation that visitors join in the formal prayer and worship unless they wish to do so. When Hindus go to the *mandir*, they usually take an offering such as food or money to give to the deities. If the visitor is not a Hindu, this would not be expected although it would be welcomed. If offering food, it should not be cooked food and especially not if it violates the principle of *ahimsa* (not-harming). Fresh fruit or nuts would be appropriate.

Food becomes sacred when given to the deity, usually prior to the ceremony called *arti*. After it becomes sacred it is called *prasada*. Often the blessed food takes the form of sweets or fruit offered on a tray. Visitors are likely to be offered one piece which they can either eat or take home. If taking a piece, hold it in cupped hands with the right hand uppermost. A visitor who is uncomfortable for religious reasons about being given some of this sacred food to eat, should let the offerer know with a quiet "No thank you". If possible, explain to the hosts in advance that this course of action will be taken for personal religious reasons, and not out of any disrespect for them.

A Note for Women

In some *mandirs* women will be expected not to enter the temple during menstruation.

VISITING A JAIN TEMPLE

Clothing in a Jain Temple

Clothing should be modest for both men and women, but need not be formal. Head coverings are not necessary for either sex. Shoes are removed before going into the temple and put on the racks provided. Clean and presentable socks, stockings, or tights are therefore a good idea. All leather objects should be left outside when entering the temple.

Entering a Jain Temple Area

No eating or chewing is allowed in the temple area. When Jains enter the temple they bow to the image in the temple and chant a *mantra*. This will not be expected of a visitor, from whom a reverent silence is appropriate. Walk in quietly and find a place to sit on the floor (usually carpeted). Sit with crossed legs, or with legs pointing to one side. It is considered disrespectful to sit with legs forward with the feet pointing towards the sacred area at the front of the temple or to stand or sit with one's back to the image.

Jain Worship

There is no expectation that visitors will join in the prayer unless they particularly wish to do so. In Jain temples, there is no custom of offering sacred food to devotees or visitors.

A Note for Women

In Jain temples women will be expected not to enter the temple during menstruation.

VISITING A JEWISH SYNAGOGUE

Clothing in a Synagogue

Dress should be modest, with arms and legs covered, but need not be formal. Women should wear a skirt or dress of reasonable length and not trousers. In an *Orthodox synagogue*, married and divorced women should cover their heads. Men and boys should cover their heads when visiting any *synagogue*.

Entering a Synagogue

Non-*kosher* food must not be brought into a *synagogue*. Check before entering whether men and women usually sit separately at the *synagogue* in question. In many *Orthodox synagogues* women sit in a separate balcony or gallery area during worship.

If the community is standing quietly in prayer, then visitors should wait at the back until the prayer has finished since this prayer should not be interrupted. *Sabbath* services in *Orthodox synagogues* can be up to two to three hours long, so visitors are advised to take this into account when planning for their arrivals and departures.

Synagogue Worship and Sacred Food

There is no expectation that visitors join in the worship unless they particularly wish to do so. *Orthodox* services, and many *Masorti* services, are conducted in Hebrew, but prayer books with translations are generally available in bookcases at the back of the *synagogue*. *Reform* services have a high proportion of English, and *Liberal* services are mostly in English.

Visitors will not be expected to make particular gestures of respect toward any objects. No sacred food is distributed during the service but *kiddush* (the Hebrew for *sanctification*) may take place after the service and visitors will be invited to join in this *blessing* which is said or sung over wine and bread in order to give thanks to God for these. The wine and bread will then be shared and will be offered to visitors as a sign of hospitality, although there is no compulsion to take them. Young children are usually given fruit juice.

VISITING A MUSLIM MOSQUE

Clothing in a Mosque

Clothing should be modest for both men and women. For women this means an ankle length skirt or trousers, which should not be tight or transparent, together with a long sleeved and high necked top. A headscarf is usually essential for women. Shoes are removed before going into the prayer hall and put on the racks provided. Clean and presentable socks, stockings, or tights are therefore a good idea.

Entering a Mosque

Where women attend the *mosque*, men and women usually enter the prayer hall by separate entrances. Visitors may be greeted by the Arabic greeting *"Asalaam-u-'alaikum"*, which means "Peace be upon you." The answer, if the visitor would like to use it, is *"Wa 'alaikum-us-salaam"*, or "Peace be upon you too." Do not offer, or expect, to shake hands with people of the opposite sex. Before entering the prayer hall or prayer room, Muslim men and women perform *wudu* or ablutions if they have not already done so earlier. This is not necessary for the non-Muslim visitor who will not be joining in the prayer.

Entering a Mosque Prayer Hall

Go quietly into the hall, and sit on the floor, avoiding pointing the feet in the direction of the *Qibla* (the wall with the niche or alcove in it indicating the direction of Makka), unless a medical condition makes this the only possible posture. If visiting as a group during a time when prayers are taking place, sit together toward the rear of the hall.

Worship in a Mosque

When *salat* (Arabic) or *namaz* (Persian/Urdu), one of the five daily prayers is in progress, non-Muslim visitors are welcomed but simply to observe rather than to join in. If arriving at such a time, find a place near the rear wall and sit quietly observing the prayer. No sacred or blessed food will be offered, nor will visitors be expected to make any physical gesture of respect to holy objects (except removing their shoes and acting respectfully in the prayer hall).

A Note for Women Visiting a Mosque

The main place of prayer is often used only by the men and a separate area is usually provided for women. Where men and women pray in the same hall, they remain in separate groups. Muslim women are expected not to come to the *mosque* during their menstrual period. *Mosque* attendance by Muslim women can vary both according to the Muslim tradition concerned, and the specific local *mosque*.

A Note for Parents of Children Visiting a Mosque

Children under the age of seven are not normally brought to *mosques*, in accordance with the request of the *Prophet*, except on the occasion of *Eid-al-Fitr* or *Eid-al-Adha*.

VISITING A SIKH GURDWARA

Clothing in a Gurdwara

This should be modest for both men and women. Women should wear a long skirt or trousers. Head covering is essential for both women and men. A large clean handkerchief is adequate for men, and women are expected to use scarves. The *gurdwara* will usually have some head coverings available for those who have not brought them, but not necessarily enough for a large group of visitors. Because shoes are removed before going into the *gurdwara* clean and presentable socks, stockings, or tights are therefore a good idea.

Entering a Gurdwara Prayer Hall

No tobacco or alcohol or drugs should ever be taken into the buildings of the *gurdwara* (not just the prayer hall). Smokers should remember to leave their tobacco or cigarettes outside. Shoes should be removed before entering the prayer hall and may also need to be left off before entering the *langar* hall. In addition to covering their heads, vistors may also be asked to wash their hands (which Sikhs do before entering to pray).

On entering, the visitor will see the *Guru Granth Sahib* (the Sikh sacred scripture) placed on a low platform, covered by a canopy. When Sikhs enter they touch the floor before this with their forehead and offer a gift such as food or money. Visitors may also bow in similar fashion as a mark of respect or, if they are uncomfortable with this for religious reasons, they may if they wish simply give a slight bow or stand for a few moments before the *Guru Granth Sahib* in silence as a mark of respect. No gift would be expected from a visitor although, of course, it would be deeply appreciated. If making a gift, leave it with the others on the floor in front of the *Guru Granth Sahib*.

Seating is on the floor (usually carpeted). Men and women usually sit in separate groupings. Sit in a position which avoids the feet being pointed toward the *Guru Granth Sahib*, or the back being turned toward it. Both those positions are considered disrespectful. A cross-legged meditational stance is the usual practice, but simply tucking one's legs in is acceptable.

Worship and Sacred Food in a Gurdwara

If arriving during a time of worship, visitors will normally be expected to join the worshippers, but there is no obligation to participate in the worship itself. At the end of the worship visitors may be offered *karah prashad* (holy food). This is a sweet pudding which has been blessed during the service. It is given to all to signify that all are equal and united in their humanity and that there are no caste distinctions. The *karah prashad* should be eaten with the right hand. It is made of clarified butter, flour, sugar and water. It is therefore buttery in texture and hands need wiping after it has been received. Often, paper napkins are distributed for this purpose.

If uncomfortable, for religious reasons, about being given some of this sacred food to eat, let the offerer know with a quiet "No thank you." If possible, explain to the hosts in advance that this is for reasons of your own personal religious position and not out of any disrespect. The same applies to *langar* (which is the food served in the communal kitchen at the *gurdwara*) since this has also been blessed.

Because the food served in the *langar* has been blessed, head covering is usually maintained in the *langar* hall. The *langar* is a meal to which outsiders are cordially welcomed. However, it is advisable to ask only for as much food as is actually wanted rather than to accept too much and then have to leave some.

VISITING A ZOROASTRIAN PLACE OF WORSHIP

There are no Zoroastrian fire temples in the United Kingdom. There is, however, a room for Zoroastrian worship in Zoroastrian House in London. People from outside the Zoroastrian community may, on occasion, be invited to attend a *jashan* (festival). Non-Zoroastrians are requested not to enter the prayer room known as the *setayeshgah*.

HOSTING VISITS TO PLACES OF WORSHIP

For members of a religious community, it is sometimes easy to forget how strange and complicated the proceedings in their place of worship or meditation may seem to outsiders. Making visitors feel at ease is important. If hosting a visit to a place of worship by people of other traditions it is helpful to think in advance about a few questions:

- What kind of service or worship or celebration would it be most appropriate for them to attend? Explain carefully in advance the nature of the event to those attending.

- Can the suggested size of the group be accommodated comfortably whilst regular worship is taking place, or would it be better to offer a guided tour outside of the times of regular worship ?

- Will visitors be expected to join in the worship in any way ? If so, has consideration been given to whether some aspects of the worship may present difficulties of conscience for some visitors and how such instances can best be handled ?

- Will visitors be expected to express respect in any particular way to any holy item within the place of worship? If so, there is a need to explain carefully what is involved.

- Are there any rules of clothing or of hygiene, or expectations concerning the handling of food which visitors must observe? If so, make sure that these are clearly explained.

- If there are any guidelines for general behaviour within the place of worship it would be helpful to tell visitors in advance.

If the place of worship is regularly visited by people of other religious traditions and those of no religious commitment, it may be helpful to create a short fact sheet about the building, its worshippers, the main forms of worship which take place and any requirements which there may be for guests who visit or attend worship.

FURTHER HELP

For further advice and information on the points discussed in this chapter, see the chapter on "Finding Out More: Some Other Relevant Publications and Resources". The Inter Faith Network (5-7, Tavistock Place, London, WC1H 9SN, Tel: (020) 7388 0008, Fax: (020) 7387 7968 or Email: ifnet@interfaith.org.uk) can help either directly or by putting the reader in touch with individuals and organisations who can advise or assist.

INTER-FAITH ACTIVITY IN THE UK

INTRODUCTION 79

TYPES OF INTER-FAITH INITIATIVE 79

MULTI-LATERAL INITIATIVES: UK AND INTERNATIONAL 80

BILATERAL INITIATIVES 83

TRILATERAL INITIATIVES 84

NORTHERN IRELAND, SCOTLAND AND WALES 84

LOCAL INTER-FAITH ACTIVITY 84

FAITH COMMUNITIES AND INTER-FAITH RELATIONS 85

PATTERN OF INVOLVEMENT IN INTER-FAITH ACTIVITIES 86

SPECIAL ISSUES 87

THE NEW MILLENNIUM AS A TIME FOR FOCUS ON SHARED VALUES 89

TOWARDS THE FUTURE 90

FURTHER READING 92

INTRODUCTION

In many parts of the world there has been contact between people of different religions in almost every century. However, as a development in the West, organised inter-faith activity began with the World Parliament of Religions held in Chicago in 1893. This brought religious leaders such as Swami Vivekananda and Paramahansa Yogananda to the attention of the Western world.

Early inter-faith encounter in the UK was on a small scale reflecting the fact that the country's population was not very religiously diverse. One of the earliest initiatives was the Religions of the Empire Conference. This was held in 1924 in conjunction with the British Empire Exhibition and was organised by Sir Denison Ross. The explorer and mystic Sir Francis Younghusband took a prominent part in it and, in 1936, convened the World Congress of Faiths. This subsequently established itself as an inter-faith organisation which still continues its work today.

It is only over the last four decades that the country has become home to an increasing range of different faith groups and only in the last two decades that inter-faith encounter and activity has taken place on a wide scale. This process has accelerated in the last five years and many inter-faith organisations and initiatives are now contributing to the development of good relations between the faith communities. There have also been a series of initiatives to bring religious communities more fully into the public life of Britain at both national and local level. In many countries Britain is now seen as being a leader in the development of structured inter-faith relations.

TYPES OF INTER-FAITH INITIATIVE

The UK is now rich in inter-faith initiatives. These are of many different kinds. Some inter-faith organisations link institutions and organisations (eg the Inter Faith Network for the UK) while others are primarily based on individual membership (eg the World Congress of Faiths). A certain amount of inter-faith work is specifically geared to social and political issues (eg that of the World Conference on Religion and Peace) while in other cases the focus is on prayer and worship or meditation (eg the Week of Prayer for World Peace). Some inter faith activity is "multi-lateral": involving several religions. Other activity is bilateral or trilateral.

There can be a number of varying motives for inter-faith activity such as: a desire for better understanding and appreciation of another religious tradition; a desire for social harmony and friendship; a wish on the part of participant groups to secure greater social and religious acceptance; or an imperative within one's own religion to work with others.

In the early days, one of the main needs was simply for information about one another's beliefs and practices and a good deal of inter-faith activity was oriented towards this aim. This remains a continuing need, but at the same time inter-faith activity has expanded and developed in a variety of ways with differing goals, participants and forms of organisation as people from various communities of faith have responded to the challenges presented by a multi-faith society.

When a society or an event or project is described as "multi-faith", it usually means that it includes a variety of religious groups. While the use of "*multi*-faith" highlights variety, use of the term "*inter*-faith" points more to the relationships *between* religions and the people who belong to them. So, for example, in an inter-faith group, people of different religious traditions come together to share their views or work together on particular projects. The term "inter-religious" is occasionally used interchangeably with "inter-faith". Sometimes this is because of a preference for the term "religion" rather than "faith" on the grounds that "religion" is a wider term which more readily covers non-theistic as well as theistic traditions. "Inter-religious" can sometimes be used in ways that denote the simple state of encounter between different religions in a religiously plural context whereas "inter-faith" tends to be used in circumstances which involve "dialogue" between the religions and faiths. The un-hyphenated term "interfaith" is found but some prefer to avoid this for fear of giving the impression of a movement that blurs the distinctiveness of the religious traditions involved.

MULTI-LATERAL INITIATIVES: UK AND INTERNATIONAL

The Inter Faith Network for the UK

The Inter Faith Network for the United Kingdom was established in 1987. Its aims are "to advance public knowledge and mutual understanding of the teachings, traditions and practices of different faith communities in Britain, including an awareness both of their distinctive features and of their common ground and to promote good relations between persons of different religious faiths."

The Network is an "organisation of organisations" linking nearly ninety organisations including: representative bodies from within the nine historic world religious traditions with significant communities in the UK that are profiled in this directory (eg bodies such as the Churches' Commission on Inter Faith Relations, the Muslim Council of Britain and the National Council of Hindu Temples); national inter-faith organisations (eg the Council of Christians and Jews and the World Congress of Faiths); local inter-faith groups (eg the Wolverhampton Inter-Faith Group and the Leicester Council of Faiths); and educational bodies, study centres and academic bodies concerned with the study of religions and the relationships between them (eg the Religious Education Council for England and Wales and the Community Religions Project of Leeds University).

The Network provides information and advice to a wide range of organisations and individuals on inter-faith matters and on how to contact communities at both national and local level. It holds regular national and regional meetings and organises seminars and conferences on a variety of issues and projects. These have explored such topics as the quest for shared values in a multi-faith society; young people and inter-faith relations; the role of the media in reporting on the religious life of Britain; and planning, registration and other issues relating to places of worship in a multi-faith society. The Network's association with the Multi-Faith Directory Research Project is an expression of its goal of encouraging and facilitating contact with and between different religious communities and their members.

The Network is a forum for information, exchange and encounter. Its aim is to promote mutual understanding rather than to represent the views and positions of its member organisations to others. On occasion, however, its officers have issued statements in relation to important issues and events which have a direct bearing on inter-religious relations in the UK, such as the Gulf War.

In 1991, the Network produced a formal *Statement on Inter-Religious Relations* and in 1993 it issued a short code of conduct on *Building Good Relations Between People of Different Faiths and Beliefs*. Both were drafted by multi-faith working groups and were endorsed by all its member organisations. It also produced a longer document entitled *Mission, Dialogue and Inter-Religious Encounter*. The Code is reproduced in an annex to this chapter. In 1995, translations of it into Bengali, Gujarati, Hindi, Punjabi and Urdu were made available and it has been widely published and circulated both here and abroad.

From the outset the Network has worked to encourage the participation of the full range of religious communities in the public life of the UK and this has become a most important dimension of its work. It has encouraged Government Departments and other public bodies to consult faith communities on the development and implementation of policies and programmes of particular concern to them. For example, it helped to facilitate the formation of the Inner Cities Religious Council in 1992 and the setting up of the 2001 Census Religious Affiliation Group which led to the inclusion of a question on religious identity in the 2001 Census. It has frequently been asked by public authorities and other organisations to help them build up their contacts with faith communities. This has encouraged the development of good working relationships between religious leaders at both national and local levels.

World Congress of Faiths

As already noted, the World Congress of Faiths (WCF) was founded in 1936 on the initiative of Sir Francis Younghusband who, whilst on a military-diplomatic mission to Tibet in 1903, had a mystical experience of the unity of all peoples. He convened a "Congress" of people of different religious traditions from Britain and from overseas which met at University College, London, in July 1936 and led to the setting up of the World Congress of Faiths.

The World Congress of Faiths aims to create understanding and a sense of unity and friendship between members of the world's faiths. The Congress's founder, Sir Francis Younghusband, deliberately chose to use the word "faiths" in order to include humanists and followers of what today are known as "New Religious Movements" within the ambit of the organisation rather than restricting membership to the generally accepted world religious traditions alone. The organisation is based on individual rather than organisational membership and is open to "seekers" as well as to those who are firmly rooted in a particular religious tradition.

The WCF sponsors a range of conferences, lectures, retreats and tours, and also publishes the journal, *World Faiths Encounter* and the newsletter *One Family*. In conjunction with the International Association of Religious Freedom, it has established the International Interfaith Centre in Oxford.

The International Interfaith Centre, Oxford

The International Interfaith Centre (IIC) was founded in 1993. Its aims are to facilitate networking, encounter, education and research on global inter-faith issues between religious and spiritual peoples, communities and organisations throughout the world. The IIC initiates programmes and publications to support these aims and is coordinator of a new network of fourteen international inter-faith orgnisations.

World Conference on Religion and Peace

Following a long history of attempts to convene a world inter-faith conference for peace, the World Conference on Religion and Peace (WCRP) met in Kyoto, Japan, in 1970. At this event it was agreed to form an organisation which would engage in at least four programmes designed to: (a) initiate inter-religious seminars and conferences at all levels in order to create a climate for the peaceful resolution of disputes among and within nations without violence; (b) encourage the establishment of national and regional committees for peace; (c) develop an inter-religious presence at the United Nations and other international conferences, through which the influence of religion could be directly exerted to resolve conflicts; (d) encourage the further development of the science of inter-religious dialogue for peace.

A European Committee of the WCRP was formed in 1975 following the 1974 meeting of WCRP International's Louvain Assembly in Belgium. The United Kingdom and Ireland Chapter (now the UK Chapter) was also formed at this time. As its name suggests, the WCRP is concerned with the resources for peace which the traditions and communities of the various religions can offer. Its work also involves bringing about inter-religious dialogue aimed at overcoming conflict rooted in religious differences. It has an international assembly every six years. The international body has consultative status in the United Nations Economic and Social Council.

International Association for Religious Freedom

The International Association for Religious Freedom (IARF) began with the 1900 International Council of Unitarian and other Liberal Religious Thinkers and Workers. Its roots lie in the Unitarian and Free Christian movements and it began as a grouping of religious believers committed to "free" or liberal religious values, rather than as a body campaigning for religious liberty. Its current agenda is reflected in its present name, adopted in 1969, which does not link it specifically either to the *Unitarian* or to the wider Christian tradition.

Today, the IARF's membership includes organisations from a range of religious communities (eg a number of Japanese Buddhist organisations and the Ramakrishna Mission) alongside those of *Unitarian* and free Christian backgrounds who continue to contribute significantly to its work. The aims of its British Chapter are: "to support the international organisation in encouraging free, critical and honest affirmation of one's own religion: religion which liberates and does not oppress; the defense of freedom of conscience and the free exercise of religion in all nations." The international headquarters of the organisation were moved from Frankfurt to Oxford in 1993.

United Religions Initiative

The United Religions Initiative (URI) has developed from a gathering convened by the Anglican Bishop of San Francisco, Bishop Bill Swing, in 1996 following the holding of an inter-faith event there to mark the fiftieth anniversary of the founding of the United Nations. The URI aims to link all those at grass roots level who have a concern for inter-faith relations. A Charter drawn up at subsequent meetings was launched in Pittsburgh, USA in the summer of 2000. The URI in Britain and

Ireland was launched at the Millennium Dome in Greenwich in August 2000.

Other International Inter-Faith Initiatives

Other international inter-faith initiatives have been launched over the last few years. The Council for a Parliament of the World Religions organised a conference in Chicago in 1993 to mark the centenary of the World Parliament of Religions and the Council organised another gathering in Cape Town in December 1999. In August 2000 a Millennium World Peace Summit of religious and spiritual leaders was held at the United Nations in New York. Participants from the UK took part in these three conferences as they have done in a variety of other international inter-faith initiatives in recent years.

BILATERAL INITIATIVES

Inter-faith activity can also focus on relationships between two or three particular religions and there are some very significant examples of such initiatives in the UK.

The Council of Christians and Jews

Apart from Christianity, Judaism is the world religious tradition which has had the longest substantial and settled presence in the UK. Not surprisingly, organisations that are specifically concerned with Christian-Jewish relations have an especially strong historical and contemporary profile in the UK.

In 1942, partly as a response to the situation of Jews in Nazi Europe, a Council of Christians and Jews (CCJ) was formed. From the outset it secured significant support from within the religious and political establishment of the UK. Its present constitution sets out its aims as: "to educate Christians and Jews to appreciate each other's distinctive beliefs and practices and to recognise their common ground; to eradicate the roots of discrimination and prejudice, especially anti-Semitism, but also all forms of intolerance and racial or religious hatred; to promote the fundamental ethical teachings which are common to Christianity and Judaism." There are now sixty local branches around the country which are linked to the national Council.

In 1946 an international conference of Christians and Jews was held at Lady Margaret Hall in Oxford and it was decided to plan for an International Council of Christians and Jews (ICCJ). Its tasks became all the more urgent as the full truth emerged concerning the Holocaust of European Jewry in the Nazi death camps. For various reasons the Council did not formally meet until 1975 in Hamburg, Germany, although from 1962 onwards an International Consultative Committee of organisations concerned with Christian-Jewish co-operation was in existence. The CCJ in this country is a member organisation of the ICCJ, which holds regular international conferences and seminars.

Other Christian-Jewish Initiatives

An early move to promote better Christian-Jewish relations was the establishment, in 1927, of the London Society for Jews and Christians. This emerged from an initiative of the Social Service Committee of the Liberal Jewish Synagogue and the Society continues to hold regular meetings today.

There are other organisations and institutions which focus on Christian-Jewish relations including the Study Centre for Christian-Jewish Relations in London run by the Roman Catholic Sisters of Sion and the Centre for Jewish-Christian Relations established in Cambridge in 1998.

The Maimonides Foundation

The Maimonides Foundation was established in 1993 and works at all levels of the Jewish and Muslim communities, both in the UK and internationally, to promote contact and understanding among other ways, through dialogue, education, sport, research and advocacy.

The Centre for the Study of Islam and Christian-Muslim Relations

The Centre for the Study of Islam and Christian-Muslim Relations at Selly Oak, Birmingham was established in 1976, and since 1999 has been part of the University of Birmingham. Postgraduate courses are available in Islamic Studies and Christian-Muslim Relations. Staff and students are Christian and Muslim from many countries.

Other Bilateral Dialogues

There have also been initiatives to promote dialogue between other traditions. A variety of conversations have been held in recent years between Buddhists and Christians. During the year 2000, a Network for Buddhist-Christian Dialogue was established. Organisations have also been launched, for example to focus on relations between the Jain and Jewish communities, and to explore the common ground between them.

TRILATERAL INITIATIVES

There is a shared agenda for dialogue among Jews, Christians and Muslims in Europe arising from their common Abrahamic inheritance.

The Calamus Foundation

The Calamus Foundation, established in 1990, focuses primarily on the encouragement of greater understanding between Christians, Jews and Muslims.

The Standing Conference of Jews, Christians and Muslims in Europe

In 1971 the Standing Conference of Jews, Christians and Muslims in Europe was formed due to the concern of European Christian and Jewish leaders that their communities should have greater mutual knowledge, particularly given the increasingly significant Muslim presence in Europe. The main activity at present of the Standing Conference is the organisation of a number of annual conferences and seminars in Bendorf, Germany, which participants from Britain regularly attend.

The Three Faiths Forum

The Three Faiths Forum was established in 1997 to encourage friendship, goodwill and understanding among people of the three Abrahamic faiths of Judaism, Christianity and Islam, both in the UK and elsewhere. The Forum organises conferences and seminars and has formed a number of local Forum groups, as well as specialist Medical Group and is preparing a Legal Group.

NORTHERN IRELAND, SCOTLAND AND WALES

The Northern Ireland Inter Faith Forum was set up in 1993. The Scottish Inter Faith Council was established in 1999 with the support and encouragement of the Inter Faith Network for the UK. Both are members of the Network. Initial steps have been taken towards setting up an Inter Faith Council for Wales. These inter faith organisations have an increasingly important role to play in relating to the devolved institutions of government in their countries.

LOCAL INTER-FAITH ACTIVITY

In the last three decades inter-faith organisations and initiatives have sprung up in towns and cities throughout the UK. This directory records over 94 such groups. Many, but not all, are members of the Inter Faith Network. Those which are members of the Network are not branches of the Network, but independent entities in their own right and in many cases were in existence before the Network was established. They have a variety of histories, self-understandings and methods of working.

The Inter Faith Network organises regular regional meetings for representatives of local inter-faith groups, both those in membership of the Network and those who are not, in order to facilitate the sharing and exchange of local experience. It also supports and encourages the launching of new local inter-faith initiatives.

The variety of approaches taken by local groups is reflected in their names. Some adopt the word "group" in their titles (eg the Derby Multi-Faith Group). This generally signifies a more informal form of organisation and an individual membership rather than an attempt to be a corporate and representative body.

On the other hand, there are those which call themselves a "council" (eg the Leicester Council of Faiths and the Birmingham Council of Faiths). These tend to be more formally structured and attempt to maintain a balanced representation from among the principal religious traditions. They often have a role in representing the concerns of their local religious communities to the local authorities and other public bodies.

Some of the local organisations (eg the Tyne and Wear Racial Equality Council Inter Faith Panel) originate in the work of local Racial Equality Councils. Consequently, these groups have a particular concern for the promotion of better community relations and an anti-racist stance figures significantly in their self-understanding.

Other local groups place a particular emphasis on individual fellowship and meeting (eg the Coventry Inter Faith Group) and may also include in their membership people who are spiritual seekers. Still others have an accent on common action in pursuit of agreed social goals (eg Rochdale Interfaith Action which has had a particular concern for immigration issues).

In some areas, local inter-faith activity has been generated by an initiative for outreach on the part of a particular religious community. For example, Westminster Interfaith was set up by the Roman Catholic Archdiocese of Westminster, but members of other faiths are involved in its activities.

There are also groups which have been formed in areas with less local religious diversity but which aim to promote a greater understanding of inter-faith issues within their area (eg the Beaminster One World Fellowship and the West Somerset Inter Faith Group).

In practice, however, most local inter-faith groups or councils embrace a variety of motivations and explore various ways to relate more effectively and relevantly to the needs and challenges of their religiously diverse local communities.

In 1999 the Inter Faith Network, in association with the Inner Cities Religious Council, published *The Local Inter Faith Guide: Faith Community Co-operation in Action* which provides advice on the setting up and running of local inter-faith initiatives. In 2000, again in association with the ICRC, the Network organised a conference to explore ways in which local authorities and local councils of faith can usefully develop good relationships with one another.

FAITH COMMUNITIES AND INTER-FAITH RELATIONS

For all religions, the existence of other religious traditions raises many profound questions. At a practical level, living together in a multi-faith society means that communities need to develop positive ways to interact and cooperate. Therefore for both theological/philosophical and practical reasons, faith communities in the UK have been giving increasing attention to relationships with people belonging to other religious traditions.

For example, the Council of Churches for Britain and Ireland has within it a Commission for Inter-Faith Relations, and a number of its member *Churches* have their own committees which focus on inter-faith issues. Some of these bodies are concerned with particular bi-lateral relations, as for example the Roman Catholic Church's Committee for Roman Catholic-Jewish Relations. These various bodies have produced material on issues which arise for Christians in a multi-faith society in both theological and social terms. Christians Aware, which is an international and ecumenical movement that aims to develop multi-cultural understanding and friendship locally, nationally and internationally, has an inter-faith programme. The Monastic Interfaith Dialogue Commission of Britain and Ireland (a branch of an international *Roman Catholic* body) promotes mutual visits and meetings between monastics of different faith traditions

Other faith communities too are developing mechanisms for inter faith activity. For example, a Sikh Council for Inter Faith Relations was formed in 1987. The Leopold Muller Interfaith Centre at the Sternberg Centre in North London was opened in 1994 as a resource for developing inter-faith relationships involving the Reform tradition of Judaism. The Islamic Foundation in Leicester has a member of staff who focuses on inter-faith issues. Within the Shi'a Muslim community, initiatives have been taken by both the Al-Khoei Foundation and the Interfaith International which has links with the World Ahl-ul-Bayt Islamic League. These are only some illustrations of this trend.

For some religious groupings the search for religious unity is central to their self-understanding. They therefore have a particular emphasis on relations between different religions although their view of this relationship will naturally be grounded in their particular tradition's perspective. These groupings include, for example, the Bahá'ís.

Among those groups often described as New Religious Movements, the Brahma Kumaris and *Unificationists* have been particularly concerned to promote the search for religious unity. A variety of groups associated with the "New Age" movement also put particular emphasis on the unity of humanity and its spiritual dimension and reflect this in their activities. In a number of local areas individuals from New Religious Movements, New Age and Pagan traditions have wished to take part in local inter-faith groups. The degree to which they have been welcomed has varied from group to group.

PATTERN OF INVOLVEMENT IN INTER-FAITH ACTIVITIES

While women have often been active in local inter faith groups they have on the whole been less prominent in inter faith events or activities organised on a representative basis, particularly where these have been at a national level. This is partly because in the majority of faith communities it is men who are in positions of power and leadership, and partly because within some religious communities there are reservations about joint activity involving both men and women. But women are now playing a more significant role in inter faith activity generally.

There has also been a tendency for the majority of key figures in inter-faith work to be in the older age group. Various efforts have been made to involve young people in inter-faith events. Sometimes these have been arranged by youth organisations and sometimes by local inter-faith groups. In the context of some emerging conflicts on higher education campuses, a pressing need is the development of appropriate inter-faith structures to bring together students from different cultural and religious backgrounds, including international as well as home students, and to enable institutions to adapt their policies and practices to meet the challenges posed by religious diversity.

Another grouping which is under-represented in many dialogues in the UK are the religious leaders (as distinct from community leaders) and scholars of faith traditions other than the longer established Christian and Jewish communities. This is in part because, for the newer communities, the more pressing concern has until recently been to establish themselves in the new context of this country. Inter-faith relations have often therefore appeared of lesser importance than these imperatives, although there are signs that this is beginning to change. In the past, one factor has also been that many of the significant figures among the religious leaders and scholars of these communities have not been comfortable using the shared language of English in contexts where nuances of language can be significant. But this situation is changing as more of the religious leaders of the communities have been born and educated in Britain.

SPECIAL ISSUES

Prayer and Worship Together

Prayer and worship involving people from different religious traditions has always been a more controversial and difficult activity than common action towards agreed social goals or engagement in theological dialogue. There are people in all religious communities who have reservations about participating in shared worship or prayer while others will feel that they can take part on particular occasions without compromising their integrity. Such gatherings have taken various forms.

A distinction has sometimes been drawn between "being together to pray" and "praying together". In the first situation each participant prays from within his or her own tradition. The second situation involves the use of prayers in common. On some occasions those present have been invited to listen respectfully to prayers and readings from different traditions, delivered in turn by their members. Sometimes the focus has been on shared silence. At other times, those present have been invited to share what is said or sung, whilst taking care that what is contributed does not contradict or offend the beliefs or practice of the participants.

It has often proved easier to organise events where people of various traditions are present at the service of another tradition and perhaps offer a reading or prayer, but where the service basically remains within the framework of the normal pattern of prayer and worship practised by the host group. This has, for example, happened at a special event such as the enthronement of the current Archbishop of Canterbury. There have been moves to include representatives of different religious communities at national events, such as the Commonwealth Day Observance held annually at Westminster Abbey, or in civic services at local level. In 2000, for the first time, in addition to Christian and Jewish faith leaders, representatives of the Buddhist, Hindu, Muslim and Sikh communities took part in the ceremony at the Cenotaph on Remembrance Sunday.

Special meetings have been held to pray together at times of crisis, for example when Christians, Muslims and others met at the time of the Gulf War to pray together for peace. Events have been organised to express concern for refugees, political prisoners, the homeless or the environment, such as the annual Amnesty International multi-faith human rights service.

The Week of Prayer for World Peace is an annual event which seeks to engage people of all religious traditions in common prayer for peace. It was initiated in 1974 and is observed during October. One World Week also takes place in October.

Prayers in the Scottish Parliament

In the consultations conducted during the preparatory stages of establishing the Scottish Parliament there was some discussion about whether sessions should begin with prayers. Initially there was some opposition to this but other faith communities gave their support to the Churches on this issue and the Parliament eventually decided that prayers should be said, but that these should be drawn from different traditions very roughly reflecting in their pattern the size of different faith communities within Scotland.

Inter-Religious Social and Political Co-operation

The establishment by the Government in 1992 of the Inner Cities Religious Council has been an important step in involving the major religious communities in tackling key issues of social and economic regeneration. It has membership from the Christian, Hindu, Jewish, Muslim, and Sikh communities and is chaired by a Minister in the Department of Transport, Local Government and the Regions. It is designed to foster partnership between Government and faith communities in tackling urban social and economic problems.

Religious individuals and groups have formed multi-faith coalitions to pursue particular social and political goals, such as help or support for the homeless, the disabled and refugees. There has also been a noticeable growth of inter-religious activities within organisations that are not themselves constituted on the basis of a religious commitment but which want, in recognition of the more religiously plural nature of British society, to engage people from various religious traditions in support of their organisations' goals.

Many of the organisations involved in this development are concerned with issues of peace and justice and of the environment. For example, the United Nations Association Religious Advisory Committee has, for many years, produced briefing papers and other materials to support religious communities in observance of worship and vigils for United Nations Day. The Amnesty International Religious Bodies Liaison Panel has furthered Amnesty's aims among the religious communities by holding an annual conference, producing relevant materials on religions and human rights, and seeking the support of religious communities and leaders, both nationally and locally, for Amnesty campaigns. Among the Panel's publications have been pamphlets about religions and the death penalty, and about arguments for human rights from the world's religions.

The Fellowship of Reconciliation, whose international organisation dates back to 1919, has both national and international branches. It is a pacifist organisation with Christian roots, which has now established a Multi-Faith Non-Violence Group. Various Gandhian organisations are active for peace, and invite participation from all religious traditions.

The World Wide Fund for Nature is very active in ecology and inter-religious concerns and has sponsored inter-faith events concerned with ecology and produced books and booklets on ecology and the world religions. Out of its work has come the Alliance of Religions and Conservation.

The Quest for Common Values

As the UK grows more culturally and religiously diverse, concerns are sometimes expressed that the process is leading to the fragmentation of social unity. These concerns link with an anxiety that, alongside the strains imposed by economic change, there is an erosion of traditional sources of moral authority underpinning both civic and personal values.

Within a plural society agreement is unlikely to be reached on the authority of the sources to which various religious groupings and others look for their values. At the same time, there has been an increasing interest in exploring the extent to which a set of common or shared values can be identified which might provide a sufficient degree of coherence for a plural society in terms of morality in the public sphere. There are different views on how far in practice this can be achieved. However, it is clearly important to try at least to identify procedures for constructive engagement with tensions or conflicts arising from values issues.

In a global context, these issues have been explored and developed in the *Declaration Toward a Global Ethic* of the World Parliament of Religions, held in Chicago, USA, in 1993 to mark the centenary of the first Parliament of the World's Religions, also held in Chicago. The Declaration affirms "a minimum fundamental consensus concerning binding values, irrevocable standards and fundamental moral attitudes" among the religions. It affirms that the principles of a Global Ethic, to which both religious people and humanists might be able to subscribe, are as follows: no new global order without a new global ethic; a fundamental demand: every human being must be treated humanely; four irrevocable directives – commitment to a culture of non-violence and respect for life, commitment to a culture of solidarity and a just economic order, commitment to a culture of tolerance and a life of truthfulness, and commitment to a culture of equal rights and partnership between men and women; and a transformation of consciousness. Other international declarations have been produced in recent years including the Earth Charter and the Charter of the United Religions Initiative.

The Values Education Council of the UK was established in 1995 linking a range of religious and secular bodies concerned with the relationship between education and values. In the same year, the School Curriculum and Assessment Authority (SCAA) convened a National Forum for Values in Education and the Community. This led to an agreed statement as a framework for moral education in schools. The work of the Forum has been reflected in guidance for schools on moral education produced in 2000 by the Qualifications and Curriculum Authority (the successor body to SCAA).

The Inter Faith Network's 1991 *Statement on Inter-Religious Relations in Britain* said, "Our religious traditions offer values and insights of great worth to society, and provide a framework of meaning within which individuals can interpret their experience" and "Both within and between our communities there are significant differences in the ways in which we translate these values and ideals into ethical judgements concerning specific personal and social issues. But a recognition of the extent to which we share a range of common values and ideals can contribute to a wider sense of community in our society."

THE NEW MILLENNIUM AS A TIME FOR FOCUS ON SHARED VALUES

In the new century, the quest for common values appears likely to become an increasingly significant dimension of inter-faith relations in the UK since this debate is seen as being of crucial importance to the development of a shared and stable framework for plural society.

In 1996 a Committee was established to advise the Government department that was in charge of Millennium matters about religious issues relating to these. Its full title was "the Churches and Other Faiths Subgroup of the Millennium Co-ordinating Group of the Department for Culture, Media and Sport". It later became known as the "Lambeth Group" as it held its meetings at Lambeth Palace, the official residence of the Archbishop of Canterbury. Representatives of the Christian Churches, the Hindu, Jewish, Muslim and Sikh communities were involved in its work as were representatives of the Inter Faith Network. The Group gave advice to Government on the religious dimensions of national celebrations and Millennium projects, as well as to the New Millennium Experience Company concerning the Faith Zone in the Greenwich Dome.

Out of the Lambeth Group came the idea for a special inter-faith event to mark the Millennium. This was the Shared Act of Reflection and Commitment by the Faith Communities of the UK which took place at the House of Lords in January 2000 and was hosted by Government and arranged for the Government by the Inter Faith Network. It focused on values held in common by the religious traditions represented at it, with a contribution offered by an individual of each tradition on a particular value. There were speakers from leaders of all the world religious traditions with significant communities in the UK and the Prime Minister also spoke. The event was broadcast on national TV and highlights were featured on the BBC's world news. It was the first such event ever hosted by a UK Government. It concluded with leaders from all the religions present joining in the following Act of Commitment which formed its centrepiece and which was also used in a number of subsequent Millennium events in different parts of the UK.

Faith community representatives:

In a world scarred by the evils of war, racism, injustice and poverty, we offer this joint Act of Commitment as we look to our shared future.

All:

We commit ourselves,
as people of many faiths,
to work together for the common good,
uniting to build a better society,
grounded in values and ideals we share:
community,
personal integrity,
a sense of right and wrong,
learning, wisdom and love of truth,
care and compassion,
justice and peace,
respect for one another,
for the earth and its creatures.
We commit ourselves,
in a spirit of friendship and co-operation,
to work together
alongside all who share our values and ideals,
to help bring about a better world
now and for generations to come.

TOWARDS THE FUTURE

In its beginnings over 100 years ago, modern inter-faith activity was often seen as a fringe activity undertaken by people who were less central to their own religious tradition. But it is now seen as an important and necessary part of the life and witness of all religious communities in a multi-faith society.

New initiatives are constantly emerging at all levels and many secular bodies are also developing their consultative processes and their activities to take account of Britain's increased religious diversity. There is a clear desire to work together to build a better society founded on a shared citizenship. The Inter Faith Network's Code of Practice, on *Building Good Relations with People of Different Faiths and Beliefs* (see the facing page), provides a framework within which religious communities can find helpful and constructive ways of living and working together for the positive benefit of all, with mutual integrity.

The intention of Britain's faith communities to follow this path was clearly expressed in the Act of Commitment held in the Houses of Parliament, in which representatives of them joined together at the start of the new Millennium.

BUILDING GOOD RELATIONS WITH PEOPLE OF DIFFERENT FAITHS AND BELIEFS

In Britain today, people of many different faiths and beliefs live side by side. The opportunity lies before us to work together to build a society rooted in the values we treasure. But this society can only be built on a sure foundation of mutual respect, openness and trust. This means finding ways to live our lives of faith with integrity, and allowing others to do so too. Our different religious traditions offer us many resources for this and teach us the importance of good relationships characterised by honesty, compassion and generosity of spirit. The Inter Faith Network offers the following code of conduct for encouraging and strengthening these relationships.

As members of the human family, we should show each other respect and courtesy. In our dealings with people of other faiths and beliefs this means exercising good will and:

- Respecting other people's freedom within the law to express their beliefs and convictions
- Learning to understand what others actually believe and value, and letting them express this in their own terms
- Respecting the convictions of others about food, dress and social etiquette and not behaving in ways which cause needless offence
- Recognising that all of us at times fall short of the ideals of our own traditions and never comparing our own *ideals* with other people's *practices*
- Working to prevent disagreement from leading to conflict
- Always seeking to avoid violence in our relationships

When we talk about matters of faith with one another, we need to do so with sensitivity, honesty and straightforwardness. This means:

- Recognising that listening as well as speaking is necessary for a genuine conversation
- Being honest about our beliefs and religious allegiances
- Not misrepresenting or disparaging other people's beliefs and practices
- Correcting misunderstanding or mis-representation not only of our own but also of other faiths whenever we come across them
- Being straightforward about our intentions
- Accepting that in formal inter-faith meetings there is a particular responsibility to ensure that the religious commitment of all those who are present will be respected

All of us want others to understand and respect our views. Some people will also want to persuade others to join their faith. In a multi-faith society where this is permitted, the attempt should always be characterised by self-restraint and a concern for the other's freedom and dignity. This means:

- Respecting another person's expressed wish to be left alone
- Avoiding imposing ourselves and our views on individuals or communities who are in vulnerable situations in ways which exploit these
- Being sensitive and courteous
- Avoiding violent language, threats, manipulation, improper inducements, or the misuse of any kind of power
- Respecting the right of others to disagree with us

Living and working together is not always easy. Religion harnesses deep emotions which can sometimes take destructive forms. Where this happens, we must draw on our faith to bring about reconciliation and understanding. The truest fruits of religion are healing and positive. We have a great deal to learn from one another which can enrich us without undermining our own identities. Together, listening and responding with openness and respect, we can move forward to work in ways that acknowledge genuine differences but build on shared hopes and values.

The Inter Faith Network, 5-7 Tavistock Place, London, WC1H 9SN. Tel: (0207) 388 0008

FURTHER READING

Abe, M, *Buddhism and Interfaith Dialogue*, Marathon, Basingstoke, 1995.

Ahmed, I, et al, "Bradford: between co-existence and dialogue", in *World Faiths Encounter*, No 1, March 1992, pp 32-42.

Amnesty International, *Arguments for Human Rights from the World's Religions*, Amnesty International, London, nd.

Amnesty International, *Helping Amnesty's Work: Ideas for Religious Bodies*, Amnesty International, London, nd.

Amnesty International, *Religions and the Death Penalty: The Case for Abolition*, Amnesty International, London, nd.

Andrews, A, "The Inter-Faith movement in the UK", in *The Indo-British Review: A Journal of History*, Volume XX, No 1, pp 123-130.

Anees, M A, Abedin, S Z and Sardar, Z, *Christian-Muslim Relations: Yesterday, Today, Tomorrow*, Grey Seal, 1991.

Bayfield, T and Braybrooke, M, *Dialogue With a Difference: The Manor House Group Experience*, SCM Press, London, 1992.

Beales, C, "Partnerships for a change: the Inner Cities Religious Council", in *World Faiths Encounter*, No 8, July 1994, pp 41-46.

Bennett, C, "Within God's gracious purposes: a review of fifteen years of ecumenical interfaith collaboration in Britain, 1977-1992", in *Discernment: A Christian Journal of Inter-Religious Encounter*, Volume VI, No 3, 1993, pp 3-16.

Beverluis, J (ed), *A Sourcebook for the Community of Religions*, The Council for a Parliament of the World's Religions, Chicago, 1993.

Braybrooke, M, *Time to Meet: Towards a Deeper Relationship Between Jews and Christians*, SCM, London, 1990.

Braybrooke, M, *Children of One God: A History of the Council of Christians and Jews*, Valentine Mitchell, London, 1991.

Braybrooke, M, *Pilgrimage of Hope: One Hundred Years of Interfaith Dialogue*, SCM Press, London, 1992.

Braybrooke, M (ed), *Stepping Stones to a Global Ethic*, SCM Press, London, 1992.

Braybrooke, M, "Interfaith in Europe", in Gill, S, D'Costa, G and King, U (eds), *Religion in Europe: Contemporary Perspectives*, Kok Pharos, Kampen, 1994, pp 201-213.

Braybrooke, M, *Faith in a Global Age: The Interfaith Movement's Offer of Hope to a World in Agony. A Personal Perspective*, Marcus Braybrooke, Oxford, 1995.

Braybrooke, M, *A Wider Vision: A History of the World Congress of Faiths*, One World, Oxford, 1996.

Braybrooke, M, *Testing the Global Ethic*, International Interfaith Centre, Oxford, 1996.

Brockington, J, *Hinduism and Christianity*, Macmillan, London, 1992.

Brockway, A, *The Theology of the Church and the Jewish People*, World Council of Churches, Geneva, 1988.

Brown, S, *Meeting in Faith: Thirty Years of Christian-Muslim Conversations Sponsored by the World Council of Churches*, World Council of Churches, Geneva, 1989.

Cole, W O and Sambhi, P Singh, *Sikhism and Christianity: A Comparative Study*, Macmillan, London, 1993.

Council of Churches for Britain and Ireland, *In Good Faith: The Four Principles of Interfaith Dialogue*, Council of Churches for Britain and Ireland, London, 1992.

Cohn-Sherbok, D, *World Religions and Human Liberation*, Orbis, New York, 1992.

Coward, H (ed), *Hindu-Christian Dialogue: Perspectives and Encounters*, Orbis, New York, 1990.

Cragg, K, *Troubled by Truth: Life Studies in Inter-Faith Concern*, Pentland Press, London, 1992.

D'Costa, G (ed), *Faith Meets Faith: Interfaith Views on Interfaith*, BFSS Religious Education Centre, 1988.

D'Costa, G, *The Meeting of Religions and the Trinity*, T&T Clark, Edinburgh 2000.

Esack, F, *Qur'an, liberation and Pluralism: An Islamic Perspective of Interreligious Solidarity Against Oppression*, Oneworld Publications, Oxford, 1996.

Fry, H (ed), *Christian-Jewish Dialogue: A Reader*, Exeter Press, Exeter, 1996.

Goddard, H, *Christians and Muslims: from Double Standards to Mutual Understanding*, Curzon Press, London, 1995.

Griffiths, P (ed), *Christianity Through Non-Christian Eyes*, Orbis, New York, 1990

Hare, W L (ed), *Religions of the Empire: A Conference on Some Living Religions Within the Empire*, Duckworth, London, 1925.

Herne, R, "The Challenge of Paganism Within Inter Faith Work", in *World Faiths Encounter*, No. 23, July 1999, pp 32-37.

Houston, G W, *The Cross and the Lotus: Christianity and Buddhism in Dialogue*, Motilal Banarasidass, New Delhi, 1985.

Ingram, P O and Streng, F J, *Buddhist-Christian Dialogue: Mutual Renewal and Transformation*, University of Hawaii Press, Honolulu, 1986.

Inter Faith Network for the United Kingdom, *Statement on Inter-Religious Relations*, Inter Faith Network for the UK, London, 1991.

Inter Faith Network for the United Kingdom, *Building Good Relations With People of Different Faiths and Beliefs*, Inter Faith Network for the UK, London, 1993.

Inter Faith Network for the United Kingdom, *Mission, Dialogue and Inter-Religious Encounter*, Inter Faith Network for the UK, London, 1993.

Inter Faith Network for the United Kingdom, *The Local Inter Faith Guide: Faith Community Cooperation in Action*, The Inter Faith Network for the UK in association with the Inner

Cities Religious Council of the Department for the Environment, Transport and the Regions, London, 1999.

Inter Faith Network for the United Kingdom, *The Quest for Common Values: Conference Report*, Inter Faith Network for the United Kingdom, London, 1997.

Islamic Foundation, *Christian Mission and Islamic Da'wah: Proceedings of the Chambesy Dialogue Consultation,* The Islamic Foundation, Leciester, 1982.

Jack, H A, *A History of the World Conference on Religion and Peace*, New York, 1993.

King, U, "Hindu-Christian dialogue in historical perspective", in *The Indo-British Review: A Journal of History*, Volume XX, No 1, pp 169-176.

Knitter, P, *One Earth Many Religions: Multifaith Dialogue and Global Responsibility*, Orbis, M??, 1995.

Küng, H (ed), *Yes to a Global Ethic*, SCM Press, London, 1996.

Küng, H and Ching, J, *Christianity and Chinese Religions*, SCM Press, London, 1993.

Küng, H and Kuschel, K-J (eds), *A Global Ethic: The Declaration of the Parliament of the World's Religions*, SCM Press, London, 1993.

Lefebure, L, *The Buddha and the Christ: Explorations in Buddhist and Christian Dialogue*, Orbis, New York, 1993.

Magonet, J, *Towards a Jewish-Muslim Dialogue*, Maimonides Foundation, London, 1998.

Marty, M, and Greenspahn, F, *Pushing the Faith: Proselytism in a Pluralistic World*, Crossroad, 1991.

Millard, D (ed), *Faiths and Fellowship: The Proceedings of the World Congress of Faiths*, held in London, July 3rd-17th, 1936, J M Watkins, London, 1937.

Moayyad, H (ed), *The Bahá'í Faith and Islam: Proceedings of a Symposium*, McGill University, March 23rd-25th, 1984, Association for Bahá'í Studies, Ottawa, 1990.

Mohammed, D, *Muslim-Christian Relations: Past, Present and Future*, Orbis Books, Maryknoll, 1999.

Momen, M, *Hinduism and the Bahá'í Faith*, George Ronald, Oxford, 1990.

Muslim-Christian Research Group, *The Challenge of the Scriptures: The Bible and the Qur'an*, Orbis, New York, 1989.

Nazir Ali, M, *Citizens and Exiles*, SPCK, London, 1998.

Novak, D, *Jewish-Christian Dialogue: A Jewish Justification*, Oxford University Press, Oxford, 1989.

Osten-Sachen, P von der, *Christian-Jewish Dialogue: Theological Foundations*, Fortress Press, Philadelphia, 1986.

O'Neill, M, *Women Speaking Women Listening: Women in Interreligious Dialogue*, Orbis, New York, 1990.

Palmer, M, Nash, A and Hattingh, I, (eds), *Faith and Nature: Our Relationship With the Natural World Explored Through Sacred Literature*, Century, London (undated).

Peters, F, *Children of Abraham: Judaism, Christianity, Islam*, Princeton University Press, New Jersey, 1982.

Potter, J and Braybrooke, M (eds), *All in Good Faith: A Resource Book for Interfaith Prayer*, World Congress of Faiths, Oxford, 1997.

Race, A, *Christians and Religious Pluralism*, second edition, SCM Press, London, 1993.

Race, A, *Interfaith Encounter*, SCM Press, London, 2001.

Seager, R M, *The World's Parliament of Religions: The East-West Encounter*, Chicago, 1893, Indiana University Press, Indianapolis, 1995.

Siddiqi, A, *Christian-Muslim Dialogue in the Twentieth Century*, Macmillan, Basingstoek, 1997.

Simpson, B and Weyl, R, *The International Council of Christians and Jews*, International Council of Christians and Jews, Heppenheim, Germany, 1988.

Smith, G, "Religious Belonging and Inter-Faith Encounter: Some Survey Findings from Easy London", in *Journal of Contemporary Religion*, Volume XIII, pp 333-351.

Storey, C, and Storey, D, *Visions of an Interfaith Future*, International Interfaith Centre, Oxford, 1994.

Suffolk Interfaith Resource, *Finding our Way and Sharing Our Stories*, Suffolk College Publishing, Suffolk, 1995.

Swidler, L, Cobb Jr, J, Knitter, P and Hellwig, M, *Death or Dialogue: From the Age of Monologue to the Age of Dialogue*, SCM Press, London, 1990.

Taylor, J H and Gebhardt, G (eds), *Religions for Human Dignity*, World Conference on Religion and Peace, Geneva, 1986.

Weller, C F (ed), *World Fellowship: Addresses and Messages by Leading Spokesmen of all Faiths, Races and Countries*, Liversight Publishing Company, New York, 1935.

Weller, P, "'Inheritors Together': the Interfaith Network for the United Kingdom", in *Discernment: A Christian Journal of Inter-Religious Encounter*, Volume III, No 2, Autumn, 1988, pp 30-34.

Weller, P, "The Inter Faith Network for the United Kingdom", in *The Indo-British Review: A Journal of History*, Volume XX, No 1, pp 20-26.

Weller, P, "Inter-Faith roots and shoots: an outlook for the 1990s", in *World Faiths Encounter*, No 1, March, 1992, pp 48-57.

Weller, P, "Faith and Justice: Issues of Justice Within Differing Faith Communities", in *World Faiths Encounter*, No. 22, March, 1997, pp 21-35.

Yates, G, (ed), *In Spirit and in Truth, Aspects of Judaism and Christianity: A Jewish Christian Symposium*, Hodder and Stoughton, London, 1934.

Zebiri, K, *Muslims and Christians Face to Face*, Oneworld, Oxford, 1997.

INTER FAITH UNITED KINGDOM ORGANISATIONS

The organisations listed in this section are either organisations operating at a United Kingdom level formed by individuals and groups in two or more religious traditions; or are sections of secular organisations, formed in order to engage the religious communities more effectively on a multi-faith basis in meeting the organisations' aims and objectives; or are organisations based within a single religion but with a specific brief for inter-faith relations.

All organisations included in these listings have "inter-faith" as one of their activities, so this is not recorded in their activities field in each individual case, but is presupposed for all.

Alliance of Religions and Conservation*
c/o International Consultancy on Religion, Education and Culture, 3 Wynnstay Grove, Fallowfield, Manchester M14 6XG
Tel: (0161) 2485731 **Fax:** (0161) 2485736
Contact: Mr Martin Palmer
Position: Secretary General
Activities: Resources, newsletters
ARC is designed to help religious communities and environmental organisations work together on faith based conservation projects which respect and build upon the teaching of the world religions. It currently has projects in India, China, Europe, Africa, Thailand, Canada and the Middle East.

Amnesty International Religious Liaison Panel*
99-119 Rosebery Avenue, London EC1R 4RE
Tel: (020) 7814 6200 **Fax:** (020) 7833 1510
Contact: Asad Rehman

Asaholah (Ministries of God)*
137a Ormside Street, Ilderton Road, Peckham, London SE15 1TF
Tel: (020) 7635 9374 **Fax:** (020) 7639 7218
Email: asaholah@talk21.com
Contact: Revd Isaac Yumi Akinkunmi
Position: Minister
Activities: Umbrella body, newsletter/journal, books
Started work in Africa to create religious understanding and stop conflicts, especially between the Christians and Muslims. Regular symposia and lectures are organised and visits are arranged to religious centres.

Association for Pastoral and Spiritual Care and Counselling (APSCC)*
1 Regent Place, Rugby CV21 2JP
Tel: (0870) 4435252 **Fax:** (0870) 4435160
Email: bacp@bacp.co.uk
Website: http://www.bacp.co.uk/
Activities: Umbrella body, newsletter/journal
The Association represents pastoral and spiritual carers and counsellors who work in different faith settings, or are concerned that spiritual and pastoral issues are raised in the lead counselling organisation in the country.

Buddhist Christian Network*
43 Bramley Road, Southgate, London N14 4HD
Tel: (020) 8216 5677
Email: ewest@onetel.net.uk
Contact: Elizabeth West
Position: Founder

Activities: Worship/practice/meditation, newsletter/journal, resources
The Network was founded to give support to spiritual practitioners who find themselves involved in more than one tradition for their personal development. Mainly Buddhist and Christian but open to anyone interested.

Calamus Foundation, The*
18j Eaton Square, London SW1W 9DD
Tel: (020) 7235 0302 **Fax:** (020) 7245 6821
Email: 100537.2412@compuserve.co
Contact: Mr M Risaluddin
Affiliations: Inter Faith Network for the UK
Informal membership group. A Muslim-led, multi-religious organisation, dedicated to building bridges of understanding between followers of the Abrahamic faiths and the faith traditions of the Indian subcontinent.

Churches' Commission for Inter-Faith Relations*
Church House, Great Smith Street, London SW1P 3NZ
Tel: (020) 7898 1000 **Fax:** (020) 7898 1431
Website: http://www.ctbi.co.uk/
Contact: Revd Canon Michael Ipgrave
Position: Secretary
Contact Email: michaelipgrave@c-of-e.org.uk
Activities: Umbrella body, visits, resources
Traditions: Ecumenical
Other Languages: Welsh
Affiliations: Churches Together in Britain and Ireland; Inter Faith Network for the UK
CCIFR is the main agency of the British Churches in their relationship with other faith communities. It co-ordinates the involvement of the Christian Churches, in inter-faith activities within Britain and Ireland.

Council of Christians and Jews*
5th Floor Camelford House, 87-89 Albert Embankment, London SE1 7TP
Tel: (020) 7820 0090 **Fax:** (020) 7820 0504
Email: cjrelations@ccj.org.uk
Website: http://www.ccj.org.uk/
Contact: Sr Margaret Shepherd
Position: Director
Contact Tel: (020) 7820 0090
Contact Email: margaret@ccj.org.uk
Activities: Central body, youth, newsletter/journal, radio, television, visits, inter-faith, resources
Affiliations: Inter Faith Network for the UK

CCJ brings together the Christian and Jewish communities in a common effort to fight the evils of prejudice, intolerance and discrimination in our society.

Holy Island Project*
Kagyu Samyeling, Eskdalemuir, Langholm DG13 0QL
Tel: (01387) 373232 **Fax:** (01387) 373223
Email: office@holyisland.org
Website: http://www.holyisland.org/
Contact: Rinchen Khandro
Position: Public Relations
Activities: Worship, visits, newsletter, media
Affiliations: Alliance of Religion and Conservation

Inner Cities Religious Council*
DTLR, Floor 4/K10, Eland House, Bressenden Place, London SW1E 5DU
Tel: (020) 7944 3704 **Fax:** (020) 7944 3709
Email: icrc@detr.gov.uk
Website: http://www.regeneration.detr.gov.uk/icrc/index.htm
Contact: David Rayner
Position: Secretary
Activities: Umbrella body
The ICRC is chaired by a DTLR Government Minister and acts as a consultative forum across Departments on faith issues. It is particularly concerned with social inclusion and urban renewal.

Inspire: The Spirit of Regeneration*
11 Birch Grove, Rusholme, Manchester M14 5JX
Tel: (0161) 2244985 **Fax:** (0161) 2249533
Email: inspire@transcending images.org
Website: http://www.transcendingimages.org/
Position: Programme Co-ordinator
Activities: Inter-faith, resources
Working with faith communities and supporting local people in determining what regeneration and social cohesion mean in their neighbourhoods. It is a partnership between United Religions Initiative, Human City Institute and Community Pride.

Inter Faith Network for the UK, The*
5-7 Tavistock Place, London WC1H 9SN
Tel: (020) 7388 0008 **Fax:** (020) 7387 7968
Email: ifnet@interfaith.org.uk
Website: http://www.interfaith.org.uk/
Contact: Mr Brian Pearce
Position: Director
Activities: Umbrella body, newsletter/journal,

books, inter-faith

The UK's national inter-faith body, linking nearly 90 faith community, inter faith and educational bodies. It promotes good relations between the faiths in this country and gives information and advice on inter faith issues. For more details see the display pages 12-13.

Interfaith Centre*

43 Bramley Road, Southgate, London N14 4HD
Tel: (020) 8216 5677
Email: ewest@onetel.net.uk
Contact: Elizabeth West
Position: Co-ordinator
Activities: Worship/practice/meditation, community centre, visits, inter-faith, resources
The Centre has a good interfaith library for local use. There is one guest room in the Centre, and there are others in the Monastery Guest House for interested persons to stay. Also runs courses and arranges visits etc.

Interfaith Foundation, The*

64 Portobello Road, London SE1 6E3
Tel: (020) 7727 9738 **Fax:** (020) 7727 7762
Contact: Mrs Tessa Boteler
Position: Co-ordinator
Other Languages: Arabic, Hebrew
Affiliations: Inter Faith Network for the UK
The aim of the Interfaith Foundation, an established charity, is to promote greater mutual understanding between Christians, Jews and Muslims in regard to all contemporary, social and ethical issues.

International Association for Religious Freedom (British Chapter)*

Upper Chapel, Norfolk Street, Sheffield S1 2JD
Tel: (0114) 2767114
Contact: Revd Geoffrey R Usher
Position: Chairman
Contact Tel: (0114) 2331218
Activities: Newsletter/journal, inter-faith
Affiliations: Inter Faith Network for the UK

International Association for Religious Freedom (International Secretariat)*

2 Market Street, Oxford OX1 3EF
Tel: (01865) 202744 **Fax:** (01865) 202746
Email: hq@iarf.net
Website: http://www.iarf-religiousfreedom.net/
Contact: Andrew C Clark
Position: General Secretary
Activities: Central body, umbrella body, youth, newsletter/journal, books

Other Languages: Japanese, Tamil, German, Hungarian
Founded in 1900 it is the oldest international interfaith organisation. It is currently undergoing major strategic planning, focusing on religious freedom and its preconditions.

International Interfaith Centre*

2 Market Street, Oxford OX1 3EF
Tel: (01865) 202745 **Fax:** (01865) 202746
Email: iic@interfaith-center.org
Website: http://www.interfaith-center.org/
Contact: Mrs Sandy Bharat
Position: Co-ordinator
Activities: Newsletter/journal, books, inter-faith, resources
Affiliations: Inter Faith Network for the UK
A registered charity for international interfaith encounter; facilitates interfaith conferences/seminars and courses as well as engages in networking; acts as a coordinator of the international interfaith organisations' network; publishes bi-annual newsletter and occasional publications.

Jain-Christian Association*

20 St James Close, London NW11 9QX
Tel: (020) 8455 5573 **Fax:** (020) 8922 7619
Email: natubhaishah@aol.com
Contact: Dr Natubhai Shah
Position: Chairman
Activities: Inter-faith
Involved in organising annual lectures on the theme 'Reverence for Life' for five years on a variety of topics including, overcoming violence, justice, peace, human rights, animal welfare and environment.

Jain-Jewish Association*

Star House, 104-108 Grafton Road, Kentish Town, London NW5 4BD
Tel: (020) 7485 2538 **Fax:** (020) 7485 4512
Email: sidney@sternberg-foundation.co.uk
Contact: Mr Sidney L Shipton
To promote fellowship and understanding among the members of the Jain and Jewish communities; to have dialogue and promote non-violence, peace and respect for the sanctity of life.

Maimonides Foundation*

38 Great Smith Street, London SW1P 3BU
Tel: (020) 7222 1992 **Fax:** (020) 7233 0161
Email: steve@maimonides.org.uk
Contact: Mr Steven Fine
Position: Executive Director
Contact Tel: (020) 7222 4852

Activities: Youth, women, inter-faith, resources
Traditions: Cross-community
Affiliations: Inter Faith Network for the UK
An organisation which promotes contact and understanding between Jews and people of different faiths in the UK and abroad through dialogue and the exchange of culture, in particular between Jews and Muslims.

Multifaith and Multicultural Mediation Services*

Camlad House, Fardern, Welshpool SY21 8NZ
Tel: (01938) 580319 **Fax:** (01938) 580319
Email: iipspg@clara.net
Contact: Dr Thomas Daffern
Position: Director
Contact Tel: (0788) 1694414

Multi Faith Nonviolence Group (International Fellowship of Reconciliation)*

49 Langton Grove, Sydenham, London SE26 6QQ
Tel: (020) 8778 4124 **Fax:** (020) 8659 2419
Contact: Abbas Baba
Position: Secretary
Activities: Newsletters
Produces leaflets on eight religions' views on peace, available from The Old School, Clopton, Kettering, Northamptonshire.

Religious Advisory Committee of the United Nations Association - UK*

3 Whitehall Court, London SW1A 2EL
Tel: (020) 7930 2931 **Fax:** (020) 7930 5893
Email: unauk@compuserve.com
Website: http://www.una-uk.org/
Contact: Betty Scharf
Position: Honorary Secretary
Contact Tel: (020) 8458 3532
Activities: Umbrella body
An inter-faith committee based on a belief in a common religious obligation to seek peace and in the principles and potential of the UN as an instrument of peace.

Sikh Council for Interfaith Relations UK*

1st Floor Office Suite, 192 The Broadway, London SW19 1RY
Tel: (020) 8540 3974
Contact: Mr Indarjit Singh OBE
Position: General Secretary
Affiliations: Network of Sikh Organisations
Aims to develop and focus interest on interfaith dialogue in the Sikh community; to promote a greater understanding of Sikhism among non-Sikhs;

to produce suitable literature and disseminate information on interfaith dialogue with meetings and seminars.

Three Faiths Forum*

Star House, 104–108 Grafton Road, Kentish Town, London NW5 4BD
Tel: (020) 7485 2538 **Fax:** (020) 7485 4512
Email: sidney@sternberg-foundation.co.uk
Contact: Mr Sidney L Shipton
Position: Co-ordinator
Activities: Central body, umbrella body, youth, elderly, women, inter-faith, resources
Affiliations: Inter Faith Network for the UK; The International Council of Christians and Jews
The Three Faiths Forum is a council and forum for the three Abrahamic and monotheistic faith communities of Islam, Judaism and Christianity. It encourages friendship, understanding and goodwill.

United Religions Initiative (Britain and Ireland)*

11 Birch Grove, Rusholme, Manchester M14 5JX
Tel: (0161) 2244985 **Fax:** (0161) 2249533
Email: info@uri.org.uk
Website: http://www.uri.org.uk/
Contact: Craig Russell
Position: Development Manager
Contact Tel: (07753) 962614
Contact Email: craig.russell@uri.org.uk
Activities: Umbrella body, youth, resources
URI's purpose is to promote enduring, daily interfaith cooperation, to end religiously motivated violence and to create cultures of peace, justice and healing for the Earth and living beings.

Week of Prayer for World Peace*

The Bungalow, Bremilham Road, Malmesbury SN16 0DQ
Tel: (01666) 825249
Email: sidney@fish.co.uk
Contact: Revd Sidney Hinkes
Publishes a multi faith leaflet of prayers each year for use in the Week of Prayer for World Peace in October.

World Conference on Religion and Peace (UK Chapter)*

London Inter Faith Centre, 125 Salusbury Road, London NW6 6RG
Tel: (020) 7604 3053 **Fax:** (020) 7604 3052
Email: 125.salusbury@london.anglican.org
Contact: Revd Fergus Capie
Position: Chair

Activities: Youth, newsletters, books
Affiliations: Inter Faith Network for the UK
An international, "religions working together" organisation, with (global) regional/national and local chapters. It is a recognised Non-Governmental Organisation at the United Nations.

World Congress of Faiths*
2 Market Street, Oxford OX1 3EF
Tel: (01865) 202751 **Fax:** (01865) 202746
Email: worldconfaiths@aol.com
Website: http://www.worldfaiths.org/
Contact: Rev Dr Richard Boeke
Position: Chair
Contact Tel: (01403) 257801
Contact Email: r.boeke@virgin.net
Activities: Newsletter/journal, books, inter-faith, resources
Traditions: Cross-community
Affiliations: International Interfaith Centre; Inter Faith Network for the UK
The World Congress of Faiths offers the opportunity to get to know people of other faiths in a practical way by listening and talking to people of other religions.

Wyndham Place Charlemagne Trust*
Copper Beeches, Gough Road, Fleet GU13 8LL
Tel: (01252) 612527 **Fax:** (01252) 612527
Email: j.keep@btinternet.com
Contact: Mrs Judy Keep
Position: Executive Secretary
The Trust aims to bring together people of different cultural political and religious backgrounds to address European and world issues and to enlighten public opinion and influence those who shape policy.

INTER-FAITH REGIONAL AND LOCAL ORGANISATIONS

Most of the organisations included in this section are groups which are not based in any one single religious community, but involve two or more religious traditions. However, also included are a small number of organisations based in one religion but concerned with inter-faith relations.

ENGLAND   101

NORTH EAST   101

YORKSHIRE AND THE HUMBER   101

NORTH WEST   102

EAST MIDLANDS   103

WEST MIDLANDS   104

EAST OF ENGLAND   105

LONDON   105

SOUTH EAST   106

SOUTH WEST   107

NORTHERN IRELAND   108

SCOTLAND   108

WALES   108

ENGLAND

NORTH EAST

Cleveland Interfaith Group*
1 Linden Road, Great Ayton, Middlesborough
TS9 6AN
Tel: (01642) 722589
Contact: Mr Richard Stainsby
Affiliations: Inter Faith Network for the UK

Gateshead Interfaith Forum*
391 Durham Road, Gateshead NE9 5AL
Tel: (0191) 487 1468
Contact: Mr Edward Brown
Position: Treasurer

Hindu-Sikh Friendship Society*
13 Ilford Road, West Jesmond, Newcastle-upon-Tyne NE2 3NX
Tel: (0191) 2843494
Contact: Davender Kumar Ghai
Position: Chair
Contact Tel: (0191) 2852888
Activities: Youth, elderly, women

Tyne and Wear Racial Equality Council (Inter Faith Panel)*
2nd Floor, MEA House, Ellison Place, Newcastle-upon-Tyne NE1 8XS
Contact: Simon Banks
Position: Director
Contact Tel: (0191) 232 7639
Activities: Umbrella body
Other Languages: Punjabi, Urdu, Bengali
Affiliations: Commission for Racial Equality; Inter Faith Network for the UK

YORKSHIRE AND THE HUMBER

Bradford Concord Interfaith Society*
c/o Interfaith Education Centre, Listerhills Road, Bradford BD7 1HD
Tel: (01274) 731674 **Fax:** (01274) 731621
Contact: Mr Rashmik Parmar
Position: Secretary
Activities: Inter-faith
Affiliations: Inter Faith Network for the UK

Q21 Centre for Dialogue and Action, The*
c/o Interfaith Education Centre, Listerhills Road, Bradford BD7 1HD
Tel: (01274) 731674 **Fax:** (01274) 731621

Website:
http://www.bradford.gov.uk/education/interfaith/q21
Contact: David Fitch
Position: Secretary
Contact Tel: (01274) 731674
Contact Email: admin@q21.org.uk

Kirklees and Calderdale Inter-Faith Fellowship*
316 Huddersfield Road, Mirfield WF14 9RY
Affiliations: Inter Faith Network for the UK

North Kirklees Interfaith Council*
5 Selbourne Road, Dewsbury, West Yorkshire WF12 9PB
Tel: (01924) 326367
Email: kaushar_Tai@hotmail.com
Contact: Mr Kaushar Tai
Position: Co-Chair
Contact Tel: (0781) 3811914
Activities: Umbrella body

Leeds Concord Inter-Faith Fellowship*
Aire Valley Marina, Redcote Lane, Leeds LS4 2AL
Tel: (0113) 214 5155
Contact: Mr Robin Fishwick
Position: General Secretary
Activities: Youth, elderly, women, resources
Other Languages: German, French, Hebrew, Persian
Affiliations: Inter Faith Network for the UK

Leeds Faith Communities Liaison Forum*
Leeds Church Institute, 20 New Market Street, Leeds LS1 6DG
Tel: (0113) 2454700 **Fax:** (0113) 3917939
Email: davidrhorn@leedschurchinstitute.org
Contact: Revd David Randolph-Horn
Position: Secretary
Activities: Umbrella body, newsletter/journal
Other Languages: Gujarati, Hindi, Punjabi, Urdu

Sheffield Christian Muslim Common Concern*
402 Abbeydale Road, Sheffield S1 1FU
Tel: (0114) 2509448
Contact: Qari Abdul Hamid
Position: Co-ordinator
Activities: Inter-faith, visits, resources
Other Languages: Urdu, Punjabi, Arabic

Sheffield Interfaith*
20 Thornsett Road, Sheffield S7 1NB
Tel: (0114) 2553896
Email: efratel@aol.com
Website:

http://www.shu.ac.uk/city/community/si
Contact: Cath Platt
Position: Secretary
Activities: Newsletters
Affiliations: Inter Faith Network for the UK

York Interfaith Group*
Forge Cottage, Linton-on-Ouse, York YO30 2AY
Tel: (01347) 848336
Contact: Ms Jan Jauncey
Activities: Newsletters

NORTH WEST

Blackburn With Darwen Interfaith Council*
Blackburn with Darwen Borough Council, Regeneration Department, Jubilee Street, Blackburn BB1 1EP
Tel: (01254) 585624 **Fax:** (01254) 265340
Email: fawad.bhatti@blackburn.gov.uk
Contact: Fawad Ahmad Bhatti
Position: Interfaith Development

Bolton Interfaith Council*
754 Blackburn Road, Sharples, Bolton BL1 7JW
Tel: (01204) 303257
Email: tony.mcneile@virgin.net
Contact: Mr Tony McNeile
Other Languages: Hindi, Gujarati
Affiliations: Inter Faith Network for the UK

Hyndburn Inter-Faith Forum*
St Peter's Vicarage, 151 Willows Lane, Accrington BB5 0LN
Tel: (01245) 382173
Contact: Revd David Lyon

Building Bridges Inter-Faith Community Project (Pendle)*
19 Market Square, Nelson, Lancashire BB9 7LP
Tel: (01282) 719303 **Fax:** (01282) 619335
Email: interfaith@buildingbridges.freeserve.co.uk
Contact: Mr Damian Duggan

Northwest Standing Conference on Inter-Faith Dialogue in Education*
1 Saint Paul's Close, Clitheroe BB7 2NB
Tel: (01200) 424719 **Fax:** (01200) 425538
Email: deved@btinternet.com
Contact: Colin Scott
Position: Secretary

Interfaith Circle Kendal*
68 Cleveleys Avenue, Lancaster LA1 5HD

Contact: Mrs Dorothea Williamson
Position: Facilitator
Contact Tel: (01524) 36709
Activities: Worship/practice/meditation

Merseyside Council of Faiths*
c/o The Dean's Office, Liverpool Cathedral, St James' Mount, Liverpool L1 7AZ
Tel: (0151) 7096271 **Fax:** (0151) 7091112
Contact: Rt Revd Dr Rupert Hoare
Position: Chair
Activities: Umbrella body

Merseyside Inter-Faith Group*
c/o 23 Hunter's Lane, Wavertree, Liverpool L15 8HL
Tel: (0151) 7331541
Contact: Revd Canon Michael M Wolfe
Position: Co-ordinator
Activities: Worship/practice/meditation, umbrella body, newsletter/journal, inter-faith
Affiliations: Merseyside and Region Churches' Ecumenical Assembly, (MARCEA); Inter Faith Network for the UK

Bury Inter-Faith Council*
13 Penryth Avenue, Whitefield, Manchester M45 6UJ
Tel: (0161) 7736529
Contact: Mrs Phyllis Vallon

Manchester Interfaith Forum*
10 Lynwood Avenue, Whalley Range, Manchester M16 8JZ
Tel: (0161) 8604716
Email: vjrosbuck@appleonline.net
Contact: Dr Valerie J Roebuck
Position: Secretary
Activities: Umbrella body

Manchester Inter-Faith Group*
St Margaret's Rectory, Rufford Road, Manchester M16 8AE
Tel: (0161) 2261289
Email: boulter@mighty_micro.co.uk
Contact: Robert Boulter
Position: Secretary
Activities: Umbrella body, women, newsletter/journal, television, visits, inter-faith, resources
Other Languages: Urdu, Arabic, Punjabi
Affiliations: Inter Faith Network for the UK

Preston Inter-Faith Forum*
University of Central Lancashire, 33-35 St Peter's Square, Preston PR1 2HE
Tel: (01772) 892615
Contact: Revd Peter James Thomas
Position: Convenor
Activities: Umbrella body

Rochdale Interfaith Action*
3 Middle Field, Rochdale OL11 5RD
Contact: Mr Razzak Ahmed
Position: Member
Contact Tel: (07899) 003017
Contact Email: razzak_ahmed@yahoo.com
Affiliations: Inter Faith Network for the UK

EAST MIDLANDS

Derby Open Centre Multi-Faith Group*
43 Pear Tree Road, Normanton, Derby DE23 6PZ
Tel: (01332) 360737
Contact: Project Director
Position: Ms Janine Shrigley
Contact Tel: (01332) 360737
Activities: Community centre, youth, inter-faith, resources.
Other Languages: Urdu, Hindi, Punjabi
Affiliations: Inter Faith Network for the UK

Leicester Council of Faiths*
Pilgrim House, 10 Bishop Street, Leicester LE1 6AF
Tel: (0116) 2546868 **Fax:** (0116) 2543528
Email: lco.faiths@webleicester.co.uk
Website: http://homepages.webleicester.co.uk/lco.faiths/index.html
Contact: Mr Tony Stokes
Position: Co-ordinator
Activities: Central body, umbrella body, newsletter/journal, visits
Other Languages: Gujarati, Punjabi, Urdu
Affiliations: Inter Faith Network for the UK

Leicester Inter Faith Council*
6 Half Moon Crescent, Oadby, Leicester LE2 4HD
Tel: (0116) 2712339
Contact: Dr David Russell
Position: President
Activities: Worship/practice/meditation, umbrella body, visits, inter-faith

Lincoln Inter Faith Group*
2 Thornton Close, Washingborough, Lincoln
LN4 1HQ
Tel: (01522) 790838
Contact: Lily Amery
Position: Secretary
Activities: Inter-faith
Other Languages: Urdu, Hindi

Loughborough Council of Faiths*
74 Cobden Street, Loughborough LE11 1AQ
Tel: (01509) 561306 **Fax:** (01509) 267826
Email: mark@druid.here.co.uk
Contact: Mark Graham
Position: Secretary
Affiliations: Inter Faith Network for the UK

Loughborough Inter-Faith Group*
c/o 21 Mayfield Drive, Loughborough LE11 2EA
Tel: (01509) 265277
Contact: Anthony Gimpel
Position: Contact
Contact Email: agimpel@aol.com
Activities: Inter-faith

Nottingham Inter-Faith Council*
St Francis House, 20 Leslie Road, Nottingham
NG7 6PD
Tel: (0115) 9783889
Contact: Sister Kathleen Harman
Position: Secretary
Activities: Central body, inter-faith
Other Languages: Punjabi, Hebrew, Urdu
Affiliations: Inter Faith Network for the UK

Peterborough Inter-Faith Council*
2 Burns Road, Stamford PE9 2XD
Tel: (01780) 762787
Contact: Mrs Anne Emery
Position: Honorary Secretary
Affiliations: Inter Faith Network for the UK

Wellingborough Multi-Faith Group*
Victoria Centre, Palk Road, Wellingborough
NN8 1HR
Tel: (01933) 277400 **Fax:** (01933) 275443
Contact: Cynthia June Bailey
Position: Centre Manager
Activities: Community centre, youth, elderly
Affiliations: Inter Faith Network for the UK

WEST MIDLANDS

Birmingham Council of Faiths*
St Philip's 6th Form College, 153 Hagley Road,
Birmingham B16 8UF
Tel: (0121) 6946206
Email:
birmingham_council_of_faiths@hotmail.com
Contact: Vajragupta
Position: Chair
Activities: Newsletters
Affiliations: Inter Faith Network for the UK

Coventry Inter Faith Group*
55 St Paul's Road, Coventry CV6 5DE
Tel: (024) 7668 8264
Contact: Revd Supriyo Mukherjee
Position: Secretary
Activities: Inter-faith
Affiliations: Inter Faith Network for the UK

Dudley Council of Faiths*
c/o Russells Hall Hospital, Dudley DY1 2HQ
Tel: (0121) 4264580 **Fax:** (01384) 244051
Contact: Revd Mark Stobert
Position: Secretary
Activities: Inter-faith
Affiliations: Inter Faith Network for the UK

Walsall Inter-Faith Group*
193 Lichfield Road, Rushall, Walsall WS4 1EA
Tel: (01922) 621703 **Fax:** (01922) 621703
Email: m.z.wilkins@zoo.co.uk
Contact: Margaret Wilkins
Position: Secretary

North Staffordshire Faiths in Friendship*
20 Tettenhall Road, Wolverhampton WV1 4SL
Tel: (01902) 771375
Email: ifofficer@aol.com
Activities: Inter-faith

Wolverhampton Inter-Faith Group*
The Inter-Faith Centre, 43 Princess Street,
Wolverhampton WV1 1HD
Tel: (01902) 427601 **Fax:** (01902) 427601
Email: interfwolv@aol.com
Contact: Revd J McManus
Position: Honorary Secretary
Contact Tel: (01902) 833436
Contact Email: jimvicar@aol.com
Activities: Umbrella body, newsletters, books,
inter-faith
Other Languages: Hindi, Punjabi
Affiliations: Inter Faith Network for the UK

EAST OF ENGLAND

Bedford Council of Faiths*
7 Wingfield Close, Bedford MK40 4PB
Tel: (01234) 307281
Contact: Monica Whitmore
Affiliations: Inter Faith Network for the UK

Cambridge Inter-Faith Group*
45 Walpole Road, Cambridge CB1 3TH
Tel: (01223) 510442
Contact: Ralph Nimmann
Affiliations: Inter Faith Network for the UK

Suffolk Inter-Faith Resource*
c/o Suffolk College, Rope Walk, Ipswich IP4 1LT
Tel: (01473) 233447 **Fax:** (01473) 289360
Email: c.capey@sifre.org.uk
Website: http://www.sifre.org.uk/
Contact: Mrs Cynthia Capey
Position: Hon Managing Director
Contact Tel: (01473) 233447
Activities: Practice/meditation, community centre, umbrella body, youth, elderly, women, newsletter/journal, books, radio, visits, inter-faith, resources
Other Languages: Punjabi, Bengali, Arabic, Farsi
Affiliations: Inter Faith Network for the UK; World Congress of Faiths

Luton Council of Faiths (LCOF)*
102a Dunstable Road, Luton LU1 1EH
Tel: (01582) 416946 **Fax:** (01582) 483507
Email: grassrootsp@cs.com
Contact: Mr Shanthi Hettiarachchi
Position: Secretary
Activities: Umbrella body, newsletters
Other Languages: Urdu, Gujarati, Punjabi, Hindi
Affiliations: Inter Faith Network for the UK

Norwich Inter Faith*
Reiukai, Unit 24, St Mary's Works, Duke Street, Norwich NR3 1QA
Tel: (01603) 630857 **Fax:** (01603) 760749
Contact: Mr Hiromi Hasegawa

Watford Inter-Faith Association
11 Frankland Road, Croxley Green WD3 3AS
Tel: (01923) 774812
Contact: Ms Judith Bruni
Position: Secretary
Affiliations: Inter Faith Network for the UK

LONDON

Harrow Inter-Faith Council*
121 Strongbridge Close, Harrow HA2 0XP
Tel: (020) 8864 8403
Contact: Mrs Phiroza Gan
Position: Chair
Activities: Youth, elderly, newsletter/journal, visits, inter-faith, resources
Affiliations: Inter Faith Network for the UK

Westminster Interfaith*
17 Garrison Close, Hounslow TW4 5EZ
Tel: (020) 8570 8639 **Fax:** (020) 8570 8639
Email: A Agius@aol.com
Website: http://www.westminster.interfaith.org.uk/
Contact: Alfred Agius
Position: Director
Activities: Newsletters, books
Affiliations: Inter Faith Network for the UK

Redbridge Council of Faiths*
2 Northbrook Road, Ilford IG1 3AQ
Tel: (020) 8478 6451 **Fax:** (020) 8478 6451
Contact: B K Mark Fleming
Position: Secretary
Contact Tel: (020) 8478 0850
Contact Email: mark-fleming@tudor-york.freeserve.co.uk
Activities: Worship/practice/meditation, youth, elderly, inter-faith
Other Languages: Hindi, Hebrew, Arabic, Punjabi
Affiliations: Inter Faith Network for the UK

Brent Inter Faith*
125 Salusbury Road, London NW6 6RG
Tel: (020) 7604 3053 **Fax:** (020) 7604 3052
Email: 125.salusbury@london.anglican.org
Contact: Mrs Gillian Jones
Position: Minutes Secretary
Activities: Umbrella body, inter-faith
Affiliations: Inter Faith Network for the UK

Croydon Interfaith Group*
Bridleways, Haling Grove, South Croydon CR2 6DQ
Tel: (020) 8680 4460 **Fax:** (020) 8681 5103
Email: revkevin19@hotmail.com
Contact: Revd Ken Smith
Position: Chair
Activities: Umbrella body

Greenwich Multi-Faith Forum*
41 Malton Street, Wellington Street, London
SE18 2EH
Tel: (020) 8854 4688
Contact: Ms Augusta Gibrill
Contact Tel: (07949) 117429
Activities: Central body, visits, inter-faith, resources
Other Languages: Punjabi, Arabic, Hindi

Hampstead Interfaith Group*
63b Belsize Park Gardens, Hampstead, London
NW3 4JN
Contact: Mrs Eva Tucker
Position: Organiser
Contact Tel: (020) 7722 9010
Activities: Inter-faith

Inter-Faith Refugee Network - Westminster Diocese Refugee Service*
Vaughan House, 46 Francis Street, London
SW1P 1QN
Tel: (020) 7798 9027 **Fax:** (020) 7798 9010
Email: aomara@westminsterdiocese.org.uk
Website: http://www.wdrs.org/
Contact: Mr Augustine Omara
Position: Director
Activities: Umbrella body

Kenton Inter Faith Group*
c/o All Saints Church, Claremont Avenue, Kenton
HA3 0UL
Contact: Sister Elizabeth
Contact Tel: (020) 7272 8048

Lambeth Multi Faith Action Group*
11 Trent Road, Brixton, London SW2 5BJ
Tel: (020) 7274 4625 **Fax:** (020) 7738 4513
Email: damianh@btinternet.com
Position: Co-ordinator

London Inter Faith Centre*
125 Salusbury Road, London NW6 6RG
Tel: (020) 7604 3053 **Fax:** (020) 7604 3052
Email: 125.salusbury@london.anglican.org
Contact: Mrs Gillian Jones
Position: Centre Manager
Activities: Resources

London Society of Jews and Christians*
28 St John's Wood Road, London NW8 7HA
Tel: (020) 7432 1283 **Fax:** (020) 7266 3591
Email: j.shopper@ljs.org
Website: http://www.ljs.org/
Contact: Rabbi David J Goldberg

Position: Joint Chairman
Activities: Inter-faith, resources
Affiliations: Inter Faith Network for the UK

Newham Association of Faiths*
The Shalom Centre, 395 High Street North,
London E12 6EL
Tel: (020) 8471 6545
Contact: Secretary
Affiliations: Inter Faith Network for the UK

Richmond Inter-Faith Group*
Richmond and Putney Unitarian Church, Ormond
Road, Richmond TW10 6TH
Tel: (020) 8332 9675
Contact: Revd Anne McClelland
Position: Acting Secretary
Contact Tel: (020) 8892 6373
Activities: Umbrella body
Affiliations: Inter Faith Network for the UK

South London Inter-Faith Group*
23 Holmewood Gardens, London SW2 3RS
Tel: (020) 8674 5447
Contact: Ms Sarah Thorley
Position: Contact Person
Contact Email: helericb@cs.com
Activities: Newsletter/journal, inter-faith
Affiliations: Inter Faith Network for the UK

Wimbledon Interfaith Group*
55 Dora Road, Wimbledon, London SW19 7EZ
Contact: John Elderton
Position: Secretary

SOUTH EAST

Basingstoke Association of Faiths and Cultures
16 Harwood Gardens, Basingstoke RG21 3NR
Tel: (01256) 350187
Contact: Mr Zarin Hainsworth
Position: Secretary

Brighton and Hove Inter-Faith Contact Group*
PO Box 2882, Brighton BN1 1PU
Tel: (01273) 722438
Email: p.sharrock@mistral.co.uk
Contact: Imam Dr Abduljalil Sajid
Position: Chair
Contact Tel: (07971) 861972
Contact Email: ajsajid@ibelieve.co.uk
Activities: Worship/practice/meditation,
community centre, umbrella body, youth, elderly,

women, newsletter/journal, books, newspapers, radio, television, inter-faith, resources
Affiliations: World Conference on Religion and Peace (WCRP), Inter Faith Network for the UK

Canterbury and District Inter Faith Action*
23 South Canterbury Road, Canterbury CT1 3LH
Tel: (01227) 463180
Email: wallings@surfaid.org
Contact: Revd Michael J Walling

Medway and Maidstone Inter-Faith Group*
Emmaus Church Centre, Chatham ME4 4DT
Tel: (01634) 404877 **Fax:** (01634) 404877
Affiliations: Inter Faith Network for the UK

Faith Awareness: The Interfaith Programme of Christians Aware*
208 Botwell Lane, Hayes UB3 2AJ
Tel: (020) 8573 8658 **Fax:** (020) 8561 3478
Email: barbarabutler@christiansaware.co.uk
Website: http://www.christiansaware.co.uk/
Contact: Dr Joy Barrow
Position: Co-ordinator
Contact Email: joybarrow@aol.com
Activities: Women, newsletter/journal, books, inter-faith
Affiliations: Inter Faith Network for the UK

Wycombe Sharing of Faiths*
35 Trees Road, Hughenden Valley, High Wycombe HP14 4PN
Tel: (01494) 564445
Email: mbowker@doctors.org.uk
Contact: Anne Bowker
Position: Chair
Other Languages: Farsi, Punjabi/Urdu
Affiliations: Inter Faith Network for the UK

Hitchin Sikh-Christian Forum*
St Faiths Vicarage, 31 Meadowbank, Hitchin SG4 0HY
Tel: (01462) 432179
Contact: Revd Pamela Wise

North Kent Council for Inter-faith Relations*
1 Crest View, Greenhithe Quay DA9 9QY
Tel: (01233) 381215
Contact: Revd Malcom Cooper

Oxford Round Table of Religions*
The Old Rectory, Middleton Stoney OX6 8RZ
Tel: (01865) 343317 **Fax:** (01865) 550781
Contact: Mr S K Vadivale

Position: Liaison Officer
Contact Email: saivale@aol.com
Affiliations: Inter Faith Network for the UK

Inter Faith MK*
11 Fairways, Two Mile Ash, Milton Keynes MK8 8AL
Tel: (01908) 560714 **Fax:** (01908) 560714
Email: hzfriedman@aol.com
Contact: Mr H Z Friedman
Position: Secretary

Reading Inter-Faith Group*
Lukers, Theale, Reading RG7 5AH
Tel: (0118) 930 3182
Contact: Mr Hugh Boulter
Affiliations: Inter Faith Network for the UK

Southampton Council of Faiths and Southampton Inter Faith Link*
135 St Mary Street, St Mary's, Southampton SO15 1NX
Tel: (023) 8033 0851
Email: d.white@southamptonvs.org.uk
Contact: Ian Johnson
Position: Member
Other Languages: Gujarati, Hebrew, Arabic

Woking Multi-Faith Group*
17 Kettlewood Close, Horsell, Woking GU21 4HY
Contact: Mrs Elizabeth Elton

SOUTH WEST

Bath Inter-Faith Group*
45 Brooklyn Road, Larkhall, Bath BA1 6TF
Tel: (01225) 422252
Contact: Shelagh James
Position: Chair

One World Fellowship*
8 Whitcombe Road, Beaminster DT8 3NE
Tel: (01308) 862470
Contact: Mr Roger Lake
Position: Secretary
Contact Email: rogerlake8@cs.com
Activities: Newsletter/journal, inter-faith

Bristol Inter Faith Group*
Underhill, Shorthill Road, Westerleigh, Bristol BS37 8QN
Tel: (01454) 313042 **Fax:** (01454) 313042
Contact: Mrs June Ridd

Position: Membership Secretary
Activities: Umbrella body, inter-faith
Affiliations: Inter Faith Network for the UK

Exeter Interfaith Group*
Coombe Farm, Knowle, Cullumpton EX15 1PT
Contact: Isabel Jeffrey
Position: Honorary Secretary
Contact Tel: (01884) 33533

Frome Interfaith Group*
Behindtown, Park Road, Frome Selwood BA11 1EU
Tel: (01373) 466371
Contact: Mrs Annette Burkitt

Gloucestershire Inter Faith Action Group*
Barton and Tredworth Community Centre,
Conduit Street, Gloucester GL1 4LX
Tel: (01452) 530337 **Fax:** (01452) 530337
Email: michaeldadson@aol.com
Contact: Mr Gulam Musa
Position: Secretary
Activities: Umbrella body, youth, elderly,
newsletter/journal
Affiliations: Inter Faith Network for the UK

Torbay Interfaith Forum*
143 Southfield Avenue, Paignton TQ3 1LD
Tel: (01803) 556632
Contact: Mrs Jan Mughrabi
Position: Secretary
Affiliations: Linked with Torbay Standing
Advisory Council on Religious Education

Plymouth Interfaith Group*
3A Watts Road, St Judes, Plymouth PL4 8SE
Tel: (01752) 2254438 **Fax:** (01752) 2254438
Contact: Mr Jonathon Marshall
Position: Chair

Taunton Inter Faith Group*
1 Pickenbridge, Compton Durville, South
Petherton TA13 5EY
Tel: (01460) 241235
Email: ngarwhiteford@hotmail.com
Contact: Mrs N A Whiteford

Swindon Interfaith Group*
2 Brecon Close, Swindon SN3 1JT
Tel: (01793) 534923
Email: vernon.griffiths@ukgateway.net
Contact: Mrs Margaret Griffiths
Position: Secretary
Activities: Umbrella body, inter-faith

Totnes and District Inter Faith*
"Lyndene", Station Road, Totnes TQ9 5HW
Tel: (01803) 863454

West Somerset Inter Faith Group*
Old Cleeve Priory, Watchet TA23 0JS
Tel: (01984) 631098
Contact: A Groos
Position: General Secretary

NORTHERN IRELAND

Northern Ireland Inter Faith Forum
Stranmillis University College, Stranmillis Road,
Belfast BT9 5DY
Tel: (028) 9038 4328
Email: n.richardson@stran.ni.ac.uk
Contact: Mr Norman Richardson, MBE
Position: Secretary

SCOTLAND
Scottish National Bodies

Scottish Inter Faith Council*
c/o St Mungo's Museum, 2 Castle Street,
Glasgow G4 0RH
Tel: (0141) 5532557 **Fax:** (0141) 5524744
Email: sifc@freeuk.com
Website: http://www.scottishinterfaith.org
Contact: Sister Isabel Smyth
Activities: Umbrella body, newsletter/journal
Affiliations: Inter Faith Network for the UK

City, Town or Local Bodies

Aberdeen Inter Faith Group*
66a Hamilton Place, Aberdeen AB2 4BA
Contact: Ms Kathryn Hendry

Dundee Inter Faith Group*
11 Rosewood Terrace, Dundee DD2 1NS
Tel: (01382) 667119
Contact: Mrs Rosemary Eddy

Edinburgh Inter Faith Association*
6 Ventnor Terrace, Edinburgh EH9 2BL
Tel: (0131) 667 4360
Email: andrew@unitarian.ednet.co.uk
Contact: Revd Andrew Hill
Position: Secretary

Glasgow Sharing of Faiths Group*
1 Leverndale Court, Crookston, Glasgow G53 7SJ
Contact: Rose Goodenough
Position: Secretary
Affiliations: Inter Faith Network for the UK

WALES

Cardiff Interfaith Association*
23 Solva Avenue, Llanishen, Cardiff CF14 0NP
Tel: (029) 2075 0990
Email: schwartz@otago.co.uk
Contact: Mr Alan Schwartz
Activities: Visits, inter-faith, resources
Affiliations: Inter Faith Network for the UK

Newport Interfaith Group (South Wales)*
Community House, Eton Road, Newport
NP9 0BL
Contact: Mrs Geraldine Layton
Position: Secretary
Contact Tel: (01495) 791618
Activities: Worship/practice/meditation,
community centre, inter-faith

INTRODUCING BAHÁ'ÍS IN THE UK

BAHÁ'ÍS IN THE UNITED
KINGDOM   111

ORIGINS AND DEVELOPMENT
OF THE BAHÁ'Í FAITH   111

SOURCES OF BAHÁ'Í BELIEFS
AND PRACTICES   112

KEY BAHÁ'Í BELIEFS   113

BAHÁ'Í LIFE   114

TRADITIONS IN THE BAHÁ'Í
FAITH   115

BAHÁ'Í WORSHIP   115

BAHÁ'Í CALENDAR AND
FESTIVALS   116

BAHÁ'Í ORGANISATIONS   117

FURTHER READING   119

BAHÁ'ÍS IN THE UNITED KINGDOM

History

Bahá'ís have been present in the UK since 1899, when Miriam Thornburgh-Cropper, the first Bahá'í to live in London, started to attract others to this new faith. She had been inspired by her visit to the Holy Land to meet *'Abdu'l-Bahá*, eldest son and successor of *Bahá'u'lláh*, the founder of the faith.

The growth of the faith was greatly stimulated by the visits of *'Abdu'l-Bahá* to a number of cities in England and Scotland during 1911-13. By then groups of Bahá'ís were holding regular meetings in London, Bournemouth and Manchester.

Up until 1939 most Bahá'í activity was centred in England, but in the years following the Second World War the Bahá'í Faith was also established in Scotland, Wales and Ireland. Now there are around 399 Local Groups and 125 Local Spiritual Assemblies.

Origins

Most Bahá'ís in the UK are of indigenous ethnic origin and the majority are converts from other religions or are former agnostics or atheists. There are also Bahá'ís whose family roots are in Iran, most of whom have arrived since the Iranian Revolution. Most Bahá'ís in the UK pray and read their scriptures in English. Some of Iranian descent also use Persian and Arabic.

ORIGINS AND DEVELOPMENT OF THE BAHÁ'Í FAITH

The Báb

The Bahá'í Faith began in Persia on 23rd May 1844, with the declaration of a new religion, distinctive from the *Shi'a* Islam found there. Four people were central to the development of the Bahá'í Faith: the *Báb*, *Bahá'u'lláh*, *'Abdu'l-Bahá* and Shoghi Effendi.

The person known to Bahá'ís by the title of the *Báb* (the Gate or Door, 1819-1850) was born in Shiraz, Persia. The *Báb* was originally known by the personal name of Ali-Muhammad and was a descendant of the Prophet Muhammad. In 1844 the *Báb* proclaimed himself the *Messenger* of God and heralded the coming of *One Greater* who would bring a new age of civilisation characterised by world peace. He was executed in Persia on 9th July 1850 under the charge of heresy against Islam. Many of his early followers, known as *Bábis*, were also persecuted after his death.

Bahá'u'lláh

Husayn Ali (1817-1892), known to Bahá'ís by the title of *Bahá'u'lláh* (the Glory of God) was born in Tehran, Persia. In 1863, he claimed to be the *Greater One* whose coming the *Báb* had foretold. He said he was the bringer of divine revelation who was to fulfil the promises made by the previous *Messengers* of other religions. *Bahá'u'lláh* was banished from Persia, and later exiled to Palestine by the Ottoman Turkish authorities in 1868. He died in Akka in 1892 and was buried at nearby Bahji which is the holiest shrine of the Bahá'í world and provides a physical focus of its global unity.

'Abdu'l-Bahá

After the death of *Bahá'u'lláh* his son *'Abdu'l-Bahá* (Servant of the Glory - also known among Bahá'ís as the *Master*) was appointed in *Bahá'u'lláh's Will* as the authorised interpreter of Bahá'í teachings. *'Abdu'l-Bahá* was born in 1844 and died in Haifa in 1921.

Shoghi Effendi

On the death of *'Abdu'l-Bahá*, his grandson Shoghi Effendi (1897-1957), as appointed in *'Abdu'l-Bahá's Will*, became the *Guardian of the Faith* and *Interpreter of Scripture*. Shoghi Effendi died whilst on a private visit to London, where there was already an established community of Bahá'ís. With his death authority passed to the elected body called the *Hands of the Cause of God*. This was a group of twenty-seven people

appointed by Shoghi Effendi to be the *Chief Stewards of the Faith*.

Universal House of Justice

In 1963 the *Universal House of Justice* was established as a guiding body for the Bahá'í community. It is now based at the Bahá'í World Centre in Haifa in Israel and is re-elected every five years.

Recent Decades

Over the past thirty years, the Bahá'í Faith has experienced major expansion, especially in India, Africa, South America, the Pacific and more recently in Eastern Europe.

SOURCES OF BAHÁ'Í BELIEFS AND PRACTICES

Bahá'í Scriptures

Bahá'ís believe their scriptures to be the revealed message of God. These scriptures consist of the *Writings* of the three central figures of the Bahá'í Faith: the *Báb*, *Bahá'u'lláh*, and *'Abdu'l-Bahá*. They include all documents hand-written by them; all documents signed by them; and records of their spoken words, authenticated either directly or indirectly by the speakers. The *Kitáb-i-Iqán* (*The Book of Certitude*) contains the key doctrinal beliefs and *Bahá'u'lláh's Hidden Words* is a frequently used collection of ethical aphorisms.

Most of the *Writings* of *Bahá'u'lláh* and *'Abdu'l-Bahá* are in the form of letters known as *Tablets* and are written in Persian or Arabic. The collection and classification of Bahá'í sacred *Writings* as well as of their authoritative interpretations by Shoghi Effendi still continues today. There are now over 60,000 original documents or copies kept at the Bahá'í World Centre in Haifa and the Bahá'í scriptures have been translated into over 820 languages. Foremost among these scriptures is *Bahá'u'lláh's* 1873 *Kitáb-i-Aqdas* (*Most Holy Book*) which is considered the basis for Bahá'í moral principles and institutions.

KEY BAHÁ'Í BELIEFS

A Summary

A summary of key Bahá'í beliefs can be found in the various collections of the talks which 'Abdu'l-Bahá gave in America. The key Bahá'í beliefs are belief in one God; the unity of mankind; independent investigation of truth; the common foundation of all religions; the essential harmony of science and religion; equality of opportunity for men and women; elimination of prejudice of all kinds; universal compulsory education; a universal auxiliary language; abolition of extremities of poverty and wealth through international legislation; the establishment of universal peace by world government which will have international courts of justice and an international military force; and, finally, the concept of progressive revelation.

Progressive Revelation

Unity and its establishment in the world is a central theme of the Bahá'í religion. Its followers share a conviction that there has only ever been one religion and one God though people have called God by different names. This conviction was continually emphasised by 'Abdu'l-Bahá.

God is seen as being beyond gender and as infinite and unknowable in Divine Essence, yet revealed to humanity through a series of *Messengers* sent to different places at different times. Moses, Krishna, Zoroaster, *Buddha*, *Christ* and Muhammad are all believed by Bahá'ís to be *Messengers* from God and are described by *Bahá'u'lláh* as *Manifestations* of God. Bahá'ís believe that every people on earth have, at some point in their history, been recipients of a Divine *Manifestation* or *Prophet*.

There is therefore a progressive view of revelation in which each recognised *Messenger* is believed to have passed on divine law informing society how to live and behave. All *Messengers* are also believed to have promised a time when a great *Messenger* would come and bring peace to the world and Bahá'ís believe that *Bahá'u'lláh* was that *Messenger*.

Oneness of Humankind

Bahá'ís believe that the future of the world lies in a single world order existing for the benefit of everyone regardless of race, religion, class or gender. This will involve the abolition of prejudices; equality for men and women; abolition of the extremes of wealth and poverty; universal compulsory education; and a world commonwealth with a world parliament.

It is within this context that the Bahá'í commitment to a universal auxiliary language should be understood. This does not entail a commitment to any particular language to serve this purpose - the choice of such a language is to be left to the people of the world to choose, through their representatives. But its introduction and use is seen as both an aid to practical communication and as a force to help develop even further the world unity which is seen as necessary for the survival and prosperity of humanity.

It is believed that once the unity of humankind has been firmly established world peace will follow. The establishment of Bahá'í communities and groups throughout the world is seen as contributing to this process and, indeed, as modelling a new world order.

Nature and Goal of Human Life

Bahá'ís believe that the basic purposes of human life are to know and worship God, developing spiritual qualities which enable individuals to fulfil their God-given potential and to become better people.

Bahá'ís believe that each human being has a separate rational soul which is related to, but also distinct from, the human body and persists after death. The world is understood as a place where this soul can develop. The analogy is often used of the world as a womb, in which the foetus is growing arms, legs, eyes and other organs whose purpose will only become clear when it moves into the next phase of existence by being born into the world. Similarly, human beings, in this life, are seen as developing positive spiritual qualities, the true importance of which will only be appreciated in the next world. To the extent that spiritual qualities have been developed in this world, to that extent will the soul to able to progress in the next world.

Heaven is seen as a state of nearness to God and hell as being remoteness from God, each of which follows as a consequence of efforts, or the lack of them, to develop spiritually. The Bahá'í teachings emphasise that death is a "messenger of joy" and deal with the subject of the life to come in great depth. *Bahá'u'lláh* states that there are many worlds of God through which our souls will pass on their journey towards Him.

Education and Spirituality

The importance of education is a central theme in the Bahá'í understanding of one's place in the world. There is no dichotomy between what are often called the secular and the spiritual dimensions of life. Religion and science are viewed as being complementary ways of discovering truth: science through investigation and religion through revelation.

Ethics and Spirituality

Bahá'í ethics are understood as being both individual and social. As already indicated in terms of the analogy of the womb, the development of positive spiritual qualities is seen as the individual task of every human being. At the same time, humankind is understood to be social with the relationships between individuals also being part of the task of spiritual development. Hence Bahá'í ethics include both individual and social dimensions, as explained in the following section.

BAHÁ'Í LIFE

Joining the Community

A person becomes a member of the Bahá'í community by applying to a Bahá'í administrative body such as a *Local Spiritual Assembly* (see below). An *Assembly* will accept them if it is satisfied that they truly believe the tenets of the Bahá'í Faith and are basically informed about the central figures of the Faith, the existence of laws they must follow, as well as the administrative system with which they must live in conformity. Being a part of the Bahá'í worldwide *Administrative Order* gives individual Bahá'ís confidence that they can contribute in the best way to the goals of the Bahá'í religion.

Teaching and Pioneering

Bahá'ís are forbidden to proselytise in the sense of holding out the promise of reward or the threat of punishment (whether material or spiritual) in order to make converts. However, Bahá'ís are always eager to share their vision and beliefs with enquirers and hold out a welcome to people who wish to join the Bahá'í community. This sharing of vision and belief is known among Bahá'ís as teaching. Many are also involved in what is known as *pioneering*, which is spreading the Faith by means of moving where there are currently few or no Bahá'ís.

Women and Men

Men and women have equal status in the Bahá'í community. Any distinctions in gender roles are culture-specific rather than religious and there is a strongly held view that both men and women should receive education of equal standard. If for any reason education is not available to all, then women, as the first educators of the next generation, should have priority.

Diet

There are no specific dietary laws in the Bahá'í Faith, although vegetarianism is commended as a healthier and more natural lifestyle and one which it is anticipated will become the norm for human beings in the future. However, the consumption of alcohol is strictly forbidden (including its use in cooking and sauces) as is the taking of habit-forming drugs, and smoking is discouraged.

Voluntary Sharing

Bahá'u'lláh advocated voluntary sharing rather than an externally imposed equalisation of wealth. Sharing is a matter of free choice and therefore is seen as more desirable.

TRADITIONS IN THE BAHÁ'Í FAITH

The Bahá'í community is tightly structured and organised. At each stage in the development of the Bahá'í religion there have been those who have split off from the community because they disputed the succession and leadership set out in the *Wills* of *Bahá'u'lláh* and *'Abdu'l-Bahá*, and who have tried to establish an alternative movement under the Bahá'í name.

These groups are referred to by Bahá'ís as *Covenant-breakers*, since the *Covenant* which binds Bahá'ís together is seen to consist of the unity of the line of authority from *Bahá'u'lláh* through to the *Universal House of Justice*. The consequence of such *Covenant-breaking* is expulsion.

Covenant-breaking is understood by Bahá'ís to be fundamentally different from simply leaving the religion or behaving in a way that falls short of Bahá'í ideals, since it is seen as disobeying the *Wills* of *Bahá'u'lláh* and *'Abdu'l-Bahá*. Bahá'ís are forbidden to have social relationships with those who have attempted to establish alternative authorities and groups. None of the groups viewed as *Covenant-breakers* have gained a major following and some of the people involved in them have subsequently gone on to practise other religions or philosophies.

Bahá'ís are not organised into any identifiably distinct traditions of interpretation or practice. It is a part of the Bahá'í self-understanding that their religion is unique among the world's religions in that it has not only survived a century and a half without splitting into sects, but it is believed that it will continue to be united in the future.

BAHÁ'Í WORSHIP

Daily Prayers

Every Bahá'í over the age of fifteen must recite daily one of three prayers known as the "obligatory" prayers. These three prayers differ in length and must be recited in differing ways. The three prayers are: a short prayer which should be recited once every twenty-four hours between noon and sunset; a medium length prayer which should be recited three times in a day - morning, noon and evening; and a long prayer which should be recited once every twenty-four hours. In addition to reciting one of these obligatory prayers, Bahá'ís are required to read extracts from the scriptures every morning and evening. When praying, Bahá'ís turn in the direction of Bahji, near Akka in Israel, which is the burial place of *Bahá'u'lláh*.

Regular Worship

The Bahá'í religion has no set worship services and no ordained priesthood. Devotional programmes are simple and consist of prayers, meditations, and the reading of sections from the sacred scriptures of the Faith and of other world religions. Music is encouraged and in the *Houses of Worship* (see below) this is provided by an unaccompanied choir.

Firesides

Most Bahá'í gatherings take place in people's homes. Small regular meetings in homes for discussion are known as *Firesides*. Outsiders who have expressed an interest in the Faith may be present at these. *Firesides* usually begin and end with prayers and include information and discussion. Other meetings, for example *Nineteen-Day Feasts* (see below), may be held in local Bahá'í Centres.

Houses of Worship

Across the world there are seven purpose-built *Houses of Worship* (Sydney in Australia; Wilmette near Chicago in the USA; Frankfurt in Germany; Panama City in Central America; New Delhi in India; Apia in Western Samoa; and Kampala in Uganda). *Houses of Worship* are at present of continental rather than national or local significance. There are regular services at the *Houses of Worship* which are open to all. The oldest surviving *House of Worship* is the one at Wilmette, otherwise known as the *Mother Temple of the West*, which was dedicated in 1953. A considerable number of sites for the development of future *Houses of Worship* have been purchased.

They were built at the request of *Bahá'u'lláh*, who gave them the name Mashriqu'l–Adhkar (*Dawning Place of God's Praise*), and they are built to *'Abdu'l-Bahá's* specifications. Each is nine sided and surmounted by a dome, standing in large gardens with fountains, trees and flowers. In addition to the place of worship itself, there are also buildings for educational, charitable and social purposes, for example old people's homes and orphanages. *Bahá'u'lláh* believed that this would ensure that Bahá'í worship would always be closely associated with the beauty of nature and art as well as with practical work for the amelioration of poor social conditions, the promotion of general education and the conduct of administration.

BAHÁ'Í CALENDAR AND FESTIVALS

Calendar

Bahá'ís follow a solar calendar which was inaugurated by the *Báb* and consists of nineteen months each containing nineteen days. The Bahá'í era (denoted by the letters "BE") dates from the declaration of the *Báb* in 1844. Thus, 2001-2 CE is 159 BE. The *Báb* named the months after what he considered to be God's attributes. For example, the first two months of the Bahá'í year as translated into English are called *Splendour* and *Glory*. Each day begins at sunset. *Nineteen-Day Feasts* are held on the first day of each Bahá'í month. The year is fixed and begins at the March equinox.

Festivals

The following are notable occasions in the Bahá'í calendar (dates are given according to their location in the Gregorian calendar):

Feast of Naw–Rúz (20th or 21st March depending on the Spring Equinox)
This is the Bahá'í New Year and the first of the nine Bahá'í holy days. On this day the nineteen day fast of the month of Alá (see below) finishes. This is a particularly joyful time of celebration.

Feast of Ridván (21st April – 2nd May)
This is the most important day in the Bahá'í calendar, described by *Bahá'u'lláh* as "*the Lord of Feasts*". It commemorates *Bahá'u'lláh's Declaration* of his mission. Celebrations take place and the feast commemorates the twelve days *Bahá'u'lláh* spent in Ridván garden before leaving Baghdad and during which his *Declaration* took place. On the first day of Ridván the *Local Spiritual Assemblies* are elected in Bahá'í communities.

Ninth Day of Ridván (see above).

Twelfth Day of Ridván (see above).

Anniversary of the Declaration of the Báb (23rd May)

This date also coincides with the birthday of *Abdu'l-Bahá*. Celebrations take place relating to the *Báb's* revelation of his mission to his first disciple, Mulla Husayn, in 1844.

Anniversary of the Ascension of Bahá'u'lláh (29th May)

A solemn day of prayer and discussion commemorating *Bahá'u'lláh's* passing away, in 1892 in Akka, after being released from prison there.

Martyrdom of the Báb (9th July)

A day of solemn commemoration of the death by firing squad of the *Báb*.

Anniversary of the Birth of the Báb (20th October)

The *Báb* was born in Shiraz, Persia, in 1819.

Anniversary of the Birth of Bahá'u'lláh (12th November)

Bahá'u'lláh was born in Tehran, Persia, in 1817.

Day of the Covenant (26th November)
This day is dedicated to *'Abdu'l-Bahá*.

Ascension of Abdu'l-Bahá (28th November)
A day of marking the *Ascension* of *'Abdu'l-Bahá*.

Intercalary Days (Ayyam-i-Ha)
(26th February - 1st March)
These days, in preparation for *The Fast* (see below) are days of celebration, charity and parties.

Period of the Fast (2nd - 21st March)
This is the Bahá'í month of 'Alá in which Bahá'ís abstain from food and drink from sunrise to sunset. *The Fast* is not binding for children under fifteen years or adults over seventy, nor for travellers or those who are too old or too weak (for example because of illness or giving birth). It is considered a time for reflection on spiritual progress and for detachment from material desires. During the *Feast of Ridván* Bahá'ís are forbidden to work during its first, ninth and twelfth days. On all the other festival days throughout the year, Bahá'ís should not work at all, except for the *Day of the Covenant* and the *Ascension* of *'Abdu'l-Bahá* on which they may work.

The Nineteen-Day Feast

The *Nineteen Day Feast*, which is rooted in a spirit of hospitality and conviviality, has three parts: devotional (recitation of prayers and readings), business (consultation on the affairs of the community) and a social time for fellowship and refreshment. Only Bahá'ís may attend the *Nineteen Day Feast*, but if a non-Bahá'í does appear he or she is made welcome and the consultative part can be omitted.

BAHÁ'Í ORGANISATIONS

The Consultative Principle

Bahá'í organisations work on the basis of the principle of consultation. This entails gathering information from a wide range of sources and perspectives; being frank but courteous about one's views; owning as the idea of the group an idea put forward by an individual; and striving for unanimity. However, if unanimity cannot be achieved then a majority vote may be taken although, in this case, all must be united behind the final decision of the majority.

Local Spiritual Assemblies

The key Bahá'í organisations are administrative bodies called *Spiritual Assemblies*, which are to be found throughout the world at local and national levels, and whose members are elected by and from among the Bahá'ís in their areas of jurisdiction. Each *Spiritual Assembly*, whether local or national, has nine members and elects officers to help conduct its affairs. This pattern was laid down by *'Abdu'l-Bahá* and developed by *Shoghi Effendi* based on guidance in *Bahá'u'lláh's* writings.

Local Spiritual Assemblies have responsibility for deciding on all matters of common action on the part of the local community, such as arranging the *Nineteen Day Feast* and other kinds of meetings, engaging in projects of social and economic development, of humanitarian service, and organising activities to promote the Bahá'í teachings. They undertake external affairs activities, often in partnership with local government and non-governmental organisations, in order to influence processes towards world peace.

A Bahá'í community must have a minimum of nine members aged twenty-one or older before it can form its *Local Spiritual Assembly*. Each year, on the first day of Ridván, nine people (including both men and women) are elected to serve on the *Local Assembly*. All Bahá'ís of twenty-one years or more who reside in the *Assembly's* area of jurisdiction have the right to vote and to serve on the *Assembly* if elected. There are no prior candidatures or nominations and canvassing is forbidden. Strict secrecy in the personal duty of election is understood to be Divinely ordained even amongst members of the same family.

Local Groups

A Bahá'í *Local Group* is formed where there are not sufficient numbers to meet the criteria for forming a *Local Spiritual Assembly*.

Regional Level

In some countries, where circumstances warrant, there are bodies known as *Regional Bahá'í Councils*. These nine-member bodies have a considerable degree of autonomy and are elected annually by the members of the *Local Spiritual Assemblies* in the *Bahá'í Council's* area of jurisdiction. There are four such bodies in the UK, one each in England, Northern Ireland, Scotland and Wales. They are responsible for planning regional-level activities, for developing the functional capacities of the *Local Spiritual Assemblies* in their region and for regional external affairs, especially in relation to the Regional Development Agencies in England, the Scottish Parliament and the Northern Ireland and Welsh Assemblies.

National Spiritual Assemblies

Each national Bahá'í community which has a significant numerical presence and a well established network of *Local Spiritual Assemblies* elects a *National Spiritual Assembly* as its national governing council. In the year 2001 there were 181 of these bodies worldwide. These bodies have authority over all the Bahá'ís activities and agencies in their area of jurisdiction and play a central role in promoting the Bahá'í teachings, social and economic development, and external relations with government and other non-governmental organisations. Most have their own headquarters building known as the *Hazìratu'l-Quds* (the *Sacred Fold*).

The *National Spiritual Assembly* of the British Isles was first elected in 1923 and was one of the earliest to be established anywhere in the world. It became the National Spiritual Assembly of the Bahá'ís of the United Kingdom in 1972, when a separate *National Spiritual Assembly* was established in the Republic of Ireland.

The *National Assembly* appoints volunteer agencies and committees for specialist work and also employs a number of specialist it administrative and executive staff for its Secretariat and various Offices, such as those for External Affairs, the Advancement of Women, and Religious and Educational Affairs.

The agency that has been longest in existence is the Bahá'í Publishing Trust, established in 1937 to publish and sell Bahá'í literature.

International Level

The *Universal House of Justice*, based in Haifa, Israel, is the international governing council of the Bahá'ís. Ordained in *Bahá'u'lláh's* writings, the *House of Justice* was first elected in 1963 and published its formal constitution in 1972. It has authority over all other Bahá'í institutions. The nine members of the *Universal House of Justice* are elected every five years by secret ballot and without candidature or canvassing from among all the adult male Bahá'ís in the world. The electors are the members of the *National Spiritual Assemblies* acting as delegates on behalf of their Bahá'í communities. This is the only Bahá'í institution whose membership is restricted to men.

The *Universal House of Justice* appoints the members of a parallel institution known as the *International Teaching Centre*. This body, whose members, men and women alike, are known as *International Counsellors*, monitors Bahá'í activity and progress throughout the world and advises the *Universal House of Justice*. It also oversees the working of *Continental Boards of Counsellors*, whose members are appointed by the *House of Justice* and which work closely with the *National Spiritual Assemblies* and with the *Regional Bahá'í Councils* in their respective continents, advising and guiding and sharing information between countries.

The *Continental Boards of Counsellors*, which came into existence in 1968, appoint members to *Auxiliary Boards*. The *Auxiliary Board* members work in an advisory and partially pastoral capacity with *Local Spiritual Assemblies* and individuals in sub-national territories; they also appoint assistants to help them with their work.

In 1948 the *Bahá'í International Community* was established as the international Bahá'í non-governmental organisation linked to the United Nations. All *National Spiritual Assemblies* are affiliated and it has offices in New York and Geneva. It acts under the supervision of the *Universal House of Justice* to participate in international conferences on a wide range of issues, such as human rights, social development, economic development, and the status of women; it also advises *National Spiritual Assemblies* and provides training and support for national external affairs work. It gained consultative status with the United Nations Economic and Social Council in 1970 and with UNICEF in 1976. It undertakes projects in a number of countries in partnership with UN and government agencies as well as with other non-governmental organisations. In the year 2000 the *Bahá'í International Community's* Principal Representative to the United Nations was one of the co-chairs of the Millennium NGO Forum that took place in New York in the run-up to the UN Millennium Summit of Heads of State and Government.

Personnel

Bahá'ís have no priesthood or clergy, professional or volunteer. Contact with Bahá'í communities and organisations can be made at local level through the secretaries of the *Local Spiritual Assemblies* and at national level through the Secretary of the *National Spiritual Assembly*.

FURTHER READING

Bahá'í International Community, *The Bahá'ís: A Profile of the Bahá'í Faith and its Worldwide Community*, Bahá'í International Community, New York, 1992.

Bahá'í Publishing Trust, *Bahá'í Prayers*, Bahá'í Publishing Trust, London, 1975.

Bahá'í Publishing Trust, *Principles of Bahá'í Administration*, Bahá'í Publishing Trust, London, (4th edition), 1976.

Balyuzi, H M, *Baha'u'llah: The King of Glory*, George Ronald, Oxford, 1963.

Balyuzi, H M, *Abdu'l-Bahá*, George Ronald, Oxford, 1971.

Balyuzi, H M, *The Báb*, George Ronald, Oxford, 1973.

Collins, W, *Bibliography of English-Language Works on the Bábi and Bahá'í Faiths, 1844-1985*, George Ronald, London, 1990.

Finch, T, "Unclipping the Wings: A Survey of Secondary Bahá'í Literature in English on Bahá'í Perspectives on Women", in *The Bahá'í Studies Review*, Volume IV, No 1, 1994, pp 9-26.

Gouvion, C and Jouvion, P, *The Gardeners of God: An Encounter with Five Million Bahá'ís*, One World, Oxford, 1995.

Hainsworth, P, *Bahá'í Focus on Human Rights*, Bahá'í Publishing Trust, London, 1985.

Hainsworth, P, *Bahá'í Focus on Peace*, Bahá'í Publishing Trust, London, 1986.

Hatcher, W S and Martin, J D, *The Bahá'í Faith: The Emerging Global Religion*, Harper and Row, San Francisco, 1984.

Momen, M, *A Short Introduction to the Bahá'í Faith*, Oneworld, Oxford, 1997.

Momen, M, *The Bábi and Bahá'í Religions, 1844-1944: Some Contemporary Western Accounts*, George Ronald, Oxford, 1981.

Smith, P, *The Bábi and Bahá'í Religions: From Messianic Shi'ism to a World Religion*, Cambridge University Press, 1987.

Smith, P and Momen, M, "The Bahá'í Faith 1957-1988: A Survey of Contemporary Developments", in *Religion*, Volume XIX, 1989, pp 63-91.

Smith, P, *A Short History of the Bahá'í Faith*, Oneworld, Oxford, 1996.

BAHÁ'Í UNITED KINGDOM ORGANISATIONS

Along with details of Bahá'í UK organisations, this section includes details of Bahá'í *Local Groups* (see page 121) listed under the entry for the Bahá'í Community of the United Kingdom. A *Local Group* can be formed where there are a number of Bahá'ís in a locality but the criteria for forming a *Local Spiritual Assembly* are not met. One criterion is that there should be at least nine Bahá'ís over the age of twenty-one.

Association of Bahá'í Studies - English speaking Europe*
27 Rutland Gate, London SW7 1PD
Tel: (020) 7584 2566 **Fax:** (020) 7584 9402
Email: absese@hotmail.com
Contact: Nazila Ghanea-Hercock
Position: Secretary

Bahá'í Academy for the Arts*
6 Weavers Ring, Angmering, Littlehampton BN16 4AJ
Email: margaretappa@hotmail.com
Contact: Mrs Margaret Appa
Position: Secretary
Activities: Resources

Bahá'í Office of Religious and Educational Affairs*
Rowan House, Oxenton, Cheltenham GL52 9SE
Email: borea@oxenton.demon.co.uk
Contact: Mrs Jennifer Lockwood
Position: Director
Activities: Inter-faith, resources

Bahá'í Publishing Trust*
4 Station Approach, Leicester LE15 6QW
Tel: (01572) 722780 **Fax:** (01572) 724280

Bahá'í Service for the Visually Impaired*
23 Percy Road, Warwick CV34 5EU
Email: connect@hearts.co.uk
Website: http://www.bahai.org.uk/svic
Contact: Mr Robin Christopherson
Position: Secretary
Activities: Resources

Children's Educational Service*
45 Suez Road, Cambridge CB1 3QB
Email: mitali@mpeckham.freeserve.co.uk
Website: http://www.bci.org/ukschools
Contact: Mrs Mitali Peckham
Position: Secretary
Activities: Youth, resources
Other Languages: Iranian

National Spiritual Assembly of the Bahá'ís of the United Kingdom*
27 Rutland Gate, London SW17 1PD
Tel: (020) 7584 2566 **Fax:** (020) 7584 9402
Email: oea@bahai.org.uk
Website: http://www.bahai.org.uk/
Contact: Ms Carmel Momen
Position: Public Information Rep
Activities: Central body, visits, inter-faith
Other Languages: Farsi
Affiliations: Inter Faith Network for the UK

Office for the Advancement of Bahá'í Women*
27 Rutland Gate, London SW7 1PD
Email: zarinhainsworth-f@virgin.net
Contact: Mrs Zarin Hainsworth-Fadaei

LOCAL GROUPS AFFILIATED TO THE NATIONAL SPIRITUAL ASSEMBLY:

ENGLAND

North East
Alnwick Bahá'í Local Group
Castle Morpeth Bahá'í Local Group
Chester-le-Street Bahá'í Local Group
Darlington Bahá'í Local Group
Derwentside Bahá'í Local Group
Gateshead Bahá'í Local Group
Hambleton Bahá'í Local Group
Hartlepool Bahá'í Local Group
Kingston-Upon-Hull Bahá'í Local Group
North Tyneside Bahá'í Local Group
Redcar and Cleveland Bahá'í Local Group
Richmondshire Bahá'í Local Group
Sedgefield Bahá'í Local Group
South Tyneside Bahá'í Local Group
Sunderland Bahá'í Local Group
Teeside Bahá'í Local Group
Tynedale Bahá'í Local Group
Wear Valley Bahá'í Local Group

Yorkshire and the Humber
Barnsley Bahá'í Local Group
Craven (N Yorks) Bahá'í Local Group
East Riding of Yorkshire Bahá'í Local Group
Harrogate Bahá'í Local Group
North East Lincolnshire Bahá'í Local Group
North Lincolnshire Bahá'í Local Group
Rotherham Bahá'í Local Group
Scarborough Bahá'í Local Group
Selby Bahá'í Local Group

North West
Blackburn Bahá'í Local Group
Blackpool Bahá'í Local Group
Bolton Bahá'í Local Group
Bury (Manchester) Bahá'í Local Group
Carlisle Bahá'í Local Group
Chorley Bahá'í Local Group
Colne (Lancs) Bahá'í Local Group
Congleton Bahá'í Local Group
Copeland Bahá'í Local Group

Crewe and Nantwich Bahá'í Local Group
Eden Bahá'í Local Group
Ellesmere Port and Neston Bahá'í Local Group
Fylde Bahá'í Local Group
Gosport Bahá'í Local Group
Grange-Over-Sands Bahá'í Local Group
Hyndburn Bahá'í Local Group
Isle of Man Bahá'í Local Group
Kendal Bahá'í Local Group
Knowsley Bahá'í Local Group
Lancaster Bahá'í Local Group
Macclesfield Bahá'í Local Group
Milnthorpe Bahá'í Local Group
Nelson Bahá'í Local Group
Oldham Bahá'í Local Group
Ribble Valley Bahá'í Local Group
Rochdale Bahá'í Local Group
South Lakeland Bahá'í Local Group
South Ribble Bahá'í Local Group
St Helens Bahá'í Local Group
Stockport Bahá'í Local Group
Tameside Bahá'í Local Group
Vale Royal Bahá'í Local Group
Warrington Bahá'í Local Group
West Lancashire Bahá'í Local Group
Wigan Bahá'í Local Group
Wilmslow Bahá'í Local Group
Wyre Bahá'í Local Group
Wyre Forest Bahá'í Local Group

East Midlands
Amber Valley Bahá'í Local Group
Bassetlaw Bahá'í Local Group
Blaby Bahá'í Local Group
Bolsover Bahá'í Local Group
Boston Bahá'í Local Group
Broxtowe Bahá'í Local Group
Charnwood Bahá'í Local Group
Daventry Bahá'í Local Group
East Lindsey Bahá'í Local Group
East Northamptonshire Bahá'í Local Group
Gedling Bahá'í Local Group
High Peak Bahá'í Local Group
Hinckley and Bosworth Bahá'í Local Group
Mansfield Bahá'í Local Group
Newark and Sherwood Bahá'í Local Group
North East Derbyshire Bahá'í Local Group
North Kesteven Bahá'í Local Group
Oadby and Wigston Bahá'í Local Group
Rushcliffe Bahá'í Local Group
Rutland Bahá'í Local Group
South Derbyshire Bahá'í Local Group
South Holland Bahá'í Local Group

South Kesteven Bahá'í Local Group
South Northamptonshire Bahá'í Local Group
Stilton Bahá'í Local Group
West Derbyshire Bahá'í Local Group
West Lindsey Bahá'í Local Group

West Midlands
Bridgnorth Bahá'í Local Group
Cannock Chase Bahá'í Local Group
Chepstow Bahá'í Local Group
Dudley Bahá'í Local Group
Earley Bahá'í Local Group
Herefordshire Bahá'í Local Group
Kenilworth Bahá'í Local Group
Knightlow Bahá'í Local Group
Lichfield Bahá'í Local Group
Malvern Hills Bahá'í Local Group
Newcastle-Under-Lyme Bahá'í Local Group
North Shropshire Bahá'í Local Group
North Warwickshire Bahá'í Local Group
Oswestry Bahá'í Local Group
Redditch Bahá'í Local Group
Rugby Bahá'í Local Group
Sandwell Bahá'í Local Group
Shrewsbury and Atcham Bahá'í Local Group
South Shropshire Bahá'í Local Group
South Staffordshire Bahá'í Local Group
Stafford Bahá'í Local Group
Staffordshire Moorlands Bahá'í Local Group
Stoke-on-Trent Bahá'í Local Group
Stratford Upon Avon Bahá'í Local Group
Stroud Bahá'í Local Group
Tamworth Bahá'í Local Group
Tewkesbury Bahá'í Local Group
Walsall Bahá'í Local Group
Warwick Bahá'í Local Group
Wellingborough Bahá'í Local Group
Wolverhampton Bahá'í Local Group
Worcester Bahá'í Local Group

East of England
Babergh Bahá'í Local Group
Basildon Bahá'í Local Group
Beccles Bahá'í Local Group
Braintree Bahá'í Local Group
Breckland Bahá'í Local Group
Brentwood Bahá'í Local Group
Broadland Bahá'í Local Group
Broxbourne Bahá'í Local Group
Carlton Colville Bahá'í Local Group
Chelmsford Bahá'í Local Group
Cottenham Bahá'í Local Group
Dacorum Bahá'í Local Group

East Cambridgeshire Bahá'í Local Group
East Hertfordshire Bahá'í Local Group
Epping Forest Bahá'í Local Group
Fenland Bahá'í Local Group
Forest Heath Bahá'í Local Group
Godmanchester Bahá'í Local Group
Great Yarmouth Bahá'í Local Group
Harlow Bahá'í Local Group
Harpenden Bahá'í Local Group
Hemel Hempstead Bahá'í Local Group
Hertsmere Bahá'í Local Group
Huntingdon Bahá'í Local Group
King's Lynn and West Norfolk Bahá'í Local Group
Loughton Bahá'í Local Group
Mid Bedfordshire Bahá'í Local Group
Mid Suffolk Bahá'í Local Group
Needingworth Bahá'í Local Group
North Hertfordshire Local Group
North Norfolk Bahá'í Local Group
Pyefleet Bahá'í Local Group
Reigate and Banstead Bahá'í Local Group
Rochford Bahá'í Local Group
South Bedfordshire Bahá'í Local Group
South Cambridgeshire Bahá'í Local Group
South Norfolk Bahá'í Local Group
St Albans Bahá'í Local Group
St Neots Bahá'í Local Group
Stanway Bahá'í Local Group
Suffolk Coastal Bahá'í Local Group
Tendering Bahá'í Local Group
Three Rivers Bahá'í Local Group
Thurrock Bahá'í Local Group
Wainford Bahá'í Local Group
Waveney Bahá'í Local Group

London
City of London Bahá'í Local Group
Tower Hamlets Bahá'í Local Group
Waltham Forest Bahá'í Local Group

South East
Adur Bahá'í Local Group
Amersham Bahá'í Local Group
Arun Bahá'í Local Group
Ashford Bahá'í Local Group
Aylesbury Bahá'í Local Group
Beaconsfield Bahá'í Local Group
Bexley Bahá'í Local Group
Bracknell Forest Bahá'í Local Group
Broadstairs Bahá'í Local Group
Canterbury Bahá'í Local Group
Caterham Bahá'í Local Group
Cherwell Bahá'í Local Group

Chichester Bahá'í Local Group
Chiltern Bahá'í Local Group
Christchurch Bahá'í Local Group
Crawley Bahá'í Local Group
Danehill Bahá'í Local Group
Dartford Bahá'í Local Group
Eastleigh Bahá'í Local Group
Elmbridge Bahá'í Local Group
Fareham Bahá'í Local Group
Gerrards Cross Bahá'í Local Group
Goring Bahá'í Local Group
Hart Bahá'í Local Group
Havant Bahá'í Local Group
Henley (Oxon) Bahá'í Local Group
Herne Bay Bahá'í Local Group
Horsham Bahá'í Local Group
Isle of Wight Bahá'í Local Group
Kennet Bahá'í Local Group
Leatherhead Bahá'í Local Group
Limpsfield Bahá'í Local Group
Maidenhead Bahá'í Local Group
Maidstone Bahá'í Local Group
Maldon Bahá'í Local Group
Marlow Bahá'í Local Group
Medway Bahá'í Local Group
Mid Sussex Bahá'í Local Group
Mole Valley Bahá'í Local Group
Rossendale Bahá'í Local Group
Rother Local Group
Rushmoor Bahá'í Local Group
Sevenoaks Bahá'í Local Group
Shepway Bahá'í Local Group
South Buckinghamshire Bahá'í Local Group
South Oxfordshire Bahá'í Local Group
South Hams Bahá'í Local Group
Southampton Bahá'í Local Group
Southborough Bahá'í Local Group
Southend-on-Sea Bahá'í Local Group
Spelthorne Bahá'í Local Group
Sunningdale and South Ascot Bahá'í Local Group
Surrey Heath Bahá'í Local Group
Swale Local Bahá'í Group
Tandridge Bahá'í Local Group
Test Valley Bahá'í Local Group
Thanet Bahá'í Local Group
Tonbridge and Malling Bahá'í Local Group
Tunbridge Wells Bahá'í Local Group
Twyford and Ruscombe Bahá'í Local Group
Wallingford Bahá'í Local Group
Warlingham Bahá'í Local Group
Waverley Bahá'í Local Group
Wealdon Bahá'í Local Group
West Berkshire Bahá'í Local Group

West Oxfordshire Bahá'í Local Group
Windsor Bahá'í Local Group
Winnersh Bahá'í Local Group
Wokingham Bahá'í Local Group
Wolderham Bahá'í Local Group
Wycombe Bahá'í Local Group

South West
Bridgwater Bahá'í Local Group
Caradon Bahá'í Local Group
Cheltenham Bahá'í Local Group
Cotswold Bahá'í Local Group
East Devon Bahá'í Local Group
Gloucester Bahá'í Local Group
Guernsey Bahá'í Local Group
Isles of Scilly Bahá'í Local Group
Jersey Bahá'í Local Group
King's Isle Bahá'í Local Group
Kingston (Lewes) Bahá'í Local Group
Knoll Bahá'í Local Group
Lewes Bahá'í Local Group
Mendip Bahá'í Local Group
Mevagissey Bahá'í Local Group
Mid Devon Bahá'í Local Group
New Forest Bahá'í Local Group
Newton Abbot Bahá'í Local Group
North Cornwall Bahá'í Local Group
North Devon Bahá'í Local Group
North Dorset Bahá'í Local Group
North Somerset Bahá'í Local Group
North Wiltshire Bahá'í Local Group
Paignton Bahá'í Local Group
Penwith Bahá'í Local Group
Purbeck Bahá'í Local Group
Restormal Bahá'í Local Group
Salisbury Bahá'í Local Group
Sedgemoor Bahá'í Local Group
South Gloucestershire Bahá'í Local Group
South Hams Bahá'í Local Group
South Somerset Bahá'í Local Group
Taunton Deane Bahá'í Local Group
Teignbridge Bahá'í Local Group
Torbay Bahá'í Local Group
West Devon Bahá'í Local Group
West Dorset Bahá'í Local Group
West Somerset Bahá'í Local Group
West Wiltshire Bahá'í Local Group
Weymouth and Portland Bahá'í Local Group
Wimborne (East Dorset) Bahá'í Local Group

NORTHERN IRELAND

Antrim Bahá'í Local Group
Ards Bahá'í Local Group
Armagh Bahá'í Local Group
Ballymena Bahá'í Local Group
Ballymoney Bahá'í Local Group
Banbridge Bahá'í Local Group
Castlereagh Bahá'í Local Group
Cookstown Bahá'í Local Group
Craigavon Bahá'í Local Group
Donaghadee Bahá'í Local Group
Down Bahá'í Local Group
Dungannon Bahá'í Local Group
Fermanagh Bahá'í Local Group
Kerrier Bahá'í Local Group
Larne Bahá'í Local Group
Lisburn Bahá'í Local Group
Moyle Bahá'í Local Group
Newry and Mourne Bahá'í Local Group
Omagh Local Bahá'í Group
Strabane Bahá'í Local Group

SCOTLAND

Alford Bahá'í Local Group
Angus Bahá'í Local Group
Annandale and Eskdale Bahá'í Local Group
Argyll and Bute Bahá'í Local Group
Badenoch and Strathspey Bahá'í Local Group
Banff and Strathbogie Bahá'í Local Group
Black Isle South Bahá'í Local Group
Bridge of Weir Bahá'í Local Group
Buchan Bahá'í Local Group
Caithness Bahá'í Local Group
Carrick Bahá'í Local Group
Central Fife Bahá'í Local Group
Chirnside Bahá'í Local Group
Clackmannan Bahá'í Local Group
Donside Bahá'í Local Group
Dumfries Bahá'í Local Group
Dunfermline Bahá'í Local Group
Duns Bahá'í Local Group
Deeside Bahá'í Local Group
East Ayrshire Bahá'í Local Group
East Dunbartonshire Bahá'í Local Group
East Fife Bahá'í Local Group
East Kilbride Bahá'í Local Group
East Lothian Bahá'í Local Group
East Renfrewshire Bahá'í Local Group
Eastern Borders Bahá'í Local Group
Falkirk Bahá'í Local Group
Inverclyde Bahá'í Local Group
Irvine Bahá'í Local Group
Kincardine Bahá'í Local Group
Kirkcudbright Bahá'í Local Group
Lewis and Harris Bahá'í Local Group
Linlithgow Bahá'í Local Group
Lochaber Bahá'í Local Group
Lochmaben Bahá'í Local Group
Midlothian Bahá'í Local Group
Moray Bahá'í Local Group
Mull Bahá'í Local Group
Nairn and Glen Mor Bahá'í Local Group
Nithsdale Bahá'í Local Group
North Ayeshire Bahá'í Local Group
North Lanarkshire Bahá'í Local Group
Pendle Bahá'í Local Group
Perth Bahá'í Local Group
Renfrewshire Bahá'í Local Group
Shetland Bahá'í Local Group
Skye and Lochalsh Bahá'í Local Group
South Ayeshire Bahá'í Local Group
Ross and Cromarty Bahá'í Local Group
Rutherglen Bahá'í Local Group
South Lanarkshire Bahá'í Local Group
Stewarthy Bahá'í Local Group
Stirling Bahá'í Local Group
Stornaway Bahá'í Local Group
Sutherland Bahá'í Local Group
Uist Bahá'í Local Group
West Fife Bahá'í Local Group
West Kilbride Bahá'í Local Group
West Lothian Bahá'í Local Group
Western Borders Bahá'í Local Group
Wigtown Bahá'í Local Group

WALES

Abergavenny Bahá'í Local Group
Blaenau Gwent Bahá'í Local Group
Brecon Bahá'í Local Group
Bridgend Bahá'í Local Group
Caerphilly Bahá'í Local Group
Carmarthenshire Bahá'í Local Group
Ceredigion Bahá'í Local Group
Conwy Bahá'í Local Group
Denbighshire Bahá'í Local Group
Flintshire Bahá'í Local Group
Gwynedd Bahá'í Local Group
Llandrindod Wells Bahá'í Local Group
Llandyfriog Bahá'í Local Group
Menai Bridge Bahá'í Local Group
Merthyr Tydfil Bahá'í Local Group
Monmouth Bahá'í Local Group
Monmouthshire Bahá'í Local Group

Neath Port Talbot Bahá'í Local Group
Newtown Bahá'í Local Group
Pembrokeshire Bahá'í Local Group
Powys Bahá'í Local Group
Rhondda Cynon Taff Bahá'í Local Group
Swansea Bahá'í Local Group
Torfaen Bahá'í Local Group
Trefriw Bahá'í Local Group
Trellech (Monm) Bahá'í Local Group
Vale of Glamorgan Bahá'í Local Group
Wrexham Bahá'í Local Group
Ynys Mon Bahá'í Local Group
Torridge Bahá'í Local Group
Wansbeck Bahá'í Local Group
Ashfield Bahá'í Local Group
Calderdale Bahá'í Local Group
Easington Bahá'í Local Group
Limavady Bahá'í Local Group

BAHÁ'Í LOCAL SPIRITUAL ASSEMBLIES

Bahá'í *Local Spiritual Assemblies* can be formed when there are at least nine Bahá'ís over the age of twenty-one in a locality. No affiliation fields are included in this chapter because all Bahá'í *Local Spiritual Assemblies* are affiliated to the Bahá'í Community of the UK and therefore local *Spiritual Assemblies* also engage in the kind of activities described in "Introducing Bahá'ís in the United Kingdom".

ENGLAND	126
NORTH EAST	126
YORKSHIRE AND THE HUMBER	126
NORTH WEST	127
EAST MIDLANDS	128
WEST MIDLANDS	129
EAST OF ENGLAND	129
LONDON	130
SOUTH EAST	133
SOUTH WEST	135
NORTHERN IRELAND	136
SCOTLAND	137
WALES	137

ENGLAND

NORTH EAST
City, Town or Local Bodies

Spiritual Assembly of the Bahá'ís of Durham*
14 Mayorswell Field, Durham DH1 1JW
Tel: (0191) 3861698 **Fax:** (0191) 3861698
Contact: Mrs Margaret Gosden
Position: Secretary
Other Languages: Farsi

Spiritual Assembly of the Bahá'ís of Newcastle-upon-Tyne*
30d Victoria Square, Jesmond, Newcastle-upon-Tyne NE2 4DE
Tel: (0191) 2401836
Email: amelialal@hotmail.com
Contact: Ms Pat Furness
Position: Vice-Chairman
Activities: Worship/practice/meditation, community centre, inter-faith, resources

Spiritual Assembly of the Bahá'ís of Allendale*
The Barns, Burnlaw, Whitfield NE7 8HF
Tel: (01434) 345391
Email: lornasilverstein@btinternet.com.
Contact: Mrs Lorna Silverstein
Position: Secretary
Contact Tel: (01434) 345391
Activities: Worship/practice/meditation, youth

YORKSHIRE AND THE HUMBER
City, Town or Local Bodies

Spiritual Assembly of the Bahá'ís of Bradford*
Moor House, 607 Allerton Road, Allerton, Bradford BD15 8AB
Tel: (01274) 544758
Contact: Mrs Chris Hallam
Position: Secretary
Activities: Worship/practice/meditation, central body, visits, inter-faith
Other Languages: Persian, French, Urdu

Spiritual Assembly of the Bahá'ís of Doncaster
87 Albany Road, Balby, Doncaster DN4 0QN
Tel: (01302) 810350
Email: anne123@blueyonder.co.uk
Contact: Ms Anne Ward
Position: Secretary

Spiritual Assembly of the Bahá'ís of Kirklees*
65 Grosvenor Road, Dalton, Huddersfield
HD5 9JB
Tel: (01484) 429490
Email: khosro@deihim.freeserve.co.uk
Website:
http://www.jenks.demon.co.uk/kbahai.htm
Contact: Mr Khosro Deihim
Position: Secretary
Activities: Resource, media, visits, youth, elderly, women, newsletter
Other Languages: Persian

Spiritual Assembly of the Bahá'ís of Leeds*
15 Moorland Rise, Leeds LS17 6HZ
Other Languages: Persian

Spiritual Assembly of the Bahá'ís of Sheffield*
18 Lawson Road, Broomhill, Sheffield S10 5BW
Tel: (0114) 2670400
Contact: Mrs Sandra Agahi
Position: Secretary
Activities: Newsletter/journal, visits, inter-faith
Other Languages: Persian

Spiritual Assembly of the Bahá'ís of Skipton*
32 Burnside Avenue, Skipton BD23 2BS
Tel: (01756) 795496
Email: peter@pwomersley.freeserve.co.uk
Website: http://www.bahai.org.uk/craven
Contact: Mr Peter Womersley
Position: Secretary
Activities: Worship/practice/meditation

Spiritual Assembly of the Bahá'ís of Wakefield*
23 Balne Lane, Wakefield WF2 0DL
Tel: (01924) 378970
Email: ian.helen@lineone.net
Contact: Ms Louise Morley
Position: Secretary
Activities: Resource, visits, youth, inter-faith activity
Other Languages: Swedish

Spiritual Assembly of the Bahá'ís of York*
West View, 112 Clifton, Clifton, York Y030 6BA
Tel: (01904) 641657
Contact: Mrs Patricia Castle
Position: Secretary
Activities: Inter-faith
Other Languages: Farsee

NORTH WEST
City, Town or Local Bodies

Spiritual Assembly of the Bahá'ís of Burnley*
9 Colne Road, Burnley BB10 1LD
Tel: (01282) 439862
Contact: Mrs Diane Cleasby
Position: Secretary
Contact Email: dmprcleas@aol.com
Activities: Worship/practice/meditation, umbrella body, youth, inter-faith, resources
Other Languages: Farsi

Spiritual Assembly of the Bahá'ís of Chester*
2 Devonshire Place, Chester CH4 7BZ
Tel: (01244) 680947 **Fax:** (01244) 675278
Email: annemaund@hotmail.com
Contact: Miss Anne Maund
Position: Secretary
Activities: Worship/practice/meditation

Spiritual Assembly of the Bahá'ís of Liverpool
125 Abbottshey Avenue, Liverpool L18 7JS
Contact: Mrs Denia Kincade
Position: Secretary

Spiritual Assembly of the Bahá'ís of Manchester*
360 Wilmslow Road, Fallowfield, Manchester
M14 6AB
Tel: (0161) 2246490
Email: manchester@bci.org
Website: http://www.bahai.org.uk/manchester
Contact: Mr Andrew Turvey
Position: Secretary
Activities: Worship/practice/meditation, community centre, youth, visits, inter-faith, resources
Other Languages: Farsi

Spiritual Assembly of the Bahá'ís of Preston*
19 Dunbar Road, Ingol, Preston PR2 3YE
Tel: (01772) 733294
Email: joysabour@talk21.com
Website: http://www.bahai.org.uk/preston
Contact: Mrs Joy Sabour
Position: Secretary
Activities: Inter-faith
Other Languages: Arabic, Persian

Spiritual Assembly of the Bahá'ís of Salford*
10 Pendlecroft Avenue, Pendlebury, Swinton,
Manchester M27 2TH

Email: mw malacebtinternet.com
Contact: Mrs May Lang Grimshaw
Position: Secretary

Spiritual Assembly of the Bahá'ís of Sefton*
36 Claremont Road, Birkdale, Southport
PR8 4DY
Tel: (01704) 563197
Email: lmc@lion29.junglelink.co.uk
Contact: Mrs Linda Coulter
Position: Secretary

Spiritual Assembly of the Bahá'ís of Stockport*
19 Cheadle Road, Cheadle Hulme, Stockport
SK8 5HL
Contact: Dr Shahla Haqjoo
Position: Secretary
Activities: Youth, elderly, women, inter-faith

Spiritual Assembly of the Bahá'ís of Trafford*
7 Park Avenue, Sale M33 6HB
Email: nadia.taleb@fsmail.net
Contact: Mrs Nadia Taleb
Position: Secretary

Spiritual Assembly of the Bahá'ís of Wirral
7 Kimberley Road, Wallasey L45 7NU
Tel: (0151) 2010129
Contact: Mr Carl Wharton
Position: Secretary

EAST MIDLANDS
City, Town or Local Bodies

Spiritual Assembly of the Bahá'ís of Brixworth*
75 Froxhill Crescent, Brixworth, Northampton
NN6 9LN
Tel: (01604) 881547
Email: kmbeint@aol.com
Contact: Mr Kevin Beint
Position: Secretary

Spiritual Assembly of the Bahá'ís of Chesterfield*
16 Park Hall Avenue, Somersal, Chesterfield
S42 7LR
Tel: (01246) 569316
Email: nimatina@unity.freeserve.co.uk
Contact: Mr Rouhollah Aminian
Position: Secretary
Contact Tel: (0798) 0505667
Contact Email: emysroh@nottingham.ac.uk
Activities: Inter-faith
Other Languages: Farsi, Arabic, Basic Esperanto

Spiritual Assembly of the Bahá'ís of Derby*
100 Broadway, Derby DE22
Email: maryam@djavid.freeserve.co.uk
Contact: Ms Maryam Djavid
Position: Secretary
Contact Tel: (01332) 741132
Activities: Worship/practice/meditation, youth, elderly, women, newsletter/journal, radio, inter-faith, resources

Spiritual Assembly of the Bahá'ís of Kettering*
Kettering
Fax: (0870) 1313202
Email: russell.attwood@btinternet.com
Website: http://www.northantsbahai.org.uk/
Contact: Mrs Terri Attwood
Position: Secretary
Other Languages: Persian, Spanish

Spiritual Assembly of the Bahá'ís of Leicester*
22 Percival Street, Leicester LE5 3NP
Tel: (0116) 2126286
Email: rodmaude@yahoo.com
Contact: Mr Roderic Maude
Position: Secretary
Activities: Inter-faith, women
Other Languages: Persian

Spiritual Assembly of the Bahá'ís of Lincoln*
161 Carholme Road, Lincoln LN1 1RU
Tel: (01522) 522748
Email: tully@tullyg.fsnet.co.uk
Contact: Mrs Gillian Tully
Position: Secretary
Activities: Worship/practice/meditation, youth, elderly, women, newsletter/journal, radio, inter-faith, resources

Spiritual Assembly of the Bahá'ís of Loughborough*
1 Outwoods Drive, Loughborough LE11 3LR
Tel: (01509) 232252
Contact: Mrs Ferdousieh Catling
Position: Secretary
Activities: Youth, elderly, women

Spiritual Assembly of the Bahá'ís of Northampton*
15 Spyglass Hill, Northampton NN4 0US
Tel: (01604) 769825 **Fax:** (01604) 709200
Contact: Mrs Susan Phillips
Position: Secretary
Other Languages: Farsi

Spiritual Assembly of the Bahá'ís of Nottingham*
2 Southey Street, Hyson Green, Nottingham NG7 4BG
Tel: (0115) 9249140
Email: nottinghambahais@bci.org
Website: http://www.bci.org/nottinghambahais
Contact: Mrs Jane Pearce
Activities: Worship/practice/meditation, youth, visits, inter-faith
Other Languages: Persian, Arabic, Albanian

Spiritual Assembly of the Bahá'ís of West Bridgford*
The Flat, 65 Clumber Road, West Bridgford, Nottingham NG2 6DP
Tel: (0115) 8469365
Email: sandraj9@ntlworld.com
Contact: Mrs Sandra Jenkins

WEST MIDLANDS
City, Town or Local Bodies

Spiritual Assembly of the Bahá'ís of Birmingham
3 Britannic Gardens, Yew Tree Road, Moseley, Birmingham B13 8QX
Tel: (0121) 442 6272
Contact: Mrs Nassrin Afnan
Contact Email: nassrin.afrnan@virgin.net
Activities: Resource, media, umbrella, youth, elderly, women
Languages: Persian, Urdu, French, German

Spiritual Assembly of the Bahá'ís of Coventry
26 Old Mill Avenue, Cannon Park, Coventry CV4 7DY
Tel: (024) 7641 3486
Email: k.porooshasp@coventry.ac.uk
Contact: Mr Kambiz Porooshasp

Spiritual Assembly of the Bahá'ís of Hereford*
104 Penn Grove Road, Hereford HR1 1BX
Tel: (01432) 277903
Email: petehulme@lineone.net
Contact: Mr Pete Hulme
Activities: Visits, inter-faith

Spiritual Assembly of the Bahá'ís of Leamington Spa*
18 Blakelands Avenue, Sydenham, Leamington Spa CV31 1RJ
Tel: (01926) 812342

Email: lsa@mercia.demon.co.uk
Website: http://www.bahai.org.uk/warwick
Contact: Mrs Appleton
Contact Tel: (01926) 778779
Contact Email: fariba@furughi.freeserve.co.uk
Activities: Youth, books, visits, inter-faith, resources
Other Languages: Persian, Spanish

Spiritual Assembly of the Bahá'ís of Nuneaton*
120 Higham Lane, Nuneaton CV11 6AX
Tel: (024) 7635 0268
Email: john@lcneal.worldonline.co.uk
Website: http://www.bahai.org./uk/nuneaton
Contact: Mr John Longcroft-Neal
Position: Secretary
Activities: Visitors, women, inter-faith
Other Languages: Persian

Spiritual Assembly of the Bahá'ís of Solihull*
7 Cedarwood Drive, Balsall Common, Coventry CV7 7DS
Tel: (01676) 530019
Email: bahai@nigelshome.com
Website: http://www.bahai.org.uk/solihull
Contact: Mr Nigel Austin-Weeks
Position: Secretary
Contact Email: nigel@nigelshomes.com
Activities: Worship/practice/meditation, inter-faith
Other Languages: Persian

Spiritual Assembly of the Bahá'ís of Telford and Wrekin
54 Castlecroft, Stirchley, Telford TF3 1UE
Tel: (01952) 592947 **Fax:** (01952) 592947
Email: stda@yahoo.com
Contact: Mrs Kerry Day
Position: Secretary

EAST OF ENGLAND
Regional or County Bodies

Spiritual Assembly of the Bahá'ís of Cambridge*
45 Suez Road, Cambridge CB1 3QB
Tel: (01223) 573873
Email: www.bahai.org.uk
Contact: Mr M Sukumaran
Contact Tel: (01223) 762399
Contact Email: ms29@biotech.com.ac.uk
Activities: Resource, visits, youth, newsletters, inter-faith
Other Languages: Persian, French, Arabic, Malay

Spiritual Assembly of the Bahá'ís of Colchester*
16 Mayberry Walk, Colchester C02 8PS
Tel: (01206) 513713)
Email: Angela.tidswell@bigfoot.com
Website: www.bahai.org.uk
Contact: Mrs Angela Tidswell
Position: Secretary

Spiritual Assembly of the Bahá'ís of Ipswich*
140 Dover Road, Ipswich IP3 8JJ
Tel: (01473) 421975
Email: nghanea@hotmail.com
Website: http://www.bahai.org.uk/
Contact: Dr N Ghanea-Hercock
Position: Secretary
Activities: Worship, newsletters, books, inter-faith
Other Languages: Persian

Spiritual Assembly of the Bahá'ís of Luton*
6 Kinross Crescent, Sundon Park, Luton LU3 3JS
Tel: (01582) 753904
Email: samtaylor1@btinternet.com
Website: http://www.bahais-luton.org.uk/
Contact: Mr Samuel Taylor
Position: Secretary
Activities: Youth, women, radio, inter-faith
Other Languages: Persian, Italian, Spanish

Spiritual Assembly of the Bahá'ís of Norwich*
65 Netherwood Green, Lakenham, Norwich NR1 2JG
Tel: (01603) 449760
Contact: Mrs Mildred Hayden
Position: Secretary
Activities: Worship/practice/meditation

Spiritual Assembly of the Bahá'ís of Watford*
104 Meriden Way, Watford WD25 9DQ
Tel: (01923) 676856
Email: shahinkhazali@hotmail.com
Contact: Mr Shahin Khazali
Position: Secretary

LONDON
Borough or Local Bodies

BARKING AND DAGENHAM

Spiritual Assembly of the Bahá'ís of Barking and Dagenham*
9 Langley Gardens, Dagenham RM9 4RR
Tel: (020) 8593 1085

Email: rana@elephant.demon.co.uk
Contact: Mrs Sharareh Walker
Position: Secretary

BARNET

Spiritual Assembly of the Bahá'ís of Barnet*
6 Laurel Court, 9 St Mary's Avenue, London N3 1SW
Tel: (020) 8343 0215
Email: sakhavan@roweandmaw.co.uk
Website: http://www.bahai.org.uk/barnet
Contact: Miss Sahba Akhavan
Position: Secretary
Other Languages: Persian, French, German

BRENT

Spiritual Assembly of the Bahá'ís of Brent*
PO Box 392, Wembley HA9 8AW
Tel: (020) 8930 8104 **Fax:** (020) 8385 2698
Email: lsabrent@aol.com
Website: http://www.bahai.org.uk/brent
Contact: Mr Farid A Afnan
Position: Secretary
Activities: Youth, women, books, inter-faith, resources
Other Languages: Farsi, Arabic, Hindi, Spanish

BROMLEY

Spiritual Assembly of the Bahá'ís of Bromley*
43 Ravensbourne Road, Bromley BR1 1HN
Tel: (020) 8290 1989
Email: aqdasi_klimo_i@yahoo.com
Contact: Mrs Iqbal Aqdasi-Klimo
Position: Secretary
Activities: Worship, resource media, visits, youth, elderly
Other Languages: Arabic, Persian, German

CAMDEN

Spiritual Assembly of the Bahá'ís of Camden*
Flat 12, 1 Platt's Lane, Camden, London NW3 7NP
Tel: (020) 7431 5324
Email: camden@bahaimail.com
Contact: Mr Guy Sinclair
Position: Secretary
Activities: Worship/practice/meditation

CROYDON

Spiritual Assembly of the Bahá'ís of Croydon*
32 Woodside Court Road, Croydon CR0 6RU
Email: alvani@croydon.ac.uk
Contact: Mr Nasrin Mahingostar
Position: Secretary

EALING

Spiritual Assembly of the Bahá'ís of Ealing*
Basement Flat, 41 Alfred Road, Acton, London
W3 6LH
Tel: (020) 8993 8476
Email: swaincam@talk21.com
Contact: Mrs Barbara Cameron
Position: Secretary

ENFIELD

Spiritual Assembly of the Bahá'ís of Enfield
73 Merlin House, 2 Napier Road, Enfield, London
EN3 4QJ
Contact: Mrs N Kazempour-Vojdani
Position: Secretary

GREENWICH

*Spiritual Assembly of the Bahá'ís of
Greenwich**
32 Eastnor Road, New Eltham, London SE9 2BG
Tel: (020) 8859 0301
Email: jilayousefzadeh@aol.com
Contact: Ms Jila Yousefzadeh
Position: Secretary
Other Languages: Persian, French, Russian,
Bulgarian

HACKNEY

Spiritual Assembly of the Bahá'ís of Hackney
Flat 3, 50 Lee Street, London E8 4DY
Tel: (020) 7684 1389
Email: jhaughton32@ukonline.co.uk
Contact: Mr James Haughton
Position: Secretary

HAMMERSMITH AND FULHAM

*Spiritual Assembly of the Bahá'ís of
Hammersmith and Fulham*
27 Clybrook Road, Hammersmith, London
W6 8LN

Email: orkyde@hotmail.com
Contact: Miss Orkyde Razavi
Position: Secretary

HARINGEY

Spiritual Assembly of the Bahá'ís of Haringey*
79 Muswell Hill Place, Muswell Hill, London
N10 3RP
Tel: (020) 8883 7658
Email: featherman66@hotmail.com
Contact: Mr Matthew Feather
Position: Secretary
Activities: Worship/practice/meditation, central
body, inter-faith
Other Languages: Farsi, French, Arabic,
Mandarin

HARROW

Spiritual Assembly of the Bahá'ís of Harrow*
8 Limedene Close, Uxbridge Road, Pinner
HA5 3PX
Tel: (020) 8868 0130 **Fax:** (020) 8868 4690
Email: homa@saadat.co.uk
Contact: Mrs Homa Saadat
Position: Secretary
Activities: Resource, newsletters, books, inter-faith
Other Languages: Persian, Arabic

HAVERING

Spiritual Assembly of the Bahá'ís of Havering*
12 Lytton Road, Romford RM2 5SL
Tel: (01708) 446297
Email: havering@bci.org
Website: http://www.bci.org/havering
Contact: Dr John Lester
Position: Secretary
Activities: Inter-faith
Other Languages: Persian

HILLINGDON

Spiritual Assembly of the Bahá'ís of Hillingdon*
1 Curlew Way, Willow Tree Lane Estate, Yeading
UB4 9UH
Tel: (020) 8581 4572
Email: aicha@griguer.freeserve.co.uk
Contact: Mrs Aicha Mehdaoui
Position: Secretary

HOUNSLOW

Spiritual Assembly of the Bahá'ís of Hounslow
4 Pownall Road, Hounslow TW3 1YN
Tel: (020) 8572 7479
Email: cannm@bv.com
Contact: Miss N Nagaratnam
Position: Secretary

ISLINGTON

Spiritual Assembly of the Bahá'ís of Islington*
27 Thornhill Road, London N1 1JR
Tel: (07867) 533400
Email: hoda-mohtadi@yahoo.com
Contact: Miss Hoda Mohtadi
Position: Secretary

KENSINGTON AND CHELSEA

Spiritual Assembly of the Bahá'ís of Kensington and Chelsea*
64-1 Addison Road, London W14 8JL
Tel: (020) 7371 6022
Contact: Mrs Mirta Lopez
Position: Secretary
Activities: Worship/practice/meditation, umbrella body, youth, newsletter/journal, inter-faith, resources
Other Languages: Persian, Welsh, Arabic

KINGSTON UPON THAMES

Spiritual Assembly of the Bahá'ís of Kingston-upon-Thames*
6 The Mall, Surbiton KT6 4EQ
Tel: (020) 8390 4886
Email: dianne.mahboubi@virgin.net
Contact: Mrs Dianne Mahboubi
Position: Secretary
Contact Email: dianne.mahboubi@virgin.net
Activities: Newsletter/journal, inter-faith, resources
Other Languages: Persian German, Afrikaans French

LAMBETH

Spiritual Assembly of the Bahá'ís of Lambeth*
32 Crescent Grove, Clapham, London SW4 7AH
Tel: (020) 7584 2566
Contact: Carmel Momen

Position: Secretary
Activities: Newsletter/journal, visits, inter-faith
Other Languages: French, Spanish, Arabic, Farsi

LEWISHAM

Spiritual Assembly of the Bahá'ís of Lewisham
7 Whidbourne Close, New Cross, London
SE8 4DL
Tel: (020) 8691 2623 **Fax:** (020) 8852 5615
Contact: Miss Annette Smith
Position: Secretary

MERTON

Spiritual Assembly of the Bahá'ís of Merton*
18 Compton Road, Wimbledon, London
SW19 7QD
Tel: (020) 8944 1303
Email: renooz@hotmail.com
Contact: Mrs Renoo Zaiwalla
Position: Secretary
Activities: Resource, media, youth, women, newsletters, books,

NEWHAM

Spiritual Assembly of the Bahá'ís of Newham*
13 East Avenue, Manor Park, London E12 6SG
Tel: (020) 84707596
Email: sureshacca@hotmail.com
Contact: Mr Suresh Marappan
Position: Secretary
Contact Tel: 07931 514726
Activities: Inter-faith,education
Other Languages: Persian, Tamil, Chinese, French

REDBRIDGE

Spiritual Assembly of the Bahá'ís of Redbridge
5 Long Green, Chigwell IG7 4JB
Tel: (020) 8501 3037
Contact: Mrs Roya Rostami
Position: Secretary

RICHMOND UPON THAMES

Spiritual Assembly of the Bahá'ís of Richmond-upon-Thames
15 Leeson House, Haggard Road, Twickenham
TW1 3AJ
Tel: (020) 8891 0901

Contact: Miss Iris Foster
Position: Secretary

SOUTHWARK

Spiritual Assembly of the Bahá'ís of Southwark*
PO Box 20872, London SE22 9YQ
Email: southwarkbahais@hotmail.com
Website: http://www.bahai.org.uk/southwark
Contact: Secretary
Contact Email: southwarkbahais@hotmail.com
Activities: Worship/practice/meditation, newsletter/journal, visits, inter-faith
Other Languages: Farsi, Hindi

SUTTON

Spiritual Assembly of the Bahá'ís of Sutton*
29 Ingleby Way, Wallington, Sutton SM6 9LP
Tel: (020) 8647 6303
Email: mariam@homedesignfsnet.co.uk
Contact: Mrs M Fallah
Position: Secretary
Activities: Worship/practice/meditation, visits, inter-faith
Other Languages: Persian, French

WANDSWORTH

Spiritual Assembly of the Bahá'ís of Wandsworth
1043 Garratt Lane, London SW17 0LN
Tel: (020) 8682 3394
Email: jim@tooting.u-net.com
Contact: Jim Jenkins
Position: Secretary

WESTMINSTER, CITY OF

Spiritual Assembly of the Bahá'ís of City of Westminster*
27 Rutland Gate, London SW7 1PD
Tel: (020) 7584 2566 **Fax:** (020) 7584 3108
Website: http://www.bahaisofwestminster.co.uk/
Contact: Mr Vafa Payman
Position: Secretary
Contact Tel: (020) 7589 2526
Contact Email: vafapayman@aol.com
Activities: Worship/practice/meditation, youth, elderly, women, newsletter/journal, inter-faith, resources
Other Languages: Persian, Arabic

SOUTH EAST
City, Town or Local Bodies

Spiritual Assembly of the Bahá'ís of Abingdon*
66 Jackman Close, Abingdon OX14 3GA
Tel: (01235) 202447
Email: msammi@light.win-uk.net
Contact: Mr Manoocher Samii
Position: Secretary
Activities: Resource, inter-faith
Other Languages: Persian, Hindi, French, Spanish

Spiritual Assembly of the Bahá'ís of Basingstoke*
16 Horwood Gardens, Cranbourne, Basingstoke RG21 3NR
Tel: (01256) 350187
Email: zarin.handsworth@NTLWORLD.com
Contact: Mrs Zarin Hainsworth-Fadaei
Position: Secretary
Activities: Youth, inter-faith
Other Languages: Dutch, Persian, French, Phillipino

Spiritual Assembly of the Bahá'ís of Bedford*
Bedford
Tel: (01234) 312638
Contact: Mrs Sepideh Mostaghimi
Position: Secretary
Activities: Worship/practice/meditation, youth, elderly, women, inter-faith
Other Languages: Farsi

Spiritual Assembly of the Bahá'ís of Brighton and Hove*
19 Stanford Avenue, Brighton BN1 6GA
Tel: (01273) 505895
Website: http://www.bahai.org.uk/
Contact: Secretary
Activities: Worship, resource, media, visits, youth, women, inter-faith
Other Languages: Persian

Spiritual Assembly of the Bahá'ís of Eastbourne*
4 The Retreat, 33 Avard Crescent, Eastbourne BN20 8TY
Tel: (01323) 430405
Contact: Mr Chris Cook
Position: Chairman

Spiritual Assembly of the Bahá'ís of Epsom and Ewell*
Epsom

Tel: (020) 8393 3574
Contact: Mrs Christine Beer
Position: Secretary
Activities: Youth, elderly, women, inter-faith, resources
Other Languages: Persian

Spiritual Assembly of the Bahá'ís of Gillingham*

39 Moor Park Close, Rainham, Gillingham
ME8 8QS
Tel: (01634) 389364
Email: faran@forghani.fsnet.co.uk
Website: http://www.medwaybahais.co.uk/
Contact: Mr F Forghani Ashrafi
Position: Secretary
Contact Tel: (01634) 389364

Spiritual Assembly of the Bahá'ís of Gravesham*

Mehrangiz, 77 Vale Road, Northfleet, Gravesend
DA11 8DD
Tel: (01474) 564972
Email: bruce@showghian.freeserve.co.uk
Contact: Mr Behrooz Showghian
Position: Secretary
Contact Tel: (07931) 144390
Other Languages: Farsi, Urdu, Spanish, French

Spiritual Assembly of the Bahá'ís of Guildford*

12 Lapwing Grove, Merrow Park, Guildford
GU4 7DZ
Tel: (01483) 568926 **Fax:** (01483) 568926
Email: 106131.1062@compuserve.com
Contact: Mr Edgar Boyett
Position: Secretary
Contact Tel: (01483) 568926
Other Languages: Persian

Spiritual Assembly of the Bahá'ís of Hastings*

57 Milward Road, Hastings TN34 3RP
Tel: (01424) 430783 **Fax:** (01424) 430783
Email: mahin@infinnet.co.uk
Contact: Mrs M H McCandless
Position: Vice-Chairman
Activities: Visits, inter-faith
Other Languages: French, Persian

Spiritual Assembly of the Bahá'ís of Hazlemere*

11 Wellfield, Hazlemere, High Wycombe HP15 7TJ
Tel: (01494) 814551
Email: shahram.alaee@lineone.net
Contact: Mr Shahram Alaee
Position: Secretary

Activities: Visits, inter-faith
Other Languages: Iranian

Spiritual Assembly of the Bahá'ís of Margate

4 Buckhurst Drive, Cliftonville, Margate CT9 3HT
Tel: (01843) 225402
Email: farrid@bahaimail.com
Contact: Dr Fereidoun Abbasi
Position: Secretary

Spiritual Assembly of the Bahá'ís of Milton Keynes*

38a Bradwell Road, Loughton, Milton Keynes
MK5 8AJ
Tel: (01908) 671734
Email: m.sanatian@open.ac.uk
Contact: Mrs Malihe Sanatian
Position: Secretary
Activities: Worship, youth, inter-faith
Other Languages: Persian, Spanish

Spiritual Assembly of the Bahá'ís of Oxford*

185 Banbury Road, Oxford OX2 7AR
Tel: (01865) 311940
Email: oxfordbahais@hotmail.com
Website: http://www.oxfordbahais.org/
Contact: Juliet Maybe
Position: Secretary
Activities: Worship, women, youth, inter-faith

Spiritual Assembly of the Bahá'ís of Portsmouth*

109 High Street, Portsmouth PO1 2HJ
Tel: (023) 9281 4516 **Fax:** (023) 9281 4516
Email: neville.hill@btinternet.com
Contact: Mr Neville Hill
Position: Secretary
Activities: Youth, elderly, women, inter-faith
Other Languages: Farsi, Spanish

Spiritual Assembly of the Bahá'ís of Reading

222 Tilehurst Road, Reading RG30 2NE
Email: chris@peopleplus.co.uk
Contact: Mr Christopher Nash
Position: Secretary

Spiritual Assembly of the Bahá'ís of Redhill*

6 Woodlands Road, Redhill RH1 6HA
Email: falconkay@onetel.co.uk
Contact: Mr Martin Kay
Position: Secretary
Activities: Worship/practice, youth, women

Spiritual Assembly of the Bahá'ís of Ryde, Isle of Wight*
5 King Arthur Close, Arthur Street, Ryde
PO33 3DA
Tel: (01983) 613902
Email: clairpope@freeuk.com
Contact: Clair Pope
Position: Secretary
Activities: Worship/practice/meditation, youth, elderly, women, newsletter/journal, visits, inter-faith, resources

Spiritual Assembly of the Bahá'ís of Sandhurst
10 Reynolds Green, Sandhurst GU47 0FL
Tel: (01276) 600735
Email: maryamkhorassani@hotmail.com
Contact: Miss Maryam Khorassani
Position: Secretary

Spiritual Assembly of the Bahá'ís of Slough*
94 Upton Park, Slough SL1 2DG
Tel: (01753) 676002
Email: elamigo@onetel.net.uk
Contact: Mr Imkan Hayati
Position: Secretary
Activities: Inter-faith

Spiritual Assembly of the Bahá'ís of Stevenage
60 Buckthorn Avenue, Stevenage SG1 1TU
Tel: (01438) 220483
Email: oliver.c@virgin.net
Contact: Mr Oliver Christopherson
Position: Secretary

Spiritual Assembly of the Bahá'ís of Welwyn Garden City
12 The Links, Welwyn Garden City AL8 7DS
Contact: Mrs Niamh Hynes
Position: Secretary

Spiritual Assembly of the Bahá'ís of Winchester*
12 St Paul's Hill, Winchester SO22 5AB
Tel: (01962) 861130
Contact: Miss Anna Seifert
Position: Secretary
Activities: Worship, visits, youth, elderly, women, newsletter
Other Languages: Italian, German, Persian

Spiritual Assembly of the Bahá'ís of Woking
3 Queensdale Court, Goldsworth Park, Woking GU21 3RJ
Tel: (01483) 797779

Contact: Miss Ladan Lamakan
Position: Secretary

Spiritual Assembly of the Bahá'ís of Worthing*
1 Galsworthy Close, Goring by Sea, Worthing BN12 6LP
Tel: (01903) 601923
Contact: Mr Gareth Jones
Position: Secretary
Activities: Worship/practice/meditation, central body, youth, elderly, women, newsletter/journal, inter-faith, resources
Other Languages: Persian

SOUTH WEST
City, Town or Local Bodies

Spiritual Assembly of the Bahá'ís of Bath*
16 Magdalen Avenue, Bath BA2 4QB
Tel: (01225) 447254
Email: janefa@iplbath.com
Contact: Dr Jane Aldred
Position: Secretary
Activities: Worship/practice/meditation

Spiritual Assembly of the Bahá'ís of Bournemouth*
16 St Luke Road, Bournemouth BH3 7LT
Tel: (01202) 527988
Contact: Mrs Rosita Abrahim
Position: Secretary

Spiritual Assembly of the Bahá'ís of Bristol
33 Northumbria Drive, Henleaze, Bristol BS9 4HL
Email: bristollsa@mail.com
Contact: Mrs Mary Sabet
Position: Secretary

Spiritual Assembly of the Bahá'ís of Exeter
24 Margaret Road, Exeter EX4 7DJ
Contact: Mrs Jennifer Miller
Position: Secretary

Spiritual Assembly of the Bahá'ís of Plymouth*
32 Dale Gardens, Mutley, Plymouth PL4 6PX
Tel: (017520) 227834
Email: plymouthassembly@hotmail.com
Contact: Mr Navid Sharghi
Position: Secretary
Contact Email: navid@sharghi.freeserve.co.uk
Activities: Worship/practice/meditation, central body, inter-faith
Other Languages: Iranian

Spiritual Assembly of the Bahá'ís of Poole*
8 Scarf Road, Canford Heath, Poole BH17 8QQ
Tel: (01202) 382377
Email: miketempest@lineone.net
Contact: Mr Michael Tempest
Position: Secretary
Activities: Worship/practice/meditation

Spiritual Assembly of the Bahá'ís of Swindon
22 Brixham Avenue, Swindon SN3 1EW
Tel: (01793) 336676
Email: swindon9@dialstart.net
Contact: Mrs Janet Justnes
Position: Secretary

NORTHERN IRELAND

Regional or County Bodies

Bahá'í Council for Northern Ireland
8 Kensington Manor, Coleraine BT52 1WD
Tel: (028) 2075 8435
Contact: Mrs Viny Robinson

Association of Bahá'í Women - Northern Ireland
32a Beverley Crescent, Newtownards BT23 3UN
Tel: (028) 9182 3285
Contact: Mrs Marie Whiteside

City, Town or Local Bodies

Spiritual Assembly of the Bahá'ís of Belfast*
399 Lisburn Road, Belfast BT9 7EW
Tel: (028) 9066 7402 **Fax:** (028) 9066 6801
Email: sherwani@btinternet.com
Contact: Mr Antony Sherwani
Position: Secretary
Contact Tel: (028) 9066 6212
Activities: Worship/practice/meditation, umbrella body, youth, elderly, women, newsletter/journal, visits, inter-faith, resources
Other Languages: Persian, Spanish, Italian, Hindi

Spiritual Assembly of the Bahá'ís of Castlereagh*
85 Ravenswood Park, Belfast BT5 7PT
Tel: (028) 9050 4614
Contact: Mrs Stella Brew

Spiritual Assembly of the Bahá'ís of Carrickfergus
Abbotford, 50 Cable Road, Whitehead BT38 9PZ

Contact: Miss Marie Baillie
Position: Secretary

Spiritual Assembly of the Bahá'ís of Coleraine*
63 Elms Park, Coleraine BT52 2QF
Tel: (028) 7032 7104
Email: georgiegalj@yahoo.com
Contact: Miss Judith George
Position: Secretary
Activities: Inter-faith

Spiritual Assembly of the Bahá'ís of Londonderry*
PO Box 95, Londonderry BT47 6FS
Tel: (028) 7134 7357 **Fax:** (028) 7126 5932
Email: isp@iol.ie
Website: http://www.bci.org/bahais_of_derry
Contact: Dr Iain Palin
Position: Secretary
Activities: Worship/practice/meditation, youth, elderly, women
Other Languages: Persian, Russian, Esperanto

Spiritual Assembly of the Bahá'ís of Newtonabbey*
122a Hydepark Road, Mallusk, Newtownabbey BT36 8PZ
Tel: (028) 9084 1685
Website: http://www.abbey bahai.freeserve.co.uk/
Contact: Mr Ralph Rossi
Position: Chairman
Contact Tel: (028) 9084 1685
Activities: Worship/practice/meditation, educational

Spiritual Assembly of the Bahá'ís of Newtownards*
32a Beverley Crescent, Newtownards BT23 3UN
Tel: (028) 9182 3285
Email: mariew@talk21.com
Contact: Mrs Marie Whiteside
Position: Secretary
Activities: Worship/practice/meditation, community centre, youth, elderly, women, inter-faith, resources

Spiritual Assembly of the Bahá'ís of North Down*
41 Station Road, Carnalea BT19 1EZ
Tel: (028) 9146 2301
Email: wecrawley@aol.com
Contact: Mrs Wendy Crawley
Position: Secretary

SCOTLAND

Scottish National Bodies

Association of Bahá'í Women - Scotland*
16 Weavers Close, Arbroath DD11 1UT
Tel: (01241) 870101
Email: jshelagh@aol.com
Contact: Miss Shelagh Gudmundsson
Activities: Central body, women

Bahá'í Council for Scotland*
2 Burgess Hill, Linlithgow EH49 6BZ
Tel: (01506) 840034
Contact: Mrs Anwen Swahim
Contact Email: bcs@bahai.org.uk
Activities: Youth, women, newsletter/journal,
inter-faith

City, Town or Local Bodies

Spiritual Assembly of the Bahá'ís of Aberdeen
Manilla, 147 North Deeside Road, Bieldside,
Aberdeen AB15 9EA
Tel: (01224) 861217
Email: samyandmona@compuserve.com
Contact: Mrs Mona Helmy
Position: Secretary

Spiritual Assembly of the Bahá'ís of Dundee*
10 Maryfield Terrace, Dundee DD4 7AE
Tel: (01382) 454459
Email: ruth.riding@virgin.net
Contact: Miss Ruth Riding
Position: Secretary
Activities: Youth, women, newsletter/journal,
visits, inter-faith, resources

Spiritual Assembly of the Bahá'ís of Edinburgh
28 Craigleith View, Ravelston, Edinburgh EH4 3JZ
Tel: (0131) 3370731 **Fax:** (01506)434644
Email: john@jparris.demon.co.uk
Contact: Dr John Parris
Position: Secretary

Spiritual Assembly of the Bahá'ís of Glasgow*
226 Nithsdale Road, Glasgow G41 5PZ
Tel: (0141) 4270802
Contact: Mr Farahbod Nakhaei

Spiritual Assembly of the Bahá'ís of Inverness*
6a Green Drive, Inverness IV2 4EX
Email: mackenzie@inverness9.freeserve.co.uk
Contact: Mr Thomas Mackenzie
Position: Secretary
Activities: Inter-faith
Other Languages: Persian

Spiritual Assembly of the Bahá'ís of Lerwick*
9 Millgaet, Gilbertson Road, Lerwick, Shetland
ZE1 0HG
Tel: (01595) 692035
Email: robert.bennet@ukonline.co.uk
Website: http://www.bci.org/shetland
Contact: Mrs Audrey Bennet
Position: Secretary
Activities: Youth, women, inter-faith, resources

Spiritual Assembly of the Bahá'ís of Orkney*
Norvana, Rendall, Orkney KW17 2NZ
Tel: (01856) 761624
Email: loughlin@onetel.net.uk
Contact: Mrs Rosemary McLaughlin
Position: Secretary

Spiritual Assembly of the Bahá'ís of Skye Central*
Corriegour, Heaste Road, Broadford, Isle of Skye
IV49 9AQ
Tel: (01471) 822292
Email: judy@rukaruka.freeserve.co.uk
Contact: Mrs Judy Finlay
Position: Secretary
Activities: Visits, youth, newsletters, books, inter-
faith
Other Languages: Gaelic, German

WALES

Welsh National Bodies

Association of Bahá'í Women - Wales*
Karma Moel View Road, Gronant, Prestatyn
LL19 9SU
Tel: (01745) 85763 **Fax:** (01745) 85763
Email: alicia@bancroft-lloyd.freeserve.co.uk
Contact: Ms Alicia Bancroft-Lloyd
Website: http://www.abw-uk.net/
Activities: Women

Bahá'í Council for Wales*
15 Parrot Row, Blaina NP13 3AH
Tel: (01495) 291874
Contact: Mrs Christine Abbas
Activities: Central body, youth, women,
newsletter/journal, radio, television, visits, inter-
faith, resources

City, Town or Local Bodies

Spiritual Assembly of the Bahá'ís of Cardiff*
20 Wordsworth Avenue, Roath, Cardiff CF24 3FR
Email: mcazami@altavista.co.uk
Contact: Mrs Elizabeth Azami
Position: Secretary

**Spiritual Assembly of the Bahá'ís of Bay of
Colwyn***
1 Maes Madog, Old Colwyn, Colwyn Bay
LL29 8LL
Tel: (01492) 514064
Email: alun-m-jones@lineone.net
Contact: Mr Alun Jones
Position: Secretary
Activities: Worship, inter-faith

Spiritual Assembly of the Bahá'ís of Newport
183 Risca Road, Newport NP9 3PQ
Contact: Mrs Helen Taghidiri
Position: Secretary

Spiritual Assembly of the Bahá'ís of Swansea
37 Bayview Terrace, Swansea SA1 4LT
Tel: (01792) 425200
Email: l_bartlett@hotmail.com
Contact: Mrs Leila Jenkins
Position: Secretary

INTRODUCING BUDDHISTS IN THE UK

BUDDHISTS IN THE UNITED
KINGDOM 139

ORIGINS AND DEVELOPMENT
OF BUDDHISM 140

SOURCES OF BUDDHIST
BELIEFS AND PRACTICES 141

KEY BUDDHIST BELIEFS 143

TRADITIONS IN BUDDHISM 145

BUDDHIST LIFE 148

BUDDHIST WORSHIP 150

BUDDHIST CALENDAR AND
FESTIVALS 151

BUDDHIST ORGANISATIONS 152

FURTHER READING 156

BUDDHISTS IN THE UNITED KINGDOM

A wide variety of Buddhist organisations, *viharas*, *monasteries*, centres and more informal groups are to be found in the UK today. They reflect both the variety of ethnic groups and the different schools of Buddhism found among UK Buddhists.

Buddhist activity is not as focused upon religious buildings as that of some other religious traditions. Nevertheless, the directory records approximately 148 *viharas*, *monasteries* and other Buddhist centres in the UK and many other groups meet in private houses or in hired halls.

Beginnings in the UK

The nineteenth century saw the development of the western academic study of Buddhism. As scholars produced an increasing number of English translations of Buddhist texts, more and more individuals developed an interest in Buddhism as a philosophy, a way of life, and a religion.

In 1881 the Pali Text Society was founded, which further fostered this development. In 1899, Gordon Douglas, the first English person to be ordained as a Buddhist monk, took his vows in Colombo, Sri Lanka and became Bhikkhu Asoka. He did not, however, return to Britain. In 1898 another Englishman, Alan Bennett, went to study Buddhism in Sri Lanka. In 1901, whilst in Burma, he was ordained as a *monk*, taking the name Ananda Metteyya.

In 1907, a Buddhist Society of Great Britain and Ireland was formed to receive a Buddhist mission which eventually arrived in 1908, led by Ananda Metteyya. The Society did not, however, become firmly established and in 1924 Christmas Humphreys founded the Buddhist Centre of the Theosophical Society which incorporated its remnants. In 1926, this new foundation became the Buddhist Lodge of the Theosophical Society and, in 1943, it was constituted as a new and independent organisation, known as The Buddhist Society. Christmas Humphreys remained as its President until his death in 1983.

In 1926, Humphreys had welcomed the Sinhalese Anagarika Dharmapala who had previously visited Britain in 1893, 1896 and again in 1904 on a mission. Subsequently, a branch of the Maha Bodhi Society was founded in London followed, in 1928, by the first *monastery* for Sinhalese *monks*.

Up until the 1960s, Western engagement with Buddhism was often of an individual, and sometimes rather theoretical, kind. In recent times, however, increasing numbers of Westerners have begun to practise Buddhist meditation and apply Buddhist ethical norms, seeing them as vehicles for bringing about change in their lives and ultimate awakening.

Migration

Individuals and small groups of migrants with Buddhist beliefs have arrived throughout the century from Sri Lanka, Thailand and Burma. Indian (mostly *Ambedkarite* - see below) Buddhists and the Hong Kong Chinese came mainly with the New Commonwealth migrations of the 1950s and 1960s. The number of Buddhists in the UK has been further expanded by refugees including those following the *Dalai Lama's* 1959 flight from Chinese-occupied Tibet; then by Vietnamese Buddhist refugees who arrived in the late 1960s and early 1970s; and more recently by refugees from the Sri Lankan civil war.

Buddhists in the UK speak English and a variety of languages reflecting their countries of origin. Most teaching is conducted in English. The Buddhist scriptures are preserved in *Pali* (in the case of the *Southern Canon*, which forms the basis of the *Theravada* tradition - see section below on "Traditions in Buddhism") and Chinese, Japanese, Sanskrit and Tibetan (in the case of the *Mahayana* scriptures - see section below on "Traditions in Buddhism").

Ethnic Chinese

The position of the ethnically Chinese population is complex with regard to religious affiliation. Some Chinese are *Evangelical* Christians, others are Buddhists of the *Cha'n* tradition, yet others mingle Buddhist, Taoist and Confucian elements within the traditional religious practice of their families. It is hard to be certain of the exact number of Chinese Buddhists, but the number is not insubstantial.

ORIGINS AND DEVELOPMENT OF BUDDHISM

Gautama Buddha/Gotama Buddha

Buddhism does not believe in a personal deity. It makes no claims to possess a divinely revealed book and it has no central organisational authority. The teachings of Buddhism are the inheritance of Siddhartha Gautama/Siddhattha Gotama's search for truth. (Here and throughout the chapter, key names and concepts are introduced in both their Sanskrit and Pali forms. Thereafter, only the Sanskrit form is used in the main body of the text).

According to Buddhist tradition, Siddhartha Gautama was born in Lumbini, in what is today Nepal, in around the fifth century BCE, and then grew up nearby in Kapilavatthu. As a prince, his early life was rich and comfortable. Eventually, however, he asked his charioteer to take him to see life in the city. Here he saw for himself, the suffering of a sick person and an old man as well as seeing a corpse, but he also saw the serenity of a *mendicant*. This experience awakened in him a wish to understand and alleviate suffering. So, at the age of twenty-nine, he began a spiritual search which lasted for six years until it reached its culmination in his *Enlightenment* under the *Bo Tree* (now known as the *Bodhi Tree*), at the place in North India now known as Bodh Gaya.

During Gautama's period of searching, he studied with two important teachers of his time, but he was still dissatisfied and decided to continue alone. He underwent extremes of self-denial and self-mortification. But these, too, did not satisfy him and he finally decided on a less *ascetic* approach. He ate some food and regained his strength. At this point five *ascetics* who had previously joined up with him left him in disapproval. He then sat down under the *Bodhi Tree* in a determined attempt to break through to that which he was seeking.

It is said that on the night of the full moon in May he finally attained the state of *nirvana/nibbana* (see section on "Key Buddhist Beliefs" below). He then sought out the five *ascetics* who had previously been with him. With them as his first followers, the *samgha/sangha* (Buddhist community) was born, in the Deer Park near Benares. At the age of eighty he passed away at Kushinagara and entered into what Buddhists describe as his *parinirvana/parinibbana* (final entry to *nirvana*).

Transmission

The form of the Buddhist tradition that spread south is known as the *Theravada* tradition. It was brought to Sri Lanka in 250BCE and spread to those countries now known as Thailand, Cambodia, Laos and Burma as well as to the southern part of Vietnam. Between the first and seventh century of the Common Era Buddhism spread slowly north-eastwards into Central Asia and into what is now China, Korea, Japan, the northern part of Vietnam and (in the seventh and eighth centuries) northwards into Tibet.

The forms of Buddhism traditionally associated with these countries are therefore often known as the *Northern Transmission*, or the *Mahayana* tradition. In India itself, after the first millennium CE Buddhism almost died out (apart from in what is now Bangladesh) until its revival this century,

through the attraction of the *Ambedkarite* (named after the Indian social reformer Dr Ambedkar) movement for the Indian *scheduled castes*, popularly referred to as *untouchables*.

SOURCES OF BUDDHIST BELIEFS AND PRACTICES

The Buddha

The historical *Buddha* is revered as the uncoverer of the teachings or *dharma/dhamma* which exist independently of him. He himself claimed only to have rediscovered "an ancient way leading to an ancient city". Therefore, the emphasis is upon the *Buddha* as guide and upon the *dharma* rather than on the person of Gautama. Strictly speaking, therefore, Gautama is not viewed as the founder of the *dharma*.

Buddhists are those who claim to have found these teachings to be valid for themselves. In the early stages of Buddhist training one can learn the details of the teachings, but in the end every individual must discover them in their own experience and not simply as what they have been taught.

The Three Refuges

Buddhists speak of "going for refuge" or "taking refuge" in the *triratna/tiratana* (*Three Jewels*). This is an affirmation of their commitment as Buddhists and to the sources of Buddhist life: "I take refuge in the *Buddha*; I take refuge in the *dharma* (the *Buddha's* teachings); I take refuge in the *samgha/sangha* (the Buddha's community)."

Buddha

Siddhartha Gautama was acknowledged by his followers to be a *Buddha* or *Enlightened* one (from *Budh* meaning to be enlightened or awakened). In the *Mahayana* Buddhist tradition, Siddhartha Gautama is also known as *Shakyamuni/Sakyamuni* (the silent sage of the Shakya/Sakya people). In the *Theravada* tradition references to the *Buddha* are usually to the historical figure of Gautama, who is venerated as the one who initiated the transmission of the teaching in the current era.

Both the *Mahayana* and *Theravada* tradition also assume the existence of numerous *Buddhas* before and after him as well as of the *Buddha-nature* in all beings of which the historical *Buddha* is but one manifestation. Going to the *Buddha* for refuge not only means accepting the *Buddha* as the ultimate spiritual guide and example for one's life, but also appreciating one's own *Buddha-nature* and potential for *enlightenment*. Many Buddhist homes and temples contain *rupas* (statues) or pictures of the *Buddha* as aids to devotion and meditation.

Dharma

Dharma has no single meaning. It is quintessentially expressed in the so-called *Four Noble Truths* (see section below on "Key Buddhist Beliefs"). Going for refuge to the *dharma* is understood to involve focusing one's energies to understand, practise and realise the *dharma* in one's own life, thus also bringing about understanding of others and expressing goodwill towards them.

Samgha

Historically, for many Buddhists, *samgha* has been understood as the community of celibate Buddhist *monks* and *nuns*. However, in some *Japanese* groups and movements there are no *monks* and *nuns*. Many *Tibetan* Buddhists are guided by married *lamas*, and *monks* and *nuns* have no particular status in the Friends of the Western Buddhist Order. Among other Buddhists in the *Mahayana* tradition, and particularly in some parts of western Buddhism, the *samgha* is understood primarily as the totality of followers of the *Buddha* who have had a significant transformative experience of transcendental insight. For some Buddhists, the meaning of the *samgha* can be taken to embrace all who potentially possess the *Buddha-nature*, in other words all sentient beings.

The Southern Canon

Several *canons* of scripture help explain the *dharma*. Most were eventually committed to writing from an original oral transmission. The southern, Pali language *canon* contains some of the oldest material which is ascribed to the *Buddha* and his disciples and in general is acceptable to all Buddhist schools. This canon is also known as the *Tipitaka*, meaning the *Three Baskets*, since its palm leaf manuscripts were originally kept in three different baskets – the *Vinaya-pitaka* (Basket of [Monastic] Discipline); the *Sutta-pitaka* (Basket of Discourses); and the *Abhidhamma-pitaka* (Basket of Further Teachings).

The Northern Canon

The *Mahayana canon* is extensive. Its wide variety of texts include many which were written down in Sanskrit and then translated into Tibetan and Chinese, plus some which were originally written in these languages. Some texts, known in the Far East as the *Agama*, are held in common with the *Pali canon*. The term *sutra/sutta* is used of the texts and refers to the idea of a single "thread" running through the discourse.

Among the more widely known *Mahayana sutras* are the *Saddharma-pundarika* (the Lotus of the True Dharma), the vast collection of the *Prajna-paramita sutras* (the Perfection of Wisdom), the long *Mahayana Parinirvana Sutra*, and the compilation known as *Avatamsaka Sutra* (the Flower Ornament).

These *sutras* were gathered into canonical collections of writings. The *Chinese canon* is known as the *Ta-ts'ang-ching* (Great Scripture Store) and its standard modern edition consists of fifty-five volumes with forty-five supplementary volumes. In Japan, this standard compilation is known as *Taizokyo*. The equally vast *Tibetan canon* consists of the *bKa'gyur* (pronounced "Kangyur" and meaning "the Translation of the Word of the Buddha") which is ninety-eight volumes long, and the *bsTan'gyur* (pronounced "Tengyur" and meaning "Translation of

Treatises"). This, in its Peking edition, is in two hundred and twenty-four volumes and it can also be found in Japan in its original wood-block print copies.

Jataka Stories

In addition to the canonical texts, both *Theravada* and *Mahayana* Buddhists refer to the over five hundred *Jataka* stories said to have been told by the *Buddha* to his followers about his former lives. They form the basis of much popular teaching and reflection in some eastern countries where Buddhism is the predominant tradition and serious practitioners also attest that their seeming simplicity contains unexpected depths.

KEY BUDDHIST BELIEFS

Four Noble Truths

The *Catur Aryasatya/Cattari Ariyasaccani* (Four Noble Truths) are at the heart of Buddhism. These four truths are: *duhkha/dukkha* (unsatisfactoriness), *samudaya* (the origin of unsatisfactoriness), *nirodha* (the cessation of unsatisfactoriness) and *marga/magga* (the way leading to contentment).

Duhkha (Unsatisfactoriness)

Duhkha has often been translated as "suffering". However, suffering is only one of its meanings and it is better understood in terms of "unsatisfactoriness", a word that also implies imperfection and impermanence. In his first teaching, the Buddha said: "Birth is *duhkha*, ageing is *duhkha*, sickness is *duhkha*, death is *duhkha*; sorrow, lamentation, grief and despair are *duhkha*; association with what one dislikes is *duhkha*; separation from what one likes is *duhkha*; not to get what one wants is *duhkha*."

Duhkha is one of the *Three Signs of Being* or characteristics of existence, the other two are *anitya/anicca* (impermanence), and *anatman/anatta* (no-self). One cannot expect to find permanent happiness from impermanent causes. *Anitya* (impermanence or change) means all conditioned phenomena are impermanent and are "coming to be and ceasing to be". Change is a constant characteristic of all things. *Anatman* is the teaching that there is no permanent or immortal self.

An "everyday self" is recognised but is understood as an ever-changing composite of five *skandhas/khandhas* (aggregates) which are themselves forever changing. They are: *rupa* (material form), *vedana* (feelings), *samjna/sanna* (perceptions), *samskaras/sankharas* (mental configurations), and *vijnana/vinnana* (discriminatory consciousness).

Samudaya (Origin of Unsatisfactoriness)

The origin of *duhkha* is seen by Buddhists to lie in *trishna/tanha*. This is a powerful thirsting or craving which, of its very nature, can never be satisfied and goes on reproducing itself. It manifests itself as desire for, and attachment to, material things and mental objects; including a thirst for continued existence and its opposite desire for non-existence. Such craving or thirst results in *duhkha* and in behaviour which will lead to undesired *rebirth*. This *rebirth* is not understood as the transmigration of a soul, which would be inconsistent with the teaching of *anatman*. Rather, the habits which are reinforced by craving are to bring about a "rebecoming", instead of a continuation of a soul.

Nirodha (Cessation of duhkha)

The transcendence of *trishna* (craving) leads to the cessation of *duhkha* and is known as *nirvana*. The full meaning of *nirvana* cannot adequately be described. In literal terms it means the "quenching" or "extinction" of the thirst and craving that results in *duhkha*. It does not therefore mean, as it has often been misunderstood to mean, a state of annihilation. The "quenching" and "extinction" to which it refers is rather that of the fires of greed, hatred, ignorance and craving which cause *duhkha*. It is seen as deliverance from *samsara* (see below), which is the world in which *duhkha* holds sway. Buddhists affirm that this deliverance can be realised in this life, as in the case of Gautama Buddha himself.

Marga (The Way)

The first three *Noble Truths* analyse the human condition and affirm the possibility of transcending *duhkha*. The fourth, more fully known as the *Arya Ashtangika Marga/Ariya Atthangika Magga* (The Noble Eightfold Path – see section below on "Buddhist Life"), is a way of life to be practised and that leads one out of *samsara*. This path is often known as the *Middle Way*, the course between and beyond the excesses of self-indulgence and self-denial.

Dependent Origination

Dependent origination is a sequence or consequence according to which all phenomena arise in dependence upon their interrelated causes. In relation to sentient beings, it is often seen in terms of a chain with twelve links, each link/cause depending upon the previous one and leading to the next.

Karma and Vipata

Karma/Kamma (literally meaning "deed") is understood in Buddhism as a law of consequences inherent in the nature of things. Technically, *karma* is the deed and *vipata* the consequence, but popularly *karma* refers to both deeds and consequences. All deliberate actions have their consequences and whether a particular action has useful or negative *karmic/kammic* effects depends predominately upon the intentions.

Samsara

Samsara (the wheel of birth and death) is not the *reincarnation* or *transmigration* of a soul because, as has been noted, Buddhism does not posit the continuing existence of such a substantial or permanent *soul* or self. This is because the individual is understood to be a cluster of various aggregates held together by desire. Buddhists therefore usually speak of a

"*rebirth*" or "*rebecoming*" of these aggregates rather than of the *transmigration* of an entity.

This *rebirth* is possible on a number of levels (not just the human) and throughout aeons. The "wheel" of birth and death is divided into six realms or states illustrative of these possibilities. Depending on the *karma* accumulated in one lifetime the *rebirth* or *rebecoming* will be of different kinds. The principal concern is ultimately not to gain a better future *rebirth*, but to escape altogether from this wheel of rebirth and death and to attain *nirvana*.

Being born as a human being is viewed as a precious opportunity since it is believed that from the human state there is no better chance that deliverance can be achieved. In *Mahayana* Buddhism, having escaped from the wheel of birth and death, the *enlightened* being may compassionately return to the world, without being *karmically* bound to it, in order to assist others to awaken.

Shunyata/Sunnata

Shunyata (Voidness or Emptiness) is a concept of great importance in the *Mahayana* tradition where the idea of *anatman* or no-self has undergone further development. In the *Mahayana* view, all that exists is devoid of any abiding essence, and "empty" of any ultimate characteristics. To understand this is to recognise the ultimately fluid and inter-connected nature of all phenomena. The deep realisation of *shunyata* is believed to end fear.

Bodhi

Bodhi literally means "awakening" and refers to *Enlightenment*. This is the state of *Buddhahood* or spiritual perfection which is the goal of the Buddhist spiritual life. It comes about with the perfection of *prajna/panna* (wisdom) and *karuna* (compassion). It brings a complete seeing into the ultimate nature of existence and a totally self-less and compassionate response to all beings and situations.

TRADITIONS IN BUDDHISM

The central teachings are common to all the traditions and schools, but they contain differences in emphasis, as well as some differences in practice. The principal traditions are the *Theravada* (Way of the Elders) or the *Southern Transmission*, found principally in South East Asia, and the *Mahayana* (often translated as the *Great Vehicle* - from *maha* meaning "great" and *yana* meaning "vehicle") or *Northern Transmission*, with its two main branches of the *Far Eastern* and *Tibetan* Buddhism. Within *Tibetan* Buddhism, there is a tendency to refer to three "vehicles" or transmissions of Buddhism, namely, the *Theravada*, the *Bodhisattvayana* and the *Vajrayana*.

In some books on Buddhism the *Theravada* is sometimes referred to as the *Hinayana* (*Little Vehicle*). However, the origins of the term *Hinayana* are to be found in a disparaging contrast with the *Mahayana* (Great Vehicle). More properly *Hinayana* historically refers to spiritual tendencies which existed in India and were criticised by followers of the *Mahayana* as being rigid and limited, rather than to the later developed forms of *Theravada* Buddhism found in Sri Lanka and the *Southern Transmission*. The correct term for *Theravada* is *Shravakayana* (Vehicle of the Disciples). Fundamentally the *Theravada* accepts the validity *Mahayana* and visa versa. The *Yajrayana* is to be understood as "skilful means" to achieve the goals of the *Mahayana*.

Within each of the major traditions there are also many different schools which emphasise particular beliefs and practices. In the West there are, also, newer developments which do not fully identify with any one traditional branch of Buddhism. Some of these are working to evolve new western styles of Buddhism.

Theravada

The ideal of the *Theravada* tradition is that of the *arahat*, an individual who has found release from the cycle of birth and death. Its hallmarks are renunciation, self-reliance and a focus upon the historical *Buddha*. This tradition is based upon the *Pali canon* and is today mainly represented in the Buddhism of the South Asian countries of Sri Lanka, Burma, Laos, Cambodia and Thailand, as well as in southern Vietnam. It is therefore sometimes known by the name of *Southern Transmission*. Variations within the *Theravada* tradition reflect the different cultural contexts in which the tradition has taken shape rather than the existence of distinctive schools as such.

Mahayana

In addition to the concept of *shunyata* and a belief in many simultaneously present *Buddhas*, the particular characteristics of the *Mahayana* tradition include an emphasis on the ideal of the *Bodhisattva*. A *Bodhisattva* among humans is one who vows to practice the Buddhist path totally in order to help and liberate both themselves and all beings (for example, Avalokiteshvara or Chenrezig, the Bodhisattva of Compassion and Manjushri, the Bodhisattva of Wisdom).

Bodhisattva-Mahasattvas are fully perfected *Bodhisattvas*, greater than any other being except *Buddhas*. They live permanently in the realm of "transcendence" and from this position strive constantly for the welfare of others. Hence the *Mahayana* is sometimes referred to as the *Bodhisattvayana* (the way of the *Bodhisattva*). The *Theravada* also accepts the existence of the *Bodhisattvas* or *Bodhissatas* (Pali) albeit primarily in the *Jakata* stories about Siddhatta's previous lives.

Mahayana is a generic name for a wide movement embracing many different groups in the northern countries of China, Japan, Vietnam, Korea and Tibet. It is sometimes known as the *Northern Transmission* because it came via the Northern Silk Road and therefore reached these countries first. All have in common the same basic principles, but each grouping has developed in a different cultural setting or is often associated with one or more of the great *sutras* and has thus evolved variations in practice.

Due to repeated persecutions most of these groups became extinct in China by the 15th century, but many were introduced to Japan and some are still extant there as the *Tendai*, *Pure Land*, *Shingon* and *Zen* schools, with one temple of the *Kegon* school. In China itself, an amalgamation of the groups took place within the broader *Ch'an* tradition (see below).

Tibetan Buddhism

Buddhism first came to Tibet during the reign of Trisong Detsen (755-797CE) through the activities of the Indian sage, Padmasambhava (meaning "Lotus-Born'). Distinctively, the *Tibetan* traditions use among others, *tantric* rituals and *visualisation* to accelerate inward transformation. The goal of "diamond-like" clarity and indestructible unity of wisdom and compassion, gives it the name V*ajrayana* (or "Diamond Vehicle'). *Tantric* practices are regarded as very powerful. Certain advanced practices (such as those known as "protection practices" – see below) are regarded as spiritually/psychologically dangerous in the "wrong hands".

Some claim the *Vajrayana* reaches back to esoteric practices taught by *Shakyamuni Buddha*, which were passed down from teacher to teacher. *Tibetan Schools* are very conscious of their *lineages*, which are recited in rituals and displayed in lineage trees, linking present-day teachers to the "founders" of the particular school. The relation of the *guru* to the disciple is a very important one.

Shakyamuni himself is no longer accessible, but the *Mahayana* tradition offers access to "transcendent support", notably *Maha-Bodhisattvas* (such as *Avalokiteshvara* (the Buddha of Compassion) and *Manjushri* (the Buddha of Wisdom), who have postponed final *nirvana* to work for the *Enlightenment* of all beings (practising *bodhicitta*).

In a simple visualisation, a person may symbolically breathe in "dark smoke" and exhale it as "white light" – radiating calm, and joyous peacefulness. At a more advanced level, a meditator will visualise a *Bodhisattva*, and introject the image so as to "become" the *Bodhisattva*. *Dharma Protectors* are also visualised as *wrathful deities*, to strengthen inner commitment. According to legend when Padmasmbhava subdued the daemons of Tibetan folk religion, they were transformed and joined the ranks of the *Dharma Protectors*.

These visualised entities should be regarded neither as independent realities, nor as psychological representations, but rather as generated phenomena embodying real potentials of the mind. The development of compassion and the practice of *bodhicitta* (compassion, loving kindness, impartiality, joy) is regarded as essential to the attainment of the clear light of *Enlightenment*.

There are four main schools of *Tibetan* Buddhism. The *Nyingma* (Old School) originated in Tibet with the arrival of successive Indian sages, including Padmasambhava (Guru Rinpoche), but it traces its lineage back to an emanation of the *Primordial Buddha*. The famous so-called *Tibetan Book of the Dead* originated in this school as a hidden teaching (or *terma*) of Guru Rinpoche, discovered by Karma Lingpa in the fourteenth century and transmitted to his *Kagyu* disciples. It describes how to control the journey from death to *rebirth* through the various *bardo* states. This process is visualised during a *Bardo Retreat* lasting forty-nine days in total darkness and isolation.

The *Kagyu* ("Teaching Lineage") traces its origins to the Indian sage, Tilopa (988-1069), said to have received teachings from *Vajradhara*, an emanation of the *Buddha's* "Enjoyment Body". The lineage continues via Naropa to Marpa, the first Tibetan, and thence to Milarepa and Gampopa, whence derive the main sub-schools, e.g. the *Karma Kagyu*, headed by the first *Karmapa*. His

Holiness, the seventeenth *Karmapa*, though recognised by the Chinese authorities, has recently fled Tibet and taken asylum in India. Emphasis is placed on direct experience as, for example, in the *mahamudra* solitary retreat of three years and three months.

The *Sakya* lineage begins with the Indian master, Virupa (1034-1102), and owes its name ("Grey Earth") to the site of the monastery built by Gonchok Gyelpo (in 1073).

The most recent school, the *Geluk* ("System of Virtue"), was created by Je Tsong Khapa Losang Drakpa (1357-1419). He built the Ganden monastery in 1410, and reformed the *Kadampa* tradition, founded by the Indian master, Atisha (982-1054).

The different schools have sometimes had turbulent relationships in Tibetan history, though leading figures have practised under masters from different schools. The nineteenth century saw the rise of a non-sectarian movement (*Rimé*) associated with Jamgon Kongtrul.

Tibetan Buddhism has evolved a unique institutional interpretation of *reincarnation*, whereby high *lamas* may decide to be "reborn" to continue their work. The discovery, recognition and education of reincarnate *lamas* (or *tulkus*) allows a celibate lineage to preserve continuity. (It is common to find these persons erroneously referred to as "god kings" in the Western media.)

The most well-known of these reincarnate *lamas* is Tenzin Gyatso, His Holiness the Fourteenth *Dalai Lama* (meaning "Ocean of Wisdom" a title bestowed by the Mongol Emperor Altan Khan). The Fifth *Dalai Lama* used these inherited alliances to consolidate his power, and that of the *Geluk* School, over the whole of Tibet by 1640, thus establishing the *Dalai Lamas* as both religious and political leaders.

The second highest *lama* in the School is the *Panchen Lama*, whose recent *reincarnation* is a matter of dispute between the *Dalai Lama* and the Chinese authorities. This has long-term implications for *Tibetan* Buddhist religious structures, since it is the *Panchen Lama* who should oversee the discovery of the next *Dalai Lama*.

Recently, a controversy has arisen in relation to a practice involving the propitiation of Dorje Shugden. In popular culture, Shugden is a "worldly deity", bringing good luck and success in enterprise. Those in the *New Kadampa* tradition believe that they experience Shudgen as a supra-mundane deity, able to strengthen their inner resolve to keep the *dharma*.

The controversy developed when the *Dalai Lama* declared that Shugden was an "evil force", harmful both to himself and to the cause of the Tibetan people. He noted that the origins of the propitiation of Dorje Shugden had arisen during a conflict with the Fifth *Dalai Lama*, and he saw it as being associated with "sectarianism". Members of the NKT took part in highly publicised demonstrations against the *Dalai Lama* for what they saw as an attack on their human rights. This campaign has now finished, but there are continuing tensions arising from the controversy.

Ch'an (Chinese) and Zen (Japanese) Buddhism

Ch'an is an abbreviated form of the Chinese word *Ch'an-na*, which is derived from the Sanskrit word *dhyana* which refers to the state of mind during meditation in which the distinctions between subject and object is transcended. *Zen* is a shortened form of *zenna*, which derives from a Japanese pronounciation of the word *Ch'an-na*.

Although meditation is important in all Buddhist schools, *Zen* stresses the practice of *zazen* (sitting meditation) in developing awareness. Zen affirms that direct insight into true reality is possible through this practice, hence the Japanese name of *satori* or *kensho*, meaning "seeing into one's true nature".

Shikantaza (or just sitting) was introduced into China by the Indian monk Bodhidhamma in the 6th century CE, when other Buddhist schools had already been established. The *Rinzai* lineage developed in the 9th century. What was to become *Soto Zen* was introduced into Japan in the 8th century by Dosen Risshi. The *Rinzai* lineage found its way to Japan in the 12th century CE. *Soto Zen* emphasises *Shikantaza* (or 'just sitting'), which is sometimes known as *Serene Reflection Meditation*. In the *Rinzai* tradition, *zazen* is combined with the use of *koan* (questions employed by a *Zen Master* designed to engender and test genuine insight).

Pure Land Buddhism

Pure Land Buddhists are devoted to Amitabha, a cosmic *Buddha* who vowed to bring liberation to all. In *Japanese* Buddhism (where Amitabha is known as Amida) the school has two main branches - the *Jodo Shu* (*Pure Land* school) and the *Jodo Shinshu* (*True Pure Land* school, often simply known as *Shin*).

Both schools are products of an emphasis in Buddhist teaching on adaptation of the *dharma* to the world in forms that are most suitable for people. They therefore offer a path which people can follow in difficult times, teaching dependence upon the infinite merit of *Amida Buddha* and his *tariki* (or "other power").

The difference between the *Jodo Shu* and the *Jodo Shinshu* is that the latter emphasises the complete abandonment of all *jiriki* (self-effort). As a central part of their practice both recite the *Nembutsu*, which is an invocation of the *mantra Namu-Amida-butsu* (hail to Amida Buddha).

Nichiren Buddhism

The *Nichiren* tradition draws upon the teachings of the Japanese teacher Nichiren (1222-1282CE), who saw the *Lotus Sutra* as the highest form of Buddhist teaching, the essence of which could be found in its title. Nichiren taught that recitation of the *sutra's* name was all that was necessary for liberation. Recitation of the *mantra* having the name of

the *sutra*, *Namu myoho renge-kyo* (Veneration to the Lotus of the Good Law), was therefore introduced as a key practice within this tradition.

BUDDHIST LIFE

The Five Precepts

The *Five Precepts* (or *Panca Silani*) are the basic rules of living for lay Buddhists. They express the intention to refrain from: harming living beings; taking what is not given; sexual misconduct and misuse of the senses; harmful speech; and drink or drugs which cloud the mind. For the lay Buddhist this is the basis of *samyakkarmanta/samma kammanta* (Right Action), which is one aspect of the *Noble Eightfold Path*. Buddhists who are *ordained* take additional vows (see section below on "Buddhist Organisations").

Noble Eightfold Path

In Buddhist teaching the *Noble Eightfold Path* (*Arya Astangika Marga*) is the fourth of the *Four Noble Truths* and is the way to overcome *duhkha*. The eight aspects of the Path are traditionally grouped into three. The first two are concerned with wisdom, the next three with morality, and the final three with concentration and meditation. All aspects of the *Eightfold Path* are, however, interdependent.

Right Understanding
Samyagdrishti/samma ditthi (meaning right understanding) is the corrected viewpoint, acquired through familiarity with the Buddhist teachings, that all life is impermanent.

Right Intention
Samyaksamkalpa/samma sankappa (right intention) is the changed motivation which develops with corrected vision.

Right Speech
Samyagvac/samma vaca (right speech) emerges from right understanding and intention and

causes no injury to oneself or others and thus avoids lying, abuse, slander and gossip.

Right Action

Samyakkarmanta/samma kammanta (right action) consists of refraining from what is harmful and involves, among other things, cultivating the *Five Precepts* and practising what is beneficial for oneself and others.

Right Livelihood

Samyagajiva/samma ajiva (right livelihood) includes right daily conduct and not earning one's living in ways inconsistent with the *Five Precepts* and the *Noble Eightfold Path*.

Right Effort

Samyagvayama/samma vayama (right effort) requires constant attentiveness and effort to sustain and generate good, as well as to refrain from what is harmful.

Right Mindfulness

Samyaksmriti/samma sati (right mindfulness) is rooted in the body and its activity; feelings; states of mind; and mental contents. Whatever enters a mind that is aware will be found to be subject to the *Three Signs of Being*.

Right Concentration

Samyaksamadhi/samma samadhi (meaning right concentration) is nurtured through the practice of meditation.

Paramitas

In the *Theravada* tradition, the main emphasis is on the *Four Noble Truths* and the practice of the *Noble Eightfold Path*. In *Mahayana* the stress is on the traditional practice of the *paramitas*, and especially the first six of these. *Paramitas* is usually translated as "perfections". The six specially emphasised *paramitas* are: giving; keeping the moral precepts; patience; strength to persevere; meditation (see below), and wisdom (the genuine insight which results from this practice and has compassion as its natural accompaniment).

Meditation

Meditation plays a central role in the practice of the Buddhist teachings. Through such meditation, faith (as confidence), concentration, mindfulness, energy and wisdom are cultivated as the five foundations of the developing spiritual life. Meditation is also rooted in right action. There are numerous methods of meditation within the various branches of Buddhism and they all require training and practice. There are, however, two basic forms which underlie the variety of methods. These are *shamatha/samatha* (tranquillity meditation) and *vipashyana/vipassana* (insight meditation).

Shamatha meditation is concerned with promoting states of mind characterised by calm, concentration and mindfulness in order to integrate the emotions and develop positive energies. Common forms of *shamatha* meditation are awareness or mindfulness of breathing and the practice of positive good will, radiating "loving-kindness" to the whole world.

Vipassana meditation is concerned with the clarity of seeing things as they really are and in realising the *Three Signs of Being* (see under the *Four Noble Truths*). This realisation is seen as breaking the bondage of *samsara* and thus as bringing liberation from *duhkha*.

There are a variety of ways in which meditation may be aided. *Rupas* (material forms) of Gautama *Buddha* are a reminder of his life and teaching. The *Tibetan* Buddhist tradition has a rich artistic heritage and teaches visualisation of many *Buddhas* and *Bodhisattvas*.

Mantras, when chanted, are believed to resonate in ways that have a deep efficacy. *Mandalas* are sacred diagrams in the shape of circles, squares or angles that depict the teachings of Buddhism. In *Tibetan* Buddhism they are either permanently constructed, such as those painted on *thang-ka* (scrolls) or are temporarily made from different coloured sands or other such materials. *Mudras* are hand gestures which, like *mantras*, are believed to have a spiritual effect.

In *Zen* Buddhism great attention is paid to sitting meditation as well as to practice of the *precepts* and meditation in daily life. The state of mind cultivated is known as "empty heart", which is not one of thoughtlessness, but of an "at-one-ness" which has passed beyond the distinction of subject and object. When practised this state prevails not only when sitting in meditation but also in the activities of daily life, including all kinds of work.

Vegetarianism

Buddhism emphasises the avoidance of intentional killing. However, there is a variety of practice with regard to the eating of meat. Many *Tibetan* Buddhists do eat meat and, in *Theravada* Buddhism, *monks* and *nuns* are allowed to eat meat if they have not seen, heard or suspected that the animal has been specifically killed for them. In particular they are able to accept meat if it is offered to them as alms, which is the only way in which they are able to obtain food.

Chinese Zen has become strictly vegetarian, whereas in *Japanese Zen* the same rules apply as in *Theravada*, although meat is never served in *monasteries*. In general, even where Buddhists are not fully vegetarian, what are perceived as the higher forms of life are often avoided. In *Chinese* forms of Buddhism garlic and onions are also avoided since they are thought to heat the blood and so make meditation more difficult. The precept of right livelihood certainly excludes the "trade in flesh" entailed in being a butcher, hunter or fisher.

BUDDHIST WORSHIP

Buildings for Devotional Practice

Buddhist buildings of various types can be found in the UK, each reflecting the different traditions, schools and ethnic groupings of the Buddhists who use them. Styles range from the stark simplicity of meditation halls through to the elaborate ornateness of some temples.

Some places for devotion may be in residential houses with a room acting as the central shrine or meditation room. Others are extensive purpose-built buildings such as the Samye Ling Tibetan Centre in Scotland and the Thai Buddhapadipa Theravada Temple in Wimbledon. Some are relatively small structures such as the Peace Pagodas in Milton Keynes and Battersea Park in London.

Despite this variety there are a number of common features. A Buddhist temple or *monastery* usually contains at least a *Buddharupa* (statue of the *Buddha*) and a *stupa/thupa*, which is a characteristic form of Buddhist architecture (representing the mind of the *Buddha*) originally built over relics of the *Buddha* or other saints or other typically holy objects. The temple is commonly a place where teaching, religious observance and meditation takes place, and it may have adjacent accommodation for resident *monks* or *nuns*. It can thus physically focus the three refuges of Buddhism - the *Buddha*, the *dharma* and the *samgha*.

Shrines and Buddharupas

Most Buddhists also have a small shrine in their homes. The *Buddharupa* is usually found in a central position within the shrine area. In front of the *Buddharupa* will usually be an incense holder and the *rupa* will be flanked by flowers and candles. *Puja*, which involves the offering of food, flowers, incense and water, together with chanting, is carried out by all schools within Buddhism as a devotional observance alongside meditation, although it takes different forms in each school. Such observance expresses *shraddha/saddha* (faith) in the *Buddha*. This is not blind faith, but confidence based on knowledge and awareness.

The offering of incense is symbolic of devotion. Candles symbolise the light that the

Buddha's teaching brings to the world. There are vases of cut flowers as a reminder of impermanence and sometimes a Buddhist text wrapped in silk cloth. *Tibetan* Buddhists offer bowls of water to represent water for bathing, washing the feet, rinsing the mouth and drinking, as well as food, flowers, incense and light. In the *Zen* tradition, offerings of fruit, tea and water are made.

BUDDHIST CALENDAR AND FESTIVALS

Calendar

Buddhist religious festivals are based on the lunar calendars of the countries concerned. However the actual festivals and their dates and meanings vary according to Buddhist tradition and the national/ethnic origins of the group concerned. Because of these national/ethnic variations and the lunar cycle, individuals cannot easily predict the exact dates of particular festivals. Some, as in Japan, have fixed dates by the Western calendar. But many other Buddhists rely for moon dates on printed calendars, such as the one produced at the Tibetan Medical Centre in Dharamsala, India, which is consulted by *Tibetan* Buddhists all over the world.

Festivals

Uposatha Days
Are observed at full moon and new moon and also on the days half way through the lunar fortnight. The full moon and new moon observances are the most important. On these days *monks* and devout lay Buddhists engage in more intense religious activities. The way in which these days are observed varies considerably among Buddhists, but their observance usually includes a visit to a monastery to make offerings of food to the *monks* and to pay one's respect to *Buddha* images and shrines.

Parinirvana (15th February)
Far Eastern Mahayana Buddhists mark the final passing away of Gautama *Buddha* at Kushinagara, India, at the age of eighty.

Buddha's Birthday (8th April in Japan)
Far Eastern Mahayana Buddhists celebrate this as a festival of flowers, reflecting the *Buddha's* birth in a garden. Sweet tea or water is ceremonially poured over a statue of the infant *Buddha*.

Wesak or Buddha Day (May)
Known as *Wesak* in Sri Lankan Buddhism and *Vaisakha Puja* in *Theravada Buddhism*, generally this festival occurs on the full moon day in May. It commemorates the *Birth*, *Enlightenment* and *Parinirvana* (passing away) of the *Buddha*, all of which, according to the *Theravada* tradition, occurred on the full moon day in May. *Far Eastern Mahayana* Buddhists celebrate these three events on different dates (see above). In the West, the day is generally known as *Buddha Day* and it is usually observed in common by Buddhists of all schools.

Poson (June)
Is the Sri Lankan name for the month and the festival which mark the conversion of Sri Lanka to Buddhism through the Venerable Mahinda, son of the Emperor Asoka, who brought the *dharma* to what is now Sri Lanka in c.250BCE.

The Rains Retreat (June/July – September/October)
The retreat is known in South Asian countries as *Vassa* and is an annual feature of the *Theravada monastic* calendar which *monks* and *nuns* observe for three months. During this period *monks* and *nuns* should remain in one place except for emergencies. In the *Northern Transmission* and in the West, dates vary in accordance with the climate. The *Zen* school has two such retreats each year, each one for three months. Special services are held on the opening and closing days.

Asalha **(Dharmachakra Day)** (July/August)
This is the anniversary of the *Buddha's* first
sermon to the five ascetics in the Deer Park
near Benares in India. It is celebrated by
Theravadins and the Friends of the Western
Buddhist Order. The discourse was called the
first *Turning of the Wheel of the Law*, which is
the meaning of *Dharmachakra*. The day also
marks the beginning of the *Rains Retreat*.

Kathina Day (October/November)
This is celebrated by *Theravadins* and follows
the *Rains Retreat* either on its final day or
within one month. On this day, the laity
present *monks* and *nuns* with a cloth which is
made into a robe for a *monk* on the same day.
The precise date of its observance varies
according to the end of the rainy season in
the various countries.

Samgha Day (November)
Is celebrated by the Friends of the Western
Buddhist Order and sometimes by other
Western Buddhists as an expression of the
spiritual community of all Buddhists.

Enlightenment Day (8th December)
This is celebrated by *Far Eastern Mahayana
Buddhists*. In India, *Mahayana* Buddhists
observe this by celebrating under the *Bodhi
Tree* in Bodh Gaya.

New Year
Although it is generally celebrated by
Buddhists as a major festival, apart from the
incorporation of some elements of Buddhist
practice into its observance, *New Year* is not a
specifically religious festival for Buddhists.
The Sri Lankan and Thai New Year fall in
mid-April and, in Thai tradition, New Year
also involves a water festival. It is of greater
importance in the *Mahayana* countries with
their colder and darker winters. The Chinese
New Year falls at the end of January or the
beginning of February. In Japan, the western
New Year date has been adopted.

Padmasambhava Day
There is a *Padmasambhava Day* in every
Tibetan Lunar month, it is celebrated among
Nyingmapa Tibetan Buddhists in honour of
Padmasambhava as the founder of Buddhism
in Tibet.

Some *Mahayana* Buddhists also have festival
days for various *Bodhisattvas* and for the
founders of particular *temples* and *monasteries*.
In *Japanese* schools of Buddhism, the Spring
and Autumn equinoxes are celebrated as times
of change and for remembrance of the dead.

BUDDHIST ORGANISATIONS

Due to the lack of firm statistics on the
Buddhist population in the UK and the
question of how to categorise large numbers
of the ethnically Chinese population, it is
difficult to give any precise indication of the
relative proportions of the various traditions
and groups among Buddhists.

Buddhist Link Organisations

The Buddhist Society, the history of which
was described above, provides a central source
of information about Buddhism, running a
series of educational courses and publishing a
widely read journal. The Network of
Buddhist Organisations was formed in 1992
and now links fifty member bodies and
groups (including the Buddhist Society). It
provides a forum for discussion and a point of
contact for information and advice.

Theravada Organisations

Followers of the *Theravada* tradition in the
UK include many who are ethnically
European. There are also substantial groups of
people with personal or ancestral roots in the
traditional *Theravada* countries such as Sri
Lanka, Burma and Thailand. Another group
are the *Ambedkarites*, who are followers of Dr
Ambedkar who led a social movement in
India among low and "scheduled *caste*"
Indians, many of whom converted to
Buddhism from Hinduism.

A Sri Lankan *vihara* which opened in London in 1928 operated until 1940. In 1954, the London Buddhist Vihara was established with Sri Lankan teachers. A Thai Buddhist *vihara* of the traditional Thai style, known as the Buddhapadipa Temple, was opened in South West London in 1966 by the King and Queen of Thailand. Ananda Metteya's mission had been funded by the Burmese Buddhists who had also given substantial assistance to the Buddhist Society. In 1978, the Burmese community opened the West Midlands Buddhist Centre/Birmingham Buddhist Vihara.

In 1956 the English Sangha Trust was set up to establish a Western Theravada Sangha and in 1962 it founded the Hampstead Buddhist Vihara. In 1979, the Venerable Sumedho, an American-born *monk*, founded the Chithurst Forest Monastery with a group of western *monks* and *nuns* trained in the Thai forest tradition. This now has branches opened in Northumberland (1981), in Devon (1984), and in 1985 the Amaravati Buddhist Monastery was established near Hemel Hempstead. This Western Theravada Sangha should be distinguished from the Friends of the Western Buddhist Order (see below).

Mahayana Buddhist Organisations

The *Mahayana* tradition in Britain is represented by diverse religious and ethnic groups.

Tibetan Buddhist Organisations
In 1959 there was a great diaspora of Tibetan *Lamas* following the Lhasa uprising against Chinese rule and the flight into exile of the *Dalai Lama*. European Buddhists offered help to Tibetan refugees such as Chogyam Trungpa, a one time Abbot of the Surmang group of monasteries in Tibet, who came to study in Oxford in 1963. In 1967 he and Akong Rinpoche, the former Abbot of the Drolma Lhakhang Monastery, founded the first Tibetan Buddhist Centre in the West at Johnstone House in Dumfriesshire. It was named Samye Ling, after the first Buddhist

monastery in Tibet. There are now many other *Tibetan Buddhist* centres in the UK.

The *Kagyupa* and *Gelugpa* schools are numerically the strongest *Tibetan* Buddhist traditions in Britain. An example of a centre in the *Kagyupa* school is the Samye Ling monastery in Eskdalemuir, Scotland built in traditional Tibetan style. The Jamyang Centre in London, begun in 1978 by pupils of Lama Thubten Yeshe and the *Lam Rim* centres in Bristol and Wales are examples of *Gelugpa* centres. The *New Kadampa* tradition emerged from the *Gelugpa* school and has centres and groups throughout the UK under the leadership of Geshe Kelsang Gyatso. Four *Sakyampa* centres have been established with the *Dechen* community directed by the English Lama Nyakpa Jampa Thaye.

Zen Buddhist Organisations
The Japanese Buddhist Dr D T Suzuki attended the 1936 World Congress of Faiths in London and, although some of his work was concerned with *Pure Land* and other forms of *Mahayana* Buddhism, he is considered to have introduced *Zen* to the West, and specifically the *Rinzai* school. Both *Rinzai* and *Soto* schools can be found in Britain together with the Korean *Son* and the Chinese *Ch'an*.

Rinzai Zen is practised at The Buddhist Society and at Shobo-an, a training temple founded in 1984 in North London by the Venerable Myokyo-ni. There are other *Zen* organisations in London and in the rest of the country, the largest of which is the Throssel Hole Priory, founded in Northumberland in 1972 by Revd Master Ptnh Jiy-Kensett, a training monastery and retreat centre, which practises *Soto Zen*.

Pure Land Buddhist Organisations
Shin Buddhism has been the most influential *Pure Land* school in Britain. The Shin Buddhist Association of Great Britain was founded in 1976 and the Pure Land Buddhist Fellowship in 1977.

Shingon Mahayana Buddhism

Shingon is a Sino-Japanese form of esoteric Buddhism based on the *Mahavairocara (Great Sun) Sutra* and the *Kongocho (Diamond Peak) sutra*. The first Shingon Association in the west was founded in 1958 and the Kongoryuji Temple in Norfolk is a centre for *Shingon* Buddhism.

Some Other Japanese Buddhist Groups

Soka Gakkai International of the UK and a range of similar Japanese groups tend to have a lay orientation and non-ascetic approach to Buddhist practice. *Soka Gakkai* is one such movement which came to Britain during the 1980s. It is based on faith in the power of the mantra *Nam-myoho-renge-kyo* (as distinct from the *Namu-myoho-renge-kyo* mantra of some other schools); on study of Buddhist teaching as presented by Nichiren and his successors; and the twice daily practice of reciting the mantra, which is the Japanese name of the *Lotus Sutra*, in front of the *Gohonzon* (a scroll on which the *mantra* is written).

Other Japanese groups include Rissho Kosei-Kai, founded by Revd Nikkyo Niwano and Mrs M Nagakuma, Reiyukai, and the Nipponzan Myohoji Order, founded by Nichidatsu Fuji. The last of these is well-known for its campaign for peace and the Peace Pagodas it built in Milton Keynes (1980) and Battersea in London (1985). It is based on the recitation of the mantra, *Namu-myoho-renge-kyo*.

Friends of the Western Buddhist Order

In 1967, the Venerable Sangharakshita, an Englishman who was ordained into the three major traditions of Buddhism while living in India, returned to the UK and established the Western Buddhist Order later supported by the Friends of the Western Buddhist Order (FWBO). This is a new Buddhist movement which draws upon all the traditions of Eastern Buddhism whilst maintaining a strong engagement with Western culture. It seeks to find new ways of living out the basic principles of Buddhism through the commitment of its members to the *Three Jewels* shared by all Buddhists. Many people involved in the FWBO live in single-sex residential communities and work in co-operative right-livelihood businesses, but there are also those who live monastic lives in retreat centres and others who have ordinary jobs.

Social Action Groups

A number of Buddhist groups have emerged in recent years to address social issues from the perspective of Buddhism. These include the Network of Engaged Buddhists and groups with specific foci such as the Buddhist Hospice Trust.

Personnel

The *samgha* or community of *monks* and *nuns* is central in traditional Buddhism. *Monks* are known as *bhikshu/bhikkhus* and *nuns* as *bhikshuni/bhikkhunis*, which literally means "almsmen" and "almswomen", reflecting the originally mendicant lifestyle of the *samgha*. The original role of the *samgha* was to work for their own spiritual development and to share the *dharma* with others, but Buddhist *monks* have often also called upon them to officiate in *priest*-like ways at rites of passage, and they have also often become involved in tasks related to education and health care.

The *Theravada samgha* can be recognised by their shaved heads and orange or ochre robes. They do not personally possess money and do not eat after mid-day. They differ from Christian *monks* and nuns in that they do not take vows of obedience and the vows that they do take are not necessarily binding upon them for life. Indeed, among Thai and Burmese Buddhists it is typical for young men temporarily to take on the *sharmanera* (lower) *ordination* as a kind of rite of passage into adulthood.

Those who take the lower *ordination* are called upon to live by the *Ten Precepts*. These include the *Five Precepts* together with the refraining from misuse of the senses being extended to total chastity. In addition, it entails refraining from eating at unseasonable times; dancing, singing and visiting musical shows; and wearing garlands, perfumes and unguents, finery and adornments; high or luxurious beds; and the handling of gold, silver or money in general.

After higher *ordination, monks* and *nuns* live according to the full *monastic* code known as the *vinaya* which entails extensive additional obligations set out in the 227 disciplinary rules for *monks* and 348 for *nuns*. The *ordination* of women as *nuns* was, in the Buddha's day, a revolutionary innovation and the *Buddha* only instituted the *bhikshuni* order after the pleading of his widowed foster mother and at the request of the *monk* Ananda.

The *order* was founded on the basis that the *nuns* followed additional special rules, intended for their protection. Generally, Buddhism argues for the equality of men and women in their spiritual potential and on several occasions Gautama defended the equality of the sexes in this regard. In the highest realms of *rebirth* a person or entity is not conceived of as having any gender.

The *bhikshuni* order survived only in *Northern Buddhism*. In *Tibetan* Buddhism there was controversy over the validity of their *ordination*, which did not come from the Indian line but was introduced in the twelfth century. In other *Mahayana* schools, the spiritual equality of women and men is recognised and women receive full *ordination* and follow the same *precepts* as men.

Today, in the *Theravada* tradition, *nuns* may again be *ordained* and the total number of *nuns* worldwide in all traditions has been increasing throughout this century. In recent times, especially in the West, a *Theravada nuns"* *samgha* has been re-established. The *Northern*, and especially the *Far Eastern, Transmission*, have always included *nuns*, who live on a similar basis to *monks*. Their codes of living differ according to the different schools to which they belong.

In the *Tibetan* tradition a *Lama* (teacher) is often a *monk* or a *nun*, but does not need to be so, and there are lay people who are skilful teachers and are revered as *Lamas*. In the *Far Eastern Mahayana* schools, except for the *Pure Land School*, both *monks* and *nuns* shave their heads at first *ordination* and live in monastic communities. Robes, rules and practices differ from school to school, but all are dedicated to the *Bodhisattva Way*, wishing to be of benefit to all living beings. In the *Mahayana* tradition, a lay person of either gender may take a *Bodhisattva* commitment and may then be recognised as being of higher spiritual attainment than either a *monk* or a *nun*.

In the *Japanese* schools, the teachers are generally *monks* and *nuns* or *ministers*, although in Britain there are also a number of *lay ministers* who have a limited role in teaching. In the *Rinzai* school, *koans* are only taught by teachers authorised to do so. In all *Japanese* schools a *priesthood* – as distinct from *monks* and *nuns* – was introduced after the Meiji Restoration of 1868, when the Japanese Government encouraged temple incumbents/ *abbots* to marry (although *nuns* remained celibate). Today, there are training monasteries with celibate *monks* or *nuns* and a celibate *Zen Master*, and temples with *ordained priests* who may be married and train *postulants* for entry into a *monastery*.

In the Western Buddhist Order members are ordained either as *Dharmacharis* (males) or as *Dharmacharinis* (females). Some members of the Order live monastic lifestyles whilst others have families. Within the Order these differences in lifestyle are not seen as being differences in status. All members of the Order follow *Ten Precepts* (a different list from the ten *shramanera precepts* of the *Theravada monastic* tradition) which lay down basic ethical principles governing actions of body, speech and mind.

FURTHER READING

Almond, P C, *The British Discovery of Buddhism*, Cambridge University Press, Cambridge, 1988.

Armstrong, K, *Buddha*, Weidenfield and Nicholson, London, 2000.

Batchelor, S, *The Awakening of the West: The Encounter of Buddhism and Western Culture*, Aquarian Press, London, 1994.

Batchelor, S, "Buddhism and European Culture", in Gill, S, D'Costa G and King, U (eds), *Religion in Europe: Contemporary Perspectives*, Kok Pharos, Kampen, 1994, pp 86-104.

Bechert, H and Gombrich, R, *The World of Buddhism*, Thames and Hudson, London, 1984.

Buddhist Society, The, *The Buddhist Directory*, The Buddhist Society, London, 1997.

Connolly, P and Erricker, C, *The Presence and Practice of Buddhism*, West Sussex Institute of Higher Education, 1985.

Conze, E, *Buddhist Scriptures*, Penguin, Harmondsworth, 1959.

Conze, E, *A Short History of Buddhism*, Allen and Unwin, 1980.

Dalai Lama, H H, *The World of Tibetan Buddhism*, Wisdom Publications, Boston, 1995.

Gombrich, R, *Theravada Buddhism: A Social History from Ancient Benares to Modern Colombo*, Routledge and Kegan Paul, London, 1988.

Goonewardene, A, *Introducing Buddhism*, Paper 2; *Life of the Buddha*, Paper 4; *Life of the Buddha*, Paper 5; *Geographical Development of Buddhism In Outline, Part I*, Paper 6, *Geographical Development of Buddhism in Outline, Part II*, Paper 7; *The Buddhist Councils*, Paper 8; *The Schools and Traditions of Buddhism (in outline)* and *Their Common Features*, Paper 9; *The Fundamental Buddhist Philosophy of the Four Noble Truths and the Noble Eightfold Path*, Buddhism for Schools and Colleges Series, Papers 10 and 11, The Buddhist Society, London, 1989-1993.

Green, D, "Buddhism in Britain: Skilful Means or Selling Out?", in Badham, P (ed), *Religion, State and Society in Modern Britain*, Edwin Mellen Press, Lampeter, 1989, pp 277-291.

Gross, R, *Soaring and Settling: Buddhist Perspectives on Contemporary Social and Religious Issues*, Continuum, New York, 1998.

Harris, E, *What Buddhists Believe*, Oneworld, Oxford, 1998.

Harvey, P, *An Introduction to Buddhism: Teachings, History, and Practices*, Cambridge University Press, Cambridge, 1990.

Harvey, P, *An Introduction to Buddhist Ethics: Foundations, Values and Issues*, Cambridge University Press, Cambridge, 2000.

Hawkins, B, *Buddhism*, Routledge, London, 1999.

Humphreys, C, *Sixty Years of Buddhism in England 1907-1967: A History and a Survey*, The Buddhist Society, London, 1968.

Kasulis, T, *Zen Action, Zen Person*, UPH, 1981.

Keown, D, *Buddhism: A Very Short Introduction*, Oxford University Press, Oxford, 2000.

King, R, *Indian Philosophy: An Introduction to Hindu and Buddhist Thought*, Edinburgh University Press, Edinburgh, 1999.

Lopez, D, *Prisoners of Shangri-La: Tibetan Buddhism and the West*, University of Chicago Press, Chicago, 1999.

Myokyo-ni, *The Zen Way*, The Zen Centre, London, 1978.

Myokyo-ni, *Gentling the Bull*, The Zen Centre, London, nd.

Pauling, C, *Introducing Buddhism*, Windhorse Publications, Glasgow, 1993.

Powell, A, *Living Buddhism*, British Museum, London, 1989.

Powers, J, *Introduction to the Tibetan Buddhism*, Snow Lion, Ithaca, New York, 1995.

Robinson, R and Johnson, W, *The Buddhist Religion*, 3rd edition, Wadsworth, 1982.

Saddhatissa, Venerable H, *The Buddha's Way*, Allen and Unwin, London, 1971.

Sangharakshita, Venerable, *New Currents in Western Buddhism*, Windhorse Publications, Glasgow, 1990.

Snelling, J, *The Buddhist Handbook: A Complete Guide to Buddhist Teaching and Practice*, Rider, London, 1987.

Snelling, J, *The Elements of Buddhism*, Element Books, Dorset, 1990.

Subhuti, *Buddhism for Today*, Element Books, London, 1983.

Suzuki, Shunryu, *Zen Mind, Beginner's Mind*, Weatherhill, New York, 1970.

Walpola, R, *What the Buddha Taught*, Oneworld, Oxford, 1998.

Williams, P, *Mahayana Buddhism: The Doctrinal Foundations*, Routledge and Kegan Paul, London, 1989.

Wisdom Publications, *The International Buddhist Directory*, Wisdom Publications, London, 1984.

BUDDHIST UNITED KINGDOM ORGANISATIONS

Together with a number of Buddhist bodies set up to operate beyond local and regional boundaries, this list of UK-wide Buddhist organisations also includes a number of monasteries or centres. In some cases these include more than one centre in a particular tradition and/or movement. Whilst these are based in particular localities (and some may also therefore be found listed in the regional or local sections of this chapter), they are included in this section because they are also points of reference for wider networks which look to them for guidance and support.

Ambedkar International Mission*
Buddha Vihara, 84 Dacre Road, Plaistow, London E13 0PR
Tel: (020) 8470 1879 **Fax:** (020) 8470 8898
Email: bhanteji.n@virgin.net
Website: http://www.buddhavihara.org.uk/
Contact: Bhikkhu Nagasena
Position: Patron/Chairman
Activities: Worship/practice/meditation, community centre, newsletter/journal, visits, inter-faith
Traditions: Theravada
Movements: Ambedkarite, Samatha, Vipassana
Other Languages: Hindi, Thai, Sinhalese, Burmese
Free, daily meditation classes. All are welcome. Regular Dharma discussion held on every first Sunday of the month - in the evening 6-8pm.

Amida Trust*
12 Coventry Road, Narborough, Leicester LE9 5GB
Tel: (0116) 2867476
Email: amida@amida.demon.co.uk
Website: http://www.amidatrust.com
Contact: Sr Prasada
Position: Order Member
Activities: Worship/practice/meditation, central body, newsletter/journal, resources
Traditions: Multi-traditional
The Trust has an international membership and promotes projects in East Europe and the "Third World". It does humanitarian, psychotherapeutic, educational and pastoral work, and religious vocational training. Moving to Leicester in Summer 2001, email and website will stay the same.

Aukana Trust*
9 Masons Lane, Bradford-on-Avon BA15 1QN
Tel: (01225) 866821
Email: aukana@globalnet.co.uk
Website: http://www.aukana.org.uk/
Contact: Mr Stephen Small
Position: Trustee
Activities: Worship/practice/meditation, newsletter/journal, books, visits
Traditions: Theravada
Movements: Samatha, Vipassana
The Aukana Trust runs a registered charity that administers a meditation centre, the House of Inner Tranquillity, plus two monasteries, one for monks and one for nuns.

Barn, The*
The Barn, Lower Sharpham, Barton, Ashprington, Totnes TQ9 7DX
Tel: (01803) 732661 **Fax:** (01803) 732718
Email: barn@sharphamcollege.org
Website: http://www.sharpham-trust.org/
Contact: The Managers
Activities: Resource
Traditions: Multi-Traditional
Affiliations: Sharpham Trust
We promote organic gardening, meditation, yoga and community living. We hold retreats, Sunday-Sunday throughout the year.

Britain Burma Trust*
1 Old Church Lane, London NW9 8TG
Tel: (020) 8200 6898
Contact: Patricia Grey
Position: Trustee/Secretary

British Buddhist Association*
11 Biddulph Road, London W9 1JA
Tel: (020) 7286 5575 **Fax:** (020) 7289 5545
Email: enquiries@britishbuddhistassociation.org.uk
Contact: A Haviland-Nye
Position: Director
Contact Email:
a.haviland-nye@britishbuddhistassociation.org.uk
Activities: Worship/practice/meditation, resources
Traditions: Western
Movements: Maha Bodhi
Promotes educational, religious and meditation aspects of the Buddha's teaching at evening and weekend sessions. It is non-sectarian and seeks to express devotion in ways suitable to Western practitioners.

British Shingon Buddhist Association*
Kongoryuji Temple, 29 London Road, East Dereham NR19 1AS
Tel: (01362) 693692 **Fax:** (01362) 693962
Email: kongoryuji@x-stream.co.uk
Website: http://website.lineone.net/~kongoryuji
Contact: Shifu Nagaboshi Tomio
Position: Head Teacher
Activities: Worship/practice/meditation, umbrella body, youth, elderly, women, newsletter/journal, books, inter-faith, resources
Traditions: Shingon
Movements: Gelugpa, Kagyupa, Maha Bodi, Rinzai Zen, Rissho Kosei-Kai, Samatha, Soto Zen, Vipassana, Chen-yen
Other Languages: Japanese, Sanskrit, Croatian

Affiliations: Network of Buddhist Organisations; European Buddhist Union
The Association provides study and retreat facilities for members. It sponsors training and teacher training in healing and remedial sciences according to Buddhist tradition.

Buddha Dharma Association*
12 Featherstone Road, Southall UB9 5AA
Tel: (020) 8571 5131 **Fax:** (020) 8575 3134
Position: Assistant Secretary
Activities: Worship/meditation, visits, youth, elderly, women,
Traditions: Theravada
Movements: Ambedkarite, Maha Bodhi
Other Languages: Hindi, Punjabi, Maharashti
Affiliations: London Buddhist Vihara; Federation of Ambedkarite and Buddhist Organisations.

Buddhapadipa Temple*
14 Calonne Road, Wimbledon, London SW19 5HJ
Tel: (020) 8946 1357 **Fax:** (020) 8944 5788
Email: buddhapadipa@hotmail.com
Website: http://www.buddhapadipa.org/
Contact: The Venerable Phrakru S Lom
Position: Temple Secretary
Contact Tel: (020) 8879 7542
Activities: Worship/practice/meditation, newsletter/journal, books, visits, inter-faith
Traditions: Theravada
Movements: Vipassana
Other Languages: Thai, Pali, Chinese
Affiliations: Thai Embassy
The Buddhapadipa Temple now holds a Buddhist Sunday School, and is a member of the Wimbledon and Merton Tourism Group.

Buddhavihara Temple*
5 Hampton Road, Aston, Birmingham B6 6AN
Tel: (0121) 5151518 **Fax:** (0121) 2401468
Email: laow.panyasiri@cableinet.co.uk
Website: http://www.watthaiuk.com/
Contact: Venerable Panyasiri
Position: Abbot
Activities: Worship/practice/meditation, community centre, newsletter, resource
Traditions: Theravada
Other Languages: Thai
Affiliations: Wat Sanghathan, Birmingham; Wat Buddhapadipa, London; Wat Srinagarindaravaram, Switzerland
The Temple runs most Thai festivals, Thai language and Buddhist studies, meditation and retreats.

Buddhism Psychology and Psychiatry Group*

8 Notre Dame Mews, Northampton NN1 2BG
Tel: (01604) 604608 **Fax:** (01604) 604531
Email: kedarnd@doctors.org.uk
Contact: Dr Kedar Nath Dwivedi
Position: Chair
Activities: Resource
Traditions: Multi-Traditional
A membership group and forum for sharing experience, interests and ideas regarding links and parallels between Buddhism and modern psychology, psychiatry and allied professions.

Buddhist Co-operative*

5 Hindmans Road, Dulwich, London SE22 9NF
Tel: (020) 8693 9951
Email: buddhistcoop@england.com
Website:
http://www.yell.co.uk/sites/buddhist-coop
Contact: Venerable U Dhammasami
Position: Spiritual Director
Activities: Resource, visits, youth, elderly, women, newsletter
Traditions: Multi-traditional
Movements: All movements
Other Languages: Burman
Affiliations: European Buddhist Union
Promoting the study of Buddhist Economics.

Buddhist Hospice Trust*

5 Grayswood Point, Norley Vale, Roehampton, London SW15 4BT
Tel: (020) 8789 6170
Email: dsibley@ukonline.co.uk
Website: http://www.buddhisthospice.cjb.net/
Contact: Mr Ray Wills
Position: Honorary Secretary
Activities: Newsletter/journal, resources
Traditions: Multi-Traditional
Affiliations: Network of Buddhist Organisations
The Buddhist Hospice Trust is primarily concerned with the spiritual care of the terminally ill. The Ananda Network is a nationwide visiting service offering spiritual friendship.

Buddhist Interhelp*

12 Shell Road, London SE13 7TW
Tel: (020) 8692 1737
Email: cm90@supanet.com
Contact: Ms Mai Nguyen
Position: General Secretary
Activities: Worship/practice/meditation, newsletter/journal, books, resources
Traditions: Theravada, Zen

Other Languages: Vietnamese
Affiliations: Community of Interbeing; Network of Buddhist Organisations; Plum Village, France
A registered charity since 1998. Sponsors various projects in Vietnam, holds mindfulness practices and organises retreats.

Buddhist Publishing Group*

Sharpham Coach Yard, Ashprington, Totnes TQ9 7UT
Tel: (01803) 732082 **Fax:** (01803) 732037
Email: buddhist.publishing@dial.pipex.com
Contact: Richard Charles St. Ruth
Position: Partner
Activities: Books
Traditions: Multi-Traditional
Affiliations: Network of Buddhist Organisations

Buddhist Society, The*

58 Eccleston Square, London SW1V 1 PH
Tel: (020) 7834 5858 **Fax:** (020) 7976 5238
Email: buddsoc@buddsoc.org.uk
Website: http://www.buddsoc.org.uk/
Contact: Mr Ronald Maddox
Position: General Secretary
Activities: Worship/practice/meditation, newsletter/journal
Traditions: Multi-Traditional
Affiliations: Network of Buddhist Organisations; World Federation of Buddhists; Inter Faith Network for the UK
Open to all who feel able to subscribe to its aims, the Society was founded in 1924 by Christmas Humphreys. It aims to publish and make known the principles of Buddhism and to encourage the study and practice of these principles.

Clear Vision Trust, The*

16/20 Turner Street, Manchester M4 1DZ
Tel: (0161) 8399579 **Fax:** (0161) 8394815
Email: clearvision@clear-vision.org
Website: http://www.clear-vision.org/
Contact: Dharmachari Bodhiketu
Position: Director
Activities: Youth, books, television, visits, resources
Traditions: Western
Movements: Friends of the Western Buddhist Order
Affiliations: Manchester Buddhist Centre; Friends of the Western Buddhist Order
A charitable trust promoting Buddhism through visual media. We supply teaching resources and teacher training and keep a substantial Buddhist photographic and video archive.

Community of Interbeing*
19 Shipka Road, London SW12 9QP
Tel: (020) 8673 5548
Website: http://www.interbeing.org.uk/
Contact: Glynis Roberts
Position: Secretary
A network of people who are inspired by the teachings and practice of Zen master, Thich Nhat Hahn, and who try to study and practise mindful living.

Dhanakosa Buddhist Retreat Centre*
Ledcreich, Balquhidder, Lochearnhead FK19 8PQ
Tel: (01877) 384213
Email: dhanakosa@compuserve.co
Website: http://www.dhanakosa.com/
Contact: Mr Gordon O'Connor
Position: Secretary
Activities: Worship/practice/meditation, community centre, women, newsletter/journal, resources
Traditions: Multi-traditional
Movements: Friends of the Western Buddhist Order
Affiliations: Glasgow Buddhist Centre, Friends of the Western Buddhist Order

Dharma School*
The White House, Ladies Mile Road, Patcham, Brighton BN1 8TB
Tel: (01273) 502055 **Fax:** (01273) 556580
Contact: Headteacher
Activities: Resource, visits, inter-faith
Traditions: Multi-Traditional
Affiliations: Theravadin Forest Sangha; Network of Buddhist Organisations; Tibetan Government in Exile
The Dharma School Trust was established in 1992 to provide high quality primary and secondary education. It currently runs a pre-school nursery and primary school for children aged 3-11 and is Buddhist in the values it imparts. Open to children of all backgrounds.

Dharmachakra*
P O Box 50, Cambridge CB1 3BG
Tel: (01223) 216821 **Fax:** (01223) 566568
Email: info@dharmachakra.com
Website: http://www.dharmachakra.com/
Contact: Mr Michael Venditozzi
Position: Manager
Activities: Resources
Traditions: Western

Movements: Friends of the Western Buddhist Order
A registered charity distributing CD lectures by Urgyen Sangharakshita, talks by other members of the Western Buddhist Order, and other audio material on Buddhism and meditation.

Dr Ambedkar Memorial Committee of Great Britain*
Buddha Vihara, Upper Zoar Street, Pennfields, Wolverhampton WV3 0HJ
Tel: (01902) 715094 **Fax:** (01902) 715094
Contact: Mr Mohan Lal
Position: General Secretary
Contact Tel: (01902) 730664
Activities: Worship/practice/meditation, community centre, youth, elderly, women, newsletter/journal, books, visits, inter-faith
Traditions: Theravada
Movements: Ambedkarite, Friends of the Western Buddhist Order, Maha Bodhi, Vipassana
Other Languages: Punjabi, Hindi, Sinhalese, Thai

Dzogchen Community UK*
2 Quickswood, London NW3 3SJ
Website:
http://www.redsandstonehill.net/dzogchen/
Contact: Geoffrey Blundell
Position: Secretary
Contact Tel: (020) 7586 1507
Contact Email: geoffgblundell@cs.com
Activities: Practice/meditation, community centre, newsletter/journal, books, newspaper
Traditions: Tibetan
Movements: Non-sectarian
Other Languages: Italian, French, German, Russian
Affiliations: MERIGAR, 58031, Arcidosso, GR, Italy
Dissemination of the teachings of Chogyal Namkhai Norbu.

Fa Yue Buddhist Monastery*
Cottage Street, Brierley Hill, Dudley DY5 1RE
Tel: (01384) 484552 **Fax:** (01384) 481209
Email: fayue@hotmail.com
Contact: Venerable Hin Hung Sik
Position: Abbot/Chairman
Activities: Worship/practice/meditation, youth, elderly, newsletter, visits
Traditions: Mahayana
Movements: Ch'an
Other Languages: Cantonese, Mandarin

*Federation of Ambedkarite and Buddhist Organisations UK**

Milan House, 8 Kingsland Road, Shoreditch, London E2 8DA
Tel: (020) 7729 6341 **Fax:** (020) 7729 6341
Contact: Mr C Gautam
Position: General Secretary
Activities: Media, umbrella body, newsletters, books, inter-faith
Traditions: Theravada
Movements: Ambedkarite, Vipassana
Other Languages: Hindi, Punjabi, Gujarati, Urdu
The Federation has been set up to propagate Ambedkar's thought and Buddhist ideas throughout the world. The Federation represents the amalgamation of many groups in the UK.

*Friends of the Western Buddhist Order (Communications)**

12 Park Road, Moseley, Birmingham B13 8AB
Tel: (0121) 4498272 **Fax:** (0121) 4498272
Email: communications@fwbo.org
Website: http://www.fwbo.org
Contact: Vishvapani
Position: Communications Officer
Activities: Resources
Traditions: Western
Movements: Friends of the Western Buddhist Order
The Communications Office handles contact with the media and those engaged in academic research.

*Friends of The Western Buddhist Order**

c/o London Buddhist Centre, 51 Roman Road, Bethnal Green, London E2 0HU
Tel: (020) 8981 1225 **Fax:** (020) 8980 1968
Email: info@lbc.org.uk
Website: http://www.lbc.org.uk/
Contact: Maitreyaraja
Position: Assistant Centre Director
Activities: Worship/meditation, visits, newsletters
Traditions: Multi-traditional
Movements: Friends of the Western Buddhist Order
Other Languages: Marathi, Hindi
Affiliations: Network of Buddhist Organisations; European Buddhist Union; Inter Faith Network for the UK
The Friends of the Western Buddhist Order seeks to apply the central principles of Buddhism in the context of the modern world through its thirty UK centres and retreat centres.

*Friends of the Western Buddhist Order Study Centre**

Blaenddol House, Corwen LL21 0EN
Tel: (01490) 460648
Email: vajra.kuta@virgin.net
Website: http://www.dharmavastu.org/
Contact: Dharmacari Jinaraja
Position: Secretary
Activities: Worship/practice/meditation, resources
Traditions: Western
Movements: Friends of the Western Buddhist Order
Other Languages: Hindi, German, Finnish, Spanish
Affiliations: Vajraloka Meditation Centre; Madhyamaloka, Office of the Western Buddhist Order

*Friends of the Western Buddhist Order Taraloka**

Taraloka Buddhist Retreat Centre for Women, Cornhill Farm, Bettisfield, Nr Whitchurch SY13 2LD
Tel: (01948) 710646 **Fax:** (01948) 710646
Email: enquiries@taraloka.org.uk
Website: http://www.taraloka.org.uk/
Contact: Dharmacarini Dharmapeta
Position: Secretary
Contact Email: admin@taraloka.org.uk
Activities: Worship/practice/meditation, women, newsletter/journal
Traditions: Multi-Traditional
Movements: Ambedkarite, Friends of the Western Buddhist Order
Other Languages: German, Dutch
Affiliations: Friends of the Western Buddhist Order, Manchester Buddhist Centre; Friends of the Western Buddhist Order, Central, Birmingham
Our retreats are for women of all ages and from all walks of life to explore the relevance of meditation and Buddhist teaching to our lives.

*Indian Buddhist Society UK**

Anad Bhawan, 9 Carlyle Road, Edgbaston, Birmingham B16 9BH
Contact: Hind Ratan Sansari Lal
Position: General Secretary
Contact Tel: (0121) 4557285
Activities: Worship/practice/meditation, visits
Traditions: Theravada
Movements: Maha Bodhi
Other Languages: Hindi, Punjabi

Institute of Oriental Philosophy European Centre*

Taplow Court, Taplow, Maidenhead SL6 0ER
Tel: (01628) 591213 **Fax:** (01628) 591244
Email: jc@iopec.org
Contact: Jamie Cresswell
Position: Director
Contact Email: jc@iopec.org
Activities: Resource, books
Traditions: Nichiren
Movements: Soka Gakkai
Other Languages: Japanese
Affiliations: SGI-UK

A research and study centre based on a growing library (11,000 books) on Buddhism and related religions/philosophies. We hold lectures and seminars in all areas of Asian religion and Buddhism.

International Ambedkar Institute UK*

90 Pennine Way, Kettering NN16 9AX
Tel: (01536) 522057
Email: sarvasinni@aol.com
Contact: Nagan Srinivasan
Activities: Resource
Traditions: Theravada
Movements: Ambedkarite
Other Languages: Kannada, Hindi, Punjabi, Urdu
Affiliations: Federation of Ambedkarite and Buddhist Organisations in the UK

International Buddhist Progress Society, UK*

Fo Guang Shan Temple, 84 Margaret Street, London W1W 8TD
Tel: (020) 7636 8394 **Fax:** (020) 7580 6220
Email: ibpslondon@hotmail.com
Contact: Venerable Man Jang
Position: Director
Activities: Worship/practice/meditation, youth, elderly, women, newsletter/journal, books, newspapers, visits, inter-faith, resources
Traditions: Zen
Movements: Ch'an
Other Languages: Mandarin, Cantonese
Affiliations: Buddhist Light International Association, London

Holds regular Sunday Services and other services, for example, New Year, Buddhist festivals and celebrations. Any social group/any religious background are welcome to attend.

International Zen Association, UK*

91-93 Gloucester Road, Bishopston, Bristol BS7 8AT
Tel: (0117) 9424347

Email: bristol@zen-izauk.org
Website: http://www.zen-izauk.org/
Contact: Ms Carol Young
Position: Chairperson
Activities: Worship/meditation, umbrella body, visits, newsletter
Traditions: Zen
Movements: Soto Zen
Other Languages: French, Spanish, German
Affiliations: Association Zen Internationale, France National headquarters, with Zen sitting groups throughout the country. These are open to the public. Also organises Zen retreats regularly.

Jodo Shu Foundation of Great Britain*

48 Laburnum Crescent, Kettering NN16 9PJ
Tel: (01536) 517782
Traditions: Zen
Movements: Jodo Shu

Kagyu Samye Ling*

Samye Ling Tibetan Centre Tibetan Buddhist Monastery, Eskdalemuir, Langholm DG13 0QL
Tel: (01387) 373232 **Fax:** (01387) 373222
Email: scotland@samyeling.org
Website: http://www.samyeling.org/
Contact: J Tsering
Position: Bookings Office
Activities: Worship/meditation, visits, resources
Traditions: Tibetan
Movements: Kagyupa
Other Languages: Tibetan
Affiliations: ROKPA International

Founded in 1967, Samye Ling has branches throughout Europe and Africa. It established Rokpa Foreign Aid, the Holy Island Project and the Tara College of Tibetan Medicine.

Karuna Trust*

St Mark's Studio, Chillingworth Road, London N7 8QJ
Tel: (020) 7700 3434 **Fax:** (020) 7700 3535
Email: info@karuna.org
Website: http://www.karuna.org/
Contact: Peter Joseph
Position: Director
Traditions: Multi-Traditional
Movements: Friends of the Western Buddhist Order
Affiliations: North London Buddhist Centre; Friends of the Western Buddhist Order

A Buddhist-inspired charity supporting long term development work in India. Projects are run in the areas of education, health, and skill-training for all communities affected by poverty and discrimination.

Lam Rim Buddhist Centre*
Pentwyn Manor Penrhos, Raglan, Usk NP15 2LE
Tel: (01600) 780383 **Fax:** (01600) 780383
Email: david@lamrim.org.uk
Website: http://www.lamrim.org.uk/
Contact: Venerable Geshe Damcho Yonten
Position: Spiritual Director
Activities: Worship/meditation, resources, umbrella body, visits, youth, elderly, women, books, inter-faith
Traditions: Tibetan
Movements: Gelugpa
Other Languages: German, Tibetan
Affiliations: Network of Buddhist Organisations; Drepung Loseling Monastery, South India

Lights In The Sky*
39a Lough Road, London N7 8RH
Tel: (020) 7607 9480 **Fax:** (020) 7607 9480
Email: surya@intonet.co.uk
Contact: Suryaprabha
Position: Director
Activities: Resource, media
Traditions: Western
Movements: Friends of the Western Buddhist Order
Other Languages: Spanish
Affiliations: North London Buddhist Centre; Friends of the Western Buddhist Order (Central)
We make videos and films of interest to (Western) Buddhists, though they also suit a wide audience. We have training facilities and modern computer-based editing. Work to commission also undertaken.

Linh-Son Buddhist Association in the UK*
76 Beulah Road, Norwood, London SE19 3EW
Tel: (020) 8771 5933
Contact: Secretary
The Vietnamese Buddhist Temple serves the Chinese as well as the Vietnamese community. It is under the guidance of the Venerable Thich Huyen Vi and, in England, the Venerable Thich Tri Camh (resident).

London Buddhist Vihara*
Dharmapala Building, The Avenue, Chiswick, London W4 1UD
Tel: (020) 8995 9493 **Fax:** (020) 8994 8130
Email: Londonvihara@virgin.net
Website: http://www.londonbuddhistvihara.co.uk/
Contact: Most Venerable Vajiragnana
Position: Head of the Vihara

Activities: Worship/practice/meditation, youth, newsletter/journal, visits, inter-faith, resources
Traditions: Theravada
Movements: Maha Bodhi, Vipassana
Other Languages: Sinhalese
Affiliations: Network of Buddhist Organisations; The Anagarika Dharmapala Trust

Longchen Foundation*
30 Beechey Avenue, Old Marston, Oxford OX3 0JU
Tel: (01865) 725569 **Fax:** (01865) 725569
Email: enquiries@longchen.demon.co.uk
Website: http://www.longchen.demon.co.uk/
Contact: Sally Sheldrake
Position: Administrator
Activities: Worship/practice/meditation, central body, newsletters, books, resource
Traditions: Tibetan
Movements: Nyingma, Kagyu
Other Languages: German, French
Offers training in the practice of Buddhism through day and weekend courses and retreats, oriented to the Mahayana and Dzogchen, led by Rigdzin Shikpo, the principal teacher.

Lumbini Nepalese Buddha Dharma Society UK*
11 Mulberry Drive, Slough SL3 7JU
Tel: (01753) 549370
Website: http://www.lumbini.org.uk/
Contact: Dr Dharma Shakya
Position: Secretary
Contact Email: dharma_shakya@hotmail.com
Activities: Worship/practice/meditation
Traditions: Multi-traditional
Other Languages: Nepali, Newari, Tamang, Gurung
Publication of the Society's journal "Lumbini".

Network of Buddhist Organisations UK*
The Old Courthouse, 43 Renfrew Road, Kennington, London SE11 4NA
Tel: (020) 8682 3442 **Fax:** (020) 7582 5797
Contact: Paul Seto
Position: Honorary Secretary
Activities: Resource, umbrella body
Traditions: Multi-Traditional
Affiliations: Inter Faith Network for the UK
A representative body that shares the experience and resources of many of the various Buddhist teaching, charitable, educational and cultural organisations and individual practitioners in the UK.

Network of Engaged Buddhists (UK)*
Truedrhiwsebon, Cwmrheidol, Aberystwyth
SY23 3NB
Tel: (01970) 880603
Email: kennora@onetel.net.uk
Website: http://www.engaged_buddhists.org.uk
Contact: Ken Jones
Position: Secretary
Contact Tel: (01970) 880603
Contact Email: kennore@onetel.net.uk
Activities: Newsletters, inter-faith, resource
Traditions: Non-denominational
Affiliations: International Network of Engaged
Buddhists
Engaged Buddhism is engagement in caring and
service, in social and environmental protest and
analysis, and in non-violence as a creative way of
overcoming conflicts.

New Kadampa Tradition*
NKT Office, Conishead Priory, Ulverston
LA12 9QQ
Tel: (01229) 588533 **Fax:** (01229) 588533
Email: kadampa@dircon.co.uk
Website: http://www.kadampa.net/
Contact: James A Belither
Position: Secretary
Activities: Umbrella body, books
Traditions: Western
Movements: New Kadampa
Other Languages: Spanish, German, French,
Portuguese
The NKT is a charitable organisation which helps to
facilitate and co-ordinate the activities, such as
retreats, of its members and their centres, who
remain legally and financially separate.

Nipponzan Myohoji (Peace Pagoda)*
Willen, Milton Keynes MK15 0BA
Tel: (01908) 663652 **Fax:** (01908) 663652
Contact: Revd Handa Astrid
Position: Abbot
Activities: Worship/practice/meditation, visits,
inter-faith, resources
Traditions: Nichiren
Movements: Nipponzan Myhohoji
Other Languages: Japanese, Dutch
Nipponzan Myohoji is a small order of mostly
Japanese monks and nuns dedicated to prayer, action,
for example, peacewalks, vigils etc. Visitors and help
are always welcome.

Nipponzan Myohoji*
The London Peace Pagoda, c/o Park Office, Albert
Bridge Road, London SW11 4NJ
Tel: (020) 7228 9620 **Fax:** (020) 7228 9620
Contact: Revd G Nagase
Position: Resident Monk
Activities: Worship/meditation, visits, inter-faith
Traditions: Nichiren
Movements: Nipponzan Myhohoji
Other Languages: Japanese

Office of Tibet*
Tibet House, 1 Culworth Street, London
NW8 7AF
Tel: (020) 7722 5378 **Fax:** (020) 7722 0362
Email: tibetlondon@gn.apc.org
Contact: T Samdup
Position: Press and Information
Activities: Newsletters, inter-faith
Traditions: Tibetan
Movements: Multi-Movements
Other Languages: Tibetan
Established in 1981, the Office is the official agency
of the Dalai Lama. It represents Tibetan affairs in the
UK, supervises arrangements for his visits, and looks
after the welfare of Tibetans living in the UK and
Northern Europe.

Padmaloka Retreat Centre*
Lesingham House, The Covey, Surlingham,
Norwich NR14 7AL
Tel: (01508) 538112 **Fax:** (01508) 538076
Email: padmaloka@compuserve.com
Contact: Dharmachari Mahjupriya
Position: Manager
Activities: Worship/practice/meditation
Traditions: Multi-traditional
Movements: Friends of the Western Buddhist
Order
Other Languages: Spanish, German
Affiliations: Norwich Buddhist Centre; Friends of
the Western Buddhist Order Madhyakaloka,
Birmingham.
The Centre is focused mainly around training for
men who want to be ordained into the Friends of
the Western Buddhist Order. It also runs a number of
retreats open to beginners as well.

Pure Land Buddhist Fellowship*
c/o 3 Field Road, Kingham, Chipping Norton
OX7 6XR
Tel: (01608) 658425 **Fax:** (01608) 658425
Contact: Jim Pym

Activities: Newsletter/journal, inter-faith
Traditions: Pure Land
Movements: Jodo Shin Shu, Jodo, Jishu
Non-sectarian group of persons interested in and practising Pure Land Buddhism.

Reiyukai*
Unit 24, Saint Mary's Works, Duke Street, Norwich NR3 1QA
Tel: (01603) 630857 **Fax:** (01603) 760749
Email: reiyukai.uk@tinyworld.co.uk
Contact: Lyn Cashley
Position: Secretary
Contact Tel: (07890) 913803
Activities: Practice/meditation, community centre, youth, elderley, women, visits, inter-faith, resources
Traditions: Nichiren
Other Languages: Japanese, Thai
We are committed to the promotion and encouragement of inter faith understanding as one way of contributing to world peace.

RIGPA Fellowship*
330 Caledonian Road, London N1 1BB
Tel: (020) 7700 0185 **Fax:** (020) 7609 6068
Email: 114335.615@compuserve.com
Contact: Sonia Magrath
Position: National Director
Contact Email: 106443.361@compuserve.com
Activities: Worship/practice/meditation, newsletter/journal, visits
Traditions: Tibetan
Movements: Nyingmapa

Rissho Kosei-Kai of the UK*
c/o International Association for Religious Freedom, 2 Market Street, Oxford OX1 3EF
Tel: (01865) 241131 **Fax:** (01865) 202746
Email: rkk-uk@jais.co.uk
Website: http://www.kosei-kai.or.jp/
Contact: Revd Megumi Hirota
Position: Representative
Activities: Worship/practice/meditation, inter-faith
Traditions: Multi-traditional
Movements: Rissho Kosei-Kai
Other Languages: Japanese
Affiliations: World Conference on Religions and Peace, UK Chapter; International Association for Religious Freedom

Rivendell Buddhist Retreat Centre*
Clillies Lane, High Hurstwood, Uckfield TN22 4AB
Tel: (01825) 732594

Email: info@fwborivendell.freeserve.co.uk
Contact: Dharmachari Jnanagarbha
Position: Community Member
Contact Email: Jnanagarbha@fwborivendell.freeserve.co.uk
Activities: Worship/practice/meditation, visits
Traditions: Western
Movements: Friends of the Western Buddhist Order
Affiliations: Friends of the Western Buddhist Order

Samatha Trust*
The Samatha Centre, Greenstreete, Llangunllo, Knighton LD7 1SP
Contact: David Hall
Position: Secretary
Contact Tel: (01223) 249732
Activities: Worship/practice/meditation, newsletter/journal, books, visits
Traditions: Theravada
Movements: Samatha

Sang-ngak-cho-dzong*
PO Box 65, Penarth CF64 1XY
Tel: (029) 2021 7517
Email: sang-ngak-cho-dzong@yahoogroups.com
Website: http://www.aroter.org/
Contact: Naljorma Sel-zer Pamo
Position: Administrative Secretary
Activities: Newsletter/journal
Traditions: Tibetan
Affiliations: Aro Gter Lineage
Founded to establish in the west the Ngakphang tradition of non-celibate, non-monastic practitioners. Spiritual directors are holders of the Aro gTer lineage which emanates from a succession of enlightened women.

Sayagyi U Ba Khin Memorial Trust*
International Meditation Centre, Splatts House, Heddington, Calne SN11 0PE
Tel: (01380) 850238 **Fax:** (01380) 850833
Email: mail@imc-uk.org
Website: http://www.ubakhin.com/
Contact: Miss Virginia Judkins
Position: Secretary
Activities: Worship/practice/meditation
Traditions: Theravada
Movements: Sayagyi U Ba Khin Tradition
Other Languages: German, Italian, French, Burmese
Affiliations: International Meditation Centre

Yangon, Myanmar

Ten day residential courses in Anapana and Vipassana Theravada Buddhist meditation held once a month beginning on Friday evening and ending the following Monday.

Shambhala Meditation Centre*

27 Belmont Close, Clapham, London SW4 7AY
Tel: (020) 7720 3207 **Fax:** (020) 7627 4224
Email: info@shambala.org.uk
Website: http://www.shambala.org.uk/
Contact: Linus Bewley
Position: Director
Contact Tel: (020) 8673 6115
Activities: Worship/practice/meditation, central body
Traditions: Tibetan
Movements: Kagyupa, Nyingmapa
Affiliations: Shambhala International

Sharpham College For Buddhist Studies And Contemporary Enquiry*

Sharpham College, Sharpham House, Ashprington, Totnes TQ9 7UT
Tel: (01803) 732521 **Fax:** (01803) 732037
Email: college@sharpaham-trust.org
Website: http://www.sharpham-trust.org/
Contact: Mr Colin Moore
Position: Manager
Contact Email: college@sharpham-trust.org
Activities: Worship/practice/meditation, resources
Traditions: Multi-Traditional
Movements: Non-denominational
Although inspired and informed by Buddhist teachings the college does not adhere to any school and does not require commitment to Buddhism as a belief system.

Society for the Advancement of Buddhist Understanding*

Joule Road, West Point Business Park, Andover SP10 3UX
Tel: (01264) 353123 **Fax:** (01264) 354883
Contact: Mr Hiroyuki Suzuki
Position: Director
Traditions: Multi-Traditional
Other Languages: Japanese
Represents Bukkyo Dendo Kyokai in Japan. We propagate a modern understanding of the Buddhist spirit to reach out to strive towards global peace and harmony.

Soka Gakkai International UK*

Taplow Court, Taplow, Maidenhead SL6 0ER

Tel: (01628) 773163 **Fax:** (01628) 773055
Website: http://www.sgi-uk.org/
Contact: Mr Robert Samuels
Contact Tel: (01628) 591215
Contact Email: robert.samuels@sgi-uk.org
Activities: Central body, youth, women, newsletter/journal, books, inter-faith, resources
Traditions: Nichiren
Movements: Soka Gakkai
Affiliations: The Network of Buddhist Organisations
SGI - UK holds monthly discussion meetings in members' homes at over 300 venues throughout the UK to which guests are warmly welcomed.

Sri Lankan Sangha Sabha UK*

c/o London Buddhist Vihara, Dharmapala Building, The Avenue, Chiswick, London W4 1UD
Tel: (020) 8995 9493 **Fax:** (020) 8994 8130
Email: londonvihara@virgin.net
Website: http://www.londonbuddhistvihara.co.uk/
Contact: Most Venerable Medagama Vajiragnana
Position: President
Activities: Umbrella body, inter-faith
Traditions: Theravada
Other Languages: Sinhala
Affiliations: Inter Faith Network for the UK
The organisation links a number of Sri Lankan Buddhist centres in the country, including the London Buddhist Vihara which is the national focal point for this community.

Sri Saddhatissa International Buddhist Centre*

309-311 Kingsbury Road, Kingsbury, London NW9 9PE
Tel: (020) 8204 3301 **Fax:** (020) 8933 9395
Email: ssibc@dircon.co.uk
Website: http://www.ssibc.dircon.co.uk/
Contact: Venerable Galayaye Piyadassi
Position: Head of Centre
Activities: Worship/practice/meditation, youth, newsletter, books, visits, inter-faith, resources
Traditions: Theravada
Movements: World Buddhist Foundation
Other Languages: Sinhalese, Hindi, Burmese
Runs a newspaper called "Budumaga" for Buddhist, Christian and Hindu communities. Also runs Sinhala classes for children and adults, meditation classes, Buddhism classes for all and Pali classes.

Throssel Hole Buddhist Abbey*

Carrshield, Hexham NE47 8AL
Website: http://www.throssel.org.uk/
Contact: The Guestmaster

Position: The Guestmaster
Contact Tel: (01434) 345204
Contact Email: gd.thba@btclick.com
Activities: Worship/practice/meditation
Traditions: Zen Buddhism
Movements: Soto Zen
Other Languages: Dutch, German,

Tiratanaloka Women's Retreat Centre*
Aberclydach House, Aber, Tallybont-on-Usk
LD3 7YS
Tel: (01874) 676482
Email: tiratanaloka@compuserve.com
Contact: Dharmacharini Akasasuri
Position: Secretary
Activities: Worship/practice/meditation, central
body, women
Traditions: Multi-traditional
Movements: Friends of the Western Buddhist
Order

Vajrasana Retreat Centre, Suffolk*
c/o London Buddhist Centre, 51 Roman Road,
London, E2 0HU, Walsham Le Willows
Tel: (020) 8981 1225 **Fax:** (020) 8980 1960
Email: info@lbc.org.uk
Website: http://www.lbc.org.uk/
Contact: Dharmachari Maitreyaraja
Position: Assistant Centre Director
Activities: Worship/practice/meditation
Traditions: Multi-traditional
Movements: Friends of the Western Buddhist
Order
Other Languages: Marathi, Hindi, Spanish,
German
Affiliations: London Buddhist Centre; San
Francisco Buddhist Centre, USA
The Centre is the venue for Introductory Meditation
Retreats organised by the London Buddhist Centre.
It offers a beautiful context in the Suffolk
countryside in which individuals can practise and
explore the benefits of meditation.

Western Ch'an Fellowship*
c/o 24 Woodgate Avenue, Bury BL9 7RU
Tel: (0161) 7611945 **Fax:** (0161) 7633221
Website: http://www.w-c-f.org.uk/
Contact: Simon Child
Position: Secretary
Contact Email: secretary@w-c-f.org.uk
Activities: Worship/practice/meditation, central
body, umbrella body, newsletter/journal, visits, inter-
faith, resources

Traditions: Zen
Movements: Ch'an
Affiliations: Institute of Chung Hwa Buddhist
Culture, New York, USA; Ch'an Meditation Centre
We run residential meditation retreats throughout
the year, and we also have locally-based meditation
groups meeting in various towns and cities in the
UK.

White Plum Zen Sangha*
21a Aigburth Drive, Liverpool L17 4JQ
Tel: (0151) 7287829 **Fax:** (0151) 7093515
Email: dl.scott@virgin.net
Contact: David Dohi Scott
Position: Admin
Activities: Worship/practice/meditation
Traditions: Zen
Movements: Rinzai Zen, Soto Zen
Affiliations: Kanzeon Zen Sangha, Main Temple,
Salt Lake City, Utah, USA; Zen Mountain Center,
California, USA.

BUDDHIST REGIONAL AND LOCAL CENTRES AND ORGANISATIONS

There are a variety of forms of Buddhist local organisations listed in this directory. These include *viharas*, where *monks* live; centres with residential Buddhist communities, lay and/or monastic; as well as groups which meet in the homes of members or in hired premises. Some UK organisations also appear in these listings where these are also rooted in a region or a locality.

In this chapter, groups which appear as regional or county bodies are centres and groups that may be based in one geographical location, but which have a more wide-ranging function.

ENGLAND   169

NORTH EAST   169

YORKSHIRE AND THE HUMBER   170

NORTH WEST   173

EAST MIDLANDS   177

WEST MIDLANDS   179

EAST OF ENGLAND   182

LONDON   185

SOUTH EAST   191

SOUTH WEST   195

NORTHERN IRELAND   198

SCOTLAND   198

WALES   200

ENGLAND

NORTH EAST
Regional or County Bodies

Atisha Buddhist Centre*
9 Milton Street, Darlington DL1 4ET
Tel: (01325) 365265
Email: atisha@rmplc.co.uk
Contact: Kelsan Wangyal
Position: Resident Teacher
Activities: Worship/meditation, resources, visits, newsletter
Traditions: Mahayana
Movements: New Kadampa
Local Groups:
Barnard Castle
Durham
Hartlepool
Middlesborough
Newton Aycliffe

City, Town or Local Bodies

Aruna Ratanagiri: Harnham Buddhist Monastery*
2 Harnham Hall Cottages, Harnham, Belsay NE20 0HF
Tel: (01661) 881612 **Fax:** (01661) 881019
Email: community@ratanagiri.org.uk
Website: http://www.ratanagiri.org.uk/
Contact: Ajahn Bhikkhu Munindo
Position: Abbot
Contact Tel: (01661) 881612
Activities: Worship/practice/meditation, newsletter/journal, books, visits
Traditions: Theravada
Movements: Vipassana
Other Languages: English, Thai
Affiliations: Wat Pah Pong - Thailand

Atisha Buddhist Centre*
9 Milton Street, Darlington DL1 4ET
Tel: (01325) 365265
Email: atisha@rmplc.co.uk
Contact: Kelsan Wangyal
Position: Resident Teacher
Activities: Worship/meditation, resources, visits, newsletter
Traditions: Mahayana
Movements: New Kadampa

Local Groups:
Barnard Castle
Durham
Hartlepool
Middlesbrough
Newton Aycliffe

Durham Buddhist Meditation Group*
c/o 10 Cedar Drive, Farewell Hall, Durham
DH1 3TF
Tel: (0191) 3843913
Email: peter.harvey@sunderland.ac.uk
Contact: Professor Peter Harvey
Position: Meditation Teacher
Traditions: Theravada
Movements: Samatha
Affiliations: Samatha Trust

Newcastle Theravadin Buddhist Group*
c/o 221 Eastbourne Avenue, Gateshead NE8 4UL
Tel: (0191) 4782726 **Fax:** (0191) 4782726
Email: adaptvix@tesco.net
Contact: Andrew Hunt
Position: Co-ordinator
Activities: Worship/practice/meditation
Traditions: Theravada
Affiliations: Harnham Buddhist Monastery

Hexham Buddhist Group*
10 Tynedale Terrace, Hexham NE46 3JE
Tel: (01434) 602759
Email: robert.bluck@hexham.net
Contact: Robert Bluck
Position: Co-ordinator
Activities: Worship/practice/meditation
Traditions: Theravada
Movements: Vipassana
Affiliations: Harnham Buddhist Monastery;
Amaravati Buddhist Monastery; Forest Sangha

Compassion Buddhist Centre
c/o Ouston Street, Scotswood, Newcastle-upon-
Tyne NE15 6AS
Tel: (0191) 2746100

Newcastle Buddhist Centre*
Friends of the Western Buddhist Order, 12 Pilgrim
Street, Newcastle-upon-Tyne NE1 6QG
Tel: (0191) 2611722
Email: nbudc@aol.com
Contact: Dharmachari Nandavajra
Position: Chairman
Activities: Worship/practice/meditation, resources

Traditions: Western
Movements: Friends of the Western Buddhist
Order

**Newcastle University Buddhist Meditation
Society***
The Union, Newcastle University, Newcastle-upon-
Tyne NE1 7RU
Email: t.g.street@ncc.ac.uk
Contact: T G Street
Activities: Worship/practice/meditation, resources
Traditions: Western
Movements: Friends of the Western Buddhist
Order
Affiliations: Newcastle Buddhist Centre

**University of Sunderland Buddhist Meditation
Group***
c/o 10 Cedar Drive, Farewell Hall, Durham City
DH1 3TF
Tel: (0191) 3843913
Email: peter.harvey@sunderland.ac.uk
Contact: Professor Peter Harvey
Position: Meditation Teacher
Traditions: Theravada
Movements: Samatha
Affiliations: Samatha Trust

YORKSHIRE AND THE HUMBER
Regional or County Bodies

Atisha Buddhist Centre*
9 Milton Street, Darlington DL1 4ET
Tel: (01325) 365265
Email: atisha@rmplc.co.uk
Contact: Kelsan Wangyal
Position: Resident Teacher
Activities: Worship/meditation, resources, visits,
newsletter
Traditions: Mahayana
Movements: New Kadampa
Local Groups:
Richmond

Madhyamaka Buddhist Centre*
Kilnwick Percy Hall, Kilnwick Percy, Pocklington,
York YO42 1UF
Tel: (01759) 304832 **Fax:** (01759) 305962
Email: info@madhyamaka.org
Website: http://www.madhyamaka.org/
Contact: Adrian Jones
Position: Education Co-ordinator

Activities: Worship/practice/meditation, central body, visits, resources
Traditions: Tibetan
Movements: New Kadampa

Gyaltsabje Buddhist Centre*
13 Sharrow View, Netheredge, Sheffield S7 1ND
Tel: (0114) 2509663 **Fax:** (0114) 2509663
Email: info@sheffmeditation.org.uk
Website: http://www.sheffmeditation.org.uk/
Contact: Liz Williams
Position: Adminstrative Director
Contact Email: liz@sheffmeditation.org.uk
Activities: Worship/practice/meditation, central body, youth, newsletter/journal, visits, resources
Traditions: Tibetan
Movements: New Kadampa
Local Groups:
Doncaster

City, Town or Local Bodies

Beverley Mahayana Buddhist Centre*
Beverley, c/o Khedrubje Centre, 43 Hutt Street,
Beverley HU3 1QL
Tel: (01482) 229899

Bradford Dhammapala*
123 Cooper Lane, Bradford BD6 3PB
Tel: (01274) 670865
Contact: Ann Voist
Traditions: Theravada

Kagyu Changchub Choling*
c/o Interfaith Education Centre, Listerhills Road,
Listerhills, Bradford BD7 1HD
Tel: (01943) 602956
Email: bradford@dechen.org
Website: http://www.dechen.org/
Contact: Tenzin Phuntsok
Position: Co-ordinator
Activities: Worship/practice/meditation,
newsletters, books
Traditions: Tibetan
Movements: Kagyupa
Affiliations: Dechen Community, European
Buddhist Union (EBU)

Kashyapa Buddhist Centre*
299 Manningham Lane, Bradford BD8 7NA
Tel: (01274) 542065
Email: info@kashyapa.f9.co.uk
Website: http://www.kashyapa.f9.co.uk/

Contact: Mr Tim Allan
Position: Assistant Admin Director
Activities: Worship/practice/meditation, visits,
inter-faith
Traditions: Western
Movements: New Kadampa
Affiliations: Manjushri Mahayana Buddhist
Centre, Cumbria

Harrogate Serene Reflection Meditation Group*
7 Rudbeck Close, Harrogate HG2 7AG
Tel: (01423) 885490
Email: poldham@cwcom.net
Contact: Marjorie Patricia Oldham
Position: Lay Minister
Activities: Practice/meditation
Traditions: Zen
Movements: Soto Zen
Other Languages: English, French
Affiliations: Throssel Hole Buddhist Abbey; Order
of Buddhist Contemplatives

Kagyu Dechen Dzong*
Wharfedale House, 28 Harlow Moor Drive,
Harrogate HG2 0JY
Tel: (01423) 522233
Email: harrogate@dechen.org
Website: http://www.dechen.org/
Contact: Howard Peter Quinn
Position: Co-ordinator
Activities: Worship/practice/meditation,
newsletter, books
Traditions: Tibetan
Movements: Kagyupa
Affiliations: Dechen Community, European
Buddhist Union (EBU)

Hull Serene Reflection Meditation Group*
28 Salisbury Street, Hull HU5 3HA
Tel: (01482) 346784
Email: mike@horne28.freeserve.co.uk
Website:
http://www.horne28.freeserve.co.uk/srmgp.htm
Contact: Mike Horne
Position: Joint Organiser
Activities: Worship/practice/meditation,
newsletter/journal
Traditions: Zen
Movements: Soto Zen
Affiliations: Throssel Hole Buddhist Abbey; Order
of Buddhist Comtemplatives

Kagyu Naro Ling*
297 Park Avenue West, Chanterlands Avenue, Hull
HU5 4DG
Tel: (01482) 472040
Email: hull@dechen.org
Website: http://www.dechen.org/
Contact: Sue Sidwell
Position: Co-ordinator
Activities: Worship/practice/meditation,
newsletter, books
Affiliations: Dechen Community, European
Buddhist Union (EBU)

Zen Practice Centre Trust*
The White Cottage, Halsham, Hull HU12 0BY
Tel: (01964) 612296
Contact: John Oldham

Jamyang Buddhist Centre*
95 Harehills Avenue, Leeds LS8 4ET
Tel: (0113) 2624052

Leeds Buddhist Centre*
9 Heddon Place, Meanwood, Leeds LS6 4EL
Tel: (0113) 2783395
Email: enq@leedsbuddhistcentre.org
Website: http://www.leedsbuddhistcentre.org/
Contact: Samanatha
Activities: Meditation
Movements: Friends of the Western Buddhist
Order

Leeds Buddhist Council*
c/o 12 Granby View, Leeds LS6 3AT
Tel: (0113) 2752353

Leeds Buddhist Group*
28 Wellstone Drive, Leeds LS13 4DZ
Tel: (0113) 2564330
Contact: Kenneth Brown
Position: Secretary
Contact Email: kenneth.brown1@btinternet.com
Activities: Umbrella body, resources
Traditions: Multi-Traditional

Leeds SGI-UK
12 Granby View, Leeds LS6 3AT
Tel: (0113) 2752353

Leeds University Buddhist Society
c/o Students Union, Leeds University, Leeds
LS2 9JT
Contact: Secretary
Traditions: Western
Movements: Friends of the Western Buddhist
Order

Yorkshire Dales Mahayana Centre*
"Buckles", Caldbergh, Leyburn DL8 4RW
Tel: (01969) 640686
Activities: Worship/practice/meditation,
newsletter/journal
Traditions: Tibetan
Affiliations: Manjushri Centre

Dharmaratna Mahayana Buddhist Group*
Alexandra House, 1 Alexandra Road, Ashby,
Scunthorpe DN16 2SF
Tel: (0115) 9857356 **Fax:** (0115) 8421651
Email: info@akshobya.com
Website: http://www.akshobya.com/
Contact: Csaba Margitai
Position: Branch Co-ordinator
Activities: Worship/practice/meditation
Traditions: Western
Movements: New Kadampa

**Friends of the Western Buddhist Order
(Sheffield)***
499 Glossop Road, Broomhill, Sheffield S10 2QE
Tel: (0114) 2685070
Contact: Dharmacari Amoghavamsa
Position: Chairman
Activities: Worship/practice/meditation, youth,
elderly, women, visits
Traditions: Western

Gyaltsabje Buddhist Centre*
13 Sharrow View, Netheredge, Sheffield S7 1ND
Tel: (0114) 2509663 **Fax:** (0114) 2509663
Email: info@sheffmeditation.org.uk
Website: http://www.sheffmeditation.org.uk/
Contact: Liz Williams
Position: Adminstrative Director
Contact Email: liz@sheffmeditation.org.uk
Activities: Worship/practice/meditation, central
body, youth, newsletter/journal, visits, resources
Traditions: Tibetan
Movements: New Kadampa

**Sheffield Buddhist Centre (Friends of the
Western Buddhist Order)***
499 Glossop Road, Broomhill, Sheffield S10 2QE
Tel: (0114) 2685070
Contact: Dharmachari Amoghavamsa
Position: Chairman
Activities: Worship/practice/meditation
Traditions: Western
Movements: Friends of the Western Buddhist
Order

Sheffield Zen Buddhist Meditation Group*
c/o 115 Rustlings Road, Sheffield S11 7AB
Tel: (0114) 2686826
Contact: John Darwin
Position: Contact Person
Contact Tel: (0114) 2686826
Contact Email: johndarwin@compuserve.com
Activities: Worship/practice/meditation
Traditions: Zen
Movements: Soto Zen
Affiliations: Throssel Hole Priory,
Northumberland

Stillness on Sundays*
10 Beaufort Road, Broomhill, Sheffield S10 2ST
Email: ajohnwragg@yahoo.com
Contact: John Wragg
Position: Member
Contact Tel: (0114) 2663922
Activities: Meditation

Wakefield Mahayana Buddhist Centre*
Wakefield, c/o Losang Dragpa Centre, Todmorden
Tel: (01706) 812247
Email: info@losangdragpa.co.uk
Website: www.losangdragpa.com
Contact: Hanah

Madhyamaka Buddhist Centre*
Kilnwick Percy Hall, Kilnwick Percy, Pocklington,
York YO42 1UF
Tel: (01759) 304832 **Fax:** (01759) 305962
Email: info@madhyamaka.org
Website: http://www.madhyamaka.org/
Contact: Adrian Jones
Position: Education Co-ordinator
Activities: Worship/practice/meditation, central
body, visits, resources
Traditions: Tibetan
Movements: New Kadampa

NORTH WEST
Regional or County Bodies

Lancashire Buddhist Centre*
Richmond Chambers, Richmond Terrace,
Blackburn BB1 7AR
Tel: (01254) 889228
Website: http://www.geocities.com/fwboeastlancs
Contact: Kamalavajri
Position: Centre Director
Activities: Worship/meditation, visits, women,
books, inter-faith

Traditions: Western
Movements: Friends of the Western Buddhist
Order

Amitayus Centre*
173 Ruskin Road, Crewe CW2 7JX
Tel: (01270) 664050
Email: amitayus@netcentral.co.uk
Contact: Marilyn Jones
Activities: Worship/meditation, resources, visits,
newsletters
Movements: New Kadampa
Local Groups:
Chester

Duldzin Buddhist Centre*
25 Aigburth Drive, Sefton Park, Aigburth, Liverpool
L17 4JH
Tel: (0151) 7268900
Email: duldzin@centre25.freeserve.co.uk
Contact: Mr Roy Crate
Position: Administrative Director
Activities: Worship/practice/meditation, visits,
inter-faith, resources
Movements: New Kadampa
Local Groups:
Kailas

Vairochana Buddhist Centre*
84 Dudley Road, Whalley Range, Manchester
M16 8BR
Tel: (0161) 8617012 **Fax:** (0161) 882 0531
Email: relax@vairochana.freeserve.co.uk
Contact: Ian Povey
Position: Administrative Director
Activities: Worship/practice/meditation
Traditions: Tibetan
Movements: New Kadampa
Local Groups:
Stockport

Vajravarahi Buddhist Centre*
66 West Cliff, Preston PR1 8HU
Tel: (01772) 259094
Email: mail@vajravarahi.freeserve.co.uk
Website: http://www.vajravarahi.freeserve.co.uk/
Contact: Kelsang Pagpa
Position: Principal Teacher
Activities: Worship/practice/meditation, central
body, visits, resources
Traditions: Tibetan
Movements: New Kadampa

Manjushri Mahayana Buddhist Centre*
Conishead Priory, Priory Road, Ulverston
LA12 9QQ
Tel: (01229) 584029 **Fax:** (01229) 580080
Email: info@manjushri.org.uk
Website: http://www.manjushri.org.uk/
Contact: Kelsang Namgyal
Position: Education Co-ordinator
Contact Email: education@manjushri.org.uk
Activities: Worship/practice/meditation, visits
Traditions: Western
Movements: New Kadampa Tradition
Local Groups:
Barrow
Carlisle
Cockermouth
Coniston
Millom
Wigan

City, Town or Local Bodies

Mahasi Dhamma Fellowship*
73 Royden Road, Billinge WN5 7LP
Tel: (01744) 895612
Email: mahasi@ukgateway.net
Website: http://www.panditarama.co.uk/
Activities: Meditation
Traditions: Theravada
Other Languages: Burmese
Affiliations: Panditarama Meditation Centre,
Yangon, Myanmar.

Lancashire Buddhist Centre*
Richmond Chambers, Richmond Terrace,
Blackburn BB1 7AR
Tel: (01254) 889228
Website: http://www.geocities.com/fwboeastlancs
Contact: Kamalavajri
Position: Centre Director
Activities: Worship/meditation, visits, women,
books, inter-faith
Traditions: Western
Movements: Friends of the Western Buddhist
Order

Bury Ch'an Group*
Room 2, The Mosses Centre, Cecil Street, Bury
BL9 0SB
Website: http://www.w-c-f.org.uk/
Contact: Simon Child
Position: Leader
Contact Tel: (0161) 7611945

Contact Email: simon@child.w-c-f.org.uk
Activities: Meditation, resources
Traditions: Zen
Movements: Ch'an

South Manchester Ch'an Group*
c/o 15 St Davids Road, Cheadle SK8 2HE
Website: http://www.w-c-f.org.uk/
Contact: Ron Henshall
Position: Group Leader
Contact Tel: (0161) 4910612
Contact Email: ron@rhenshall.fsnet.co.uk
Activities: Meditation
Traditions: Zen
Affiliations: Western Ch'an Fellowship

Samatha Group*
63 Woodlands Drive, Chester CH2 3QJ
Tel: (01244) 342272

Kagyu Dzong*
36 Charles Street, Colne BB8 0LZ
Tel: (01282) 864537
Email: colne@dechen.org
Website: http://www.dechen.org/
Contact: John Rowan
Position: Co-ordinator
Activities: Worship/practice/meditation,
newsletters, books
Movements: Kagyupa
Affiliations: Dechen Community, European
Buddhist Union (EBU)

Amitayus Centre*
173 Ruskin Road, Crewe CW2 7JX
Tel: (01270) 664050
Email: amitayus@netcentral.co.uk
Contact: Marilyn Jones
Activities: Worship/meditation, resources, visits,
newsletters
Movements: New Kadampa

Isle of Man Vipassana Group*
38 Oakhill Close, Glen Park, Douglas IM2 6HU
Tel: (01624) 621782
Email: michaelkewley@hotmail.com
Contact: Mike Kewley
Position: Guiding Teacher
Activities: Worship/practice/meditation, umbrella
body, newsletter/journal, books
Traditions: Theravada
Movements: Rinzai Zen, Soto Zen, Vipassana
Affiliations: Birmingham Buddhist Vihara

Kagyu Osel Choling*
c/o 24 Birkey Lane, Formby L37 4BU
Tel: (01704) 872169
Email: southport@dechen.org
Website: http://www.dechen.org/
Contact: The Secretary
Activities: Worship/practice/meditation, newsletter, books
Traditions: Tibetan
Movements: Kagyupa
Affiliations: Network of Buddhist Organisations

Buddhist Group of Kendal (Theravada)*
c/o Fellside Centre, Low Fellside, Kendal LA9 4NH
Contact: J Gomes
Position: Secretary
Activities: Worship/practice/meditation
Traditions: Theravada

Keswick Buddhist Group*
Sundance Wholefoods, 33 Main Street, Keswick CA12 5BL
Tel: (01768) 774712
Contact: Julian Holdswirth
Traditions: Theravada

Chenrezig Centre*
21 Portland Street, Lancaster LA1 1SZ
Tel: (01524) 68437
Contact: Richard Lupsom
Traditions: Tibetan
Movements: New Kadampa

Lancaster Friends of the Western Buddhist Order Centre*
98 High Road, Halton, Lancaster LA2 6PU
Tel: (01524) 811418
Email: jnanaketu@aol.com
Contact: Dharmachari Jnanaketu
Position: Chairman
Activities: Worship/practice/meditation, women, resources
Traditions: Western
Movements: Friends of the Western Buddhist Order

Lancaster Serene Reflection Meditation Group*
c/o 7 Portland Street, Lancaster LA1 1SZ
Tel: (01524) 34031 **Fax:** (01524) 63503
Contact: Mr Paul Taylor
Position: Lay Minister
Activities: Worship/practice/meditation
Traditions: Zen
Movements: Soto Zen

Affiliations: Throssel Hole Buddhist Priory, Order of Buddhist Contemplatives

Duldzin Buddhist Centre*
25 Aigburth Drive, Sefton Park, Aigburth, Liverpool L17 4JH
Tel: (0151) 7268900
Email: duldzin@centre25.freeserve.co.uk
Contact: Mr Roy Crate
Position: Administrative Director
Activities: Worship/practice/meditation, visits, inter-faith, resources
Movements: New Kadampa

Friends of the Western Buddhist Order (Liverpool)*
Liverpool Meditation Centre, 37 Hope Street, Liverpool L1 9EA
Tel: (0151) 7095489
Contact: Dharmachari Mangala
Position: Chairman
Contact Email: mangala@bun.com
Activities: Worship/practice/meditation, visits, resources
Traditions: Western
Movements: Friends of the Western Buddhist Order
Affiliations: Friends of the Western Buddhist Order

Shedrup Ling*
15 Hawarden Avenue, Liverpool L17 2AJ
Tel: (0151) 7227649
Email: liverpool@dechen.org
Website: http://www.dechen.org/
Contact: Russ Davidson
Position: Publicity Officer
Contact Tel: (0151) 932 0202
Contact Email: Russ Davidson
Activities: Worship/practice/meditation
Affiliations: Member of the Dechen Community, European Buddhist Union (EBU)

Vairochana Buddhist Centre*
84 Dudley Road, Whalley Range, Manchester M16 8BR
Tel: (0161) 8617012 **Fax:** (0161) 882 0531
Email: relax@vairochana.freeserve.co.uk
Contact: Ian Povey
Position: Administrative Director
Activities: Worship/practice/meditation
Traditions: Tibetan
Movements: New Kadampa

Buddha's Light International Association Manchester*
540 Stretford Road, Old Stafford, Manchester
M16 9AF
Tel: (0161) 8723338 **Fax:** (0161) 8723334
Email: ibps-man-uk@hotmail.com
Contact: Ven. Chueh-Teng
Position: Director
Contact Tel: (07714) 766696
Other Languages: Chinese, Cantonese

Buddhist Society of Manchester*
c/o 3 Grosvenor Square, Sale, Manchester
M33 1RW
Tel: (0161) 9737588
Contact: David Johnson
Position: Secretary

International Zen Association, UK Izauk - Manchester*
Mill Street Venture Centre, 491 Mill Street,
Openshaw, Manchester M11 2AD
Tel: (0161) 2312040
Email: alan.m.smith@capgemini.co.uk
Website: http://www.zen-izauk.org/
Contact: Alan Smith
Position: Zen monk
Activities: Worship/practice/meditation, visits
Traditions: Zen
Other Languages: French, German, Spanish
Affiliations: International Zen Association UK;
Association Zen Internationale (AZI)

Kagyu Ling*
20 Macefin Avenue, Chorlton, Manchester
M21 7QQ
Tel: (0161) 4453044
Email: manchester@dechen.org
Website: http://www.dechen.org/
Contact: Jonathon Macaskill
Position: Centre Co-ordinator
Activities: Worship/practice/meditation,
newsletter, books
Traditions: Tibetan
Movements: Kagyupa, Sakyapa
Affiliations: Dechen Community; European
Buddhist Union (EBU)

Manchester Buddhist Centre (Friends of the Western Buddhist Order)*
16-20 Turner Street, Manchester M4 1DZ
Tel: (0161) 8349232 **Fax:** (0161) 8394815
Email: info@manchesterbuddhistcentre.org.uk
Website:
http://www.manchesterbuddhistcentre.org.uk/

Contact: Mahasraddha
Position: Manager
Contact Tel: (0161) 8349232
Activities: Worship/meditation, resources, visits,
newsletter, inter-faith
Traditions: Multi-Traditional
Movements: Ambedkarite, Friends of the Western
Buddhist Order
Affiliations: Network of Buddhist Organisations;
European Buddhist Union

Manchester Centre for Buddhist Meditation*
21 High Lane, Chorlton-cum-Hardy, Manchester
M21 9DJ
Contact: Mrs Debbie End
Position: Chair
Contact Tel: (0161) 7230377
Contact Email: debbiekaren@totalise.co.uk
Activities: Worship/practice/meditation
Traditions: Theravada
Movements: Samatha
Affiliations: Manchester University Buddhist
Society; The Samatha Trust

Manchester Theravada Buddhist Group*
26 Kirkby Avenue, Sale, Manchester M33 3EP

Samatha Group*
3 Nuneham Avenue, Withington, Manchester
M20 9PZ
Tel: (0161) 4459746 **Fax:** (01928) 734998
Email: lescallow@hotmail.com
Contact: Dr Callow
Position: Chair
Activities: Worship/practice/meditation
Traditions: Theravada
Movements: Samatha
Affiliations: Samatha Association; Samatha Trust

Karme Choling*
Flat 2, 9 Dudley Road, New Brighton CH45 9JP
Tel: (0151) 6382568
Email: wirral@dechen .org
Website: http://www.dechen.org/
Contact: Mrs V Taylor
Position: Co-ordinator
Activities: Worship/practice/meditation,
newsletter, books
Traditions: Tibetan
Movements: Kagyupa
Affiliations: Dechen Community, European
Buddhist Union (EBU)

Odiyana Buddhist Centre*
76 Carlton Road, Witton Park, Northwich
CN9 5PG
Tel: (01606) 41356 **Fax:** (01606) 46660
Contact: John Davies
Position: Director
Contact Tel: (01606) 40040
Activities: Community centre, central body, visits,
resources
Traditions: Tibetan
Movements: New Kadampa
Affiliations: Tara Buddhist Centre

Kagyu Choling*
c/o 6 Faversham Brow, Oldham OL1 2XS
Tel: (0161) 8606524
Email: oldham@dechen.org
Website: http://www.dechen.org/
Contact: Franz Nevotne
Position: Co-ordinator
Activities: Worship/practice/meditation,
newsletter, books
Traditions: Tibetan
Movements: Kagyupa
Affiliations: Dechen Community, European
Buddhist Union (EBU)

Ketumati Buddhist Vihara Trust*
3 Pretoria Road, Hollins, Oldham OL2 6HA
Tel: (0161) 6789726
Email: ketumati@altavista.net
Contact: Ven Pidiville Piyatissa
Position: Chief Incumbent
Activities: Worship/practice/meditation,
community centre, youth, newsletter/journal, visits,
inter-faith, resources
Traditions: Theravada
Other Languages: Sinhala

Vajravarahi Buddhist Centre*
66 West Cliff, Preston PR1 8HU
Tel: (01772) 259094
Email: mail@vajravarahi@freeserve.co.uk
Website: http://www.vajravarahi.freeserve.co.uk/
Contact: Kelsang Pagpa
Position: Principal Teacher
Activities: Worship/practice/meditation, central
body, visits, resources
Traditions: Tibetan
Movements: New Kadampa

Wilmslow Samatha Group*
41 Yew Tree Lane, Poynton SK12 1PT
Tel: (01625) 850709

Website: http://www.samatha.demon.co.uk/
Contact: Mr Robert Adkins
Position: Contact person
Contact Email: robert@adkins.easynet.co.uk
Activities: Worship/practice/meditation
Traditions: Theravada
Movements: Samatha
Affiliations: Manchester Samatha Association; The
Samatha Trust

Rochdale Zen Retreat*
5 Oak Street, Rochdale OL16 1FD
Tel: (01706) 525951
Contact: Revd Peter Bonati
Position: Chief priest
Activities: Worship/practice/meditation
Traditions: Zen
Movements: Soto Zen
Affiliations: Throssel Hole Buddhist Abbey; Order
of Buddhist Contemplatives

Samye Dzong North-West*
St Helens, c/o Samye Ling Tibetan Centre,
Eskdalemuir, Langholm, DG13 0QL
Tel: (01387) 373232 **Fax:** (01387) 373223
Email: scotland@samyeling.org
Website: http://www.samyeling.org/
Contact: J Tsering
Position: Bookings Office
Activities: Worship/practice/meditation
Traditions: Tibetan
Movements: Kagyupa

Manjushri Mahayana Buddhist Centre*
Conishead Priory, Priory Road, Ulverston
LA12 9QQ
Tel: (01229) 584029 **Fax:** (01229) 580080
Email: info@manjushri.org.uk
Website: http://www.manjushri.org.uk/
Contact: Kelsang Namgyal
Position: Education Co-ordinator
Contact Email: education@manjushri.org.uk
Activities: Worship/practice/meditation, visits
Traditions: Western
Movements: New Kadampa Tradition

EAST MIDLANDS
Regional or County Bodies

Tara Buddhist Centre*
Ashe Hall, Ash Lane, Etwall DE65 6HT
Tel: (01283) 732338 **Fax:** (01283) 733416

Email: meditate@taracentre.org.uk
Website: http://www.taracentre.org.uk/
Contact: Miss Lorraine Quin
Position: Assistant Administrative
Activities: Worship/meditation, umbrella body, visits, resources
Traditions: Mahayana (Kadampa)
Movements: New Kadampa
Other Languages: Spanish, Polish, Chinese, French
Local Groups:
Derby
Ilkeston
Matlock

Akshobya Buddhist Centre*

52 Mayo Road, Sherwood Rise, Nottingham
NG5 1BL
Tel: (0115) 9857356 **Fax:** (0115) 8411651
Email: info@akshobya.com
Website: http://www.akshobya.com/
Contact: Kelsang Monlam
Position: Education Co-ordinator
Activities: Worship/practice/meditation, central body, umbrella body, visits, resources
Traditions: Western
Movements: New Kadampa
Local Groups:
Boston
Grantham
Loughborough
Mansfield
Nottingham University
Peterborough
Spalding

Gyaltsabje Buddhist Centre*

13 Sharrow View, Netheredge, Sheffield S7 1ND
Tel: (0114) 2509663 **Fax:** (0114) 2509663
Email: info@sheffmeditation.org.uk
Website: http://www.sheffmeditation.org.uk/
Contact: Liz Williams
Position: Adminstrative Director
Contact Email: liz@sheffmeditation.org.uk
Activities: Worship/practice/meditation, central body, youth, newsletter/journal, visits, resources
Traditions: Tibetan
Movements: New Kadampa
Local Groups:
Chesterfield
Lincoln

City, Town or Local Bodies

Bakewell Samatha Meditation Class*

Bakewell
Contact: Mrs Rosemary Rose
Position: Contact
Contact Tel: (01629) 814617
Activities: Worship/practice/meditation
Traditions: Theravada
Movements: Samatha
Affiliations: The Samatha Trust

Tara Buddhist Centre*

Ashe Hall, Ash Lane, Etwall DE65 6HT
Tel: (01283) 732338 **Fax:** (01283) 733416
Email: meditate@taracentre.org.uk
Website: http://www.taracentre.org.uk/
Contact: Miss Lorraine Quin
Position: Assistant Administrator
Activities: Worship/meditation, umbrella body, visits, resources
Traditions: Mahayana (Kadampa)
Movements: New Kadampa
Other Languages: Spanish, Polish, Chinese, French

Kagyu Samye Dzong Northamptonshire*

149 Kingsley Avenue, Kettering NN16 9ES
Tel: (01536) 522395
Email: northampton@samye.org
Website: http://www.samye.org/northampton
Contact: Mr Stephen Scofield
Position: Programme Director
Contact Email: sjscofield@ksdn.fsnet.co.uk
Activities: Worship/practice/meditation, newsletter/journal, resources
Traditions: Tibetan
Movements: Kagyupa
Affiliations: Rokpa Trust

East Midlands Buddhist Association*

Leicester Buddhist Vihara, 9 Una Avenue, Braunstone, Leicester LE3 2GS
Tel: (0116) 2825003
Contact: Venerable Ratanajothi
Position: Resident Monk
Activities: Worship/practice/meditation, resources
Traditions: Theravada
Other Languages: Sinhalese

Leicester Buddhist Society*

6 Half Moon Crescent, Oadby, Leicester LE2 4HD
Tel: (0116) 2712339
Contact: Dr D Russell

Position: President
Activities: Worship/practice/meditation
Traditions: Multi-Traditional

Nagarjuna Buddhist Centre*
27 Knighton Road, Stoneygate, Leicester LE2 3HL
Tel: (0116) 2700785
Contact: Marc Thompson
Position: Secretary

Akshobya Buddhist Centre*
52 Mayo Road, Sherwood Rise, Nottingham
NG5 1BL
Tel: (0115) 9857356 **Fax:** (0115) 8411651
Email: info@akshobya.com
Website: http://www.akshobya.com/
Contact: Kelsang Monlam
Position: Education Co-ordinator
Activities: Worship/practice/meditation, central
body, umbrella body, visits, resources
Traditions: Western
Movements: New Kadampa

Friends of the Western Buddhist Order (Nottingham)*
Nottingham Buddhist Centre, 9 St Mary's Place,
Nottingham NG1 1PH
Tel: (0115) 9561008
Email: nottfwbo@aol.com
Contact: Dharmachari Vimalaprabha
Position: Chairman
Activities: Worship/practice/meditation, visits
Traditions: Western
Movements: Friends of the Western Buddhist
Order

Nottingham Serene Reflection Meditation Group*
Friends Meeting House, Clarendon Street,
Nottingham NG1 5JD
Tel: (0115) 9603450
Contact: Mr Teddy Fullick
Position: Senior Member
Activities: Worship/practice/meditation
Traditions: Zen
Movements: Soto Zen
Other Languages: French, Italian
Affiliations: Throssel Hole Buddhist Abbey

Western Ch'an Fellowship Nottingham Branch*
c/o 8 Park Terrace, The Park, Nottingham
NG1 5DN
Tel: (0115) 924975
Contact: Ms Hilary Richards

Position: Regional representative
Traditions: Ch'an
Affiliations: Institute of Chung Hwa Buddhist
Culture, New York, USA

WEST MIDLANDS
Regional or County Bodies

Midlands Buddhist Association*
49 Brecon Road, Handsworth, Birmingham
B20 3RW
Tel: (0121) 5518614 **Fax:** (0121) 5518614
Email: tudamtu@hotmail.com
Contact: Revd T P Hue
Position: President
Contact Tel: (0121) 5518616
Activities: Worship/practice/meditation, youth,
elderly, newsletter/journal
Traditions: Pure Land
Other Languages: Vietnamese, Chinese
Affiliations: World Linh-Son Buddhist
Congregation

Midlands International Buddhist Association in the UK*
23 Weycroft Road, Perry Common, Birmingham
B23 5AD
Tel: (0121) 3827108 **Fax:** (0121) 3848333
Email: mibauk86@hotmail.com
Contact: Uen W Kassapa
Position: President
Contact Tel: (0121) 3827108

Samantabhadra Buddhist Centre*
46 Poplar Road, Kings Heath, Birmingham
B14 7AG
Tel: (0121) 4435422 **Fax:** (0121) 4432255
Email: info@samantabhadra.co.uk
Website: http://www.samantabhadra.co.uk/
Contact: Ms Georgina Pugh
Position: Administrative Director
Activities: Worship/practice/meditation,
community centre, central body, young, elderly,
women, newsletter, resource
Traditions: Tibetan
Movements: New Kadampa

Amitayus Centre*
173 Ruskin Road, Crewe CW2 7JX
Tel: (01270) 664050
Email: amitayus@netcentral.co.uk
Contact: Marilyn Jones

Activities: Worship/meditation, resources, visits, newsletters
Movements: New Kadampa
Local Groups:
Newcastle-under-Lyme
Stafford

Tara Buddhist Centre*
Ashe Hall, Ash Lane, Etwall DE65 6HT
Tel: (01283) 732338 **Fax:** (01283) 733416
Email: meditate@taracentre.org.uk
Website: http://www.taracentre.org.uk/
Contact: Miss Lorraine Quin
Position: Assistant Administrative
Activities: Worship/meditation, umbrella body, visits, resources
Traditions: Mahayana (Kadampa)
Movements: New Kadampa
Other Languages: Spanish, Polish, Chinese, French
Local Groups:
Burton
Cannock
Dudley
Halesowen
Lichfield
Redditch
Solihull
Tamworth
Telford
Walsall
Worcester

City, Town or Local Bodies

Birmingham Buddhist Centre*
11 Park Road, Moseley, Birmingham B13 8AB
Tel: (0121) 4495279
Email: fwbomidlands@compuserve.com
Website:
http://www.birminghambuddhistcentre.org.uk/
Contact: Mr John Hudson
Position: Centre Manager
Activities: Worship/practice/meditation, visists
Traditions: Western
Movements: Friends of the Western Buddhist Order
Affiliations: Friends of the Western Buddhist Order

Birmingham Buddhist Vihara*
47 Carlyle Road, Edgbaston, Birmingham
B16 9BH

Tel: (0121) 4546591 **Fax:** (0121) 454 0374
Email: dhamma@globalnet.co.uk
Website: http://www.nibbana.com/
Contact: Venerable Dr Rewata Dhamma
Position: Spiritual Director
Activities: Worship/meditation, visits, newsletters, books, inter-faith
Traditions: Theravada
Movements: Vipassana
Other Languages: Burmese, Hindi

Buddhavihara Temple*
5 Hampton Road, Aston, Birmingham B6 6AN
Tel: (0121) 5151518 **Fax:** (0121) 2401468
Email: laow.panyasiri@cableinet.co.uk
Website: http://www.watthaiuk.com/
Contact: Venerable Panyasiri
Position: Abbot
Activities: Worship/practice/meditation, community centre, newsletter, resource
Traditions: Theravada
Other Languages: Thai
Affiliations: Wat Sanghathan, Birmingham; Wat Buddhapadipa, London; Wat Srinagarindaravaram, Switzerland

Jethavana Buddhist Vihara Trust*
13 Booth Street, Handsworth, Birmingham
B21 0NG
Contact: Chandra Pathirana
Position: General Secretary
Contact Tel: (0121) 5541466
Activities: Worship/practice/meditation, visits
Traditions: Theravada
Movements: Maha Bodhi
Other Languages: Sinhalese, Hindi

Karma Do-Ngak Kunchab Ling*
41 Carlyle Road, Edgbaston, Birmingham
B16 9BH
Tel: (0121) 4542782
Contact: Simon Romer
Position: Facilitator
Activities: Worship/practice/meditation, visits, inter-faith, resources
Traditions: Tibetan
Movements: Kagyupa
Other Languages: Tibetan
Affiliations: Sherab Ling, Himachal, Pradesh, India

Midlands Buddhist Association*
49 Brecon Road, Handsworth, Birmingham
B20 3RW
Tel: (0121) 5518614 **Fax:** (0121) 5518614

Email: tudamtu@hotmail.com
Contact: Revd T P Hue
Position: President
Contact Tel: (0121) 5518616
Activities: Worship/practice/meditation, youth, elderly, newsletter/journal
Traditions: Pure Land
Other Languages: Vietnamese, Chinese
Affiliations: World Linh-Son Buddhist Congregation

Midlands International Buddhist Association in the UK*
23 Weycroft Road, Perry Common, Birmingham B23 5AD
Tel: (0121) 3827108 **Fax:** (0121) 3848333
Email: mibauk86@hotmail.com
Contact: Uen W Kassapa
Position: President
Contact Tel: (0121) 3827108

Rigpa Fellowship*
171 Pineapple Road, Stirchley, Birmingham B30 2FU
Tel: (0121) 4411698

Samatha Group*
105 Middleton Hall Road, King's Norton, Birmingham B30 1AG
Tel: (0121) 4582353 **Fax:** (0121) 4597847
Email: keith@eskola.freeserve.co.uk
Website: http://www.samatha.demon.co.uk/
Contact: Keith Munnings
Activities: Meditation
Affiliations: Samatha Trust

Wat Sanghathan*
107 Handsworth Wood Road, Handsworth Wood, Birmingham B20 2PH
Tel: (0121) 5515729 **Fax:** (0121) 5152213
Email: wat@sanghathan.com
Contact: Phra Aod Titajaro
Position: Abbot's Assistant
Traditions: Theravada

House of Inner Tranquillity*
Aukana Trust 9 Masons Lane, Bradford-on-Avon BA15 1QN
Tel: (01225) 866821 **Fax:** (01225) 865262
Email: info@aukana.org.uk
Website: http://www.aukana.org.uk/
Traditions: Theravada

Smiling Mountain Meditation Group*
19 Fox Lane, Hilltop, Bromsgrove B61 7NJ

Tel: (01527) 876588 **Fax:** (01527) 559506
Contact: Organiser
Contact Email: info@zazensacredicons.co.uk
Activities: Worship/practice/meditation
Traditions: Zen
Movements: Sanbo Kyodan Kai
Affiliations: Oxford Zen Centre; Sanbo Kyodan Kai (Japan)

Sakya Goshak Choling Buddhist Centre*
55 Russell Road, Moseley, Birmingham B13 8RB
Tel: (0121) 4493296
Email: birmingham@dechen.org
Website: http://www.dechen.org/
Contact: Secretary
Activities: Worship/practice/meditation, newsletter, books, resources
Traditions: Tibetan
Movements: Sakyapa
Affiliations: Dechen Community, European Buddhist Union (EBU)

Samantabhadra Buddhist Centre*
46 Poplar Road, Kings Heath, Birmingham B14 7AG
Tel: (0121) 4435422 **Fax:** (0121) 4432255
Email: info@samantabhadra.co.uk
Website: http://www.samantabhadra.co.uk/
Contact: Ms Georgina Pugh
Position: Administrative Director
Activities: Worship/practice/meditation, community centre, central body, young, elderly, women, newsletter, resource
Traditions: Tibetan
Movements: New Kadampa

Sugata Centre*
Coventry, c/o 27 Knighton Road, Stoneygate, Leicester, LE2 3HL
Tel: (0116) 2700785
Contact: Nick Bramble
Position: Co-ordinator

Fa Yue Buddhist Monastery*
Cottage Street, Brierley Hill, Dudley DY5 1RE
Tel: (01384) 484552 **Fax:** (01384) 481209
Email: fayue@hotmail.com
Contact: Venerable Hin Hung Sik
Position: Abbot/Chairman
Activities: Worship/practice/meditation, youth, elderly, newsletter, visits
Traditions: Mahayana
Movements: Ch'an
Other Languages: Cantonese, Mandarin

Community of Interbeing*
8 Lansdowne Circus, Leamington Spa CV32 4SW
Contact: Mr Mike Regan
Position: Contact
Contact Tel: (024) 7645 8222
Activities: Worship/practice/meditation
Traditions: Zen
Affiliations: Community of Interbeing UK; Plum Village, France

Shen Phen Thubten Choeling*
The Nurses Cottage, Long Lane, Peterchurch HR2 0TE
Tel: (0845) 4584718 **Fax:** (0845) 4584718
Email: elaine@greeengate.org.uk
Contact: Paul Swatridge
Position: Director
Activities: Practice/meditation, visits, inter-faith, resources
Traditions: Tibetan
Movements: non-sectarian
Other Languages: French, Spanish, Nepalese, Tibetan
Affiliations: The Foundation for the Preservation of the Mayahana Tradition

Telford Buddhist Priory*
Old Meadows, 49 The Rock, Ketley, Telford TF3 5BH
Tel: (01952) 615574 **Fax:** (01952) 615574
Website: http://www.obcon.org/
Contact: Rev DHS Kennaway
Position: Resident Monk
Activities: Worship/practice/meditation
Traditions: Zen
Movements: Soto Zen
Affiliations: Order of Buddhist Contemplatives

Telford Buddhist Group*
8 Wheatley Crescent, Hadley, Telford TF1 6PZ
Tel: (01952) 240283
Email: d.d.ahir@ukonline.co.uk
Contact: Mr D D Ahir
Position: Organiser
Activities: Resource, inter-faith
Traditions: Theravada
Movements: Ambedkarite
Other Languages: Punjabi

Wat Pah Santidhamma - The Forest Hermitage*
Lower Fulbrook, nr Sherbourne, Warwick CV35 8AS
Tel: (01926) 624385 **Fax:** (01926) 624385
Email: prakhem@foresthermitage.org.uk
Website: http://www.foresthermitage.org.uk/
Contact: Ven Phra Ajahn Khemadhammo
Traditions: Theravada, Thai Forest Tradition

Friends of the Western Buddhist Order Taraloka*
Taraloka Buddhist Retreat Centre for Women, Cornhill Farm, Bettisfield, Nr Whitchurch SY13 2LD
Tel: (01948) 710646 **Fax:** (01948) 710646
Email: enquiries@taraloka.org.uk
Website: http://www.taraloka.org.uk/
Contact: Dharmacarini Dharmapeta
Position: Secretary
Contact Email: admin@taraloka.org.uk
Activities: Worship/practice/meditation, women, newsletter/journal
Traditions: Multi-Traditional
Movements: Ambedkarite, Friends of the Western Buddhist Order
Other Languages: German, Dutch
Affiliations: Friends of the Western Buddhist Order, Manchester Buddhist Centre; Friends of the Western Buddhist Order, Central, Birmingham

Buddha Vihara: Ambedkar Nagar*
Upper Zoar Street, Pennfields, Wolverhampton WV3 0JH
Tel: (01902) 730664 **Fax:** (01902) 341186
Contact: Mr Mohan Lal
Position: General Secretary
Contact Tel: (07775) 963657
Activities: Worship/meditation, resources, visits, youth, elderly, women, newsletter, books, inter-faith
Traditions: Theravada
Movements: Ambedkarite
Other Languages: Punjabi, Hindi, Thai

EAST OF ENGLAND
Regional or County Bodies

Heruka Buddhist Centre*
13 Woodstock Road, Golders Green, London NW11 8ES
Tel: (020) 8455 7563 **Fax:** (020) 8905 5280
Email: info@heruka.org
Website: http://www.meditateinlondon.com/
Contact: Mr John McBretney
Position: Director
Contact Tel: (020) 8455 7563
Contact Email: john@heruka.org
Activities: Worship/practice/meditation, community centre, central body, visits, inter-faith

Movements: New Kadampa
Other Languages: Spanish, French
Local Groups:
Epping
Southend-on-Sea

Akshobya Buddhist Centre*
52 Mayo Road, Sherwood Rise, Nottingham
NG5 1BL
Tel: (0115) 9857356 **Fax:** (0115) 8411651
Email: info@akshobya.com
Website: http://www.akshobya.com/
Contact: Kelsang Monlam
Position: Education Co-ordinator
Activities: Worship/practice/meditation, central
body, umbrella body, visits, resources
Traditions: Western
Movements: New Kadampa

City, Town or Local Bodies

Dr Ambedkar Mission Society Bedford*
25 Hartwell Drive, Kempston, Bedford MK42 8US
Tel: (01234) 312976
Email: arun.kumar@ntlworld.com.uk
Contact: Mr Arun Kumar
Position: General Secretary
Activities: Newspapers, radio, television, visits,
inter-faith, resources
Traditions: Theravada
Movements: Ambedkarite
Other Languages: Punjabi, Hindi
Affiliations: Federation of Ambedkarite and
Buddhist Organisations of the UK

Friends of the Western Buddhist Order (Bury St Edmunds)*
Friends Meeting House, St Johns Street, Bury St
Edmunds IP33 1SJ
Tel: (01284) 756500 **Fax:** (01284) 750254
Contact: Dharmacarini Dhammapattiya
Position: Resident Member
Activities: Worship/meditation, resources
Traditions: Western
Movements: Friends of the Western Buddhist
Order

Cambridge Amaravati Group*
59 Cavendish Avenue, Cambridge CB1 7UR
Tel: (01223) 246257
Contact: Dan Jones
Position: Contact Person
Traditions: Theravada

Movements: Thai Forest Tradition
Affiliations: Buddhist Organisations in
Cambridge; Sangha of Amaravati and Chithurst

Cambridge Buddhist Centre: Friends of the Western Buddhist Order*
36/38 Newmarket Road, Cambridge CB5 8DT
Tel: (01223) 577553
Email: cambudcen@cwcom.net
Website:
http://www.cambridgebuddhistcentre.com/
Position: Centre Manager
Activities: Worship/practice/meditation,
community centre, central body, newsletter/journal,
visits, resources
Traditions: Multi-traditional
Movements: Friends of the Western Buddhist
Order
Other Languages: Spanish, German, French

Cambridge Buddhist Society*
32 Greens Road, Cambridge CB4 3EF
Tel: (01223) 366079
Email: baugh@beeb.net
Contact: Simon and Mary Rose Baugh
Position: Secretaries
Activities: Inter-faith
Traditions: Multi-Traditional
Movements: Kagyupa, Samatha
Affiliations: Nezang Meditation group (Tibetan);
The Samatha Association (Theravada)

Cambridge Serene Reflection Meditation Group*
8 Leyburn Close, Cherry Hinton, Cambridge
CB1 9XR
Tel: (01223) 411018
Website: http://www.obcon.org/
Contact: Richard Potter
Position: Lay Minister
Contact Tel: (01223) 411018
Contact Email:
richardpotter@potterhorgan.clara.co.uk
Activities: Worship/practice/meditation
Traditions: Zen
Affiliations: Order Of Buddhist Contemplatives

Cambridge University Buddhist Society*
Faculty of Oriental Studies, Sidgwick Avenue,
Cambridge CB3 9DA
Email: soc-buddha@lists.cam.ac.ukl
Website: http://www.cam.ac.uk/societies/buddha
Contact: Dr Rachael Harris
Position: Senior Treasurer
Contact Tel: (01223) 335124

Contact Email: rmh1001@cam.ac.uk
Activities: Resource
Traditions: Multi-Traditional

Cambridge University Meditation and Buddhism Society*
36/38 Newmarket Road, Cambridge CB5 8DT
Tel: (01223) 577553
Email: sundara@vajraguru.fsnet.co.uk
Contact: Dharmacari Sundara
Activities: Worship/practice/meditation, youth, resources
Traditions: Multi-traditional
Movements: Friends of the Western Buddhist Order
Affiliations: Cambridge Buddhist Centre

Nezang Buddhist Meditation Group*
5 Sedley Taylor Road, Cambridge CB2 2PW
Contact: Mrs Ato
Activities: Worship/practice/meditation
Traditions: Tibetan
Movements: Kagyupa

Colchester Buddhist Centre*
11 Manor Road, Colchester C03 3LX
Tel: (01206) 576330
Contact: Dharmachari Harshaprabha
Position: Chairman
Activities: Worship/practice/meditation, youth, elderly, women, visits, inter-faith
Traditions: Western
Movements: Friends of the Western Buddhist Order, Ambedkarite

Kongoryuji Temple*
London Road, East Dereham NR19 1AS
Tel: (0870) 4589666 **Fax:** (01362) 693962
Email: kongoryuji@x-stream.co.uk
Website: http://website.lineone.net/~kongoryuji
Contact: Secretary
Contact Email: shingon@buddhistnetwork.com
Activities: Worship/meditation, resources, umbrella body, newsletter, books
Traditions: Shingon Esoteric Buddhism
Other Languages: Croatian/Serbian, Japanese, Sanskrit, French
Affiliations: Network of Buddhist Organisations; Mushindokai; European Buddhist Union

Harlow Buddhist Society*
Dana House, 385 Longbanks, Harlow CM18 7PG
Tel: (01279) 303287
Contact: Dennis Wood
Position: Secretary
Activities: Worship/meditation, visits
Traditions: Theravada

Ipswich Buddhist Centre*
1st Floor, 5 The Thoroughfare, Ipswich IP1 1BX
Tel: (01473) 211516
Email: info@ipswichbuddhistcentre.org
Website: http://www.ipswichbuddhistcentre.org/
Contact: Dharmachari Jnanamitra
Position: Chairman
Activities: Practice/meditation
Traditions: Western
Movements: Friends of the Western Buddhist Order
Affiliations: Friends of the Western Buddhist Order

Community of Interbeing, Norfolk Sangha*
23 Havelock Road, Norwich NR2 3HQ
Tel: (01603) 613798
Website: http://www.interbeing.org.uk/
Contact: Dr Andrew Boswell
Position: Secretary
Contact Email: a.boswell@uea.ac.uk
Activities: Worship/practice/meditation, newsletter/journal, inter-faith
Traditions: Zen
Other Languages: Vietnamese, French
Affiliations: Community of Interbeing UK; Plum Village Practice Centre, France

Norfolk Zen Dojo*
Norwich
Tel: (01603) 754184
Email: norfolk@zen-izauk.org
Website: http://www.zen-izauk.org/
Activities: Worship/practice/meditation
Traditions: Zen
Movements: Soto Zen
Affiliations: International Zen Association UK; Association Zen International

Norwich Buddhist Centre*
41 All Saints Green, Norwich NR1 3LY
Tel: (01603) 627034
Email: fwbonorwich@paston.co.uk
Website: http://www.norwichbuddhistcentre.com/
Contact: Dharmachari Satyadaka
Position: Chair

Activities: Worship/practice/meditation, community centre, women, newsletter/journal, visits, resources
Traditions: Multi-traditional
Movements: Friends of the Western Buddhist Order

Norwich Serene Reflection Buddhist Meditation Group*
19 The Street, Matlaske, Norwich NR11 7AQ
Contact: Faith Broadbent
Position: Lay Minister
Contact Tel: (01263) 577661
Contact Email: faithb@waitrose.com
Activities: Worship/practice/meditation, newsletter
Traditions: Zen
Movements: Soto Zen
Affiliations: Throssel Hole Buddhist Abbey, Northumberland

Padmaloka Retreat Centre*
Lesingham House, The Covey, Surlingham, Norwich NR14 7AL
Tel: (01508) 538112 **Fax:** (01508) 538076
Email: padmaloka@compuserve.com
Contact: Dharmachari Mahjupriya
Position: Manager
Activities: Worship/practice/meditation
Traditions: Multi-traditional
Movements: Friends of the Western Buddhist Order
Other Languages: Spanish, German
Affiliations: Norwich Buddhist Centre; Friends of the Western Buddhist Order Madhyakaloka, Birmingham.

Rigpa Fellowship*
4 Girton Road, Norwich NR1 1BB
Tel: (01603) 259957
Email: mkchambers@hotmail.com
Contact: M Chambers
Position: Manager
Activities: Worship/practice/meditation

Stamford Buddhist Vihara*
97 Empingham Road, Stamford PE9 2SU
Tel: (01780) 756280 **Fax:** (01780) 756280
Contact: Venerable B Ananda
Position: Abbot and President
Contact Tel: (07764) 607873
Activities: Meditation
Traditions: Theravada
Other Languages: Pali, Japanese, Singhalese

Vajrasana Retreat Centre, Suffolk*
Walsham Le Willows c/o London Buddhist Centre, 51 Roman Road, London E2 0HU
Tel: (020) 8981 1225 **Fax:** (020) 8980 1960
Email: info@lbc.org.uk
Website: http://www.lbc.org.uk/
Contact: Dharmachari Maitreyaraja
Position: Assistant Centre Director
Activities: Worship/practice/meditation
Traditions: Multi-traditional
Movements: Friends of the Western Buddhist Order
Other Languages: Marathi, Hindi, Spanish, German
Affiliations: London Buddhist Centre; San Francisco Buddhist Centre, USA

LONDON
Regional and Area Bodies

Heruka Buddhist Centre*
13 Woodstock Road, Golders Green, London NW11 8ES
Tel: (020) 8455 7563 **Fax:** (020) 8905 5280
Email: info@heruka.org
Website: http://www.meditateinlondon.com/
Contact: Mr John McBretney
Position: Director
Contact Tel: (020) 8455 7563
Contact Email: john@heruka.org
Activities: Worship/practice/meditation, community centre, central body, visits, inter-faith
Movements: New Kadampa
Other Languages: Spanish, French
Local Groups:
West Hampstead

Kagyu Samye Dzong London*
Carlisle Lane, off Royal Street, Lambeth, London SE1 7LG
Tel: (020) 7928 5447 **Fax:** (020) 7633 9339
Email: london@samye.org
Website: http://www.samye.org/london
Contact: Ani Zangmo
Position: Director
Activities: Practice/meditation, umbrella body
Traditions: Tibetan
Movements: Kagyupa
Affiliations: Kagyu Samye Ling Monastery, Eskdalemuir, Scotland; Kagyu Samye Dzong, Brussels

London Buddhist Arts Centre*
Eastbourne House, Bullards Place, Bethnal Green,
London E2 0PT
Tel: (020) 8983 6134
Contact: Clare Barton-Harvey
Position: Director
Activities: Practice, community centre
Traditions: Western
Movements: Friends of the Western Buddhist
Order

London Buddhist Centre*
51 Roman Road, Bethnal Green, London E2 0HU
Tel: (0845) 4584716 **Fax:** (020) 8980 1960
Email: info@lbc.org.uk
Website: http://www.lbc.org.uk/
Contact: Dharamchari Maiteycraya
Position: Assistant Centre Director
Activities: Worship/practice/meditation,
community centre, youth, elderly, women,
newsletter/journal, books, visits, inter-faith,
resources
Traditions: Multi-traditional
Movements: Friends of the Western Buddhist
Order
Other Languages: French, German, Polish,
Spanish
Affiliations: Friends of the Western Buddhist
Order, Birmingham

London Retreats*
67 Strafford Gate, Potters Bar EN6 1PR
Contact: Clare Brunt
Contact Tel: (020) 8755 0353
Activities: Meditation
Traditions: Theravada
Movements: Vipassana
Affiliations: Insight Meditation Centre, Gaia
House, Devon

North London Buddhist Centre*
St Mark's Studios, Chillingworth Road, Holloway,
London N7 8SJ
Tel: (020) 7700 3075 **Fax:** (020) 7700 3535
Email: nlbc@cwcom.net
Website: http://www.nlbc.cwc.net/
Contact: Dharmachari Manjudeva
Position: Centre Manager
Activities: Worship/practice/meditation,
newsletter/journal, visits
Traditions: Western
Movements: Friends of the Western Buddhist
Order

Thames Meditation Society*
Thames Buddhist Vihara, 49 Dulverton Road,
Selsdon CR2 8PJ
Tel: (020) 8657 7120 **Fax:** (020) 8651 3776
Contact: Ven P Somaratana Thera
Position: Head of Vihara
Contact Email: henia_nanda@yahoo.com
Activities: Worship/practice/meditation,
newsletter/journal
Traditions: Theravada
Movements: Maha Bodhi
Other Languages: Sinhalese
Affiliations: London Buddhist Vihara

West London Buddhist Centre*
West London Buddhist Centre, 94 Westbourne Park
Villas, London W2 5PL
Tel: (0845) 4585461
Email: centre@wlbc.freeserve.co.uk
Website: http://www.wlbc.freeserve.co.uk/
Contact: Dharmachari Sahananda
Position: Chairman
Contact Email: sahananda@wlbc.freeserve.co.uk
Activities: Worship/practice/meditation
Traditions: Western
Movements: Friends of the Western Buddhist
Order
Affiliations: Friends of the Western Buddhist
Order

West London Zen Dojo*
The Shiatsu College, c/o 85 Gascony Avenue,
NW6 4ND
Tel: (020) 7625 9142
Email: 100451.2721@compuserve.com
Contact: Jim Elliott
Position: Treasurer

Borough or Local Bodies

BARNET

Heruka Buddhist Centre*
13 Woodstock Road, Golders Green, London
NW11 8ES
Tel: (020) 8455 7563 **Fax:** (020) 8905 5280
Email: info@heruka.org
Website: http://www.meditateinlondon.com/
Contact: Mr John McBretney
Position: Director
Contact Tel: (020) 8455 7563
Contact Email: john@heruka.org
Activities: Worship/practice/meditation,

community centre, central body, visits, inter-faith

Movements: New Kadampa

Other Languages: Spanish, French

BRENT

Association for Insight Meditation*

3 Clifton Way, Alperton HA0 4PQ

Contact: Bhikkhu Pesala

Position: Director

Activities: Meditation

Traditions: Theravada Mahasi

Sri Saddhatissa International Buddhist Centre*

309-311 Kingsbury Road, Kingsbury, London NW9 9PE

Tel: (020) 8204 3301 **Fax:** (020) 8933 9395

Email: ssibc@dircon.co.uk

Website: http://www.ssibc.dircon.co.uk/

Contact: Venerable Galayaye Piyadassi

Position: Head of Centre

Activities: Worship/practice/meditation, youth, newsletter, books, visits, inter-faith, resources

Traditions: Theravada

Movements: World Buddhist Foundation

Other Languages: Sinhalese, Hindi, Burmese

CAMDEN

Hampstead Buddhist Group*

Burgh House, New End Square, Hampstead, London NW3 1LT

Tel: (020) 8452 4174

Contact: Susan Jordan

Position: Secretary

Traditions: Theravada, Thai Tradition

Affiliations: Buddhist Monastery, Hemel Hempstead; Other Forest Sangha Monasteries

London Serene Reflection (Soto Zen) Meditation Group*

Basement, 2 Pilgrim's Place Cottages, Rosslyn Hill, London NW3 5UJ

Tel: (020) 7385 1901

Contact: James Donegan

Position: Co-ordinator

Zen Practice Centre Trust*

Flat 3, 32 Shirlock Road, London NW3 2HS

Tel: (020) 7267 4167

Email: haztmoon@onetel.co.uk

Contact: Manu

Position: Editor/Co-ordinator

CROYDON

Croydon Buddhist Centre*

98 High Street, Croydon CR0 1ND

Tel: (020) 8688 8624 **Fax:** (020) 8688 8624

Email: croydonbc@lineone.net

Website: http://www.croydonbuddhistcentre.com/

Contact: Ms F Henley

Position: Receptionist

Activities: Worship/practice/meditation, community centre, women, newsletter, visits, inter-faith, resources

Traditions: Multi-traditional

Movements: Friends of the Western Buddhist Order

Thames Meditation Society*

Thames Buddhist Vihara, 49 Dulverton Road, Selsdon CR2 8PJ

Tel: (020) 8657 7120 **Fax:** (020) 8651 3776

Contact: Ven P Somaratana Thera

Position: Head of Vihara

Contact Email: henia_nanda@yahoo.com

Activities: Worship/practice/meditation, newsletter/journal

Traditions: Theravada

Movements: Maha Bodhi

Other Languages: Sinhalese

Affiliations: London Buddhist Vihara

EALING

Karunamaya Buddha Vihara*

12 Featherstone Road, Southall UB2 5AA

Tel: (020) 8571 5131

Contact: Mr B. R. Birdi

Position: Chairman

Contact Tel: (020) 8574 2316

Activities: Worship/practice/meditation

Traditions: Theravada

Other Languages: Sinhala, Hindi

Three Wheels*

55 Carbery Avenue, Acton, London W3 9AB

Tel: (020) 8248 2542 **Fax:** (020) 8248 2578

Email: t-wheels@jais.co.uk

Website: http://www.threewheels.org.uk/

Contact: Revd Prof Kemmyo Taira Sato

Position: Director

Activities: Worship/practice/meditation, community centre, youth, elderly, women, newsletter/journal, visits, inter-faith, resources

Traditions: Pure Land

Movements: Jodo Shin Shu
Other Languages: Japanese

ENFIELD

Buddhist Realists' Vihara*
85 Highworth Road, New Southgate, London
N11 2SN
Tel: (020) 8361 6394
Email: vimalo 742@hotmail.com
Contact: Dr Sumana Siri
Position: Executive Director
Contact Email: revdress@yahoo.com
Activities: Worship/practice/meditation
Traditions: Theravada
Other Languages: Singhal, Malay, Hindi

GREENWICH

Kagyu Telo Ling*
48 Tyler Street, London SE10 9EX
Tel: (020) 8269 1119
Email: slondon@dechen.org
Website: http://www.dechen.org/
Contact: Fred Tyler
Position: Co-ordinator
Contact Tel: (020) 8269 1119
Activities: Worship/practice/meditation,
newsletter, books
Traditions: Tibetan
Movements: Kagyu
Affiliations: Dechen Community, European
Buddhist Union (EBU)

Woolwich Meditation Group
120 Woodhill, London SE18 5JL

HARROW

Harrow Zazenkai*
Flat 3, 4 Stuart Avenue, Harrow HA2 9BB
Tel: (020) 8422 9757
Email: franktettsu@ukgateway.net
Website: http://www.wwzc.org/
Contact: Mr Frank Tettsu Woods
Position: Administrator
Activities: Practice/meditation, newsletter/journal,
books, visits
Traditions: Zen
Movements: Soto Zen
Affiliations: Zen Centre of Ottawa

HILLINGDON

Lelung Dharma Trust*
12 Meadow Close, Ruislip HA4 8AP
Tel: (01895) 624147 **Fax:** (01895) 624147
Email: jasmine@jpkoller.freeserve.co.uk
Website: http://www.lelungdharmatrust.org.uk/
Contact: Jasmine Koller
Position: Chairperson
Activities: Radio
Traditions: Tibetan
Movements: Nyingmapa, Rime
Other Languages: Finnish, French, Italian

Ruislip Meditation and Retreat Centre*
12 Meadow Close, Ruislip HA4 8AP
Tel: (01895) 624147 **Fax:** (01895) 624147
Email: jasmine@jpkoller.freeserve.co.uk
Website: http://www.lelungdharmatrust.org.uk/
Contact: Mrs Jasmine Koller
Position: Chair
Activities: Worship/practice/meditation,
community centre
Traditions: Tibetan
Movements: Nyingmapa
Other Languages: French, Finnish, Italian

HOUNSLOW

London Buddhist Vihara*
Dharmapala Building, The Avenue, Chiswick,
London W4 1UD
Tel: (020) 8995 9493 **Fax:** (020) 8994 8130
Email: Londonvihara@virgin.net
Website: http://www.londonbuddhistvihara.co.uk/
Contact: Most Venerable Vajiragnana
Position: Head of the Vihara
Activities: Worship/practice/meditation, youth,
newsletter/journal, visits, inter-faith, resources
Traditions: Theravada
Movements: Maha Bodhi, Vipassana
Other Languages: Sinhalese
Affiliations: Inter Faith Network for the UK;
Network of Buddhist Organisations; The Anagarika
Dharmapala Trust

ISLINGTON

London Zen Group*
6 Edward Friend House, Brodia Road, London
N16 0ET
Tel: (0973) 147853
Contact: Mary Butler

North London Buddhist Centre*
St Mark's Studios, Chillingworth Road, Holloway,
London N7 8SJ
Tel: (020) 7700 3075 **Fax:** (020) 7700 3535
Email: nlbc@cwcom.net
Website: http://www.nlbc.cwc.net/
Contact: Dharmachari Manjudeva
Position: Centre Manager
Activities: Worship/practice/meditation,
newsletter/journal, visits
Traditions: Western
Movements: Friends of the Western Buddhist
Order

Sakya Chogyal Sechen Dzong*
47 Davenant Road, Holloway, London N19 3NW
Tel: (020) 7281 5340
Email: nlondon@dechen.org
Website: http://www.dechen.org/
Contact: Stephen Mulligan
Position: Co-ordinator
Activities: Worship/practice/meditation,
newsletter, books
Traditions: Tibetan
Movements: Sakyapa
Affiliations: Dechen Community, European
Buddhist Union (EBU)

Sukhavati (Buddhist Temple and Community)*
21 Sussex Way, Finsbury Park, London N7 6RT
Tel: (020) 7263 0921
Email: amida@quannon.demon.co.uk
Website: http://www.amidatrust.com/
Contact: Sr Prasada
Position: Order Member
Activities: Worship/practice/meditation, inter-
faith, resources
Traditions: Pure Land
Movements: Socially Engaged
Other Languages: Assamese, Bengali, French
Affiliations: Amida Trust

KENSINGTON AND CHELSEA

West London Zen Dojo*
The Shiatsu College, c/o 85 Gascony Avenue,
NW6 4ND
Tel: (020) 7625 9142
Email: 100451.2721@compuserve.com
Contact: Jim Elliott
Position: Treasurer

LAMBETH

Heart of London Sanga, The*
34a Kennington Lane, Kennington, London
SE11 4LS
Contact: Bridget Holding
Contact Tel: (020) 7820 9703
Contact Email: bridgetholding@dial.pipex.com
Activities: Meditation
Traditions: Thich Nhat Hanh
Affiliations: Community of Interbeing UK

Jamyang Buddhist Centre*
The Old Court House, 43 Renfrew Road,
Kennington SE114NA
Tel: (020) 7810 8787 **Fax:** (020) 7810 8605
Email: admin@jamyang.co.uk
Website: http://www.jamyang.co.uk/
Contact: Mr Jon Underwood
Position: Activities Manager
Contact Email: jon@jamyang.co.uk
Activities: Worship/practice/meditation,
community centre, central body, newsletter/journal,
visits, inter-faith, resources
Traditions: Tibetan
Movements: Foundation for the preservation of
the Mahayana Tradition
Affiliations: Network of Buddhist Organisations

Sasana Ramsi Vihara*
18 Ospringe House, Wootton Street, London
SE1 8TP
Tel: (020) 7261 1492 **Fax:** (020) 7261 1492
Email: uuttara@talk21.com
Contact: Venerable Uuttara
Position: Abbot
Contact Tel: (07932) 792556
Activities: Worship/practice/meditation,
community centre, umbrella body
Traditions: Theravada
Movements: Vipassana
Other Languages: Burmese, Chinese

Shambhala Meditation Centre*
27 Belmont Close, Clapham, London SW4 7AY
Tel: (020) 7720 3207 **Fax:** (020) 7627 4224
Email: info@shambala.org.uk
Website: http://www.shambala.org.uk/
Contact: Linus Bewley
Position: Director
Contact Tel: (020) 8673 6115
Activities: Worship/practice/meditation, central
body

Traditions: Tibetan
Movements: Kagyupa, Nyingmapa
Affiliations: Shambhala International

South London Buddhist Centre

c/o 24 Guernsey Grove, London SE24 9YZ
Tel: (020) 8671 7115
Email: slbc@sangha.demon.co.uk
Traditions: Western
Movements: Friends of the Western Buddhist
Order

MERTON

Buddhapadipa Temple*

14 Calonne Road, Wimbledon, London SW19 5HJ
Tel: (020) 8946 1357 **Fax:** (020) 8944 5788
Email: buddhapadipa@hotmail.com
Website: http://www.buddhapadipa.org/
Contact: The Venerable Phrakru S Lom
Position: Temple Secretary
Contact Tel: (020) 8879 7542
Activities: Worship/practice/meditation,
newsletter/journal, books, visits, inter-faith
Traditions: Theravada
Movements: Vipassana
Other Languages: Thai, Pali, Chinese
Affiliations: Thai Embassy

Dorjechang Buddhist Centre*

12 Springfield Road, Wimbledon, London
SW19 7AL
Tel: (020) 8946 5140
Email: dorjechang@lineone.net
Website: http://www.meditateinlondon.com/
Contact: Josephine Percival
Position: Director
Contact Tel: (020) 8946 5140
Contact Email: dorjechang@lineone.net
Activities: Worship/practice/meditation,
community centre, central body
Traditions: Western
Movements: New Kadampa
Other Languages: Spanish, French

Putney Mahayana Buddhist Centre*

c/o Dorjechang Centre, 12 Springfield Road,
London SW19 7AL
Tel: (020) 8946 5140
Email: dorjechang@lineone.net
Website: http://www.meditateinlondon.com/
Contact: Josephine Percival
Position: Director

Activities: Meditation
Movements: New Kadampa

RICHMOND UPON THAMES

Tisarana Vihara Association*

357 Nelson Road, Whitton, Twickenham
TW2 7AG
Tel: (020) 8898 6965 **Fax:** (020) 8898 6965
Website: http://www.tisarana.com/
Contact: Venerable U Nyakina
Position: Spiritual Instructor
Activities: Worship/meditation, visits, youth,
elderly, women, newsletters, books
Traditions: Theravada
Movements: Vipassana, Buddhist Psychology
Other Languages: Hindi, Myanmar

SOUTHWARK

Buddhist Co-operative*

5 Hindmans Road, Dulwich, London SE22 9NF
Tel: (020) 8693 9951
Email: buddhistcoop@england.com
Website:
http://www.yell.co.uk/sites/buddhist-coop
Contact: Venerable U Dhammasami
Position: Spiritual Director
Activities: Resource, visits, youth, elderly, women,
newsletter
Traditions: Multi-traditional
Movements: All movements
Other Languages: Burman
Affiliations: European Buddhist Union

Community of Interbeing*

102 Alleyn Road, West Dulwich, London
SE21 8AH
Tel: (020) 8670 6388
Contact: Mrs Marie Pompe
Position: Facilitator
Contact Email: marie.pompe@virgin.net
Activities: Practice/meditation
Traditions: Multi-traditional
Other Languages: French, Dutch
Affiliations: Community of Interbeing UK;
Community of Interbeing, Plum Village, France

Kagyu Samye Dzong London*

Carlisle Lane, off Royal Street, Lambeth, London
SE1 7LG
Tel: (020) 7928 5447 **Fax:** (020) 7633 9339
Email: london@samye.org

Website: http://www.samye.org/london
Contact: Ani Zangmo
Position: Director
Activities: Practice/meditation, umbrella body
Traditions: Tibetan
Movements: Kagyupa
Affiliations: Kagyu Samye Ling Monastery,
Eskdalemuir, Scotland; Kagyu Samye Dzong,
Brussels

TOWER HAMLETS

Bodywise Natural Health*
119 Roman Road, London E2 0QN
Tel: (020) 8981 6938

London Buddhist Arts Centre*
Eastbourne House, Bullards Place, Bethnal Green,
London E2 0PT
Tel: (020) 8983 6134
Contact: Clare Barton-Harvey
Position: Director
Activities: Practice, community centre
Traditions: Western
Movements: Friends of the Western Buddhist
Order

London Buddhist Centre*
51 Roman Road, Bethnal Green, London E2 0HU
Tel: (0845) 4584716 **Fax:** (020) 8980 1960
Email: info@lbc.org.uk
Website: http://www.lbc.org.uk/
Contact: Dharamchari Maiteycraya
Position: Assistant Centre Director
Activities: Worship/practice/meditation,
community centre, youth, elderly, women,
newsletter/journal, books, visits, inter-faith,
resources
Traditions: Multi-traditional
Movements: Friends of the Western Buddhist
Order
Other Languages: French, German, Polish,
Spanish
Affiliations: Friends of the Western Buddhist
Order, Birmingham

WANDSWORTH

Nipponzan Myohoji*
The London Peace Pagoda, c/o Park Office, Albert
Bridge Road, London SW11 4NJ
Tel: (020) 7228 9620 **Fax:** (020) 7228 9620
Contact: Revd G Nagase
Position: Resident Monk

Activities: Worship/meditation, visits, inter-faith
Traditions: Nichiren
Movements: Nipponzan Myhohoji
Other Languages: Japanese

WESTMINSTER, CITY OF

Buddhist Centre*
The Meeting Room, 51 Roman Road, London
E2 0HU
Tel: (020) 8981 1225
Contact: Dh Prasama Vira
Position: Centre Manager
Contact Tel: (0845) 458 4716

West London Buddhist Centre*
West London Buddhist Centre, 94 Westbourne Park
Villas, London W2 5PL
Tel: (0845) 4585461
Email: centre@wlbc.freeserve.co.uk
Website: http://www.wlbc.freeserve.co.uk/
Contact: Dharmachari Sahananda
Position: Chairman
Contact Email: sahananda@wlbc.freeserve.co.uk
Activities: Worship/practice/meditation
Traditions: Western
Movements: Friends of the Western Buddhist
Order
Affiliations: Friends of the Western Buddhist
Order

SOUTH EAST
Regional or County Bodies

Bodhisattva Centre*
3 Lansdowne Road, Brighton BN3 1DN
Tel: (01273) 732917 **Fax:** (01273) 736936
Email: bodhisattva@clara-net
Website: http://www.bodhisattva.co.uk
Contact: Kelsang Dana
Position: Education Co-ordinator
Activities: Meditation
Traditions: Western
Movements: New Kadampa
Local Groups:
Chichester
Maidstone
Reigate
Sevenoaks
St Margaret's-at-Cliffe
Tunbridge Wells

Hampshire Buddhist Society (Zen Group)*
32 Norfolk Road, Shirley, Southampton SO15 5AS
Contact: Mrs Roberta Mansell
Position: Publicity Officer
Contact Tel: (023) 8049 6315
Activities: Worship/practice/meditation, visits, resources
Traditions: Zen
Movements: Rinzai Zen
Affiliations: Fairlight Zen Buddhist Temple, Luton; The Buddhist Society, London; The Zen Centre, London; Daitoku-Ji Temple, Kyoto

Hampshire Buddhist Society*
15 St Anne's Gardens, Woolston, Southampton S019 9FJ
Contact: Rosalind Dean
Position: Secretary
Contact Tel: (023) 8042 2430
Activities: Worship/practice/meditation
Traditions: Theravada, Zen
Movements: Rinzai Zen
Affiliations: Chithurst Buddhist Monastery; Network of Buddhist Organisations; European

City, Town or Local Bodies

Aylesbury Meditation Group*
9 Recreation Ground, Wingrave, Aylesbury HP22 4PH
Tel: (01296) 681161
Contact: Christa Wright
Movements: Kagyupa, Theravadin Forest Tradition

Being in Practice
Flat 1, 2 Preston Park Avenue, Brighton BN1 6HJ

Bodhisattva Centre*
3 Lansdowne Road, Brighton BN3 1DN
Tel: (01273) 732917 **Fax:** (01273) 736936
Email: bodhisattva@clara-net
Website: http://www.bodhisattva.co.uk
Contact: Kelsang Dana
Position: Education Co-ordinator
Activities: Meditation
Traditions: Western
Movements: New Kadampa

Brighton Buddhist Centre*
17 Tichborne Street, Brighton BN1 1UR
Tel: (01273) 772090
Email: brightonbuddhist@aol.com
Website:

http://www.brightonbuddhistcentre.co.uk/
Contact: Dharmacari Jnanottara
Position: Administrator
Contact Tel: (01273) 711392
Contact Email: jnanottara@aol.com
Activities: Worship/practice/meditation
Traditions: Western
Movements: Friends of the Western Buddhist Order
Other Languages: Spanish

Dharma School*
The White House, Ladies Mile Road, Patcham, Brighton BN1 8TB
Tel: (01273) 502055 **Fax:** (01273) 556580
Contact: Headteacher
Activities: Resource, visits, inter-faith
Traditions: Multi-Traditional
Affiliations: Theravadin Forest Sangha; Network of Buddhist Organisations; Tibetan Government in Exile

Evolution Arts and Health Centre*
2 Sillwood Terrace, Brighton BN1 2LR
Tel: (01273) 729803 **Fax:** (01273) 381670
Email: evolutionarts@compuserve.com
Website: http://www.evolutionarts.co.uk/
Contact: Dharmachari Viprasanna
Position: Director
Activities: Community centre, youth
Traditions: Multi-traditional
Movements: Friends of the Western Buddhist Order
Other Languages: Spanish
Affiliations: Brighton Buddhist Centre, Madhyamaloka

Maitrikara*
24 Freshfield Street, Queen's Park, Brighton BN2 2ZG
Tel: (01273) 675803 **Fax:** (01273) 675803
Email: info@maitrikara.org
Website: http://www.maitrikara.org/
Contact: Larry Gethin
Position: Group Co-ordinator
Activities: Worship/meditation
Traditions: Tibetan
Movements: Nyingmapa
Affiliations: Network of Buddhist Organisations; Centre de'Etudes de Chanteloube

Canterbury Tibet Link*
55 Havelock Street, Canterbury CT1 1NP
Tel: (01227) 763505

Contact: Caroline Latham
Position: Founder
Activities: Worship/practice/meditation
Traditions: Tibetan

Jampel Kadampa Buddhist Centre*
26 Cherry Garden Road, Canterbury CT2 8EP
Tel: (01227) 760955
Email: info@jampel.org
Website: http://www.jampel.org/
Contact: Kunden
Position: Programme Co-ordinator
Contact Email: kelsang kunden@hotmail.com
Activities: Worship/practice/meditation
Affiliations: NKT

Bodhicharya Buddhist Group*
Richmond Field, West Ashling, Chichester
PO18 8DA
Tel: (01243) 575951 **Fax:** (01243) 575851
Website: http://www.bodhicharya.org/
Contact: Cait Collins
Contact Email: cait@bodhicharya.org
Activities: Worship/practice/meditation
Traditions: Tibetan
Movements: Gelugpa, Kagyupa, Nyingmapa
Affiliations: Network of Buddhist Organisations
of the UK; Bodhicharya

Hastings Buddhist Meditation and Discussion Group*
Cincla Cottage, Cliff End, Pett Level, Hastings
TN35 4EE
Tel: (01424) 813176
Email: a.dipper@talk21.com
Contact: Mr Alan Dipper
Position: Chair
Activities: Worship/practice/meditation
Traditions: Zen
Movements: Rinzai Zen
Affiliations: The Buddhist Society

Maidstone Meditation Group*
Maidstone
Tel: (01622) 670587
Email: alpatching@lineone.net
Website:
http://www.longchenmeditation.org.uk/
Contact: Andrew
Activities: Practice/meditation, resources
Traditions: Tibetan
Movements: Nyingmapa
Affiliations: Longchen Foundation

Mid Kent and Medway Buddhist Group*
c/o Friends Meeting House, Union Street,
Maidstone
Tel: (01634) 375728
Email: anthony.millett@virgin.net
Contact: Tony Millett
Activities: Worship/meditation

Zen Practice Centre Trust*
26 Milford Close, Maidstone ME16 0EX
Contact: Barbara Hussong
Contact Tel: (01622) 670587
Activities: Worship/practice/meditation

Milton Keynes Meditation Association*
Milton Keynes, c/o Cambridge Buddhist Centre,
36/38 Newmarket Road, Cambridge, CB5 8DT
Tel: (01223) 577553
Email: cambudcen@cwcom.net
Website:
http://www.cambridgebuddhistcentre.com/
Activities: Worship/practice/meditation,
community centre
Traditions: Multi-traditional
Movements: Friends of the Western Buddhist
Order

Isle of Wight Buddhist Group*
19 Watergate Road, Newport PO30 1XN
Tel: (01983) 520795

Friends of the Western Buddhist Order (Oxford)
46 Derwent Avenue, Headington, Oxford
OX3 0AP
Tel: (01865) 61973
Email: odec@gn.apc.org
Contact: Shantiprabha
Activities: Youth, elderly, women, inter-faith
Traditions: Western
Movements: Friends of the Western Buddhist
Order

Kagyu Donak Ling*
c/o 7 Bateman Street, Headington, Oxford
OX3 7BG
Email: oxford@dechen.org
Website: http://www.dechen.org/
Contact Tel: (01865) 453574

Mahasiddha Yoga Group (Stillness in Action)*
Orchard House, 11 Church Street, Beckley, Oxford
OX3 9UT
Contact: Maarten Vermaase
Contact Tel: (01865) 351650

Oxford Buddhist Centre
16 Bhandari Close, Cricket Road, Oxford
OX4 3DT

Oxford Community of Interbeing*
17 Elmthorpe Road, Wolvercote, Oxford OX2 8PA
Tel: (01865) 552833
Contact: Mrs Ruth Dowley
Position: Sangha Member
Activities: Practice/meditation
Traditions: Zen
Affiliations: UK Community of Interbeing;
International Centre at Plum Village, France

Oxford University Buddhist Society*
14 Southmoor Road, Oxford
Tel: (01865) 454149
Contact: Dr Elsner

Samatha Association Oxford Group
8 Earl Street, Oxford OX2 0JA
Tel: (01865) 726312
Contact: Colin George
Position: Facilitator
Activities: Worship/meditation
Traditions: Theravada
Movements: Samatha
Affiliations: Samatha Association, Powys

Thrangu Rinpoche Trust*
42 Magdalen Road, Oxford OX4 1RB
Tel: (01865) 241555 **Fax:** (01865) 790096
Email: rosie@thrangu.clara.net
Website: http://www.thrangu.clara.net/
Contact: Rosie Green
Position: Secretary
Activities: Worship/practice/meditation,
community centre, umbrella body, women,
newsletter/journal, visits, inter-faith, resources
Traditions: Tibetan
Movements: Kagyupa
Affiliations: Thrangu Tashi Choling, Nepal

Chithurst Buddhist Monastery*
Chithurst, Petersfield GU31 5EU
Tel: (01730) 814986 Fax: (01730) 817334
Contact: Dr Barry Durrant
Position: Secretary
Activities: Worship/practice/meditation, visits
Traditions: Theravada
Movements: Forest Sangha Tradition
Other Languages: German
Affiliations: English Sangha Trust

Oxford Prasangika Centre*
c/o Shantideva Centre, 40 Alexandra Road,
Reading RG1 5PF
Tel: (0118) 9262198 **Fax:** (0118) 9262198
Email: info@learntomeditate.org
Website: http://www.learntomeditate.org/
Activities: Worship/practice/meditation

Reading Buddhist Priory
176 Cressingham Road, Reading RG2 7LW
Tel: (0118) 9860750 **Fax:** (0118) 9860750
Contact: The Prior
Activities: Worship/meditation
Traditions: Zen
Movements: Soto Zen
Affiliations: Throssel Hole Buddhist Abbey

Shantideva Centre
40 Alexandra Road, Reading RG1 5FP
Tel: (0118) 9262198
Email: kadampa@shantideva.co.uk
Website: http://www.shantideva.co.uk

Romsey Buddhist Group - Yakushi-Do*
44 Alma Road, Romsey SO51 8ED
Tel: (01794) 512735
Contact: Revd Ganshin E Rock
Position: Priest
Activities: Worship/practice/meditation
Traditions: Japanese Tendai
Movements: Tendai School
Other Languages: Japanese
Affiliations: Enryaku-Ji Temple, Mt Hiei, Japan

Dharma Trust, The*
Marpa House, Rectory Lane, Ashdon, Saffron
Walden CB10 2HN
Tel: (01799) 584415 **Fax:** (01799) 584415
Email: mail@marphahse.globalnet.co.uk
Website: http://www.marpahouse.org.uk/
Contact: The House Manager
Activities: Newsletter/journal
Traditions: Tibetan
Movements: Kagyupa

Chichester Serene Reflection Meditation Group*
22 Large Acres, Chichester, Selsey PO20 9BA
Tel: (01243) 604180
Email: escoffan@aol.com
Contact: Roy Foley
Position: Secretary
Activities: Worship/practice/meditation
Traditions: Zen

Movements: Soto Zen
Affiliations: Reading Buddhist Priory; Throssel Hole Priory Northumberland

Southampton Buddhist Centre
Southampton SO14 0EP
Tel: (023) 8057 6134 **Fax:** (023) 8036 5578
Email: buddsoc@soton.ac.uk
Traditions: Western
Movements: Friends of the Western Buddhist Order

Thekchen Mahayana Buddhist Centre*
76 Whitworth Crescent, Bitterne Park,
Southampton SO18 1GA
Tel: (023) 8055 7077
Email: ask@why meditate.com
Contact: Kelsang Nyingpo
Position: Admin Director
Activities: Worship/practice/meditation

Steyning Meditation Group*
37 Hills Road, Steyning BN44 3QG
Tel: (01903) 812130
Contact: Annie Cousins
Contact Email:
anniecousins@lantean.freeserve.co.uk
Activities: Worship/practice/meditation
Traditions: Theravada
Affiliations: Chithurst Buddhist Monastery

Surrey Buddhist Centre Meditation Group
Wold Cottage, Goose Lane, Mayford, Woking
GU22 0NW
Tel: (01483) 727170
Contact: Chris Hidred
Traditions: Multi-Traditional
Movements: Multi-Movements

Surrey Buddhist Meditation Group*
143 York Road, Woking GU22 7XS
Tel: (01483) 761398
Contact: Rocana
Position: Co-ordinator
Activities: Worship/practice/meditation, resources
Traditions: Theravada
Movements: The Forest Tradition
Affiliations: Chithurst Buddhist Monastery,
Amravati Buddhist Centre

SOUTH WEST
Regional or County Bodies

Sharpham College For Buddhist Studies And Contemporary Enquiry*
Sharpham College, Sharpham House, Ashprington,
Totnes TQ9 7UT
Tel: (01803) 732521 **Fax:** (01803) 732037
Email: college@sharpham-trust.org
Website: http://www.sharpham-trust.org/
Contact: Mr Colin Moore
Position: Manager
Contact Email: college@sharpham-trust.org
Activities: Worship/practice/meditation, resources
Traditions: Multi-Traditional
Movements: Non-denominational

Amitabha Buddhist Centre*
St Audries House, West Quantoxhead, Taunton
TA4 4DS
Tel: (01984) 633200 **Fax:** (01984) 633807
Email: buddha@amitabha.net
Website: http://www.amitabha.net/
Contact: Kelsang Donyo
Position: Education Co-ordinator
Activities: Worship/practice/meditation, visits
Traditions: Tibetan
Movements: New Kadampa
Affiliations: Manjushri Mahayana Buddhist Centre

City, Town or Local Bodies

Bath Buddhist Group*
1 Laura Place, Bath BA2 4BH
Contact: Catherine Hewitt
Position: Contact Person
Contact Tel: (01225) 405235
Activities: Worship/practice/meditation, umbrella body, newsletter/journal, visits
Traditions: Multi-Traditional
Movements: Gelugpa, Kagyupa, Nyingmapa, Soto Zen, Vipassana
Affiliations: The Buddhist Society

Bath Theravada Group*
54 Claude Avenue, Oldfield Park, Bath BA2 1AG
Tel: (01225) 405235
Contact: Miss Alice Catherine Hewitt
Position: Contact
Activities: Worship/practice/meditation
Traditions: Theravada
Movements: Vipassana
Affiliations: Amaravati Buddhist Monastery

Bournemouth Area Buddhist Group*
2 Wollstonecraft Road, Boscombe, Bournemouth
BH5 1JQ
Tel: (01202) 304207
Contact: Nigel Watkins
Position: Chairman

Bristol Buddhist Centre*
162 Gloucester Road, Bishopston, Bristol BS7 8NT
Tel: (0117) 9249991
Email: office@bristol-buddhist-centre . Fsnet.co.uk
Contact: Dave Sage
Position: Administrator
Activities: Worship/meditation, resources, visits,
youth, women
Traditions: Western
Movements: Friends of the Western Buddhist
Order

Bristol Shambhala Meditation Group*
13 Clifton Vale, Clifton, Bristol BS8 4PT
Tel: (0117) 9292511
Email: bristol@shambhala.org.uk
Website: http://www.shambhala.org.uk/bristol
Contact: Paul Harris
Position: Publicity Officer
Contact Email: paul.mercurius@virgin.net
Activities: Practice/meditation, resources
Traditions: Tibetan
Movements: Kagyupa
Affiliations: London Shambhala Meditation
Centre;

Bristol Soto Zen Dojo*
91-93 Gloucester Road, Bishopston, Bristol
BS7 8AT
Tel: (0117) 9424347
Email: bristol.zen.dojo@virgin.net
Contact: Adrian Tuttiett
Position: Trustee
Activities: Meditation
Traditions: Zen
Movements: Soto Zen
Other Languages: French
Affiliations: International Zen Association

Sakya Thinley Rinchen Ling*
121 Sommerville Road, St Andrews, Bristol
BS6 5BX
Tel: (0117) 9244424
Email: bristol@dechen.org
Website: http://www.dechen.org/
Contact: David Armstrong
Position: Co-ordinator

Activities: Worship/practice/meditation, books,
visits
Traditions: Tibetan
Movements: Sakyapa
Affiliations: Dechen Community, European
Buddhist Union (EBU)

White Clouds Sangha*
13 York Avenue, Ashley Down, Bristol BS7 9LH
Tel: (0117) 9512591
Email: whitecloudssangha@hotmail.com
Contact: Mr Duncan Liddle
Position: Contact
Activities: Worship/practice/meditation,
newsletter/journal
Traditions: Multi-traditional
Movements: Rinzai Zen, Vipassana
Affiliations: Community of Interbeing UK

Akanishta Buddhist Centre*
c/o Evelyn Court, Malvern Road, Cheltenham
GL50 2JR
Tel: (01242) 262840
Contact: Mr Rob Frost
Position: Administrative Director
Contact Tel: (01452) 414601
Activities: Worship/practice/meditation
Traditions: Tibetan
Movements: New Kadampa
Affiliations: Amitabha Buddhist Centre; Manjushri
Mahayana Buddhist Centre

Pure Land Buddhist Centre*
c/o 2 Westwood Cottages, Crediton EX17 3PE
Tel: (01363) 773112
Email: eddiej@compuserve.com
Contact: Mr Eddie Johnson
Position: Secretary
Activities: Worship/practice/meditation
Traditions: Tibetan
Movements: New Kadampa
Affiliations: Amitabha Buddhist Centre; Manjushri
Mahayana Buddhist Centre

Sakya Namgyal Ling*
3 Belvidere Road, Pennsylvania, Exeter EX4 4RU
Tel: (01392) 258021
Email: exeter@dechen.org
Website: http://www.dechen.org/
Contact: Martyn Samuel
Position: Co-ordinator
Contact Email: msamuel@ukgateway.net
Activities: Worship/practice/meditation,
newsletters, books

Traditions: Tibetan
Movements: Sakyapa
Other Languages: French
Affiliations: Dechen Community, European Buddhist Union (EBU)

Karma Pakshi Centre
8 Catherine Street, Frome BA11 1DB
Tel: (01373) 451289
Contact: Chris Hollingworth
Position: Secretary
Activities: Worship/meditation
Traditions: Tibetan
Movements: Kagyupa
Affiliations: Dhagpo Kagyu Ling, SW France

Naropa Buddhist Centre*
c/o Puddledock Cottage, Hill Corner, Frome
BA11 5JB
Tel: (01373) 462242
Contact: Mrs Susan Sampter
Position: Admin, Director
Activities: Worship/practice/meditation
Traditions: Tibetan
Movements: New Kadampa
Affiliations: Amitabha Buddhist Centre; Manjushri Mahayana Buddhist Centre

Sakya Orgyen Khandro Ling*
'Classeys', High Street, Butleigh, Glastonbury
BA6 8DD
Tel: (01458) 850958
Contact: Jenny Samson
Position: Chair

Hartridge Buddhist Monastery*
Odle Cottage, Uppottery, Honiton EX14 9QE
Tel: (01404) 891251 **Fax:** (01404) 890023
Contact: Retreats Manager
Activities: Worship/practice/meditation, youth
Traditions: Theravada

Gaia House*
West Ogwell, Newton Abbot TQ12 6EN
Tel: (01626) 333613 **Fax:** (01626) 352650
Email: gaiahouse@gn.apc.org
Website: http://www.gn.apc.org/gaiahouse
Contact: The Managers
Activities: Practice/meditation
Traditions: Multi-Traditional
Movements: Vipassana

Whitecross Buddhist Centre*
Gilly Lane, Whitecross, Penzance TR20 8BZ

Tel: (01736) 754342
Contact: Ms Carol Blackwell
Position: Trustee
Activities: Worship/practice/meditation
Traditions: Theravada

Ashoka Buddhist Centre*
2 Chaddlewood Avenue, St Judes, Plymouth
PL4 8RE
Tel: (01752) 224137
Contact: Mrs Jackie Hand
Position: Group Leader
Activities: Worship/practice/meditation
Traditions: Tibetan
Movements: New Kadampa
Affiliations: Amitabha Buddhist Centre; Manjushri Mahayana Buddhist Centre

Wellbeing Centre Buddhist Society, The*
The Self Heal Trust, Old School House,
Churchtown, Illogan, Redruth TR16 4SW
Tel: (01209) 842999
Contact: Fiona Ryall
Position: Co-ordinator
Activities: Worship/practice/meditation

Saltash Buddhist Group*
7 Tavy Road, Saltash PL12 6DE
Tel: (01752) 846096
Contact: Dharmachari Jayaratna
Activities: Worship/practice/meditation, inter-faith, resources
Traditions: Western
Movements: Friends of the Western Buddhist Order
Affiliations: Bristol Buddhist Centre

Western Ch'an Fellowship*
Winterhead Hill Farm, Shipham BS25 1RS
Email: teacher@w-c-f.org.uk
Website: http://www.w-c-f.org.uk/
Contact: Teacher
Activities: Resource, umbrella body, newsletters, inter-faith
Traditions: Zen
Movements: Ch'an
Other Languages: French, German, Greek
Affiliations: Bristol Ch'an Group; Western Ch'an Fellowship; Chung Hwa Institute of Buddhist Culture, New York and Taiwan

Saraswati Buddhist Group*
The Market House, St James Street, South
Petherton TA13 5BN

Tel: (01460) 241339
Email: andy.wistreich@btinternet.com
Contact: Andy Wistreich
Activities: Worship/practice/meditation
Traditions: Tibetan
Movements: Gelugpa
Affiliations: Network of Buddhist Organisations

Swindon Buddhist Fellowship*
1, Wharf Road, Wroughton, Swindon SN4 9LE
Tel: (01793) 812409
Contact: Irwin Brohier
Position: Lay Guide
Activities: Inter-faith
Traditions: Theravada
Movements: Maha Bodhi, Vipassana

Swindon Buddhist Meditation Group*
84 Lansdown Road, Swindon SN1 3ND
Tel: (01793) 343447
Email: hughie@carrollonline.co.uk
Contact: Hugh Carroll
Activities: Worship/meditation
Traditions: Multi-Traditional
Movements: Ch'an, Kagyupa
Affiliations: Western Ch'an Fellowship

Amitabha Buddhist Centre*
St Audries House, West Quantoxhead, Taunton
TA4 4DS
Tel: (01984) 633200 **Fax:** (01984) 633807
Email: buddha@amitabha.net
Website: http://www.amitabha.net/
Contact: Kelsang Donyo
Position: Education Co-ordinator
Activities: Worship/practice/meditation, visits
Traditions: Tibetan
Movements: New Kadampa
Affiliations: Manjushri Mahayana Buddhist Centre

**Sharpham College For Buddhist Studies And
Contemporary Enquiry***
Sharpham College, Sharpham House, Ashprington,
Totnes TQ9 7UT
Tel: (01803) 732521 **Fax:** (01803) 732037
Email: college@sharpaham-trust.org
Website: http://www.sharpham-trust.org/
Contact: Mr Colin Moore
Position: Manager
Contact Email: college@sharpham-trust.org
Activities: Worship/practice/meditation, resources
Traditions: Multi-Traditional
Movements: Non-denominational

Forge Yoga Centre, The*
Top of Collins Road, Totnes TQ9 5PJ
Tel: (01803) 867440 **Fax:** (01803) 867440
Email: theforge@totalise.co.uk
Contact: Gretchen Caplan-Faust
Activities: Meditation

NORTHERN IRELAND

City, Town or Local Bodies

Jampa Ling Belfast*
26 Kansas Avenue, off Antrim Road, Belfast
BT15 5AW
Tel: (028) 9058 9442
Email: jampaling@compuserve.com
Activities: Meditation
Movements: Gelugpa

Tashi Khyil Tibetan Buddhist Centre and Trust
14 Drumaconnell Road, Saintfield BT24 7NB
Tel: (028) 9651 0232

SCOTLAND

Regional or County Bodies

**Aberdeen Friends of the Western Buddhist
Order***
Aberdeen Buddhist Centre, 6 Sclattie Park,
Bucksburn, Aberdeen AB21 9QR
Tel: (01224) 712489
Contact: Dh Ajitasena
Position: Chairman
Contact Email: ajitasens@netscapeonline.co.uk
Activities: Worship/practice/meditation
Traditions: Western
Movements: Friends of the Western Buddhist
Order

Portobello Buddhist Priory*
27 Brighton Place, Portobello, Edinburgh
EH15 1LL
Tel: (0131) 669 9622 **Fax:** (0131) 530 1223
Contact: The Prior
Email: leyn@pbpriory. freeserve. co.uk
Website:
http://www. geocities.com/pbpriory/portobello.html
Traditions: Zen
Movements: Soto Zen
Activities: Meditation/practice, central body,
newsletter/journal. visits, inter faith, resources

Affiliations: Order of Buddhist Contemplatives, Throstle Hole Buddhist Abbey

City, Town or Local Bodies

Aberdeen Reflection Meditation
Aberdeen, AB31 5ZZB
Activities: Worship/practice/meditation
Affiliations: Order of Buddhist Contemplatives

Galloway Serene Reflection Meditation Group*
Parkhead Cottage, Southwick DG2 8AW
Email: anne.darling@virgin.net
Contact: Keith Matherson
Position: Treasurer
Activities: Worship/practice/meditation
Traditions: Soto Zen

Dingwall Friends of the Western Buddhist Order Group*
Dingwall, c/o Flat 4, Viewmount House, 10 Culduthel Road, Inverness IV2 4AG
Tel: (01463) 714213
Email: gunasiddhi@fwbo.fsnet.co.uk
Contact: Dh Gunasiddhi
Position: Chairwoman
Activities: Worship/practice/meditation

Vajrasattva Buddhist Centre*
c/o 58 Cardoness Street, Dumfries DG1 3AJ
Tel: (01387) 254852 **Fax:** (01387) 254852
Contact: Mrs Jill McKean
Position: Co-ordinator
Activities: Worship/meditation, resources
Movements: New Kadampa

Edinburgh Buddhist Centre*
10 Viewforth, Edinburgh EH10 4JF
Tel: (0131) 2283333
Email: ebudc@supanet.com
Website:
http://www.edinburghbuddhistcentre.org.uk/
Contact: Dharmacharini Kalyanavaca
Position: Chairwoman
Activities: Worship/practice/meditation, women, visits, inter-faith, resources
Traditions: Western
Movements: Friends of the Western Buddhist Order
Affiliations: Glasgow Buddhist Centre, Friends of the Western Buddhist Order

Edinburgh Theravada Buddhist Group*
Eric Liddill Centre, 15 Morningside Road,

Edinburgh EH10 4DP
Contact Tel: (0131) 332 7987
Contact: Jody Higgs
Activities: religious, visits, inter-faith
Traditions: Theravada
Affiliations: Buddhist Organisations in Edinburgh; Ratanagiri Harnham Buddhist Monastery

Wellspring Buddhists
13 Smith's Place, Edinburgh EH6 8NT

Forres Friends of the Western Buddhist Order Group*
Forres, c/o Flat 4, Viewmount House, 10 Culduthel Road, Iverness, IV2 4AG
Tel: (01463) 714213
Email: gunasiddhi@fwbo.fsnet.co.uk
Contact: Dh Gunasiddhi
Position: Chairwoman
Activities: Worship/practice/meditation

Glasgow Buddhist Centre*
329 Sauchiehall Street, Glasgow G2 3HW
Tel: (0141) 3330524
Email: glasbud@aol.com
Website: http://www.glasgowbuddhistcentre.com/
Contact: Pam Hill
Position: Administrator
Activities: Worship/practice/meditation, central body, women, newsletter/journal, visits, inter-faith, resources
Traditions: Multi-traditional
Movements: Friends of the Western Buddhist Order
Affiliations: Friends of the Western Buddhist Order (Central), Edinburgh Buddhist Centre

Glasgow Theravada Buddhist Group*
c/o 3 Corrie Grove, Muirend, Glasgow G44 3PP
Tel: (0141) 6379731
Contact: Mr James Scott
Position: Secretary
Activities: Worship/practice/meditation
Traditions: Theravada
Affiliations: "Aruna Ratanagiri" Harnham Buddhist Monastery, Belsay; Amaravati Monastery, Great Gaddesden

Rokpa Glasgow*
7 Ashley Street, Woodlands, Glasgow G41 2NN
Tel: (0141) 3329950 **Fax:** (0141) 4290990
Email: glasgow@rokpa.org
Website: http://www.rokpa.org/glasgow
Contact: Humphrey Matthey

Position: Committee Member
Contact Tel: (0141) 4290300
Contact Email: humphrey.m@origin.net
Activities: Worship/practice/meditation, resources
Traditions: Tibetan
Movements: Kagyupa
Other Languages: Tibetan
Affiliations: Rokpa Trust

Inverness Friends of the Western Buddhist Order Group*
c/o Flat 4, Viewmount House, 10 Culduthel Road, Inverness IV2 4AG
Tel: (01463) 714213
Email: gunasiddhi@fwbo.co.uk
Contact: Dh Gunasiddhi
Position: Chairwoman
Activities: Worship/practice/meditation
Traditions: Western
Movements: Friends of the Western Buddhist Order

Kagyu Samyeling*
Tibetan Buddhist Monastery, Eskdalemuir, Langholm DG13 0QL
Tel: (013873) 73232 **Fax:** (01387) 373223
Email: scotland@samyeling.org
Website: http://www.samyeling.org/
Contact: J Tsering
Position: Bookings Office
Activities: Worship/meditation, visits, resources
Traditions: Tibetan
Movements: Kagyupa
Other Languages: Tibetan
Affiliations: ROKPA International

Dhanakosa Buddhist Retreat Centre*
Ledcreich, Balquhidder, Lochearnhead FK19 8PQ
Tel: (01877) 384213
Email: dhanakosa@compuserve.co
Website: http://www.dhanakosa.com/
Contact: Mr Gordon O'Connor
Position: Secretary
Activities: Worship/practice/meditation, community centre, women, newsletter/journal, resources
Traditions: Multi-traditional
Movements: Friends of the Western Buddhist Order
Affiliations: Glasgow Buddhist Centre, Friends of the Western Buddhist Order

Perth Friends of the Western Buddhist Order Group*
Perth, c/o Glasgow Friends of the Western Buddhist Order, 329 Sauchiehall Street, Glasgow, G2 3HW
Contact: Dh Suriyavamsa
Position: Chairman
Contact Tel: (0141) 3330524
Contact Email: glasgowbud@aol.com
Activities: Worship/practice/meditation
Traditions: Western
Movements: Friends of the Western Buddhist Order
Affiliations: Glasgow Buddhist Centre; Dhanakosa Retreat Centre

WALES

Regional or County Bodies

Dharmavajra Buddhist Centre*
13 St James's Gardens, Uplands, Swansea SA1 6DX
Tel: (01792) 458245
Email: dharmavajra@nktswansea.co.uk
Website: http://www.dharmavajra.co.uk
Contact: Ms Wendy McGill
Position: Administrative Director
Activities: Worship/practice/meditation, central body, youth, elderly, newsletter/journal, visits
Traditions: Tibetan
Movements: New Kadampa
Other Languages: Welsh
Affiliations: Manjushri Mahayana Buddhist Centre
Local Groups:
Carmarthen
Pontardawe

City, Town or Local Bodies

Kagyu Tegchen Choling*
Riverside Lodge, Pont Y Gwyddel, Llanfairtalhaiarn, Abergele LL22 9RA
Tel: (01745) 540417
Email: mold@dechen.org
Website: http://www.dechen.org/
Contact: Lyn Williams
Position: Secretary
Activities: Worship/practice/meditation, newsletter, books
Traditions: Tibetan
Movements: Kagyupa
Affiliations: Dechen Community, European Buddhist Union (EBU)

Aberystwyth Buddhist Group*
Troedrhiwsebon, Cwmrheidol, Aberystwyth
SY23 3NB
Tel: (01970) 880603
Email: kennora@onetel.net.uk
Contact: Kenneth Henry Jones
Activities: Worship/practice/meditation
Traditions: Non-Denominational
Affiliations: Gaia House

Bangor Buddhist Fellowship*
62 Carneddi Road, Bethesda, Bangor LL57 3SE
Tel: (01248) 601109
Contact: Malcolm Boater
Position: Resident Monk
Activities: Worship/practice/meditation
Traditions: Multi-Traditional

Kalpa Badra Buddhist Centre*
Bangor
Tel: (01492) 540414
Contact: Julie Bower
Position: Administrative Director

Je Tsongkhapa Buddhist Centre*
Old Penual Chapel, 118a High Street, Barry
CF62 7DS
Tel: (01446) 746691
Contact: Miss Rebecca Thomas
Activities: Worship/practice/meditation, visits
Traditions: Tibetan
Movements: New Kadampa
Affiliations: Dharmavajra Buddhist Centre,
Manjushri Mahayana Buddhist Centre

Cardiff Buddhist Centre
12 St Peters Street, Cardiff CF24 3BA
Tel: (029) 2046 2492
Traditions: Western
Movements: Friends of the Western Buddhist
Order

Cardiff Buddhist Community
97a Albany Road, Cardiff CF2 3LP

**Cardiff Serene Reflection (Soto Zen)
Meditation Group***
114 Parc-y-Fro, Creigiau, Cardiff CF15 9SB
Tel: (029) 2089 0034
Email: joycefrape@norwell.worldonline.co.uk
Website: http://www.telinco.co.uk/cardiffzen
Contact: Mrs Joyce Frape/Norwell
Activities: Worship/practice/meditation, umbrella
body, newsletter/journal, radio, television, visits,
inter-faith, resources

Traditions: Zen
Movements: Soto Zen

Kalpa Bhadra Buddhist Centre*
89 Llanerch Road West, Colwyn Bay LL28 4AS
Tel: (01492) 540414
Website: http://www.kalpa.f9.co.uk/
Contact: Nigel David Spaull
Activities: Worship/practice/meditation, resources
Traditions: Tibetan
Movements: New Kadampa
Other Languages: Welsh

**Friends of the Western Buddhist Order Study
Centre***
Blaenddol House, Corwen LL21 0EN
Tel: (01490) 460648
Email: vajra.kuta@virgin.net
Website: http://www.dharmavastu.org/
Contact: Dharmacari Jinaraja
Activities: Worship/practice/meditation, resources
Traditions: Western
Movements: Friends of the Western Buddhist
Order
Other Languages: Hindi, German, Finnish,
Spanish
Affiliations: Vajraloka Meditation Centre;
Madhyamaloka, Office of the Western Buddhist
Order

Llangollen Buddhist Group*
c/o Vajraloke: Tyn-y-Ddol, Treddol, Corwen
LL21 0EN
Tel: (01490) 460406
Email: vajraloka@compuserve.com
Contact: Dhammachari Aryacitta
Activities: Worship/practice/meditation
Traditions: Western
Affiliations: Friends of the Western Buddhist
Order

Gwent Zazen Group*
6 Ruskin Close, Silver Birches, Fairwater, Cwmbran
NP44 4QX
Tel: (01633) 874882
Contact: Mr Kevin Davies
Position: Organiser
Activities: Worship/practice/meditation
Traditions: Zen
Movements: Soto Zen
Affiliations: Bristol Zen Dojo, International Zen
Association UK, Association Zen Internationale

Samatha Group*
Letterstone
Website:
http://www.samatha.demon.co.uk/pembrokeshire/
Contact: Alex Barr
Contact Tel: (01348) 840309
Contact Email: alex@fronrhydd.demon.co.uk
Activities: Meditation
Traditions: Theravada
Affiliations: The Samatha Association

Community of Interbeing*
Coedcae, Rock House Road, Llandrindod Wells
LD1 6AF
Tel: (01597) 823672
Email: mlowe@new-leaf.demon.co.uk
Contact: Mr Michael Lowe
Activities: Worship/practice/meditation
Traditions: zen
Affiliations: Community of Interbeing UK; Order
of Interbeing

Carmarthenshire Meditation Group*
Ffynnongreck, Pumpsaint, Llanwrda SA19 8YE
Tel: (01558) 650460
Contact: Jenny M Waite
Position: Meditation Teacher
Activities: Worship/practice/meditation
Traditions: Theravada
Movements: Samatha, Vipassana

Dharmavajra Buddhist Centre*
13 St James's Gardens, Uplands, Swansea SA1 6DX
Tel: (01792) 458245
Email: dharmavajra@nktswansea.co.uk
Website: http://www.dharmavajra.co.uk
Contact: Ms Wendy McGill
Position: Administrative Director
Activities: Worship/practice/meditation, central
body, youth, elderly, newsletter/journal, visits
Traditions: Tibetan
Movements: New Kadampa
Other Languages: Welsh
Affiliations: Manjushri Mahayana Buddhist Centre

Tiratanaloka Women's Retreat Centre*
Aberclydach House, Aber, Tallybont-on-Usk
LD3 7YS
Tel: (01874) 676482
Email: tiratanaloka@compuserve.com
Contact: Dharmacharini Akasasuri
Position: Secretary
Activities: Worship/practice/meditation, central
body, women

Traditions: Multi-traditional
Movements: Friends of the Western Buddhist
Order

INTRODUCING CHRISTIANS IN THE UK

CHRISTIANS IN THE UNITED KINGDOM 203

ORIGINS AND DEVELOPMENT OF CHRISTIANITY 205

SOURCES OF CHRISTIAN BELIEFS AND PRACTICES 206

KEY CHRISTIAN BELIEFS 208

TRADITIONS IN CHRISTIANITY 211

CHRISTIAN LIFE 215

CHRISTIAN WORSHIP 218

CHRISTIAN CALENDAR AND FESTIVALS 221

CHRISTIAN ORGANISATIONS 224

CHURCHES IN THE UK 225

FURTHER READING 234

CHRISTIANS IN THE UNITED KINGDOM

Christianity is the largest and longest established of the world religious traditions in the UK. In its various forms, it has shaped the past and present life of the British Isles and helped mould legal structures, public institutions, and the social and intellectual tradition. This strong presence and influence is reflected in the number of places of worship around the country. In England and Wales, for example, at the last count there were 44,648 registered or recorded places of Christian worship, (figures are not available for the UK overall). Because there are so many Christian places of worship, and a range of extensive and detailed directories of Christian *Churches* and organisations are available, this directory lists only Christian bodies at regional and national level. More detailed information about local *churches* and Christian organisations can be obtained from these bodies.

Beginnings in the United Kingdom

Christianity was introduced into Britain from continental Europe when some of its Celtic inhabitants were converted during the early centuries of the Common Era. *Celtic* Christianity developed in parts of northern England, Ireland, Scotland and Wales. Christian life also developed in the South of England during Roman times. The distinctive ethos and loose structures of *Celtic* Christianity were independent of the organisational structures of the rest of *Western Christendom* that had developed around the *Bishop of Rome* (the *Pope*).

In 597 CE, Augustine, an emissary of *Pope* Gregory the Great of Rome, arrived in Kent. Canterbury became the base for his *missionary* work. He became *Archbishop of Canterbury* and was given authority by the *Pope* over the *bishops* in the rest of Britain, an authority which they acknowledged at the Synod of Whitby in 664 CE. The *Catholic* form of Christianity gradually displaced *Celtic*

Christianity, although in Wales and Ireland *Celtic* forms of Christianity continued independently for some centuries.

Western Christianity gradually became consolidated under the jurisdiction of the *Pope*, and Christians in the different parts of these islands remained part of what was known as the *Catholic* (meaning universal) tradition until the time of the *Reformation*.

Protestant Reformation

During the sixteenth and seventeenth centuries *Western Christendom* underwent major religious and political upheavals. This period is referred to as the *Reformation*, because of the attempts made by *Protestants* (initially those reformers who protested against certain doctrines and practices in the *Catholic Church*) in a number of European countries to remodel the Christian *Church* in a way which, they believed, reflected more truly the earliest forms of Christianity to which the *New Testament* scriptures witnessed. Key reformers were Martin Luther and John Calvin.

In England and Wales, various changes took place in the *Church* which reflected these movements. After King Henry VIII's political break with the *Papacy*, the Church of England was recognised as the *established* form of religion in England. The Church of Scotland, embodying a *Calvinist*, *Presbyterian* (see below) form of *Church* government, became the *established* religion in Scotland. In Ireland, *Presbyterianism* spread with the influence of settlers from Scotland, whilst the adherents of the majority of the population to *Catholic* Christianity also became a dimension of resistance to English attempts to establish control over Ireland.

During the sixteenth and seventeenth centuries Christians of various traditions were persecuted depending upon the balance of power at the time. Those Christians remaining loyal to the *Papacy* remained subject to legal disabilities and penalties until the nineteenth century. In addition to the Churches of England and Scotland, other forms of *Protestant* Christianity came into being during the sixteenth, seventeenth and eighteenth centuries. These movements are often known as *Nonconformist* because of their refusal to conform to ways of worship and organisation required in the Churches established by law. Like *Roman Catholics*, they were subjected to numerous civil and religious restrictions and penalties until the nineteenth century.

Denominational and Ethnic Diversity

Christianity in the UK is ethnically and denominationally very diverse. Groups of Christian immigrants have, over the centuries, brought their own distinctive traditions with them. These groups have included the French Reformed *Huguenots*, Irish *Roman Catholics* and, more recently, Greek, Russian and other *Eastern Orthodox* (see below) Christians, as well as members of the *Pentecostal*, *Holiness* and *Spiritual Churches* of mainly African-Caribbean membership. Also included are groups from Africa, Asia and Latin America, who now form a small but growing and increasingly significant proportion among practising Christians, especially in England.

There are also groupings of Chinese Christians with origins in Hong Kong and of Asian Christians with ethnic origins in the Indian sub-continent, Korea and elsewhere. One of the fastest growing sections of Christianity in the UK is the so-called *New Church* or *House Church* Movement which is *Evangelical* in flavour, and is so named because it began predominantly at meetings in the houses of its members.

Numbers and Geography

Active membership varies considerably between the four nations of these islands, with this being at its greatest in Northern Ireland and Scotland.

Concepts of membership, and therefore the basis upon which these statistics are calculated, vary significantly from *Church* to *Church*. The active strength of different denominations also varies between the four nations.

In terms of what is often called "community membership" (as distinct from "active membership") the Church of England is the largest single *Church* in England. In Scotland the largest single *Church* is the Church of Scotland (*Presbyterian*), and in Northern Ireland, it is the Roman Catholic Church. In Wales, the *Free Churches* collectively are larger than any other tradition as are the *Protestant* Churches in Northern Ireland although the Roman Catholic Church is the largest single *Church* there.

This pattern is, however, the subject of considerable variation in terms of numerical growth and decline. The Roman Catholic Church is the *Church* with the largest attendance in England. The *Independent* and *Orthodox Churches* and, in some parts of the UK, the *Baptist* and *Pentecostal* Churches, have been growing steadily in terms of active membership, while parallel to this there has been a significant decline in the "active membership", as measured by *church* attendance on Sundays, of the *Roman Catholic*, *Anglican* and *Presbyterian* Churches. This has contributed in recent decades to an overall decline of active *Church* membership in the UK.

ORIGINS AND DEVELOPMENT OF CHRISTIANITY

Early Years

Christianity began around two thousand years ago as a radical renewal movement within Judaism. It is rooted in the life and teaching of Jesus of Nazareth. The early Jesus movements were linked strongly to Jewish life, but as the tradition spread it came to include also *Gentiles*, or those of a non-Jewish background. It developed a separate life but retained a complex and often problematic link to the Jewish tradition. For a long period Christians suffered localised opposition, coupled with sporadically intense persecution throughout the Roman Empire, especially under the Emperors Decius and Diocletian. However, Christianity gradually gained a wider following and, following the conversion of the Roman Emperor Constantine in the early fourth century CE, it eventually became the official religion of the Roman Empire.

The Roman Empire became divided into Eastern and Western parts which followed distinct Christian traditions. Although the *Churches* in the East and the West had much in common, differences of doctrine and practice began to emerge within the different jurisdictions. Following the great *Schism* between these *Churches* in 1054, by the twelfth century these differences had resulted in the distinctive forms of *Eastern* and *Western Christendom* which underlie, respectively, the various forms of *Eastern Orthodox* and *Roman Catholic* Christianity.

Eastern and Western Christendom and Protestant Reformation

After the rise of Islam in the seventh century CE, the *Churches* of *Eastern Christendom* in the Middle East and in North Africa became separate religious minorities. By contrast, in *Western Christendom*, Christianity was the dominant religious tradition, largely supplanting indigenous *pagan* traditions. In the Middle Ages, *Western Christendom* was commonly understood as a socio-political unity with two poles of authority: the state power of the *Holy Roman Emperor* or an individual country's monarch, and the ecclesiastical and spiritual authority of the *Pope* (the *Bishop of Rome*, the senior *bishop* of the *Church*).

There was a continued tension between these secular and spiritual poles until, in the sixteenth century, *Western Christendom* fragmented, with many territories becoming *Protestant* and no longer acknowledging *papal* jurisdiction in the spiritual sphere. Many *Protestant Churches* developed as national *Churches* having a close relationship with the states in which they were set.

The Protestant Reformation and the Missionary Movement

With growing European awareness of the world beyond Europe, both *Protestant* and *Roman Catholic* Christians increasingly became convinced of a need to spread the message of Christianity to the countries where European colonies were being established. The *missionary* movement began with the *Roman Catholic* missions of the sixteenth and seventeenth centuries to China, Goa, Japan and the New World. It reached its peak during the latter part of the nineteenth century and the first half of the twentieth century, with the development of the *Protestant* Christian missions that led to Christian *Churches* of many denominations being established on every continent. This process then in turn contributed to the development of the *ecumenical* movement (see below) towards unity in faith, prayer and action among the Christian *Churches* of the world.

Many individual Christian *missionaries* were undoubtedly motivated by genuine Christian convictions about their responsibility for spreading the Christian message, but the relationship between the *missionary* movement and European colonialism and imperialism has, with hindsight, been criticised by the more recently founded *Churches* in other continents and by many of the European *Churches* themselves. However, the *missionaries* made a significant impact, and today the global focus of Christianity has shifted significantly from Europe and North America to Africa and Latin America.

SOURCES OF CHRISTIAN BELIEFS AND PRACTICES

Scriptures

The Christian *scriptures* comprise what Christians have traditionally called the *Old Testament* and the *New Testament* (*testament* meaning *covenant*). Together they form what is known among Christians as the *Bible*. From the earliest years of Christianity Christians have believed that one God speaks through both the Jewish law, the *prophets* and the writings as recorded in the *Hebrew Scriptures* (commonly known among Christians as the *Old Testament*), and through Jesus as testified to in the *Gospels*, *Epistles* and other writings (which collectively came to be known among Christians as the *New Testament*).

The Christian *Old Testament* is similar in content to the Jewish *Tanakh* (see chapter on "Introducing Jews in the UK"), though different in its internal order after the first five books. The *New Testament* is a collection of texts dating from the first and early second centuries which describe the impact of Jesus upon his followers who became known as "*Christians*", together with beliefs about him, the story of the formation of early Christian communities, and the elaboration of the ethical implications of Christian belief.

The *canon* (normative contents) of the Christian *New Testament* emerged out of a process of debate concerning the authenticity and authority of a wider range of writings which were in circulation among the early Christian communities. The *canon* was finalised by a *Church* Council held in Carthage in 397 CE, although there remains some difference among Christians today concerning the place of a number of Greek texts collectively known as the *Apocrypha* (literally, "the hidden things") which are not included in the Hebrew language version of the *Old Testament*. *Roman Catholics* and some other Christians understand these books to be fully a part of the scriptures, whilst others see their religious value as of less centrality.

The status of these texts is, however, different from that of texts which emerged much later in history, such as the forged *Gospel of Barnabas*, which is not accepted by Christians as authentic in any sense.

In the *New Testament* the four *Gospels* (the English term from the Saxon word *Godspell*, meaning *Good News*) tell the story and describe how Christians understand the significance of Jesus, emphasising particularly his public life, death and *resurrection*. They are named after four early followers of Jesus: *Matthew, Mark, Luke* and *John*. They are followed by the *Book of the Acts of the Apostles*, which describes the spread of early Christianity; the *Epistles*, in which the leaders of the early *Church* address problems and issues arising in the Christian communities; and finally the *Book of Revelation*, which records a series of visions.

The scriptures are central to the life of all Christians. Some Christians understand them as being the literal words of God without error or human distortion, whilst others see them as human testimony, guided by the Spirit of God in all central matters of belief and practice, and bearing witness to Jesus as the revelation of God in human nature.

The Creeds

Creeds (from the Latin *Credo*, meaning "I believe") are summary statements of orthodox beliefs hammered out during vigorous controversies throughout the first centuries of CE. The most commonly used and important are the *Apostles' Creed* and the *Nicene Creed*. There are, however, some Christian denominations which dislike the use of *credal* formulae, notably *Unitarians*, members of the Society of Friends and some *Baptists*.

Tradition

For *Orthodox, Roman Catholic* and *Anglican* Christians, *Tradition* is the third key source of belief and practice. *Tradition* is understood to embrace the authoritative understandings and interpretations of basic Christian beliefs contained in the scriptures and the *creeds* of the *Church*. The texts of the *Patristic* period (the period of the early *Church Fathers*) are of great importance for many Christians, and particularly for those within the *Orthodox Churches*, as authoritative interpretations of scripture. Also important for belief and practice, although less authoritative, are the writings of the great Christian *saints* (see below).

Reason, Conscience and Experience

Human reason, individual conscience and religious experience are also recognised sources of belief and practice when exercised in the context of the scriptures, the *creeds*, *Tradition* and the teaching of the *denomination* or the local *church*. Christians differ, however, on the scope for individual interpretation.

The Church

On the basis of its scriptures, and for many *Churches* also drawing on *Tradition*, the *Church* provides guidance to Christian individuals and Christian communities. The community of those who follow Jesus is known as the *Church* (from the Greek, *kuriakon*, meaning "belonging to the Lord").

The Greek word *ekklesia* (translated as *Church*) originally referred to the whole community of believers and is still used today with reference to the universal Christian community. Nevertheless, the English word *Church* has also come to be used in a variety of other ways. Sometimes (and usually when it begins with a capital letter) it is used to refer to particular national bodies or world communions such as the Methodist Church or the Russian Orthodox Church. At other times it refers to the buildings in which Christian worship takes place (as when people refer to "the *church* on the corner of the street" or the local Christian group which is found there. In these latter instances, the word usually begins with a small "c".

KEY CHRISTIAN BELIEFS

Jesus

The common focus of Christianity is upon the person of Jesus of Nazareth. Christian groups differ to some extent in their interpretations of his teaching, life, death and *resurrection* (being raised from the dead), but these matters are at the heart of the teaching and way of life of all of them.

The earliest Christian confession of faith appears to have been the expression "Jesus is *Lord*". In other words, he was seen as the criterion by which all of life was to be evaluated, and not simply as the *Saviour* of those who followed him. By this title of *Lord*, used also in Jewish tradition of God, the universal significance of Jesus is asserted.

The name "Christians" was originally a nickname given to the early followers of Jesus, who confessed him to be the *Christ*. The English word *Christ* comes from the Greek *Christos* which is, in turn, a translation of the Hebrew *Mashiach*. Although this word often appears together with Jesus as if Jesus Christ is a personal name, Jesus is the personal name and *Christ* is a title given to him by the early Christians, who believed that Jesus fulfilled the expectations of the Jewish people for the *Messiah* (the *Anointed One* – a coming deliverer). Other titles used of Jesus in the *New Testament* scriptures include *Son of Man*, *Son of God*, *Saviour* and *Word of God*.

Christians turn to the four *Gospels* and the *Book of the Acts of the Apostles* for an account and explanation of the origins of Christianity, the story of Jesus and its significance. These documents indicate that Jesus was born in Bethlehem, approximately two thousand years ago; that he grew up in the town of Nazareth in the region known as Galilee; that when he was about thirty years old he began to teach, heal and travel through Judaea, Samaria and Galilee with a group of *disciples* (learners) from among whom he chose twelve *apostles* (*messengers* – from the Greek *apostoloi*); that in his work, as well as associating with the ordinary people of his nation, he deliberately also associated with the disreputable and with social and religious outcasts, in order to demonstrate the love of God for all kinds of people.

The *Gospels* also indicate that Jesus called people to turn to God, repent of their sins and receive forgiveness, teaching that the self-righteous are actually those who cut themselves off from the outcasts. They indicate that although Jesus was a faithful Jew, he also came into conflict with the Jewish authorities of his day and that he was put to death by *crucifixion* by the Roman occupiers of the country, (a form of execution usually applied to slaves and political rebels which entailed hanging its victims upon a *cross* made of wood until they died by asphyxiation).

The *Gospels* recount that three days later his tomb was found empty; that he was met by one of his women followers and his disciples reported meeting with him, talking with him and eating with him; and that eventually these disciples believed that he had been *resurrected* from the dead and had *ascended* to be with God the Father.

The *Acts of the Apostles* describe the early Christians' experience of the Holy Spirit being sent down on gathered followers and also give an account of the spread of the new faith. These texts and the *Epistles* (from the Greek *epistole*, meaning "letter") reveal the significance of Jesus for the earliest Christians and show something of Christianity's development in a variety of different geographical locations throughout the eastern Mediterranean area. The *Epistles*, in particular, portray Jesus as the key to God's activity in the world, and they attempt to apply his teaching to daily life.

God, Incarnation and Revelation

Christians are *monotheists*. They believe that there is one God who has been revealed as

Father and as the Creator, Sustainer and *Redeemer* (or, restorer) of all that is. They also believe that whilst this one God has been manifested in many different places and times, and in particular through the history and faith of the Jewish people, God's nature has been shown most clearly in the life, teaching, death and *resurrection* of Jesus of Nazareth.

Indeed, it is traditionally believed that God the Son (see section below on the *Holy Trinity*) became a human being as the *Word* of God made flesh in Jesus, born as a Jew, and that in and through Jesus, God identified fully with humanity. This is called the *incarnation* (from the Latin for "enfleshed"). The classical *credal* definition of the 451CE Council of Chalcedon contains the paradoxical statement that Jesus was both fully human and fully divine. This expresses the belief that Jesus was fully human in all respects except for sin (falling short of the will of God) and yet also that God was fully present in Jesus' human vulnerability.

It is because of belief in the *incarnation* that, in Christian understanding, Jesus' teachings, such as the well-known *Sermon on the Mount*, cannot ultimately be separated from his life, death and *resurrection* as the embodiment and expression of the nature of God. Through Jesus, understood as the revelation of God made flesh, the nature of God is pre-eminently seen as being that of self-giving love (signified by the use of the Greek word *agape*, one of three Greek words rendered in English by the word "love").

Salvation

Jesus is therefore seen as the pivotal historical locus of God's activity. This activity is first of all seen as creative. God is understood as the origin of all things, both seen and unseen, which were created as good. But God's activity is also seen as *salvific* (putting right that which has gone wrong), because the world and human beings within it are understood to have become fundamentally flawed and to be in need of God's healing. This flawedness has been understood in a variety of ways within Christianity from the effect of original sin passed down the generations from the sins of the first humans, Adam and Eve, to the falling away from God of each individual human.

Whatever the cause, humans are believed by Christians to fall short of God's intention for them. Human beings are created in the image of God, but the image in each has become clouded over or damaged and is in need of restoration, so that they can come back into right relationship with God. It is believed by Christians that God takes the initiative in this restorative forgiveness and acceptance and this activity of God is known as *grace*.

God's healing *salvific* activity is understood by Christians to be most fully demonstrated in Jesus' life and teaching, which serve as a pattern for human life, and in God's participation in Jesus' death and *resurrection*. The *Gospels* show Jesus' death as the inevitable consequence of his faithful announcement of the message of the coming *Kingdom of God*. Very early on, many Christians also came to interpret the death and *resurrection* of Jesus as in some sense a sacrifice paid on behalf of human sin, to bring about an *atoned* ("at-oned") and restored relationship with God (a key theme in the writings attributed to St Paul).

It was also believed that somehow, in the *crucifixion* of Jesus, God plumbed the depths of human experience: death itself, the last enemy of human life. Death was then conquered in the *resurrection* and it is this conquest that Christians celebrate at *Easter*. In traditional belief, because of Jesus' conquest of death, no lesser powers can bind or enslave any who put their trust in him, and death itself will be overcome after this life by those who partake, through faith, in his *resurrection*.

Many Christians also hold to the traditional biblical idea that Jesus will return a second time to judge humanity and bring about a complete renewal of all creation: not just of human beings. For some *Evangelical* Christian groups, this idea of a *Second Coming* is connected with a belief that it is possible to interpret world events in the light of such biblical texts as the *Book of Revelation* to discern when Jesus will come again.

Judgement and Eternal Life

Christians believe that human beings have only one life and that they will be judged on how they have lived this life. The exact shape of beliefs about judgement has varied over time, but some biblical texts describe a *Last Judgement* which will be followed by immortal union with God or by punishment. In the *Catholic* tradition, a state called *Purgatory*, or the place where sins are purged, is seen as preparatory for entry to heaven. On the whole, contemporary *western Christianity* tends to emphasise the importance of Christian faith and love in this world and to focus less on the penal aspect of the afterlife than has been the case in some centuries.

The Holy Trinity

Jesus is seen as the most complete expression and revelation of God, expressed in traditional language as the Son of God made flesh, but the Christian vision and experience of God does not focus on the person of Jesus alone. The Christian conviction about the ultimately unfathomable nature of God came to be expressed in the Christian doctrine or *Mystery* of the *Holy Trinity*. The Christian doctrine of the *Trinity* should not be understood as *tritheism* (belief in three individual gods) since the oneness of God is emphatically affirmed by Christians. Rather, it is intended to express belief in a dynamic interrelationship of community, inter-dependence and unity within the nature of the one God. God's nature and activity are said to be expressed in what the original Greek doctrine referred to as three *hypostases* (often, somewhat misleadingly, translated into

English as three "*persons*", although *hypostasis* does not refer to an independent individual in the modern sense of the word "person").

Although expressed in highly complex language in its doctrinally developed form, by this doctrine Christians give expression to their experience that it is by the Holy Spirit of God, in and through God revealed and active in Jesus, that they worship God as the Father, the Creator and *Redeemer* of all things. Some Churches also see the union of believers in mutual love as reflecting the life of the *Trinity*.

The Virgin Mary

The *Virgin Mary*, the *Mother of Jesus*, is a focus of devotion for millions of Christians. However, Christians have varying views about the place which Mary has within Christian life and doctrine. Most Christians believe that Jesus had no human father but was conceived by the *Virgin Mary* through the Holy Spirit; therefore she is to be honoured for her role of being the *Mother of Jesus* and the first and best example of Christian faith and obedience. The *Roman Catholic, Orthodox* and *Anglo-Catholic* traditions, however, emphasise this unique role more than do the *Protestant* Churches. Hundreds of *church* buildings within the *Roman Catholic, Anglican* and *Orthodox* traditions are named after her.

Orthodox tradition calls Mary by the title of *Theotokos* (Greek for "God-bearer") since it is through her that the *incarnation* is believed to have taken place. She is therefore held to have a special role as a link between the spiritual and material worlds. Among *Roman Catholics* Mary is known as the *Queen of Heaven*. In both the *Orthodox* and *Roman Catholic* traditions, Christian believers address prayers to Mary, asking her to intercede with Jesus on behalf of those who pray to her.

Some in the *Anglican* tradition also share in the veneration of Mary as the most honoured of human beings. Very few *Protestant*

Christians pray to Mary. The official teaching of the *Roman Catholic* Church proclaims a belief that Mary, by the singular *grace* of God and through the merits of Christ's saving work, was conceived without *Original Sin*. This is known as the doctrine of the *Immaculate Conception*.

The Saints

In some branches of Christianity, individual Christian men and women who have led particularly holy and exemplary lives manifesting the grace and power of God are venerated as *saints* (from the Latin *sanctus*, meaning "holy" and "set apart") and are looked to for help and support. This is particularly true of both *Orthodox* and *Roman Catholic* Christianity where veneration of the *saints* underlines the universal Christian sense that the *Church* is composed of all Christian people, both present and past.

Many Church buildings are named after individual *saints*. *Saints* are also often associated with particular places of Christian pilgrimage. In the early Christian *Church*, the scriptures referred to all Christian believers as the *saints* as distinct from the more specialised and restrictive use of the term which developed in the course of *Church* history.

TRADITIONS IN CHRISTIANITY

Globally, the largest Christian traditions are the *Roman Catholic*, *Orthodox*, *Protestant* and *Pentecostal*. The *Anglican* tradition of Christianity understands itself as both *Reformed* and *Catholic* in tradition. These traditions share many of the key beliefs described above, but they also have their own distinctive teachings, ethos and emphases.

Roman Catholic

The *Catholic* Church embraces around half the Christians in the world. It understands itself as "one, holy, *catholic* and *apostolic*"; that is to say, as one united *Church* which is sanctified by God, which is universal in scope

(*Catholic* from the Greek, *katholos*), and in an authentic and unbroken line of transmission of the Christian faith from the earliest apostles until the present time. It is often referred to by non-*Catholics* as the Roman Catholic Church.

Its *bishops* are believed to be in direct *apostolic* line of succession from the *Apostles* of the *Church* (the twelve appointed by Jesus together with the *Apostles* Paul and Barnabas). The *Pope* is understood by *Roman Catholics* to be Peter's successor by virtue of his office as the *Bishop of Rome*. The *bishops* are nominated by the *Pope* and consecrated by other *bishops* who are in communion with the *Pope*. They are responsible for the teaching and discipline of the *Church* as well as for ordaining *priests* and *deacons* to serve local Christian communities, and thus for maintaining what is known as the *Apostolicity* of the *Church*.

In *Roman Catholic* teaching the scriptures, as interpreted according to tradition, are given the supreme authority within the *Church*. But it is believed that the teaching authority of the *Church*, known as the *magisterium*, resides in the collective role of all the *bishops* gathered in *Ecumenical Councils* such as were held in the early centuries of Christianity.

Since the time of the *Reformation*, *Roman Catholics* have recognised three further *Ecumenical Councils* – the Council of Trent (1545-1563), Vatican I (1870) and Vatican II (1962-65). At the same time, a supreme authority is given to the *Pope* as the *Bishop of Rome* and the head of the *College of Bishops*, and the right, under certain conditions, to make infallible declarations on matters of faith and morals.

The *Roman Catholic* commitment to *Catholicity* refers to the universality and the unity-in-diversity of that *Church* in all geographical contexts and also throughout space and time. There is therefore a great sense of belonging to a living tradition reflecting the diversity of humanity and yet kept in unity particularly by celebration of the *Eucharist* (see below under "Christian Worship") as the focus of unity. Participation in sacramental *Communion* at the *Mass* generally requires full initiation into the Roman Catholic Church in the sense of being in *communion* with the *bishops* and the *Pope*, who are seen as maintaining the *Church's Apostolicity*.

Orthodox

The *Churches* of the *Orthodox* tradition of Christianity understand themselves to be representing the tradition and practice of the undivided *Church* before the separation of *Eastern* and *Western Christendom*. *Orthodoxy* thus claims to represent a more original form of Christianity than others.

The *Orthodox* give central importance to the doctrine of the *Holy Trinity*. Differing interpretations of the origination of the Spirit led to the so called *filioque* controversy between *Orthodoxy* and *Western Christendom*. This is the debate over whether, within the *creeds* of the *Church*, it should be said with reference to *Trinitarian* doctrine that, the Spirit proceeds "from the Father", the source of all Godhead (which is the *Orthodox credal* form) or "from the Father and the Son" (which is the *Western credal* form).

The *Western* formulation expresses the understanding that the Spirit of God is always manifested in terms of the character and person of Jesus. The *Orthodox* are concerned that such a formulation may subordinate the role of Spirit to that of Jesus. They also see the *Western* addition, made without the authority of an *Ecumenical Council*, as an illegitimate act by one section of the *Church*.

The *Orthodox* tradition places a great emphasis on prayer, on spirituality and on celebration of the *Liturgy*. In *Church* government, the *Orthodox* tradition has *autocephalous* (Greek, meaning "independently governed") *Churches* with their own *patriarchs* (senior *bishops*) or *Archbishops*, although all *Orthodox Churches* recognise the *Patriarch of Constantinople* as the *Ecumenical Patriarch* who is first in order of seniority. In global terms, the numerical strength of the *Orthodox Churches* is to be found primarily in Eastern Europe, the Mediterranean and the Middle East.

Protestant

Protestant is the name given to the Christian groupings whose particular character derives from the sixteenth and seventeenth century division in the *Church* in Europe generally referred to as the *Reformation* (see above).

They vary in belief and practice, particularly about *Church* organisation and government. There are also significant differences between those *Protestant* Christian traditions which have seen a close relationship with the state and/or the nation in a positive light (for example, in Scotland the *Reformed* Church of Scotland) and those traditions, generally known as the *Free Churches*, which have advocated the separation of the *Church* and the state.

In general, the *Protestant* tradition declares the supremacy and authority of the *scriptures* in matters of belief and *Church* government. However, it also emphasises the role of the individual believer, under the guidance of the Holy Spirit, in reading and interpreting the text of the *Bible*. It places emphasis upon personal faith in Jesus as the means to *salvation*. In some *Protestant* traditions, such as *Methodism*, this has also been supplemented by a focus on the need for a strong personal experience of conversion, understood as a complete change of life orientation.

Most *Protestant Churches* also place particular emphasis upon *preaching* (the proclamation of the *Word of God* believed to be revealed in *scripture*). Through this, God is understood to offer eternal life in Christ and by the Holy Spirit to enable Christian hearers to deepen their faith and live in a more Christlike way.

Anglican

The *Anglican* tradition is a worldwide Christian tradition composed of autonomous *Churches* which, historically, are daughter *Churches* of the Church of England and look to the *Archbishop of Canterbury* for their international leadership. Like the Church of England, and as a consequence of the distinctive course of events of the *Reformation* in England and Wales, these *Churches* understand themselves as being both *Reformed* and *Catholic* in tradition. The *Catholic* element is part of the *Anglican* emphasis on its continuity with the past and in apostolic succession to the earliest *Church*. The *Protestant* element was rooted in the correction of matters which, at the time of the *Reformation*, were judged to be abuses and distortions of *Catholic* Christianity.

Anglicanism strives for balance in all things. In doctrine, this is expressed by affirming *scripture*, *Tradition* and human reason as God-given instruments for interpreting revelation. In matters of authority, reason is seen as a necessary interpreter of *scripture* and *Tradition*, and in matters of church order individual and *parochial* (the level of the local *parish*) freedom is combined with an *episcopal* (the order of *bishops*) *Church* structure. In recent decades most *Anglican Churches* have developed *synodical* democratic structures where key issues in the life of the *Church* are debated by both lay and ordained elected representatives.

There is also an attempt to balance a developed liturgical life and private devotion with a focus on scripture and social responsibility. There is concern, too, for comprehensiveness, which is envisaged as embracing a breadth of Christian belief and practice containing several identifiable theological and *liturgical* streams of life. These streams are known as the *Evangelical* (sometimes called *Low Church*), the *Anglo-Catholic* (sometimes called *High Church*), the *Liberal* (or *Broad Church*) and the *Charismatic* (see below for an explanation of these terms).

Pentecostal

The *Pentecostal* tradition has historical roots in *Protestantism* but there are also good reasons for regarding it as a distinctive tradition of Christianity that has come to global prominence in the course of the twentieth century. The *Pentecostal* tradition shares with the wider *Protestant* tradition a commitment to the primacy of the scriptures for individual and *Church* life, as well as the necessity of personal faith in, and commitment to, Jesus. However, the tradition of *Pentecostalism* goes further to assert that the immediacy of the power of God that was available to the first Christian believers as recorded in the scriptural book of the *Acts of the Apostles* is still available to Christians today.

Pentecostalists believe in the necessity of actually experiencing this power and love as well as believing in it. An event which they describe as the experience of *baptism in the Spirit* is seen as the occasion in and through which individuals can gain access to the spiritual gifts of God. In classical *Pentecostal* practice, the outward sign of this *baptism in the Spirit* has been seen as the ability to engage in *glossolalia* (speaking in tongues). This involves the individual producing sounds, directed in praise and worship to God, which are not the words of the person's day-to-day language. However, although this has become particularly identified with *Pentecostalism*, the tradition's own emphasis is upon all the spiritual gifts of God, including the gifts of prophecy and healing.

Restorationist and House Church Movements

During the 1970s and 1980s, European Christianity has seen the growth of the so-called *Restorationist* and *House Church* movements, organised separately from the traditional Christian *denominations*. Christians in these movements often feel that the older *Churches* have stifled the real spirit of

Christianity in outmoded structures. They therefore seek to develop forms of organisation and networking which they believe to be more consistent with those that were found among the earliest Christian communities.

Quakers and Unitarians

As well as the traditions outlined above, there are also some groups which do not fit neatly into any of these categories but which have historical roots in *Protestant* Christianity. Among these are the *Quakers* (officially known as the Religious Society of Friends) and the *Unitarian and Free Christian Churches*. Both are non-*credal* traditions, believing that *credal* statements about orthodoxies of belief or *church* order are restrictive of true religion. In the case of *Quakers* this reflects the conviction from their beginnings in the seventeenth century that the "inward light of Christ" is available to all whether or not they use *Christian* terms to describe it. To be faithful is to act in accordance with its guidance not simply to hold the right beliefs about it. Some members of the *Quaker* and *Unitarian* traditions do not wish to be identified as specifically Christian in any way which they believe implies separation from people of other religions or, sometimes, also from humanists.

Churchmanship

Within many of these major traditions of Christianity there are streams or tendencies of what often used to be called *churchmanship*, which refer to Christians in all the major traditions who have particular emphases within their Christian understanding and life. Among the principal tendencies are the following:

Anglo-Catholic

Anglo-Catholics are *Anglican* Christians who emphasise the *Catholic* inheritance of the *Anglican* tradition in various aspects of theology, doctrine and worship.

Charismatic

Charismatic Christianity is a movement that is historically related to the *Pentecostal* branch of Christianity, but which is now present in all other major branches of Christianity. It is characterised by an emphasis on the direct experience of the Holy Spirit being available to Christian believers today, including the possibility that the Holy Spirit can produce miraculous works in the contemporary world. *Charismatic* Christians do not, however, necessarily adopt particular items of *Pentecostal* theology or practice, such as the emphasis on *speaking with tongues* as a necessary evidence of *baptism in the Spirit*.

Evangelical

Evangelicals are Christians who draw upon the inheritance of the *Reformation* particularly as it developed in the eighteenth and nineteenth centuries. They try to live according to the Christian scriptures viewed as the supreme authority for Christian life, and understood as revealed and inspired without human error or distortion.

Because their personal decision to follow Jesus is so central, they feel strongly called to bring others into the Christian *Church* by means of *evangelism* (meaning *Good News* - from the Greek word *euangelion*). *Evangelism* means sharing the good news of what Christians believe God has done in and through Jesus. Whilst *Evangelical* Christians are centrally concerned with this, other Christians also engage in *evangelism*, since bearing witness to Jesus is understood to be obligatory for all Christians (see section on "Christian Life" below).

Liberal

Liberal Christians are those Christians in all traditions and denominations who place an emphasis upon the necessity for a contextualised understanding and practice of Christianity and believe that rationality and contemporary relevance are crucially important for the meaning and communication of the Christian message.

The Ecumenical Movement

Particularly during the twentieth century, the *Ecumenical Movement* (from the Greek *oikumene*, meaning "the whole inhabited earth") has developed. This represents a desire among Christians of all traditions to fulfil the prayer of Jesus for the unity of the *Church* and so to build a universal Christian fellowship which transcends or embraces all divisions and boundaries and shares resources for witness and ministry. This global movement has sometimes found expression in the search for common and unified *Church* structures and organisations in attempts to form united *Churches* out of two or more formerly separate *Churches* as, for example, the United Reformed Church (see below).

More recently, the organised *Ecumenical Movement* has also sought to achieve closer co-operation and working relationships in common projects between Christians who remain in separate *Churches*, as in the work of the Churches together in Britain and Ireland. At the European level many *Protestant* and *Orthodox* Churches belong to the Conference of European Churches (CEC). At an international level many *Anglican*, *Protestant* and *Orthodox Churches* belong to the World Council of Churches (WCC) and *Roman Catholics* participate fully in its Faith and Order Commission.

CHRISTIAN LIFE

Jesus commanded his disciples to "love one another as I have loved you", and so Christian believers are called upon to live according to the pattern of Jesus' life which was characterised by sacrificial and self-giving love or *agape* (the Greek word for this form of love).

Sin and Grace

Without the assistance of the power of God, Christianity sees human beings as being gripped by self-centredness and powers beyond their control, a condition described as enslavement to *sin*. The release which believers experience when they put their trust in God through Jesus is known as *salvation*. This means a progressive liberation from all that enslaves human beings in terms of self-centredness.

In the Christian life there is a dynamic tension between the belief that one is already, in principle, freed from the power and guilt of *sin*, whilst in this life never being entirely free from it. This is expressed in the Christian scriptures by the concept of *salvation* appearing in all three tenses: past, present and future.

The activity by which God is believed to draw people into his purposes is referred to as *grace*. This is a word that expresses dependence upon the free and unmerited gift of God's power in contrast to reliance upon human goodness or self-sufficiency, and Christians are called to put their trust in God's name.

This trust is described by the word *faith*, which is understood to be evoked and sustained through the power of God known as the Holy Spirit, who is God at work in and among believers. Christians believe that they can draw upon this power of God through their practice of prayer, and they are supported in this by participation in fellowship with other Christian believers within the *Church*.

Baptism

The rite of *baptism* (from the Greek *baptizo*, meaning to dip or immerse) in water accompanied by prayer and conducted in the name of the *Holy Trinity* marks a person's entry into the Christian *Church*. In many older *church* buildings the *baptismal font* (usually a standing receptacle which holds the water used in *baptism*) is near the door of the *Church*, to show symbolic entry. The waters of *baptism* are understood as a sign of the remission of *sins* and entry into new life in Jesus.

In the *Anglican, Roman Catholic, Reformed,* and *Orthodox Churches* the *baptismal* rite is generally administered to babies or infants. They are presented for *baptism* by their parents who, together with friends or relatives designated as *godparents,* make promises on behalf of the infant. In the *Anglican, Roman Catholic* and *Reformed Churches,* a small amount of water is usually poured on the child's head. Some then anoint with *chrism* oil. In the *Orthodox Churches,* the baby is immersed three times in the *baptismal* waters and is then *chrismated* (anointed with oil) and admitted to full *Communion.*

In other Christian traditions, such as the *Baptist* and *Pentecostal* movements, it is believed that *baptism* should only be administered to those (generally teenagers and adults) who are capable of a personal confession of Christian faith. In these traditions *baptism* is also generally by complete immersion in the *baptismal* waters. Such *Churches* usually have specially constructed sunken *baptistries* (tanks) designed for this purpose.

There are a few Christian traditions, such as the Society of Friends and the Salvation Army, which do not practise water *baptism.* Their emphasis is on a spiritual and inner *baptism* rather than on outward signs such as the rite of *baptism.*

In some traditions infant *baptism* is popularly known as *christening,* a word which derives from the ancient practice of giving candidates for *baptism* a Christian name to indicate their new identity as believers and members of the *Church.*

Confirmation and Membership

In the *Roman Catholic* tradition, *confirmation* with *Holy Communion* completes initiation into the *Church,* making possible the fuller life given at *baptism.* The Christian believer bears public witness to Jesus and is believed to receive the Holy Spirit of God in a special way. Among those who have grown up within the *Church, confirmation* often takes place in the early teenage years.

In the *Anglican* tradition, and also in some parts of the *Protestant* tradition, *confirmation* is understood in a similar way but with an emphasis on believers affirming their faith and making their own the promises made on their behalf at their *baptism* as infants.

In *episcopal Churches, confirmation* is usually administered by a *bishop* by the *laying-on of hands* on the head of the candidates, accompanied by prayer. In the *Roman Catholic* tradition, anointing with *chrism* also takes place. In the *Orthodox* tradition, the *chrismation* with oil blessed by the *bishop,* which immediately follows after *baptism,* is the equivalent of *Confirmation.*

In *Churches* of the *Reformed* tradition *confirmation* or what is sometimes otherwise known as *reception into membership* is usually administered by the *minister.* This is done within a solemn service at which *baptised* individuals (usually at least in their mid-teens) confess their own personal faith and commitment and are welcomed as full members of the world-wide *Church* and of the local worshipping community. Thereafter, those who have been welcomed play their part in the decision-making processes within their *Church,* their names being entered on the roll, or list, of *Church* members.

Christian Witness

Christians believe that Jesus' last command was to preach the *Gospel* and make *disciples.* The commitment to spread the message of Christianity is undergirded by the conviction that the Christian message is (as *euangelion,* the Greek of the word *Gospel* suggests) *Good News* to announce to people, concerning which it would be selfish to remain quiet.

Some Christians see their responsibility to bear *witness* in terms of participating in organised *evangelistic* activities known as missions, or in belonging to *missionary* organisations that are specifically concerned with presenting the claims of the Christian message, both in this country and in other parts of the world. Other Christians see the call to *witness* more in terms of the way in which they attempt to go about their day-to-day activities in conformity with the life and teaching of Jesus.

Ethics and Discipleship

Discipleship, for Christians, involves following the example or "way" of Jesus. For all Christians, the example of Jesus and the teachings of the *Bible* are key sources for decision and practice. In this context, the *Decalogue* or *Ten Commandments* (shared with Judaism) have been a key reference in Christian ethical reflection, as have Jesus' *Beatitudes* and the rest of his *Sermon on the Mount*.

For Christians in the *Protestant* tradition, individual conscience is also particularly important in deciding how to apply the teachings of the *Bible*. In the *Roman Catholic* tradition, the role of conscience is affirmed although there is a strong emphasis on informing the individual conscience by the scriptures and the corporate teaching of the *Church*. This teaching is expressed, in particular, through its *bishops* and, supremely, through the *Ecumenical* and other *Councils* of the *Church* and the official pronouncements of the *Pope* (some of which are known as *Encyclicals*). These are often very specific in the guidance they give to individual believers and some aspects of this guidance are reinforced through the application of measures of *Church* discipline.

Christianity has a strong tradition of social concern. Jesus reinforced the *Old Testament* command to love one's neighbour as oneself and he enjoined his disciples to "love as I have loved you". In his teaching concerning the *Last Judgement* of human beings he pointed out that in serving or neglecting the hungry, the sick and the imprisoned, his followers would be serving or neglecting Jesus himself. In the light of such teaching, Christians have been behind the foundation of many philanthropic and educational initiatives in the UK.

But in the twentieth century, alongside a commitment to charitable works, the Christian *Churches* have increasingly come to understand that they have a calling to oppose structural and institutionalised injustice. In the contemporary *Ecumenical Movement*, Christian ethics and discipleship are expressed by a commitment to what is known as the JPIC process - Justice, Peace and the Integrity of Creation, no one aspect of which can be fully achieved without the other two.

Dietary Issues

Christians do not have any universally agreed dietary regulations although some Christians observe, in various ways, the discipline of abstaining from certain foods during the season of *Lent* (see the section on "Calendar and Festivals"). Some Christians also *fast* at other, individually chosen times, in order to focus on prayer or as an act of solidarity with the poor, donating the money which they would have otherwise spent on food to a Christian justice and development charity such as Christian Aid, Tear Fund or the Catholic Fund for Overseas Development (CAFOD). There are also some, especially those within the *Protestant* traditions, who refrain, on principle, from drinking alcohol.

Monks, Nuns and Religious

The majority of Christians lead ordinary lives at work in the world and within family life, but from the earliest years of Christianity some have felt called to form special groups in which they could aim to share a more complete devotion to Jesus, and to the pattern of his life and work. Some groups are known as *Orders*, and those within them, generally called *monks* (men) and *nuns* (women), have taken what are known as "solemn vows" of poverty, chastity and obedience.

There are also *Congregations* whose members are known as *Religious*. There are also *Religious Brothers* who are not necessarily monks, but make vows to live in community. *Monks*, *nuns* and *Religious* can be found in the contemporary *Roman Catholic*, *Orthodox* and *Anglican Churches*. The particular pattern of life of a group of *monks*, *nuns* or *Religious* varies according to the self-understanding of the *Order* or *Congregation* of which they are a part. This, in turn, is based upon the life and teachings of its founder. Some emphasise prayer and meditation and retreat from the world, whilst for others practical service in the world is basic to their calling.

Among the more well-known *Orders* that have grown up in *Western Christianity* are the Society of Jesus (*Jesuits*, founded by St. Ignatius of Loyola and noted for teaching and missionary work); the *Benedictines* (founded by St. Benedict and with an emphasis on prayer, work and the reading of holy books); the *Dominicans* (after the spirit of St Dominic, and who are known for intellectual study and rigour); the *Carmelites* (known for silent prayer and meditation); and the *Franciscans* (who follow the rule of St. Francis of Assisi).

Many other organisations and groups exist within and with the blessing of the *Churches*, having developed as responses to particular contemporary needs or in order to strengthen and renew Christian life. These include *ecumenical* communities such as Iona in Scotland and Lee Abbey in Devon, England.

CHRISTIAN WORSHIP

Holy Communion

For the majority of Christians *Holy Communion* is the most characteristic and central act of Christian worship. Some Christians, such as the Religious Society of Friends (the *Quakers*) and the Salvation Army, do not celebrate *Holy Communion*. *Communion* means sharing (from the Latin *communio*) and refers to the sharing of bread and wine and of the life of the *Church*. Christians believe that the act was instituted by Jesus himself at what is known as the *Last Supper* when he blessed, or gave thanks over bread and wine, declaring it to be his body and his blood and then shared this with his disciples before his *crucifixion*.

Holy Communion is also known as the *Eucharist* (from the Greek word *eucharistia*, meaning "thanksgiving"); among *Roman Catholics* as the *Mass* (probably originating from Latin words spoken at the end of the service *ite, missa est*, the meaning of which has variously been translated as "It is offered" or "Go, you are sent forth"); among the *Orthodox Churches* as the *Divine Liturgy* (from the Greek word *leitourgia*, meaning service); and among some *Protestant Churches* as the *Sacrament of the Lord's Supper* or the *Breaking of Bread*.

The content, interpretation and frequency of this event vary considerably among Christians of different traditions. *Roman Catholic* churches celebrate the *Mass* daily, as do some *Anglican churches* (especially those in the *Anglo-Catholic* tradition), whilst others have one or more weekly celebrations. Some *Protestant Churches* have only monthly or quarterly celebrations, using other forms of worship at other times. The elements of the *Eucharist* also differ from *Church* to *Church*. *Roman Catholics* normally use a flat wafer of unleavened bread.

This is also an *Anglican* practice, although in an increasing number of *Anglican* churches ordinary bread is used. *Anglicans* normally receive wine also, whereas in *Roman Catholic* churches there is a variety of practice, with some offering *Holy Communion* under the appearance of both bread and wine and also under one element only. *Orthodox* Christians receive from a long spoon a small piece of bread dipped in wine. In some *Protestant Churches* pieces of bread are taken from a single loaf and each individual receives an individual cup of wine (which may be non-alcoholic). In most *Churches*, however, the wine is alcoholic and is drunk from a common cup.

In *Roman Catholic, Orthodox* and *Anglican Churches* the *congregation* usually go up to the front of the *church* to receive *communion* either from the *priest* or, in the *Anglican* and *Roman Catholic Churches*, also from lay *eucharistic* ministers, who are authorised to assist the *priest* in the distribution of the *sacrament*. In some *Protestant Churches* the bread and wine are taken out to the *congregation* by lay officers of the *church* or are passed from member to member.

The *Protestant* traditions generally see *Holy Communion* as a remembrance of Jesus' death and *resurrection* in obedience to his command to do so in remembrance of him, as recorded in the *New Testament*, with God's act of *atonement* in Jesus being symbolised by the bread and wine which represent Jesus' body and blood. There is also an emphasis on the spiritual nourishment received by believers, individually and collectively, with a sense of reliance upon the indwelling Spirit of God expressed by the idea of spiritually feeding on Christ by faith.

Among *Roman Catholics*, the *Orthodox* and many *Anglicans* within the *Anglo-Catholic* tradition, the elements of the bread and wine are seen as, in a real sense, "re-presenting" the body and blood of Christ so that, by sharing in them, the faithful can actually have *communion* with the risen Jesus. The *Eucharist* is understood as the memorial or making present of Christ's sacrifice in his saving death and *resurrection*, so that by taking part in the celebration, the faithful are united with Christ's once-for-all work of *salvation*. Among *Roman Catholics, First Communion* is usually taken by children after a period of preparation at around the age of seven or eight and is of great personal and family significance.

Preaching

All the Christian *denominations* in the UK give an important place to *preaching* or expounding the *scriptures* within worship. But among the *Churches* of the *Reformation* and among *Churches* founded following the *Evangelical Revival* of the seventeenth and eighteenth centuries, the *preaching* of the *Word* is often given greater prominence than the celebration of the *sacrament* of *Holy Communion*.

Preaching is normally a special responsibility of *ordained ministers*, but most *Churches* also authorise appropriately trained and designated *lay preachers* to share in the leading of worship, including the ministry of *preaching* based upon the *scriptures*. In the Roman Catholic Church, only *bishops, priests* and *deacons* may normally preach at *Mass*.

Prayer

In both public and private prayer the *Lord's Prayer* is important. It is the prayer which Jesus is recorded in the *Gospels* as having taught his first disciples, and is therefore a pattern for all Christian prayer. In addition to participating in corporate prayer and worship, many individual Christians have private and personal disciplines of prayer, scriptural study and meditation.

Church Buildings

Most Christian buildings for worship are referred to as *churches*, but in some *Protestant* branches of Christianity, especially among the *Free Churches*, the word "Church" is generally reserved for describing the people who make up the community of the *Church*. In these cases, in England and Wales (though not generally in Scotland or Ireland) the word *chapel* may be used to describe the building, instead of *church*. However, the word *chapel* is also used among *Roman Catholics* and *Anglicans* to denote a small *church* without a *parish* building or a small part of a larger building. Some *Nonconformist* places of worship, such as those of the *Quakers*, are called *meeting houses*. These are not *consecrated* buildings, thus underlining the belief that it is the people who are the *Church* and the place where they meet for worship does not confer sanctity on the proceedings. For the same reason they are without religious decoration or symbols of any kind. Some Christians do not meet in recognisably religious buildings but in private homes or in hired public meeting places such as schools, as with the *House Church* or Restorationists movement which is a growing form of Christian life in the UK.

From the outside, Christian places of worship vary in appearance. Many old *churches*, however, have a range of recognisable features such as a tower or spire which makes them landmarks in both town and countryside. Very old buildings of this kind are generally now of the *Anglican* Christian tradition, although a large number of them pre-date the *Reformation*. By contrast, other Christian places of worship have the external appearance of a simple square or rectangular hall. Many *churches* of all kinds have stained glass windows frequently depicting scriptural characters, stories or events.

Once inside a building there is again a very wide variety in terms of what might be found. At one end of the spectrum, *Baptist* or *Methodist chapels* can often have an interior bare of religious symbols except perhaps for a wooden *cross* on the wall, although a number of local *churches* now have colourful banners hanging from their walls. Attention is focused on the *pulpit* (the raised enclosed platform, usually at one end of the building, from which the *preacher* addresses the *congregation*) with a simple table in front of it from which the service of *Holy Communion* (see above) is led.

In most *Protestant* and *Catholic* churches there are seats for the worshippers, but in *Orthodox Churches* most of the *congregation* stand during the service. A place of worship in the *Orthodox* tradition may have brightly coloured frescoes and also many religious pictures called *icons*, whose purpose is to bring close to the worshipper the spiritual realities which they depict in *iconographic* form. As well as an elevated *pulpit*, there may

be a modest *lectern* (reading desk). Instead of a simple table for *Communion*, the *Orthodox Church* will have an *altar* which is hidden from general view behind a screen known as an *iconostasis*. This is a screen which is covered in *icons* and has doors in the middle through which the *priest* passes to bring out the bread and wine from the *altar* to the *congregation*.

In *Roman Catholic* and *Anglican Churches* in the *Catholic* tradition the main focal point is the *altar*. Another focal point is the *tabernacle*, a secure container in which is placed the consecrated bread from the *Eucharist*. The presence of the consecrated bread is indicated by a lightened lamp or candle. There will also be statues of the *Virgin Mary* and perhaps of *saints* as well. These statues help the worshippers to focus their devotion. They are not, in themselves, objects of worship.

In *Orthodox*, *Roman Catholic* and *Anglo-Catholic Anglican church* buildings, services of worship may be accompanied by the use of incense. Organs and often other musical instruments, sometimes including guitars, are used to accompany singing in *Anglican*, *Protestant* and *Roman Catholic churches*, but not in *Orthodox churches*. *Choirs* are to be found in most Christian traditions, but vary greatly in style between the traditional and formal *Cathedral choirs* and the more informal and contemporary *Gospel choirs* of the *Pentecostal* tradition.

The main church building of *Anglican*, *Roman Catholic* and *Orthodox Dioceses* is known as a *Cathedral* or, in the case of some *Anglican churches*, a *Minster*. Such buildings act as focal points for their respective *Dioceses* since they are where the bishop has his *cathedra* or seat. Church of England *Cathedrals*, in particular, are very often also seen as places where events of civic and social importance are held, as well as being important parts of the country's architectural and spiritual heritage and thus also as tourist attractions.

CHRISTIAN CALENDAR AND FESTIVALS

The Christian Calendar

The Christian calendar dates world history in relation to what was believed to have been the year of the birth of Jesus, although it is now generally accepted that this took place a number of years earlier than was originally thought. The *Millennium* which has just begun is the third *Millennium* for Christians.

Because of the Christian belief in the *incarnation*, the birth of Jesus is seen as being the pivotal point of world history. It is in this context that the letters "AD" (from the first letters of the Latin words *Anno Domini*, meaning "In the Year of our Lord") and "BC" (for "Before Christ") came to be used for dating world history, although outside of internal Christian usage this notation is now more generally becoming replaced, as in this directory, by the letters "CE" (for Common Era) and "BCE" (for Before the Common Era).

Sunday

Christianity inherited its seven day week from Judaism. Sunday (the first day of the Jewish week) is usually observed as the day of assembly for Christian worship because, as it was the day of the week on which Jesus is believed to have been raised from death, it marks *resurrection* and new beginning. However, the so-called *Sabbatarian* or *Seventh Day Churches* believe that the commandment to the Jews to keep the seventh day (Saturday) holy is still binding on Christians after the coming of Jesus.

The understanding of Sunday observance varies considerably among Christians. Many *Roman Catholics* attend *Vigil Sunday Mass* on Saturday evening since, following the Biblical tradition, the day is seen as commencing the previous evening. Some *Protestants* refrain from employment or secular recreation throughout Sunday, concentrating on participation in morning and evening worship.

The Church Year and Festivals

The Christian liturgical year begins with *Advent* at the end of November. The *liturgical* year marks key events and commemorates figures connected with the Christian story and is particularly important for *Roman Catholics*, the *Orthodox* and *Anglicans*. Most *Protestant Churches* of the *Reformed* and *Congregational* traditions observe only Sundays, *Advent, Christmas, Holy Week, Easter* and *Pentecost* (see below).

In some small Christian groupings even these days are seen as, at best, of marginal importance. At worst they are seen as a corruption of pure Christianity, introduced largely to incorporate some elements of pre-Christian tradition in order to wean Christians away from the traditional celebrations at these times of year.

There are three cycles of festivals within the Christian year. The *Christmas* cycle has dates which are fixed within the *Gregorian* calendar. Then comes the *Easter* cycle, the dates of which vary for reasons explained below under *Easter*. Finally, there is a third cycle of festivals and commemorations of *saints* and *martyrs* of the *Church*, which are observed on fixed dates. A number of *Orthodox Churches* follow the so-called *Julian* calendar which, in the present century, is thirteen days behind the date of the calendar which is in common social use in the UK.

The *Roman Catholic Church* has also prescribed certain days as holy days of obligation. On these days believers are expected to attend *Mass*. In England, Scotland and Wales, this includes all Sundays together with *Christmas Day, Ascension Day,* the *Assumption of the Blessed Virgin Mary, All Saints' Day,* the feast days of *Saints Peter and Paul, Corpus Christi* (a celebration of thanksgiving for the institution of the *Eucharist*) and *Epiphany*.

Advent (November–December)
Advent means "coming" and it refers to the coming of Jesus into the world and to his *Second Coming* at the end of time. The season is observed by *Western* Christians as a solemn preparatory season for *Christmas*, traditionally beginning on the fourth Sunday before *Christmas*.

Immaculate Conception of the Blessed Virgin Mary (8th December)
Roman Catholics celebrate the belief that Mary the Mother of Jesus was herself conceived free of *original sin* in order that she might be sinless for the bearing of Jesus.

Christmas (25th December)
Celebrates the birth of Jesus, the precise date of which is unknown, but the *Catholic Church* fixed on 25th December to coincide with the winter *solstice*. Some *Orthodox Churches* keep to the pre-*Gregorian* calendar date of 6th or 7th January celebrating the birth of Jesus. For the other *Churches*, the 6th January is the twelfth night of *Christmas*, which closes the *Christmas* season with the festival of *Epiphany*.

Epiphany (6th January)
The word *Epiphany* is Greek meaning "manifestation". In the *Orthodox Churches*, this refers to the manifestation of Jesus at his *baptism* as the *Son of God*. In the *Western Churches Epiphany* celebrates the adoration of Jesus by the *Magi* or *Wise Men*, and thus his being revealed to the *Gentiles* (non-Jews). It is sometimes referred to as the *Twelfth Night* as it is twelve days after *Christmas*.

Shrove Tuesday (February/March)
This is a popular folk festival marking the day before the start of *Lent*, and has a number of traditional and popular cultural customs attached to it. The name comes from the Middle English word *shriven* which referred to the practice of making confession before the beginning of *Lent*. The popular custom of making pancakes arose from the need to use up eggs before *Lent*, a period of *fasting*. The same day is sometimes known by the French title *Mardi Gras* (fat Tuesday) which refers to the using up of all the fats before *Lent*.

Ash Wednesday (February/March)
This is the first day of *Lent* and is so called because in some churches the *priest* marks the forehead of believers with ash as a sign of mortality and of penitence before God. In the Roman Catholic Church and in *Anglican churches* of *Catholic* tradition, it is a day of *fasting* and abstinence.

Lent (February–March/April)
This is a period of forty days, not counting Sundays, between *Ash Wednesday* and the Saturday before *Easter*. It is a preparation for *Easter*. Its roots can be found in the *Gospel* stories of Jesus being tempted for forty days in the wilderness prior to the beginning of his public ministry. In the *Orthodox* tradition it is known as the *Great Fast* and starts on the Monday (known as *Clean Monday*) before the first Sunday of *Lent* rather than on the Wednesday as in the *Western Churches*. In all traditions it is a season of penitence and preparation in which many Christians abstain from some foods and/or luxuries.

The Annunciation to the Blessed Virgin Mary (25th March)
This celebrates the announcement by the Angel Gabriel to Mary that she was to give birth to a son to be called Jesus, and her assent to this. It is celebrated nine months prior to *Christmas Day*.

Mothering Sunday (March)
This is the fourth Sunday in *Lent* and is widely known as *Mother's Day*. Though it may have begun with the idea of *Mother Church* or of Jerusalem as the "mother of us all", it has become a more popular occasion upon which to recognise and thank mothers for all that they do.

Passion Sunday (March)

This is the fifth Sunday in *Lent* when Christians begin to concentrate their thoughts on the significance of the *Passion* (or suffering) of Jesus, in preparation for recalling the events of *Holy Week*.

Palm Sunday (March/April)

This is the first day of *Holy Week*. On this day Christians are often given pieces of palm leaf in the form of a cross to recall the *Gospel* accounts of how Jesus was greeted by crowds waving palm leaves as he entered into Jerusalem a few days before his *crucifixion*.

Holy Week (March/April)

The last week of *Lent*, which is dedicated to remembering the suffering and death of Jesus.

Maundy Thursday (March/April)

The Thursday in *Holy Week* which commemorates the day on which, at his *Last Supper* with his disciples, Jesus instituted the *Holy Communion*. It was also the occasion of Jesus' command to his disciples to wash one another's feet as a sign of mutual humility and service. A *foot washing* ceremony is held on this day in some *churches*. It is also the day on which Jesus gave his *disciples* the commandment to love one another, and prayed for their unity. The name *Maundy Thursday* comes from the Latin of the beginning of the *Gospel of John* chapter 13 verse 34, where Jesus is recorded as giving the *disciples* a new commandment (*Mandatum novum*). In *churches* in the *Catholic* tradition the *altars* are generally stripped bare at the end of this day.

Good Friday (March/April)

The Friday of *Holy Week* which commemorates the *crucifixion* of Jesus is generally an austere and solemn day, but is called "Good" because Christians believe *salvation* to be effected through the *crucifixion*. In the Roman Catholic Church and in Anglican *churches* of *Catholic* tradition, it is a day of *fasting* and abstinence. In many churches a service with meditations upon Jesus' words from the *cross* is held between noon and three o'clock in the afternoon. The symbolism of the *cross* of Jesus lies behind the traditional practice of eating buns marked with a *cross* on this day.

Holy Saturday (March/April)

This is a day of prayerful waiting and preparation for *Easter*. In the *Roman Catholic* and *Orthodox* traditions and among *Anglo-Catholic Anglicans*, a special night service takes place (the *Easter Vigil*) as the main celebration of *Easter*. This involves the biblical story of creation, the solemn proclamation of the *resurrection* of Jesus, the lighting of the *Paschal* candle and the renewal of *baptismal* vows.

Easter (March/April)

Easter commemorates the *resurrection* of Jesus. It is the central Christian festival and is full of joy. It was traditionally the main time for *baptism*. In the *Western* Christian tradition it is celebrated on the first Sunday following the first full moon after the vernal equinox. The date therefore varies within the solar calendar adopted by western countries. The *Orthodox* calculate *Easter* in a different way and their celebration of the season also continues, in total, for fifty days until *Pentecost*, and therefore also includes *Ascension Day*. The name *Easter* derives from the old English *eostre* which was the name for a pre-Christian Spring festival. The giving of *Easter* eggs, symbolising new life, appears to be a survival of an ancient fertility custom.

Ascension Day (May/June)

This is celebrated on the fortieth day after *Easter* and commemorates the last earthly appearance of the Risen Christ to his first disciples which is recorded in the scriptures. His *ascension* marks his transcending of all earthly limitations and the celebration of his kingly rule. It is always celebrated on a Thursday.

Pentecost (May/June)

The name derives from the Greek *pentecoste*, meaning fiftieth day and it is celebrated on the seventh Sunday after *Easter*. *Pentecost* (or the *Feast of Weeks*) is a Jewish harvest festival which has been given a different meaning by the *Church*. For Christians, it marks the outpouring of the Holy Spirit upon the followers of Jesus, and the commencement of the *Church's* mission to spread the message about Jesus throughout the world. It is sometimes known as *Whitsun* (*White Sunday*), from the custom of converts presenting themselves on this day for *baptism* dressed in white clothes.

Trinity Sunday (June)

This is celebrated in the *West* on the Sunday following *Pentecost*. The *Orthodox Churches* celebrate *All Saints* on this day. *Trinity Sunday* is devoted to contemplation of the mystery of God, which Christians see as an indivisible unity and yet revealed in the inter-related communion of God the Father, Son and Holy Spirit.

Corpus Christi (Thursday following *Trinity Sunday*, therefore usually in June)

This is particularly a *Roman Catholic* festival and celebrates belief in the presence of Jesus in the *Eucharist* in a more joyful way than is appropriate on *Maundy Thursday*. The festival is also observed by some *Anglicans* as a thanksgiving for the institution of the *Holy Communion* or *Eucharist*.

Transfiguration (6th August)

This recalls the scriptural account of the shining of Jesus' face and clothes on the so-called Mount of Transfiguration, when his heavenly glory is believed to have been revealed to his disciples.

Assumption of the Blessed Virgin Mary (15th August)

Roman Catholics and *Orthodox* (who call it the *Dormition* – the falling asleep of the *Mother of God*) celebrate the belief that Mary, body and soul, was *assumed*, or taken up into heaven.

St. Michael and All Angels (29th September)

This day celebrates the Archangel Michael, the adversary of Satan. Sometimes known as *Michaelmas*, this is a season of the *Western* Church's year in which the *ordination* of *priests* and *deacons* may take place, though many *ordinations* also occur on *Trinity Sunday* and, in the *Anglican* tradition, at *Petertide* (at the end of June).

Harvest Festival (September/October)

Although it is not an official part of any *Church* year, the observance of a *harvest* festival has become a regular event in many *Churches*. It celebrates the bounty of God in creation. Such festivals became common from the Middle Ages onwards and were revived in the nineteenth century. Displays of foodstuffs are often made in church and these are then distributed to the needy after the festival is over.

All Saints Day (1st November)

Since the names of every saint cannot be known, this festival commemorates all the *saints*.

All Souls Day (2nd November)

Is a day upon which to remember all those who have died and are within the so-called *Communion of Saints* – the unity in Jesus of all believers, past, present and future.

CHRISTIAN ORGANISATIONS

In the UK there are numerous Christian *Churches* belonging to the principal Christian traditions described earlier. In what follows, attention is focused on these *Church* bodies as such (often described as *ecclesiastical* bodies – from the Greek word *ecclesia* meaning *Church*). There are, in addition, very many Christian organisations with particular foci for their work, some of which are *Church*-sponsored, others of which are voluntary associations of Christians.

CHURCHES IN THE UK

The principal characteristics of the *Churches* in the UK reflect the wider, global Christian traditions of which they are a part. By reason of history and contemporary circumstances they are, however, to be found in different proportions within the UK and its various nations than is the case internationally.

Arising from the history of the UK, it is more common to use the categories of *established Churches* (the Church of England and the Church of Scotland), the Roman Catholic Church, the *Orthodox Churches*, and the *Free Churches* than the categories which are more common globally of *Roman Catholic, Protestant, Orthodox, Anglican* and *Pentecostal.* The principal *Protestant Churches* in the UK, and which are also *Free Churches*, include the Methodist Church, the United Reformed Church and *Baptist churches.* The *Anglican* Churches regard themselves as drawing upon both the *Catholic* and the *Protestant* traditions.

The variations in the pattern of *Churches* in the UK are closely related to the diverse but connected national histories of these islands. In particular, the contemporary patterns of Christian organisation reflect the various national outworkings of the events of the *Reformation* as outlined below. As a religious movement which had political dimensions, the *Reformation* affected different parts of these islands in different ways.

England and Wales

In England and Wales the *Reformation* led to the establishment of what is now called the Church of England through the 1534 *Act of Supremacy* of King Henry VIII, who initially styled himself *Head of the Church.* This title was later modified under Queen Elizabeth I to *Supreme Governor.* Thus the *Church* in England and Wales became independent of the jurisdiction of Rome, but closely identified with the monarchy.

In the period which followed in England, Christians who maintained allegiance to the Bishop of Rome (*Roman Catholics*) were persecuted under King Edward VI (1549-53). Under the *Catholic* Queen Mary (1553-58), *Protestants* were persecuted. Under Queen Elizabeth I, the position was again reversed.

The Church of England preserved many of the characteristics of *Catholic* Christianity, but also embraced certain *Protestant* features, such as a stress on the availability of the Christian scriptures to be read and studied in the everyday language of ordinary believers rather than in Latin since Latin was accessible only to *priests*, scholars and others who had received a formal education and, in any case, had not been the original language of the scriptures. During the sixteenth and early seventeenth centuries the *Bible* and the *Book of Common Prayer* (containing prescribed orders of worship of the Church of England) were translated into Welsh and were quickly accepted into common use among Christians in Wales.

By the end of the sixteenth century, *Congregationalists* (whose origins lay in the conviction that the *Church* consists of committed believers and who argued that therefore spiritual authority resides in the local congregation rather than in supra-local *Church* structures) were emerging, followed during the seventeenth century by *Baptists* and *Quakers.*

In Wales, the substantial majority of the *Churches* which were formed as a result of these developments worshipped and conducted their congregational and individual Christian life in the Welsh language. Today in Wales, the Union of Welsh Independents, the majority of *congregations* in the Baptist Union of Wales and the Presbyterian Church of Wales, and all *churches* within the Cymru District of the Methodist Church, continue to conduct their worship and *congregational* life in Welsh, as do some *Anglican churches* and several *Unitarian chapels.*

After the period of political and religious upheaval which followed the English civil war and the restoration of the monarchy, the 1662 *Act of Uniformity* led to over one thousand *clergy* being ejected from their parishes in England due to their refusal to be bound by its provisions which made the *Book of Common Prayer* compulsory. This strengthened the *Presbyterian Independent* and *Congregationalist* movements as they were joined by many *Anglican clergy* who did not wish to conform to these requirements. From this non-conforming stance came the name for such Christian traditions of "*Nonconformists*".

Scotland

In Scotland, *Calvinism* had the greatest impact. In 1560 the Church of Scotland was reformed along *Calvinist* principles, with a *Presbyterian* form of *Church* government based upon a collective of local church leadership of both *clergy* and non-clerical *elders*. Known as the *presbytery* (from the Greek *presbuteros* meaning *elder*), it is not to be confused with the residence of a *Roman Catholic parish priest*, usually also known as a *presbytery*.

Following the union of the crowns of England and Scotland, unsuccessful attempts were made to introduce an *episcopalian* (from the Greek *episcope*, meaning oversight) model of *church* government into Scotland, centred upon *bishops* (*episcopoi*) operating at the regional level. Those who supported the *Episcopalian* model formed the minority Scottish Episcopal Church. The dominant *Presbyterian* form of Christianity continued to be recognised as the Church of Scotland which is the *established* Church in Scotland and is generally understood by *Presbyterians* as the national *Church. Presbyterianism* came to Ireland from Scotland and is now the largest *Protestant* Christian tradition in Northern Ireland.

Anglican Churches

There are four autonomous *Anglican Churches* in these islands which correspond to its main nations. The Church of England, the Scottish Episcopal Church, the Church in Wales, and the Church of Ireland (which operates in both Northern Ireland and the Republic of Ireland.) In England and Wales there are 16,464 *Anglican* places of worship recorded with the General Register Office in 1999.

At the regional level, the *Churches* of the *Anglican* tradition are organised into *Provinces* and *dioceses*. At the local level, they are organised into *parishes* (the neighbourhood area) and *deaneries* (groupings of *parishes*). In England, Church of England *parishes* are legal entities and taken together cover the whole country, so that there is no area which is not understood as being in a Church of England *parish*.

The Church of England is the *established Church* in England. Its special constitutional position in the UK state is currently reflected by twenty-six of its senior *bishops* having reserved places in the House of Lords. The Church of England has two *Provinces* (of Canterbury and York) and forty-three *dioceses* (42 in England and 1 in the Isle of Man). Although an *episcopal* Church (led by *bishops* who have oversight of their *dioceses*), the Church of England is governed by the *General Synod* which includes three categories of *diocesan* representatives: *laity, clergy* and *bishops*, with similar *synods* operating at *diocesan* and *deanery* levels. These *synods* have various committees which deal with different aspects of the *Church's* work.

The *Anglican* Churches in Scotland, Wales and Ireland are not *established Churches*. The Scottish Episcopal Church has seven *dioceses*. It is the smallest of the *Anglican Churches* in these islands and numerically it is concentrated in Perthshire and in the north and east of Scotland. The Church of Ireland has two *Provinces* (Dublin and Armagh). The *Province* of Dublin is almost entirely in the Irish Republic whilst Armagh is mostly in Northern Ireland. The *disestablishment* of the Church of England in Wales led, in 1920, to the formation of the Church in Wales which is one *Province*. The *Province* has six *dioceses* and is a bi-lingual *Church*.

Roman Catholic Church

Although there is a continuity in the English *Roman Catholic* tradition with Christianity before King Henry VIII's repudiation of *Papal* authority, the Roman Catholic Church's contemporary strength in England and Wales is mainly due to the nineteenth and early twentieth century immigration of *Roman Catholics* from Ireland. There were, in 1999, 3,708 places of *Roman Catholic* worship, certified as such with the Registrar General.

In Scotland in 1560 there was an attempt to suppress *Roman Catholic* Christianity and *Papal* authority by law. However, the *Catholic* tradition survived in the south-west and in the highlands and islands of the north-west of Scotland. Immigration from Ireland and Italy also increased the *Catholic* population, which is concentrated around Glasgow.

In Ireland as a whole the Roman Catholic Church is by far the largest Christian tradition. It is also numerically the largest single *Church* in Northern Ireland even though *Catholics* make up only approximately forty per cent of Northern Ireland's total population.

In these islands the Roman Catholic Church has three national *Bishops' Conferences*: the Bishops' Conference for England and Wales, another for Scotland, and another for Ireland. *Roman Catholic* life is focussed upon *parish* and *diocesan*, rather than intermediate or national levels. At regional level, the Roman Catholic Church is organised into *dioceses* and *Provinces*. There are twenty-two *dioceses* in England and Wales and eight *dioceses* in Scotland. There are currently seven *Provinces* in Great Britain, each of which has an Archbishop. The *Archdioceses* of Westminster, Cardiff and Glasgow are the seats of the *Roman Catholic Archbishops* for England, Wales and Scotland, respectively, who often give a personal focus to leadership of the Roman Catholic Church in these countries. In respect of Northern Ireland, the Archdiocese of Armagh provides a focus for *Roman Catholics* both north and south of the border, since the *Church* is organised, as most other *Churches* on the island of Ireland, on an all-Ireland basis.

Orthodox Churches

The Registrar General's list of places of worship for England and Wales does not keep a running total for a separate category of *Orthodox churches*. In the UK the *Orthodox* Churches as such are a relatively recent presence apart from a number of individuals who settled in the UK from the seventeenth century onwards.

Larger numbers resulted from the arrival of significant emigrè groups of Russians after the Russian revolution, and the post Second World War migrations of Greeks, Serbs and other ethnic groups which have a traditionally close relationship with *Orthodox* Christianity. The *Orthodox Churches* in the UK are, in fact, still related to these older national and ethnic *Orthodox Churches*. The Greek Orthodox Church is numerically the largest, principally due to immigration from Cyprus. There are also, however, numbers of individuals from other ethnic and national backgrounds who have joined *Orthodox Churches*.

There are now also a growing number of Churches of the *Oriental Orthodox* tradition including the Armenian, Coptic, Ethiopian, Indian and Syrian *Orthodox*, and there is a Council of Oriental Orthodox Churches which seeks to group these *Churches* together co-operatively. Some Rastafarians are also baptised into the Ethiopian Orthodox Church. Because the *Orthodox* in general are not numerically strong and their members are geographically scattered, there is usually only one *diocese* for each *Church*, covering the whole of the UK.

Protestant Churches

Reformed Churches

The largest non-*Anglican Protestant* tradition in the British Isles is the *Reformed* tradition, within which *Presbyterianism* is the biggest strand. The word *Presbyterian* comes from the Greek word *presbuteros*, meaning *elder* and it refers to the local leadership of a Christian community. *Presbyterianism* is so called because of its emphasis on the local and collective leadership of such *elders*. The Registrar General's 1999 list of places of worship gives 1,752 certified places of worship for the United Reformed Church in England and Wales.

The main *Reformed* Churches of the UK are the Church of Scotland, the Presbyterian Church in Ireland, the Presbyterian Church of Wales and the United Reformed Church (which also includes the *Churches of Christ* and *Congregational* traditions, having been formed initially in 1972 through the uniting of the Presbyterian Church of England and the Congregational Church, formerly the Congregational Union).

There are also a number of smaller *Presbyterian* bodies – the Free Church of Scotland, the Free Presbyterian Church of Scotland, the Reformed Presbyterian Church of Scotland and the United Free Church of Scotland. In Ireland smaller *Presbyterian* church bodies include the Reformed Presbyterian Church of Ireland, the Evangelical Presbyterian Church, the Non-Subscribing Presbyterian Church of Ireland, and the Free Presbyterian Church of Ulster.

Methodism

There are 7,576 *Methodist* places of worship recorded in the Registrar General's 1999 list of certified places of worship for England and Wales. *Methodism* is the second most numerous *Protestant* tradition in the UK and is in the *Free Church* stream of Christianity. Its origins go back to the *Evangelical Revival* of the eighteenth century and specifically to the

religious movement led by John Wesley, aided by his brother, the hymn writer Charles Wesley. The word *Methodist* describes the systematic and methodical approaches to Christian conduct and training that were adopted by its founders, John and Charles Wesley within their Society, which began as a fellowship within the Church of England.

The Methodist Church of Great Britain covering England, Scotland and Wales is the largest *Methodist* body. Smaller *Methodist* bodies are the Methodist Church in Ireland, the Free Methodist Church, the Wesleyan Reform Union, and the Independent Methodist Connexion. *Methodist* numerical strength is concentrated in England, especially in the South West and the northern counties.

Methodism is organised on the basis of local *congregations* grouped together into what are known as *circuits*, each with a *Superintendent Minister*. These *circuits* are then part of regional bodies known as *Districts*. Each *District* is overseen by a *Chairman*, who is a senior ordained *minister*, and all are governed by the national *Conference*, which annually appoints a senior ordained *minister* as *President* of the Methodist Conference and a senior lay person as *Vice-President*. *Methodists* are noted for their emphasis upon pastoral care by *lay* people; for the large proportion of worship services led by *lay Local Preachers*; for the use of *hymns* to express their faith, and for emphasising that the Christian *Gospel* is for all people.

Baptist Movement

The *Baptist* movement emerged at the beginning of the sixteenth century. The Registrar General's 1999 list for England and Wales includes 3,332 certified *Baptist* places of worship. The word *Baptist* is used because of this tradition's practice of reserving *baptism* as a rite of Christian initiation for those who have confessed personal Christian faith rather than administering it to infants. Other than in exceptional circumstances (such as on medical grounds), *baptism* is administered in

Baptist congregations by complete immersion in water.

Today *Baptists* are organised into four main *Unions* of churches with some overlap of membership: these are the Baptist Union of Great Britain (the largest), the Baptist Union of Scotland, the Baptist Union of Wales, and the Baptist Union of Ireland. There are, however, also smaller groups of *Seventh Day* and *Strict Baptists*. Though distributed nationally, there are concentrations in the counties to the north of London and around the Bristol Channel, as well as to some extent in the rest of south-east England.

The individual congregation is the basic unit of *Baptist church* life. From January 2002 the Baptist Union of Great Britain will be divided into thirteen *Associations* each of which will be led by a regional *Association* team headed by a *Senior Regional Minister*. *Congregations* are also grouped informally into *Clusters* which may vary from three or four *congregations* up to twenty. Their main purpose is to engage together in *mission*. Each of the national *Unions* has a governing *Council* and holds an annual *Assembly*. The *Unions,* together with the Baptist Missionary Society, constitute the Federation of British Baptists, an umbrella body which exists to promote consultation and cooperation, though it does not have powers itself.

Congregationalism

Congregationalism goes back to the early *Puritan Separatists* from the Elizabethan *Church*. It grew with the imposition of the *Book of Common Prayer* in 1662, following the Restoration of the Monarchy following the Commonwealth and the Protectorate. In Ireland, the Congregational Union of Ireland is the main representative of this *Congregational* tradition.

Congregationalists accounted for seventy per cent of the membership of the United Reformed Church at its formation in 1972. The United Reformed Church, which has *congregations* in England, Wales and Scotland, combines elements of both *Congregational* and *Presbyterian* patterns of Church government as well as those of the Churches of Christ. Local *congregations* are grouped into *Districts*, and *Districts* into twelve *Provinces*, each with a *Provincial Moderator*.

The Registrar General's 1999 list for England and Wales gives a total number of 1,377 certified *Congregationalist* places of worship. Continuing *Congregational* groups which did not join the United Reformed Church include the Union of Welsh Independents, the Scottish Congregational Church, the Congregational Federation (in England) and also the Evangelical Fellowship of Congregational Churches. In addition, there are a number of totally un-affiliated *Congregational* congregations which, at the time of the formation of the United Reformed Church, stated that they would not join any other body, with their structures being similar to those of the *Baptists*.

Salvation Army

The Salvation Army was founded in 1878 by William Booth who tried to respond to both the social and the spiritual needs of the industrial working class. The Registrar General's list for England and Wales gives a total of 944 certified Salvation Army places of worship.

Its members can be recognised by their distinctive uniforms and its officers have military-style ranks. It is well known for its social service projects among the poor and homeless. The Salvation Army is organised into local *corps*, which are then grouped into regional level *Divisions* overseen by its National Headquarters. It does not administer the *sacraments* of *baptism* or the *eucharist* but is firmly within the *Evangelical* Christian tradition.

Lutheran

Compared with continental Europe, the *Lutheran* Christian tradition is very small in the UK. Its origins were in the continental *Reformation* and, specifically, the work of the reformer, Martin Luther, from whose surname the tradition takes its name. The Registrar General's list for England and Wales does not keep separate cumulative totals of certified *Lutheran* places of worship. Most *Lutheran congregations* in the UK have a significant proportion of members who are of German or Scandinavian descent.

Moravian

The *Moravian* tradition, which traces its origins to 1457 in what is now the Czech Republic, has a small presence in the UK and Ireland. The Registrar General's list for England and Wales does not keep separate cumulative totals of *Moravian* places of worship.

The Moravian Church is *Free Church* and *Evangelical* in orientation while having an *episcopal* form of Church Government. Local Churches are grouped into *Districts* and *Districts* which together form the British Moravian Church Province. The *Unity* (International) *Synod* meets every seven years.

Brethren

The *Brethren* movement was formed in the nineteenth century with Plymouth as an important geographical centre. The Registrar General's 1999 list for England and Wales gives 949 certified *Brethren* places of worship.

The popular name of "Plymouth Brethren" is derived from the movement's place of origin, although its members have never accepted this designation, preferring the terminology of *Christian Brethren*. There are also other *Brethren* groups, such as those known as the *Exclusive Brethren* and the Churches of God in the British Isles and Overseas. *Churches* of the *Brethren* tradition are local, independent *congregations* following what they understand to be the pattern of Christianity found in the *New Testament*.

Pentecostal Churches

Pentecostal Churches include the Assemblies of God, the Elim Pentecostal Church, the Apostolic Church and a significant number of black-majority *Churches*, many of which have roots in Caribbean, North American and African forms of Christianity. The Registrar General's list of certified places of worship in England and Wales does not keep a separate running total of churches under the category of *Pentecostalist*.

Black-Majority Churches

The black-majority Churches are a fast-growing and increasingly significant section of the Christian population of the UK. These *Churches* are very diverse in terms of their doctrines, practices and forms of *Church* organisation. They range from *Pentecostal* and *Holiness* Churches, through to those of *Sabbatarian* and other traditions. The Registrar General's list of certified places of worship in England and Wales does not keep a separate running total of *churches* under the category of *Black-majority Churches*.

Some of these *Churches*, such as the New Testament Church of God or the Church of God of Prophecy, are becoming numerically significant. Others are quite local and consist of only one or two *congregations*, although they quite often co-operate with other larger groups within the framework of co-ordinating organisations such as the International Ministerial Council of Great Britain and the Council of African and Afro-Caribbean Churches. They are represented on the Black Christians Concerns Group of Churches Together in Britain and Ireland which also relates to the concerns of black Christians in the "historic" *Churches* of the United Kingdom.

House Churches

Over the past quarter of a century, a number of independent *House Churches* have been established under local leaderships which have gradually built patterns of wider networking and association. These *Churches* have developed new forms of worship which have often proved attractive to young people. Since these *Churches* do not necessarily meet in buildings of their own, the Registrar

General's list of certified places of worship in England and Wales does not record a total of churches under the category of *House Churches*.

Quakers

The Religious Society of Friends was founded out of the sixteenth century life and work of George Fox.

Today, two discernible strands have emerged: the primarily Christian, and the *Universalist*. The latter has attracted some members of other faiths and humanists into membership of the Society of Friends. *Quakers* do not use *creeds*, have no *ordained* ministers, embrace pacifism and have a distinctive style of worship rooted in shared silence and decision-making which aims at unity based on the leadings of the Holy Spirit.

Quakers meet in local *Meetings* and also at a national level in a *Britain Yearly Meeting* which covers England, Wales and Scotland. A separate *Yearly Meeting* covers the whole of Ireland. Those local *Quaker* groups which have their own buildings often open these up for wider use by a range of both religious and secular groups concerned with justice, peace and reconciliation.

The Registrar General's list of certified places of worship in England and Wales records 365 *Quaker* meeting places. There are 25 *Quaker Meetings* in Ireland.

Unitarian and Free Christian Churches

Unitarian Churches had their British origins in the seventeenth century, when they rejected the *Trinitarian* and *Christological* credal formulations of the then predominant Christian traditions and *Churches*, and upheld religious freedom. In the nineteenth and twentieth centuries there has been a strong influence from the Unitarian Universalist Association of North America.

The Registrar General's 1999 list gives 180 certified *Unitarian* places of worship. The General Assembly of Unitarian and Free

Christian Churches is not a member of Churches Together in Britain and Ireland.

Ecumenical Structures

Churches Together in Britain and Ireland (CTBI) was set up in 1990 under the original name of the Council of Churches for Britain and Ireland (CCBI), as a result of the *Inter-Church Process*.

This broadened the range of Christian traditions participating in the previous *ecumenical* structure known as the British Council of Churches (BCC). Amongst its thirty members are some of the largest *Churches*, including the Roman Catholic Church in England and Wales and in Scotland, which had not been part of the BCC, as well as a number of smaller *Churches*.

The CTBI relates to a number of *ecumenical* networks and organisations in Britain and Ireland and, as in the case of the other similar bodies operating at the levels of the four individual nations, it is known as an *ecumenical instrument*. The CTBI works largely through a series of *Networks*, *Agencies* and *Commissions* (see the Christian organisational listings).

The national *ecumenical instruments* are Churches Together in England (CTE), Action of Churches Together in Scotland (ACTS), Churches Together in Wales (CYTUN), the Irish Council of Churches (ICC) and Irish Inter-Church Meeting (IICM). The Free Churches Group in Churches Together in England represents the interests that were formerly embodied in the Free Churches Council, including the specifically Free Church interests in education and in chaplaincies.

At a local level, many individual *congregations* and *parishes* co-operate in what are known as local Councils of Churches or local *Churches Together* groups or in what were originally called *Local Ecumenical Projects* and are now known as *Local Ecumenical Partnerships* (LEPs). Member Churches of Churches Together in

England are also working closely together in so-called *Intermediate Bodies*. These operate at a level that approximates to a county and are serviced by a full or part-time *ecumenical officer*.

Other Interdenominational Networks

In addition to the *Churches* involved in these structures, there are also networks which link together other national bodies and local *congregations* which have an understanding of their commitment to *Evangelical* Christian tradition that requires them not to be directly involved in these formal *ecumenical* structures. There is, for example, a Fellowship of Independent Evangelical Churches (FIEC) which operates throughout the UK and there is also the Evangelical Alliance which links *Churches* and other Christian bodies which assent to its basis of faith and belief.

Other Christian Organisations

There are a vast range of Christian based organisations existing alongside the Christian Churches and *Religious Orders* and working at local, regional, national and international levels. The current directory does not attempt to give comprehensive details of this large sector of organisations, fuller details of which can be found in the *UK Christian Handbook*. These organisations operate in most fields, from social welfare to education. Some are formally sponsored by and receive significant support from national *Churches* while others are supported primarily by the donations of time or money of individual Christians.

Some organisations are aligned with a particular tradition and/or "*Churchmanship*" of Christianity, whilst others - perhaps the majority - are explicitly *ecumenical* or *inter-denominational* in character. Details of a selection of these organisations are included in this directory, but for a fuller and more comprehensive range, readers are directed to the *UK Christian Handbook*.

Personnel

Local Leadership

Members of the *Church* who are not ordained are generally known as the *laity* (from the Greek word *laos*, meaning people). In some *Protestant Churches* the *laity* can, in principle at least, conduct all the ceremonies, rites and functions of the *Church*, even if in practice these are usually carried out by designated leaders.

Ordained Leadership

The names and functions of the designated religious leadership of various Christian *Churches* vary according to their tradition. Nevertheless, broad categories of personnel can be discerned among *ordained* (set apart and recognised) leaders of the *Roman Catholic, Anglican, Orthodox* and *Protestant Churches*.

Among some of the *Churches* which have a shorter history in the UK, and which have geographical origins in Africa and the Caribbean, an even wider variety of titles and functions can be found. For example, among a number of the *African Churches* there is a specific office of *prophet* or *prophetess* and another of *apostle*.

Other Christian groups within the *House Church* and *Restorationist* movements recognise leaders who have wider than local ministries and special gifts of ministry as *apostles* (a word which other Christians generally reserve for the first *disciples* of Jesus who are believed to have had a uniquely special role within the Christian community).

In the *Roman Catholic, Anglican* and *Orthodox* traditions, *ordained* leadership at the local level is provided by religious leaders and functionaries who are known as *priests*. In the Western *Roman Catholic* tradition *priests* are not allowed to marry, although some married former *Anglican priests* have recently been *ordained*, or conditionally *ordained*, as *Roman Catholic priests*. In the *Anglican* tradition *priests* may marry; in the *Orthodox* tradition, married men may be ordained *priests* (but may not be *bishops*). In these traditions, presiding at the *Eucharist* is reserved for *priests*.

Priests are also authorised to *baptise* and to *preach*. In these traditions, *priests* are seen both as representing the people to God and also as representing Christ to the *congregation*, as the focal points through whom God cares for the Christian community. This is especially believed to be the case in the *Eucharist*.

In the *Anglican* tradition authorised lay people, known as *Readers*, can *preach*. There is also an *ordained* order of *ministry* known as *deacons* or the *diaconate* (from the Greek word – *diakonos*, meaning "servant"). This is technically an order in its own right, although *priests*-to-be are first of all *ordained deacon* as a stage on the way to full *ordination* to the *priesthood*. The *diaconate* exists in other Christian traditions, too, sometimes as a permanent order of *ministry*.

Protestant Churches generally have a more functional view of their local *ordained* leadership. In the *Protestant Churches ordained* local leaders are known as *ministers* (*Baptist*, *Methodist*, United Reformed Church, Church of Scotland as well as other *Reformed* Churches) or as *pastors* (*Christian Brethren*, many branches of the *Pentecostal* movement, and some *Baptist churches*).

In the *Roman Catholic* and *Orthodox* traditions the *priesthood* is not open to women. Women are now able to be ordained as *priests* in the *Churches* of the *Anglican* tradition in England, Ireland, Scotland and Wales. For many years there have been divided convictions on this issue even though there have been women *priests* in other parts of the worldwide *Anglican* tradition. Tensions still remain within the *Churches* which have ordained women as *priests*. Specific provision is made, for example in the Church of England, to recognise the position of those who oppose for reasons of conscience, the *ordination* of women as *priests*. In the *Protestant Churches*

women are generally able to serve as local *ministers* and some have also assumed responsibilities in regional and national leadership.

Pastoral Care

In all *Churches*, local *clergy* have a role in the pastoral care of the *congregation* as well as in *preaching* and administering the *sacraments*. In the understanding of the *established* Church of England, the *priest's* duty of pastoral care, shared with *lay* people, extends to everyone within the geographical area of the *parish*, regardless of whether or not they are *Anglican* or even *Christian*. A similar duty applies to *ministers* of the *established* Church of Scotland. In many *Churches* designated lay Christians also share in the pastoral ministry of the *Church*.

Regional, National and International Leadership

In the *Orthodox*, *Roman Catholic* and *Anglican* traditions the focus of unity of the *Church's* leadership is vested in the *bishop*. *Bishops* are senior *clergy* who are responsible for the geographical and ecclesiastical areas known as *dioceses*. *Roman Catholic bishops* and *priests* do not marry. *Anglican bishops* may be married, but whilst *Orthodox priests* may marry before *ordination* as *priests*, the office of *bishop* in the *Orthodox Churches* is open only to *monks* and therefore only to *priests* who are not married or who have become widowers.

In the *Protestant Churches* regional leaders are known by a wide variety of titles such as *Provincial Moderator* (United Reformed Church), *Area Superintendent* (*Baptists*), and *District Chairman* (Methodist Church). The Church of England has two *Archbishops*, namely, the Archbishop of Canterbury and the Archbishop of York. The Archbishop of Canterbury is the Church of England's senior *bishop* and is also recognised as having a special seniority in the worldwide *Anglican* communion.

In the *Protestant Churches* national leaders usually have very functional titles such as *General Secretary* (Baptist Union of Great Britain), *Moderator of the General Assembly* (Church of Scotland) or *President of the Conference* (Methodist Church). These indicate the different kinds of roles in each of the *Churches*. In general, *General Secretaryships* are stipendiary posts which are held for several years, whilst the offices of *Moderators of Assembly* and those of *Presidents* tend to be honorary officers, appointed annually.

In the *Orthodox Churches*, senior *Archbishops* are known by the title of *Patriarch* and they may have responsibilities which extend across national boundaries. In the Roman Catholic Church in some parts of the world there are also *Patriarchs*. A group of senior *Bishops* and *Archbishops* from all over the world are members of the *College of Cardinals*. *Cardinals* under eighty years of age at the time of an election choose the *Pope* (meaning "Father") who is installed as *Bishop of Rome* and is recognised as the chief pastor of the Roman Catholic Church throughout the world. He is often referred to by *Roman Catholics* as the *Holy Father*.

Among *Protestant Churches*, the international leadership, like the national leadership, has a variety of more functional titles. In keeping with the military imagery used by the Salvation Army, the leader of the Salvation Army worldwide is known as *General*. The World Alliance of Reformed Churches, the Lutheran World Federation and the Baptist World Alliance all have *General Secretaries*. Each of these bodies has a mainly co-ordinating and consultative role in contrast to the more integrated and hierarchical structure of the Salvation Army.

FURTHER READING

Attwater, D, *A Dictionary of Mary*, P J Kennedy, Longmans, 1957.

Ballard, P and Jones, D (eds), *This Land and People: Y Wlad a'r Bobl Hyn: A Symposium on Christian and Welsh National Identity*, Collegiate Centre of Theology, University College, Cardiff (revised edition) 1980.

Barraclough, G (ed), *The Christian World*, Abrams, London, 1981.

Barrett, D, *The World Christian Encyclopaedia: A Comparative Study of Churches and Religions in the Modern World, AD1900-2000*, Oxford University Press, Oxford, 1982.

Bettenson, H, *Documents of the Christian Church*, Oxford University Press, London, 1975.

Bisset, P, *The Kirk and Her Scotland*, Handsel Press, Edinburgh, 1986.

Bowden, J, *Dictionary of Christian Theology*, SCM Press, London, 1983.

Braybrooke, M, *The Explorer's Guide to Christianity*, Hodder and Stoughton, London, 1998.

Brierley, P, *Christianity by Numbers, No1*, Christian Research Association, London, 1989 (updated 1994).

Brierley, P, *Irish Christian Handbook, 1995-96*, Christian Research Association, London, 1994.

Brierley, P (ed), *UK Christian Handbook 2000-2001*, Christian Research Association, London, 1999.

Brierley, P and Macdonald, F, *Prospects for Scotland 2000*, Christian Research Association, London, 1995.

Catholic Bishops' Conference of England and Wales, *What Are We to Teach?*, Catholic Education Service, London, 1994.

Catholic Church, *Catechism of the Catholic Church*, Geoffrey Chapman, London, 1994.

Chadwick, O, *The History of Christianity*, Weidenfeld & Nicolson, London, 1995.

Childs, J F, and Macquarrie, J (eds), *A New Dictionary of Christian Ethics*, SCM, London, (2nd edition) 1987.

Chryssides, G, *The Elements of Unitarianism*, Element Books, Dorset, 1998.

Coggins, R J and Houlden, J L, *A Dictionary of Biblical Interpretation*, SCM, London, 1990.

Cross, F L and Livingstone, E A (eds), *Oxford Dictionary of the Christian Church*, Oxford University Press, London, (3rd revised edition) 1997.

Davies, H, *Worship and Theology in England* (Volume I: From Cranmer to Baxter and Fox, 1534-1690; Volume II: From Watts and Wesley to Martineau, 1690-1900; Volume III: The Ecumenical Century, 1900 to the Present), Eerdmans, 1996.

Davies, J G, *A New Dictionary of Liturgy and Worship*, SCM, London, 1986.

Dickens, A G, *The English Reformation*, Collins, London, 1967.

de Druille, *From East to West: A History of Monasteries*, Gracewing, 1999.

Dupre, L and Saliers, D E (eds), *Christian Spirituality: Reformation and Modern*, SCM, London, 1989.

Edwards, D L, *Christian England*, Collins, London, 1985.

Furlong, M, *C of E: The State It's In*, Hodder and Stoughton, London, 2000

Gerloff, R, *A Plea for British Black Theologies: The Black Church Movement in Britain in its Transatlantic Cultural and Theological Interaction, Parts I and II*, Peter Lang, Frankfurt am Main, Germany, 1992.

Hastings, A, *A History of English Christianity, 1920-1985*, Collins, London, 1986.

Keeley, R (ed), *The Lion Handbook of Christian Belief*, Lion Publishing, Tring, 1982.

Latourette, K, *A History of Christianity*, (2 volumes), Harper and Row, London, 1975.

Lossky, N, Bonino, M, Pobee, J, Stransky, T, Wainwright G and Webb, P, *Dictionary of the Ecumenical Movement*, World Council of Churches, Geneva, 1991.

Marthaler, B, *The Creed*, Twenty-Third Publications, 1993 (revised edition).

McAdoo, H R, *Anglican Heritage*, Canterbury Press, Norwich, 1991.

McBrien, R P, *Catholicism*, Chapman, 1980.

McGinn, B and Meyendorff, J (eds), *Christian Spirituality: Origins to the Twelfth Century*, SCM, London, 1986.

McKenzie, P, *The Christians: Their Practices and Beliefs*, SPCK, London, 1988.

McManners, J (ed), *The Oxford Illustrated History of Christianity*, Oxford University Press, Oxford, 1990.

Nunn, Roger, *This Growing Unity: A Handbook on Ecumenical Development in the Counties, Large Cities and New Towns of England*, Churches Together in England (Publications), London, 1995.

Raitt, J (ed), *Christian Spirituality: High Middle Ages and Reformation*, SCM, London, 1987.

Smart, N, *The Phenomenon of Christianity*, Collins, London, 1979.

Smith, N (ed), *Journal of George Fox*, Penguin Classics, 2000.

Strange, R, *The Catholic Faith*, Oxford University Press, 1985.

ter Haar, G, *Halfway to Paradise: African Christians in Europe*, Cardiff Academic Press, Cardiff, 1998.

Wakefield, G, *A Dictionary of Christian Spirituality*, SCM, London, 1983.

Walker, A, *Restoring the Kingdom: The Radical Christianity of the House Church Movement*, Hodder and Stoughton, London, 1988.

Ware, Kallistos, *The Orthodox Way*, Mowbray, London, 1987.

Welch, Elizabeth and Winfield, Flora, *Travelling Together: A Handbook on Local Ecumenical Partnerships*, Churches Together in England (Publications), London, 1995.

Yearly Meeting of the Religious Society of Friends in Britain, *Quaker Faiths and Practice: The Book of Christian Discipline of the Religious Society of Friends (Quakers) in Britain* (2nd edition), London, 1999.

CHRISTIAN UNITED KINGDOM ORGANISATIONS

Alongside Christian Churches there are an enormous range of other Christian organisations of varied kinds such as the Christian Ecology Group, the Christian Socialist Movement and many others. Details of many of these organisations can be found in the *UK Christian Handbook*.

The format of the Christian listings varies from the directory's normal layout. Due to the large number of Christian places of worship and local organisations and because the structures of the Churches are very developed, information is given only on UK, national and regional levels of organisation.

Churches which operate at the level of only one country of the UK (eg the Church of England) are listed in the "Christian National and Regional Listings" section under the country concerned rather than in this section.

UNITED KINGDOM ECUMENICAL INSTRUMENTS   237

UNITED KINGDOM GROUPINGS OF CHURCHES   238

CHURCHES OPERATING AT A UNITED KINGDOM OR GREAT BRITAIN LEVEL   241

BODIES CONNECTED WITH UNITED KINGDOM ECUMENICAL INSTRUMENTS   245

UNITED KINGDOM ECUMENICAL INSTRUMENTS

Churches Together in Britain and Ireland*
Inter-Church House, 35-41 Lower Marsh, London SE1 7SA
Tel: (020) 7523 2121 **Fax:** (020) 7928 0010
Email: info@ctbi.org.uk
Website: http://www.ctbi.org.uk/
Contact: Dr David Goodbourn
Position: General Secretary
Contact Email: david.goodbourn@ctbi.org.uk
Activities: Worship/practice/meditation, umbrella body, newsletter/journal, books, resources
Traditions: Ecumenical/Interdenominational
Affiliations: World Council of Churches
CTBI was renamed in 1999 and it was previously the Council of Churches for Britain and Ireland. CTBI co-ordinates the work of its 31 member churches.

Member Churches of CTBI
Baptist Union of Great Britain
Cherubim and Seraphim Council of Churches
Church in Wales
Church of England
Church of Ireland
Church of Scotland
Congregational Federation
Council for Oriental Orthodox Christian
    Churches
Council of African and Afro-Caribbean Churches
Evangelische Kirche Deutschland (German-
    speaking Synod)
Free Churches Group of Churches Together in
    England
Greek Orthodox Church
Independent Methodist Churches
International Ministerial Council of Great Britain
Joint Council of Afro-Caribbean Churches
Light and Life Mission
Lutheran Council of Great Britain
Methodist Church
Methodist Church in Ireland
Moravian Church
New Testament Assembly
Presbyterian Church of Wales
Religious Society of Friends (Quakers)
Roman Catholic Church in England and Wales
Roman Catholic Church in Ireland (associate
    member)
Roman Catholic Church in Scotland

Russian Orthodox Church
Salvation Army UK Territory
Scottish Episcopal Church
Serbian Orthodox Church
Seventh Day Adventist Church (associate member)
Undeb Yr Annibynwyr Cymraeg (Union of Welsh
    Independents)
United Free Church of Scotland
United Reformed Church
Wesleyan Holiness

Bodies in Association
Afro-West Indian United Council of Churches
Assn of Centres of Adult Theological Education
Association of Inter-Church Families in Britain and
    Ireland
Centre for Black and White Christian Partnership
Christian Education Movement
Christianity and the Future of Europe
Church Action of Christians against torture
Church Action on Poverty
Churches' East-West European Relations Network
Council on Christian Approaches to Defence and
    Disarmament
Ecumenical Council for Corporate Responsibility
Feed the minds
Fellowship of St Alban and St Sergius
Iona Community
Irish School of Ecumenics
Living Stones
Managerial and Organisational Disciplines for the
    Enhancement of Ministry (MODEM)
Nat. Assn of Christian Communities and Networks
National Christian Education Council
New Assembly of Churches
William Temple Foundation
Young Men's Christian Association (YMCA)
Young Women's Christian Association (YWCA)

Agencies
Catholic Fund for Overseas Development
Christian Aid
Christians Abroad
Churches' Commission on Overseas Students
One World Week
Scottish Catholic International Aid Fund

Formal Networks
AIDS Monitoring Group (BSR)
Church and Society Forum
Churches' Advisory Council on Local Broadcasting
Churches' Joint Education Policy Committee
Churches' Peace Forum
Churches' Stewardship Network

Churches' World Development Network
Consultative Group on Ministry among Children
Environmental Issues Network
International Affairs Liaison Group
Joint Liturgical Group

UNITED KINGDOM GROUPINGS OF CHURCHES

Afro-West Indian United Council of Churches*
New Testament Church of God, Arcadian Gardens,
High Road, Wood Green, London N22 5AA
Tel: (020) 8888 9427
Contact: Revd Eric Brown
Position: General Secretary
Affiliations: Inter Faith Network for the UK

Member Bodies:
Bibleway Church of our Lord Jesus Christ
    Worldwide
Community Church of God
Melchisedek Spiritual Baptist Church
New Testament Assembly
New Testament Church of God
Pentecostal Revival Fellowship
Redemption Church of God
Shiloh United Church of Christ Apostolic
    Worldwide
United Church of God
Wesleyan Holiness Church

Cherubim and Seraphim Council of Churches UK*
The Prayer House, 175 Earlham Grove, Forest
Gate, London E7 9AP
Tel: (020) 8534 5101 **Fax:** (020) 8534 0378
Contact: Special Apostle E O Oluwole
Position: Chairman
Activities: Worship, resource, inter-faith
Traditions: African Independent
Other Languages: Yoruba (Nigerian)
The Council was founded in 1976 to embrace all
Cherubim and Seraphim Churches in the UK and
to promote inter-relationships among all Christian
Churches in the UK and all over the world.

Council of African and African-Caribbean Churches (UK)*
31 Norton House, Sidney Road, Stockwell,
London SW9 0UJ
Tel: (020) 7274 5589 **Fax:** (020) 7274 4726
Contact: Most Revd Father Oluwole Aremu

Abiola
Position: Chairman
Contact Email: olu_abiola@lineone.net
Activities: Umbrella body
Traditions: African Independent, Pentecostal, Caribbean
Other Languages: Yoruba, Twi, French, Patua
Affiliations: Churches Together in Britain and Ireland; Churches Together in England; Conference of European Churches; Inter Faith Network for the UK

The Council is a medium through which African and Afro-Caribbean Churches may work with a joint effort to perform those services which Churches cannot conveniently provide themselves, especially in the training of ministers and officers.

Member Bodies Include:
Aladura International Church
Celestial Church of Christ
Cherubim and Seraphim Church (Imole)
Cherubim and Seraphim Church Movement
Cherubim and Seraphim Society St Stephen's
    Church
Christ Apostolic Church
Christ the King Pentecostal Church
Christ the Resurrection Church
Church of Salvation
Church of the Lord Aladura
Church of the Lord Brotherhood
Crystal El-Shaddai Church of Christ
Divine Prayer Society, 1944
ESO New Temple Cherubim and Seraphim
    Church
Eternal Glory Church
Eternal Order of Cherubim and Seraphim
Eternal Order of the Morning Star
Holy Emmanuel Church of Christ
Holy Mount Zion Revival Church
Holy Order of Cherubim and Seraphim Church
Imimsi Oluwa Cherubim and Seraphim Church
Iraw Ogo Jeusu
Kimbanguist Church
Love Divine Church of Christ
Melchisedec Spiritual Baptist Church
Musama Disco Christo Church
Newborn Apostolic Church
Pentecostal Revival Church of Christ
Redeemed Church of Christ Cherubim and
    Seraphim
St James Cherubim and Seraphim Redemption
    Church

St Francis Spiritual Baptist Church
St John the Divine Spiritual Baptist Church
United Prayerist of Christ Church

Council of Oriental Orthodox Churches UK*
34 Chertsey Road, Church Square, Shepperton
TW17 9LF
Tel: (020) 8368 8447 **Fax:** (020) 8368 8447
Contact: Aziz M A Nour
Position: Secretary
Activities: Umbrella body, youth, elderly, visits, resources
Other Languages: Arabic, Armenian, Coptic, Amharic

This ecumenical body co-ordinates the ecumenical and interfaith activities in the UK and Ireland of the Orthodox Churches which are in full communion with each other. Each Church has a supreme head who usually resides outside the UK.

Member Bodies:
Armenian Apostolic Church
Coptic Orthodox Church
Eritrean Orthodox Church
Ethiopian Orthodox Church
Syrian Orthodox Church
Syro Indian Church

Evangelical Alliance UK*
Whitefield House, 186 Kennington Park Road,
London SE11 4BT
Tel: (020) 7207 2100 **Fax:** (020) 7207 2150
Email: info@eauk.org
Website: http://www.eauk.org/
Contact: Information and Resources Centre
Position: Information Officer
Activities: Umbrella body, newsletter/journal
Traditions: Evangelical
Affiliations: European Evangelical Alliance; World Evangelical Alliance

Represents Evangelical views on social, political and moral issues. Has 44,000 individuals; 3,000 local churches and 700 organisations in membership. There are some 30 Local Evangelical Fellowships linked to the Alliance which group together a number of local churches and ministries in different areas.

Local Evangelical Fellowships:
Beckenham and Penge
Brent
Brentwood
Brighton
Bristol

Bromley
Grampian
Hull
Inverness
Ipswich
King's Lynn
Leyton
Manchester
Merseyside
Mid Cotswolds
New Forest
Paisley
Peterborough
Plymouth
Portsmouth
Southampton
South East Essex
South Wessex
Taunton
Teeside
Tiverton
Torbay
Tower Hamlets
Tunbridge Wells
Wight, Isle of
Wolverhampton

Free Churches Group*

Churches Together in England, 27 Tavistock
Square, London WC1H 9HH
Tel: (020) 7529 8141 **Fax:** (020) 7529 8134
Email: freechurch@cte.org.uk
Contact: Revd Geoffrey H Roper
Position: Secretary
Activities: Umbrella body, women,
newsletter/journal
Other Languages: Welsh
Co-ordinates and represents eighteen constituent
denominations and supports a Women's Council, an
education committee and a Health Care Chaplaincy
Steering Committee.

Constituent Denominations:
Afro-West Indian United Council of Churches
Baptist Union of Great Britain
Baptist Union of Wales
Congregational Federation
Council of African and Afro-Caribbean Churches
    UK
Countess of Huntingdon's Connexion
Fellowship of Churches of Christ
Free Church of England
Independent Methodist Churches

Methodist Church
Moravian Church
New Testament Church of God
Old Baptist Union
Presbyterian Church of Wales
Salvation Army
Undeb yr Annibynwyr Cymraeg
(Union of Welsh Independents)
United Reformed Church in the United Kingdom
Wesleyan Reform Union

International Ministerial Council of Great Britain*

93 Cecil Street, Watford WD2 4NY
Tel: (01923) 239266 **Fax:** (01923) 239266
Email: imcgb@aol.com
Contact: Revd Onye Obila
Position: General Secretary
Contact Tel: (020) 8345 5169
Contact Email: onye@dircon.co.uk
Activities: Umbrella body, resources
Traditions: Ecumenical/Interdenominational
Other Languages: African, German, Tamil
Affiliations: Churches Together in Britain and
Ireland; Christian Aid
A uniting body for all churches, IMCGB is the
licensing body for independent churches

Joint Council for Anglo-Caribbean Churches*

141 Railton Road, Brixton, London SE24 0LT
Tel: (020) 7737 6542
Contact: Revd Esme Beswick
Position: General Secretary
Activities: Youth, inter-faith
Traditions: Pentecostal

Member Bodies:
Bible Truth Church of God
Church of God Assembly
Church of God Independent
Church of God Pentecostal
Firstborn Church of the Living God
Humble Heart Church
Mount Hermon Church of God Assembly
Mount Refuge Firstborn Church
New Testament Assembly
Union Reformed Church
Universal Group of Apostles
Zion Pentecostal Church of God

New Assembly of Churches*

15 Oldridge Road, Balham, Wandsworth, London
SW12 8PL

Tel: (020) 8673 0595 **Fax:** (020) 8675 8768
Contact: Revd Carmel E Jones
Position: Chief Executive Officer
Activities: Umbrella body, youth, elderly, women, inter-faith
Traditions: Pentecostal

Member Bodies:
African Methodist Zion Church
All Nations Christian Fellowship
Assemblies of the First Born
Calvary Church of God in Christ
Church of God Worldwide Mission Faith Chapel
International Fellowship for Christ
New Life Assembly
New Testament Church of God
Seventh Day Adventists
Shiloh United Church of Christ Apostolic

Syrian Orthodox Churches Council (UK)*
Antaccia, 77 Exeter Road, London N14 5JU
Tel: (020) 8368 8447 **Fax:** (020) 8368 8447
Contact: Aziz M A Nour
Position: Secretary
Activities: Umbrella body, newsletter/journal, books, inter-faith, resources
Traditions: Orthodox
Other Languages: Syriac, Arabic, Malayalam, Turkish
Affiliations: Council of Oriental Orthodox Churches; Churches Together in Britain and Ireland; Churches Together in England

CHURCHES OPERATING AT A UNITED KINGDOM OR GREAT BRITAIN LEVEL

Aladura International Church (UK and Overseas)*
31 Norton House, Sidney Road, Stockwell, London SW9 OUJ
Tel: (020) 7274 5589 **Fax:** (020) 7274 4726
Email: adura_inter@lineone.net
Contact: Most Revd Father Oluwole Aremu Abiola
Position: General Superintendent
Contact Email: olu_abiola@lineone.net
Activities: Worship/practice/meditation
Traditions: African Independent
Other Languages: Yoruba, Twi, Patua, French
Affiliations: Council of African and Afro-Caribbean Churches; Churches Together in Britain

and Ireland; Churches Together in England
Its aim is to give professionally trained people the opportunity to minister to those around them on completion of their studies, using their spare time to preach, teach and propagate the Gospel.

Apostolic Church, The*
PO Box 389, Swansea SA1 1ZH
Tel: (01792) 473992
Email: admin@apostolic-church.org
Website: http://www.apostolic-church.org/
Contact: Rev Andrew Saunders
Position: Administrator
Activities: Worship/practice/meditation, central body, newsletter/journal, books
Traditions: Pentecostal
Affiliations: Evangelical Alliance UK

Armenian Orthodox Church in Great Britain*
Armenian Vicarage, Iverna Gardens, Kensington, London W8 6TP
Contact: Revd Shnork Bagdessarian
Position: Vicar
Contact Tel: (020) 7937 0152
Activities: Worship/practice/meditation, community centre, youth, elderly, visits
Traditions: Orthodox
Other Languages: Armenian

Assemblies of God*
16 Bridgford Road, West Bridgford, Nottingham NG2 6AF
Tel: (0115) 9811188 **Fax:** (0115) 9813377
Email: info@aog.org.uk
Website: http://www.aog.org.uk/
Contact: Mr David Gill
Position: General Administrator
Activities: Worship/practice/meditation, central body, youth, elderly, women, newsletter/journal, resources
Traditions: Pentecostal
Affiliations: Pentecostal Churches UK (PCUK); World Pentecostal Fellowship
An organisation of more than 650 autonomous churches in the British Isles.

Assyrian Church of the East*
66 Montague Road, Hanwell, London W7 3PQ
Tel: (020) 8579 7259
Contact: Revd Yonan Yowel Yonan
Position: Archdeacon
Traditions: Orthodox

Baptist Union of Great Britain*
Baptist House, PO Box 44, 129 Broadway, Didcot
OX11 8RT
Tel: (01235) 517700 **Fax:** (01235) 517715
Email: baptistuniongb@baptist.org.uk
Website: http://www.baptist.org.uk/
Contact: Revd David Coffey
Position: General Secretary
Activities: Resource, umbrella body, youth, elderly,
women, newsletters
Traditions: Free Church
Affiliations: Baptist World Alliance

Bulgarian Orthodox Church*
188 Queen's Gate, London SW7 5HL
Tel: (020) 7584 4607
Contact: Very Revd Simeon Iliev
Position: Chairman
Activities: Worship
Other Languages: Bulgarian

Byelorussian Autocephalic Orthodox Church*
11 Park Grove, Bradford BD9 4JY
Tel: (01274) 547474
Contact: Mr J Jaswilowicz
Position: Council Secretary

Coptic Orthodox Church*
509 Duncan House, Dolphin Square, London
SW1V 3PP
Tel: (020) 7937 5782
Contact: Dr Fuad Megally
Position: Secretary
Contact Tel: (020) 7834 9728
Activities: Worship
Other Languages: Arabic, Coptic

Countess of Huntingdon's Connexion*
69 Jubilee Road, Middleton, Manchester M24 2LT
Tel: (0161) 6434108
Website: http://www.cofhconnexion.org.uk/
Contact: Marjorie Jacques Crossley
Position: Secretary
Activities: Worship, youth, elderly, women
Traditions: Evangelical Free Church
Affiliations: Free Churches' Council; Evangelical
Alliance

**Ecumenical Patriarchate Archdiocese of
Thyateira and Great Britain***
Thyateira House. 5 Craven House, London
W2 3EN
Tel: (020) 7723 4787 **Fax:** (020) 7224 9301
Contact: Father Deacon Meliton Oakes

Position: Secretary
Activities: Worship/practice/meditation,
community centre, central body, newsletter/journal,
inter-faith
Traditions: Orthodox
Other Languages: Greek

Eritrean Orthodox Church*
78 Edmund Street, Camberwell, London SE5 7NR
Tel: (020) 7703 5147 **Fax:** (020) 7703 5147
Contact: Father Yohannes Sibhatu
Position: Minister
Contact Tel: (07956) 365775
Activities: Community centre, youth, elderly,
women, newspapers
Traditions: Orthodox
Other Languages: Tigrigna, Arabic

Ethiopian Orthodox Church
9 Philip House, Mortimer Place, London
NW6 5PB
Contact: Most Revd Archbishop Abuna Esaias
Position: Primate of N W Europe

Fellowship of Churches of Christ*
25 Robert Avenue, Erdington, Birmingham
B23 5RD
Tel: (0121) 3737942 **Fax:** (0121) 3737942
Email: coc-erdington@charis.co.uk
Website: http://www.charis.co.uk/coc-erdington/
Contact: Mrs Hazel Wilson
Position: Fellowship Secretary
Activities: Central body, newsletter/journal
Traditions: Evangelical Free Church
Affiliations: Free Church Group at Churches
Together in England; World Convention of
Churches of Christ
A group of autonomous churches who are part of a
wider group found in 165 countries. They believe in
Jesus Christ as founder and centre of their faith and
the authority of the Bible in matters of faith and
conduct.

**General Assembly of Unitarian and Free
Christian Churches***
Essex Hall, 1-6 Essex Street, London WC2R 3HY
Tel: (020) 7240 2384 **Fax:** (020) 7240 3089
Email: ga@unitarian.org.uk
Website: http://www.unitarian.org.uk/
Contact: Matthew Smith
Position: Information Officer
Activities: Central body, umbrella body, youth,
elderly, women, books, inter-faith
Traditions: Unitarian

Other Languages: Welsh
Affiliations: International Council of Unitarians and Universalists

Lutheran Council of Great Britain*
30 Thanet Street, London WC1H 9QH
Tel: (020) 7373 1141
Contact: Revd Thomas Bruch
Position: General Secretary

Methodist Church*
25 Marylebone Road, London NW1 5JR
Tel: (020) 7486 5502 **Fax:** (020) 7467 5226
Email: conferenceoffice@methodistchurch.org.uk
Website: http://www.methodist.org.uk/
Contact: Revd Dr Nigel T Collinson
Position: Secretary of Conference
Traditions: Free Church
The Methodist Church claims and cherishes its place in the Holy Catholic Church. It is committed to the ecumenical movement and is involved in many local ecumenical partnerships and in joint worship, witness, action and mission with other Churches.

Moravian Church in Great Britain and Ireland*
Moravian Church House, 5-7 Muswell Hill, Muswell Hill, London N10 3TJ
Tel: (020) 8883 3409 **Fax:** (020) 8365 3371
Email: moravianchurch@btinternet.com
Website: http://www.moravian.org.uk/
Contact: Mrs Jackie Morten
Position: Chair
Contact Email: jackiemorten@compuserve.com
Activities: Worship/practice/meditation, central body, newsletter/journal, books, resources
Traditions: Free Church
Affiliations: Moravian Unity

New Testament Assembly*
5 Woodstock Avenue, London W13 9UQ
Tel: (020) 8579 3841
Email: njsterlnta@aol.com
Contact: Rev Nezlin Sterling
Position: General Secretary
Traditions: Pentecostal

New Testament Church of God*
Main House, Overstone Park, Overstone NN6 0AD
Tel: (01604) 643311 **Fax:** (01604) 790254
Email: roy.mcleod@dtcg.org.uk
Contact: Revd Louis R McLeod
Position: National Secretary
Activities: Central body

Traditions: Pentecostal
Affiliations: Evangelical Alliance; Church of God, Cleveland
The New Testament Church of God is part of the International Church of God and has over 100 branches within England and Wales. Local church addresses can be obtained from the Head Office.

Old Baptist Union*
64 Kennedy Avenue, Macclesfield SK10 3DE
Tel: (01625) 422404 **Fax:** (01625) 422404
Email: theobu@xalt.co.uk
Contact: Revd Christopher N Whiteley
Position: General Secretary
Contact Email: cnwhiteley@xalt.co.uk
Activities: Newsletter
Traditions: Free Church, Evangelical Baptist
Affiliations: Evangelical Alliance; Free Churches Group; Churches Together in England

Orthodox Church of Antioch, The*
1a Redhill Street, Somers Town, London NW1 4BG
Tel: (020) 7383 0403 **Fax:** (020) 7383 0403
Email: frsamir@antiochgreekorth.fsnet.co.uk
Website: http://www.antiochgreekorth.org/
Contact: Father Samir Gholam
Position: Priest
Contact Tel: (020) 8942 9676
Activities: Worship/practice/meditation, community centre, central body, youth, elderly, women, newsletter/journal, inter-faith
Traditions: Orthodox
Other Languages: Arabic, French
Affiliations: Orthodox Churches in Great Britain; Parish of the Antiochan Greek-Orthodox Diocese for Western and Central Europe
St George's Antiochan Cathedral Church and British Antiochan Orthodox Deanery are two separated administrative church units under one bishop. Both make the Orthodox Church of Antioch in Great Britain.

Pioneer (Charismatic Evangelical)*
Waverley Abbey House, Waverley Lane, Farnham GU9 8EP
Tel: (01252) 784772 **Fax:** (01252) 784775
Email: admin@pioneer.org.uk
Website: http://www.pioneer.org.uk/
Contact: Gerald Coates
Position: Trust Director
Activities: Worship/practice/meditation, community centre, umbrella body, youth, elderly, women, newsletter/journal, radio, television, visits, resources

Traditions: Restorationist
Affiliations: Churches Together; Evangelical Alliance

Religious Society of Friends (Quakers)*
Friends House, Euston Road, London NW1 2BJ
Tel: (020) 7663 1000 **Fax:** (020) 7663 1001
Website: http://www.quaker.org.uk/
Contact: Harvey Gillman
Position: Outreach Secretary
Activities: Worship, youth, newsletter, books, inter-faith
Other Languages: Welsh
Quakers spring out of the Christian tradition but their belief of God in everyone makes them open to other traditions as well. They meet together for worship in silence. They are also noted for their concern for peace and social justice.

Roman Catholic Church in England and Wales*
39 Eccleston Square, London SW1V 1BX
Tel: (020) 7828 8709 **Fax:** (020) 7931 7678
Email: cmo@cbcew.org.uk
Website: http://www.catholic.ew.org.uk/
Contact: Revd Andrew Summersgill
Position: General Secretary
Activities: Media, newsletters

Romanian Orthodox Church in London*
c/o St Dunstans in the West, 186a Fleet Street, London EC4A 2EA
Tel: (020) 7242 6027 **Fax:** (020) 7735 3515
Email: ppufulete@compuserve.com
Contact: Revd S P Pufulete
Position: Priest in Charge
Activities: Worship/practice/meditation
Traditions: Orthodox
Other Languages: Romanian
Affiliations: The Romanian Orthodox Archdiocese for Central and Western Europe
The Church has parishes in Leeds and Birmingham.

Russian Orthodox Church*
Cathedral of the Dormition and All Saints, 67 Ennismore Gardens, Knightsbridge, London SW7 1NH
Tel: (020) 7584 0096 **Fax:** (020) 7584 9864
Email: webdeacon@sourozh.org
Website: http://www.sourozh.org/
Contact: Gillian Crow
Position: Secretary
Contact Tel: (020) 7272 9898
Contact Email: gillian@crow.co.uk
Activities: Worship, visits, youth, newsletter, books,

resources
Traditions: Orthodox
Other Languages: Russian
Affiliations: Patriarchate of Moscow

Serbian Orthodox Church*
131 Cob Lane, Bourneville, Birmingham B30 1QE
Tel: (0121) 4585273 **Fax:** (0121) 4584986
Contact: Father Zebic

Seventh Day Adventist Church*
British Isles Headquarters, BUC Office, Stanborough Park, Watford WD25 9JZ
Tel: (01923) 672251 **Fax:** (01923) 893212
Email: buc@adventist.org.uk
Website: http://www.adventist.org.uk/
Contact: Pastor John Surridge
Position: Communications Director
Contact Email: jsurridge@adventist.org.uk
Activities: Central body, umbrella body, newsletter/journal, resources
Traditions: Free Church

St James Mar Thoma Church UK*
Mar Thoma Centre, 22 Altmore Avenue, London E6 2BY
Tel: (020) 8471 2446
Contact: Revd Prasad Mathew
Position: Vicar
Activities: Worship, newsletters
Traditions: Eastern Reformed Independent
Other Languages: Malayalam, Hindi
Contact can also be made c/o Mar Thoma Centre, 22 Altmore Avenue, London, E6 2BY.

Syrian Orthodox Church of Antioch*
"Antaccia", 77 Exeter Road, London N14 5JU
Tel: (020) 8368 8447 **Fax:** (020) 8368 8447
Contact: Aziz M A Nour
Position: Secretary
Activities: Central body, newsletter/journal, books
Traditions: Orthodox
Other Languages: Syriac, Arabic, Malayalam, Turkish
Affiliations: Council of Oriental Orthodox Churches (COOC); Syrian Orthodox Churches Council (SOCC); Churches Together in Britain and Ireland
The Syrian Orthodox Church of Antioch is the first Gentile Church which was founded by Barnabas, Peter and Paul at Antioch, where the disciples were first called Christian. Worship takes place at St Marks Church, Allen Street, Kensington, London.

Ukranian Autocephalous Orthodox Church*
1a Newton Avenue, Acton, London W3 8AJ
Tel: (020) 8992 4689
Contact: Very Revd Protopresbyter Mychajlo Halycia
Position: Chairman of the Diocesan
Other Languages: Ukranian

United Reformed Church*
86 Tavistock Place, London WC1H 9RT
Tel: (020) 7916 2020 **Fax:** (020) 7916 2021
Email: urc@urc.org.uk
Website: http://www.urc.org.uk/
Contact: Revd Dr David Cornick
Position: General Secretary
Activities: Worship, resource, newsletters, books, inter-faith

Wesleyan Holiness Church*
70-72 City Road, St Pauls, Bristol BS2 8TX
Contact: Revd I N Sawyers
Position: Superintendent

Wesleyan Reform Union of Churches*
Church House, 123 Queen Street, Sheffield S1 2DU
Tel: (0114) 2721938 **Fax:** (0114) 2721965
Contact: Revd A J Williams
Position: General Secretary
Traditions: Free Church

BODIES CONNECTED WITH UNITED KINGDOM ECUMENICAL INSTRUMENTS

Action by Christians Against Torture*
40 Albert Road, Saltash PL12 4EB
Tel: (01752) 849821 **Fax:** (01752) 849821
Email: lois@acat-uk.freeserve.co.uk
Contact: Lois Stamelis
Position: Director
Activities: Resource, newsletters, inter-faith

Arthur Rank Centre, The*
National Agricultural Centre, Stoneleigh Park, Warwick CV8 2LZ
Tel: (024) 7669 6969 **Fax:** (024) 7641 4808
Email: arthur.rank.centre@virgin.net
Website: http://www.ruralnet.org.uk/~arc
Contact: Rev Dr G Gatwand
Position: Director
Activities: Umbrella body, newsletter/journal, books, visits, resources
Traditions: Ecumenical/Interdenominational

Other Languages: French, Spanish
The Centre focuses on the needs and situation of rural society. It is a partnership between Churches, the Rank Foundation and the Royal Agricultural Society of England.

Association of Interchurch Families*
Inter-Church House, 35-41 Lower Marsh, London SE1 7SA
Tel: (020) 7523 2152 **Fax:** (020) 7928 0010
Email: aife@msn.com
Website: http://interchurchfamilies.org.uk
Contact: Mr Keith Lander
Position: Executive Secretary
Contact Tel: (01462) 682444
Contact Email: aiflander@talk2i.com
Activities: Youth, newsletter/journal, books, resources
Affiliations: Churches Together in Britain and Ireland; Churches Together in England
The Association of Interchurch Families offers an information service and a network of support for mixed (inter-denominational) marriages and interchurch families, and a voice for such families in the Churches.

Bible Society*
Stonehill Green, Westlea, Swindon SN5 7DG
Tel: (01793) 418100 **Fax:** (01793) 418118
Contact: Ingrid Roderick
Position: Information
Activities: Resource, books
The Bible Society aims to communicate the credibility and relevance of the Bible message through campaigning programmes at home and overseas, in order to see the Bible at work' in changing attitudes and society.

CAFOD (Catholic Fund for Overseas Development)*
Romero Close, Stockwell Road, London SW9 9TY
Tel: (020) 7733 7900 **Fax:** (020) 7274 9630
Email: hqcafod@cafod.org.uk
Website: http://www.cafod.org.uk
Contact: Ian Smith
Position: Librarian
Activities: Resource, youth, newsletters, books
CAFOD is one of the UK's major relief and development agencies. It funds over 1,000 development projects and emergencies in 75 countries, helping people regardless of race, religion or politics.

Canon Law Society of Great Britain and Ireland*
Cathedral House, Ingrave Road, Brentwood
CM15 8AT
Tel: (01277) 265283
Contact: Mr Pearce
Position: Administrative Secretary
Activities: Resource, newsletters, books
Traditions: Roman Catholic
Other Languages: Italian, Spanish
The Society's aim is to promote understanding of Canon Law (Catholic Church Law).

Catholic Association for Racial Justice (CARJ)*
9 Henry Road, Manor House, London N4 2LH
Tel: (020) 8802 8080 **Fax:** (020) 8211 0808
Email: info@carj.co.uk
Website: http://www.carj.co.uk/
Contact: Stephen Corriette
Position: Director
Contact Email: stephen@carj.freeserve.co.uk

Catholic Education Service*
39 Eccleston Square, London SW1V 1BX
Tel: (020) 7828 7604 **Fax:** (020) 7233 9802
Contact: Ms Una Stannard
Position: Director
Activities: Resource, umbrella body, newsletters, books, inter-faith
Other Languages: French

Centre for Black and White Christian Partnership*
University of Birmingham, Selly Oak Campus, Bristol Road, Selly Oak, Birmingham B29 6LQ
Tel: (0121) 4152372 **Fax:** (0121) 4152400
Email: blackandwhite@bham.ac.uk
Website: http://www.cbwcp.com/
Contact: Bishop Joe Aldred
Position: Executive Director
Traditions: Ecumenical/Interdenominational
Bridge-building between black and white Churches.

CEWERN (Churches' East-West European Relations Network)*
81 Thorney Leys, Witney OX28 5BY
Tel: (01993) 771778
Website: http://www.cewern.org.uk/
Contact: Dr Philip Walters
Position: General Secretary
Activities: Resource, umbrella body, newsletters, inter-faith
Affiliations: Churches Together in Britain and Ireland

CEWERN is the organisation by means of which member Churches of CTBI keep each other informed about their East-West work. CEWERN holds regular briefing meetings for its members.

Christian Aid*
P O Box 100, London SE1 7RT
Tel: (020) 7620 4444 **Fax:** (020) 7620 0719
Email: caid@gn.apc.org
Contact: Dr Daleep Mukherjee
Position: Director
Activities: Resource, media, newsletters, inter-faith
Christian Aid is sponsored by 40 Churches in Britain and Ireland, supporting work in 60 countries worldwide to strengthen poor communities. In Europe it campaigns about the structural causes of global poverty.

Christian Education*
1020 Bristol Road, Selly Oak, Birmingham B29 6LB
Tel: (0121) 4724242 **Fax:** (0121) 4727575
Activities: Newsletter/journal, books
Other Languages: German, French
Affiliations: Churches Together in Britain and Ireland (Associate)
Christian Education incorporates Christian Education Movement and National Christian Educational Council.

Christianity and the Future of Europe*
Lincoln Theological Institute, University of Sheffield, 36 Wilkinson Street, Sheffield S10 2GB
Tel: (0114) 2226399
Contact: Rev Prof Kenneth Medhurst

Christians Abroad*
Suite 233, Bon Marche Centre, 241 Ferndale Road, London SW9 8B J
Tel: (020) 7346 5950 **Fax:** (020) 7346 5955
Email: admin@cabroad.org.uk
Website: http://www.cabroad.org.uk/
Contact: Rev Philip Wetherell
Position: Director
Contact Tel: (020) 7346 5957
Contact Email: director@cabroad.org.uk
Activities: Newsletter/journal
Affiliations: Churches Together in Britain and Ireland
Christians Abroad, working through its arm "World Service Enquiry", is primarily an advice and consultancy service. Also arranges and services overseas mission appointments for UK and overseas Churches.

Christians Aware*
2 Saxby Street, Leicester LE2 0ND
Tel: (0116) 2540770

Church Action On Poverty*
Central Buildings, Oldham Street, Manchester
M1 1JT
Tel: (0161) 2369321 **Fax:** (0161) 2375359
Contact: Niall Cooper
Position: National Co-ordinator
Activities: Resource, newsletters
Campaigns to raise awareness especially within the churches about poverty in the UK. Our recent initiative, Local People National Voice, aims to ensure that those with direct experience of poverty are heard more clearly at national level.

Church and Peace (Britain and Ireland)*
20 The Drive, Hertford SG14 3DF
Tel: (01992) 302681
Email: gerald.drewett@ntlworld.com
Website: http://www.bocs.hu/
Contact: Gerald Drewett
Position: Secretary
Activities: Umbrella body, newsletter/journal, books, resources
Other Languages: French, German
Affiliations: London Mennonite Centre; Religious Society of Friends (Quakers); Church and Peace International
Church and Peace was founded by the historic peace churches - Quakers, Mennonites and the Church of the Brethren. Its stance is pacifist and ecumenical. It is pan-European in its scope.

Churches' Commission for Inter-Faith Relations*
Church House, Great Smith Street, London
SW1P 3NZ
Tel: (020) 7898 1000
Contact: Revd Canon Dr Michael Ipgrave
Position: Secretary
Affiliations: Inter Faith Network for the UK
SCCIFR is the main agency of the British Churches in their relationship with other faith communities.

Churches' Commission for International Students (CCIS)*
Inter-Church House, 35-41 Lower Marsh, London
SE1 8SA
Tel: (020) 7523 2121 **Fax:** (020) 7928 0010
Email: ccis@ctbi.org.uk
Contact: Gillian Court
Position: Commission Secretary
Contact Tel: (020) 7523 2154

Activities: Umbrella body, inter-faith, resources
Traditions: Ecumenical/Interdenominational
Affiliations: Churches Together in Britain and Ireland
CCIS is part of Churches Together in Britain and Ireland.

Churches' Commission for Racial Justice (CCRJ)*
Inter Church House, 35-41 Lower Marsh, London
SE1 7RL
Tel: (020) 7620 4444 **Fax:** (020) 7928 0010
Email: ccrj@ccbi.org.uk
Website: http://www.ctbi.org.uk/
Contact: Revd Arlington Trotman
Position: Commission Secretary
Activities: Central body
Traditions: Ecumenical/Interdenominational
Affiliations: Churches Together in Britain and Ireland; Conference of European Churches

Churches' Commission on Mission*
Inter-Church House, 35-41 Lower Marsh,
Waterloo, London SE1 7SA
Tel: (020) 7523 2121 **Fax:** (020) 7928 0010
Email: ccom@ctbi.org.uk
Website: http://www.ccom.org.uk/
Contact: Mr Simon Barrow
Position: Commission Secretary
Contact Tel: (020) 7523 2122
Contact Email: simon.barrow@ctbi.org.uk
Activities: Umbrella body, newsletters

Churches' Committee for Hospital Chaplaincy*
c/o Hospital Chaplaincies Council, Church House,
Great Smith Street, London SW1P 3NZ
Tel: (020) 7898 1893 **Fax:** (020) 7898 1891
Email: tim.battle@cofe.org.uk
Contact: Mr Tim Battle
Position: Secretary
Activities: Umbrella body
The Committee brings together representatives of the Health Care Chaplaincy Steering Committee (Free Churches), Hospital Chaplaincies Council (Cof E) and of Roman Catholic Chaplaincies.

Churches' Community Work Alliance*
36 Sandygate, Wath-upon-Dearne, Rotherham
S63 7LW
Tel: (01709) 873254 **Fax:** (01709) 873254
Email: ccwa@btinternet.com
Website: http://www.ccwa.org.uk/
Contact: Revd Brian J Ruddock
Position: Resource Officer
Activities: Umbrella body, newsletters, inter-faith

Churches' Joint Education Policy Committee*
Free Church Education Unit, 25 Marylebone
Road, London NW1 5JR
Tel: (020) 7467 3783 **Fax:** (020) 7467 5282
Email: woodg@methodistchurch.org.uk
Contact: Miss Gillian Wood
Position: Secretary
Activities: Umbrella body
Traditions: Ecumenical/Interdenominational
Affiliations: Churches Together in England
The Churches' Joint Education Policy Committee is
a co-ordinating group of Churches Together in
England, and has links with CYTUN (Churches
Together in Wales).

Churches' Stewardship Network*
The Diocesan Office, Auckland Castle, Bishop
Auckland DL14 7QJ
Tel: (01388) 604823

Conference of Religious in England and Wales (CMRS)*
114 Mount Street, London W1J 5RW
Tel: (020) 7493 1817 **Fax:** (020) 7409 2321
Email: confreli@aol.com
Position: General Secretary
Activities: Central body, umbrella body, elderly,
newsletter/journal, inter-faith
Traditions: Roman Catholic
Other Languages: French, Italian, German,
Spanish
Affiliations: Bishops' Conference of England and
Wales, Roman Catholic Church
Voluntary association of Provincial Superiors in
England and Wales and one of the four consultative
bodies of the Catholic Bishops' Conference for
England and Wales. It liaises with other national
conferences of religious and lay associations.

Department of International Affairs, Catholic Bishops' Conference*
39 Eccleston Square, London SW1V 1BX
Contact: Dr David Ryall
Position: Secretary
Activities: Inter-faith, resources
Traditions: Roman Catholic
Other Languages: French, Spanish, Italian

Feed the Minds*
Albany House, 67 Sydenham Road, Guildford
GU1 3SE
Tel: (01483) 888580 **Fax:** (01483) 888581
Email: headoffice@feedtheminds.org
Website: http://www.feedtheminds.org/

Contact: Miss J Marsh
Position: Administrator
Activities: Umbrella body, newsletter/journal,
books, newspapers, radio, resources
Traditions: Ecumenical/Interdenominational
We provide financial support to Christian
organisations in Africa, Asia, Eastern Europe and
Latin America, to help with publication or
distribution of literature.

Fellowship of Reconciliation, England*
The Eirene Centre, Old School House, Clopton,
Kettering NN1 3DZ
Tel: (01832) 720257 **Fax:** (01832) 720557
Email: fellowship@gn.apc.org
Contact: Tracey Warren
Position: Administrator
Activities: Youth, newsletters, books
FOR, England is a religious society rooted in the
Christian pacifist tradition which seeks to promote
spiritual development, witness and service as a means
of reconciling all people with God and with each
other.

Fellowship of St Alban and St Sergius*
1 Canterbury Road, Oxford OX2 6LU
Tel: (01865) 552991 **Fax:** (01685) 316700
Email: gensec@sobornost.org
Website: http://www.sobornost.org/
Contact: Revd Stephen Platt
Position: General Secretary
Activities: Worship/practice/meditation, central
body, newsletter/journal, books, resources
Traditions: Ecumenical/Interdenominational
Other Languages: French, Russian, Greek
Affiliations: Churches Together in Britain and
Ireland
The fellowship exists to foster deeper friendship and
understanding between Eastern Orthodox and
Western Christians. It prays and works for Christian
unity.

Focolare Movement*
Centre for Unity, 69 Parkway, Welwyn Garden City
AL8 6DU
Tel: (01707) 323620 **Fax:** (01707) 336413
Website: http://www.focolare.org/
Contact: Celia Blackden
Position: Interfaith Contact
Contact Tel: (020) 8671 8355
Activities: Worship/practice/meditation,
community centre, youth, elderly,
newsletter/journal, books, visits, inter-faith

Traditions: Roman Catholic
Other Languages: Italian, Spanish, French, German
Affiliations: Churches Together in England
Dialogue with all believers and people is central to Focolare's spirituality of unity. More than 50,000 followers of other religions are involved in the Focolare movement worldwide.

Keston Institute*
4 Park Town, Oxford OX2 6SH
Tel: (01865) 311022 **Fax:** (01865) 311280
Email: keston.institute@keston.org
Website: http://www.keston.org/
Contact: Mr Mark Pargeter
Position: Fund-Raiser
Contact Email: mark.pargeter@keston.org
Activities: Newsletter/journal, books, resources
Other Languages: Russian, German
Research and publication on religious human rights in Communist and ex-Communist countries

Living Spirituality Network*
The Well at Willen, Newport Road, Willen, Milton Keynes MK15 9AA
Tel: (01908) 200675
Email: spirituality@cix.co.uk
Website: http://www.living-spirituality.org.uk/
Contact: Mrs Win Kennedy
Position: Administrator
Contact Email: lsn@ctbi.org.uk
Activities: Umbrella body, youth, newletter/journal, books, visits, inter-faith, resources
Traditions: Ecumenical/Interdenominational
Other Languages: Welsh
Affiliations: Milton Keynes Christian Council; Churches Together in Britain and Ireland
Produces a newsletter "The Living Spirituality News". We also arrange spirituality events.

Living Stones*
2 Castle Close, London SW19 5NH
Tel: (020) 8879 3074
Email: jamilbullata@aol.com
Contact: Mr Jamil Bullata
Activities: Resource, newsletters, inter-faith
Living Stones is an ecumenical trust which promotes contacts between Christians in Britain and those in the Holy Land and neighbouring countries.

National Association of Christian Communities and Networks (NACCAN), The*
Community House, Eton Road, Newport
NP19 0BL
Tel: (01633) 265486
Email: moderator@naccan.freeeserve.co.uk
Contact: Office Administrator
Activities: Umbrella body, newsletter/journal, resources
Traditions: Ecumenical/Interdenominational
Affiliations: Churches Together in Wales; Churches Together in Britain and Ireland; Churches Together in England
NACCAN is an association whose membership is open to communities, groups, networks and individuals who link together to live out the implications and meanings of Christian Communities.

One World Week*
PO Box 2555, Reading RG1 4XW
Tel: (0118) 9394933 **Fax:** (020) 7620 0719
Email: oneworldweek@gn.apc.org
Contact: Helen Garforth
Position: Director
Activities: Resource, youth, elderly, women, newsletters, inter-faith
OWW aims to celebrate, reflect, act and break out of our normal boxes! OWW shares the vision of Peace with Justice for the whole of creation. The Week is offered to all by the Churches as a sign of hope, a point of sharing in celebration and struggle.

William Temple Foundation*
Luther King House, Brighton Grove, Rusholme, Manchester M14 5JP
Tel: (0161) 2246404 **Fax:** (0161) 2489201
Email: temple@wtf.org.uk
Website: http://www.wtf.org.uk/
Contact: Canon Dr John Atherton
Position: Secretary
Contact Tel: (0161) 8332220
Contact Email: manchester.cathedral@btinternet.com
Activities: Newsletter/journal, visits, resources
Affiliations: Churches Together in Britain and Ireland; European Contact Group
Research and development in Christian thought and practice, with particular reference to economic marginalisation processes.

Women's Co-ordinating Group for Churches Together in England*

c/o 27 Tavistock Square, London WC1H 9HH
Tel: (020) 7529 8132 **Fax:** (020) 7529 8134
Email: pauline@cte.org.uk
Contact: Pauline Main
Position: Secretary
Activities: Umbrella body
The Co-ordinating group brings together women representatives from Christian denominations and women's organisations to plan work together and to share concerns, ideas and resources.

Young Men's Christian Association*

640 Forest Road, Walthamstow, London E17 3DZ
Tel: (020) 8520 5599 **Fax:** (020) 8509 3190
Contact: Suzanne Humphreys
Position: Public Affairs
Contact Email:
suzanne.humphreys@england.ymca.org.uk
Activities: Resource, media, umbrella body, visits, youth
YMCA England is part of the worldwide Christian movement of YMCAs. Its central purpose is to support local YMCAs and help form new YMCAs.

Young Women's Christian Association*

Clarendon House, 52 Cornmarket Street, Oxford OX1 3EJ
Tel: (01865) 304200 **Fax:** (01865) 204805
Contact: Ms Gill Tishler
Position: Chief Executive
Activities: Central body, youth, resources
The YWCA is a force for change for women facing discrimination and inequalities of all kinds.

CHRISTIAN NATIONAL AND REGIONAL ORGANISATIONS

ENGLAND 251

ENGLISH ECUMENICAL INSTRUMENTS 251

CHURCHES OPERATING AT AN ENGLISH LEVEL 252

CHURCH REGIONAL BODIES 252

NORTH EAST 252

YORKSHIRE AND THE HUMBER 254

NORTH WEST 256

EAST MIDLANDS 260

WEST MIDLANDS 263

EAST OF ENGLAND 266

LONDON 269

SOUTH EAST 270

SOUTH WEST 275

IRELAND 278

IRISH ECUMENICAL INSTRUMENTS 278

CHURCHES OPERATING AT AN IRISH LEVEL 279

CHURCH REGIONAL BODIES 280

SCOTLAND 283

SCOTTISH ECUMENICAL INSTRUMENT 283

CHURCHES OPERATING AT A SCOTTISH LEVEL 283

CHURCH REGIONAL BODIES 284

WALES 290

WELSH ECUMENICAL INSTRUMENTS 290

CHURCHES OPERATING AT A WELSH LEVEL 291

CHURCH REGIONAL BODIES 292

OTHER WELSH BODIES 295

Churches which operate across the United Kingdom are listed in the previous section of this chapter.

Churches which operate at the level of only one country in the United Kingdom (eg in England, the Church of England and in Scotland, the Church of Scotland) are listed in this part of the chapter under the relevant national sections rather than in the section on "Christian United Kingdom Organisations".

In this chapter only, entries are included on regional rather than local organisations in the UK. Each of the regional bodies listed here is able to supply detailed local information concerning places of worship and other organisations within their membership.

Some regional bodies have entries appearing in more than one region because they operate across the regional boundaries used in this directory.

ENGLAND

ENGLISH ECUMENICAL INSTRUMENTS

Churches Together in England*
27 Tavistock Square, London WC1H 9HH
Tel: (020) 7529 8141 **Fax:** (020) 7529 8134
Email: anyname@cte.org.uk
Website: http://www.churches-together.org.uk/
Contact: Revd Bill Snelson
Position: General Secretary
Activities: Umbrella body, newsletter/journal, books
Traditions: Ecumenical/Interdenominational
Affiliations: Churches Together in Britain and Ireland; Conference of European Churches

Churches Together in England North and Midlands Office*
Luther King House, Brighton Grove, Rusholme, Manchester M14 5JP
Tel: (0161) 2492515 **Fax:** (0870) 1215613
Email: jennybond@churchestogetherengland.freeserve.co.uk
Website: http://www.churches-together.org.uk

Contact: Jenny Bond
Position: Field Officer
Activities: Umbrella body, newsletter/journal, books
Traditions: Ecumenical/Interdenominational
Affiliations: Churches Together in Britain and Ireland; Conference of European Churches

CHURCHES OPERATING AT AN ENGLISH LEVEL

Church of England General Synod*
Church House, Great Smith Street, London SW1P 3NZ
Tel: (020) 7898 1000 **Fax:** (020) 7898 1369
Website: http://www.cofe.anglican.org/
Position: Secretary General

Church of Scotland England Presbytery
St Columba's Presbytery, Pont Street, London SW1X 0BD
Tel: (020) 7584 2321
Contact: Revd W A Cairns
Position: Presbytery Clerk

Congregational Federation*
4/8 Castle Gate, Nottingham NG1 7AS
Tel: (0115) 9111460 **Fax:** (0115) 9111462
Email: admin@congregational.org.uk
Website: http://www.congregational.org.uk/
Contact: Revd Michael Heaney
Position: General Secretary
Activities: Worship, newsletters
Traditions: Free Church

Free Church of England*
32 Bonny Wood Road, Hassocks BN6 8HR
Tel: (01273) 845092
Contact: Revd Ron Talbot
Position: General Secretary
Traditions: Free Church

CHURCH REGIONAL BODIES

NORTH EAST

REGIONAL ECUMENICAL INSTRUMENTS

North East Christian Churches Together*
29 Arundel Court, Kingston, Newcastle-upon-Tyne NE3 2UJ
Tel: (0191) 2866349

Email: malcoport@aol.com
Contact: Mr M Porter
Position: Secretary
Activities: Umbrella body
Traditions: Ecumenical
Affiliations: Churches Together in England

South Tees Faith In The City Group*
The Vicarage, James Street, North Ormesby, Middlesbrough T53 6LD
Tel: (01642) 271814
Email: gloa@compuserve.com
Contact: The Reverend Graham Usher
Position: Chairman
Activities: Ecumenical, inter-faith community development

ASSEMBLIES OF GOD REGIONS

Assemblies of God in Great Britain and Ireland North East Regional Council*
c/o 16 Bridgford Road, West Bridgford, Nottingham, NG2 6AF
Tel: (0115) 9811188 **Fax:** (0115) 9813377
Email: info@aog.org.uk
Website: http://www.aog.org.uk/

BAPTIST UNION AREAS

Northern Baptist Association*
Maranatha House, St Agnes Gardens North, Ryton NE40 4NR
Tel: (0191) 4132205 **Fax:** (0191) 4132205
Email: secretary@nba.netkonect.co.uk
Website: http://www.thenba.org.uk./
Contact: Mr David Lennox
Position: Secretary

CHURCH OF ENGLAND DIOCESES

Church of England Diocese of Durham*
Diocesan Office, Auckland Castle, Bishop Auckland DL14 7QJ
Tel: (01388) 604515 **Fax:** (01388) 603695
Email: diocesan.secretary@durham.anglican.org
Website: http://www.durham.anglican.org/
Contact: Mr J P Cryer
Position: Diocesan Secretary
Activities: Central body
Traditions: Anglican

Church of England Diocese of Newcastle*
Church House, Grainger Park Road, Newcastle-upon-Tyne NE4 8SX

Email: church_house@newcastle.anglican.org
Website: http://www.newcastle.anglican.org/
Contact: Mrs Lesley Carson
Position: Inter-Faith Adviser
Contact Tel: (0191) 2730120
Activities: Worship/practice/meditation, umbrella body, newsletter/journal, visits, inter-faith, resources
Traditions: Anglican
Affiliations: Committee for Inter-Faith and Ethnic Relations

METHODIST DISTRICTS

Methodist Church Darlington District*
2 Edinburgh Drive, Darlington DL3 8AW
Tel: (01325) 468119 **Fax:** (01325) 468119
Contact: Revd Graham Carter
Position: Chairman
Contact Email: graham.carter@care4free.net
Activities: Umbrella body
Traditions: Free Church

Methodist Church, Newcastle-upon-Tyne District*
15 Lynnwood Avenue, Newcastle-upon-Tyne NE4 6XB
Tel: (0191) 2731747
Email: john607williams.fsnet.ac.uk
Contact: Revd J Williams
Position: Synod Secretary
Traditions: Free Church
Affiliations: The Methodist Church; World Council of Churches

ROMAN CATHOLIC DIOCESES

Roman Catholic Diocese of Hexham and Newcastle*
Bishops House, East Denton Hall, 800 West Road, Newcastle-upon-Tyne NE5 2BJ
Tel: (0191) 2280003 **Fax:** (0191) 2740432
Email: bishop@rcdhn.org.uk
Website: http://www.rcdhn.org.uk/
Contact: Right Revd Ambrose Griffiths
Position: Bishop
Activities: Worship/practice/meditation, community centre, central body, youth, elderly, women, newsletter/journal, newspapers, inter-faith, resources
Traditions: Roman Catholic

Roman Catholic Diocese of Middlesbrough*
Bishops House, 16 Cambridge Road, Middlesbrough TS5 5NN

Tel: (01642) 818253
Contact: Rt Revd John Crowley
Position: Bishop

SALVATION ARMY DIVISIONS

Salvation Army Northern Division*
Balliol Business Park, Newcastle-upon-Tyne NE12 8EW
Tel: (0191) 2381801 **Fax:** (0191) 2381811
Email: northern@salvationarmy.org.uk
Website: http://www.salvationarmy.org.uk/northern
Contact: Lt Col Ray Kirby
Position: Divisional Commander
Traditions: Free Church
Affiliations: North East Christian Churches Together

UNITARIAN AND FREE CHRISTIANS

Northern Unitarian Association
40 The Oaklands, Middleton One Row, Darlington DL2 1BD
Tel: (01325) 332688
Contact: Freda Laverick
Position: Secretary
Activities: Umbrella body
Traditions: Free Church

UNITED REFORMED CHURCH PROVINCES

United Reformed Church Northern Synod Office*
Room 1, First Floor, 65 Westgate Road, Newcastle-upon-Tyne NE1 1SG
Tel: (0191) 2321168 **Fax:** (0191) 2321811
Email: urc.northern@ic24.net
Website: http://www.urc-northernsynod.org.uk/
Contact: Revd Peter I Poulter
Position: Moderator
Activities: Worship/practice/meditation
Traditions: Reformed
Affiliations: North East Christian Churches; Churches Together in Cumbria; World Alliance of Reformed Churches

YORKSHIRE AND THE HUMBER

REGIONAL ECUMENICAL INSTRUMENTS

Hull and District Evangelical Alliance*
17 Dene Close, Dunswell, Hull HU6 0AB
Tel: (01482) 802186
Email: evangel@mmorfin.freeserve.co.uk
Contact: Mr Michael Morfin
Activities: Umbrella body
Traditions: Evangelical
Affiliations: Evangelical Alliance

KEY (Kingston-upon-Hull and East Yorkshire) Churches Together*
The Vicarage, Skirlaugh, Hull HU11 5HE
Tel: (01964) 562259 **Fax:** (01964) 563383
Email: david@perryskirlaugh.karoo.co.uk
Website: http://www.keyct.org.uk/
Contact: Revd David William Perry
Position: Ecumenical Officer
Activities: Umbrella body

North York Moors Churches Together*
c/o Skirrid, 102 Outgang Road, Pickering
YO18 7EL
Tel: (01751) 473488
Contact: Revd H L Dixon
Position: Honorary Secretary
Activities: Central body, umbrella body
Traditions: Ecumenical/Interdenominational
Affiliations: Churches Together in England

Churches Together in South Yorkshire*
Crookes Valley Methodist Church, Crookesmoor
Road, Sheffield S6 3FQ
Tel: (0114) 2666156
Email: louise@ctsy.freeserve.co.uk
Contact: Revd Louise Dawson
Position: Ecumenical Officer
Activities: Umbrella body, newsletters

West Yorkshire Ecumenical Council*
Hinsley Hall, 62 Headingley Lane, Leeds LS6 2BX
Tel: (0113) 2618053 **Fax:** (0113) 3618054
Email: stephanierybak@compuserve.com
Website: http://www.wyec.co.uk/
Contact: Dr Stephanie Rybak
Position: County Ecumenical Officer
Activities: Umbrella body, newsletter/journal,
radio, resources
Traditions: Ecumenical/Interdenominational
Affiliations: Churches Together in England

ENVOY (Ecumenical Network in the Vale of York)*
The Manor, Moss End Farm, Hawkhills,
Easingwold YO61 3EW
Tel: (01347) 838593
Contact: Mrs Jean Abbey
Position: Secretary

ASSEMBLIES OF GOD

Assemblies of God, East Pennine Region*
16 Richard Road, Rotherham S60 2QR
Tel: (01709) 855209
Contact: Frederick Durrant
Position: Administrator
Traditions: Pentecostal

BAPTIST UNION AREAS

Yorkshire Baptist Association*
1 South Parade, Leeds LS6 3LF
Tel: (0113) 2784954
Contact: Revd Ernie Whalley
Position: Regional Minister
Activities: Worship/practice/meditation

CHURCH OF ENGLAND DIOCESES

Church of England Diocese of Bradford*
Cathedral Hall, Stott Hill, Bradford BD1 4ET
Tel: (01274) 725958 **Fax:** (01274) 726343
Website: http://www.bradford.anglican.org/
Contact: Mr Malcolm Halliday
Position: Diocesan Secretary
Activities: Central body, umbrella body,
newsletter/journal, inter-faith, resources
Traditions: Anglican

Church of England Diocese of Ripon and Leeds*
Diocesan Office, St Mary's Street, Leeds LS9 7DP
Tel: (0113) 2487487 **Fax:** (0113) 2491129
Website:
http://ourworld.compuserve.com/homepages/ripo
ncc
Contact: P M Arundel
Position: Diocesan Administration
Activities: Worship, resource

Church of England Diocese of Sheffield*
Diocesan Church House, 95-99 Effingham Street,
Rotherham S65 1BL
Tel: (01709) 309100 **Fax:** (01709) 512550
Email: admin@sheffield-diocese.org.uk

Website: http://www.sheffield-diocese.org.uk/
Contact: Mr Malcolm Robertson
Position: Education Director
Contact Tel: (01709) 309123
Activities: Central body, resources
Traditions: Anglican

Church of England Diocese of Wakefield*
Church House, 1 South Parade, Wakefield
WF1 1LP
Tel: (01924) 371802 **Fax:** (01924) 364834
Email: diocesan.secretary@wakefield.anglican.org
Website: http://www.wakefield.anglican.org/
Contact: Ashley Ellis
Position: Diocesan Secretary
Activities: Resource, umbrella body

Church of England Diocese of York*
Aviator Court, Clifton Moor, York YO30 4WJ
Tel: (01904) 699500 **Fax:** (01904) 699501
Email: york_dbf@york_diocese.org
Position: Diocesan Secretary

CONGREGATIONAL FEDERATION AREAS

Congregational Federation North East Area*
Bottom-Mill, 5 Lumb Mill Way, Skyreholme,
Skipton BD23 6DL
Tel: (01724) 720395
Contact: Mrs Andrea Adams
Position: Chair
Activities: Worship, youth, elderly, newsletter,
inter-faith
Traditions: Free Church

METHODIST DISTRICTS

Methodist Church Leeds District (including Wakefield, Harrogate and Dewsbury)*
281 Otley Road, Leeds LS16 5LN
Tel: (0113) 2785546 **Fax:** (0113) 2745611
Email: michael.townsend@leeds-methodist-district.fsnet.co.uk
Contact: Revd Michael J Townsend
Position: Chairman
Activities: Umbrella body
Traditions: Free Church
Affiliations: West Yorkshire Ecumenical Council

Methodist Church Lincoln and Grimsby District*
107 Welholme Avenue, Grimsby DN32 0BP
Contact: Revd CC Humble
Position: Synod Secretary
Contact Tel: (01472) 877644
Contact Email: chric@humblec.freeserve.co.uk
Activities: Worship/practice/meditation,
newsletter/journal
Traditions: Free Church

Methodist Church Sheffield District*
Victoria Hall Methodist Church, Norfolk Street,
Sheffield S1 2JB
Tel: (0114) 2812733 **Fax:** (0114) 2812734
Email: sheffmeth@aol.com
Website: http://www.sheffieldmethodist.org/
Contact: Revd David Halstead
Position: Chair
Activities: Central body, newsletter/journal
Traditions: Free Church

Methodist Church West Yorkshire District*
19 Wentworth Court, Rastrick, Brighouse
HD6 3XD
Tel: (01484) 719993 **Fax:** (01484) 720606
Email: pwwyks@aol.com
Website:
http://www.westyorkshiremethodist.inuk.com/
Contact: Revd Peter Whittaker
Position: Chairman
Affiliations: West Yorkshire Ecumenical Council

Methodist Church York and Hull District*
13 Lawnway, York Y03 0JD
Tel: (01904) 424739 **Fax:** (01904) 424739
Contact: Revd Stuart J Burgess
Position: Chairman of the District
Activities: Resource, newsletters, inter-faith
Affiliations: KEY Churches Together; Churches
Together in the Vale of York

MORAVIAN CHURCH DISTRICTS

Moravian Church Yorkshire District Conference*
The Parsonage, 38 Fulneck, Pudsey LS28 8NT
Tel: (0113) 2564828
Contact: David John Dickinson
Position: Chairman
Activities: Worship, newsletters
Traditions: Free Church
Affiliations: West Yorkshire Ecumenical Council

NEW TESTAMENT CHURCH OF GOD DISTRICTS

New Testament Church of God District*
Jonson Street, Nursery Street, Sheffield S3 8GL
Tel: (0114) 2725722 **Fax:** (0114) 2725722
Email: grbngry@aol.com
Contact: Bishop Benjamin Grey
Position: Minister
Activities: Worship, resource, youth, elderly, women
Traditions: Pentecostal
Affiliations: Churches Together in South Yorkshire

ROMAN CATHOLIC DIOCESES

Roman Catholic Diocese of Hallam*
Hallam Pastoral Centre, St Charles Street, Sheffield
Tel: (0114) 256 2246

Roman Catholic Diocese of Leeds*
St Mary's Presbytery, 142 East Parade, Undercliffe, Bradford BD1 5EE
Tel: (01274) 271248 **Fax:** (01274) 394123
Contact: Revd Michael Sullivan
Position: Priest
Activities: Worship/practice/meditation, central body, umbrella body, youth, elderly, women, newletter/journal, inter-faith, resources
Traditions: Roman Catholic
Other Languages: Italian, Polish, Ukraine

SALVATION ARMY DIVISIONS

Salvation Army Yorkshire Division*
1 Cadman Court, Hanley Road, Morley, Leeds LS2 0RX
Tel: (0113) 2810101 **Fax:** (0113) 2810111
Contact: Lt Col Geoff Blurton
Position: Divisional Commander

UNITARIAN AND FREE CHRISTIANS

Sheffield and District Association of Unitarian and Free Christian Churches Inc*
Upper Chapel, Norfolk Street, Sheffield S1 2JD
Tel: (0114) 2767114
Email: joannorton@upperchapel.freeserve.co.uk
Contact: Mrs Joan Norton
Position: Secretary
Contact Tel: (0114) 2305337
Activities: Worship/practice/meditation, central body
Traditions: Free Church

Yorkshire Unitarian Union*
21 Trenton Avenue, Anlaby High Road, Hull HU4 7RP
Tel: (01482) 505118
Email: spaettig@talk21. Com
Contact: Susan Raettig
Position: Honorary Secretary
Activities: Worship, umbrella body, inter-faith
Affiliations: General Assembly Of Unitarian And Free Christian Churches

UNITED REFORMED CHURCH PROVINCES

United Reformed Church Yorkshire Province*
43 Hunslet Lane, Leeds LS10 1JW
Tel: (0113) 2451267 **Fax:** (0113) 2341145
Contact: Moderator
Activities: Umbrella body, newsletters
Traditions: Free Church
Affiliations: West Yorkshire Ecumenical Council

OTHER BODIES

Touchstone*
32 Merton Road, Bradford BD7 2RE
Tel: (01274) 721626 **Fax:** (01274) 395 324
Email: touchsto@surfaid.org
Contact: Revd Geoff Ried
Position: Team Leader
Contact Email: teamleader@touchstonecentre.fsbusiness.co.uk
Activities: Worship/practice/meditation, newsletter/journal, visits, inter-faith, resources
Traditions: Ecumenical/Interdenominational
Affiliations: Methodist Church West Yorkshire District

NORTH WEST

REGIONAL ECUMENICAL INSTRUMENTS

Churches Together in Cheshire*
5 White Hart Lane, Wistaston, Crewe CW2 8EX
Tel: (01270) 568550
Email: dscott7143@aol.com
Contact: Mr David Scott
Position: Ecumenical Officer
Activities: Central body, newsletter/journal
Traditions: Ecumenical/Interdenominational
Affiliations: Churches Together in England

Churches Together in Cumbria*
Church House, West Walls, Carlisle CA3 8UE
Tel: (01228) 522573 **Fax:** (01228) 815400
Contact: Revd Andrew Dodd
Position: Ecumenical Officer
Contact Tel: (01593) 436451
Contact Email: andrew.dodd1@btinternet.com
Activities: Resource, umbrella body, newsletters

Greater Manchester Churches Together*
St Peter's House, Precinct Centre, Oxford Road,
Manchester M13 9GH
Tel: (0161) 2735508 **Fax:** (0161) 2727172
Email: sph.gmet@man.ac.uk
Contact: Revd Graham Kent
Position: Ecumenical Officer
Contact Email: sph.maureenfc@man.ac.uk
Activities: Umbrella body, newsletters

Churches Together in Lancashire*
Centre-Peace, Feilden Street, Blackburn BB2 1LQ
Tel: (01254) 699833
Email: ctloffice@dial.pipex.com
Contact: Mrs Terry Garley
Position: Development Officer

Churches Together in Man*
2 Hillberry Lakes, Governor's Hill, Douglas
IM2 7BQ
Tel: (01624) 674203
Contact: Miss Susan McCann
Position: Secretary
Activities: Central body
Traditions: Ecumenical/Interdenominational
Affiliations: Churches Together in England

**Merseyside and Region Churches Ecumenical
Assembly***
Friends Meeting House, 65 Paradise Street,
Liverpool L1 3BP
Tel: (0151) 7090125 **Fax:** (0870) 1289754
Email: marcea@surfaid.org
Contact: Revd Martyn Newman
Position: Ecumenical Officer
Activities: Umbrella body, newsletter/journal,
inter-faith
Traditions: Ecumenical/Interdenominational
Affiliations: Churches Together in England

ASSEMBLIES OF GOD REGIONS

**Assemblies of God in Great Britain and Ireland
North West Regional Council**
377 Hollinwood Avenue, New Moston,

Manchester M10 0JQ
Website: http://www.aog.org.uk/

**Assemblies of God, North Wales and Midlands
Region***
88 Queens Road, Vicars Cross, Chester CH3 5HD
Tel: (01244) 341729
Website: http://www.aog.org.uk/
Contact: Roger Jeavons
Position: Administrator
Contact Email: rjea531882@aol.com
Traditions: Pentecostal

BAPTIST UNION AREAS

North Western Baptist Association*
Latchford Baptist Church, Loushers Lane,
Warrington WA4 2RP
Tel: (01925) 633929 **Fax:** (01925) 418796
Email: baptnwi@aol.com
Contact: Revd Christopher D Haig
Position: General Secretary
Activities: Central body, youth, elderly, women,
newsletter/journal
Traditions: Free Church
Affiliations: Baptist World Alliance

CHURCH OF ENGLAND DIOCESES

Church of England Diocese of Blackburn*
St Mark's Vicarage, Buncer Lane, Witton, Blackburn
BB2 6SY
Tel: (01254) 676615
Email: vicar@tankbat.freeserve.co.uk
Website: http://www.blackburn.anglican.org/
Contact: Revd Paul Battersby
Position: Senior Chaplain
Activities: Worship
Traditions: Anglican
Affiliations: Churches Together in Lancashire

Church of England Diocese of Carlisle*
Church House, West Walls, Carlisle CA3 8UE
Tel: (01228) 522573 **Fax:** (01228) 815400
Email: chrchhse@carlisle-c-of-e.org
Contact: Revd Canon Colin Hill
Position: Diocesan Secretary
Traditions: Anglican
Affiliations: Churches Together in Cumbria

Church of England Diocese of Chester*
Church House, Lower Lane, Aldford, Chester
CH3 6HP
Tel: (01244) 620444 **Fax:** (01244) 620456

Contact: Stephen P Marriott
Position: Diocesan Secretary
Affiliations: Churches Together in Cheshire

Church of England Diocese of Liverpool*
Church House, No 1 Hanover Street, Liverpool
L1 3DW
Tel: (0151) 7099722 **Fax:** (0151) 7092885
Position: Diocesan Secretary
Affiliations: Merseyside and Region Churches
Ecumenical Assembly

Church of England Diocese of Sodor and Man*
c/o Holly Cottage, Ballaughton Meadows, Douglas
IM2 1JG
Tel: (01624) 626994 **Fax:** (01624) 626994
Email: dsec-sodor@mcb.net
Contact: Mrs Christine Roberts
Position: Diocesan Synod Secretary

CONGREGATIONAL FEDERATION AREAS

Congregational Federation North West Area*
13 Springhead Avenue, Springhead, Oldham
OL4 5SP
Contact: Revd D G Openshaw
Position: Secretary
Activities: Central body
Traditions: Free Church
Affiliations: Congregational Federation

FREE CHURCH OF ENGLAND DIOCESES

Free Church of England Northern Diocese, The
10 Hest Bank Road, Morecombe LA4 6HJ

METHODIST DISTRICTS

Methodist Church Bolton and Rochdale District*
5 Hill Side, Heaton, Bolton BL1 5DT
Contact: Revd Keith V Garner
Position: Chairman of District
Contact Tel: (01204) 843302
Activities: Worship/practice/meditation,
community centre, central body, youth, elderly,
women, newsletter/journal, inter-faith
Traditions: Free Church

Methodist Church Chester and Stoke District*
5 Sandside Road, Alsager, Stoke on Trent ST7 2XJ
Tel: (01270) 883417

Contact: Revd John D Walker
Position: Chairman
Activities: Umbrella body
Traditions: Free Church
Affiliations: Churches Together in Cheshire;
Churches Linked Across Staffordshire and the
Potteries

Methodist Church Cumbria District*
14 Monnington Way, Penrith CA11 8QJ
Tel: (01768) 866342 **Fax:** (01768) 866342
Email: david@cumbriadistrict.u-net.com
Contact: Revd David R Emison
Position: Chairman
Activities: Umbrella body
Traditions: Free Church
Affiliations: Churches Together in Cumbria

Methodist Church Isle of Man District*
Yn Conney, Shore Road, Castletown IM9 1BF
Tel: (01624) 822541
Contact: Revd Stephen Caddy
Position: Chairman
Traditions: Free Church
Affiliations: Churches Together in Man

Methodist Church Liverpool District*
Clayton House, 33 Trafalgar Road, Birkdale,
Southport PR8 2HF
Tel: (01704) 568678 **Fax:** (01704) 568678
Contact: Revd Neil A Stubbens
Position: Synod Secretary
Activities: Umbrella body
Traditions: Free Church
Affiliations: Merseyside and Region Churches
Ecumenical Assembly

Methodist Church Manchester and Stockport District*
198 Turf Lane, Royton, Oldham OL2 6EU
Tel: (0161) 6265703
Contact: Mr T F Bell
Position: Synod Secretary
Activities: Worship, community centre, central
body, youth, elderly, women
Traditions: Free Church

Methodist Church North Lancashire District*
47 Greenacres, Fulwood, Preston PR2 7DB
Tel: (01772) 861110
Email: sjpoxon@aol.com
Contact: Revd Stephen Poxon
Position: Chairman of District
Activities: Central body
Traditions: Free Church

ROMAN CATHOLIC DIOCESES

Roman Catholic Archdiocese of Liverpool*
Croxteth Drive, Sefton Park, Liverpool L17 1AA
Tel: (0151) 5221000 **Fax:** (0151) 5221001
Email: p.heneghan@rcaol.co.uk
Website: http://www.archdiocese-of-liverpool.co.uk/
Contact: Mr Peter Heneghan
Position: Press Officer
Contact Tel: (0151) 5221007
Activities: Worship/practice/meditation,
community centre, central body, umbrella body,
youth, elderly, women, newsletter/journal,
newspapers, visits, inter-faith, resources
Traditions: Roman Catholic
Affiliations: Merseyside and Region Churches
Ecumenical Assembly; The RC Bishops'
Conference of England and Wales; Roman
Catholic Church

Roman Catholic Diocese of Lancaster*
Bishop's House, Cannon Hill, Lancaster LA1 5NG
Tel: (01524) 32231 **Fax:** (01524) 849296
Contact: Bishop's Secretary
Activities: Worship, umbrella body, youth, elderly,
women, newsletter
Affiliations: Churches Together in Cumbria;
Churches Together in Lancashire

Roman Catholic Diocese of Salford*
St Johns Cathedral, 250 Chapel Street, Salford
M3 5LL
Tel: (0161) 8340333 **Fax:** (0161)8349596
Email: cathsal@aol.com
Contact: Cathedral Dean
Activities: Worship/practice/meditation, central
body, youth, elderly, women, newsletter/journal,
resources
Traditions: Roman Catholic
Other Languages: French, Spanish, Swahili

Roman Catholic Diocese of Shrewsbury*
Curial Offices, 2 Park Road South, Birkenhead
L43 4UX
Tel: (0151) 6529855 **Fax:** (0151) 653517
Contact: Father J Fagin
Position: Bishop's Secretary
Activities: Worship, resource, umbrella body,
youth, elderly, women
Affiliations: Churches Together in Cheshire and
Shropshire

SALVATION ARMY DIVISIONS

Salvation Army Central North Division*
80 Eccles New Road, Salford, Manchester
M5 2RU
Tel: (0161) 7433900 **Fax:** (0161) 7433911
Email: centralnorth@salvationarmy.org.uk
Contact: Major Chick Yuill
Position: Divisional Commander
Contact Tel: (0161) 743391
Contact Email: chick.yuill@salvation.org.uk
Activities: Worship/practice/meditation,
community centre, central body
Traditions: Free Church

Salvation Army North Western Division*
16 Faraday Road, Wavertree Technology Park,
Liverpool L13 1EH
Tel: (0151) 2526100 **Fax:** (0151) 2526111
Contact: Major Geoffrey Parkin
Position: Divisional Commander
Affiliations: Merseyside and Region Ecumenical
Council; Churches Together in Cheshire

UNITARIAN AND FREE CHRISTIANS

East Cheshire Union of Unitarian and Free Christian Churches*
260 Wood Street, Langley, Middleton M24 5GL
Tel: (0161) 6431824
Email: arp9898@hotmail.com
Contact: Revd A Parker
Position: Secretary

Manchester District Association of Unitarian and Free Christian Churches*
Fairfield, London Road, Adlington, Macclesfield
SK10 4NA
Tel: (01625) 828279 **Fax:** (01625) 828279
Contact: Revd Penny Johnson
Position: Secretary
Activities: Umbrella body, newsletters, inter-faith

Merseyside and District Missionary Association (Unitarian)*
Ullet Road Church, 57 Ullet Road, Sefton Park,
Liverpool L17 2AA
Tel: (0151) 7331927
Contact: Revd Christopher Goacher
Position: Secretary
Contact Tel: (0151) 7269162
Contact Email: revcg@aol.com
Activities: Umbrella body, youth, elderly, women,
newsletter/journal, visits, inter-faith

Traditions: Free Church
Affiliations: Merseyside and Region Churches
Ecumenical Assembly; The General Assembly of
Unitarian and Free Christian Churches

North and East Lancashire Unitarian Mission*
754 Blackburn Road, Bolton BL1 7JW
Tel: (01204) 303257
Email: tony.mcneile@virgin.net
Contact: Revd A F McNeile
Position: Secretary
Activities: Central body, umbrella body, youth,
elderly, women, newsletter/journal, inter-faith
Traditions: Free Church
Affiliations: General Assembly of Unitarian and
Free Christian Churches

UNITED REFORMED CHURCH
PROVINCES

United Reformed Church Mersey Synod*
1 Fingall Road, Wavertree, Liverpool L15 9JE
Tel: (0151) 7226590 **Fax:** (0151) 7221863
Email: office@merseysynod.dabsol.co.uk
Contact: Revd Graham Cook
Position: Moderator
Activities: Resource, youth, elderly, women,
newsletters, inter-faith
Traditions: Free Church
Affiliations: Merseyside and Region Churches
Ecumenical Assembly

United Reformed Church North Western
Province*
Synod Office, Franklin Street, Patricroft, Eccles,
Manchester M30 0QZ
Tel: (0161) 7895583 **Fax:** (0161) 7079117
Email: admin.nwsynod@urc.org.uk
Website: http://www.nwsynod.org.uk/
Contact: Revd Peter Brain
Position: Moderator
Activities: Umbrella body
Traditions: Reformed
Affiliations: Churches Together in Lancashire;
Greater Manchester and Cumbria

OTHER BODIES

Network*
c/o Nazerene Theological College, Dene Road,
Didsbury, Manchester M20 2GU
Tel: (0161) 7182863
Email: info@network-ea.org.uk
Website: http://www.network-ea.org.uk/
Contact: Debra Green

Position: Church Liaison Officer
Contact Tel: (0161) 9736334
Contact Email: debrajgreen@totalise.co.uk
Activities: Central body, umbrella body, youth,
elderly, women, newsletter/journal, visits
Traditions: Ecumenical/Interdenominational
Affiliations: Evangelical Alliance

EAST MIDLANDS

REGIONAL ECUMENICAL
INSTRUMENTS

Churches Together in Derbyshire and
Nottinghamshire*
Westbarn, Hurds Hollow, Matlock DE4 3JE
Tel: (01629) 760857
Email: philip.webb1@virgin.net
Contact: Revd Philip Webb
Position: County Ecumenical Officer
Activities: Umbrella body
Traditions: Ecumenical/Interdenominational
Affiliations: Churches Together in England

Churches Together in Leicestershire*
6 Cottesmore Avenue, Melton Mowbray
LE13 0HY
Tel: (01664) 850672
Email: rinaldi.fw@aol.com
Contact: Revd Dr Frank Rinaldi
Position: Ecumenical Development Officer
Contact Email: rinaldifw@aol.com

Churches Together in All Lincolnshire*
c/o YMCA, St Rumbold Street, Lincoln LN2 5AR
Tel: (01522) 520984
Email: john@ctal.org.uk
Contact: Revd John Cole
Position: Development Officer
Contact Tel: (01652) 657484
Activities: Umbrella body

Churches Together in All Northamptonshire*
c/o College Street Baptist Church, College Street,
Northampton NN1 2QP
Tel: (01604) 633372 **Fax:** (01604) 633372
Email: eirlys@btinternet.com
Contact: Revd Michael J Cleaves
Position: County Ecumenical Officer
Activities: Newsletter/journal
Traditions: Ecumenical/Interdenominational
Affiliations: Churches Together in England; World
Council of Churches

ASSEMBLIES OF GOD REGIONS

East Midlands Region, Assemblies of God in GB and Ireland*
Emmanuel Christian Centre, Sherwood Avenue, Newark NG24 1QF
Tel: (01636) 682240 **Fax:** (01636) 682240
Email: office@eccentres.co.uk
Website: http://www.aog.org.uk/
Contact: Pastor Kenneth Aubrey Morgan
Position: Chair
Traditions: Pentecostal

BAPTIST UNION AREAS

East Midland Baptist Association*
25 Coningsby Road, Woodthorpe, Nottingham NG5 4LH
Tel: (0115) 9679679 **Fax:** (0115) 9679679
Email: emba@surfaid.org
Contact: Mrs Rachel Tole
Position: Administrator
Activities: Central body, newsletter/journal
Traditions: Free Church

Northamptonshire Baptist Association
Baptist Association Office, Cary Chapel, 62 Main Road, Hackleton, Northampton NN7 2AH
Tel: (01908) 614847 **Fax:** (01604) 870808
Email: whysalljb@cwcom.net
Contact: Revd James Whysall
Position: Secretary

CHURCH OF ENGLAND DIOCESES

Church of England Diocese of Derby*
Derby Church House, Full Street, Derby DE1 3DR
Tel: (01332) 382233 **Fax:** (01332) 292969
Email: ddbf@talk21.com
Contact: Mr R J Carey
Position: Diocesan Secretary
Activities: Central body
Traditions: Anglican

Church of England Diocese of Leicester*
Church House, 3/5 St Martins East, Leicester LE1 5FX
Tel: (0116) 2487400 **Fax:** (0116) 2532889
Email: chouse@leicester.anglican.org
Website: http://www.leicester.anglican.org/
Contact: Andrew Howard
Position: Diocesan Secretary
Activities: Resource, newsletters, inter-faith
Affiliations: Churches Together in Leicestershire

Church of England Diocese of Lincoln*
Church House, The Old Palace, Lincoln LN2 1PU
Tel: (01522) 529541 **Fax:** (01522) 512717
Email: lincolndio@claranet.co.uk
Website: http://www.lincoln.anglican.org/
Contact: Phil Hamlyn Williams
Position: Diocesan Secretary
Activities: Resource, visits, youth, newsletters
Affiliations: Churches Together in All Lincolnshire

Church of England Diocese of Southwell*
Dunham House, 8 Westgate, Southwell NG25 0JL
Tel: (01636) 814331 **Fax:** (01636) 815084
Email: mail@southwell.anglican.org
Website: http://www.southwell.anglican.org/
Contact: Mr Peter Prentis
Position: Diocesan Secretary
Activities: Newsletters, inter-faith
Affiliations: Churches Together in Nottinghamshire

CONGREGATIONAL FEDERATION AREAS

Congregational Federation East Midlands Area*
113 Over Lane, Belper DE56 0HN
Tel: (01773) 822512
Contact: Mrs J G Smith
Position: Area Secretary
Activities: Central body
Traditions: Congregational
Affiliations: Churches Together in Leicestershire

METHODIST DISTRICTS

Methodist Church Nottingham and Derby District*
12 Cheviot Avenue, Codnor Park, Ironville NG16 5QQ
Contact: Ms Averil George
Position: Synod Secretary
Contact Tel: (01773) 603902
Contact Email: averilg@compuserve.com
Activities: Worship/practice/meditation, umbrella body, youth, elderly, women
Traditions: Free Church
Affiliations: Churches Together in Derbyshire; Churches Together in Nottinghamshire; Church of North India

MORAVIAN CHURCH DISTRICTS

Moravian Church Eastern District Conference*
Hillside, 29 The Settlement, Ockbrook, Derby
DE7 3RJ
Tel: (01332) 6745932
Contact: Revd Michael Rea
Position: Chairman
Traditions: Free Church
Affiliations: Churches Together in Derbyshire

NEW TESTAMENT CHURCH OF GOD DISTRICTS

New Testament Church of God Derby District*
Brighton Road, Alvaston, Derby DE24 8SZ
Tel: (01332) 726031
Contact: Revd Keith N Channer
Activities: Worship/practice/meditation, youth, elderly, women, visits
Traditions: Pentecostal

ROMAN CATHOLIC DIOCESES

Roman Catholic Diocese of Northampton*
Bishops House, Marriott Street, Northampton
NN2 6AW
Tel: (01604) 715635 **Fax:** (01604) 792186
Email: admin@diocnpton.fsnet.co.uk
Website: http://www.northamptondiocese.org/
Contact: Revd Peter Hocken
Position: Bishop's Chaplain
Activities: Central body
Traditions: Roman Catholic
Affiliations: Conference of Bishops of England and Wales; See of Rome (Vatican)

Roman Catholic Diocese of Nottingham*
27 Cavendish Road East, The Park, Nottingham
NG7 1BB
Tel: (0115) 9474786 **Fax:** (0115) 9475235
Email: bishop@nottinghamdiocese.org.uk
Website: http://www.nottinghamdiocese.org.uk/
Contact: Revd Father Edward Jarosz
Position: Bishop's Secretary
Contact Email:
eddy.jarosz@nottinghamdiocese.org.uk
Activities: Central body
Traditions: Roman Catholic

SALVATION ARMY DIVISIONS

Salvation Army East Midlands Division*
Paisley Grove, Chilwell, Nottingham NG9 6DJ
Tel: (0115) 9835000 **Fax:** (0115) 9835011
Email: chris.sands@salvationarmy.org
Website: http://www.salvationarmy.org.uk/
Contact: Captain Chris Sands
Position: Divisional Director
Activities: Worship/practice/meditation, community centre, central body, youth, elderly, women, newsletter/journal, books, newspapers, radio, television, visits, inter-faith, resources
Traditions: Free Church
Affiliations: Churches Together in England

SEVENTH DAY ADVENTIST CONFERENCES

Seventh Day Adventist Church North England Conference*
22 Zulla Road, Mapperley Park, Nottingham
NG3 5DB
Tel: (0115) 9606312 **Fax:** (0115) 9691476
Email: admin@nec-sda-church.co.uk
Contact: Pastor Llewellyn Edwards
Position: Executive Secretary
Activities: Central body, umbrella body, youth, elderly, women, visits
Traditions: Seventh-Day Adventist
Affiliations: South England Conference of Seventh-Day Adventists; British Union of Seventh-Day Adventists; Trans European Division of the Seventh-Day Adventist Church

UNITARIAN AND FREE CHRISTIANS

East Midlands Unitarians*
3 Plumptre Street, Lace Market, Nottingham
NG1 1JL
Tel: (0115) 9892198
Contact: Mr M Adcock
Position: Secretary
Activities: Central body, newsletter/journal, books, inter-faith
Traditions: Free Church
Affiliations: General Assembly of Unitarian and Free Christian Churches; International Association for Religious Freedom

UNITED REFORMED CHURCH PROVINCES

United Reformed Church East Midlands Synod*

Sherwood United Reformed Church, 1 Edwards Lane, Sherwood, Nottingham NG5 3AA
Tel: (0115) 9609241 **Fax:** (0115) 9609202
Email: office.urceastmid@lineone.net
Website: http://www.urc.org.uk/
Contact: Revd M G Hanson
Position: Moderator
Activities: Central body
Traditions: Reformed
Affiliations: East Midlands Churches Forum; Churches Together in England; World Alliance of reformed Churches

WEST MIDLANDS

REGIONAL ECUMENICAL INSTRUMENTS

Birmingham Churches Together*

Carrs Lane Church Centre, Birmingham B4 7SX
Tel: (0121) 6436603 **Fax:** (0121) 6325320
Email: office@birminghamchurches.org.uk
Website:
http://www.birminghamchurches.org.uk/
Contact: Revd Mark Fisher
Position: General Secretary
Activities: Newsletters
Affiliations: West Midlands Region Churches Forum

Black Country Churches Engaged*

18 Selman's Hill, Bloxwich, Walsall WS3 3RJ
Tel: (01922) 475932
Email: mike.topliss@u.genie.co.uk
Contact: Mr J M Topliss
Position: Ecumenical Officer
Activities: Umbrella body, newsletter/journal, resources
Traditions: Ecumenical/Interdenominational
Affiliations: West Midlands Region Churches' Forum; Churches Together in England

Churches Together in Coventry and Warwickshire*

59 Tiverton Drive, Nuneaton CV11 6YJ
Tel: (024) 7635 2551
Email: rowland@cwec84.freeserve.co.uk
Contact: David Rowland
Position: Secretary

Activities: Central body, newsletter/journal
Traditions: Ecumenical/Interdenominational
Affiliations: West Midlands Regional Churches Forum; Churches Together in England

Churches Together in Herefordshire*

9 Hartland Close, Abbotscroft, Belmont, Hereford HR2 7SL
Tel: (01432) 376782
Contact: Mr Raymond Rose
Position: County Ecumenical Officer
Activities: Umbrella body
Traditions: Ecumenical/Interdenominational
Affiliations: Churches Together in England; World Council of Churches

Churches Together in Shropshire*

Fern Villa, Four Crosses, Llanymynech SY22 6PR
Tel: (01691) 831374
Email: gedcliffe@barclays.net
Contact: Mr Geo Cliffe
Position: Ecumenical Secretary
Activities: Umbrella body, newsletter/journal, inter-faith
Traditions: Ecumenical/Interdenominational
Affiliations: West Midlands Regional Churches Forum; Churches Together in England; Churches Together in Britain and Ireland

Churches Linked Across Staffordshire and the Potteries (CLASP)*

18 Selman's Hill, Bloxwich, Walsall WS3 3RJ
Tel: (01922) 475932
Email: mike.topliss@u.genie.co.uk
Contact: Mr J M Topliss
Position: County Ecumenical Officer
Activities: Umbrella body, newsletter/journal, resources
Traditions: Ecumenical/Interdenominational
Affiliations: West Midlands Region Churches' Forum; Churches Together in England; Churches Together in Britain and Ireland

Telford Christian Council*

Meeting Point House, Southwater Square, Town Centre, Telford TF3 4HS
Tel: (01952) 291904 **Fax:** (01952) 213555
Contact: Revd David Lavender
Position: Ecumenical Dean
Contact Tel: (01952) 585731
Contact Email: david@lavenders.demon.co.uk
Activities: Worship/practice/meditation, umbrella body, youth, visits
Traditions: Ecumenical/Interdenominational

West Midlands Region Churches' Forum*
Carrs Lane Church Centre, Birmingham B4 7SX
Tel: (0121) 6436603 **Fax:** (0121) 6436603
Email: office@wmchurches.org.uk
Website: http://www.wmchurches.org.uk/
Contact: Revd Mark Fisher
Position: General Secretary
Activities: Umbrella body

Churches Together in Worcestershire*
The Rectory, Clifton-on-Teme, Worcester
WR6 6DJ
Tel: (01886) 812483
Email: clifford.de.clifton@dial.pipex.com
Contact: Revd Clifford Owen
Position: Secretary
Activities: Umbrella body, newsletter/journal
Traditions: Ecumenical/Interdenominational
Affiliations: Churches Together in England

BAPTIST UNION AREAS

The Heart of England Baptist Association*
137 Newhall Street, Birmingham B3 1SF
Tel: (0121) 2124842 **Fax:** (0121) 2124512
Email: mailbox@baptist-heartofengland.org
Website: http://www.baptist-heartofengland.org/
Contact: Revd Barrie Smith
Position: Secretary
Contact Email: bsmith@baptist-heartofengland.org
Activities: Umbrella body, visits, newsletters, resources
Traditions: Free Church
Affiliations: West Midlands Region Churches Forum

CHURCH OF ENGLAND DIOCESES

Church of England Diocese of Birmingham and Board of Finance*
175 Harborne Park Road, Harborne, Birmingham
B17 0BH
Tel: (0121) 4260400 **Fax:** (0121) 4281114
Contact: Mr Jim Drennan
Position: Diocesan Secretary
Affiliations: Birmingham Churches Together

Church of England Diocese of Coventry*
Church House, Palmerston Road, Coventry
CV5 6FJ
Tel: (024) 7667 4328 **Fax:** (024) 7669 1760
Email: isobel.chapman@btinternet.com

Website: http://www.coventry.anglican.org/
Contact: Ms Isobel Chapman
Position: Diocesan Secretary
Traditions: Anglican
Affiliations: Coventry and Warwickshire
Ecumenical Council

Church of England Diocese of Hereford*
Diocesan Office, The Palace, Hereford HR4 9BL
Tel: (01432) 353863 **Fax:** (01432) 352952
Email: hereford@diooffice.freeserve.co.uk
Contact: Revd Sylvia Green
Position: Diocesan Secretary
Activities: Umbrella body, newspapers, resources
Traditions: Anglican
Affiliations: Parochial Church Councils; Church
of England; Anglican Communion

Church of England Diocese of Lichfield*
St Mary's House, The Close, Lichfield WS13 7LD
Tel: (01543) 306030 **Fax:** (01543) 306039
Email: info@lichfield.anglican.org
Website: http://www.lichfield.anglican.org/
Contact: David Taylor
Position: Diocesan Secretary
Activities: Central body, youth, elderly, women,
newsletter/journal, books, newspapers, resources
Traditions: Anglican
Affiliations: Anglican Communion

Church of England Diocese of Worcester*
The Old Palace, Deansway, Worcester WR1 2JE
Tel: (01905) 20537 **Fax:** (01905) 612302
Email: ncurrie@cofe-worcester.org.uk
Website: http://www.cofe-worcester.org.uk/
Contact: Mrs Nicola Currie
Position: Communications Officer
Contact Tel: (01905) 454768
Activities: Worship/practice/meditation,
community centre, central body, youth, elderly,
women, newsletter/journal, resources
Traditions: Anglican
Affiliations: Anglican Communion

CONGREGATIONAL FEDERATION AREAS

Congregational Federation North West Midlands Area*
Swan Hill Congregational Church, Swan Hill,
Shrewsbury SY1 1NL
Tel: (01743) 247043
Contact: Mrs P Haydon
Position: Secretary

Activities: Central body
Traditions: Congregational

Congregational Federation South West Midlands Area*
Wood Street, Bishops Itchington, Southam
CV47 1PP
Email: wayne.hawkins@congregation.org.uk
Contact: Revd Wayne Hawkins
Activities: Central body
Traditions: Congregational

METHODIST DISTRICTS

Methodist Church Birmingham District*
36 Amesbury Road, Moseley, Birmingham
B13 8LE
Tel: (0121) 4490131 **Fax:** (0121) 4490131
Email:
clem@birminghamdistrict.swinternet.co.uk
Contact: Revd Christina Le Moignan
Position: Chair of District
Contact Tel: (0121) 4490131
Activities: Worship/practice/meditation, youth
elderly, women, inter-faith
Traditions: Free Church

Methodist Church Wolverhampton and Shrewsbury District*
53 York Avenue, Wolverhampton WV3 9BX
Tel: (01902) 424430 **Fax:** (01902) 424430
Email: wsmeth@naser.net
Contact: Revd Peter F Curry
Position: Chairman
Activities: Umbrella body
Affiliations: Churches Together in Shropshire;
Dudley and Worcestershire Ecumenical Council;
Staffordshire Plus Ecumenical Council

MORAVIAN CHURCH DISTRICTS

Moravian Church Eastern District Conference*
The Manse, Keys Lane, Prior Marston, Southham
CV47 7SA
Tel: (01327) 261375
Contact: Revd Michael Rea
Position: Chairman

NEW TESTAMENT CHURCH OF GOD DISTRICTS

New Testament Church of God Birmingham District*
244 Lozells Road, Lozells, Birmingham B19 1NP

Tel: (0121) 5541358
Contact: Derek Anthony Wembley
Position: District Bishop
Activities: Visits, youth, elderly, women, education
Traditions: Pentecostal

New Testament Church of God Coventry District*
83 Old Church Road, Bell Green, Coventry
Tel: (02476) 687502
Contact: Mrs Manderson
Position: Secretary

ROMAN CATHOLIC DIOCESES

Roman Catholic Archdiocese of Birmingham*
Cathedral House, St Chad's Queensway,
Birmingham B4 6EX
Tel: (0121) 2365535 **Fax:** (0121) 2339266
Email: mail@rc-birmingham.org
Contact: Revd J F Carlyle
Position: Secretary
Contact Email: revjohncarlyle@rc-birmingham.org
Activities: Worship/practice/meditation, central
body, youth, elderly, women, visits, inter-faith,
resources
Traditions: Roman Catholic

SALVATION ARMY DIVISIONS

Salvation Army West Midlands Division*
102 Unett Street, Hockley, Birmingham B19 3BZ
Tel: (0121) 5078501 **Fax:** (0121) 5078511
Contact: Lt Col Ronald Smith
Position: Divisional Commander
Traditions: Free Church
Affiliations: Birmingham Churches Together

UNITED REFORMED CHURCH PROVINCES

United Reformed Church West Midlands Province*
Digbeth-in-the-Field URC, Moat Lane, Yardley,
Birmingham B26 1TW
Tel: (0121) 7831177 **Fax:** (0121) 7898500
Contact: Mr Simon Rowntree, JP
Position: Synod Clerk
Traditions: Free Church

OTHER BODIES

Wolverhampton Evangelical Fellowship*
51 Lennox Gardens, Wolverhampton WV3 0RR

EAST OF ENGLAND

REGIONAL ECUMENICAL INSTRUMENTS

Churches Together in Buckinghamshire*
124 Bath Road, Banbury OX16 0TR
Tel: (01295) 268201 **Fax:** (01295) 268201
Email: derek.g.palmer@tesco.net
Contact: Revd Canon Derek Palmer
Position: Secretary
Activities: Central body, umbrella body,
newsletter/journal, radio, inter-faith, resources
Traditions: Ecumenical/Interdenominational
Affiliations: Churches Together in England; World
Council of Churches

Cambridgeshire Ecumenical Council*
'Kovno', 19 Abbotsmead, Heybridge, Maldon
CM9 4PT
Email: jhaywa@globalnet.co.uk
Contact: Revd John Hayward
Position: Officer

East London Church Leaders' Group*
250 High Street, Cottenham, Cambridge
CB4 8RZ
Tel: (01702) 342327 **Fax:** (01702) 342327
Email: revs@reverie.fsnat.co.uk
Contact: Revd D C Hardiman
Position: Ecumenical Officer
Activities: Umbrella body, newsletters
Affiliations: Essex Churches Consultative
Council; Churches Together in England

Essex Churches Consultative Council*
250 High Street, Cottenham, Cambridge
CB4 8RZ
Tel: (01954) 250242 **Fax:** (01954) 250242
Email: revs@reverie.fsnet.co.uk
Contact: Revd D C Hardiman
Position: Ecumenical Officer
Activities: Umbrella body, newsletter/journal
Traditions: Ecumenical/Interdenominational
Affiliations: Churches Together in England

Norfolk Churches Together*
The Rectory, Marsham, Norwich NR10 5PP

Tel: (01263) 733249
Email: robin@rhewetson.freeserve.co.uk
Contact: Revd Robin Hewetson
Position: Vicar

Greater Peterborough Ecumenical Council
61 Hall Lane, Werrington, Peterborough PE4 6RA
Contact: Secretary

Suffolk Churches Together*
34 Rectory Lane, Kirton, Ipswich IP10 0PY
Tel: (01473) 252829 **Fax:** (01473) 323552
Contact: Margaret Condick
Position: Ecumenical Officer
Contact Tel: (01394) 448576
Contact Email: n.t.condick@btinternet.com
Activities: Umbrella body

BAPTIST UNION AREAS

Cambridgeshire Baptist Association*
28 Church Street, Willingham CB4 5HT
Tel: (01954) 260665
Email: gensecambsbaptist@btinternet.com
Contact: Mr Keith Rawlinson
Position: Secretary

Eastern Baptist Association*
26 Birchwood Drive, Rushmere, Ipswich IP5 1EB

Essex Baptist Association*
40 Melville Drive, Kingsley Grange, Wickford
SS12 9FE
Tel: (01268) 571213 **Fax:** (01268) 571213
Email: richardsoar@essexbaptist.freeserve.co.uk
Contact: Revd Richard Soar
Position: Pastor Administrator
Traditions: Free Church

Suffolk Baptist Association*
26 Birchwood Drive, Rushmere, Ipswich IP5 1EB
Tel: (01473) 729652 **Fax:** (01473) 729652
Email: gensec@suffolkbaptist.freeserve.co.uk
Website: http://get.to/sba
Contact: Mr Terence Cooper
Position: Secretary

CHURCH OF ENGLAND DIOCESES

**Church of England Diocese of St Edmundsbury
and Ipswich***
Churchgates House, Cutler Street, Ipswich
IP1 1UQ
Tel: (01473) 298500 **Fax:** (01473) 298501

Email: dbf@stedmundsbury.anglican.org
Website: http://www.stedmundsbury.anglican.org/
Contact: Mr M J Green
Position: Deputy Diocesan Secretary
Contact Tel: (01473) 298500
Contact Email:
malcolm@stedmundsbury.anglican.org
Traditions: Anglican

Church of England Diocese of Ely*
Diocesan Office, Bishop Woodford House, Barton
Road, Ely CB7 4DX
Tel: (01353) 652701 **Fax:** (01353) 652700
Email: resource.centre@ely.anglican.org
Website: http://www.ely.anglican.org/
Contact: Revd Canon Tim Elbourne
Position: Diocesan Director
Contact Tel: (01353) 652724
Contact Email: tim.elbourne@ely.anglican.org
Activities: Worship, resource, media, newsletter,
umbrella body, visits youth
Traditions: Anglican
Affiliations: Churches Together in
Cambridgeshire; Greater Peterborough Ecumenical
Council, SACRE

Church of England Diocese of Norwich*
Diocesan House, 109 Dereham Road, Easton,
Norwich NR9 5ES
Tel: (01603) 880853 **Fax:** (01603) 881083
Email: diocesanhouse@norwich.anglican.org
Website: ww.norwich.anglican.org
Contact: Mr D W Adeney
Position: Diocesan Secretary
Contact Email:
davidadeney@norwich.anglican.org
Activities: Umbrella body, youth,
newsletter/journal, resources
Traditions: Anglican
Affiliations: Norfolk and Waveney Churches
Together

Church of England Diocese of Peterborough*
The Palace, Peterborough PE1 1YB
Tel: (01733) 887000 **Fax:** (01733) 555271
Email:
communications@peterboroughdiocese.org.uk
Website:
http://www.peterboroughdiocese.org.uk/
Contact: Mr Richard L Pestell
Position: Diocesan Secretary
Affiliations: Greater Peterborough Ecumenical
Council

Church of England Diocese of St Albans*
41 Holywell Hill, St Albans AL1 1HE
Tel: (01727) 854532 **Fax:** (01727) 844469
Email: maie@stalbansdioc.org.uk
Website: http://www.stalbansdioc.org.uk/
Contact: Mr L M Nicholls
Position: Diocesan Secretary
Contact Tel: (01727) 854532
Contact Email: lmnicholls@stalbansdioc.org.uk
Activities: Worship/practice/meditation, umbrella
body, youth, newsletter/journal, inter-faith,
resources
Traditions: Anglican
Affiliations: Churches Together in Hertfordshire
and Bedfordshire

CONGREGATIONAL FEDERATION
AREAS

Congregational Federation Norfolk Area*
The Old Meeting House, Colegate, Norwich
NR3 1BW
Tel: (01508) 530511 **Fax:** (01508 531536
Contact: Len Willis
Position: Secretary
Activities: Worship/meditation,
newsletter/journal, visits, inter-faith
Traditions: Free Church
Affiliations: Council for World Mission

METHODIST DISTRICTS

Methodist Church East Anglia District*
26 Wentworth Green, Norwich NR4 6AE
Tel: (01603) 452257
Contact: Malcolm Braddy
Position: District Chairman
Traditions: Free Church

Methodist Church London North West District*
37 Long Buftlers, Harpenden AL5 1JF
Tel: (01582) 460732 **Fax:** (01582) 4601218
Email: wgr@londonnw-2.freeserve.co.uk.
Contact: Revd W Garth Rogers
Position: Chairman
Activities: Umbrella body
Traditions: Free Church
Affiliations: Churches Together in Bedfordshire;
Churches Together in Hertfordshire;
Buckinghamshire Ecumenical Council

ROMAN CATHOLIC DIOCESES

Roman Catholic Diocese of East Anglia*
The White House, 21 Upgate, Poringland,
Norwich NR14 7SH
Tel: (01508) 492202 **Fax:** (01508) 495358
Email: office@east-angliadiocese.org.uk
Website:
http://website.lineone.net/~eastanglia.diocese
Contact: Revd John Warrington
Position: Private Secretary
Contact Tel: (01508) 492202
Activities: Worship, resource, youth, elderly,
women, newsletter
Affiliations: Norfolk and Suffolk Churches
Together; Cambridgeshire Ecumenical Council;
Greater Peterborough Ecumenical Council

SALVATION ARMY DIVISIONS

Salvation Army Anglia Division*
2 Barton Way, Carrow Road, Norwich NR1 1DL
Tel: (01603) 724400 **Fax:** (01603) 724411
Email: anglia@salvationarmy.org.uk
Website: http://www.salvationarmy.org.uk/
Contact: Lt Col Howard Grottick
Position: Divisional Commander
Traditions: Free Church, Holiness
Affiliations: Norfolk Churches Together/Suffolk
Churches Together; Cambridgeshire Ecumenical
Council

Salvation Army London North East Division*
Maldon Road, Hatfield Peverel CM3 2HL
Tel: (01245) 383001 **Fax:** (01245) 383011
Email: londonnortheast@salvationarmy.org.uk
Website:
http://www.salvationarmy.org.uk/londonnortheast
/index.html
Contact: Lt Col David Phillips
Position: Divisional Commander
Contact Email:
david.phillips@salvationarmy.org.uk
Activities: Worship, visits, youth, elderly, women,
newsletter
Traditions: Free Church
Affiliations: Essex Council of Churches

SEVENTH DAY ADVENTIST CONFERENCES

Seventh Day Adventist Church South England Conference*
25 St John's Road, Watford WD17 1PZ

Tel: (01923) 232728 **Fax:** (01923) 250582
Email: 102555.2314@compuserve.com
Website: http://www.secadventist.org.uk/
Contact: Pastor Humphrey Walters
Position: Executive Secretary
Activities: Central body, youth, elderly, women,
newsletter/journal, resources
Traditions: Independent
Other Languages: Spanish, Portuguese, French

UNITARIAN AND FREE CHRISTIANS

Eastern Union of Unitarian and Free Christian Churches*
Memorial Church (Unitarian), Emmanuel Road,
Cambridge CB1 1JW
Tel: (01223) 576952
Contact: Mrs Susanna Lee Brown
Position: Secretary
Contact Tel: (01223) 365848
Contact Email: susannalee.brown@virgin.net
Activities: Worship/practice/meditation, central
body
Traditions: Unitarian and Free Christian
Affiliations: The General Assembly of Unitarian
and Free Christian Churches; International Council
of Unitarian Universalists

UNITED REFORMED CHURCH PROVINCES

United Reformed Church Eastern Province*
The United Reformed Church, Whittlesford,
Cambridge CB2 4ND
Tel: (01223) 830770
Email: urc7@aol.com
Website: http://www.freebie.net/~easternurc
Contact: Revd Elizabeth Caswell
Position: Moderator
Contact Tel: (01223) 830770
Activities: Worship/practice/meditation, central
body, newsletter/journal, resources
Traditions: Free Church
Affiliations: Churches Together in Britain and
Ireland; World Council of Churches

OTHER BODIES

King's Lynn Evangelical Alliance Fellowship*
11 Gloucester Road, Gaywood, King's Lynn
PE30 4AB
Tel: (01553) 772036
Contact: Mr Mike Brown
Position: Secretary

Activities: Umbrella body
Traditions: Ecumenical/Interdenominational
Affiliations: Evangelical Alliance

Peterborough Alliance of Christian Evangelicals (PACE)*
c/o 68A Westgate, Peterborough PE1 1RG
Tel: (01733) 352701 **Fax:** (01733) 352701
Email: richard@crops.clara.net
Contact: Richard Morrison
Position: Administrative Secretary

Queens' College, Cambridge - Christian Union*
c/o Queen's College, Cambridge CB3 9ET
Tel: (01223) 335511
Email: tdh22@cam.ac.uk
Activities: Youth

LONDON

REGIONAL ECUMENICAL INSTRUMENTS

London Churches Group for Social Action*
Central Hall, Westminster, Storey's Gate, London
SW1H 9NH
Tel: (020) 7222 0281 **Fax:** (020) 7222 0298
Email: esimon@surfaid.org
Contact: Ms Elizabeth Simon
Position: Policy Officer
Activities: Umbrella body, inter-faith
Traditions: Ecumenical/Interdenominational
Affiliations: London Church Leaders

Churches Together in North London*
30 Valley Avenue, London N12 9PG
Tel: (020) 8445 5968
Email: restrick@waitrose.com
Contact: Mr David Restarick
Position: Secretary
Activities: Umbrella body

Churches Together in North West London*
34 Earl's Court Square, London SW5 9DQ
Tel: (020) 8427 3418 **Fax:** (020) 8427 3418
Contact: Revd Dr. Callan Slipper
Position: Convenor
Activities: Umbrella body

Churches Together in South London*
Hawkstone Hall, 1A Kennington Road, London
SE1 7QP
Tel: (020) 7928 5395 **Fax:** (020) 7928 8222

Contact: Revd Dr Malcolm Drummond
Position: Ecumenical Officer
Activities: Umbrella body

Churchlink West London*
Flat 6, 147 Cromwell Road, London SW7
Tel: (020) 7370 4327
Contact: Annemarie de Visser
Position: Convenor

ASSEMBLIES OF GOD REGIONS

Assemblies of God in Great Britain and Ireland Greater London Regional Council*
30 Christchurch Square, Hackney, London
E9 7HU
Tel: (020) 8985 7202 **Fax:** (020) 8985 7202
Email: JaButcher4@aol.com
Website: http://www.aog.org.uk/
Contact: John W Butcher
Position: Chairman/Administrator
Contact Tel: (0208) 985 7202

BAPTIST UNION AREAS

London Baptist Association*
235 Shaftesbury Avenue, London WC2H 8EL
Tel: (020) 7692 5592 **Fax:** (020) 7692 5593
Email: lbaoffice@cwcom.net
Contact: Revd Dr P M Took
Position: Gen Superintendent
Contact Tel: (020) 8530 8179
Contact Email: pattook@aol.com
Activities: Central body, newsletter/journal
Traditions: Free Church

CHURCH OF ENGLAND DIOCESES

Church of England Diocese of London*
London Diocesan House, 36 Causton Street,
London SW1P 4AU
Tel: (020) 7932 1100 **Fax:** (020) 7932 1112
Website: http://www.london.anglican.org/
Contact: Keith Robinson
Position: General Secretary
Traditions: Anglican

Church of England Diocese of Southwark*
Trinity House, 4 Chapel Court, Borough High
Street, London SE1 1HW
Tel: (020) 7939 9400 **Fax:** (020) 7939 9468
Email: trinity@dswark.org.uk
Website: http://www.dswark.org/
Contact: Mr Simon Parton

Position: Diocesan Secretary
Contact Email: simon.parton@dswark.org.uk
Activities: Worship/practice/meditation, community centre, central body, umbrella body, youth, elderly, women, newsletter/journal, books, newspapers, visits, inter-faith, resources
Traditions: Anglican
Affiliations: London Churches' Group; Churches Together in South London; Churches Together in Surrey,

METHODIST DISTRICTS

Methodist Church London South West District*
85 Dartnell Park Road, West Byfleet KT14 6QD
Contact: Revd Martin Broadbent
Position: Chairman
Traditions: Free Church
Affiliations: Churches Together in Surrey; Sussex Churches, London Church Leaders, Berkshire Church Leaders.

OTHER BODIES

Brent Evangelical Fellowship*
PO Box 326, Wembley HA9 6HL

Leyton Evangelical Fellowship*
St Mary's Vicarage 4 Vicarage Road, Leyton E10 5EA
Tel: (020) 8539 7882
Contact: Revd Canon David Ainge
Position: Chair
Activities: Central body, umbrella body
Traditions: Ecumenical/Interdenominational
Affiliations: Evangelical Alliance

ROMAN CATHOLIC DIOCESES

Roman Catholic Archdiocese of Southwark*
Archbishop's House, 150 St Georges Road, London SE1 6HX
Tel: (020) 7928 2495 **Fax:** (020) 7928 7833
Website: http://www.rcsouthwark.co.uk/
Contact: Revd W Saunders
Position: Private Secretary
Traditions: Roman Catholic

Roman Catholic Archdiocese of Westminster*
Archbishops House, Ambrosden Avenue, London SW1P 1QJ
Tel: (020) 7798 9000
Contact: Vicar General
Affiliations: Churches Together in Hertfordshire

SALVATION ARMY DIVISIONS

Salvation Army - Central South Division*
16c Cowley Road, Uxbridge UB8 2LT
Tel: (01895) 208800 **Fax:** (01895) 208811
Contact: Lt Col Trevor Davis
Position: Divisional Commander
Contact Email:
trevor.davis@salvationarmy.org.uk
Activities: Worship/practice/meditation, community centre, central body, youth, elderly, women, newsletter/journal, books, newspapers, radio, television, resources
Traditions: Free Church

Salvation Army London Central Division*
1st Floor, 25/27 Kings Exchange, Tileyard Road, London N7 9AH
Tel: (020) 7619 6100 **Fax:** (020) 7619 6111
Email: john.wainwright@salvationarmy.org.uk
Contact: Peter Reece
Position: Admin Officer
Activities: Worship, youth, elderly, women
Traditions: Free Church

UNITED REFORMED CHURCH PROVINCES

United Reformed Church Thames North Province*
The City Temple, Holborn Viaduct, London EC1A 2DE
Tel: (020) 7799 5000 **Fax:** (020) 7353 1558
Contact: Adrian Bulley
Position: Synod Clerk

SOUTH EAST

REGIONAL ECUMENICAL INSTRUMENTS

Bedfordshire Ecumenical Committee*
47 Main Road North, Dagnall, Berkhamsted HP4 1QZ
Tel: (01442) 843237
Contact: Miss Dorothy Green
Position: Secretary
Activities: Umbrella body, newsletters
Traditions: Ecumenical/Interdenominational
Affiliations: Churches Together in England

Churches Together in Berkshire*
16 Wises Firs, Ufton Nervet, Reading RG7 4EH
Tel: (0118) 9832253 **Fax:** (0118) 9836794
Contact: Professor Roger Mead
Position: Ecumenical Officer
Contact Tel: (0118) 9832253
Contact Email: r.mead@reading.ac.uk
Activities: Ecumenical Churches and Church Groupings
Affiliations: Churches Together In England

Churches Together in Hampshire and the Isle of Wight*
71 Andover Road, Winchester SO22 6AU
Tel: (01962) 862574 **Fax:** (0870) 1307231
Email: cthi@rolph.freeuk.com
Contact: Dr Paul Rolph
Position: Ecumenical Officer
Activities: Worship, media, umbrella body, newsletters

Churches Together in Hertfordshire*
47 Main Road North, Dagnall, Berkhamsted HP4 1QZ
Tel: (01442) 843237
Contact: Miss Dorothy Green
Position: Secretary
Activities: Umbrella body, newsletters
Traditions: Ecumenical/Interdenominational
Affiliations: Churches Together in England

Churches Together in Kent*
St Lawrence Vicarage, Stone Street, Seal, Sevenoaks TN15 0LQ
Tel: (01732) 761766
Email: info@ctkent.org.uk
Website: http://www.ctkent.org.uk/
Contact: Revd Dr Michael Cooke
Position: Ecumenical Officer
Activities: Umbrella body, newsletter/journal, inter-faith
Traditions: Ecumenical/Interdenominational
Affiliations: Churches Together in England; Council of European Churches

Milton Keynes Christian Council*
Christian Foundation, The Square, Aylesbury, Wolverton MK12 5HX
Tel: (01908) 311310 **Fax:** (01908) 311310
Email: admin@mkcc.fsnet.co.uk
Contact: Revd Murdoch MacKenzie
Position: Ecumenical Moderator
Activities: Umbrella body

Churches Together in Oxfordshire*
St Columba's URC, Alfred Street, Oxford OX1 4EH
Tel: (01865) 723801
Email: bede.gerrard@care4free.net
Website: http://www.communigate.co.uk/oxford/churchinoxon
Contact: Mr M R Bede Gerrard
Position: County Ecumenical Officer
Contact Tel: (01865) 864805
Activities: Umbrella body
Traditions: Ecumenical

Churches Together in Surrey*
10 Abbey Gardens, Chertsey KT16 8RQ
Tel: (01932) 566920
Email: sue.loveday.ctsurrey@lineone.net
Contact: Revd Susan Loveday
Position: Ecumenical Co-ordinator
Activities: Inter-faith
Traditions: Ecumenical/Interdenominational
Affiliations: Churches Together in England

Sussex Churches*
85 Hollingbury Rise, Brighton BN1 7HH
Tel: (07976) 811654 **Fax:** (07977) 991716
Email: ianpchisnall@cs.com
Contact: Mr Ian Chisnall
Position: Co-ordinator
Activities: Umbrella body

ASSEMBLIES OF GOD REGIONS

Assemblies of God in Great Britain and Ireland Eastern Regional Council
40 Noriston Road, Bedford MK41 7UQ
Tel: (01234) 309779
Website: http://www.aog.org.uk/
Contact: Brian Oxborough

BAPTIST UNION AREAS

Bedfordshire Baptist Association*
27 Luton Road, Caddington LU1 4AF
Tel: (01582) 451283 **Fax:** (01582) 484670
Contact: Mr John Williams
Position: Secretary
Contact Email: johnrwilliams@lineone.net
Activities: Worship/practice/meditation
Affiliations: Baptist Union Of Great Britain

Berkshire Baptist Association*
37 Cressingham Road, Reading RG2 7RU
Tel: (0118) 9868164 **Fax:** (0118) 9868164
Contact: Revd Sylvia Stevenson
Position: Secretary
Contact Tel: (0118) 3767748
Contact Email:
sylvia@cressingham.freeserve.co.uk

Buckinghamshire Baptist Association*
3 Selby Cottages, Windsor Avenue, Little Kingshill,
Great Missenden HP16 0DZ
Tel: (01494) 864734
Email: redsun@cpye.freeserve.co.uk
Contact: Revd Colin Pye
Position: Secretary

Hertfordshire Baptist Association*
60 Strathmore Avenue, Hitchin SG5 1ST
Tel: (01462) 442548
Email: slcopson@dial.pipex.com
Contact: Revd Stephen Copson
Position: Secretary

Kent Baptist Association*
5 Hawks Way, Ashford TN23 5UD
Tel: (01233) 612332 **Fax:** (08700) 557855
Email: revdtcross@aol.com
Contact: Revd Tony Cross
Position: Director
Contact Email: revdtcrosse.aol.com
Activities: Worship/practice/meditation
Affiliations: Baptist Union

North Downs Baptist Association*
c/o Godalming Baptist Church, Queen Street,
Godalming GU7 1BA
Tel: (01483) 423467
Contact: Mr Roger Barnett
Position: Secretary

**Oxfordshire and East Gloucestershire Baptist
Association***
Findern Mill, The Ridgeway, Bloxham, Banbury
OX15 4NF
Tel: (01295) 721899 **Fax:** (01295) 721460
Email: gill.crippen@oegba.fsnet.co.uk.
Contact: Mrs Gill Crippen
Position: Secretary

Southern Baptist Association
28 Caerleon Avenue, Bitterne, Southampton
SO19 5JX
Tel: (023) 8043 1150

Email: frankboyd@compuserve.com
Contact: Revd Frank Boyd
Position: Secretary
Traditions: Free Church
Affiliations: Churches Together in Oxfordshire,
Berkshire, Hampshire and Islands

Sussex Baptist Association*
33 Chestnut Close, Burgess Hill RH15 8HN
Tel: (01444) 870662
Email: dom@sba1.ftech.co.uk
Website:
http://www.hrbc2.freeserve.co.uk/sbaindex.htm
Contact: Revd David Hall
Position: Chief Executive
Contact Tel: (01444) 870662
Contact Email: dom@sba1.jtech.co.uk
Affiliations: Baptist Union Of Great Britain

CHURCH OF ENGLAND DIOCESES

Church of England Diocese of Canterbury*
Diocesan House, Lady Wootton's Green,
Canterbury CT1 1NQ
Tel: (01227) 459401 **Fax:** (01227) 450964
Email: reception@diocant.clara.co.uk
Website: http://www.canterbury.anglican.org/
Contact: Mr David S Kemp
Position: Diocesan Secretary
Affiliations: Churches Together in Kent

Church of England Diocese of Chichester*
Diocesan Church House, 211 New Church Road,
Hove BN3 4ED
Tel: (01273) 421021 **Fax:** (01273) 421041
Email: media@diochi.org.uk
Contact: Revd David Guest
Position: Diocesan Communications
Activities: Central body
Traditions: Anglican

Church of England Diocese of Guildford*
Diocesan House, Quarry Street, Guildford
GU1 3XG
Tel: (01483)571826 **Fax:** (01483) 790333
Email: sally.hastings@cofeguildford.org.uk
Website: http://www.guildford.anglican.org/
Contact: Stephen Marriott
Position: Diocesan Secretary
Contact Email: reception@cafeguildford.org.uk
Traditions: Anglican

Church of England Diocese of Oxford*
Diocesan Church House, Oxford OX2 0NB
Tel: (01865) 208200 **Fax:** (01865) 790470
Email: diosec@oxford.anglican.org
Website: http://www.oxford.anglican.org/
Contact: Mrs Rosemary Pearce
Position: Diocesan Secretary
Activities: Worship/practice/meditation, umbrella body, youth, elderly, women, newsletter/journal, newspaper, visits, inter-faith, resources
Traditions: Anglican
Affiliations: Anglican Communion

Church of England Diocese of Portsmouth*
Cathedral House, St Thomas's Street, Portsmouth P01 2HA
Tel: (023) 9282 5731 **Fax:** (023) 9229 3423
Email: admin@portsmouth.anglican.org
Website: http://www.portsmouth.anglican.org/
Contact: Michael Frank Jordan
Position: Diocesan Secretary
Contact Email:
diocesansecretary@portsmouth.anglican.org
Affiliations: Churches Together in Hampshire and the Islands

Church of England Diocese of Rochester*
Diocesan Office, St Nicholas Church, Boley Hill, Rochester ME1 1SL
Tel: (01634) 830333 **Fax:** (01634) 829463
Email: general.diocesan@rochester.anglican.org
Website: http://www.rochester.anglican.org/
Contact: Revd Chris Stone
Position: Communications Director
Contact Tel: (01634) 404343
Contact Email:
communications@rochester.anglican.org
Activities: Central body, newsletter/journal, inter-faith
Traditions: Anglican

Church of England Diocese of Winchester*
Church House, 9 The Close, Winchester SO23 9LS
Tel: (01962) 844644 **Fax:** (01962) 841815
Email: lyn.williams@chsewinchester.clara.net
Website: http://www.winchester.anglican.org/
Contact: Mr Ray Anderton
Position: Diocesan Secretary
Contact Tel: (01962) 624742
Contact Email:
ray.anderton@chsewinchester.clara.net
Traditions: Anglican
Affiliations: Churches Together in Hampshire and the Isle of Wight; Anglican Communion; Churches Together in Dorset

CONGREGATIONAL FEDERATION AREAS

Congregational Federation Central Southern Area*
Flat 2, The Manse, Petersfield Road, South Harting, Petersfield GU31 5QA
Tel: (01730) 825519
Contact: Revd Graham Akers
Contact Tel: (01983) 533862
Traditions: Free Church

Congregational Federation South East Area*
17 Overbrook, West Horsley, Leatherhead KT24 6BH
Tel: (01483) 282541
Email: barry@ruralmissions.org.uk
Contact: Barry Osbourne
Position: President
Contact Tel: (01323) 832445

METHODIST DISTRICTS

Methodist Church (Oxford and Leicester District)*
53 Oxford Road, Kidlington OX5 2BP
Tel: (01865) 373958 **Fax:** (01865) 373958
Contact: Revd Dr Martin Wellings
Position: District Synod Secretary
Activities: Central body, umbrella body
Traditions: Free Church
Affiliations: Greater Peterborough Ecumenical Council

Methodist Church London North East District*
51 Beattyville Gardens, Ilford IG6 1JY
Contact: Revd Ermal B Kirby
Position: Chairman
Contact Tel: (020) 8503 9854
Activities: Umbrella body
Traditions: Free Church

Methodist Church London South East District*
District Office, Bromley Methodist Church, College Road, Bromley BR1 3NS
Tel: (020) 8464 1112 **Fax:** (020) 8464 1113
Email: hrichardson@lsemethdist.fsnet.co.uk
Contact: Revd Harvey S Richardson
Position: Chairman
Activities: Umbrella body
Traditions: Free Church
Affiliations: Churches Together in Kent; Churches Together in South London

ROMAN CATHOLIC DIOCESES

Roman Catholic Diocese of Arundel and Brighton*
Bishop's House, Upper Drive, Hove BN3 6NE
Tel: (01273) 506387 **Fax:** (01273) 501527
Contact: Revd Mgr Canon J Hull
Position: Vicar General
Activities: Worship, resource, newsletters, inter-faith
Other Languages: Italian, Polish, French
Affiliations: Churches Together in Surrey and Sussex

Roman Catholic Diocese of Brentwood*
Cathedral House, Ingrave Road, Brentwood CM15 8AT
Contact: Mr G P Curran
Position: Director of Finance
Contact Tel: (01277) 265280
Activities: Worship/practice/meditation, community centre, youth, elderly, women, inter-faith, resources
Traditions: Roman Catholic
Affiliations: Essex Churches Consultative Council

Roman Catholic Diocese of Portsmouth*
Bishop's House, Edinburgh Road, Portsmouth PO1 3HG
Contact: Rt Revd Crispian Hollis
Position: Bishop
Affiliations: Churches Together in Hampshire and the Islands; Churches Together in Berkshire

SALVATION ARMY DIVISIONS

Salvation Army London South East Division*
1 East Court, Enterprise Road, Maidstone ME15 6JF
Tel: (01622) 775001 **Fax:** (01622) 775011
Email: londonsoutheast@salvationarmy.org.uk
Website: http://www.salvationarmy.org.uk/
Contact: Lt Col David Jones
Position: Divisional Commander
Traditions: Free Church
Affiliations: Churches Together in Kent; Surrey; South London; Sussex

Salvation Army Southern Division*
6/8 Little Park Farm Road, Segensworth, Fareham PO15 5TD
Tel: (01489) 566800 **Fax:** (01489) 566811
Contact: Major Ian Barr
Position: Divisional Commander
Contact Tel: (01489) 566801

Contact Email: ian.barr@salvationarmy.org.uk
Activities: Worship, resource, visits, youth, elderly, women
Traditions: Free Church
Affiliations: Churches Together in Hampshire and the Islands; Churches Together in Dorset; Churches Together in Wiltshire

UNITARIAN AND FREE CHRISTIANS

General Assembly of Unitarian and Free Christian Churches
Southern Unitarian Association, 35 Brookfield Road, Fratton PO1 5HZ
Tel: (023) 8073 6686
Contact: Daisy Roxburgh-Gunter
Position: Secretary
Activities: Worship, umbrella body, newsletter, inter-faith

UNITED REFORMED CHURCH PROVINCES

United Reformed Church Southern Province*
Synod Office, East Croydon United Reformed Church, Addiscombe Grove, Croydon CR0 5LP
Tel: (020) 8688 3730 **Fax:** (020) 8688 2698
Contact: Mrs Christine P Meekison, DCS
Position: Synod Clerk

OTHER BODIES

Beckenham and Penge Evangelical Fellowship*
76 Village Way, Beckenham BR3 3NR
Tel: (020) 8289 3572
Contact: Andrew A Cooke
Position: Chair
Activities: Umbrella body, newsletters

Brighton and Hove Evangelical Fellowship*
118 Nevill Avenue, Hove BN3 7ND

Bromley Evangelical Fellowship*
81 Kingsway, Coney Hall, West Wickham BR4 9JE

South East Essex Evangelical Fellowship*
14 Elsenham Court, Tendring Avenue, Rayleigh SS6 9SB

Southampton Evangelical Fellowship*
Central Hall, St Mary Street, Southampton SO14 1NF

SOUTH WEST

REGIONAL ECUMENICAL INSTRUMENTS

Churches Together in Cornwall*
186 Bodmin Road, Truro TR1 1RB
Tel: (01872) 223755
Contact: Revd Ian Haile
Position: Secretary
Activities: Umbrella body
Affiliations: Churches Together in England

Christians Together in Devon*
Grenville House, Whites Lane, Torrington
EX38 8DS
Tel: (01865) 625059
Email: john.bradley@care4free.net
Contact: Revd John Bradley
Position: Ecumenical Officer
Activities: Umbrella body, newsletter/journal
Traditions: Ecumenical/Interdenominational
Affiliations: Churches Together in England; World
Council of Churches

Churches Together in Dorset*
22 D'Urberville Close, Dorchester DT1 2JT
Tel: (01305) 264416
Email: ctdorset@clara.net
Website: http://www.ctdorset.clara.net/
Contact: Valerie Potter
Position: Ecumenical Officer
Activities: Umbrella body, newsletters
Affiliations: Churches Together in England

Churches Together in Greater Bristol*
9 Lodway Close, Pill, Bristol BS20 0DE
Tel: (01275) 373488 **Fax:** (01275) 373488
Email: ctgb@clara.co.uk
Website: http://www.ctgb.clara.co.uk/
Contact: Revd Brian Scott
Position: Ecumenical Officer
Activities: Resource, umbrella body, newsletters

Churches Together in Swindon*
16 Sherwood Avenue, Melksham SN12 7HJ
Tel: (01225) 704748
Email: anne.doyle@btinternet.com
Contact: Anne Doyle
Position: Ecumenical Officer
Activities: Newsletter/journal, inter-faith

Gloucestershire Churches Together
151 Tuffley Road, Gloucester GL1 5NP

Tel: (01452) 301347
Contact: Revd David Calvert
Position: Ecumenical Officer
Activities: Worship, youth, elderly, newsletter

Guernsey Council of Churches*
Le Grand Courtil, Les Tracheries, L'Islet, Guernsey
GY2 4SW
Tel: (01481) 248223
Contact: Mrs Frances Stanton
Position: Chairman
Contact Tel: (01481) 246468
Affiliations: Churches Together in England

Churches Together in Jersey*
Catholic Pastoral Centre, St Mary and St Peter's
Church, Wellington Road, St Helier, Jersey JE2 4RJ
Tel: (01534) 732583
Contact: Sr Loretta Madigan FCJ
Position: Ecumenical Officer

Somerset Churches Together*
12 Lawson Close, Saltford, Bristol BS31 3LB
Tel: (01225) 872903 **Fax:** (01225) 872903
Email: sct@ukmax.com
Contact: Mr Dixon
Position: County Ecumenical Offcier
Activities: Worship/practice/meditation, umbrella
body, youth, elderly, women, newsletter/journal,
inter-faith, resources
Traditions: Ecumenical/Interdenominational
Affiliations: Churches Together in England

Wiltshire Churches Together*
16 Sherwood Avenue, Melksham SN12 7HJ
Tel: (01225) 704748
Email: anne.doyle@btinternet.com
Contact: Anne Doyle
Position: Ecumenical Officer
Activities: Umbrella body, visits, newsletters, inter-
faith

ASSEMBLIES OF GOD REGIONS

Assemblies of God, West Country Regional Council*
Riverside Christian Centre, 13-14 Okehampton
Street, St Thomas, Exeter EX2 9HE
Tel: (01392) 210146 **Fax:** (01392) 210146
Website: http://www.aog.org.uk/
Contact: Revd John Partington
Position: Secretary
Traditions: Pentecostal

BAPTIST UNION AREAS

Bristol and District Baptist Association*
Stapleton Baptist Church, Broom Hill, Bristol
BS16 1DN
Tel: (0117) 9658828 **Fax:** (0117) 9658838
Contact: Revd Roger Short
Position: Secretary
Contact Tel: (01453) 811988

Gloucestershire Baptist Association*
7 College Fields, Longlevens, Gloucester GL2 0AG
Tel: (01452) 532310
Email: glosbaptists@kenyonbjm.freeserve.co.uk
Contact: Mr Brian Kenyon
Position: Secretary

South West Baptist Association*
13 Wrefords Drive, Cowley Park, Exeter EX4 5AU
Tel: (01392) 431097
Email: djk@ok
Contact: Revd Derek John Keenan
Position: Regional Minister
Traditions: Free Church
Affiliations: Churches Together in Cornwall

Western Baptist Association*
60 Andrew Allan Road, Rockwell Road, Rockwell
Green, Wellington TA21 9DY
Tel: (01823) 664529
Email: revelsied@howell.freeserve.co.uk
Contact: Revd Elsie Howell
Position: Secretary
Traditions: Free Church
Affiliations: Somerset Churches Together

Wiltshire and East Somerset Baptist Association*
5a Ebble Crescent, Warminster BA12 9PF
Tel: (01985) 219801
Email: g-birchwebasec.freeserve.co.uk
Contact: Revd Geoffrey Birch
Position: Secretary
Traditions: Free Church
Affiliations: Churches Together in Wiltshire

CHURCH OF ENGLAND DIOCESES

Church of England Diocese of Bath and Wells*
Diocesan Office, Old Deanery, Wells BA5 2UG
Tel: (01749) 670777 **Fax:** (01749) 674240
Email: general@bathwells.anglican.org
Website: http://www.bathwells.anglican.org/
Contact: Mr N Denison
Position: Diocesan Secretary
Affiliations: Somerset Churches Together

Church of England Diocese of Bristol*
Diocesan Church House, 23 Great George Street,
Bristol BS1 5QT
Tel: (0117) 9060100 **Fax:** (0117) 9250460
Contact: Mrs Lesley Farrall
Position: Diocesan Secretary
Activities: Resource
Affiliations: Greater Bristol Ecumenical Council;
Wiltshire Churches Together

Church of England Diocese of Exeter*
Diocesan House, Palace Gate, Exeter EX1 1HX
Tel: (01392) 272686 **Fax:** (01392) 499594
Website: http://www.exeter.anglican.org/
Contact: Diocesan Secretary
Activities: Worship/practice/meditation
Traditions: Anglican
Affiliations: Churches Together in Devon

Church of England Diocese of Gloucester*
Church House, College Green, Gloucester
GL1 2LY
Tel: (01452) 410022 **Fax:** (01452) 308324
Email: church.house@glosdioc.org.uk
Website: http://www.glosdioc.org.uk/
Contact: Mrs Hilary Penney
Position: Executive Officer
Activities: Resource, umbrella body
Affiliations: Gloucestershire Churches Together

Church of England Diocese of Salisbury*
Church House, Crane Street, Salisbury SP1 2QB
Tel: (01722) 411922 **Fax:** (01722) 411990
Email: enquiries@salisbury.anglican.org
Website: http://www.salisbury.anglican.org/
Contact: Revd Karen Curnock
Position: Diocesan Secretary
Traditions: Anglican
Affiliations: Churches Together in Dorset;
Wiltshire Churches Together

Church of England Diocese of Truro*
Diocesan House, Kenwyn, Truro TR1 1JQ
Tel: (01872) 274351 **Fax:** (01872) 222510
Website: http://www.truro.anglican.org/
Contact: Mr Ben Laite
Position: Diocesan Secretary
Contact Tel: (01872) 274351
Contact Email: sec.trurodio@virgin.net
Affiliations: Churches Together in Cornwall

Diocese of Bath and Wells Training Department*
The Old Deanery, Wells BA4 4HD
Tel: (01749) 670777 **Fax:** (01749) 674240
Email: training@bathwells.anglican.org
Contact: Preb Rev Russell Bowman-Eadie
Position: Director of Training
Activities: Central body, umbrella body, resources
Traditions: Anglican
Affiliations: Wesley College Bristol, Anglican Adult Education Network, College of Preachers

CONGREGATIONAL FEDERATION AREAS

Congregational Federation South West Area*
85 Bowden Park Road, Crownhill, Plymouth PL6 5NQ
Contact: Mrs Great White
Position: Assistant Secretary
Activities: Umbrella body
Traditions: Free Church
Affiliations: Congregational Federation

METHODIST DISTRICTS

Methodist Church Bristol District*
31 Midland Road, Bristol
Tel: (0117) 955 5606
Contact: Richard Barrett
Position: Minister
Traditions: Free Church

Methodist Church Channel Islands District*
West Lea, Route des Quennevais, St Brelade JE3 8LJ
Tel: (01534) 743933 **Fax:** (01534) 498386
Contact: Revd Ian T White
Position: Chairman
Traditions: Free Church

Methodist Church Plymouth and Exeter District*
Fairlawn, 133 New Road, Brixham TQ5 8DB
Fax: (01803) 854431
Email: revpbw@btinternet.com
Contact: Revd Peter B Williamson
Position: Synod Secretary
Activities: Central body
Traditions: Free Church
Affiliations: Churches Together in Devon; Somerset Churches Together

Methodist Church Southampton District*
4 The Glade, Thornbury, Chandlers Ford, Eastleigh SO53 5AZ

Contact: Revd Thomas J Stuckey
Position: Chairman
Activities: Umbrella body
Traditions: Methodist
Affiliations: Churches Together in Hampshire and the Isle of Wight

MORAVIAN CHURCH DISTRICTS

Moravian Church Western District Conference, The*
148 Purlewent Drive, Bath BA1 4BE
Tel: (01225) 442730
Email: paul.gubi@virgin.net
Contact: Revd Paul Gubi
Position: Chair
Activities: Umbrella body
Traditions: Free Church

ROMAN CATHOLIC DIOCESES

Roman Catholic Diocese of Clifton
Clifton Diocesan Offices, Egerton Road, Bishoptown, Bristol BS7 8HU
Tel: (0117) 9083324 **Fax:** (0117) 9424448
Contact: Mgr Canon W Mitchell
Position: Vicar General
Affiliations: Greater Bristol Ecumenical Council; Gloucestershire Churches Together; Somerset Churches Together

Roman Catholic Diocese of Plymouth*
Bishop's House, 31 Wyndham St West, Plymouth PL1 5RZ
Tel: (01752) 224414 **Fax:** (01752) 223750
Website: htttp//www.plymouth-diocese.org.uk
Contact: RT Rev Christopher Budd
Position: Bishop of Plymouth

SALVATION ARMY DIVISIONS

Salvation Army South Western Division*
Marlborough Court, Manaton Close, Matford Business Park, Exeter EX2 8PF
Tel: (01392) 822100 **Fax:** (01392) 822111
Email: southwestern@salvationarmy.org.uk
Website: http://www.salvationarmy.org.uk/
Contact: Lt Col David Lambert-Gorwyn
Position: Divisional Commander
Activities: Worship, community, youth, elderly, women, newsletters, books, inter-faith
Traditions: Free Church

UNITARIAN AND FREE CHRISTIANS

Midland Union of Unitarian and Free Christian Churches*
29 Woodlands Road, Cookley, Kidderminster
DY10 3TL
Tel: (01562) 850538
Contact: Mr Roger Mathews
Position: Secretary
Activities: Newsletters
Affiliations: Observer at Birmingham Council of
Christian Churches

Western Union of Unitarian and Free Christian Churches*
1 Parkside Avenue, Winterbourne, Bristol
BS36 1LU
Tel: (01454) 775454

UNITED REFORMED CHURCH PROVINCES

United Reformed Church South Western Synod*
The Manse, Norton Fitzwarren, Taunton TA2 6RU
Tel: (01823) 275470 **Fax:** (01823) 275470
Email: urc-southwest@beeb.net
Contact: Revd R Harrison
Position: Synod Clerk
Traditions: Free Church
Affiliations: Greater Bristol Ecumenical Council;
Somerset Churches Together; Christians Together
in Devon; Wiltshire Churches Together

United Reformed Church: Wessex Synod*
Synod Office, United Reformed Church, King
Road, Chandler's Ford, Eastleigh SO53 2EY
Tel: (023) 8026 6548 **Fax:** (023) 8026 6548
Email: wessex@urc-9.freeserve.co.uk
Website: http://www.urcwessex.org.uk/
Contact: Mr Graham N Rolfe
Position: Synod Clerk
Activities: Central body
Traditions: Free Church
Affiliations: World Alliance of Reformed
Churches

OTHER BODIES

Mid Cotswolds Evangelical Alliance*
127 Ashlands Road, Cheltenham GL51 0DJ

South Wessex Evangelical Alliance*
Delta House, 56 Westover Road, Bournemouth
BH1 2BS

Tel: (01202) 315133 **Fax:** (01202) 314219
Email: swea@lineone.net
Position: Secretary
Activities: Central body, umbrella body,
newsletter/journal
Traditions: Ecumenical/Interdenominational

Taunton Evangelical Fellowship*
Canon Street Pentecostal Church, Canon Street,
Taunton TA1 1SN
Tel: (01823) 327107
Contact: Mr Colin Ryles
Position: Secretary
Contact Tel: (01823) 252124
Contact Email: colinryles@onetel.net.uk
Activities: Umbrella body

Torbay Evangelical Fellowship*
Ellacombe Vicarage, 1a Lower Ellacombe Church,
Torquay TQ1 1JH
Tel: (01803) 293441
Contact: Revd Roy William Taylor
Position: Chair
Activities: Resource, media, umbrella body, youth

IRELAND

IRISH ECUMENICAL INSTRUMENTS

Irish Council of Churches*
Inter-Church Centre, 48 Elmwood Avenue, Belfast
BT9 6AZ
Tel: (028) 9066 3145 **Fax:** (028) 9038 2750
Email: icpep@email.com
Website: http://www.irishchurches.org/
Contact: Dr David Stevens
Position: General Secretary
Activities: Umbrella body, women, books,
resources
Traditions: Ecumenical/Interdenominational
Affiliations: Conference of European Churches

Member Bodies:
Church of Ireland
Greek Orthodox Church in Britain and Ireland
Irish District of the Moravian Church
Lutheran Church in Ireland
Non-Subscribing Presbyterian Church of Ireland
Presbyterian Church in Ireland
Religious Society of Friends
Salvation Army

Irish Inter-Church Meeting*
Inter Church Centre, 48 Elmwood Avenue, Belfast
BT9 6AL
Tel: (028) 9066 3145 **Fax:** (028) 9038 2750
Email: ccpep@email.com
Website: http://www.irishchurches.org/
Contact: Dr David Stevens
Position: Executive Secretary
Activities: Umbrella body, newsletter/journal,
books

CHURCHES OPERATING AT AN IRISH LEVEL

Assemblies of God in Great Britain and Ireland, Ireland Regional Council
5 Glenburn Park, Ballymena BT43 6HG
Website: http://www.aog.org.uk/

Association of Baptist Churches in Ireland*
117 Lisburn Road, Belfast BT9 7AF
Tel: (028) 9066 3108 **Fax:** (028) 9066 3616
Email: abcin1@aol.com
Contact: Pastor William Colville
Position: Association Secretary
Contact Email: assocsec@aol.com
Activities: Central body, youth, elderly, women,
newsletter/journal, books, resources
Other Languages: Irish

Church of Ireland*
Church of Ireland House, Church Avenue,
Rathmines Dublin 4
Tel: ++353 1497 8422 **Fax:** ++351 1499 78821
Email: office@rc bdub.org
Website: http://www.ireland.anglican.org/
Contact: Ms Valerie Beatty
Position: Head of General Office
Contact Tel: +353 1 4978422
Contact Email: synod@rcbdub.org
Traditions: Anglican
Movements: Anglican Communion
Other Languages: Irish

Congregational Union of Ireland
38 Edgecumbe Gardens, Belfast BT4 2EH
Tel: (028) 9065 3140
Contact: Revd Malcolm Coles
Position: Secretary

Irish Catholic Bishops' Conference*
St Patrick's College, Maynooth, County Kildare
Tel: ++353 1601 6700 **Fax:** ++353 1601 6698

Email: bishops@eircom.net
Contact: Revd Aidan O'Boyle
Position: Executive Secretary
Activities: Worship/practice/meditation, central
body, umbrella body, inter-faith
Traditions: Roman Catholic

Lutheran Church in Ireland*
Lutherhaus, 24 Adelaide Road, Dublin 2
Tel: ++353 1676 6548 **Fax:** ++353 1676 6548
Email: lutheranchurch@eircom.net
Contact: I G Mayer
Position: Chairman
Activities: Worship/practice/meditation,
newsletter/journal
Other Languages: German, Swedish, Finnish

Methodist Church in Ireland*
1 Fountainville Avenue, Belfast BT9 6AN
Tel: (028) 9032 4554 **Fax:** (028) 9023 9467
Email: secretary@irishmethodist.org
Contact: Revd Edmund T I Mawhinney
Position: Secretary
Contact Tel: (028) 9032 4554
Activities: Worship/practice/meditation, central
body, newsletter/journal

Moravian Church (Irish District)
Moravian Avenue, 153 Finaghy Road South, Upper
Malone, Belfast BT10 0DG
Tel: (028) 9061 9755
Contact: Leonard Broadbent
Position: Chair
Activities: Worship
Traditions: Free Church

Non-Subscribing Presbyterian Church of Ireland*
102 Carrickfergus Road, Larne BT40 3JT
Tel: (028) 2827 2600
Contact: Revd Dr John W Nelson
Position: Clerk of the Synod
Activities: Worship/practice/meditation, central
body, youth, elderly, women, newsletter/journal,
resources
Traditions: Presbyterian
Affiliations: Irish Council of Churches;
International Association for Religious Freedom

Presbyterian Church in Ireland*
Church House, Fisherwick Place, Belfast
BT1 6DW
Tel: (028) 9032 2284 **Fax:** (028) 9023 6609
Email: clerk@presbyterianireland.org

Website: http://www.presbyterianireland.org/
Contact: Revd Samuel Hutchinson
Position: Clerk of Assembly
Activities: Central body, newsletter/journal,
resources
Traditions: Presbyterian
Affiliations: Irish Council of Churches; World
Alliance of Reformed Churches

Religious Society of Friends in Ireland*
Swanbrook House, Bloomfield Avenue,
Donnybrook, Dublin 4
Tel: ++353 1668 3684 **Fax:** ++353 1668 3684
Contact: Valerie O'Brien
Position: Recording Clerk

Seventh Day Adventist Church, Ireland
9 Newry Road, Banbridge BT32 3HF

CHURCH REGIONAL BODIES

BAPTIST UNION AREAS

Northern Association of Irish Baptist Churches*
65 Taylorstown Road, Toomebridge BT41 3RW
Tel: (028) 7965 0386 **Fax:** (028) 7965 0386
Email: grodgers@freeuk.com
Website: http://www.grodgers.freeuk.com/
Contact: Pastor Gerald Rogers
Position: Secretary
Activities: Newsletters
Traditions: Free Church

CHURCH OF IRELAND DIOCESES

Church of Ireland Diocese of Armagh*
Church House, 46 Abbey Street, Armagh
BT61 7DZ
Tel: (028) 3752 2858 **Fax:** (028) 3751 0596
Email: office@armagh.anglican.org
Contact: Mrs J Montgomery
Position: Diocesan Secretary
Traditions: Anglican

Church of Ireland Diocese of Clogher*
The Deanery, 10 Augher Road, Clogher
BT76 0AD
Tel: (028) 8554 8235 **Fax:** (028) 8554 8235
Email: dean@clogher.anglican.org
Contact: Very Revd Thomas R Moore
Position: Dean of Clogher
Activities: Worship, resource, umbrella body, visits,

newsletters
Traditions: Anglican
Other Languages: French

Church of Ireland Diocese of Derry and Raphoe*
Diocesan Office, London Street, Londonderry
BT48 6RQ
Tel: (01805) 04262440
Contact: G. Kelly
Position: Diocesan Secretary
Traditions: Anglican

Church of Ireland Diocese of Down and Dromore and Diocese of Connor*
Diocesan Office, Church of Ireland House, 61-67
Donegall Street, Belfast BT1 2QH
Tel: (028) 9032 2268 **Fax:** (028) 9032 1635
Contact: Mr T N Wilson
Position: Diocesan Secretary
Contact Tel: (028) 9032 3188
Activities: Central body
Traditions: Anglican

METHODIST DISTRICTS

Methodist Church in Ireland Belfast District
10 Locksley Park, Belfast BT10 0AR
Traditions: Free Church

Methodist Church in Ireland Down District*
2 Lyndhurst Avenue, Crawford Road Church,
Bangor BT19 1NU
Tel: (028) 9147 3400
Email: k.lindsay@virgin.net
Website:
http://www.carnaleamethodist@freeserve.co.uk/
Contact: Revd Kenneth Lindsay
Position: Minister
Contact Tel: (028) 9147 3400
Activities: Worship/practice/meditation,
community centre, central body, youth, elderly,
women, newsletter/journal
Traditions: Methodist

Methodist Church in Ireland Londonderry District
48 Upper Strabane Road, Castlederg BT81 7BE

Methodist Church In Ireland North East District*
2 Balmoral Avenue, Whitehead, Carrickfergus
BT38 9QA
Tel: (028) 9337 3327

Contact: Revd Wesley Campbell
Activities: Worship, youth
Traditions: Free Church

Methodist Church in Ireland Portadown District
3 Old Rectory Park, Lurgan Road, Banbridge
BT32 4QA
Traditions: Free Church

NON-SUBSCRIBING PRESBYTERIAN CHURCH OF IRELAND

Non Subscribing Presbyterian Church of Ireland Presbytery of Bangor*
15 Windmill Hill, Comber BT23 5WH
Tel: (028) 9187 2265
Contact: Rev Ian Gilpin
Position: Clerk
Activities: Worship/practice/meditation, women
Affiliations: International Association For Religious Freedom

PRESBYTERIAN CHURCH IN IRELAND PRESBYTERIES

Presbytery of Antrim*
102 Carrickfergus Road, Larne BT40 3JX
Tel: (028) 2827 2600
Contact: Revd Dr John Wallace Nelson
Position: Presbytery Clerk
Activities: Worship/practice/meditation, central body
Traditions: Presbyterian

Presbyterian Church in Ireland Ards Presbytery*
3 Second Avenue, Baylands, Bangor BT20 5JZ
Tel: (028) 9145 0141 **Fax:** (028) 9145 0141
Email: dwatts@presbyterianireland.org
Contact: Revd Dr Donald J Watts
Position: Presbytery Clerk
Activities: Central body
Traditions: Presbyterian

Presbyterian Church in Ireland - Presbytery of Ballymena*
1 Forthill Park, Ballymena BT42 2HL
Tel: (028) 2564 5544 **Fax:** (028) 2564 5544
Email: jandrews@presbyterianireland.org
Contact: Revd J J Andrews
Position: Clerk
Contact Tel: (028) 2564 5544
Activities: Umbrella body
Traditions: Presbyterian

Affiliations: World Alliance of Reformed Churches

Presbyterian Church in Ireland Belfast East Presbytery*
Church Office, 161 Gilnahirk Road, Belfast
BT5 7QP
Contact: John McVeigh
Position: Clerk

Presbyterian Church in Ireland, Armargh Presbytery*
Greenfield Manse, 72 Newry Road, Armagh
BT60 1ER
Tel: (028) 3752 5522
Contact: Dr J Thompson
Position: Head of Presbytery

Presbyterian Church in Ireland Belfast North Presbytery
11 Waterloo Gardens, Belfast BT15 4EX

Presbyterian Church in Ireland Belfast South Presbytery*
The Manse, 3 Shrewsbury Gardens, Balmoral
Avenue, Belfast BT9 6PJ
Tel: (028) 9066 7247
Email: tanderson@presbyterianireland.org
Contact: Revd R Trevor Anderson
Position: Presbytery Clerk

Presbyterian Church in Ireland, Carrickfergus Presbytery*
22 Brustin Braes, Larne BT38 7US

Presbyterian Church in Ireland Derry and Strabane Presbytery*
19 Clearwater, Londonderry BT47 6BE
Tel: (028) 7131 1425 **Fax:** (028) 7131 1425
Email: jfell@presbyterianireland.org
Website: http://www.presbyterianireland.org/
Contact: Revd Dr Joseph Fell
Position: Clerk
Traditions: Presbyterian
Affiliations: World Alliance of Reformed Churches

Presbyterian Church in Ireland Down Presbytery*
35 Manse Road, Ballygowan, Newtonards
BT23 6HE
Tel: (01238) 528962 **Fax:** (01283) 528962
Contact: Revd James Harper
Position: Clerk of Presbytery
Contact Tel: (07833) 635669

Contact Email: jharper@easicom.com
Activities: Umbrella body

Presbyterian Church in Ireland, Dromore Presbetery*
2 Lisburn Road, Hillsborough BT26 6AA
Tel: (028) 9268 3696
Contact: Revd John Davey

Presbyterian Church in Ireland Foyle Presbytery*
68 Donagheady Road, Strabane BT82 0LR
Tel: (028) 7184 1320
Contact: Revd S Stewart
Traditions: Anglican

Presbyterian Church in Ireland Iveagh Presbytery
19 Shimna Road, Newcastle BT33 0AT

Presbyterian Church in Ireland, Newry Presbytery*
156 Glasdrumman Road, Annalong, Newry BT34 4QL

Presbyterian Church in Ireland Route Presbytery*
134 Filbey Road, Ballymouney, Belfast BT53 8HY
Contact: Revd Wallace

Presbyterian Church in Ireland Tyrone Presbytery*
17 Bankfield Drive, Coagh, Cookstown BT80 0BG
Tel: (028) 8673 7690 **Fax:** (028) 8673 7690
Contact: James B McCormick
Position: Presbytery Clerk
Traditions: Presbyterian

ROMAN CATHOLIC DIOCESES

Roman Catholic Archdiocese of Armagh*
Ara Coeli, Armagh City BT61 7QY
Tel: (028) 3752 2045 **Fax:** (028) 3752 6182
Email: admin@aracoeli.com
Contact: Archbishop Seán Brady
Position: Archbishop of Armagh

Roman Catholic Diocese of Derry*
Derry Diocese Office, Bishop's House, St Eugene's Cathedral, Derry BT48 9AP
Tel: (01504) 262302 **Fax:** (01504) 371960
Email: derrydiocese@aol.com
Contact: The Most Revd Seamus Hegarty
Position: Bishop of Derry
Other Languages: Irish, French, Italian, German

Roman Catholic Diocese of Down and Connor*
"Lisbreen", 73 Somerton Road, Belfast BT15 4DE
Tel: (028) 9077 6185
Contact: Most Revd Patrick Walsh
Position: Bishop

Roman Catholic Diocese of Dromore, St Colamn's College*
Newry BT35 6PN
Tel: (028) 3026 2451 **Fax:** (028) 3026 7422
Email: fbrown@stcolmans.newry.ni.sch.uk
Website: http://www.stcolmans.org.uk/
Contact: Revd Francis Brown

SALVATION ARMY DIVISIONS

Salvation Army Northern Ireland Division*
12 Station Mews, Sydenham, Belfast BT4 1TL
Tel: (028) 9067 5000 **Fax:** (028) 9067 5011
Contact: George A Pilkington
Position: Divisional Commander
Activities: Youth, elderly, women, newsletters, books
Traditions: Free Church

OTHER IRISH BODIES

Evangelical Alliance, Northern Ireland*
218 York Street, Belfast BT15 1GY
Contact: General Secretary

Irish Fellowship of Reconciliation
224 Lisburn Road, Belfast BT9 6GE

Irish School of Ecumenics (Trinity College Dublin)*
Bea House, Milltown Park Dublin 6
Contact: Revd Canon Kenneth Kearon
Position: Director
Contact Tel: +353 1 260114
Contact Email: ise@iol.ie
Activities: Women, newsletter/journal, visits, inter-faith, resources
Traditions: Ecumenical
Other Languages: German, French

National Council of YMCAs of Ireland Limited
St Georges Building, 37/41 High Street, Belfast BT1 2AB
Tel: (028) 9032 7757 **Fax:** (028) 9043 8809
Email: bev@ymca-ire.dnet.co.uk
Contact: Beverley Cuthbert
Position: Administration/Finance Manager

Activities: Umbrella body, youth, women
Traditions: Cross-denominational

SCOTLAND

SCOTTISH ECUMENICAL INSTRUMENT

Action of Churches Together in Scotland*
Scottish Churches House, Kirk Street, Dunblane
FK15 0AJ
Tel: (01786) 823588 **Fax:** (01786) 825844
Email: acts.ecum@dial.pipex.com
Website: http://www.acts-scotland.org/
Contact: Dr Kevin Franz
Position: General Secretary
Activities: Central body, umbrella body,
newsletter/journal, books, visits, inter-faith,
resources
Traditions: Ecumenical/Interdenominational

Member Bodies:
Church of Scotland
Congregational Union of Scotland
Methodist Church
Religious Society of Friends
Roman Catholic Church in Scotland
Salvation Army
Scottish Episcopal Church
United Free Church
United Reformed Church

CHURCHES OPERATING AT A SCOTTISH LEVEL

Assemblies of God Scottish Regional Council*
12 Carrick Place, Carron, Falkirk FK2 8BT
Tel: (01324) 885934 **Fax:** (01324) 885934
Email: rolloaogscot@compuserve.com
Website: http://www.aog.org.uk/
Contact: Revd Michael George Rollo
Position: Regional Administrator
Activities: Central body, youth, elderly, resources
Traditions: Pentecostal
Affiliations: Assemblies of God in Great Britain
and Ireland

Church of Scotland*
121 George Street, Edinburgh EH2 4YN
Tel: (0131) 240 2240 **Fax:** (0131) 240 2239
Email: fmacdonald@cofscotland.org.uk

Website: http://www.churchofscotland.org.uk
Contact: Revd Dr Finlay MacDonald
Activities: Resource, youth, elderly, women,
newsletters, book
Traditions: Presbyterian

Methodist Church in Scotland*
Central Hall, West Tollcross, Edinburgh EH3 9BP
Tel: (0131) 2219029 **Fax:** (0131) 2219029
Email: edinmethodistmission@talk21.com
Contact: David Cooper
Position: Synod Secretary
Activities: Worship, youth, women, newsletter,
inter-faith
Traditions: Free Church

Roman Catholic Church in Scotland*
Bishops' Conference of Scotland, 64 Aitken Street,
Airdrie ML6 6LT
Tel: (01236) 764061 **Fax:** (01236) 762489
Contact: Revd Mgr Henry Docherty
Position: General Secretary
Activities: Worship, resource, media, umbrella
body, youth, elderly
Other Languages: Gaelic

Scottish Episcopal Church*
General Synod Office, 21 Grosvenor Crescent,
Edinburgh EH12 5EE
Tel: (0131) 2256357 **Fax:** (0131) 3467247
Email: office@scotland.anglican.org
Website: http://www.scotland.anglican.org/
Contact: John F Stuart
Position: Secretary General
Activities: Worship/practice/meditation,
community centre, central body, youth, elderly,
women, newsletter/journal, newspapers, inter-faith
Traditions: Anglican
Affiliations: Anglican Communion

Scottish Unitarian Association*
74 Craigie Drive, Dundee DD4 7PB
Tel: (01382) 455588
Email: liz.shepherd@tinyworld.co.uk
Contact: Liz Shepherd
Position: Secretary
Activities: Resource, media, umbrella body, visits,
youth, elderly

Seventh Day Adventist Church, Scotland*
5 Ochilview Gardens, Crieff PH7 3EJ
Contact: A R Rodd
Position: President
Contact Tel: (01764) 652090
Contact Email: 100616.1703@compuserve.com

Activities: Worship/practice/meditation, youth, elderly, women, newsletter/journal, books, television, visits, inter-faith, resources
Traditions: Free Church
Other Languages: Spanish

United Free Church of Scotland*

11 Newton Close, Glasgow G3 7PR
Tel: (0141) 3323435 **Fax:** (0141) 3323435
Email: ufcos@charis.co.uk
Website: http://www.ufcos.org.uk/
Contact: Revd John Fulton
Position: General Secretary
Activities: Central body, newsletter/journal
Traditions: Presbyterian
Affiliations: Action of Churches Together in Scotland; Churches Together in Britain and Ireland; World Council of Churches

United Reformed Church Synod of Scotland*

PO Box 189, Glasgow G1 9BX
Tel: (0141) 332 7667 **Fax:** (0141) 332 8463
Email: scotland@urc.org.uk
Contact: Revd Kenneth Forbes
Position: Synod Clerk

CHURCH REGIONAL BODIES

CHURCH OF SCOTLAND PRESBYTERIES

Church of Scotland Aberdeen Presbytery*

c/o Mastrick Church, Greenfern Road, Aberdeen AB21 9QU
Tel: (01224) 690494 **Fax:** (01224) 690494
Email: aberdeen@dial.pipex.com
Website: http://www.presbaberdeen.org.uk/
Contact: Revd Andrew M Douglas
Position: Presbytery Clerk
Activities: Central body
Traditions: Presbyterian

Church of Scotland Abernethy Presbytery*

The Manse, Nethy Bridge PH25 3DG
Tel: (01479) 821280 **Fax:** (01479) 821280
Email: manse@nethybridge.freeserve.co.uk
Contact: Revd James A I MacEwan
Position: Presbytery Clerk
Activities: Central body
Traditions: Presbyterian

Church of Scotland Angus Presbytery*

Presbytery Office, St Margaret's Church, West High Street, Forfar DD8 1BJ
Tel: (01302) 464224 **Fax:** (01302) 465589
Email: anguspresbytery@dial.pipex.com
Contact: Presbytery Clerk

Church of Scotland Annandale and Eskdale Presbytery

The Manse, Gretna Green DG16 5DU
Tel: (01461) 338313
Contact: Rev C Bryan Haston
Position: Presbytery Clerk
Traditions: Presbyterian

Church of Scotland Ardrossan Presbytery*

St Columba's Manse, Kilbirnie KA25 7JU
Tel: (01505) 683342 **Fax:** (01505) 684024
Email: pres@davbros.demon.co.uk
Website: http://www.davbros.demon.co.uk/
Contact: Revd David Broster
Position: Presbytery Clerk
Activities: Worship/practice/meditation, youth, elderly, women, inter-faith
Traditions: Presbyterian

Church of Scotland Buchan Presbytery*

The Manse, Hatton, Peterhead AB42 0QQ
Tel: (01779) 841229 **Fax:** (01779) 841822
Email: buchan@dial.pipex.com
Contact: Revd Rodger Neilson
Position: Presbytery Clerk
Activities: Central body
Traditions: Presbyterian

Church of Scotland Caithness Presbytery*

Ardachadh, Halladale, Forsinard, Sutherland KW13 6YT
Tel: (01641) 571241 **Fax:** (01641) 571288
Email: myrtle.gillies@btinternet.com
Contact: Myrtle A Gillies
Position: Presbytery Clerk
Traditions: Presbyterian

Church of Scotland Dumbarton Presbytery*

14 Birch Road, Killearn, Glasgow G63 9SQ
Tel: (01360) 550098 **Fax:** (01360) 551198
Email: dmunro@dial.pipex.com
Contact: Revd David P Munro
Position: Presbytery Clerk
Traditions: Presbyterian

Church of Scotland Dumfries and Kirkcudbright Presbytery*

11 Laurieknowe, Dumfries DG2 7AH
Tel: (01387) 252929 **Fax:** (01387) 252929
Contact: Revd Gordon M A Savage

Position: Presbytery Clerk
Activities: Central body
Traditions: Presbyterian

Church of Scotland Dundee Presbytery*
Presbytery Office, Nicoll's Lane, Dundee
DD2 3HG
Tel: (01382) 611415
Contact: James A Roy
Position: Presbytery Clerk

Church of Scotland Dunfermline Presbytery*
Townhill Manse, Dunfermline KY12 0EZ
Tel: (01383) 723835 **Fax:** (01383) 723835
Email: dunfpres@dial.pipex.com
Contact: Revd William Farquhar
Position: Presbytery Clerk
Activities: Central body
Traditions: Presbyterian

Church of Scotland Dunoon Presbytery*
9 Bishop Terrace, Rothesay, Isle of Bute PA20 9HF
Tel: (01700) 504378 **Fax:** (01700) 504378
Email: ronaldd.samuel@ukgateway.net
Contact: Revd Ronald Samuel

Church of Scotland Duns Presbytery*
The Manse, Coldstream Guards, TN12 4DP
Tel: (01890) 882537
Contact: Mr Cutler
Position: Presbytery Clerk
Traditions: Presbyterian

Church of Scotland Edinburgh Presbytery*
10 Palmerston Place, Edinburgh EH12 5AA
Tel: (0131) 2259137
Email: peter.graham@dial.pipex.com
Contact: Revd W Peter Graham
Position: Presbytery Clerk
Activities: Central body
Traditions: Presbyterian

Church of Scotland Falkirk Presbytery*
Zetland Manse, Ronaldshay Crescent,
Grangemouth FK3 9JH
Tel: (01324) 471656
Email: gni53@dial.pipex.com
Website: http://www.falkirkp.dabsol.co.uk/
Contact: Revd I W Black
Position: Presbytery Clerk
Activities: Central body, youth, elderly, women,
inter-faith
Traditions: Presbyterian

Church of Scotland Glasgow Presbytery*
260 Bath Street, Glasgow G2 4JP
Tel: (0141) 3326606 **Fax:** (0141) 3326606
Email: coss.glasgow.presbytery@dial.pipex.com
Contact: Revd Alex Cunningham
Position: Presbytery Clerk
Activities: Worship, resource, media, youth, elderly,
women, newsletter
Traditions: Presbyterian
Other Languages: Gaelic, German, South Korean

Church of Scotland Gordon Presbytery*
The Manse, 26 St Ninians, Monymusk AB51 7HF
Email: gordonpresb@dial.pipex.com
Contact: Revd Euan Glen
Position: Presbytery Clerk
Contact Tel: (01467) 651470
Activities: Worship/practice/meditation, central
body, umbrella body, youth, elderly, women, inter-
faith
Traditions: Presbyterian

Church of Scotland Greenock Presbytery*
105 Newark Street, Greenock PA16 7TW
Tel: (01475) 639602
Contact: Revd David Mill
Position: Presbytery Clerk
Activities: Inter-faith
Traditions: Presbyterian

Church of Scotland Hamilton Presbytery*
Presbytery Office, 18 Haddow Street, Hamilton
ML3 7HX
Tel: (01698) 286837 **Fax:** (01698) 457258
Email: clerk@presbyteryofhamilton.co.uk
Website: http://www.presbyteryofhamilton.co.uk/
Contact: Revd James H Wilson
Position: Presbytery Clerk
Activities: Central body
Traditions: Presbyterian

Church of Scotland Irvine and Kilmarnock Presbytery*
51 Portland Road, Kilmarnock KA1 2EQ
Contact: Revd Coline G F Brockie
Position: Presbytery Clerk
Activities: Worship, resource, youth, elderly,
women, newsletter
Traditions: Presbyterian

Church of Scotland Jedburgh Presbytery*
The Manse, Newcastleton TD9 0QX
Tel: (013873) 75242
Email: jedburghpresbytery@dial.pipex.com

Contact: Revd Alan D Reid
Position: Presybtery Clerk
Activities: Worship/practice/meditation, central body
Traditions: Presbyterian
Affiliations: World Alliance of Reformed Churches

Church of Scotland Kincardine and Deeside Presbytery*

Aboyne Dinnet Parish Church, Huntly Road, Aboyne AB34 5HH
Tel: (01339) 886989
Email: aboynedinnetcos@freezone.co.uk
Contact: Revd David J Devenney
Position: Presbytery Clerk
Activities: Worship/practice/meditation, youth, elderly, women, newsletter/journal, visits
Traditions: Presbyterian

Church of Scotland Lanark Presbytery*

c/o The Manse,61 High Street, Biggar ML8 5AA
Tel: (01899) 220227 **Fax:** (01899) 220227
Email: biggarkirk@biggar-net.co.uk
Contact: RevdGavin Elliott
Position: Presbytery Clerk
Contact Tel: (01899) 220227
Traditions: Presbyterian

Church of Scotland Lewis Presbytery*

Martin's Memorial Manse, Matheson Road, Stornoway HS1
Tel: (01851) 702206
Email: gof39@dial.pipex.com
Contact: Revd T S Sinclair
Position: Presbytery Clerk
Traditions: Presbyterian

Church of Scotland Lochaber Presbytery*

26 Riverside Park, Lochyside, Fort William PH33 7RB
Tel: (01397) 702054
Email: aramsay@dial.pipex.com
Website: http://www.cofslochaber.f9.co.uk/
Contact: Revd Alan Ramsay
Position: Presbytery Clerk
Activities: Central body
Traditions: Presbyterian
Affiliations: World Alliance of Reformed Churches

Church of Scotland Lochcarron and Skye Presbytery*

High Barn, Croft Road, Lochcarron, Strathcarron IV54 8YA

Tel: (01520) 722278 **Fax:** (01520) 722674
Email: a.macarthur@btinternet.com
Contact: Revd Allan I MacArthur
Position: Presbytery Clerk
Activities: Central body, umbrella body
Traditions: Presbyterian
Other Languages: Gaelic

Church of Scotland Lorn and Mull Presbytery*

Ardchtran Manse, North Connel, Argyll PA67 1QZ
Tel: (01631) 710364
Contact: Jesse McCormack
Position: Presbytery Clerk

Church of Scotland Melrose and Peebles Presbytery*

St Aidan's Manse, High Road, Galashiels TD1 2BD
Tel: (01896) 752420
Contact: Revd Jack M Brown
Position: Presbytery Clerk
Activities: Central body
Traditions: Presbyterian

Church of Scotland Moray Presbytery*

The Manse, 3 Seafield Place, Cullen AB56 4UU
Tel: (01542) 841851 **Fax:** (01542) 841991
Email: melvynwood@cullenmanse.freeserve.co.uk
Website: http://www.moraypresbytery.org.uk/
Contact: Revd G Melvyn Wood
Position: Presbytery Clerk
Activities: Central body
Traditions: Presbyterian

Church of Scotland Orkney Presbytery*

Finstown Manse, Finstown, Orkney KW17 2EG
Tel: (01856) 761328 **Fax:** (01856) 761328
Email: presb.orkney@dial.pipex.com
Contact: Revd Trevor G Hunt
Position: Presbytery Clerk
Traditions: Presbyterian

Church of Scotland Paisley Presbytery*

6 Southfield Avenue, Paisley PA2 8BY
Tel: (0141) 8843600 **Fax:** (0141) 8843600
Email: gmw86@dial.pipex.com
Contact: Revd David Kay
Position: Presbytery Clerk
Activities: Umbrella body
Traditions: Presbyterian

Church of Scotland Perth Presbytery*

209 High Street, Perth PH1 5PB
Email: perth@dial.pipex.com
Contact: Revd Derek G Lawson
Position: Presbytery Clerk

Contact Tel: (01738) 828247
Traditions: Presbyterian

Church of Scotland Ross Presbytery*
Contin Manse, Contin, Strathpeffer IV14 9ES
Tel: (01997) 421380
Contact: Revd T M McWilliam
Position: Presbytery Clerk
Traditions: Presbyterian

Church of Scotland South Argyll Presbytery*
Tigh-Na-Coille, Ardrishaig, Argyll PA30 8EP
Tel: (01546) 603454 Fax: (01546) 603454
Email: gossip@dial.pipex.com
Contact: Mr Michael Arthur John Gossip
Position: Presbytery Clerk
Activities: Worship/practice/meditation, central
body, youth, elderly, women
Traditions: Presbyterian
Other Languages: Gaelic

Church of Scotland St Andrews Presbytery*
7 Lorraine Drive, Cupar KY15 5DY
Fax: (01334) 656991
Contact: Revd Peter Meager
Position: Presbytery Clerk
Contact Tel: (01334) 656991
Contact Email: st.andrews.clerk@dial.pipex.com
Activities: Central body
Traditions: Presbyterian
Affiliations: World Council of Churches

Church of Scotland Sutherland Presbytery*
The Manse, Lairg, Sutherland IV27 4EH
Tel: (01549) 402373
Contact: Revd J L Goskirk
Position: Presbytery Clerk
Traditions: Presbyterian

Church of Scotland Uist Presbytery*
The Manse, Scarista, Isle Of Harris HS3 3HZ
Tel: (01870) 602180
Contact: Murdo Smith
Position: Presbytery Clerk
Activities: Resource, umbrella body
Traditions: Presbyterian
Other Languages: Gaelic

Church of Scotland West Lothian Presbytery*
St John's Manse, Mid Street, Bathgate EH48 1QD
Contact: Revd Duncan Shaw
Position: Presbytery Clerk
Contact Tel: (01506) 653146
Activities: Worship
Traditions: Presbyterian

**Church of Scotland Wigtown and Stranraer
Presbytery**
High Kirk Manse, Leswalt High Road, Stranraer
DG9 0AA
Tel: (01776) 854225
Contact: Revd D W Dutton
Position: Presbytery Clerk
Traditions: Presbyterian

METHODIST DISTRICTS

**Methodist Church in Scotland Edinburgh
District***
Methodist Central Hall, West Tollcross, Edinburgh
EH3 9BT
Tel: (0131) 2219029 Fax: (0131) 2219029
Email: edinmethodistmission@talk21.com
Contact: Revd David Cooper
Activities: Worship/practice/meditation,
community centre, central body, youth, elderly,
women, visits
Traditions: Free Church

Methodist Church Shetland District*
Wesley Manse, 9 Hillhead, Lerwick ZE1 0EJ
Tel: (01595) 692874 Fax: (01595) 692874
Email: richard.bielby@lineone.net
Contact: Revd Richard Bielby
Position: Chairman
Activities: Umbrella body
Traditions: Free Church

ROMAN CATHOLIC DIOCESES

Roman Catholic Archdiocese of Glasgow*
Curial Offices, 196 Clyde Street, Glasgow G1 4JY
Tel: (0141) 2265898 Fax: (0141) 2252600
Email: curia@rcag.org.uk
Website: http://www.rcag.org.uk/
Contact: The Chancellor
Contact Email: chancellor@rcag.org.uk
Activities: Resource, media, youth, newsletters,
inter-faith
Traditions: Roman Catholic

**Roman Catholic Archdiocese of St Andrews and
Edinburgh***
Diocesan Offices, Gillis Centre, 113 Whitehouse
Loan, Edinburgh EH9 1BB
Tel: (0131) 4528244 Fax: (0131) 4529153
Contact: Archdiocesan Secretary
Activities: Worship, resource, media, umbrella
body, visits, youth

Roman Catholic Diocese of Aberdeen*

Bishop's House, 3 Queen's Cross, Aberdeen
AB15 4XU
Tel: (01224) 319154 **Fax:** (01224) 325570
Email: bishopconti@hotmail.com
Contact: Bishop Mario Joseph Conti
Position: Bishop
Traditions: Roman Catholic

Roman Catholic Diocese of Argyll and the Isles*

Bishop's House, Esplanade, Oban PA34 5AB
Tel: (01631)571395 **Fax:** (01631) 564986
Email: bip.arg@virgin.net.
Contact: Bishop

Roman Catholic Diocese of Dunkeld*

Diocesan Centre, 24-28 Lawside Road, Dundee
DD3 6XY
Contact: Revd Michael Milton
Position: Chancellor
Contact Tel: (01382) 225453
Activities: Central body, youth, elderly, women,
newsletter/journal, resources
Traditions: Roman Catholic

Roman Catholic Diocese of Galloway*

8 Corsehill Road, Ayr KA7 2ST
Tel: (01292) 266750 **Fax:** (01292) 266750
Email: stninian@globalnet.co.uk
Website: http://www.gallowaydiocese.i12.com/
Contact: Rt Revd Maurice Taylor
Position: Bishop
Activities: Central body, umbrella body, youth,
elderly, women, newsletter/journal, inter-faith,
resources
Traditions: Roman Catholic
Affiliations: Bishops' Conference of Scotland

Roman Catholic Diocese of Motherwell*

Diocesan Centre, Coursington Road, Motherwell
ML1 1PP
Tel: (01698) 269114 **Fax:** (01698) 275630
Email: chancellor@dioceseofmotherwell.co.uk
Contact: Mr Frank Cassidy
Position: Chancellor
Activities: Central body
Traditions: Roman Catholic
Affiliations: Scottish Catholic Conference of
Bishops

Roman Catholic Diocese of Paisley*

Diocesan Offices, 6 Kilmacolm Road, Greenock
PA15 4XP
Tel: (01475) 892143 **Fax:** (01475) 892146

Email: diocesanoffice@paisleydiocese.org.uk
Website: http://www.paisleydiocese.org.uk/
Contact: Bishop John A Mone
Position: Bishop
Activities: Central body
Traditions: Roman Catholic

SALVATION ARMY DIVISIONS

Salvation Army Northern Ireland Division*

12 Station Mews, Sydenham, Belfast BT4 1TL
Tel: (028) 9067 5000 **Fax:** (028) 9067 5011
Contact: George A Pilkington
Position: Divisional Commander
Activities: Youth, elderly, women, newsletters,
books
Traditions: Free Church

SCOTTISH EPISCOPAL CHURCH

Scottish Episcopal Church Diocese of Aberdeen & Orkney*

Diocesan Office, 39 King's Crescent, Aberdeen
AB24 3HP
Tel: (01224) 636653 **Fax:** (01224) 636186
Email: office@aberdeen.anglican.org
Contact: Mrs Sue Pike
Position: Bishop's Secretary
Activities: Worship/practice/meditation, central
body, youth, elderly, women, newsletter/journal,
inter-faith, resources
Traditions: Anglican
Affiliations: Regional Ecumenical Team, Anglican
Communion

Scottish Episcopal Church Diocese of Argyll & The Isles*

The Pines, Ardconnel Road, Oban PA34 5DR
Tel: (01631) 566912 **Fax:** (01631) 566912
Contact: Douglas Cameron
Position: Bishop
Traditions: Anglican

Scottish Episcopal Church Diocese of Brechin*

Diocesan Centre, Pine Grove, 334 Perth Road,
Dundee DD2 1EQ
Tel: (01382) 640007
Email: office@brechin.anglican.org
Traditions: Anglican

Scottish Episcopal Church Diocese of Edinburgh*

Diocesan Centre, 21a Grosvenor Crescent,
Edinburgh EH12 5EL
Tel: (0131) 5387033 **Fax:** (0131) 5387088

Contact: Elizabeth A Brady
Position: Diocesan Secretary
Traditions: Anglican

Scottish Episcopal Church Diocese of Glasgow and Galloway*

Diocesan Office, St Vincent Place, Glasgow
G1 2DH
Tel: (0141) 2215720 **Fax:** (0141) 2217014
Contact: The Diocesan Secretary
Activities: Resource, newsletters, inter-faith
Traditions: Anglican

Scottish Episcopal Church Diocese of Moray, Ross and Caithness*

11 Kenneth Street, Inverness IV3 5NR
Tel: (01463) 226255 **Fax:** (01463) 226255
Email: office@moray.anglican.org
Contact: Rt Revd J Crook
Position: Bishop
Activities: Resource, youth, elderly, women, newsletters, inter-faith
Traditions: Anglican
Other Languages: Gaelic

UNITED REFORMED CHURCH AREA COUNCILS

Scottish United Reformed Church East Scotland Area Council

'Kerrlynn', Eyemouth Road, Coldingham, Berwickshire EH54 6PR

Scottish United Reformed Church Glasgow Area Council

Flat 4/1, 74 Woodside Road, Glasgow, G4 9HG

Scottish United Reformed Church Mid Scotland Area Council

77 Glan Lednock Drive, Craigmarloch, Cumbernauld G68 8ED

Scottish United Reformed Church Northern Area Council*

20 Forvie Circle, Bridge of Don, Aberdeen
AB22 8TA
Traditions: Free Church

Scottish United Reformed Church West Scotland Area Council

150 West Princes Street, Helensburgh G84

Scottish United Reformed Church Solway Area Council

6 Greenlea Road, Annan DG12 5LB

OTHER SCOTTISH BODIES

Churches' Agency for Inter-Faith Relations in Scotland (CAIRS)*

326 West Princes Street, Glasgow G4 9HA
Tel: (0141) 3398174
Email: ismyth@bigfoot.com
Contact: Sister Isabel Smyth
Position: Secretary
Activities: Umbrella body, inter-faith, resources
Traditions: Ecumenical/Interdenominational
Affiliations: Inter Faith Network for the UK;
Action of Churches Together in Scotland

Evangelical Alliance Scotland*

Challenge House 29 Canal Street, Glasgow
G4 0AD
Tel: (0141) 3228700 **Fax:** (0141) 3228700
Email: scotland@eauk.org
Website: http://www.eauk.org/
Contact: Revd David J B Anderson
Position: General Secretary
Activities: Umbrella body, newsletter/journal, books, radio, television, resources
Traditions: Evangelical
Affiliations: World Evangelical Fellowship

Fellowship of Reconciliation Scotland

The Manse, Kirkton of Airlie, Kirriemuir Angus
DD8 5NL
Tel: (01575) 530245
Contact: Robert J Ramsey
Position: Chair
Activities: Resource, visits, newsletters, inter-faith
Traditions: All Christian Denominations

Iona Community*

840 Govan Road, Govan, Glasgow G51 3UU
Tel: (0141) 4454561 **Fax:** (0141) 4454295
Email: ionacomm@gia.iona.org.uk
Website: http://www.iona.org.uk/
Contact: Revd Norman Shanks
Position: Leader
Activities: Worship/practice/meditation, central body, youth, elderly, women, newsletter/journal, books, visits, inter-faith, resources
Traditions: Ecumenical/Interdenominational
Affiliations: Action of Churches Together in Scotland; National Association of Christian Communities and Networks; United Nations Associations

WALES

WELSH ECUMENICAL INSTRUMENTS

CYTUN: Churches Together in Wales (Eglwysi Ynghyd Yng Nghymru)*

11 St Helen's Road, Swansea SA1 4AL
Tel: (01792) 460876 **Fax:** (01792) 469391
Email: anyname@cytun.freeserve.co.uk
Website: http://www.cytun.freeserve.co.uk/
Contact: Revd Gethin Abraham-Williams
Position: General Secretary
Activities: Umbrella body, visits, newsletter, books, resources
Traditions: Ecumenical/Interdenominational
Other Languages: Welsh

Full Members:
Churches and Denominations with Headquarters in Wales:Eglwys Bresbyteraidd Cymru (Presbyterian Church of Wales)
Eglwys Yng Nghymru (Church in Wales)
Undeb Bedyddwyr Cymru (Baptist Union of Wales)
Undeb Yr Annibynwyr Cymraeg (Union of Welsh Independents)

Churches and Denominations with Headquarters in England:
Byddin Yr Iachawriaeth (Salvation Army)
Cymdeithas Grefyddol Y Cyfeillion (Religious Society of Friends)
Eglwys Ddiwyiedig Unedig (United Reformed Church)
Eglwysi Cyfamodol Uned Bedyddwyr Prydain (Baptist Union of Great Britain Covenanted Churches)
Eglwys Fethodistaidd (Methodist Church)
Eglwys Gatholig Rufeinig (Roman Catholic Church)
Y Gynghrair Gynulleidfaol (Congregational Federation)

Observers:
Eglwys Adfentaidd Y Seithfed Dydd (Seventh Day Adventist Church)
Eglwys Liwtheraidd (Lutheran Church)
Yr Eglwys Uniongred (Orthodox Church)

ENFYS - Covenanted Churches in Wales (Eglwysi Cyfamodol Yng Nghymru)*

25 Talbot Road, Wrexham LL13 7DY
Tel: (01978) 354448 **Fax:** (01978) 354448
Email: sionaled@prifardd.fsnet.co.uk
Website: http://www.prifardd.fsnet.co.uk/
Contact: Dr Sion Aled Owen
Position: General Secretary
Activities: Umbrella body, newsletter/journal, books
Traditions: Ecumenical/Interdenominational
Other Languages: Welsh
Affiliations: Cytun (Churches Together in Wales); Churches Together in Britain and Ireland; World Council of Churches

Bodies covenanted together:
Eglwys Bresbyteraidd Cymru (Presbyterian Church of Wales)
Eglwys Ddiwygiedig Unedig (United reformed Church)
Eglwys Fethodistaidd (Methodist Church)
Eglwys Yng Nghymru (Church in Wales)
Yr Eglwysi Bedyddiedig Cyfamodol yng Nghymru (Covenanted Baptist Churches)

Free Church Council for Wales (Cyngor Eglwysi Rhyddion Cymru)*

18 Lon y Wennol, Llanfairpwll LL61 5JX
Tel: (01248) 715402
Email: harri@lonywennol.fsnet.co.uk
Contact: Revd Harri Owen
Position: Secretary
Activities: Umbrella body
Traditions: Ecumenical/Interdenominational
Other Languages: Welsh

Member Bodies:
Byddin Yr Iachawdriaeth (Salvation Army)
Eglwys Bresbyterraid Cymru (Presbyterian Church of Wales)
Eglwys Fethodistaidd (Methodist Church)
Undeb Beddyddwr Cymru (Baptist Union of Wales)
Undeb Bedyddwr Prydain (Baptist Union of Great Britain)
Undeb Yr Annibynwyr Cymraeg (Union of Welsh Independents)
Y Cyngraiu Gynwelleidfaol (Congregational Federation)
Yr Eglwys Unedig Ddiwygiedig (United Reformed Church)

CHURCHES OPERATING AT A WELSH LEVEL

Baptist Union of Wales (Undeb Bedyddwr Cymru)*
Ilston House 94 Mansel Street, Swansea SA1 5TZ
Tel: (01792) 655468 **Fax:** (01792) 469489
Email: peter@15penmean15.freeserve.co.uk
Website: http://www.welshbaptists.com/
Contact: Revd Peter Dewi Richards
Position: General Secretary
Contact Tel: (01269) 592848
Contact Email:
peter@denmaen15.freeserve.co.uk
Activities: Worship/practice/meditation, central
body, elderly, women, newsletter/journal, resources
Traditions: Free Church
Other Languages: Welsh
Affiliations: Free Church Council for Wales;
European Federation of Baptists; World Baptisit
Alliance; Churches Together in Wales (Cytun)

Church in Wales (Eglwys Yng Nghymru)*
39 Cathedral Road, Cardiff CF11 9XF
Tel: (029) 2034 8200 **Fax:** (029) 2038 7835
Email: information@churchinwales.org.uk
Website: http://www.churchinwales.org.uk/
Contact: Mr David Llewellyn
Position: Information Co-ordinator
Activities: Worship/practice/meditation, umbrella
body, youth, elderly, women
Traditions: Anglican
Other Languages: Welsh
Affiliations: CYTUN Churches Together in
Wales; Council of Churches for Britain and Ireland;
Anglican Consultative Council

Church of the Holy Protection*
11 Manod Road, Blaenau Ffestiniog LL41 4DE
Tel: (01766) 831272 **Fax:** (01766) 831272
Contact: The Very Revd Father Deiniol
Position: Administrator
Activities: Worship, central body, youth, books,
visits, resources
Traditions: Orthodox
Other Languages: Welsh, Greek, Old Church
Slavonic
Affiliations: Belarusian Autocephalous Orthodox
Church

Congregational Federation in Wales (Gynghrair Gynulleidfaol)*
Crosslyn, Spittal, Haverfordwest SA62 5QT
Tel: (01437) 741260 **Fax:** (01437) 741566
Email: tabernacle@haverfordwest.freeserve.co.uk

Website:
http://www.haverfordwest.freeserve.co.uk/cfwales
Contact: Revd Christopher Gillham
Position: Secretary
Activities: Central body, youth, elderly, women,
newsletter/journal
Traditions: Congregational
Affiliations: CYTUN - Churches Together in
Wales; CWM

Covenanted Baptist Churches in Wales (Yr Eglwysi Bedyddiedig Cyfamodol Yng Nghymru)*
3 Edith Road, Dinas Powys CF64 4AD
Tel: (029) 2051 4630 **Fax:** (029) 2051 4630
Contact: Revd J M Garland
Position: Chairman
Contact Tel: (029) 2051 4630
Contact Email: jmgarland@freenet.co.uk
Activities: Umbrella body
Traditions: Free Church
Affiliations: ENFYS - The Commission of the
Covenanted Churches in Wales

General Assembly of Unitarian and Free Christian Churches South East Wales Society
10 Tan y Lan Terrace, Morriston, Swansea
SA6 7DU
Tel: (01792) 794542
Contact: Revd E W Phillips
Position: Secretary

Lutheran Church Wales (Yr Eglwys Liwtheraidd)
32 Heol-y-Felin, Rhiwbina, Cardiff CF4 6NT
Tel: (029) 2061 6481
Contact: Revd H Volker
Position: Minister
Activities: Elderly, women, newsletters, inter-faith
Other Languages: German

Methodist Church*
Heulfryn, Barmouth Road, Dolgellau LL40 2YT
Tel: (01341) 422524 **Fax:** (01341) 422524
Email: slattery@heulfryn50.freeserve.co.uk
Website: http://www.westwales.co.uk/methodism
Contact: Revd Patrick Slattery
Position: Secretary
Activities: Umbrella body, newsletter/journal,
inter-faith
Traditions: Ecumenical/Interdenominational
Other Languages: Welsh

Presbyterian Church of Wales (Eglwys Bresbyteraidd Cymru)*
53 Richmond Road, Cardiff CF24 3WJ
Tel: (029) 2049 4913 **Fax:** (029) 2046 4293
Email: ebcpcw@aol.com
Website: http://www.ebcpcw.org.uk/
Contact: Revd W Gareth Edwards
Position: General Secretary
Activities: Worship/practice/meditation, community centre, central body, youth, elderly, women, newsletter/journal, books, newspapers, visits, resources
Traditions: Presbyterian
Other Languages: Welsh
Affiliations: CYTUN - Churches Together in Wales; Council of Churches for Britain and Ireland; Council for World Mission

Seventh Day Adventists Church (Welsh Mission)
Glan Yr Afon, 10 Heol Y Wen, Caerphilly CF3 3EY
Tel: (029) 2088 2097
Email: 100527.3046@compuserve.co
Contact: John Charles Surridge
Position: Communications Director
Activities: Worship, resource, visits, youth, elderly, women
Traditions: Evangelical
Other Languages: Spanish, Ghanaian

Union of Welsh Independents (Undeb yr Annibynwyr Cymraeg)
Y John Penry, 11 St Helen's Road, Swansea SA1 4AL
Tel: (01792) 650647 **Fax:** (01792) 650647
Contact: Revd Derwyn Morris Jones
Position: General Secretary
Traditions: Ecumenical
Other Languages: Welsh

United Reformed Church, National Synod of Wales*
Minster Road, Roath, Cardiff CF23 5AS
Tel: (029) 2049 9938
Email: admin@urcwales.org.uk
Website: http://www.urcwales.org.uk/
Contact: Mr Geoff Griffiths
Position: Synod Clerk
Activities: Central body, newsletter/journal
Traditions: United Reformed Church
Other Languages: Wales
Affiliations: CYTUN Churches Together in Wales

CHURCH REGIONAL BODIES

ASSEMBLIES OF GOD REGIONS

Assemblies of God South Wales Office
Cwmbran Christian Centre, Bellevue Road, Cwmbran NP44 3LF
Tel: (01663) 483335
Email: swregionorg@aol.com
Contact: Revd Phillipps
Position: Administrator
Traditions: Pentecostal

BAPTIST UNION AREAS

Anglesey Baptist Association*
Tyn Llwyn, Paradwys, Llangristiolus, Anglesey LL62 5PG
Tel: (01248) 724400
Contact: Mr Arnold Milburn
Traditions: Free Church
Other Languages: Welsh

Arfon Baptist Association*
Ael y Bryn, Chwilog, Pwllheli LL53 6SH
Tel: (01766) 810092
Contact: Revd Dafydd Aled Davies
Position: Secretary
Traditions: Free Church

Baptist Union of Great Britain South Wales Area*
19 Melrose Close, St Mellons, Cardiff CF3 9SW
Tel: (029) 2079 5919 **Fax:** (029) 2079 5919
Email: peter@manson.f9.co.uk
Contact: Peter D Manson
Position: General Superintendent
Activities: Umbrella body
Traditions: Free Church

Baptist Union of Wales (Undeb Bedyddwr Cymru)*
Ilston House 94 Mansel Street, Swansea SA1 5TZ
Tel: (01792) 655468 **Fax:** (01792) 469489
Email: peter@15penmean15.freeserve.co.uk
Website: http://www.welshbaptists.com/
Contact: Revd Peter Dewi Richards
Position: General Secretary
Contact Tel: (01269) 592848
Contact Email: peter@denmaen15.freeserve.co.uk
Activities: Worship/practice/meditation, central body, elderly, women, newsletter/journal, resources

Traditions: Free Church
Other Languages: Welsh
Affiliations: Free Church Council for Wales;
European Federation of Baptists; World Baptist
Alliance; Churches Together in Wales (Cytun)

Carmarthenshire and Cardiganshire Baptist Association*
Llwynrhosyn, Maesycrugiau, Pencader SA39 9DH
Tel: (01559) 395438
Contact: Revd Wynn Vittle
Position: Secretary
Traditions: Free Church

East Glamorgan Welsh Baptist Association*
17 Ivor Terrace, Dowlais CF48 3SW
Tel: (01685) 377896
Contact: Revd Eifion Wynne
Traditions: Free Church

Gwent (Welsh) Baptist Association*
9 Colin Way, Ely, Cardiff CF5 5AJ
Tel: (029) 2057 5380
Email: itutton@aol.com
Contact: Revd Ian Tutton
Position: Secretary
Traditions: Free Church

Pembrokeshire (Welsh) Baptist Association*
Morawel, 78 Heol Fawr, Abergwaun, Fishguard
SA65 9AU
Contact: Revd David Carl Williams
Position: Secretary
Contact Tel: (01348) 872190
Activities: Worship/practice/meditation
Other Languages: Welsh
Affiliations: Baptist Union of Wales

Pembrokeshire Baptist Association (English Wing)*
50 Whitlow, Saundersfoot SA69 9AU
Tel: (01834) 813750 **Fax:** (01834) 813750
Email: dfgpusey@aol.com
Contact: Revd Dr D F G Pusey
Position: Secretary
Activities: Worship/practice/meditation
Traditions: Free Church
Affiliations: Baptist Unions Of Wales and Great
Britain.

Radnor and Montgomery Baptist Association*
Arosfa, Hillfield, Llanidloes SY18 6ET
Tel: (01686) 412452
Contact: Meredith Powell
Position: Secretary

South Wales Baptist Association (BUGB)*
126A Heol Uchaf, Rhiwbina, Cardiff CF14 6SS
Tel: (029) 2069 2175 **Fax:** (029) 2069 2175
Contact: Mrs Diane Tyson
Position: Administrator

West Glamorgan (Welsh) Baptist Association*
Little West, Southerndown CF32 0PY
Tel: (01656) 880022
Contact: Revd D E Miles
Position: Secretary
Traditions: Free Church

CHURCH IN WALES DIOCESES

Church in Wales Diocese of Bangor*
Diocesan Office, Cathedral Close, Bangor
LL57 1RL
Tel: (01248) 354999 **Fax:** (01248) 353882
Contact: Stella Schultz
Position: Diocesan Secretary
Activities: Central body
Traditions: Anglican
Other Languages: Welsh

Church in Wales Diocese of Llandaff*
Board for Social Responsibility, Heol Fair, Llandaff
CF5 2EE
Tel: (029) 2057 8899 **Fax:** (029) 0205 6198
Email:
garethfoster.dbf.llandaff@churchinwales.org.uk
Contact: Gareth Foster
Position: Executive Officer
Activities: Central body, youth, women,
newsletter/journal, inter-faith, resources
Traditions: Anglican
Other Languages: Welsh

Church in Wales Diocese of Monmouth*
64 Caerau Road, Newport NP20 4HJ
Tel: (01633) 267490 **Fax:** (01633) 265586
Contact: Richard John Tarran
Position: Secretary
Activities: Umbrella body
Traditions: Anglican
Other Languages: Welsh

Church in Wales Diocese of St Asaph*
Escrobty, St Asaph LL17 0RL
Tel: (01745) 583503 **Fax:** (01745) 584301
Email: bishop.stasaph@churchinwales.org.uk
Contact: Rt Revd John Stewart
Position: Bishop
Activities: Worship/practice/meditation, central

body, youth, elderly, women, newsletter/journal, visits, resources
Traditions: Anglican
Other Languages: Welsh
Affiliations: Churches Together in Wales; Churches Together in Britain and Ireland; World Council of Churches

Church in Wales Diocese of St Davids*
Diocesan Office, Abergwili, Carmarthen SA31 2JG
Tel: (01267) 236145
Contact: Mr D Vincent Lloyd
Position: Diocesan Secretary
Traditions: Anglican

Church in Wales Diocese of Swansea and Brecon*
Swansea and Brecon Diocesan Centre, Cathedral Close, Brecon LD3 9DP
Tel: (01874) 623716 **Fax:** (01874) 623716
Contact: Heather Price
Position: Diocesan Secretary
Activities: Central body, visits, youth, elderly, women, newsletters
Traditions: Anglican
Other Languages: Welsh

CONGREGATIONAL FEDERATION AREAS

Congregational Federation in Wales (Gynghrair Gynulleidfaol)*
Crosslyn, Spittal, Haverfordwest SA62 5QT
Tel: (01437) 741260 **Fax:** (01437) 741566
Email: tabernacle@haverfordwest.freeserve.co.uk
Website:
http://www.haverfordwest.freeserve.co.uk/cfwales
Contact: Revd Christopher Gillham
Position: Secretary
Activities: Central body, youth, elderly, women, newsletter/journal
Traditions: Congregational
Affiliations: CYTUN - Churches Together in Wales; CWM

METHODIST DISTRICTS

Methodist Church in Wales, Cymru District*
Heulfryn, Ffordd Tyn-y-Coed, Dolgellau
LL40 2YT
Tel: (01341) 422524
Contact: Chair of District
Other Languages: Welsh

Methodist Church North Wales District*
Abbey View, Pant Lane, Gresford, Wrexham
LL12 8HB
Tel: (01978) 852883 **Fax:** (01978) 852883
Email: methnwales@enterprise.net
Contact: Revd B Bircumshaw
Position: Chair
Activities: Central body, newsletter/journal, visits
Traditions: Free Church

Methodist Church South Wales District*
12 Llwyn-y-Grant Road, Cardiff CF23 9ET
Tel: (029) 2048 6751 **Fax:** (029) 2048 2006
Email: willmorrey@enterprise.net
Contact: Revd William R Morrey
Position: Chairman
Traditions: Free Church
Other Languages: Welsh

ROMAN CATHOLIC DIOCESES

Roman Catholic Archdiocese of Cardiff*
Archbishop's House, 41-43 Cathedral Road, Cardiff
CF11 9HD
Tel: (029) 2022 0411 **Fax:** (029) 2034 5950
Contact: Archbishop's Secretary
Activities: Worship, resource, media, umbrella body, newsletters, inter-faith
Other Languages: Welsh

Roman Catholic Diocese of Menevia*
Curial Office, 27 Convent Street, Swansea
SA1 2BX
Tel: (01792) 644017
Contact: Monsignor Clyde Hughes Johnson
Position: Chancellor
Activities: Worship, resource, women, newsletters, inter-faith
Other Languages: Welsh

Roman Catholic Diocese of Wrexham*
Bishop's House, Sontley Road, Wrexham
LL13 7EW
Contact: Mrs Coppack
Position: Secretary
Contact Tel: (01978) 262726
Contact Email: diowxm@globalnet.co.uk
Activities: Worship/practice/meditation, central body, umbrella body, youth, elderly, women, inter-faith, resources
Traditions: Roman Catholic
Other Languages: Welsh

SALVATION ARMY DIVISIONS

Salvation Army South and Mid Wales Division*
East Moors Road, Ocean Park, Cardiff CF24 5SA
Tel: (029) 2044 0601 **Fax:** (029) 2044 0611
Email: southmidwales@salvationarmy.org.uk
Contact: Major Michael Parker
Position: Divisional Commander
Contact Email:
michael.parker@salvationarmy.org.uk
Activities: Worship, resource, media, visits, youth,
elderly, women, newsletters, books
Traditions: Free Church, Holiness
Other Languages: Welsh

UNITARIAN AND FREE CHRISTIANS

South Wales Unitarian Association*
2 Morfa Gwyn House, Newquay SA45 9SB
Tel: (01545) 560995 **Fax:** (01545) 560940
Email: celticwaves@enterprise.net
Contact: Revd Alun-Wyn Dafis
Position: Secretary
Activities: Central body, umbella body, youth,
elderly, women, newsletter/journal, books,
newspapers, radio, television, visits, inter-faith,
resources
Traditions: Free Church
Other Languages: Welsh
Affiliations: General Assembly Welsh Department;
General Assembly of Unitarian and Free Christian
Churches; International Association for Religious
Freedom

OTHER WELSH BODIES

CAFOD Wales*
National Office, 11 Richmond Road, Roath,
Cardiff CF24 3AQ
Tel: (029) 2045 3360 **Fax:** (029) 2045 3360
Email: cafod@wales.org.uk
Contact: Mr Elfed Jones
Position: National Organiser
Activities: Youth, resources
Traditions: Roman Catholic
Other Languages: Welsh
Affiliations: CARITAS, CIDSE

Christians Against Torture*
25 Ronald Place, Ely, Cardiff CF5 4BJ
Tel: (029) 2065 9306 **Fax:** (029) 2065 9307
Email: efa.chwil@ntlworld.com
Website:

http://homepage.ntlworld.com/efa.chwil/cat/
Contact: Efa Wulle
Position: Co-ordinator
Activities: Resource, newsletters
Other Languages: Welsh

**Cymdeithas Y Cymod Yng Nghymru (Fellowship
of Reconciliation in Wales)***
Eglwys Noddfa, Lon Peblig, Caernarfon LL55 2RS
Tel: (01286) 676342
Contact: Miss Anna Jane Evans
Position: General Secretary
Contact Tel: (01286) 672257
Traditions: Ecumenical/Interdenominational
Other Languages: Welsh

Evangelical Alliance Wales*
20 High Street, Cardiff CF10 1PT
Tel: (029) 2022 9822 **Fax:** (029) 2022 9741
Email: cymru@eauk.org
Contact: Rev Elfed Godding
Position: General Secretary
Activities: Umbrella body, newsletter/journal
Traditions: Ecumenical/Interdenominational
Other Languages: Welsh

INTRODUCING HINDUS IN THE UK

HINDUS IN THE UNITED KINGDOM 297

ORIGINS AND DEVELOPMENT OF THE HINDU TRADITION 298

SOURCES OF HINDU BELIEFS AND PRACTICES 299

KEY HINDU BELIEFS 301

TRADITIONS IN HINDUISM 303

HINDU LIFE 305

HINDU WORSHIP 308

HINDU CALENDAR AND FESTIVALS 310

HINDU ORGANISATIONS 311

FURTHER READING 314

HINDUS IN THE UNITED KINGDOM

Migration

Small numbers of Hindus have visited and worked in the United Kingdom for centuries and the number of students and professionals increased greatly from the late nineteenth century onwards. However, it was not until the 1950s and 1960s that significant numbers of Hindus settled here. Some came to Britain directly from India. With the development of Africanisation policies in the newly independent African states, others came from the countries to which their foreparents had previously migrated, such as Kenya, Tanzania, Uganda, Zambia, and Malawi. Between 1965 and 1972 some of these came as economic migrants and others, especially those from Uganda, came seeking refuge from persecution.

Hindu migrants also came from Fiji, and from Trinidad and other Caribbean islands. Hindus are now settled in most large towns and cities in the UK. The largest Hindu communities are in Greater London (especially in Wembley and Harrow), Birmingham, Coventry and Leicester. This directory records around 131 Hindu places of worship in the UK.

Ethnic Composition

Between fifty-five and seventy per cent of Hindus in the UK are thought to be Gujarati (including those from the Northern Kutch region) and between fifteen and twenty per cent Punjabi, with the remainder having their ancestral origins in other parts of India such as Uttar Pradesh, West Bengal, and the Southern states, as well as in other countries such as Sri Lanka. Even where a family has lived for generations in another part of India, or outside India, its members often maintain links with their ancestral region and often speak their ancestral language among themselves. Thus the Hindu population is constituted of many ethnic groups, each of which was originally often based in a particular geographical region of India.

Languages

Hindus in the UK, in addition to English, speak one or more other languages. The most common are Gujarati, Hindi, Punjabi, Bengali and Tamil. They mostly use the ancient language Sanskrit in their worship, and the majority of the sacred texts are in this language. Most of the Indian words and names used below are Sanskrit. However, Sanskrit words are adapted in form and pronunciation to the different regional languages, and this accounts for some variations in the transliteration of such words: eg. Siva or Shiv; Rama or Ram.

ORIGINS AND DEVELOPMENT OF THE HINDU TRADITION

Origins

The term "Hindu" is related to the Sanskrit word Sindhu which is the name of the river which in English is called the Indus. In Iranian languages such as Persian, this river was called "Hindu", and the name "Hindu" was applied also to the country adjoining the river, and to its people. The name "Hindusthan" was also applied to the whole of North India, and sometimes to the whole of India. These names were made current in India by Persian-speaking people from Afghanistan.

Some Hindus refer to the origin of the terms "Hindu" and "Hindusthan" as being found in the scripture known as the *Brihaspati Agam*. The term "Hinduism" became current in English during the nineteenth century. The Hindu way of life is referred to as *Dharma* or sometimes as the *Sanatana Dharma* (eternal way of life), and many Hindus prefer this description to the word "Hinduism".

Sanatana Dharma is a tradition which is believed by many Hindus to go beyond time and space. It has no precisely traceable beginning, nor a single founder or teacher.

Modern historians, including many who are themselves Hindus, point to some formative periods in Indian religious history. The Indus Valley civilisation flourished in north-west India in the third and second millennia BCE, but is known only from archaeological finds.

Other Hindus do not accept this view of the ancient history of India and believe that key events such as the birth of Krishna and the Battle of Kurukshetra (see section on the *Mahabharata*, below) can be dated to a period around 3100 BCE by utilising interpretations of astrological data in the *Vedas*. What many identify as the *Vedic* period (1500-500 BCE) has left a large body of literature.

The time of the *Buddha* (c.450 BCE) was a period of great social and political change. Since then, the tradition has undergone further transformations (see section below on "Traditions in Hinduism") and developed into richly diverse ways of life and thought. Some of the famous figures in this development who are given prominence by many Hindus are: Shankara (seventh century CE), Ramanuja (eleventh century CE), Madhva (eleventh to twelfth century CE), Nimbarka (twelfth century CE), Chaitanya (fifteenth to sixteenth century CE), Vallabha (fifteenth to sixteenth century CE) and Sahajananda (eighteenth to nineteenth century CE).

Some Hindus reject the notion of an historical development of the tradition since it conflicts with the idea of degenerative time (see *Yuga* below), according to which past ages were more glorious and closer to the eternal truth than this one. However, many Hindus see Hinduism as evolving and as coming to fresh understandings throughout time in ways that do not conflict with the idea of an eternal *dharma*.

Variety

Because of its ancient origins and its visions of truth, the Hindu traditions embrace a very wide range of belief and practices, with regional, linguistic, and doctrinal variations. Within the Hindu traditions various schools of thought, a whole range of philosophical positions, religious practices and devotional foci are accepted.

The Hindu traditions are often described as more a way of life than a religion based upon commonality of belief. However, within this diversity there are a number of beliefs and practices which are more commonly accepted, and the diverse systems of thought have themselves been tested, codified and accepted throughout the centuries. Perhaps the greatest degree of commonality concerns acceptance of the authority of the *Vedas* (see below).

SOURCES OF HINDU BELIEFS AND PRACTICES

Hindus hold a number of texts to be sacred and at the root of their beliefs and practices. Many of them are in Sanskrit, and fall into two broad categories: *shruti* (that which is heard) and *smriti* (that which is remembered).

The four *Vedas* (see below) are *shruti*. Some Hindus believe that *smriti* such as the *Puranas* and the *Ramayana* are less authoritative than the *shruti*, although others stress that *smriti* texts are extensions of the truths hidden in the *shruti*, made accessible through story and simple language. For example, many *Vaishnavas* (see below) consider the *shruti* and the *smriti* to be on the same level, and call the *Bhagavata Purana* (or *Shrimad Bhagavatam*) the "fifth Veda". The text known as the *Mahabharata* also is often considered to be the "fifth *Veda*".

Sacred texts are treated with great respect. They are often wrapped in silk or cotton cloth and devout Hindus will avoid placing them on the floor and touching them with feet or with dirty hands. Prayers are often recited before reading from such texts.

Shruti

Oral Tradition

For Hindus, sacred texts are essentially spoken rather than written. This is why the *Vedas*, the most ancient sacred texts, are referred to as *shruti* (that which is heard). Some Hindus believe that the original revelations were given in *Dev Vak* (the language of God) and that Sanskrit later emerged from this, modifying and adapting the original language of revelation in order to make it understandable to human beings. Some Hindus believe that there are some revelations which have, until now, been kept as unwritten secrets which are only orally passed on to those qualified to receive them.

The Four Vedas

The sacred texts known as *Vedas* (meaning "knowledge") are believed to be eternal. Tradition says that there was originally one *Veda*, but it was divided into four at the beginning of the third age of the world (see *Yuga* below), and learnt by the four *rishis* (sages): Paila, Jaimini, Vaishampayana and Sumantu. They are then said to have been passed on by word of mouth by the people of that age who possessed remarkable memories until the beginning of the *Kali-Yuga* (3102 BCE, see below), the present age of degeneration. After that it became necessary to commit the teachings to writing in the form of the four books in which they are known today.

The four *Vedas* are: the *Rig Veda*, which contains *mantras* (verses) spoken in worship; the *Sama Veda*, containing sung mantras with their tunes; the *Yajur Veda*, containing further *mantras*, and instructions for the actions (*karma*) used in worship; and the *Atharva Veda*, containing *mantras* for particular purposes such as cure of diseases. There are altogether over 20,000 *mantras* in the *Vedas*, including *mantras* which some believe deal in ways ahead of their times with matters of physics, astronomy and mathematics.

According to some traditions, there are also five main *Upavedas* (sub-branches of the *Vedas*). The *Upavedas* are: *Ayurveda*, which is related to the *Rig Veda*, and is concerned with medical knowledge; the *Gandharvaveda*, which is related to the *Sama Veda*, and is concerned with expertise in music, dance and drama; the *Dhanurveda*, which is related to the *Yajur Veda*, and is concerned with military science; the *Arthaveda*, which is related to the *Artharva Veda*, and is concerned with the practice of government; and the *Shilpaveda*, which deals with architecture.

Each of the four *Vedas* consists of four parts: the *Samhitas*, the *Brahmanas*, the *Aranyakas* and the *Upanishads*. The *Samhitas* contain mantras for recitation; the *Brahmanas* are concerned with ritual and sacrifice, the purpose of which is material prosperity on earth and joy in heaven after death; the *Aranyakas* reflect on the cosmic role of *Vedic* rituals; and the *Upanishads* contain more philosophical and meditative material and discuss the knowledge through which one is liberated from ignorance and finds self-realisation.

Smriti

The *smriti* consist of six categories: *Itihasa*, *Purana*, *Grihya Sutra*, *Vedanga*, *Dharma Shastra* and *Prasthana Vakya*. The *Itihasas* (histories) consist of the two epics: the *Ramayana* (written by Valmiki) and the *Mahabharata*, which includes the *Bhagavad Gita*. The *Ramayana* and *Mahabharata* are believed by some Hindus to be historical, whilst others see them in more symbolic terms. They contain accounts of the *Lilas* (pastimes) of the divine manifested in human form, as Rama and Krishna.

Some Hindus believe that it is Vishnu who was manifested in this way, whilst others see the manifestations as those of Krishna in his divine form (for further information on Rama, Krishna and Vishnu see section below on "Key Hindu Beliefs"). The *Ramayana* and the *Mahabharata* illustrate Hindu conceptions of divinity, of human nature and of *dharma* (see below). They deal with the morality which can guide personal life and protect the social order. Both epics illustrate and inspire perseverance and detachment in dealing with adverse circumstances.

Ramayana

The *Ramayana* is set in ancient India and tells the story of how King Rama fought against the forces of evil headed by Ravana. For many Hindus, Rama and his wife Sita are the epitome of right action and righteousness. Rama acts as the dutiful son, obeying his father's every wish, whilst Sita is seen as the perfect wife. Rama Rajya, the reign of Rama as King of ancient Bharat (India), is considered an ideal example of social and political leadership.

Mahabharata

The *Mahabharata* is also set in ancient India. It contains the *Bhagavad Gita* or the *Song of the Blessed Lord* which is a discourse between Krishna and his devotee Prince Arjuna. The *Mahabharata* tells a story which culminates in the battle of Kurukshetra, which marks the beginning of the present degenerate age, the *Kali Yuga*.

Immediately before the war, Prince Arjuna, who is called upon to fight, is perplexed at a situation in which he might have to kill his relatives in the enemy's army. Responding to Arjuna's questions, Krishna (who is in human form as Arjuna's charioteer) speaks to Arjuna and teaches him that the essence of *dharma* is to discharge all duties without selfishness or attachment to their rewards and in dedication to the divine.

The *Bhagavad Gita* is one of the most important scriptures for many Hindus throughout the world because of its teachings about *dharma* and about the different ways of reaching the divine, including through right action. Through the characters of the *Mahabharata*, a code of conduct and a social and ethical philosophy of human relations and problems are presented.

Puranas

The *Puranas* contain stories about the deities Brahma, Vishnu and Shiva and stories about the great sages of Hindu tradition, together with expositions of Hindu theology and religious practice. Whilst some Hindus see these as historical, many understand them as colourful mythology and interpret them in symbolic terms. There are traditionally eighteen principal *Puranas*, the most widely used of which is the *Bhagavata Purana*, which tells of the activities of Vishnu and some of the famous stories about Krishna.

Other Texts

The *Grihya Sutras* are instructions for domestic rituals, including a special emphasis upon the fire sacrifice and the rites of passage through life.

There are six *Vedangas* (literally limbs of the *Vedas*). These are: *Shiksa*, dealing with phonetics; *Vyakarana*, dealing with Sanskrit grammar; *Nirukti*, dealing with Sanskrit etymology; *Chandas*, dealing with the rules of metre; *Jyotisha*, dealing with astrology and astronomy; and *Kalpa*, setting out regulations for ritual.

The *Dharma Shastras* (law books), the most famous of which is the *Manusmriti* (see also below under "Gender Roles") or *Laws of Manu* (the ancestor of humankind), contain codes of conduct.

The *Prasthana-vakyas* is a generic title for a wide range of literature, much of which is often specific to particular traditions found among Hindus. The most significant of these are the *Vedanta-Sutras* which summarise the key aspects of *Vedic* philosophy and the *Tantras*, which are esoteric texts related to Shiva or to Shakti (the Goddess).

KEY HINDU BELIEFS

One and Many

Some non-Hindus have perceived Hindu belief as *polytheistic* because of its multiplicity of forms and representations of the divine and of *devas* and *devis* (see below – often inadequately rendered into English as gods and goddesses), which the *Vedas* number symbolically at 330 million.

The Hindu traditions allow the use of a variety of symbols, names, terms and images which enable people to discover the divine in ways which are appropriate to them. Within the Hindu *dharma* there are both *monotheists* (believers in one God, and for whom there is a clear distinction between God and the world) as well as *monists* who argue that it is not contradictory to believe that the divine is simultaneously both one and many.

Most Hindus in the UK adhere either to a philosophy of *Advaita*, a form of *monism*, or to a philosophy of *Dvaita*, which is *monotheistic* (For both *Advaita* and *Dvaita* see section below on "Traditions in Hinduism"). Both schools accept the existence of the One Supreme. This is understood either impersonally as the all-pervading *Brahman* (the *Advaita* position) or as a Supreme Person (the *Dvaita* position). The divine is often represented in a threefold form as *trimurti*. This consists of Brahma with his consort, Saraswati; Vishnu with his consort, Lakshmi; and Shiva with his consort, Parvati (also known by many other names, eg Durga or Shakti).

Simultaneously with accepting the One Supreme in either understanding outlined above, the Hindu traditions also refer to many other beings. Among the best known of these *devas* and *devis* are: Indra (god of rain), Surya (sun god), Chandra (moon god), Ganesha (remover of obstacles), Yama (god of death), Sarasvati (goddess of learning), Lakshmi (goddess of wealth), Hanuman, the ardent devotee of Rama (who is believed to have assumed the monkey-form to fulfil the prophecy of Nandi whom Ravana called "monkey-face") and also Murugan (with Ganesha, one of the two sons of Shiva and Parvati). Some Hindus see these as manifestations of different powers and functions of the divine, whilst others accept them as distinctly existing beings.

The Hindu tradition recognises a female principle as a form, and in some cases as the highest form, of the divine. The universal energy of existence is referred to as Shakti, the consort of Shiva, who is considered as the personification of the material energy or Mother Nature. She has various forms, some gentle and nurturing and others fierce and terrible. These go by different names such as Devi, Ambaji, Parvati, Durga and Kali. She is often referred to simply as Mataji (meaning "respected mother").

Atman

Atman is understood to be the spirit which is present in all life and not just human life. It is the energy which activates the body and fills it with consciousness and is distinct from the material body, which consists of *prakriti* (inert matter). *Prakriti* is understood to be composed of three *gunas* (qualities) namely: *sattva* (goodness), *rajas* (passion) and *tamas* (ignorance). These affect the make-up of each individual human being according to the proportions in which they are found. The *atman* is eternal, but is repeatedly embodied, so that it goes through a cycle of birth and death. At death the *atman* is believed to leave the body and, in accordance with the law of *karma* (see below), its actions in one life are believed to determine the nature and circumstances of its future lives.

Moksha

Hindus understand the ultimate goal of all living beings to be the transcendence of *samsara* (the cycle of birth and death). This is known as *moksha* (liberation). The goal of Hindu practice is to realise union between *atman* and *Brahman*. In the *Advaita* perspective this is understood as the *atman* recognising its identity with *Brahman*, the Supreme Spirit. In the *Dvaita* view (also see below), union is understood as serving God eternally and the union is a qualitative rather than a quantitative one. In either case it is believed that it can take many lives to reach this goal.

Dharma

The concept of *dharma* is central to the Hindu traditions. It has no exact English equivalent,

although it is often loosely translated as "religion", "law", "duty" or "righteousness". Its linguistic root is the Sanskrit *dhr* meaning "to sustain" or "hold together". Its meaning is therefore approximately "that which sustains", "that which upholds" or "the intrinsic property of something". Thus, for example, the *dharma* of water is its wetness. Following one's *dharma* is essential to achieving *moksha*.

Karma

For Hindus, *karma* is the universal principle of actions and their consequences. While one is free to act, all actions have consequences – good, bad or mixed, depending upon the nature of the act and the intention behind its performance. Because of the relationship between actions and consequences, the results shape one's destiny, whether in the present or in a future life. Whilst one remains ignorant of the principle of *karma*, it leads to *janma* (birth), resulting in *dukkha* (unsatisfactoriness). Hindu teaching advises that, in order to be released from *karma*, every action should be carried out from a holy sense of duty and dedication, shunning attachment to its results.

Maya

Maya (sometimes explained as meaning "that which is not") is the state of illusion which comes about through ignorance of the *Sanatana Dharma* (the eternal truth). Many Hindus speak more of "ignorance" and "knowledge" than of "evil" and "good". The illusion of *maya* and our dependence upon the world of appearances decreases as our knowledge increases.

Yuga

A very common belief is that there has been a gradual spiritual degradation of civilisation in the current age, which is itself part of a cycle of four ages, called *Yugas*. This present age is known as the *Kali Yuga* (Kali in this context is not to be confused with the name of the goddess Kali) or "dark age". It is believed to have begun with the departure of Krishna after the destruction of the *Mahabharata* war, in 3102BCE. At the end of the *Kali Yuga* it is believed that the divine will appear in human form in order to eradicate all evil from the world and clear the way for the return of the next cycle of four ages, beginning with the perfect age.

TRADITIONS IN HINDUISM

The Six Darshanas

Classically, there are six *Darshanas* (systems of Hindu philosophy). These are the *Purva Mimamsa* (also called *Mimamsa* for short), *Nyaya*, *Vaisheshika*, *Samkhya*, *Yoga* and *Vedanta* (otherwise known as the *Uttara Mimamsa*).

They are each concerned with different aspects of knowledge: *Mimamsa* is concerned with action and with responsibility; *Nyaya* with logic; *Vaisesika* with the analysis of matter in terms of its atomic structure; *Samkhya* with the analysis of matter in terms of its functioning; *Yoga* with training of the mind and body; and *Vedanta* with knowledge of ultimate reality.

The six different systems developed at different points in time and exist side by side in the Hindu tradition, resulting in a variety of philosophies ranging from *atheistic* to *theistic* and from *monistic* to *dualistic*. Despite their differences, in most of these systems the common theme is that the goal of human existence is liberation of the *atman* from the cycle of birth and death.

There is also a commitment to the idea that the spiritual life consists of four principal paths: *karma yoga* (way of action), *jnana yoga* (way of knowledge), *raja yoga* (way of self-control) and *bhakti yoga* (way of devotion). The systems do not exclude one another; for instance, a person who follows the *Vedanta* as the way to liberation may also use *Purva Mimamsa* as a guide to ritual practice, *Nyaya* as a system for conducting arguments, and *Yoga* as a means of self-discipline.

Vedanta: Dvaita and Advaita

Many Hindus today subscribe to the *Vedanta* system in one form or another, which seeks to understand the teaching of the *Upanishads*. *Vedanta* literally means "the ultimate purpose of the *Vedas*" or "the conclusion of all knowledge". It is concerned with three ultimate entities: God, the *atman* (spirit) and *prakriti* (matter). Within *Vedanta* there are different views of the relation between these three. However, there are two main tendencies – the *dvaita* (dualist) and the *advaita* (monist).

Dvaita

The term *dvaita* refers to *personalist monotheism*, in which the nature of God is that of an unlimited supreme personality. In this tendency, the *atman* and *prakriti* are seen as eternally distinct from God, and the *atman* depends upon God for its liberation. *Dvaitins* believe some deities to be *avataras* (manifestations and descents) of God. Besides these, it is also believed that there are numerous *devas* and *devis*, each of whom has specific functions within the material sphere.

Advaita

The *Advaita* or *monist* tendency insists that the *atman* and *prakriti* have no existence of their own, but depend for their existence on God, often called *Brahman*. *Brahman* is not a personal name, since God has no name or gender and is seen more in terms of permeative energy than of personality. The *atman* which is the eternal spirit in each conscious being is a manifestation of *Brahman*. Most humans are seen as being unaware of this identity, and think that they exist as separate beings. *Moksha* (salvation) is reached when this limited outlook is overcome and identity with *Brahman* is realised.

Brahman is believed to have been manifested in a variety of different times and places and personified in many different forms. Because of this, *Advaitins* believe that union with *Brahman* can be attained through the worship of any deity which is chosen as one's personal object of devotion.

In the *Advaita* view, *Brahman* can be seen as the underlying principle behind the universe from which is manifested the trinity of creative force (personified as Brahma), preservative force (personified as Vishnu) and dissolving force (personified as Shiva). Everything is therefore seen as being part of an eternal cycle in which is created, maintained for some time, and then destroyed.

Dvaita and *Advaita*, as summarised above, represent two poles of thought within the *Vedanta*. Between these poles can be found a range of subtly varied schools of thought associated with famous Hindu teachers and philosophers. These include the following:

Advaita Vedanta

Non-dualist Vedanta, a philosophy that was propounded by Shankara (7th-8th century CE), in which it is believed that the *atman* or *jiva* (living entity) is identical with God and this has simply to be realised. Only the divine is absolutely real, and everything else is *maya* (illusion or provisional), being real only in a relative and limited sense.

Vishishta-Advaita

A qualified *non-dualism* propounded by Ramanuja (c.1017-1137CE), which holds that there is a difference between God, the living entities, and *prakriti* (nature). Nevertheless, the *atman* and *prakriti* are God, in rather the same way as a person's body is that person: it is God who permeates them and gives them purpose and meaning. Ramanuja identified God as Vishnu.

Navya Vishishta-Advaita

A qualified *non-dualism*, propounded by Sahajananda (c.1781-1830CE). Five eternal realities are distinguished: *jivas* (living entities that are infinite in number); Ishwara or the Lord (cosmic self-omniscience); *maya* (matter in both manifested and unmanifested forms); Akshar Brahman (supreme divine abode of God); and Parabrahman (Supreme Godhead).

Shuddha-Dvaita

A pure *dualism* propounded by Madhva (c.1239-1319CE), also known as *Swaminarayan* (see section on "Spiritual Movements" below), in which God (seen as Vishnu), the living entities and the material world (*prakriti*) are eternally distinct. Madhva maintained even more strongly than Ramanuja the distinctness of these three, and particularly the distinction between the individual soul and God.

Dvaita-Advaita

A philosophy of oneness and difference propounded by Nimbarka (13th or 14th century CE), a worshipper of Krishna.

Shuddha-Advaita

A purified *monism* taught by Vishnuswami and his successor Vallabha (c.1479-1531BCE) (see "Spiritual Movements" below), who rejected the doctrine of *maya*.

Achintya-Bhedha-Abheda

A doctrine of inconceivable simultaneous oneness and difference, propounded by Chaitanya (c.1486-1534CE) and by his successors, including Bhaktivedanta Swami Prabhupada (1896-1977) (see "Spiritual Movements" below). It holds that God (identified as Krishna), the living entities and *prakriti* are both one and different at the same time, in a way that cannot be conceived by the human mind.

Shaiva Siddhanta

The system of the worshippers of Shiva, codified in the 12th-14th centuries CE. This system teaches that there are innumerable living entities, trapped in the world of *rebirth*, but enabled to escape from it by the grace of Shiva.

Sampradaya

The above are the doctrines of some of the many *sampradayas* (traditions) which can be encountered among Hindus in the UK. Each *sampradaya* has its set of doctrines and its form of worship, usually directed to a particular personal form of God, flourishing in a particular region of India and passed down through a succession of *gurus*. *Gurus* are spiritual leaders who are seen by their followers as providing great insight and guidance in spiritual matters. (See further "Spiritual Movements" below.)

Not all Hindus are members of *sampradayas*. However, many Hindus worship a particular form of God, called their *ishta-devata* (choicest deity). On the basis of the form of God which they chiefly worship, they can be classed as *Vaishnavas*, *Shaivas* and *Shaktas*.

Vaishnavas, Shaivas and Shaktas

The term *Vaishnava* is applied to worshippers of Vishnu who understand the Divine and its relationship with humanity in the *Dvaita* way, seeing Vishnu as the supreme divine personal reality and also to those who see Krishna as the divine personal reality. Many British Hindus belong to one or another of the *Vaishnava sampradayas*.

Shaivas are worshippers of Shiva, and *Shaktas* are worshippers of Shakti or the Goddess (also known by other names including Durga and Parvati) and sometimes seen as the consort of Shiva. Some see Shiva and Shakti as alternative and complementary manifestations of Brahman, understood as supra-personal in the *Advaita* manner.

HINDU LIFE

The Four Aims

The traditional Hindu view of human life is characterised by the four *purusharthas* (aims for human existence). These are: *dharma* (religious life) as a foundation for everything else; *artha* (economic development) as a necessity for life; *kama* (sense gratification) in order to keep a healthy body and mind, but the desire for which should also be controlled through regulation; and *moksha* (liberation, salvation) from the cycle of birth and death.

Most Hindus consider liberation to be the ultimate goal, but among *Vaishnavas* some would say that *bhakti* (devotion to the divine) is a fifth and final goal and that *prema* (love of God) and selfless devotion is higher than liberation (which for the devotees comes by means of the *grace* of God and not just by personal efforts).

Values

There are a number of core ideals and values which are shared by most Hindus, although in practice they are subject to different interpretations which result in varying degrees of observance. These ideals and values include: respect for parents and elders; reverence for teachers; regard for guests; a general adoption of vegetarianism; *ahimsa* (non-violence); tolerance of all races and religions; controlled relations between the sexes in which marriage is considered sacred and divorce, and pre-marital or extra-marital sexual relationships are strongly discouraged; sacredness of the cow whose milk sustains human life; and an appreciation of the equality of all living beings and the sanctity of life.

Hindus seek to promote the *Sanatana Dharma* among all people although, in general, they do not engage in activity aimed at converting non-Hindus to Hindu practice. Nevertheless, individuals are generally welcome to embrace the Hindu way.

Varnashrama Dharma

An understanding of one's personal and social role within the cosmic order of things is at the centre of Hindu life. Understanding *sva-dharma* (literally, "one's own *dharma*") in its relationship to *varna* (social position, or class) and *ashrama* (meaning "stage in life" or "spiritual order") is crucial. *Dharma*, understood as a whole, is the morality by which righteousness and religious codes and duties are protected.

The mutual obligations involved in this system are symbolised for many by the ceremony of

Rakshabandhan, which involves the tying of a thread (*rakhi*) by sisters around the wrist of their brothers, by students around the wrist of their teachers, and by people in general around the wrist of their leaders. This symbolises the vow to protect *dharma* and promote unity within society.

Various *dharmas* correspond with particular *varnas* and *ashramas* (see below) of which, in each case, there are believed to be four. As already noted (see *dharma* above), *dharma* can mean "intrinsic property", which is different for different things. Similarly, there are different *dharmas* for different people. Among the factors that differentiate people are the four *varnas* and four *ashramas* described below.

The Four Varnas

In the Hindu ideal, everyone belongs to one of four *varnas*, traditionally and ideally perceived as having complementary, separate and distinct social roles. These are defined in a well-known *Vedic* hymn, the *Purusha Sukta* (*Rig-Veda*, book 10, hymn 90), in which the whole of society is seen as one person and the *varnas* as interdependent parts of the one social body. A person's *varna* traditionally indicates his or her status and responsibility, and thus the kind of duty which he or she must execute to transmigrate into a higher existence.

According to some interpretations of the scriptures, the system of the four *varnas* is not wholly applicable in this age (*Kali Yuga*). Some Hindus say that it was only after the *Vedic* period that this social system became rigidly hereditary, whereas others maintain that it was always so. According to the *Bhagavad Gita* an individual's *varna* should be understood according to the person's qualities and the tendency towards a particular kind of work. The traditional *varnas* consist of:

Brahmins
Intelligentsia and priests who are characterised by austerity, knowledge, self-control, honesty and cleanliness and who seek to promote these more widely.

Kshatriyas
Administrators and military characterised by power, courage and leadership whose purpose in life is to establish peace and prosperity.

Vaishyas
Agriculturalists and merchants whose work is in producing and trading, being responsible for the generation and distribution of material wealth.

Sudras
Workers who provide labour and service.

The four-fold differentiation of varnas is no longer rigidly followed among contemporary Hindus. However it does reflect the broad outlines of a division of labour and responsibilities which are found in many historical and contemporary societies.

Jati

The ideal division of society into four *varnas* is an important concept in *dharma*. But in practice a person tends to identify himself or herself with an hereditary group called a *jati* that is associated with one of the *varnas*. These groups are often referred to in English as *castes* or *sub-castes*. This should not be taken as implying any inherent differences between groups.

While the system of four *varnas* is known throughout India, the pattern of *jatis* varies from region to region. In each region there are dozens of *jatis*, many of them unknown even by name in other regions, and in India as a whole there are thousands.

Many *jatis* are traditionally linked to particular occupations, although their members do not necessarily practise them. *Jati* remains a significant social, cultural and economic factor for many aspects of Hindu life in the UK; for instance, many Hindus marry within their *jati*. Examples of *jatis* include: *Patidars* (traditionally, traders), *Mochis* (traditionally, shoemakers), *Lohanas* (traditionally, traders), *Anavil Brahmins* (traditionally, agriculturalists), *Khattris* and

Aroras (both traditionally traders), *Balmikis* (traditionally, manual workers), *Ravidasis* (traditionally, shoemakers), *Rarhi Brahmins* (traditionally, priests) and *Baidyas* (traditionally, physicians).

Certain *jatis*, generally associated with what are viewed as polluting occupations, have historically been identified as *"outcastes"* and *"untouchables"*, and have often suffered social discrimination as a result. The official term used in India to describe this group of people is the *"scheduled castes"*, and following independence, the Indian Government granted a special status to this group with the intention of achieving social equity.

Many of the present leaders of this group now prefer the self-designation of *Dalit* (oppressed). The majority contemporary Hindu position is that *untouchability* has no sanction within the Hindu *dharma*. The Hindu leader *Mahatma* (Great Soul) Gandhi called such people *Harijans* (children of God).

Gender Roles

The Hindu tradition has advocated equality of worth between women and men but with differentiation of social roles. These are set out in the *Manusmriti* (the *Law of Manu*), where a woman's role is defined primarily as that of an educator of children and housekeeper, with a man's role being one of overall authority coupled with financial responsibility for the family. Views as to how far the *Manusmriti* applies in the circumstances of contemporary society vary within different sections of the Hindu population and, in the UK, specific gender roles vary from family to family. In spiritual terms, many Hindu women point to the strength and dignity which they derive from the Hindu tradition's representation of the divine in female as well as male forms.

Ashramas

The *ashramas* are the four stages which have traditionally and ideally been followed in the course of one's life. In this ideal sequence one first becomes a *brahmacharin* (student) living a celibate life of study under a *guru*.

Next, one becomes a *grihastha* or *grihini* (householder). In this stage, marriage, family and the bringing up and educating of children, together with hospitality for guests and care for the elderly and disabled, are the main focus of responsibility.

The third stage is that of a *vanaprastha* (hermit who has retired to the forest). This stage can only be entered after the completion of social obligations through the marriage of all one's daughters and preferably also of one's sons, and the handing over to them of all business affairs. This *ashrama* is traditionally a time in which there are increasing periods of withdrawal from society to enable more concentration on the spiritual dimension of life.

The fourth and final stage which may be undertaken is that of the *sannyasin*, who has renounced all earthly ties and looks to the whole world as a family rather than to an immediate biologically-related unit. When a husband becomes a *sannyasin*, the husband and wife part, with the husband going to live in an *ashram* and the wife coming under the care of her sons. This stage is followed only very rarely in conventional society.

Traditionally, *brahmins* go through all four *ashramas*, *kshatriyas* never directly take *sannyasa*, and *vaishyas* do not take *vanaprastha* or *sannyasa*, with *sudras* only accepting the householder *ashrama*. Some early Hindu texts allow for the possibility of becoming a *sannyasi* soon after completing the *brahmacharin* stage. Whilst the *ashrama* system has not been fully operative since medieval times, a sequence of study followed by familial responsibilities and finally withdrawal from the world remains a powerful ideal for many Hindus, including those in the UK, since these stages are seen as based on a natural progression through life.

Guru-Disciple Relationship

For many Hindus, the *Guru Shishya Sambandh* (*Guru*-disciple relationship) is of great importance. *Gurus* are revered as those who have attained a spiritual perfection and as embodiments of the divine. The guidance and grace of a *guru* is therefore often seen as being essential for those who aspire to liberation.

Vegetarianism

Within the Hindu tradition there is a variety of views on the permissibility of a range of foods and drinks. Whilst Hindus recognise that every living organism depends upon others for food, many Hindus are vegetarians and even those who eat meat normally abstain from beef. Hindu vegetarianism arises from a belief in the principle of *ahimsa* (non-harming) and thus generally precludes the eating of meat, fish or eggs. Sometimes onions and garlic are also not eaten.

However, as well as the principle of *ahimsa*, there is also a positive conviction concerning the effect of food upon human development, especially for those who practise spiritual disciplines. Milk, yoghurt, butter, ghee (clarified butter) and fruits are usually acceptable because no killing has taken place and they are considered to be foods which promote *sattva* (purity and harmony). When preparing their own food, many Hindus offer their food to a deity before eating it, and keep aside a portion for animals.

Products which have been cooked in, or contain, by-products from slaughtered animals would not be acceptable to strict Hindu vegetarians. For example, neither conventional ice cream (which may contain animal fats) nor cheese which contains rennet (extracted from the pancreas of the cow), nor chips which have been cooked in animal fats, would be acceptable. Hindus may also refrain from intoxicating drinks such as alcohol, and in some cases from tea and coffee too.

Fasting

Many Hindus (and especially women) observe *fasts* or *vrats* (vows) as devotion to a deity and on behalf of the well-being of themselves and their family. These vows entail the avoidance of certain foods at certain times, such as on particular days of the week, of the lunar month, and of the year.

HINDU WORSHIP

The practice of domestic worship is widespread. In their own homes, most Hindus have a shrine or small area for worship (*ghar mandir*, "house temple") containing pictures and/or *murtis* (see below) of favourite deities and the women of the household have an important role in the religious devotions centred on these shrines. In addition to private worship some fairly large gatherings for worship may also take place in private homes. *Havan* (the rite of the sacred fire) may also be performed at home on important occasions.

However, many Hindus also attend a place of worship to associate with saintly persons from whom they can learn about spiritual topics. In a land in which Hindus are in a minority, worship at the *mandir* (see below) also fulfils an important social function, providing an opportunity to engage in community and cultural activities and consolidate faith together.

Mandirs

At present *mandirs* (temples) in the UK are generally converted public or religious buildings and private houses, with only a few purpose-built buildings. One such is the recently completed Shri Swaminarayan Mandir in Neasden, North West London. This is the first ever traditional *mandir* carved in white marble stone to be built in Europe and was opened in August 1995.

Within individual *mandirs*, one may see different *murtis* (sacred images or figures that represent deities) and pictures of holy people. This variety can reflect the range of *sampradayas* that use the temple. *Mandirs* are more likely than in India to cater for a variety of *sampradayas*. This may be partly because of the minority position of Hindus in the UK and the financial constraints within which they must operate, but it is also made possible by the inclusive approach of the Hindu traditions with respect to the commonalities shared by different deities. As well as the hall for worship, *mandirs* may also have other facilities on their premises, such as social, cultural, educational, and administrative rooms.

Murtis

Inside the *mandir*, there is usually a main hall with a shrine where the *murtis* of the *mandir* are installed. There may also be other side shrines. For those who are outsiders to the Hindu tradition, it is sometimes difficult to gain an accurate understanding of the nature of *murtis*. They are more than purely symbolic representations of deities and yet Hindus do not believe that the reality of a deity is limited to a particular *murti* in a particular place. *Murtis* are specifically dedicated and they are venerated as deities, being dressed in the finest fabrics and decorated with ornaments, jewellery and garlands of flowers. This is in order to foster a mood of *seva* (sacrifice and selfless service) by centring people's devotion on the deity.

The *murtis* are usually made of marble, but can also be made of other kinds of stone, wood or metal. For the believer, the presence of a particular deity is manifested by *murtis* with specific characteristics. For example, Ganesha is represented by an elephant-headed *murti* with four arms; Krishna is represented as a cowherd seen standing with one leg crossing the other at the ankles, playing a flute, and accompanied by his favourite devotee, a *gopi* (cowherd girl) Radha.

Deities are often accompanied by *murtis* of their *vahana* (a vehicle, the animal or bird on which they ride). For example, Shiva rides on the bull, Nandi. Brightly coloured and sweet-smelling flowers are laid before the *murtis* or hung over them as garlands. The *murtis* may be housed in a *garbha-griha* (inner sanctum), which only the *priest* is permitted to enter.

Other Features and Activities

In the main hall there may also be one or more *vyasasanas*. These are decorated thrones on which *swamis* (religious teachers) sit when they deliver discourses to religious gatherings. In a *mandir* it is also likely that there will be incense to purify the air and create a spiritual atmosphere; the *AUM* (or *OM*) symbol to symbolise the primaeval sound representing God in the simplest form; and the *swastika*. This is not to be confused with the *swastika* of Nazism. The original Hindu form of this symbol is a sign of auspiciousness. Hindus feel a sense of outrage at the Nazi co-option and distortion of such a sacred symbol, and also at the use of *OM* on some hallucinogenic drugs.

One might also find a conch shell, the sound of which assists concentration on worship; a *trishul*, which is the trident weapon of Shiva and represents God, the soul and the ignorance through which the soul is held in bondage; a coconut, which is believed to represent the three-eyed Shiva and is symbolic of life by being hard on the outside but sweet on the inside; images of the *lotus*, which is an ancient symbol of the cosmos, of wisdom and of humanity; and a *kalasha*, which is a pot representing the human body. The mouth of a *kalasha* is considered as Vishnu; its base as Brahma; and its middle as Shiva. The water within it stands for purity and love of the divine.

Corporate devotional activities include *bhajan* and *kirtan* (singing songs and *mantras*); *pravachan* (sermon); *havan* (the sacred fire ceremony); and the *arti* ceremony (see below). Private devotions, in the temple and at home, include *japa* (*mantra* meditation), prayer, *puja* (worship of the *murti*) and the study of sacred texts.

When visiting a *mandir*, it is customary for Hindus to take some kind of offering for the deity, such as food, money or flowers, *haldi* (turmeric) and *kumkum* (red powder). Anyone entering a *mandir* for any purpose must remove their shoes. A bell may be hung for worshippers to ring on entering, to invite the presence of the gods and to ward off evil spirits. The worshipper then comes face to face with the *murti*. This is called taking *darshan* (sight) of the deity, which is understood as a blissful experience.

The worshipper offers respect to the deity/deities by folding hands or by bowing down, and may then offer prayers and a gift, or respectfully sip a few drops of *charnamrita* (holy water used to bathe the deity). The worship of the *murti* with offering of gifts is called *puja*. More formal *puja* is performed by the temple priest.

In the *arti* ceremony, performed several times a day, the priest offers articles of worship to the deity including lighted ghee lamps, incense, water for bathing, small napkins for drying, flowers and peacock and yak-tail fans, during which worshippers play musical instruments, sing *bhajans*, and clap their hands in rhythm.

Almost all Hindu *mandirs* welcome people from all religions to visit them and, if they wish, to take part in the worship. Prior to *arti*, food is offered to the deity and is blessed for later distribution. Food that has been offered to a deity is said to be sanctified and is known as *prasad* or *prasadam*.

HINDU CALENDAR AND FESTIVALS

Calendar

The Hindu year is based on the waxing and waning of the moon. Since it consists normally of twelve lunar months, it is ten days shorter than it is in the *Gregorian* calendar year. Approximately once every three years an extra month is added to bring the lunar year in phase with the solar year. Hindu years carry a name instead of the numbers of the *Gregorian* calendar. For example, 1996-97 was Dhatu; 1997-98 was Ishvara, and 1998-99 was Bahudaanya.

Hindu seasons and festival dates do not remain the same each year within the framework of the *Gregorian* calendar, except for a few which are timed by the sun and not the moon. The Hindu calendar is set out in *panchang* (almanacs) which provide information on the dates of festivals and other rituals to be followed by various Hindu groups.

Festivals

There are many Hindu festivals, but the following are some of the principal ones. The approximate time of their occurrence indicated below refers to the *Gregorian* calendar in common use in the UK:

Shivaratri or Mahashivaratri (February /March)
Worship dedicated to Lord Shiva. Devotees spend the night at the temple chanting and singing. Milk is poured continuously, as an offering, on to the *linga*, the symbolic form of Lord Shiva. Among some families, there is also a tradition of *fasting*.

Holi (February/March)
This festival of colours is associated with many stories of Vishnu and his devotees, and with that of the half-man, half-lion incarnation, Narasimha or Narasingha, and Prahlada, a devotee of Krishna. In India, traditionally, liquid dyes, coloured powders and water are liberally sprinkled on the participants as fun. In the UK the inclement climate, and the fact that it could easily be misunderstood by the wider society, can curtail this traditional practice, but many British Hindus enjoy the bonfire which is another traditional feature of *Holi*.

Yugadi or Gudi Parva (March–April)
For many Hindus, this festival marks the beginning of the New Year. *Puja*, feasting and greetings are common. A special mixture of neem leaves and jaggery is eaten to symbolise acceptance of both bitter and happy things in life.

Rama Navami/Hari Jayanti (March/April)
Celebrates the birth of Lord Rama as an *avatar* at Ayodhya in India. Devotees fast, and the

Ramayana, the story of Rama and Sita, is read aloud in temples. Devotees of *Lord Swaminaryan* also celebrate his birth on this day by fasting, prayers, *bhajans* and discourses about his life.

Janmashtami (August/September)

Marks the birth of Lord Krishna who is believed to have appeared in human form in the fourth century BCE, or in traditional chronology five thousand years ago shortly before the *Kali Yuga*, in the district of Mathura, India, in order to deliver the pious, destroy miscreants and establish the principles of the *Sanatana Dharma*. Devotees perform *puja* and sing *bhajans*.

Navaratri (September/October)

Navaratri means "nine nights". It is celebrated with dancing and is held in honour of Lakshmi, Durga and Sarasvati, as well as other goddesses worshipped in this season. It ends with *Dussehra* or *Vijayadashami*, the tenth day, a time of celebration of the victory of good over evil.

Diwali or Deepawali (October/November)

According to some Hindu groups, this festival marks the beginning of a new Hindu year. It is concerned with the celebration of the victory of light over darkness and knowledge over ignorance. The festival is also a time when Hindus worship the Goddess Lakshmi (Goddess of prosperity) and is known as the "festival of lights" because of the lighting everywhere of *dipas* or *divas* (small oil lamps). These are lit to illuminate Lakshmi's way to the home and to celebrate the return of Rama and Sita to Rama's kingdom of Ayodhya after fourteen years of exile.

Annakuta or Nutan Varsh (October/November)

This is the day after *Diwali*. Large quantities of sweets and other food stuffs are brought to the temple to be offered to the deities in celebration of a story from Krishna's childhood and concerned with Mount Govardhan.

Pilgrimages

Pilgrimages also form an important part of Hindu religious observance. Visits to holy places in India may be undertaken with special intentions in mind, such as cure of disease or blessing for the family.

In the *Advaita* Hindu tradition, the most holy of all places of pilgrimage is Varanasi (also known as Benares or Kashi). This is situated on the sacred River Ganga (Ganges) and is especially sacred to those Hindus who venerate Shiva and Rama. Pilgrims who have visited the River Ganga often bring home bottles of water from the river to place in their family shrines. Dying people may request to sip Ganges water and also to have their ashes spread in the river.

In the *Vaishnava* Hindu tradition, Vrindavan and Nathdwar are of special importance because of their connections with Krishna. Ayodhya, Badrinath, Kedaranath, Mathura, Tirupathi and Vaishnodevi, Kashmir, Dwarka are other important places of pilgrimage. There are also some more recently evolved centres of pilgrimage such as Akshardham, in Gandhinagar, Gujarat, a memorial to *Lord Swaminarayan*.

HINDU ORGANISATIONS

The first Hindu organisations in the UK were set up in the late 1950s. Since then a number of different kinds of organisation have developed, many of which serve multiple functions, including lobbying and campaigning groups, youth activities, language classes, women's groups, trust funds, education and propagation of Hindu culture, in addition to more specifically religious activities. Some of the local and national groupings are part of international organisations mainly based in India.

Jati (Community) Associations

Although *jatis* may be historically associated in India with particular occupations, in the UK they do not generally correlate with one's social, economic or occupational status. *Jati* groups do, however, remain a significant social, cultural and economic factor for many aspects of internal Hindu community life in the UK. Different patterns of settlement have influenced organisational development and therefore *jati* groups are concentrated in particular localities in the UK. For example, there has been a concentration of *Mochis* in Leeds, and of *Lohanas* in Leicester and North London.

Jati associations exist at both national and local levels. They have functions ranging from social networking through to voluntary welfare support and provision. Local organisations may be affiliated to a national organisation. As one example, the Gujarati Federation of Anavil Samaj is an organisation representing members of the *Anavil jati* and has local branches in various parts of the country.

National *jati* organisations are much more characteristic of Gujarati Hindus than Punjabi Hindus and they co-ordinate joint events between local groups and provide a networking function across the country. National *jati* organisations often produce annual directories of members of the local *jati* groups affiliated to them, although these are not readily available to the general public.

Jati associations are sometimes recognisable from the *jati* name in their title, for example, the National Association of Patidar Samaj (*Patidar*), the Shri Kutch Leva Patel Samaj (members of the *Leva Patel jati* from the Kutch region of the state of Gujarat), or Brahma Samaj (*Brahmin*). The Brahma Samaj is a Gujarati *Brahmin* association and should not be confused with the Brahmo Samaj, which is a religious society founded in Calcutta in 1828.

Spiritual Movements

Another form of organisation, often with a regional base in India, is the *sampradaya* or spiritual tradition (see above). A number of *sampradayas*, some relatively modern, have a strong presence in the UK.

Swaminaryans

Swaminarayan Hindus in the UK are predominantly of Gujarati origin and follow teachers in the line of Sahajananda Swami (1781-1830), also called *Swaminarayan*, who is believed to have been an incarnation of the Supreme Lord. *Swaminarayanis* combine traditional Hindu practices with specific customs of their own, including the strict separation of men and women in the temple.

There are various *Swaminarayan* groupings in the UK, reflecting different views concerning the proper line of succession to Sahajananda Swami. The largest in the UK is the Akshar Purushottam Sanstha (the Swaminarayan Hindu Mission) which looks to the leadership of Pramukh Swami and whose main UK centre is in Neasden, London. Another is the group which looks for leadership to Acharya Tejendraprasad Pande and whose main UK centre is in Willesden Lane, London.

Pushtimargis

Other devotional groups include the *Pushtimarg* or *Vallabha sampradaya* (founded in the sixteenth century). Its members, who are largely *Lohana* by *jati*, follow the teachings of Vallabha (c.1479-1531CE) and worship Krishna, particularly in the form of Srinathji and as the infant Krishna.

Krishna Consciousness

There is also the International Society for Krishna Consciousness (ISKCON) whose devotees follow the teachings propounded by A C Bhaktivedanta Swami Prabhupada (1896-1977) in the Chaitanya Vaishnava tradition which flourishes in Bengal. The first ISKCON temple in the UK was opened in 1969 in central London. Later, George Harrison (one of the Beatles) donated Bhaktivedanta Manor in Hertfordshire where, every year, a festival involving thousands of Hindus from all over the UK has been held to celebrate *Krishna-Janmashtami*. A long-running planning dispute which threatened this temple with closure for public worship was settled in 1996.

Arya Samajis

Members of the Arya Samaj follow the teachings of Swami Dayananda Saraswati (1824-1883CE) who rejected the concept of *jati* and the worship of *murtis*. Hindus in the Arya Samaj, who are mainly Punjabis, stress belief in, and the purity of, the *Vedas* and reject those parts of post-*Vedic* Hindu teachings which they believe do not conform to the *Vedic* revelation, including parts of the *Puranas* and *Tantras*.

Ramakrishna Mission

The Ramakrishna Mission was founded by the Bengali Swami Vivekananda (1863-1902CE) in the name of his master Ramakrishna (1836-1886). It teaches *Advaita Vedanta*, and is headed by a highly disciplined and organised body of *sannyasins*.

Hindu-Related Groups

There are also many Hindu-related movements and groups which practise the disciplines of *Yoga*. Some of these focus purely on the more physical exercises of *Hatha Yoga* whilst others seek to present a complete religious approach through *Raja Yoga*. Some of these *Yoga* groups are closely connected with the wider Hindu tradition, whilst others have recruitment and management from a cross section of the wider community. These include the Divine Life Society, the Transcendental Meditation movement and others.

Educational Organisations

The Swaminarayan Hindu Mission in London has started an independent Hindu school where, in addition to the National Curriculum, students are taught about moral and ethical values and Hindu religion, culture and music. There are also many supplementary schools which teach Indian languages and Hindu religion and culture out of school hours.

Regional/Linguistic Groups

Some groups are organised on the basis of a specific shared regional or linguistic background. Punjabis or Gujaratis or Bengalis have often joined together to form associations. Such groups can sometimes be recognised by the inclusion of regional names in their organisational titles, as in for example, the Preston Gujarat Hindu Society.

Representative Groups

There is no single national representative organisation of Hindus in the UK, although the Hindu Council of the UK, founded in November 1994, aspires to a role as an umbrella organisation for the various national groupings. Among these groupings are the National Council of Hindu Temples, which played a significant role in the formation of the Hindu Council of the UK. There is also a UK branch of the international organisation, the Vishwa Hindu Parishad (The World Council of Hindus) which has local branches throughout the UK.

A number of local and regional areas have seen the development of representative groups such as the Hindu Council (Brent), the Hindu Council of Birmingham, the Leicester Gujarat Hindu Association, the Hindu Council of the North, the Hindu Council of Nottingham, and the Hindu Resource Centre (Croydon).

Personnel

A Hindu *priest* is often referred to as *pandit*, *swami*, or *maharaj*. A *priest* whose function is to perform *puja* in a temple is called a *pujari*. One who performs life-cycle rituals for families in their homes is called a *purohit*. Traditionally, these roles have been restricted to those of the Brahmin *varna*. However (as explained in the section on *varna* above), the term *Brahmin* can be understood in a qualitative sense, so that anyone who is knowledgeable and shows *Brahmin*-like qualities can be a *priest*.

Priests are usually male, but can also be female. In some other temples wives of *priests* act as *pujari* when their husbands are away. *Priests* may be resident in the *mandir*, and may be appointed and paid by the congregation. Their role is to conduct religious ceremonies and to care for the holy shrines.

The *mandir* is usually governed by a managing committee including the offices of temple president and a secretary. Many *pandits* are from India, staying only for a temporary period before returning home. As such, they will not necessarily speak English. Therefore when wishing to visit a *mandir* it may be preferable to contact the secretary or president of the *mandir*.

Swamis or *gurus* are religious teachers, and they are venerated by Hindus because they are learned in the scriptures, know the methods of worship and have renounced all worldly attachments. Some have authority in relation to particular *sampradayas*, but they also receive respect from non-members.

FURTHER READING

Ballard, R (ed), *Desh Pardesh: The South Asian Presence in Britain*, C. Hurst and Co, London, 1994.

Barot, R, "Caste and Sect in the Swaminarayan Movement", in Burghart, R (ed), *Hinduism in Great Britain*, Tavistock Publications, London, 1987.

Bharatiya Vidya Bhavan, *Hindu Dharma: The Universal Way of Life*, Bharatiya Vidya Bhavan, London, nd.

Bowen, D G (ed), *Hinduism in England*, Faculty of Contemporary Studies, Bradford College, Bradford, 1986.

Brockington, J L, *The Sacred Thread: Hinduism in Its Continuity and Diversity*, Edinburgh University Press, Edinburgh, 1981.

Burghart, R (ed), *Hinduism in Great Britain: The Perpetuation of Religion in an Alien Cultural Milieu*, Tavistock, London, 1987.

Carey, S, "The Hare Krishna movement and Hindus in Britain", in *New Community*, Volume X, Spring 1983, pp 477-486.

Carey, S, "The Indianisation of the Hare Krishna movement in Britain", in Burghart, R (ed), *Hinduism in Great Britain*, Tavistock, London, 1987.

Chandrashekharendra Sarasvati Swami, His Holiness, *Hindu Dharma: The Universal Way of Life*, Bharatiya Vidya Bhavan, Bombay, 1995.

Dwyer, R, "Caste, Religion and Sect in Gujarat: Followers of Vallabhacharya and Swaminarayan" in Ballard, R (ed), *Desh Pardesh: The South Asian Presence in Britain*, C. Hurst and Co, London, 1994, pp 165-190.

Elgood, H, *Hinduism and the Religious Arts*, Cassells, London, 1998.

Firth, S, "Changing Patterns in Hindu Death Rituals in Britain", in Killingley, D; Menski, W; and Firth, S, *Hindu Ritual and Society*, S.Y. Killingley, Newcastle-upon-Tyne, 1991.

Firth, S, *Death, Dying and Bereavement in a British Hindu Community*, Kok Pharos, Kampen, 1997.

Flood, G, *An Introduction to Hinduism*, Cambridge University Press, Cambridge, 1996.

Henley, A, *Caring for Hindus and Their Families: Religious Aspects of Care*, National Extension College, Cambridge, 1983.

Jackson, R, "Holi in North India and in an English city: some adaptations and anomalies", in *New Community*, Volume V, 1976, pp 203-209.

Jackson, R and Nesbitt, E, *Listening to Hindus*, Unwin Hyman, London, 1990.

Jackson R and Killingley, D, *Approaches to Hinduism*, John Murray, London, 1988.

Jackson R and Killingley, D, *Moral Issues in the Hindu Tradition*, Trentham Books, Stoke-on-Trent, 1991.

Jackson, R and Nesbitt, E, *Hindu Children in Britain*, Trentham Books, Stoke-on-Trent, 1993.

Kanitkar, H and Cole, O, *Teach Yourself Hinduism*, Hodder, 1995.

Killingley, D (ed), *A Handbook of Hinduism for Teachers*, Grevatt & Grevatt, Newcastle-upon-Tyne, 1984.

Killingley, D, Menski, D and Firth, S, *Hindu Ritual and Society*, S Y Killingley, Newcastle-upon-Tyne, 1991.

King, R, *Indian Philosophy: An Introduction to Hindu and Buddhist Thought*, Edinburgh University Press, Edinburgh, 1999.

King, U, *A Report on Hinduism in Britain*, Community Religions Project Research Papers, No 2, University of Leeds Department of Theology and Religious Studies, Leeds, 1984.

Klostermaier, K, *A Short Introduction to Hinduism*, Oneworld, Oxford, 1998.

Knott, K, *Hinduism in Leeds: A Study of Religious Practice in the Indian Hindu Community and in Hindu-Related Groups*, Community Religions Project Monograph, University of Leeds, 1986 (reprinted, 1994).

Knott, K, *My Sweet Lord: The Hare Krishna Movement*, Aquarian Press, Wellingborough, 1986.

Knott, K, "Hindu Communities in Britain", in Badham, P (ed), *Religion, State and Society in Modern Britain*, Edwin Mellen Press, Lampeter, 1989, pp 243-257.

Knott, K, "The Gujarati Mochis in Leeds: From Leather Stockings to Surgical Boots and Beyond", in Ballard, R (ed), *Desh Pardesh: The South Asian Presence in Britain*, C. Hurst and Co, London, 1994, pp 213-230.

Knott, K, *Hinduism: A Very Short Introduction*, Oxford University Press, Oxford, 2000.

Knott, K, "Hinduism in Britain", in Coward, H, Hinnells, J and Williams, R, *The South Asian Religious Diaspora in Britain, Canada and the United States*, State University of New York Press, New York, 2000, pp 89-107.

Law, J, *The Religious Beliefs and Practices of Hindus in Derby*, Community Religions Project Papers (new series), University of Leeds, Leeds, 1991.

Lipner, J, *Hindus: Their Religious Beliefs and Practices*, Routledge, London, 1994.

Logan, P, "Practising Religion: British Hindu Children and the Navraratri Festival", in *British Journal of Religious Education*, Volume X, No. 3, pp 160-169.

Michaelson, M, "The relevance of caste among East African Gujaratis in Britain", in *New Community*, Volume VII, pp 350-360.

National Council of Hindu Temples, *Hinduism*, National Council of Hindu Temples, 1983.

Nesbitt, E, *My Dad's Hindu, My Mum's Side Are Sikhs: Studies in Religious Identity*, Arts, Culture and Education Research Papers, National Foundation for Arts Education, University of Warwick, Coventry, 1991.

Nesbitt, E, "Gender and religious traditions: the role learning of British Hindu children", in *Gender and Education*, Volume V, No. 1, 1993, pp 81-91.

Nye, M, "Temple congregations and communities: Hindu constructions in Edinburgh", in *New Community*, Volume XXIX, 1993, pp 201-215.

Nye, M, *A Place for Our Gods: The Construction of a Hindu Temple Community in Edinburgh*, Curzon Press, London, 1995.

Nye, M, "Hare Krishna and Sanatan Dharma in Britain: The Campaign for Bhaktivedanta Manor", in *Journal of Contemporary Religion*, Volume XI, No. 1, pp 37-56, 1996.

Pandey, R, *Hindu Samskaras*, Motilal Banarsidass, Delhi, 1993.

Pearson, A, *"Because It Gives Me Peace of Mind": Ritual Fasts in the Religious Lives of Hindu Women*, State University of New York Press, New York, 1996.

Pocock, D, "Preservation of the religious life: Hindu immigrants in England", in *Contributions to Indian Sociology*, ns. Volume X, 1976, pp 341-165.

Prabhupada, A.C. Bhaktivedanta Swami, *Bhagavad-Gita As It Is*, Bhaktivedanta Book Trust, London, 1986.

Radhakrishnan, S, *Indian Religions*, Vision Books, Delhi, 1983.

Renard, J, *Responses to 101 Questions on Hinduism*, Paulist Press, New York, 1999.

Shattuck, S, *Hinduism*, Routledge, London, 1999.

Stutley, M, *Hinduism: The Eternal Law*, Crucible, Wellingborough, 1985.

Stutley, M and J, *A Dictionary of Hinduism*, Routledge and Kegan Paul, London, 1987.

Subramaniyaswami, Satguru Sivaya, *Dancing with Siva: Hinduism's Contemporary Catechism*, Himalayan Academy Publications, Hawaii, 1993.

Thomas, T, "Hindu Dharma in Dispersion", in Parsons, G (ed), *The Growth of Religious Diversity: Britain from 1945, Volume I: Traditions*, Routledge, 1993, pp 173-204.

Vertovec, S (ed), *Aspects of the South Asian Diaspora*, Oxford University Press, Delhi, 1991.

Vertovec, S, "Community and congregation in London Hindu Temples: divergent trends", in *New Community*, Volume XVIII, 1992, pp 251-264.

Vertovec, S, "Caught in an Ethnic Quandary: Indo-Caribbean Hindus in London", in Ballard, R (ed), *Desh Pardesh: The South Asian Presence in Britain*, C. Hurst and Co, London, 1994, pp 272-290.

Vishwa Hindu Parishad, *Explaining Hindu Dharma: A Guide for Teachers*, Chansitor Publications, 1996.

Warrier, Shrikala, "Gujarati Prajapatis in London: Family Roles and Sociability Networks", in Ballard, R (ed), *Desh Pardesh: The South Asian Presence in Britain*, C. Hurst and Co, London, 1994, pp 191-212.

Williams, R B, *A New Face of Hinduism: The Swaminarayan Religion*, Cambridge University Press, Cambridge, 1984.

Zaehner, R C (ed), *Hindu Scriptures*, J M Dent and Sons, London, 1986.

HINDU UNITED KINGDOM ORGANISATIONS

The organisations listed in this section include both head offices of organisations with branches throughout the country and organisations which aspire to serve the Hindu community on a UK-wide basis.

Arya Pratinidhi Sabha (UK)*
69a Argyle Road, West Ealing, London W13 0LY
Tel: (020) 8991 1732
Contact: Professor S N Bharadwaj
Position: President
Affiliations: Inter Faith Network for the UK
Aims to propagate the Vedic religion in the UK; to devise means and measures for its propagation; and to establish and maintain libraries and centres of learning for the Vedic Dharma (religion).

Basava International Foundation*
59 Kingsfield Avenue, Harrow HA2 6AQ
Contact: Mr S Mahadevaiah
Position: Executive Chairman
Activities: Youth, elderly, women, visits, inter-faith, resources
Traditions: Multi-traditional
Other Languages: Kannada

Bochasanwasi Shri Akshar Purushottamni Sansatha, The Swaminarayan Hindu Mission*
PO Box 7122, 23-43 Ivor Road, Sparkhill, Birmingham B11 4NR
Tel: (0121) 7723086
Contact: Madhu Joshee
Contact Tel: (0121) 2464602
Activities: Worship/practice/meditation, community centre, youth, elderly, newsletter/journal
Traditions: Sanatan
Movements: Swaminarayan
Other Languages: Gujarati, Hindi
Affiliations: Hindu Council of Birmingham

Brahmrishi Mission*
Yoga and Cultural Centre, 278 Heston Road, Hounslow TW5 0RT
Tel: (020) 8571 3879 **Fax:** (020) 8571 3879
Contact: Swami Vishva Bharti
Position: Religious Preacher
Activities: Worship/practice/meditation, youth, elderly, women, newsletter/journal, books, television
Traditions: Sanatan
Other Languages: Hindi, Punjabi
An international organisation working for the welfare of humanity through educational institutions. Teaches Hindi and Punjabi to children and teaches Yoga and meditation free of charge.

Confederation of Indian Organisations*
5 Westminster Bridge Road, London SE1 7XW

Tel: (020) 7928 9889 **Fax:** (020) 7620 4025
Email: cio@gn.apc.org
Website: http://www.blink.org.uk/organ/cio.htm
Contact: Ms Rashmi Varma
Position: Chief Executive
Activities: Umbrella body, visits, newsletters, books, inter-faith
Other Languages: Hindi, Gujarati, Urdu, Bengali
Aims to provide services to strengthen and support voluntary organisations so they may have sustainable structures allowing them to deliver effective services and attract and manage resources.

Federation of Brahmin Associations UK*
53 West Hill, Wembley HA9 9RW
Tel: (020) 8904 2898
Contact: Ashok Pandya
Position: Secretary
Activities: Umbrella body

Federation of Patidar Associations*
Patidar House, 22 London Road, Wembley HA9 7EX
Tel: (020) 8795 1648 **Fax:** (020) 8795 1648
Contact: Ramesh Patel
Position: Honorary Secretary
Activities: Youth, elderly, women
Traditions: Sanatan
Other Languages: Gujarati

Gaudiya Mission (Vasudev Gaudiya Math)*
27 Cranhurst Road, Willesden Green, London NW2 4LJ
Tel: (020) 8452 2733 **Fax:** (020) 8452 2733
Email: ramgaudiyamission@hotmail.com
Website: http://www.gaudiyamission.org/
Contact: Mr Ramchandra Pakhira
Position: Superintendent
Activities: Worship/practice/meditation, inter-faith
Traditions: Vaishnava
Other Languages: Bengali, Hinhi, Gujarati, Sanskrit
Affiliations: International Society for Krishna Consciousness
The first Vaishnava organisation in the western world.

Gujarati Arya Kashktriya Mahasubha (UK)*
1 Wavertree Drive, Leicester LE4 7NX
Contact: Mr Chimanbhai B Champaneria
Position: President
Contact Tel: (0116) 2218436
Activities: Community centre, youth, elderly,

women, newsletter/journal, books, radio, inter-faith
Traditions: Sanatan
Movements: Arya Samaj
Other Languages: Gujarati, Hindi,

Hindu Centre London*
39 Grafton Road, Chalk Farm, London NW5 4JA
Tel: (020) 7485 8200
Contact: Mr D Gopee
Position: Trustee
Activities: Worship/practice/meditation, community centre, newsletter/journal, resources
Traditions: Multi-Traditional
Movements: Arya Samaj
Other Languages: Hindi, Punjabi

Hindu College London*
50 Morland Avenue, Croydon CR0 6EA
Tel: (020) 8656 1835 **Fax:** (020) 8656 1835
Contact: Dr J C Sharma
Position: Principal
Contact Tel: (020) 8656 1835
Activities: Youth, books, resources
Traditions: Multi-traditional
Movements: Arya Samaj
Other Languages: Hindi, Punjabi, Sanskrit

Hindu Council (UK)*
74 Llanover Road, North Wembley HA9 7LT
Tel: (07779) 583066
Contact: Mr Romapada Dasa
Position: General Secretary
Affiliations: Inter Faith Network for the UK
The Council was founded in 1994 and links a wide range of Hindu organisations.

Hindu Cultural Trust Centre*
55 Manor Avenue, Hounslow TW4 7JN
Tel: (020) 8230 0571
Contact: Gian Chand Gaur
Position: General Secretary
Activities: Worship, resource, umbrella body, visits, youth, elderly women, newsletters, books, inter-faith
Traditions: Sanatan
Movements: Vedic, Cultural or Sanatanic
Other Languages: Hindi, Punjabi, Gujarati

Hindu Marathon*
15 Higher Downs, Fairweather Green, Bradford BD8 0NA
Tel: (01274) 577395 **Fax:** (01274) 521211
Contact: Rajnikant B Parmar
Position: National Secretary

Activities: Youth
Traditions: Multi-Traditional
Movements: Hindutva
Other Languages: Hindi, Gujarati, Punjabi
Affiliations: Vishwa Hindu Parishad, West
Yorkshire; Hindu Swayamsevak Sangh (UK)
Organises annual half marathon and fun runs. The
event is open to all.

Hindu Resource Centre*

10 De Montfort Road, London SW16 1LZ
Tel: (020) 8675 6717 **Fax:** (020) 8675 6717
Contact: Mrs Saraswati Dave
Position: Chair
Activities: Resource, media, umbrella body, youth,
elderly, women, inter-faith
Traditions: Multi-Traditional
Other Languages: Gujarati, Panjabi, Hindi, Tamil
Affiliations: Vishwa Hindu Parishad
An umbrella organisation providing services to the
cross-section of the community including
counselling and advice on all matters to various age
groups. Also acts as a pressure group.

Hindu Swayamsevak Sangh (UK)

Keshav Pratishthan, 46-48 Loughborough Road,
Leicester LE4 5LD
Tel: (0116) 2665665 **Fax:** (0116) 2611931
Contact: Mr Pravin V Ruparelia
Position: General Secretary
Activities: Youth
Traditions: Cultural Organisation
Movements: Hindutva
Other Languages: Hindi, Gujarati, Punjabi,
Marathi
Affiliations: Vishwa Hindu Parishad
The organisation's objective is to provide and
propagate Hindu thoughts, ideals and values of life,
and to promote unity among Hindus and
harmonious relations with other faiths. Working
mainly with Hindu youth it has branches all over the
country.

International Society for Krishna
Consciousness (ISKCON)*

Bhaktivedanta Manor, Dharam Marg, Hilfield Lane,
Aldenham, Watford WD25 8EZ
Tel: (01923) 857244 **Fax:** (01923) 852896
Email: bhaktivedanta.manor@pamho.net
Website: http://www.bhaktivedantamanor.org/
Contact: Bimal Krishna das
Position: Public Relations Officer
Contact Tel: (01923) 856259
Contact Email: bimal.krsna.bcs@pamho.net

Activities: Worship/practice/meditation,
community centre, central body, umbrella body,
youth, elderly, women, newsletter/journal, books,
newspapers, radio, television, visits, inter-faith,
resources
Traditions: Vaishnava
Movements: Chaitanya
Other Languages: Gujarati, Hindi, Polish, Spanish
Affiliations: National Council of Hindu Temples;
Shree Mayapur Chandro Daya Mandir, Bengal,
India.
A centre of living Hindu spirituality which
promotes Vedic culture, especially through the
Gaudiya Vaishnava teachings of Chaitanya Maha
Prabhu. Also a Vedic college for theological training.

ISKCON Communications*

Bhaktivedanta Manor, Hilfield Lane, Aldenham,
Watford WD2 8EZ
Tel: (01923) 852819
Contact: Varshana devi das
Position: Communications Officer
Activities: Media
Traditions: Vaishnava
Movements: Chaitanya
Other Languages: Gujarati, Hindi, Bengali
Affiliations: National Council of Hindu Temples;
ISKCON Communications is the registered office
of the charity and deals with financial and
membership matters. It aims to facilitate
communications between the movement and
interested groups such as the media, educationalists
and other religious faiths.

ISKCON Educational Services*

Bhaktivedanta Manor, Hilfield Lane, Aldenham,
Watford WD2 8EZ
Tel: (01923) 859578 **Fax:** (01923) 859578
Email: ies@pamho.net
Website: http://www.iskcon.org.uk/ies/
Contact: Indriyesha
Position: Co-Director
Activities: Worship/practice/meditation, books,
visits, resources
Traditions: Vaishnava
Movements: Chaitanya
Other Languages: Gujarati,
Affiliations: The International Society for Krishna
Consciousness
Information, artefacts and other resources covering
all aspects of Hinduism. Guest speakers, dance and
drama available for schools, colleges, INSET etc. Free
correspondence service. All enquiries welcome.

Iyengar Yoga Institute*
223a Randolph Avenue, London W9 1NL
Tel: (020) 7624 3080 **Fax:** (020) 7372 2726
Email: office@iyi.org.uk
Website: http://www.iyi.org.uk/
Contact: Angus Fookes
Position: Manager
Activities: Resource
Traditions: Yoga
Movements: Iyengar Yoga
Runs over 50 classes a week for all levels of ability, including children's classes, pregnancy, remedial, teacher training and classes for 59+.

Jignyasu Satsang Seva Trust*
12 Sidmouth Road, Willesden Green, London
NW2 5JX
Tel: (020) 8459 4466 **Fax:** (020) 8145 9400
Contact: Miss Prabha Bhagat
Position: Secretary
Contact Tel: (020) 8908 4978
Activities: Worship/practice/meditation, youth, elderly
Traditions: Sanatan
Movements: Pushtimargi, Chaitanya
Other Languages: Hindi, Gujarati,
Affiliations: Rambapa Sadhu Seva Trust
(London); Maruti Rambaba Seva Trust
The Trust, through founder Pujya Rambapa, provides idols of Hindu deities to any Hindu temple, free of charge. Also runs yearly food camps in India which feed thousands of people.

Lohana Community of the UK*
16 Fortescue Chase, Southend-on-Sea SS1 3SS
Tel: (01702) 582992
Email: secretary@lcuk.org.uk
Website: http://www.lcuk.org.uk/
Contact: Harishbhai Raichura
Position: Secretary General

National Association of Patidar Samaj*
77 Brockenhurst Avenue, Worcester Park
KT4 7RH
Email: pravinamin@aol.com
Contact: Pravinbhai Amin
Position: President
Activities: Worship, youth, elderly, women, visits
Traditions: Multi-Traditional
Movements: Sanatan
Social Groups: Patidar
Affiliations: National Council of Hindu Temples
Hindu community centre and temple with an advisory service for immigration, unemployment, family concerns and education. There are language classes for adults in England and Gujarati. Religious services and marriage registration, hall hire and library.

National Council of Hindu Temples (UK)*
c/o Shree Sanatan Mandir, Weymouth Street, off
Catherine Street, Leicester LE4 6FP
Tel: (0116) 2661402 **Fax:** (01923) 856269
Contact: Mr Bimal Krishna das
Position: Secretary
Contact Tel: (01923) 856269
Contact Email: bimal.krsna.bcs@pamho.net
Activities: Umbrella body, youth, elderly, women, newsletters, books, inter-faith
Traditions: Sanatan
Other Languages: Gujarati, Hindi
Affiliations: Inter Faith Network for the UK;
Hindu Council of the UK
The Council aims to promote the Hindu religion; maintain uniformity among Hindu Temples; provide advice and information for local and public authorities and government departments.

National Council of Vanik Associations*
37 Howberry Road, Edgeware HA8 6SS
Tel: (020) 8952 1165
Contact: Mr Manhar Mehta
Position: Chairman

National Hindu Students Forum (UK)*
46-48 Loughborough Road, Leicester LE4 5LD
Tel: (07779) 303476
Email: info@nhsf.org.uk
Website: http://www.nhsf.org.uk/
Contact: Mr Keshava Shastry
Position: Communications Officer
Contact Email: mks98@doc.ic.ac.uk
Activities: Central body, youth, visits, inter-faith, newsletter/journal, resources
Traditions: Multi-Traditional
Other Languages: Hindi, Sanskrit
Affiliations: World Organisation of Students and Youth
Largest Hindu student body in Europe. We work towards the better understanding of Hindu Dharma, and to provide a platform for Hindu youth to express their views.

Pancholi Samaj*
143 Loughborough Road, Leicester LE4 5LR
Tel: (0116) 276864

Contact: Mr B G Pancholi
Position: Senior Trustee

Rushi Panchang*
60 Belgrave Road, Leicester LE4 5AS
Tel: (0116) 2622662 **Fax:** (0116) 2622662
Email: rushi_panchang@hotmail.com
Contact: Mr Vanmali
Position: Chair
Activities: Books, inter-faith
Traditions: Sanatan
Other Languages: Gujarati, Hindi,
Affiliations: Hindu Religion and Astrological
Education Society
Produces an Almanac for Hindus based on UK time
which Hindus can use for any auspicious event.

Shree Mirzapur Association (UK)*
37 Prout Grove, Neasden, London NW10 1PU
Tel: (020) 8452 1394 **Fax:** (020) 8208 1968
Contact: Mr Veljibhai Hirani
Position: Secretary
Activities: Resource, youth, elderly, women
Movements: Swaminarayan
Other Languages: Gujarati
Affiliations: Hindu Council (Brent)

Shree Swaminarayan Mandir*
105-119 Brentfield Road, Neasden, London
NW10 8JP
Tel: (020) 8965 2651 **Fax:** (020) 8965 6313
Website: http://www.swaminarayan.org/
Contact: Mr N Palan
Position: Interfaith Representative
Contact Tel: (07715) 110293
Contact Email: npalan@aol.com
Activities: Worship/practice/meditation,
community centre, newsletter/journal, inter-faith
Traditions: Vaishnava
Movements: Swaminarayan
Other Languages: Gujarati
Affiliations: National Council of Hindu Temples;
Inter Faith Network for the UK

Shri Vallabh Nidhi UK*
Opposite Baptist Church, Ealing Road, Wembley
HA0 4LT
Tel: (020) 8795 1051 **Fax:** (020) 8903 7750
Contact: Nalinikarit T Pandia
Position: Hon General Secretary
Contact Tel: (020) 8922 7093
Activities: Umbrella body, youth, elderly,
newsletter/journal, inter-faith, resources
Traditions: Sanatan
Movements: Pushtimargi, Sanatani

Social Groups: Various
Other Languages: Gujarati, Hindi
Affiliations: National Council of Hindu Temples;
Hindu Council (Brent)

Sivananda Yoga Vedanta Centre*
51 Felsham Road, Putney, London SW15 1AZ
Tel: (020) 8780 0160 **Fax:** (020) 8780 0128
Email: london@sivananda.org
Website: http://www.sivananda.org/
Contact: Swami Saradananda
Position: Director
Activities: Worship, umbrella body, visits, youth,
elderly, women, newsletter, books, inter-faith
Traditions: Yoga, Vedanta
Movements: Swami Sivananda
Affiliations: Sivananda Yoga Vedanta Centres
Headquarters, Quebec, Canada
The Centre offers Yoga classes, meditation and
chanting classes; also organises fasting weekends,
retreats, and a wide range of workshops. Courses
from beginners to advanced levels. All welcome.

Swaminarayan Satsang Organisation*
Shree Hari House, 99B Cobbold Road, Willesden,
London NW10 9SL
Tel: (020) 8830 0771 **Fax:** (020) 8830 0804
Email: issoeurope@compuserve.com
Website:
http://www.shreeswaminarayan-online.org/
Contact: Mr Ashok Patel
Position: Public Relations Officer
Contact Tel: (020) 8830 0803
Contact Email: info@interpharm.co.uk
Activities: Worship/practice/meditation,
community centre, central body, youth, elderly,
women, books, radio, visits, inter-faith, resources
Traditions: Sanatan
Movements: Swaminarayan
Other Languages: Gujarati, Hindi
Affiliations: Shree Swaminarayan Temple, Kalupur,
Ahmedabad, India
ISSO is an umbrella organisation of Shree
Swaminarayan Temples outside India. The first
Swaminarayan Temple in the world was built in
Ahmedabad by the founder Bhagan Shree
Swaminarayan.

Swaminarayan Temple*
847 Finchley Road, Golders Green, London
NW11 8LX
Tel: (020) 8458 5356 **Fax:** (020) 8458 4950
Email: london@swaminarayangadi.com
Website: http://www.swaminarayangadi.com/

Contact: Mr P D Varsani
Position: Secretary
Contact Tel: (020) 8202 0229
Contact Email: tantri@swaminarayangadi.com
Activities: Worship/practice/meditation, community centre, youth, elderly, women, television, visits, resources
Traditions: Sanatan
Movements: Swaminarayan
Other Languages: Gujarati, Hindi, Sanskrit
Affiliations: Shree Swaminarayan Sidhant Sajivan Mandal, London; Shree Swaminarayan Gadi Sansthan - Maninagar
A centre for spiritual, cultural and social welfare.

Vanik Association of the United Kingdom*
5 Beechdene, Tadworth KT20 5EA
Tel: (01737) 813977
Contact: Mrs Mradula S Shah
Position: General Secretary

Vedanta Movement*
13 Elsenham Street, Southfields, London SW18 5UN
Contact: Mrs Iris Rafferty
Position: General secretary
Activities: Umbrella body, newsletters, books, inter-faith
Traditions: Yoga
Movements: Chaitanya, Rama Krishna Order
Affiliations: Rama Krishna Order

Veerashaiva Samaja United Kingdom (VSUK)*
c/o The Forge, Shaftesbury Road, Fovant, Salisbury SP3 5JA
Tel: (01722) 714511 **Fax:** (01722) 714699
Email: moksha@kmcl.com
Website: http://www.vsuk.org.uk/
Contact: Mrs Moksha Darnton
Position: Vice-President
Activities: Worship/practice/meditation, youth, elderly, women
Traditions: Multi-traditional
Movements: Basaveshwara
Other Languages: Kannada, Hindi, Tamil, Marati
Affiliations: Veerashaiva Samaja (UK); Veerashaiva Samaja of North America
Veerashaivism, also known as Lingayatism, was started by the great man called Basaveshwara in the 12th century. The motto is "work is worship" and "all are equal".

Vishwa Hindu Parishad (UK)*
48 Wharfedale Gardens, Thornton Heath, Croydon CR7 6LB
Tel: (020) 8684 9716 **Fax:** (020) 8684 9716
Contact: Mr Kishor Ruparelia
Position: General Secretary
Activities: Worship, resource, umbrella body, media, visits, youth, elderly, women, newsletters, books
Traditions: Multi-traditional
Other Languages: Hindi, Gujarati
Affiliations: Vishwa Hindu Parishad, India and Europe; Inter Faith Network for the UK
Provides religious, social, educational and welfare services to all communities; runs centres for the elderly, women and youth. Its office bearers play an active part in governmental organisations and agencies and strive for equal opportunity for all.

Vivekananda Centre*
6 Lea Gardens, Wembley HA9 7SE
Tel: (020) 8902 0840 **Fax:** (020) 8903 0763
Email: hindu@btinternet.com
Website: http://www.vivekananda.co.uk/
Contact: Mr Jay Lakhani
Position: Chief Executive
Activities: Youth, elderly, women, radio, television, inter-faith, resources
Traditions: Sanatan
Other Languages: Gujarati, Hindi, Tamil
Education/media participation and inter-faith work is our speciality. Popular Hinduism for schools website: www.hinduism.fsnet.co.uk. We also teach Hinduism at GCSE and Advanced Levels.

HINDU REGIONAL AND LOCAL ORGANISATIONS AND MANDIRS

Various forms of Hindu local organisations are listed in this directory. These include *mandirs*, many of which are in buildings adapted from other original uses, but increasing numbers of which are purpose-built. Also listed are *caste* groups and other organisations which often meet either in hired premises or in the homes of their members.

ENGLAND   323

NORTH EAST   323

YORKSHIRE AND THE HUMBER   324

NORTH WEST   326

EAST MIDLANDS   329

WEST MIDLANDS   336

EAST OF ENGLAND   340

LONDON   342

SOUTH EAST   353

SOUTH WEST   354

NORTHERN IRELAND   355

SCOTLAND   355

WALES   356

ENGLAND

NORTH EAST
City, Town or Local Bodies

Hindu Cultural Society*
54 Westbourne Grove, North Ormesby, Middlesbrough TS3 3EF
Tel: (01642) 218428
Email: prem@ghimire.fqbusiness.co.uk
Contact: Acharya P Sharma
Position: Head of Religious Study
Activities: Worship/practice/meditation, community centre, youth, elderly, women, newsletter/journal, radio, television, visits, inter-faith
Traditions: Sanatan
Other Languages: Hindi, Punjabi, Gujarati, Bengali

Hindu Temple*
172 West Road, Newcastle-upon-Tyne NE4 9QB
Tel: (0191) 2733364
Contact: Attri
Position: Priest
Activities: Worship, resource, youth, elderly, women, inter-faith
Traditions: Multi-Traditional
Other Languages: Hindi, Gujarati, Bengali

ISKCON Newcastle*
304 Westgate Road, Newcastle-upon-Tyne NE4 5QU
Tel: (0191) 2721911 **Fax:** (0191) 2721911
Website: http://www.iskcon.org.uk/
Contact: Bhakti Rasa Das
Position: Temple President
Activities: Worship/practice/meditation, youth, elderly, women, newsletter/journal, visits, inter-faith, resources
Traditions: Vaishnava
Movements: Chaitanya
Other Languages: Hindi, Finnish
Affiliations: National Council of Hindu Temples; ISKCON

Istree Samaj*
10 Eastlands, High Heaton, Newcastle-upon-Tyne NE7 7YE
Tel: (0191) 2811509

Contact: Mrs Ravi Chowdhry
Position: Sectretary
Activities: Elderly, women, youth, inter-faith
Traditions: Sanatan
Movements: Arya Samaj
Other Languages: Hindi, Punjabi

Mahakaal Bheiro Group*
13 Ilford Road, West Jesmond, Newcastle-upon-Tyne NE2 3NX
Tel: (0191) 2843494 **Fax:** (0191) 2852888
Contact: Ghai Baba Ji
Position: Chair
Activities: Worship/practice/meditation, visits, inter-faith
Traditions: Tantra
Movements: Shiv Shakti
Other Languages: Hindi, Urdu, Punjabi, Gujarati
Affiliations: Hindu Sikh Friendship Society; Kirklees Hindu Society; Mahakaal Bheiro India Group

YORKSHIRE AND THE HUMBER
Regional or County Bodies

Hindu Education Council (Yorkshire)*
52 Rugby Place, Bradford BD7 2DF
Tel: (01274) 577395
Contact: Joniah Parthasarathi
Position: Secretary
Contact Tel: (01422) 361381
Activities: Resource, umbrella body, inter-faith
Traditions: Multi-Traditional
Movements: Vedanta
Other Languages: Hindi, Gujarati
Affiliations: Vishwa Hindu Parishad (Yorkshire); Vishwa Hindu Parishad (UK); World Council of Hindus

Leuva Patidar Samaj Yorkshire*
Legramms Mill Lane, off Legramms Lane, Lidget Green, Bradford BD7 2BA
Tel: (01274) 521185
Contact: Mr G V Patel
Position: Secretary
Activities: Worship/practice/meditation, community centre, youth, elderly, women, visits, inter-faith, resources
Traditions: Sanatan

Movements: Arya Samaj
Other Languages: Gujarati

Vishwa Hindu Parishad Yorkshire*
10 Ashville Croft, Pellon, Halifax HX2 0QJ
Tel: (01422) 361381
Contact: Mr Joniah Partha-Sarathi
Position: Secretary
Activities: Umbrella body
Traditions: Multi-traditional
Other Languages: Hindi, Gujarati, Punjabi, Bengali
Affiliations: Vishwa Hindu Parishad (UK); Vishwa Hindu Parishad (International)

City, Town or Local Bodies

Hindu Cultural Society of Bradford*
321 Leeds Road, Bradford BD3 9LS
Tel: (01274) 395603 **Fax:** (01274) 395603
Contact: Mr R Dewedi
Position: Honorary Secretary
Activities: Worship/practice/meditation, community centre, youth, elderly, women, books, visits, inter-faith
Traditions: Sanatan
Movements: Arya Samaj
Other Languages: Punjabi, Hindi
Affiliations: National Council of Hindu Temples; Vishwa Hindu Parishad

Hindu Education Council (Yorkshire)*
52 Rugby Place, Bradford BD7 2DF
Tel: (01274) 577395
Contact: Joniah Parthasarathi
Position: Secretary
Contact Tel: (01422) 361381
Activities: Resource, umbrella body, inter-faith
Traditions: Multi-Traditional
Movements: Vedanta
Other Languages: Hindi, Gujarati
Affiliations: Vishwa Hindu Parishad (Yorkshire); Vishwa Hindu Parishad (UK); World Council of Hindus

Hindu Swayamsevak Sangh*
52 Rugby Place, Bradford BD7 2DF
Tel: (01274) 577395 **Fax:** (01274) 521211
Contact: Bhupendra Mistry
Position: Assistant Secretary
Other Languages: Hindi, Gujarati, Punjabi

Affiliations: Vishwa Hindu Parishad (Yorkshire); Vishwa Hindu Parishad (UK); Vishwa Hindu Parishad (International)

Leuva Patidar Samaj Yorkshire*
Legramms Mill Lane, off Legramms Lane, Lidget Green, Bradford BD7 2BA
Tel: (01274) 521185
Contact: Mr G V Patel
Position: Secretary
Activities: Worship/practice/meditation, community centre, youth, elderly, women, visits, inter-faith, resources
Traditions: Sanatan
Movements: Arya Samaj
Other Languages: Gujarati

Shree Prajapati Association*
Thornton Lane, off Little Horton Lane, Bradford BD5 9DN
Tel: (01274) 578115
Contact: Mr Balu Lad
Position: Hon President
Contact Tel: (01274) 499841
Activities: Worship/practice/meditation, community centre, youth, elderly, women, visits, inter-faith
Traditions: Sanatan
Other Languages: Gujarati
Affiliations: Hindu Council of the North; Shree Prajapati Association UK

Sri Jalaram Shakti Mandal*
148 Arncliffe Terrace, Bradford BD7 3AG
Tel: (01274) 572337
Contact: Mr Kunverji Jivanji Mistry
Position: Secretary
Activities: Worship, visits
Traditions: Multi-Traditional
Other Languages: Gujarati
Affiliations: Hindu Cultural Society Community Centre

Swaminarayan Hindu Mission*
11 West View Close, Shipley, Bradford BD18 1NF
Contact: Mr Rasik Patel
Position: Branch Representative
Contact Tel: (01274) 585740
Other Languages: Gujarati, Hindi

Vidhya Varg*
c/o 52 Rugby Place, Lidget Green, Bradford BD7 2DF

Sanatan Dharam Society*
2 Holyrood Road, Town Moor, Doncaster DN2 5HB
Tel: (01302) 363732

Vishwa Hindu Parishad Yorkshire*
10 Ashville Croft, Pellon, Halifax HX2 0QJ
Tel: (01422) 361381
Contact: Mr Joniah Partha-Sarathi
Position: Secretary
Activities: Umbrella body
Traditions: Multi-traditional
Other Languages: Hindi, Gujarati, Punjabi, Bengali
Affiliations: Vishwa Hindu Parishad (UK); Vishwa Hindu Parishad (International)

Hindu Society of Kirklees and Calderdale*
Shree Sita Ram Temple, 20 Zetland Street, Huddersfield HD1 2RA
Tel: (07715) 611343
Contact: Miss Kiran Bali
Position: Assistant Secretary
Contact Email: kiran_bali@hotmail.com
Activities: Worship/practice/meditation, community centre, youth, elderly, women, visits, resources
Traditions: Sanatan
Movements: Sai Baba Community
Other Languages: Punjabi, Hindi, Gujarati
Affiliations: Vishwa Hindu Parishad; National Council of Hindu Temples

Hindu Charitable Trust*
6 Moor Allerton Gardens, Leeds L17 6QU
Tel: (0113) 2757024
Contact: A P Sekhri
Position: President
Contact Tel: (0113) 2371027
Contact Email: apsekhri@hotmail.com
Activities: Worship/practice/meditation, community centre, newsletter
Other Languages: Hiindi, Gujarati
Affiliations: Vishwa Hindu Parishad

Shree Hindu Mandir
36 Alexandra Road, Leeds LS6 1RF
Tel: (0113) 2612342

NORTH WEST
Regional or County Bodies

Hindu Council of the North
348 Denton Lane, Chadderton, Oldham
OL9 8QE
Tel: (0161) 236 6089   **Fax:** (0161) 236 6089
Contact: Mr Ratilal Chohan
Position: General Secretary
Contact Tel: ((0161) 2843023
Email: anantchohan@cwcom.net
Activities: Worship, resource, media, umbrella body, visits, youth, women, interfaith
Movements: Arya Samaj
Other Languages: Gujarati, Hindi
Affiliations: Hindu Council of UK, National Council of Hindu Temples.

City, Town or Local Bodies

Shree Bhartiya Mandal*
103 Union Road, Ashton-under-Lyne, Tameside OL6 8JN
Tel: (0161) 3302085 **Fax:** (0161) 3302085
Contact: Mr Balvant Mistry
Position: Honorary Secretary
Activities: Elderly, education
Other Languages: Gujarati, Hindi
Affiliations: Hindu Council of the North

Shree Jalaram Bhajan Mandal*
58 Kenyon Street, Ashton-under-Lyne OL6 7DU
Tel: (0161) 343 4639
Contact: Mr V Kara
Position: General Secretary
Contact Tel: (0161) 343 1939
Other Languages: Gujarati

Swaminarayan Hindu Mission*
29 Russell Street, Ashton-under-Lyne OL6 9QS
Contact: Vinubthai D Patel
Position: President
Contact Tel: (0161) 3305196

Blackburn Hindu Centre*
c/o 11 The Dene, Beardwood, Blackburn BB2 7QS

Tel: (01254) 678183
Email: ashokchudasama@hotmail.com
Website: http://www.blackburnhinducentre.co.uk/
Contact: Mr Ashok Chudasama
Position: Honorary General Secretary
Activities: Central body, youth, elderly, women, newsletter/journal, inter-faith, resources
Traditions: Multi-traditional
Other Languages: Gujarati, Hindi, Swahili
Affiliations: Hindu Council of the North

Shree Jansari Gnati Mandal*
33 Maple Street, Blackburn BB1 6LP
Tel: (01254) 677988
Contact: Mr Shantilal Vadher
Position: Secretary
Activities: Community centre
Traditions: Sanatan
Other Languages: Gujarati
Affiliations: Jansari Organisations UK

Mandhata Hitradak Mandal (Bolton)
Krishna Temple, 10 Beverley Road, Bolton BL1 4DT

Shree Krishna Mandir*
10 Beverley Road, Bolton BL1 4DT
Contact: Mr G B Patel
Position: Secretary
Contact Tel: (01204) 391392

Shree Kutch Satsang Swaminarayan Temple*
11 Adelaide Street, Bolton BL3 3NT
Tel: (01204) 652604 **Fax:** (01204) 652604
Contact: Secretary
Activities: Worship, resource, visits, youth
Traditions: Sanatan
Movements: Swaminarayan
Other Languages: Gujarati
Affiliations: Shree Swaminarayan Temple, Bhuj-Kutch, India

Shree Kutchhi Leva Patel*
Crook Street, Bolton BL3 6AS
Tel: (01204) 383297
Contact: Dev Halal
Position: Treasurer
Contact Tel: (01204) 660962
Other Languages: Gujarati

Shree Swaminarayan Sidhant Sajivan Mandal*
161 Deane Road, Bolton BL3 5AH
Tel: (01204) 533558
Contact: Mr Kanji V Naran
Position: Trustee
Contact Tel: (0161) 2803508
Activities: Worship/practice/meditation,
community centre, youth, elderly, women, visits,
inter-faith
Traditions: Swaminarayan
Movements: Swaminarayan
Other Languages: Gujarati

Vishwa Hindu Parishad (UK) Bolton*
1 Thomas Holden Street, Bolton BL1 2QG
Tel: (01204) 527492
Email: udmistry@madasafish.com
Website: http://www.vishwahinduparishad.co.uk/
Contact: Mr Uttambhai D Mistry
Position: Secretary
Contact Tel: (01204) 840611
Activities: Worship/practice/meditation,
community centre, youth, elderly, women, visits,
inter-faith, resources
Traditions: Sanatan
Other Languages: Gujarati, Hindi
Affiliations: Vishwa Hindu Parishad (UK)

Hindu Society - Lancaster and Morecambe*
10 Langton Close, Halton Road, Lancaster
LA1 2TJ
Tel: (01524) 849705
Contact: Mr Praful Upadhyay
Position: Chair
Activities: Worship/practice/meditation, inter-
faith
Traditions: Multi-Traditional
Other Languages: Gujarati, Punjabi, Hindi

Hare Krishna Centre (ISKCON)
114a Bold Street, Liverpool L1 4HY
Tel: (0151) 5129319
Email: liverpool@iskcon.org.uk
Contact: Arjunanatha das
Position: Secretary
Activities: Worship, visits, newsletter, books, inter-
faith
Traditions: Vaishnava
Movements: Chaitanya
Other Languages: French, Mauritian
Affiliations: International Society for Krishna
Consciousness

Hindu Cultural Organisation*
253 Edge Lane, Liverpool L7 2PH
Tel: (0151) 2637965 **Fax:** (0151) 2637965
Email: kirankhaneja@l7kensington.net
Contact: Ms Kiran Khaneja
Position: Youth Worker
Activities: Worship/practice/meditation,
community centre, youth, elderly, visits
Traditions: Sanatan
Movements: Arya Samaj
Other Languages: Hindi, Punjabi, Gujarati,
Bengali
Affiliations: Vishwa Hindu Parishad

Shri Radha Krishna Temple*
253 Edge Lane, Liverpool L7 2PH
Tel: (0151) 2637965 **Fax:** (0151) 2637965
Contact: Kiran Khaneja
Position: Youth Worker
Contact Email: kirankhaneja@l7kensington.net
Activities: Worship/practice/meditation, elderly
Traditions: Sanatan
Movements: Arya Samaj
Other Languages: Hindi, Punjabi, Gujarati,
Bengali

Bharatiya Vidya Bhavan (Manchester)*
Unit 5 West Point Enterprise Park, Clarence
Avenue, Manchester M17 1QS
Email: nprinja@aol.com
Website: http://www.bhavan.com/
Contact: Dr N Prinja
Position: Chairman, Education
Activities: Youth, newsletter/journal, resources
Other Languages: Hindi, Gujarati, Sanskrit
Affiliations: Vishwa Hindu Parishad (UK)

Gita Bhawa*
231 Withington Road, Whalley Range, Manchester
M32 8JT
Tel: (0161) 8610606
Contact: Mr S L Jairath
Position: Chairman
Activities: Worship/practice/meditation,
community centre, newsletter/journal, visits, inter-
faith
Traditions: Sanatan
Other Languages: Panjabi, Hindi, Gujarati, Tamil

Hindu Swayamsevak Sangh*
Karam House, 79 Lever Street, Manchester
M1 1FL

Tel: (0161) 2368621 **Fax:** (0161) 2280056
Contact: Mr T L Gupta
Position: Public Relations
Activities: Youth

Indian Association Manchester*

Gandhi Hall, Brunswick Road, Manchester
M20 9QB
Tel: (0161) 4451134 **Fax:** (01625) 548200
Contact: Mrs R M Oza
Position: President
Contact Tel: (01625) 531156
Activities: Resource, media, visits, youth, elderly,
women, newsletters
Traditions: Sanatan
Other Languages: Gujarati, Hindi

Indian Women's Organisation*

Gandhi Hall, Brunswick Road, Manchester
M20 9QB
Tel: (0161) 4451134 **Fax:** (01625) 548200
Contact: Dr Yogesh Virmani
Position: President
Contact Tel: (0161) 4457732
Activities: Resource, media, youth, elderly,
women, inter-faith
Traditions: Sanatan
Movements: Swaminarayan
Other Languages: Gujarati, Hindi
Affiliations: International Women's Organisation

ISKCON Manchester*

Hare Krishna Centre, 20 Mayfield Road, Whalley
Range, Manchester M16 8FT
Tel: (0161) 8606117 **Fax:** (0161) 8606117
Email: manchester@iskcon.org.uk
Website: http://www.iskcon.org.uk/manchester
Contact: His Grace Krishna Dharma
Position: Manager
Contact Email:
krishna@dharma16.freeserve.co.uk
Activities: Worship/practice/meditation,
newsletter/journal, books, newspapers, visits, inter-
faith, resources
Traditions: Vaishnava
Movements: Chaitanya
Affiliations: Society for Krishna Consciousness

Vishwa Hindu Parishad*

Karam House, 79 Lever Street, Manchester
M1 1FL

Tel: (0161) 2368621 **Fax:** (0161) 2280056
Contact: Mr Tarsem Lal Gupta
Position: Treasurer
Activities: Resource, umbrella body, youth, elderly,
newsletters, books, inter-faith
Traditions: Multi-Traditional
Movements: All Sampradayas
Other Languages: Hindi, Gujarati, Punjabi,
Kannada
Affiliations: Vishwa Hindu Parishad (UK); Vishwa
Hindu Parishad, India

India Culture and Social Centre*

53 Ashley Street, Oldham OL1 6HR
Tel: (0161) 6825189
Contact: Mr R C Chohan
Position: President
Contact Tel: (0161) 2843023
Activities: youth
Other Languages: Gujarati, Hindi
Affiliations: Hindu Council of the North

Indian Association*

Schofield Street, Oldham OL8 1JQ
Tel: (0161) 6330043 **Fax:** (0161) 6330043
Email:
indian_association_oldham_r@hotmail.com
Contact: Mr Shashi Mohandas
Position: Secretary
Activities: Worship/practice/meditation,
community centre, youth, elderly, women,
newsletter/journal, visits, inter-faith
Traditions: Sanatan
Other Languages: Gujarati, Hindi
Affiliations: Hindu Council of the North;
National Council of Hindu Temples

Shree Swaminarayan Temple*

270 Lee Street, Oldham OL8 1BG
Tel: (0161) 6520993
Contact: Mr P Naran
Position: Secretary
Activities: Worship/practice/meditation,
community centre, youth, elderly, women,
newsletter/journal, visits, resources
Traditions: Vaishnava
Movements: Swaminarayan
Other Languages: Gujarati, Hindi

Andhra Social and Community Organisation*

28 St Mary's Street, Preston PR1 5LN

Tel: (01772) 793924
Contact: Mr K V Babu
Position: President
Contact Tel: (01772) 798374
Activities: Worship/practice/meditation
Other Languages: Telugu

Gujarat Hindu Society*
South Meadow Lane, off Fishergate Hill, Preston
PR1 8JN
Tel: (01772) 253901 **Fax:** (01772) 882221
Contact: D H Nayee
Position: Secretary
Activities: Worship, resource, visits, youth, elderly,
women, newsletters, books, inter-faith
Traditions: Sanatan
Other Languages: Gujarati, Hindi
Affiliations: Hindu Council of the North;
National Council of Hindu Temples; National
Congress of Gujarati Organisations

Shree Prajapati Association*
105 Lowndes Street, Preston PR1 7XU
Tel: (01772) 821487
Email: dineshmistry@mcmail.com
Contact: Mr N A Tailor
Position: Trustee
Other Languages: Gujarati
Affiliations: All UK Prajapati Associations

Swaminarayan Hindu Mission*
8 Avenham Place, Avenham, Preston PR1 3SX
Tel: (01772) 562252
Contact: Mr Gerry Limbachia
Contact Tel: (01772) 704174
Contact Email: gerry.limbachia@baesystems.com
Activities: Worship/practice/meditation,
community centre, youth, elderly, women, visits,
inter-faith, resources
Traditions: Sanatan
Movements: Swaminarayan
Other Languages: Gujarati, Hindi
Affiliations: Swaminarayan Hindu Mission,
London

Lord Rama Krishna Temple*
7 Haydock Street, Warrington WA2 7UW
Tel: (01925) 572042
Contact: Mr O N Sud
Position: Secretary
Activities: Worship/practice/meditation,

community centre, umbrella body, youth, elderly,
women, visits, inter-faith, resources
Traditions: Multi-traditional
Other Languages: Hindi, Punjabi, Gujarati

Brahma Samaj Manchester*
c/o 26 Prestbury Road, Wilmslow SK9 2LL
Tel: (01625) 531156 **Fax:** (01625) 548200
Contact: Mrs Ramaben M Oza
Position: President
Contact Email: westfield.textilesuk@virgin.net.
Activities: Resource, media, youth, elderly,
women, newsletter, inter-faith
Traditions: Sanatan
Movements: Swaminarayan
Other Languages: Gujarati
Affiliations: Hindu Council of the North;
National Council of Hindu Temples; Federation of
Brahmin Associations of Europe

EAST MIDLANDS
Regional or County Bodies

**Lohana Community: Derbyshire and
Nottinghamshire***
312 Normanton Road, Derby DE3 6WE
Tel: (01332) 380407 **Fax:** (0115) 9308145
Contact: Mr Mansukh Modi
Position: Committee Member
Contact Tel: (01332) 771285
Activities: Worship/practice/meditation, central
body, umbrella body, youth, elderly, women, visits
Traditions: Sanatan
Movements: Arya Samaj, Pushtimargi
Other Languages: Gujarati
Affiliations: Geeta Bhawan, Derby

Shree Prajapati Association*
Shree Prajapati Community Centre, Ulverscroft
Road, Leicester LE4 6BY
Tel: (0116) 2628560
Website: http://www.prajapati.org.uk/
Contact: Mr Jay Mistry
Position: Vice President
Contact Email: harish_mistry@ntlworld.com
Activities: Worship/practice/meditation,
community centre, umbrella body, youth, elderly,
women, newsletter/journal, radio, television, visits,
inter-faith, resources
Traditions: Sanatan

Movements: Arya Samaj
Other Languages: Gujarati
Affiliations: Leicester Hindu Council

City, Town or Local Bodies

Geeta Bhawan Hindu Temple*
312 Normanton Road, Derby DE23 6WE
Tel: (01332) 380407
Contact: Raj Bali
Position: President
Contact Tel: (01332) 735908
Activities: Worship/practice/meditation, youth, elderly, women, visits, resource
Traditions: Sanatan
Other Languages: Hindi, Gujarati, Punjabi
Affiliations: National Council of Hindu Temples

Gujarati Arya Association*
1 Wavertree Drive, Leicester LE4 7NX
Contact: Mr C B Champaneria
Position: General Secretary
Contact Tel: (0116) 2218436
Activities: Community centre, central body, youth, elderly, women, newsletter/journal, radio, visits
Traditions: Sanatan
Movements: Arya Samaj
Other Languages: Gujarati, Hindi,

Hindu Welfare Association*
c/o Geeta Bhawan Temple, 312 Normanton Road, Derby DE3 6WE
Tel: (01332) 380407

Asian Sports Club and Cultural Centre*
29 Coral Street, Leicester LE4 5BF
Tel: (0116) 2669207
Contact: Maganbhai P Patel
Position: General Contact
Activities: Resource, youth, inter-faith
Traditions: Sanatan
Other Languages: Gujarati, Hindi
Affiliations: Leicester Hindu Festival Council

Audich Gadhia Brahmasamaj*
62 Lockerbie Avenue, Leicester LE4 7NJ
Tel: (0116) 2660612
Contact: Mr Indubhai Vyas
Affiliations: Leicester Gujarat Hindu Association

Charotar Patidar Samaj (Leicester)*
20 Southchurch Gate, Entrance on Bay Street, Leicester LE1 3EA
Tel: (0116) 2514465
Contact: Mr A M Amin
Position: Secretary
Contact Tel: (0116) 2899007
Contact Email: ashu.amin@ntlworld.com
Activities: Worship/practice/meditation, community centre, youth, elderly, women
Traditions: Vaishnava
Other Languages: Gujarati, Hindi

Friends of Vrindavan*
43 Stanhope Street, Leicester LE1 5DG
Tel: (0116) 2217314
Contact: Ram Pillai

Gujarati Arya Association*
1 Wavertree Drive, Leicester LE4 7NX
Contact: Mr C B Champaneria
Position: General Secretary
Contact Tel: (0116) 2218436
Activities: Community centre, central body, youth, elderly, women, newsletter/journal, radio, visits
Traditions: Sanatan
Movements: Arya Samaj
Other Languages: Gujarati, Hindi

Gujarat Hindu Association*
51 Loughborough Road, Leicester LE4 5LJ
Tel: (0116) 2668266 **Fax:** (0116) 2613066
Contact: Mr M P Patel
Position: President
Activities: Resource, media, umbrella body, youth, elderly, newsletters
Traditions: Sanatan
Other Languages: Gujarati

Hindu Religious and Cultural Society*
Geeta Bhavan, 70 Clarendon Park Road, Knighton, Leicester LE2 3AD
Tel: (0116) 2707756
Contact: Mahesh Chander Prasher
Position: Secretary
Contact Tel: (0116) 2350667
Activities: Worship, youth, elderly
Traditions: Sanatan
Other Languages: Hindi, Punjabi
Affiliations: Council of Hindu Organisations, Leicester; National Council of Hindu Temples

Hindu Sahitya Kendra*

46/48 Loughborough Road, Leicester LE4 5LD
Tel: (0116) 2611303 **Fax:** (0116) 2611931
Email: admin@hss-leic.demon.co.uk
Contact: Mr L B Raithatha
Position: Manager
Traditions: Sanatan
Other Languages: Gujarati, Hindi, Punjabi

Hindu Temple and Community Association

75 Prospect Hill, Leicester LE5 9BW
Tel: (0116) 2622221
Contact: Mr Rashmikant Joshi
Position: Honorary Secretary
Affiliations: Leicester Gujarat Hindu Association

Hindu Temple (Sanatan Mandir)*

84 Weymouth Street, Leicester LE4 6FP
Tel: (0116) 2661402
Contact: Mr Patel
Position: President

Indian Cultural Society*

47 Tavistock Drive, Leicester LE5 5NT
Tel: (0116) 2730357
Contact: Dr H D Vyas
Position: Honorary Secretary
Affiliations: Leicester Gujarat Hindu Association

Indian Education Society*

10 Woodbridge Road, Leicester LE4 7RF
Tel: (0116) 2681071
Contact: Mr Jayantilal Mistry
Position: Honorary Secretary
Other Languages: Gujarati
Affiliations: Leicester Gujarat Hindu Association

International Swaminarayan Satsang Organisation (ISSO)*

Shree Swaminarayan Temple, 139/141
Loughborough Road, Leicester LE4 5LQ
Tel: (0116) 266210 **Fax:** (0116) 266210
Activities: Worship/practice/meditation
Traditions: Sanatan
Movements: Swaminarayan
Other Languages: Gujarati, Hindi

ISKCON Leicester*

21 Thoresby Street, North Evington, Leicester LE5 4GU
Tel: (0116) 2762587 **Fax:** (0116) 2367723

Email: gauranga@gauranga.org
Website: http://www.gauranga.com/
Contact: Gauranga Sundara Das
Position: President
Contact Tel: (07887) 560260
Activities: Worship, resource, media, visits, youth, elderly, women, newsletters, books, inter-faith
Traditions: Vaishnava
Movements: Chaitanya
Other Languages: Gujarati, Hindi
Affiliations: International Society for Krishna Consciousness

Leicester Hindu Festival Council*

51 Loughborough Road, Leicester LE4 5LJ
Tel: (0116) 2668266 **Fax:** (0116) 2613066
Contact: Maganghai P Patel
Position: President
Activities: Umbrella body, youth, elderly, women, inter-faith
Traditions: Multi-Traditional
Other Languages: Hindi, Gujarati

Leicester Sangit Kala Kendra*

c/o Mr Patel, 27 Bradbourne Road, Leicester LE5 5AL

Leicestershire Brahma Samaj

15 Belgrave Road, Leicester LE4 6AR
Tel: (0116) 2624359

Leuva Patidar Samaj (SD)*

3 Saltcoates Avenue, Leicester LE4 7NP
Contact: Mr Ratilal Patel
Position: Secretary
Affiliations: Leicester Gujarat Hindu Association

Lohana Mahila Mandal*

3 Dorset Street, Leicester LE4 6BG

Maher Community Association*

15 Ravenbridge Drive, Leicester LE4 0BZ
Tel: (0116) 2425360 **Fax:** (0116) 2625637
Contact: Mr Harbhambhai Keshwala
Position: Office Manager
Activities: Community centre
Traditions: Sanatan
Movements: Arya Samaj
Other Languages: Gujarati, Hindi

Pancholi Samaj*
143 Loughborough Road, Leicester LE4 5LR
Tel: (0116) 276864
Contact: Mr B G Pancholi
Position: Senior Trustee

Rana Samaj*
85 Coral Street, Leicester LE4 5BG
Contact: Mr Bharatbhai Rana
Position: Honorary Secretary
Affiliations: Leicester Gujarat Hindu Association

Shree Anavil Samaj*
11 Saltersford Road, Leicester LE5 4DF
Tel: (0116) 2213246
Contact: Mr N Desai
Position: Honorary Secretary
Affiliations: Leicester Gujarat Hindu Association

Shree Darji Gnati Mandal (SD) Leicester*
21 Sawley Street, Leicester LE5 5JR
Contact: Mr Navin Topiwala
Position: Committee Member
Activities: Youth, elderly, women, inter-faith
Traditions: Multi-Traditional
Other Languages: Gujarati

Shree Gurjar Kshatriya Gnati Mandal*
3 Agar Street, Leicester LE4 6NE
Tel: (0116) 2386228
Email: barkmanani@compuserve.com
Contact: Mr Prabhulal Jivanlal Manani
Position: Trustee
Activities: Youth, elderly, women, newsletters,
inter-faith
Traditions: Sanatan
Movements: Swaminarayan, Ramanandi
Other Languages: Gujarati
Affiliations: Leicester Hindu Festival Council;
Gujarat Hindu Association; Vision Hindu Parishad

Shree Hindu Temple and Community Centre*
34 St Barnabas Road, Leicester LE5 4BD
Tel: (0116) 2464590 **Fax:** (0116) 2464590
Contact: Mr Govindbhai Rambhai Patel
Position: President
Contact Tel: (0116) 2122943
Activities: Worship/practice/meditation,
community centre, youth, elderly, women,
newsletter/journal, visits
Traditions: Sanatan

Other Languages: Gujarati, Hindi
Affiliations: Gujarat Hindu Association; National
Council of Hindu Temples

Shree Jalaram Prathna Mandal*
85 Narborough Road, Leicester LE3 0LF
Tel: (0116) 2540117 **Fax:** (0116) 2547488
Email: jalarambapa@endland.com
Website: http://www.jalarambapa.com./
Contact: Thakersi Vithaldas Morjaria
Position: President
Activities: Worship, resource, visits, youth, women,
inter-faith
Traditions: Sanatan
Movements: Sanatan Dharma
Other Languages: Gujarati, Hindi, Punjabi
Affiliations: Leicestershire Hindu Council;
National Council of Hindu Temples

Shree Jansari Gnati Mandal Leicester*
109 Burfield Street, Leicester LE4 6AQ
Tel: (0116) 2714372
Contact: Mr Mahesh K Chauhan
Position: Secretary
Activities: Youth, elderly, newsletters
Traditions: Sanatan
Movements: Arya Samaj
Other Languages: Gujarati, Hindi
Affiliations: Gujarat Hindu Association; Jansari
Organisation UK

Shree Mandata Samaj Sahayak Mandal*
1 Hartington Rd, Leicester LE2 0GP
Tel: (0116) 2623648
Contact: Mr M R Patel
Position: Secretary
Affiliations: Leicester Gujarat Hindu Association

Shree Navrang Society*
20 Wetherby Road, Leicester LE4 9UF
Tel: (0116) 2767816
Contact: Mr Nitin Vyas
Position: Honorary Secretary
Contact Tel: (0116) 2665540
Activities: Worship/practice/meditation
Other Languages: Gujarati, Hindi

Shree Prajapati Association*
Shree Prajapati Community Centre, Ulverscroft
Road, Leicester LE4 6BY
Tel: (0116) 2628560

Website: http://www.prajapati.org.uk/
Contact: Mr Jay Mistry
Position: Vice President
Contact Email: harish_mistry@ntlworld.com
Activities: Worship/practice/meditation, community centre, umbrella body, youth, elderly, women, newsletter/journal, radio, television, vists, inter-faith, resources
Traditions: Sanatan
Movements: Arya Samaj
Other Languages: Gujarati
Affiliations: Leicester Hindu Council

Shree Rajput Bhoiraj Gnati*
2 Jubilee Drive, Leicester LE3 9LJ
Tel: (0116) 2916685
Email: kivit.j@hotmail.com
Contact: Mr Kivit Jethwa
Position: Chair
Other Languages: Gujarati
Affiliations: Leicester Gujarat Hindu Association

Shree Ram Mandir*
Hildyard Road, Off Ross Walk, Leicester LE4 5GG
Tel: (0116) 2664643
Email: agk@africamail.com
Contact: Narandas Adatia
Position: President
Contact Tel: (0116) 2663820
Activities: Worship/practice/meditation, community centre, umbrella body, youth, elderly, women, radio, television, visits, inter-faith, resources
Traditions: Multi-traditional
Movements: Rahuvansi
Other Languages: Gujarati, Hindi
Affiliations: National Council of Hindu Priests; National Hindu Council

Shree Sanatan Mandir and Community Centre*
Weymouth Street, off Catherine Street, Leicester LE4 6FQ
Tel: (0116) 2661402 **Fax:** (0116) 2661402
Contact: Mr Dullabhbhai B Patel
Position: President
Contact Tel: (0116) 2761356
Activities: Worship/practice/meditation, community centre, youth, elderly, newsletter/journal, books, radio, visits, inter-faith
Traditions: Sanatan
Movements: Sanatan Dharma
Affiliations: Hindu Council of Leicestershire; Gujarat Hindu Association, Leicester; National Council of Hindu Temples

Shree Sarvodaya Samaj*
20 Ingersby Drive, Leicester LE5 6HA
Tel: (0116) 2219727
Contact: Mr Kantilal Solanki
Position: Honorary Secretary
Affiliations: Leicester Gujarat Hindu Association

Shree Satsang Mandal*
53 Moira Street, Leicester LE4 6LB
Tel: (0116) 2241390
Contact: Mrs P J Patel
Position: Honorary Secretary
Activities: Worship, visits, elderly
Traditions: Sanatan
Other Languages: Gujarati, Hindi
Affiliations: National Council of Hindu Temples

Shree Shakti Mandir*
73 Canon Street, Leicester LE4 6NH
Tel: (0116) 2663349 **Fax:** (0116) 2236536
Email: jp-crazybeats@hotmail.com
Contact: J P Purohit
Position: Secretary
Activities: Worship, resource, visits, youth, elderly, women, inter-faith
Traditions: Sanatan
Other Languages: Gujarati, Hindi, Punjabi
Affiliations: Leicester Gujarat Hindu Association; Hindu Council of Leicestershire; National Council of Hindu Temples

Shree Sitaram Seva Trust (UK)*
54 Woodville Road, off Glenfield Road, Leicester LE9 6DU
Tel: (0116) 2557177
Contact: Ratilad G Vegad
Position: Honorary Secretary
Affiliations: Leicester Gujarat Hindu Association

Shree UK R K Seva Samaj
9 Osmaston Road, Leicester LE5 5JF

Shree UK Luhar Gnati Mandal*
32 Evington Drive, Leicester LE5 5PB
Tel: (0116) 2740401
Contact: Mr Ramesh Purshottam Sidpara
Position: Secretary
Activities: Resource, youth, elderly, women, inter-faith
Traditions: Multi-Traditional
Other Languages: Gujarati
Affiliations: Leicester Hindu Festival Council; Gujarat Hindu Association; Vishwa Hindu Parishad

Shree Wanze Community
Pasture Lane, off Sanvey Gate, Leicester LE1 4EY

Shreeji Dwar Haveli*
58 Loughborough Road, Leicester LE4 5LD
Tel: (0116) 2682425 **Fax:** (0116) 2258565
Contact: H H Giriraj Prasad Goswami
Position: Priest
Activities: Worship/practice/meditation, visits,
inter-faith
Traditions: Vaishnava
Movements: Pushtimargiya, Shuddhadvita
Other Languages: Gujarati, Hindi, Vraj, Bhasa

Swaminarayan Hindu Mission*
3 St James Street, Off Humberstone Gate, Leicester
LE1 3SU
Tel: (0116) 2623791
Contact: Mr Bhubendra Bhadd
Position: President
Activities: Worship/practice/meditation
Affiliations: Leicester Gujarat Hindu Association

Vanik Samaj (Leicester)*
60 Belgrave Road, Leicester LE4 5AS
Tel: (0116) 2622662
Contact: Vanmali Gordhandas
Position: President
Other Languages: Gujarati

Vasenev Satsang Mandal
44 Paton Street, Leicester LE3 0BE

Vishwa Hindu Parishad (Leicester Branch)*
46-48 Loughborough Road, Leicester LE5 5LD
Tel: (0116) 2665665 **Fax:** (0116) 2611931
Contact: Mr Ashok Kumar Verma
Position: Chairman
Contact Tel: (0116) 2701686
Activities: Youth, elderly, women, inter-faith
Traditions: Sanatan
Other Languages: Hindi, Gujarati, Punjabi
Affiliations: Vishwa Hindu Parishad, UK

Geeta Bhawan*
Lemyngton Street, Loughborough LE11 1UH
Tel: (01509) 233570
Contact: Dr Sri Ram Chhabra
Position: Honorary Secretary
Activities: Worship/practice/meditation,
community centre, elderly, women, visits, inter-faith

Traditions: Sanatan
Other Languages: Punjabi, Hindi
Affiliations: National Council of Hindu Temples

Shree Ram Krishna Centre*
Alfred Street, Loughborough LE11 1NG
Tel: (01509) 232401 **Fax:** (01509) 237396
Contact: Mr Khandubhai Mistry
Position: Trustee
Contact Tel: (01509) 550612
Activities: Worship/practice/meditation, youth,
elderly, woman, visits, inter-faith
Traditions: Sanatan
Movements: Arya Samaj
Other Languages: Gujarati

Charotar Patidar Samaj
c/o 52 Thorburn Road, Northampton NN5 5BG

Indian Hindu Welfare Association
Hayworth House, 20 Thenford Street,
Northampton NN1 5QT
Tel: (01604) 637900

Northampton Hindu Samaj
c/o 93 Weldon Road, Northampton NN5 5BG

Hindu Swayamsevak Sangh*
1 East Leys Court, Moulton, Northampton
NN3 7TX
Contact: Mr M Mistry
Position: Co-ordinator
Contact Tel: (01604) 493434
Activities: Youth, resources
Traditions: Multi-traditional
Other Languages: Hindi, Gujarati, Punjabi
Affiliations: Hindu Swayamsevak Sangh UK

Vishwa Hindu Parishad*
108 St James Road, St James, Northampton
NN5 5LD
Tel: (01604) 404869
Contact: Chhotubhai Vasanji Mistry
Position: Chair
Contact Tel: (01604) 753100
Activities: Resource, media, umbrella body, visits,
youth, elderly, women, books
Traditions: Multi-Traditional
Other Languages: Gujarati, Hindi
Affiliations: Vishwa Hindu Parishad, National;
Vishwa Hindu Parishad (International)

Brahma Samaj Nottingham*
34 Russell Drive, Wollaton, Nottingham NG8 2BH
Tel: (0115) 9164664 **Fax:** (0115) 9153515
Email: bhareshpjani@hotmail.com
Contact: P B Jani
Position: Member
Contact Tel: (0115) 9500667
Other Languages: Gujarati, Hindi, Swaheli

Gujarat Samaj*
28 Handel Street, St Anns, Nottingham NG3 1JE
Tel: (0115) 9119007 **Fax:** (0115) 9119007
Email: gujarat.samaj@tinyworld.com
Contact: Sapna Pandya
Position: Administrator
Other Languages: Gujarat

Hindu Temple Cultural and Community Centre*
215 Carlton Road, Nottingham NG8 5FX
Tel: (0115) 9113384
Contact: Mrs K S Mohindra
Position: Secretary
Contact Tel: (0155) 9131426
Activities: Worship/practice/meditation, community centre, youth, elderly, women, newsletter/journal, books, visits, inter-faith, resources.
Traditions: Multi-Traditional
Other Languages: Hindi, Punjabi
Affiliations: Council of Hindu Temples

Hindu Youth Group*
Radford Youth and Community Centre, Lenton Boulevard, Radford, Nottingham NG7 2BY
Tel: (0115) 9231595
Contact: Sudheer Kumar Gupta
Position: Honorary Secretary
Activities: Youth, women
Traditions: Multi-Traditional
Other Languages: Hindi
Affiliations: Hindu Swayamsevak Sangh UK

Radha Kripa Trust*
44 Bressingham Drive, West Bridgford, Nottingham NG2 7PD
Tel: (0115) 9847217
Contact: Mrs Usha J Gadhia
Position: Secretary

Sri Nama Hatta, ISKCON Nottingham*
Srivasa-Angang, 24 Manor Close, Bleasby, Nottingham NG14 7GE
Tel: (01636) 830077
Contact: His Grace Pundarika Das
Position: President
Activities: Worship/practice/meditation, youth, elderly, women, newsletter/journal, radio, visits, inter-faith, resources
Traditions: Vaishnava
Movements: Chaitanya
Other Languages: Gujarati, Hindi

Swaminarayan Hindu Mission*
8 Howseman Gardens, Nottingham NG2 2HX
Tel: (0115) 9865848
Contact: Diyeshbhai Rughani

Vishwa Hindu Parishad (UK)*
21 Kenneth Road, Redhill, Nottingham NG5 8HY
Tel: (0115) 9559251 **Fax:** (0115) 9559251
Contact: D V Dhanda
Position: Chairman
Activities: Youth, elderly, inter-faith, resources
Traditions: Multi-Traditional
Movements: All movements
Other Languages: Hindi, Gujarati, Punjabi

Pravasi Mandal (Asian Elders)*
65 Elsden Road, Wellingborough NN8 1QD
Tel: (01933) 442955
Contact: Niraj Jani
Position: Development Officer
Activities: Elderly, women, inter-faith
Other Languages: Gujarati, Hindi

Swaminarayan Hindu Mission*
16-20 Mill Road, Wellingborough NN8 1PE
Tel: (01933) 315961
Contact: Mukeshbhai Pabari

Wellingborough District Hindu Association*
133 Highfield Road, Wellingborough NN8 1PL
Tel: (01933) 274330 **Fax:** (01933) 440732
Contact: Mr Ranesh Ganatra
Position: Community Centre Manager
Activities: Worship, resource, visits, youth, elderly, women, newsletters
Traditions: Multi-Traditional
Other Languages: Gujarati
Affiliations: National Council of Hindu Temples

WEST MIDLANDS
Regional or County Bodies

Arya Samaj (Vedic Mission) West Midlands*
Erskine Street, Nechells, Birmingham B7 4SA
Tel: (0121) 3597727
Contact: Mr Brit Bhushan Aggarwal
Position: Secretary
Contact Tel: (0121) 6826222
Activities: Worship/practice/meditation,
community centre, youth, elderly, women,
newsletter/journal, books, radio, visits, inter-faith,
resources
Traditions: Sanatan
Movements: Arya Samaj
Other Languages: Hindi, Punjabi
Affiliations: Hindu Council of Birmingham

City, Town or Local Bodies

Arya Samaj (Vedic Mission) West Midlands*
Erskine Street, Nechells, Birmingham B7 4SA
Tel: (0121) 3597727
Contact: Mr Brit Bhushan Aggarwal
Position: Secretary
Contact Tel: (0121) 6826222
Activities: Worship/practice/meditation,
community centre, youth, elderly, women,
newsletter/journal, books, radio, visits, inter-faith,
resources
Traditions: Sanatan
Movements: Arya Samaj
Other Languages: Hindi, Punjabi
Affiliations: Hindu Council of Birmingham

**Bochasanwasi Shri Akshar Purushottamni
Sansatha, The Swaminarayan Hindu Mission***
PO Box 7122, 23-43 Ivor Road, Sparkhill,
Birmingham B11 4NR
Tel: (0121) 7723086
Contact: Madhu Joshee
Contact Tel: (0121) 2464602
Activities: Worship/practice/meditation,
community centre, youth, elderly,
newsletter/journal
Traditions: Sanatan
Movements: Swaminarayan
Other Languages: Gujarati, Hindi
Affiliations: Hindu Council of Birmingham

Hindu Council of Birmingham*
c/o Shree Geeta Bhavan Mandir, 107-115
Heathfield Road, Birmingham B19 1YL
Tel: (0121) 5544120
Contact: T R Varma
Position: Chairman
Activities: Umbrella body

Hindu Swayamsevak Sangh*
36 Rothwell Drive, Solihull, Birmingham
B91 1HG
Tel: (0121) 7732214
Contact: Mr Ramesh Shah

ISKCON Birmingham*
84 Stanmore Road, Edgbaston, Birmingham
B16 9BT
Tel: (0121) 4204999
Contact: Mr Nitai Charan
Position: President
Contact Tel: (0121) 3500628
Activities: Worship/practice/meditation,
community centre, youth, newsletter/journal,
books, visits, inter-faith, resources
Traditions: Vaishnava
Movements: Chaitanya
Affiliations: Hindu Council of Birmingham;
National Council of Hindu Temples

Kalyan Ashram Trust Aid Committee*
231 Walford Road, Sparkbrook, Birmingham
B11 1QJ
Tel: (0121) 6935020
Contact: Mr Gurbachan Bhara
Position: President

Shree Gita Bhavan and Charitable Trust*
107-115 Heathfield Road, Handsworth,
Birmingham B19 1HE
Tel: (0121) 5544120
Contact: Mr Jagdish Chander Gupta
Position: General Secretary
Activities: Worship, resource, visits, youth, elderly,
newsletters, books
Traditions: Sanatan
Other Languages: Hindi, Punjabi, Gujarati,
Andhra
Affiliations: Birmingham City Hindu Council;
National Council of Hindu Temples

Shree Jansari Gnati Mandal*

5 Glover Close, Hall Green, Birmingham B28 0JG
Tel: (0121) 7332583
Email: chan-jansari@see.co.uk
Contact: Mr Chandrakant Jansari
Activities: Community centre, youth, elderly
Traditions: Sanatan
Other Languages: Gujarati
Affiliations: Shree Hindu Community Centre

Shree Krishna Mandir (Birmingham Prabati Mandal)*

10 Sampson Road, Sparkbrook, Birmingham
B11 1JL
Tel: (0121) 7714478
Contact: Raman Bulsara
Position: Secretary
Activities: Worship, visits, youth
Other Languages: Gujarati, Hindi
Affiliations: National Council of Hindu Temples

Shree Laxmi Narayan Mandir and Shree Hindu Community Centre*

541a Warwick Road, Tyseley, Birmingham B11 2JP
Tel: (0121) 7073154 **Fax:** (0121) 7644214
Email: pradip_patel@bigfoot.com
Activities: Worship, resource, umbrella body, visits,
youth, elderly, women, newsletters, inter-faith
Traditions: Multi-Traditional
Other Languages: Gujarati, Hindi, Bengali,
Punjabi
Affiliations: Hindu Council of Birmingham;
National Council of Hindu Temples

Shree Pajapati Association (Birmingham)*

249 Warwick Road, Tyseley, Birmingham B11 2QX
Tel: (0121) 7532893
Position: Secretary
Activities: Resource, youth, elderly, women,
newsletters, inter-faith
Traditions: Multi-Traditional
Other Languages: Gujarati, Hindi
Affiliations: Hindu Council, Midlands, Shree
Pargapati Association, UK

Shree Ram Mandir*

8 Walford Road, Sparkbrook, Birmingham
B12 1NR
Tel: (0121) 7735735
Contact: Dhirubhai Rajgor
Position: Priest

Activities: Worship, resource, youth, elderly,
women, newsletters, inter-faith
Traditions: Multi-Traditional
Other Languages: Gujarati, Hindi, Punjabi
Affiliations: Hindu Council of Birmingham;
Shree Sorathia Prajapati Community (UK)

Shree Sorathia Prajapati (UK)*

8 Walford Road, Sparkbrook, Birmingham
B11 1NR
Tel: (0121) 7735735
Contact: Dr N M Gohil
Position: Honorary Secretary
Activities: Worship, visits, youth, women,
newsletter
Traditions: Multi-Traditional
Other Languages: Gujarati
Affiliations: Hindu Council of Birmingham

Shree Vishwakarma Association of UK*

PO Box 33918, Birmingham B91 1NJ
Tel: (020) 8200 8958
Contact: Mr Bakrania
Position: Secretary
Contact Tel: (020) 8200 8958
Activities: Youth
Other Languages: Gujarati, Hindi
Affiliations: Hindu Council (Brent) Brent Indian
Association

Shri Venkateswara Bahaji Temple

119 New Road, Rubery, Birmingham B45 9JR
Tel: (0121) 4577597 **Fax:** (0121) 4577770
Contact: Mrs S A Gurney
Position: Office Coordinator
Activities: Resource, youth, newsletters, inter-faith
Traditions: Sanatan
Other Languages: Telegu, Tamil, Kannada,
Maharashtra
Affiliations: Hindu Council of Birmingham;
National Council of Hindu Temples

Charotaria Leuva Patidar Samaj

38 Leacrest Road, Coventry CV6 2NW
Tel: (024) 733 8791
Contact: Mr Dilip T Patel
Position: Chairman

Hindu Sevika Samiti (Ladies Group)*

75 Knoll Drive, Coventry CV3 5JP

Hindu Sevika Samiti - Coventry*
Harp Place, 2 Sandy Lane, Radford, Coventry
CV1 4DX
Tel: (024) 7655 5222
Contact: Miss Kajal Jagatia
Position: Public Relations
Traditions: Multi-Traditional
Other Languages: Hindi, Gujarati, Punjabi
Affiliations: Vishwa Hindu Parishad

Hindu Temple Society*
274 Stoney Stanton Road, Coventry CV6 5DJ
Tel: (024) 7668 5898
Contact: Mr Ram Krishna Prashar
Position: Secretary
Contact Tel: (024) 7650 2443
Activities: Worship/practice/meditation, women,
visits, inter-faith
Traditions: Sanatan
Other Languages: Hindi, Punjabi
Affiliations: National Council of Hindu Temples

Leuva Patidar Youth Samaj*
63 Grangemouth Road, Coventry CV6 3EZ
Activities: Elderly
Other Languages: Gujarati
Affiliations: Coventry Leuva Patidar Samaj

Sanatan Dharm*
56 Mason Road, Foleshill, Coventry CV6 7FJ
Tel: (024) 7668 5125
Contact: Mr Yash Pal Takiar
Position: President
Contact Tel: (024) 7668 2082
Activities: Worship/practice/meditation
Traditions: Sanatan
Other Languages: Hindi, Punjabi
Affiliations: Council of Hindu Temples,
Birmingham

Sat Sang Janki Mandli*
c/o Hindu Temple Society, 274 Stoney Stanton
Road, Foleshill, Coventry CV6 5DJ
Tel: (024) 7659 3554
Contact: Mrs Sudarshan Bhakri
Position: Secretary
Activities: Worship, visits, elderly, women
Traditions: Multi-Traditional
Movements: Arya Samaj, ISKCON
Other Languages: Punjabi, Hindi, Urdu
Affiliations: National Council of Hindu Temples;
Hindu Council (UK)

**Shree Gujarati Hindu Satsang Mandal and
Shree Krishna Temple***
Harnall Lane West, Nr Halfords, Coventry
CV1 4FB
Tel: (024) 7625 6981 **Fax:** (024) 7622 7911
Contact: C R Thakey
Position: Secretary
Contact Tel: (07931) 968858
Other Languages: Gujarati, Hindi

Shree Shakti Bhajan Mandal*
6 Talland Avenue, Coventry CV6 7NX
Tel: (024) 7668 5368
Contact: Mr Kanti M Patel
Position: Secretary
Activities: Visits, youth, elderly, women, inter-faith
Traditions: Multi-Traditional
Movements: Sanatan Dharma
Other Languages: Gujarati, Hindi
Affiliations: Shree Krishna Temple, Coventry

Shree Radha Krishna Cultural Centre*
Kingfield Road, Radford, Coventry CV1 4DW
Tel: (024) 7655 2822 **Fax:** (024) 7623 0467
Contact: Mr Arun Bhandari
Position: President
Contact Tel: (024) 7655 5420
Contact Email:
haridas@harekrsna.freeserve.co.uk
Activities: Worship/practice/meditation, youth,
women, newsletter/journal, visits, inter-faith,
resources
Traditions: Vaishnava
Movements: International Society for Krishna
Consciousness
Other Languages: Hindi, Gujarati, Bengali
Affiliations: International Society for Krishna
Consciousness, UK

Hindu Samaj Mandir*
18 Salisbury Street, Darlaston WS10 8BQ
Contact: Mr Arvind G Patel
Position: President
Contact Tel: (0121) 5262344
Activities: Worship, youth, visits
Traditions: Sanatan
Other Languages: Gujarati
Affiliations: National Council of Hindu Temples
(UK)

Hindu Cultural Association (Mata Da Mandir)*
57-59 King Street, Dudley DY2 8PY
Contact: Mr Hari K Ahluwalia
Position: President
Contact Tel: (01384) 569858
Contact Email: hari_ahluwalia@hotmail.com
Activities: Worship/practice/meditation,
community centre, youth, elderly, women, visits,
inter-faith, resources
Traditions: Sanatan
Other Languages: Hindi, Punjabi, Gujarati
Affiliations: National Council of Hindu Temples

Krishna Temple and Gujarati Hindu Centre*
Hope Street, Off Churchfield Street, Dudley
DY2 8RS
Tel: (01384) 253253
Contact: Mr R D Patel
Position: Secretary

Hindu Religious Association and Temple*
10b High Street, Leamington Spa CV31 1LW
Tel: (01926) 452247
Contact: Yash Paul Tara
Position: Chair
Contact Tel: (01926) 422077
Activities: Worship, visits, inter-faith
Traditions: Multi-Traditional
Other Languages: Punjabi, Hindi
Affiliations: National Council of Hindu Temples

Shri Hindu Gujarati Samaj*
45 Upper Abbey Street, Nuneaton CV11 6PL
Tel: (024) 7673 5989
Contact: Mahendra Soni
Position: Secretary
Activities: Worship, resource, umbrella body, visits,
youth, elderly, women, newsletters, inter-faith
Traditions: Sanatan
Movements: Arya Samaj
Other Languages: Gujarati, Hindi
Affiliations: National Council Of Hindu Temples

Bharat Sevak Samaj Rugby
Hindu Swayam Sevak Sangh, 4 Kimberley Road,
Rugby CV21 3EZ
Tel: (01788) 565105
Contact: Vasant Mistry
Position: Vice President
Activities: Worship, visits, youth, elderly, women
Traditions: Sanatan
Other Languages: Gujarati, Hindi, Punjabi

Affiliations: Kalyan Prathna Mandir; Hindu
Swayam Sevak Sangh; Vishva Hindu Parishad

Shree Kalyan Mandal*
4/6 Kimberley Road, Rugby CV21 2SU
Tel: (01788) 573515
Contact: Mr Ambaram Mistry
Position: Chair
Contact Tel: (01788) 573515
Activities: Worship
Traditions: Sanatan
Other Languages: Gujarati, Hindi
Affiliations: National Council of Hindu Temples

Hindu Cultural Society, Staffordshire*
The Dudson Centre, Hope Street, Hanley, Stoke-
on-Trent ST1 5DD
Tel: (01782) 683046 **Fax:** (01782) 683199
Contact: Mr S Roy Chowdhury
Position: Coordinator
Activities: Resource, visits, elderly, women,
newsletters
Traditions: Multi-Traditional
Other Languages: Hindi, Gujarati, Marathi,
Punjabi

Mandir Baba Balak Nath (Temple)*
96a Caldmore Road, Walsall WS1 3PD
Tel: (01922) 621177 **Fax:** (01922) 621177
Contact: Jaspal Singh Bhatti
Position: Priest
Contact Tel: (07860) 528245
Activities: Worship/practice/meditation
Traditions: Sanatan
Movements: Baba Balak Nath
Other Languages: Punjabi, Hindi

Shree Ram Mandir*
Ford Street, Pleck, Walsall WS2 9BW
Tel: (01922) 724024

Hindu Samaj Mandal Temple
18 Salisbury Street, Wednesbury WS10 8BQ

Shree Krishna Mandir*
81 Old Meeting Street, West Bromwich B70 9SZ
Tel: (0121) 5535375
Contact: Chandhu Patel
Position: President
Contact Tel: (01958) 437003
Activities: Worship, visits, youth, elderly, women,
newsletter, inter-faith

Traditions: Multi-traditional
Other Languages: Gujarati, Hindi, Punjabi

Hindu Association Bilston*
54 Villiers Avenue, Bilston, Wolverhampton
WV14 6QY
Tel: (01902) 652643 **Fax:** (01902) 552269
Contact: Mr Bavant Patel
Position: President
Activities: Community centre, youth, elderly, women, newsletter, visits, inter-faith
Traditions: Sanatan
Other Languages: Gujarati, Hindi
Affiliations: Wolverhampton Interfaith

Hindu Sabha*
54 Goldthorn Crescent, Penn, Wolverhampton
WV4 5TX
Contact: Mr Tirath Ram Bhardwaj
Position: President
Contact Tel: (01902) 330735
Activities: Community centre, elderly, women, visits
Traditions: Sanatan
Movements: Arya Samaj, Sanatan Dharam
Other Languages: Hindi, Punjabi, Gujarati, Urdu
Affiliations: Wolverhampton Interfaith; National Council of Hindu Temples; Vishwa Hindu Parishad

Leuva Patidar Samaj (Bilston, Wolverhampton, Willenhall)*
4 Fenmere Close, Goldthorn Park, Wolverhampton
WV4 5EN
Tel: (01902) 332545
Contact: Mr Hasmukh Patel
Position: Chair
Activities: Youth, elderly, women
Traditions: Shaiva
Movements: Arya Samaj
Other Languages: Gujarati, Hindi
Affiliations: Leuva Patidar Samaj UK

Shree Krishan Mandir*
123 Penn Road, Wolverhampton WV3 0DR
Contact: Mr D L Chadha
Position: President
Contact Tel: (01902) 772416
Activities: Worship/practice/meditation, youth, elderly, women, visits, inter-faith
Traditions: Sanatan
Movements: Arya Samaj

Other Languages: Hindi, Gujarati, Punjabi, Urdu
Affiliations: Wolverhampton Interfaith; National Council of Hindu Temples; Hindu Swayam Sevak Sang; ISKCON

Sri Ram Krishna*
39 Wellington Road, Bilston, Wolverhampton
WV14 6AH
Tel: (01902) 492190
Contact: Priest Vinod Kumar
Activities: Worship/practice/meditation
Traditions: Sanatan
Other Languages: Hindi

EAST OF ENGLAND
City, Town or Local Bodies

Gujarati Mitra Mandal (Bedford)*
11 Ullswater Close, Kempston, Bedford MK42 8JX
Tel: (01234) 303179
Contact: Mr M Mistry
Contact Tel: (01234) 855696
Activities: Youth, elderly, women, visits, resources
Traditions: Multi-Traditional
Other Languages: Gujarati

Hindu Society of Bedford
105 Wentworth Drive, Bedford MK41 8QE
Tel: (01234) 215717 **Fax:** (01234) 400648
Email: mohankhiani@hotmail.com
Contact: Dr Khiani

Shri Saisidh Baba Balaknath Temple*
2 Derwent Place, Bedford MK42 9HY
Tel: (01234) 214891
Contact: Santosh Kumari
Position: Chairwoman
Activities: Worship/practice/meditation, youth, elderly, women, inter-faith
Other Languages: Hindi, Punjabi, Gujarati, Bangladeshi

North Harrow Satsang Mandal*
"Shri Kunj", 121 Chiltern Avenue, Bushey
WD2 3QE
Tel: (020) 8950 1172
Contact: Mrs Manorama Ghelani
Activities: Elderly
Traditions: Vaishnava
Movements: Pushtimargi
Other Languages: Gujarati

Indian Community and Cultural Association*
Bharat Bhavan, 217 Mill Road, Cambridge
CB1 2AZ
Fax: (01223) 473237
Email: rajan.badi@arm.com
Website: http://www.indian.ic24.net/
Contact: Mr Suresh Patel
Position: Chairman
Contact Email: karyakar@hotmail.com
Activities: Community centre, youth, elderly,
women, newsletter, visits, inter-faith
Traditions: Sanatan
Movements: Arya Samaj
Other Languages: Gujarati, Hindi
Affiliations: National Council of Hindu Temples

Jan Kshatriya Sevak Mandal (UK)*
32 Mount Pleasant Road, Chigwell IG7 5ER
Tel: (020) 8500 4639
Contact: Babual Vadher
Position: President

Ipswich Hindu Samaj*
72 Belmont Road, Pinewood, Ipswich IP2 9XT
Contact: Dr Sushil Kumar Soni
Activities: Radio, inter-faith
Traditions: Sanatan
Movements: Arya Samaj
Other Languages: Hindi, Punjabi
Affiliations: SIFRE (Suffolk Inter Faith Centre
for Religious Education)

Shree Sanatan Seva Samaj*
Hereford Road, Lewsey Farm, Luton LU4 0PS
Tel: (01582) 663414 **Fax:** (01582) 663414
Contact: Mr Pravin Shah
Position: Administrative Officer
Activities: Worship/practice/meditation,
community centre, youth, elderly, women, visits,
inter-faith, resources
Traditions: Sanatan
Other Languages: Gujarati, Hindi
Affiliations: National Council of Hindu Temples

Bharat Hindu Samaj*
6 New England Complex, Rock Road,
Peterborough PE1 3BU
Tel: (01773) 347188 **Fax:** (01773) 554805
Contact: Pandit Kaushikbhai
Position: Temple Priest
Activities: Worship, visits, youth, elderly, women,
inter-faith

Traditions: Sanatan
Other Languages: Gujarati, Hindi, Tamil, Bengali
Affiliations: National Council of Hindu Temples

Bavis Gam Patidar Samaj UK*
22 Elderway, Stevenage SG1 1SE
Tel: (020) 8904 8519
Contact: Mr Jagdish Patel
Position: Vice President
Contact Tel: (01438) 362476
Affiliations: Hindu Council (Brent)

**International Society for Krishna
Consciousness (ISKCON)***
Bhaktivedanta Manor, Dharam Marg, Hilfield Lane,
Aldenham, Watford WD25 8EZ
Tel: (01923) 857244 **Fax:** (01923) 852896
Email: bhaktivedanta.manor@pamho.net
Website: http://www.bhaktivedantamanor.org/
Contact: Bimal Krishna das
Position: Public Relations Officer
Contact Tel: (01923) 856259
Contact Email: bimal.krsna.bcs@pamho.net
Activities: Worship/practice/meditation,
community centre, central body, umbrella body,
youth, elderly, women, newsletter/journal, books,
newspapers, radio, television, visits, inter-faith,
resources
Traditions: Vaishnava
Movements: Chaitanya
Other Languages: Gujarati, Hindi, Polish, Spanish
Affiliations: National Council of Hindu Temples;
Shree Mayapur Chandro Daya Mandir, Bengal,
India.

Shree Prajapati Association UK
28 Colne Way, Watford WD2 4NA
Contact: Jayantilal Mistry
Position: Treasurer
Activities: Youth, elderly, women, newsletters,
inter-faith
Traditions: Sanatan
Movements: Arya Samaj
Other Languages: Gujarati, Hindi
Affiliations: Hindu Council (Brent); Vishwa
Hindu Parishad

Watford Indian/Hindu Community*
Watford
Email: yogesh.joshi@bbc.co.uk
Contact: Yogesh Joshi
Activities: Resource, youth, elderly, women,
inter-faith

Traditions: Sanatan
Other Languages: Gujarati, Hindi, Punjabi

LONDON
Regional and Area Bodies

Aryasamaj London*
69a Argyle Road, West Ealing, London W13 0LY
Tel: (020) 8991 1732 **Fax:** (020) 8991 1732
Contact: Professor S N Bharadwaj
Position: President
Contact Tel: (020) 8569 6403
Activities: Worship, visits, youth, elderly,
newsletter, inter-faith
Movements: Arya Samaj
Other Languages: Hindi, Punjabi, Sanskrit
Affiliations: Arya Pratinidhi Sabha (UK);
Sarvadeshik Arya Partinidhi Sabha, New Delhi,
India

Bardai Brahmin Samaj London*
86/88 South Ealing Road, London W5 4QB
Contact: Mr Bipin Thanki
Position: Secretary
Contact Tel: (01923) 670911
Contact Email: bipin.thanki@ntl.com
Activities: Youth, elderly, women, inter-faith,
resources
Traditions: Multi-Traditional
Movements: Arya Samaj
Other Languages: Gujarati
Affiliations: Brent Indian Association Community
Centre; The Federation of Sri Bardai Brahman
Samajs UK; The Federation of Brahmin
Associations of Europe

Brahmin Society - North London*
BSNL House, 128 East Lane, Wembley HA0 3NL
Tel: (020) 8997 8511
Contact: Mr Vijay Mehta
Position: Secretary
Affiliations: Hindu Council (Brent); Hindu
Council (Harrow); National Congress of Gujarat
Organisations

Hindu Centre (East London) and Radha Krishna Temple*
5 Cedars Road, Stratford, London E15 4NE
Tel: (020) 8534 8879
Contact: Mr S R Mittal
Position: Joint Secretary
Contact Tel: (020) 8252 1261
Activities: Worship/practice/meditation, youth,

elderly, women, visits
Traditions: Sanatan
Other Languages: Hindi, Gujarati, Punjabi, Urdu

Hindu Centre London*
39 Grafton Road, Chalk Farm, London NW5 4JA
Tel: (020) 7485 8200
Contact: Mr D Gopee
Position: Trustee
Activities: Worship/practice/meditation,
community centre, newsletter/journal, resources
Traditions: Multi-Traditional
Movements: Arya Samaj
Other Languages: Hindi, Punjabi

Hindu College London*
50 Morland Avenue, Croydon CR0 6EA
Tel: (020) 8656 1835 **Fax:** (020) 8656 1835
Contact: Dr J C Sharma
Position: Principal
Contact Tel: (020) 8656 1835
Activities: Youth, books, resources
Traditions: Multi-Traditional
Movements: Arya Samaj
Other Languages: Hindi, Punjabi, Sanskrit

Lohana Community North London*
28 North Way, Kingsbury, London NW9 0RG
Tel: (020) 8204 4407
Contact: Mr Mansuhbhai
Position: Asst Hon. Secretary
Activities: Community centre, youth, elderly,
women, newsletter/journal
Traditions: Multi-Traditional
Movements: Sanatan
Other Languages: Gujarati

Mohyal Community Association (UK) London*
84b Telephone Place, London SW6 1TH
Tel: (020) 7385 8592
Contact: Mr S L Mehta
Position: Secretary
Activities: Youth, elderly, women, newsletters
Other Languages: Hindi, Punjabi, Urdu

London Sri Murugan Temple*
78 Church Road, Manor Park, London E12 6AF
Tel: (020) 8478 8433
Position: Secretary

Vanza Society of London, The*
PO Box 48, Wembley HA9 9EP
Email: mail@vanzasociety.co.uk
Website: http://www.vanzasociety.co.uk/

Contact: Mr M Sonigra
Position: President
Contact Tel: (020) 8905 0138
Contact Email: k_sonigra@hotmail.com
Activities: Youth, elderly, women,
newsletter/journal
Traditions: Sanatan
Other Languages: Gujarati
Affiliations: Hindu Council (Brent);
Confederation of Indian Organisations

Borough or Local Bodies

BARNET

Hindu Cultural Society*
321 Colney Hatch Lane, Friern Barnet, London
N11 3DH
Tel: (020) 8446 9873 **Fax:** (020) 8446 9873
Email: soniathcs@aol.com
Contact: Mr Harshed Soni
Position: Secretary
Contact Email: jarshsoni@aol.com
Activities: Worship/practice/meditation,
community centre, youth, elderly, women,
newsletter/journal, visits, inter-faith
Traditions: Multi-traditional
Other Languages: Hindi, Gujarati, Punjabi

Shree Aden Depala Mitra Mandal (UK)*
67a Church Lane, East Finchley, London N2 8DR
Tel: (020) 8446 5057
Contact: Madhusudan C Jogani
Position: Secretary
Activities: Worship, visits, youth, elderly, women
Traditions: Sanatan
Other Languages: Gujarati

Swaminarayan Sidhant Sajivan Mandal
874 Finchley Road, Golders Green NW11 8LX

Vishwakarma Association*
75 Birchen Grove, Kingsbury, London NW9 8RY
Tel: (020) 8200 8958
Contact: Jivan M Bakrania
Position: General Secretary
Affiliations: Hindu Council (Brent); Hindu
Council (Harrow)

BRENT

Athia Samaj*
Heather Park Community Centre, Mount Pleasant,
Wembley HA0 1SH

Tel: (020) 8903 6563 **Fax:** (020) 8451 4698
Contact: Subhas Patel
Position: President
Contact Tel: (07958) 531819
Affiliations: Hindu Council (Brent)

Brahmin Society - North London*
BSNL House, 128 East Lane, Wembley HA0 3NL
Tel: (020) 8997 8511
Contact: Mr Vijay Mehta
Position: Secretary
Affiliations: Hindu Council (Brent); Hindu
Council (Harrow); National Congress of Gujarat
Organisations

Gujarati Literary Academy*
32 Beechcroft Gardens, Wembley HA9 8ER
Tel: (020) 8908 6673
Contact: Mr Vipool Kalyani
Position: Secretary General
Activities: Resources
Other Languages: Gujarati

Hindu Council (Brent)*
7 The Leadings, Wembley Park HA9 9DT
Tel: (020) 8961 5444 **Fax:** (020) 8961 6811
Contact: Mr Venilal Vaghela
Position: Secretary General
Contact Tel: (020) 8908 0192

Hindu Young Persons and Professionals
Dennis Jackson Centre, London Road, Wembley
HA9 7EU
Tel: (020) 8903 2965
Contact: Dr Subash Patel
Activities: Worship, resource, visits, youth, elderly,
women
Traditions: Multi-Traditional
Other Languages: Gujarati, Tamil, Bengali, Hindi

Jignyasu Satsang Seva Trust*
12 Sidmouth Road, Willesden Green, London
NW2 5JX
Tel: (020) 8459 4466 **Fax:** (020) 8459 4000
Contact: Shree Rambapa
Activities: Worship, religious, youth, elderly, inter-
faith
Traditions: Sanatan
Other Languages: Hindi, Gujarati, Sindhi,
Punjabi

Kadwa Patidar Samaj UK*
c/o 8 Mayfields, Wembley Park, Wembley HA9 9PS
Tel: (020) 8909 2711
Contact: Mr Suryakant A Patel

Position: Secretary
Activities: Youth, elderly, women, newsletters, inter-faith
Traditions: Multi-Traditional
Other Languages: Gujarati, Hindi
Affiliations: Hindu Council (Brent); Patidar Association

Kshatriya Association UK*
2a Villiers Road, Willesden, London NW2 5PH
Tel: (020) 8451 4693
Email: dmotiram@aol.com
Contact: Mr Dilip Motiram
Position: Secretary
Contact Tel: (020) 8961 6512
Other Languages: Gujarati, Hindi
Affiliations: Hindu Council (Brent)

Lohana Community North London*
28 North Way, Kingsbury, London NW9 0RG
Tel: (020) 8204 4407
Contact: Mr Mansuhbhai
Position: Asst Hon. Secretary
Activities: Community centre, youth, elderly, women, newsletter/journal
Traditions: Multi-Traditional
Movements: Sanatan
Other Languages: Gujarati

Navnat Vanik Association of the United Kingdom
43 Burgess Avenue, London NW9 8TX
Tel: (020) 8205 0856
Contact: Mr Bhupendra J Shah
Position: General Secretary
Affiliations: Hindu Council (Brent)

Palana Europe Society*
47 Glendale Gardens, Wembley HA9 8PR
Contact: Mr Amritlal Patel
Position: Secretary
Contact Tel: (020) 8904 5760
Affiliations: Hindu Council (Brent)

Prajapati Association*
519 North Circular Road, London NW2 7QG
Tel: (020) 8907 5086
Position: Secretary
Affiliations: Hindu Council (Brent)

Sanatan Seva Mandal*
21 Dean Court, Wembley HA0 3PU
Tel: (020) 8904 1759 **Fax:** (020) 7371 1902
Contact: Chhotalal Damji Pattni

Position: Chairperson
Contact Tel: (020) 7602 9249
Contact Email: chhota_pattni@hotmail.com
Activities: Central body, resources
Traditions: Sanatan
Movements: Sanatan Dharma
Other Languages: Gujarati, Hindi

Sattavis Gam Patidar Samaj*
52 Dersingham Road, Cricklewood, London NW2 1SL
Tel: (020) 8452 3561
Contact: Mr Ashokumar Patel
Position: Secretary
Affiliations: Hindu Council (Brent)

Shakti Mandir
28 Talbot Road, Wembley HA0 4UE

Shishukunj- Youth Group*
98 Chaplin Road, London NW2 5PR
Tel: (020) 8459 1545
Contact: Mr M Gandhi
Position: President
Affiliations: Hindu Council (Brent)

Shree Cutch Leva Patel Community (UK)
43 Chaplin Road, London NW2 5PP

Shree Swaminarayan Mandir*
105-119 Brentfield Road, Neasden, London NW10 8JP
Tel: (020) 8965 2651 **Fax:** (020) 8965 6313
Website: http://www.swaminarayan.org/
Contact: Mr N Palan
Position: Interfaith Representative
Contact Tel: (07715) 110293
Contact Email: npalan@aol.com
Activities: Worship/practice/meditation, community centre, newsletter/journal, inter-faith
Traditions: Vaishnava
Movements: Swaminarayan
Other Languages: Gujarati
Affiliations: National Council of Hindu Temples; Inter Faith Network for the UK

Shri Param Hans Advait Mat
41-43 Brondesbury Park, London NW6 7AY

Shri Swaminarayan Temple*
220-222 Willesden Lane, Brent, London NW2 5RG
Tel: (020)8459 4506 **Fax:** (020) 8830 4651
Email: info@shreeswaminarayan.org.uk

Website: http://www.shreeswaminarayan.org.uk/
Contact: Mr K D Patel
Position: Secretary
Contact Tel: (020) 8459 4506
Activities: Worship, resource
Traditions: Sanatan
Movements: Swaminarayan
Other Languages: Gujarati, Hindi
Affiliations: Shree Swaminarayan Temple - Bhuj

Shri Vallabh Nidhi UK*
80 Ealing Road, Wembley HA0 4TH
Tel: (020) 8922 7093
Contact: Mr Nalinikant Pandya
Position: Hon Secretary General
Contact Tel: (020) 8503 7737
Traditions: Sanatan
Affiliations: Hindu Council (Brent)

UK Valam Brahmin Association*
32 Annesley Close, Neasden NW10
Tel: (020) 8930 0238
Contact: Mrs D Mehta
Position: President
Other Languages: Gujarati
Affiliations: Hindu Council (Brent)

Vishwa Hindu Parishad Wembley*
93 Swinderby Road, Wembley, Middlesex
HA0 4SE
Tel: (020) 8903 2466
Contact: Vinod Wadher
Position: Secretary
Traditions: Sanatan
Movements: Sanatan
Other Languages: Hindi, Gujarati
Affiliations: Hindu Council (Brent)

Wanza Samaj UK*
7 The Leadings, Wembley Park HA9 9DT
Tel: (020) 8908 0192
Contact: Mr Venilal Vaghela
Position: Secretary
Affiliations: Hindu Council (Brent)

CAMDEN

Hindu Centre London*
39 Grafton Road, Chalk Farm, London NW5 4JA
Tel: (020) 7485 8200
Contact: Mr D Gopee
Position: Trustee
Activities: Worship/practice/meditation,
community centre, newsletter/journal, resources

Traditions: Multi-Traditional
Movements: Arya Samaj
Other Languages: Hindi, Punjabi

CROYDON

Arya Samaj Croydon*
50 Morland Avenue, Croydon CR0 6EA
Tel: (020) 8656 1835 **Fax:** (020) 8656 1835
Contact: Dr J C Sharma
Position: President
Activities: Worship/practice/meditation,
community centre, youth, elderly, women, inter-
faith
Traditions: Vedic Dharma
Movements: Arya Samaj
Other Languages: Hindi, Sanskrit
Affiliations: Arya Pratinidhi Sabha (London)

Global Sanskritik Cultural Society*
24 Limes Road, Croydon CR0 2HE
Tel: (020) 8684 7298 **Fax:** (020) 8239 1606
Contact: Jagan Nath Kharbanda
Position: Chair
Activities: Resource, youth, elderly, women,
newsletters, books inter-faith
Traditions: Yoga
Movements: Arya Samaj, Swaminarayan
Other Languages: Hindi, Urdu, Panjabi, Sanskrit
Affiliations: Croydon Ethnic Forum; National
Hindu Council; Hindu College, Bhaivir Singh
Sadan, New Delhi, India

Hindu College London*
50 Morland Avenue, Croydon CR0 6EA
Tel: (020) 8656 1835 **Fax:** (020) 8656 1835
Contact: Dr J C Sharma
Position: Principal
Contact Tel: (020) 8656 1835
Activities: Youth, books, resources
Traditions: Multi-Traditional
Movements: Arya Samaj
Other Languages: Hindi, Punjabi, Sanskrit

Hindu Swayamsevak Sangh*
58 Greenwood Road, Mitcham, Croydon
CR4 1PE
Tel: (020) 8764 2805
Contact: Mr R A Shah

Oshwal Mahajanwadi
Corner of London Road and Campbell Road,
Croydon CR0 2SQ

Shree Radha Krishna Cultural Centre (ISKCON)*

42 Enmore Road, South Norwood, London
SE25 5NG
Tel: (020) 8656 4296
Contact: Nabhinandana Das
Position: President
Contact Tel: (020) 8764 7765
Contact Email: nmalde@investec.co.uk
Activities: Worship, resource, visits, youth, elderly,
women, newsletters, books, inter-faith
Traditions: Vaishnava
Movements: Chaitanya
Other Languages: Gujarati, Hindi
Affiliations: International Society for Krishna
Consciousness

Vishwa Hindu Parishad*

10 Thornton Row, Thornton Heath Pond,
Croydon CR7 6JN
Tel: (020) 8675 6717 **Fax:** (020) 8665 5502
Contact: Mr Ramesh Jhalla
Position: Honorary Secretary
Contact Tel: (020) 8764 2738
Contact Email: rameshjhalla@yahoo.co.uk
Activities: Community centre, central body,
umbrella body, youth, elderly , women, visits, inter-
faith, resources
Traditions: Multi-Traditional
Other Languages: Hindi, Gujarati,

EALING

Aryasamaj London*

69a Argyle Road, West Ealing, London W13 0LY
Tel: (020) 8991 1732 **Fax:** (020) 8991 1732
Contact: Professor S N Bharadwaj
Position: President
Contact Tel: (020) 8569 6403
Activities: Worship, visits, youth, elderly,
newsletter, inter-faith
Movements: Arya Samaj
Other Languages: Hindi, Punjabi, Sanskrit
Affiliations: Arya Pratinidhi Sabha (UK);
Sarvadeshik Arya Partinidhi Sabha, New Delhi,
India

Bardai Brahmin Samaj London*

86/88 South Ealing Road, London W5 4QB
Contact: Mr Bipin Thanki
Position: Secretary
Contact Tel: (01923) 670911
Contact Email: bipin.thanki@ntl.com
Activities: Youth, elderly, women, inter-faith,
resources

Traditions: Multi-Traditional
Movements: Arya Samaj
Other Languages: Gujarati
Affiliations: Brent Indian Association Community
Centre; The Federation of Sri Bardai Brahman
Samajs UK; The Federation of Brahmin
Associations of Europe

Kalaniketan*

31 Horsenden Crescent, Greenford UB6 0JF
Tel: (020) 8422 7647
Contact: Mr Mansukh Unadkat
Position: Secretary
Affiliations: Hindu Council (Brent)

Shree Baba Balaknathji Temple

51 Orchard Road, Southall

Shree Ram Mandir

22 King Street, Southall UB2 4DA
Tel: (020) 8574 5376
Contact: Mrs S Whig
Position: Trustee/Co-ordinator

Vishwa Hindu Kendra*

2 Lady Margaret Road, Southall UB1 2RA
Tel: (020) 8574 3870
Contact: Ms Meenu Dhiri
Position: Trustee
Contact Email: minoo@blueyonder.co.uk
Activities: Worship, resource, visits, youth
Traditions: Sanatan
Other Languages: Hindi, Punjabi, Gujarati

ENFIELD

Darji Mitra Mandal of the UK*

62 Whitmore Close, New Southgate, London
N11 1PB
Tel: (020) 8361 5981
Contact: R Taylor
Position: Secretary

Krishna Yoga Mandir*

57 Balham Road, Edmonton, London N9 7AH
Tel: (020) 8363 9187
Contact: Pandit Keshava C Krishnatreya
Position: Chairman
Activities: Worship/practice/meditation,
community centre, youth, elderly, women, visits,
inter-faith, resources
Traditions: Multi-Traditional
Movements: Sanatan Dharma
Other Languages: Hindi, Punjabi, Tamil

GREENWICH

Greenwich Hindu Mandir (Temple)*
63-67 Bannockburn Road, London SE18 1ET
Tel: (020) 8854 4566
Contact: Mrs Madhu Baksh
Position: President
Contact Tel: (020) 8467 0141
Activities: Worship/practice/meditation, youth, elderly, women, visits, inter-faith, resources
Traditions: Sanatan
Movements: Sanatan
Other Languages: Hindi, Punjabi, Gujarati, Tamil

Hindu Mandir
51 Crescent Road, Plumstead, London SE18 7BL
Tel: (020) 8855 1148

Hindu Swayamsevak Sangh
Woolwich Branch, 27 Vicarage Park, Plumstead, London SE18 7SU
Tel: (020) 8854 4143

Rama Sri Krishna*
76 Herbert Road, Plumstead, London SE18 3PP
Tel: (020) 8854 3964

Shree Kutch Satsang Swaminarayan Temple*
St Margaret's Grove, Plumstead, London SE18 7RL
Tel: (020) 8855 0823 **Fax:** (020) 8317 0020
Email: info@swaminarayan.gb.net
Website: http://www.swaminarayan.gb.net/
Contact: Dr Ravji Dhanji Pindoria
Position: Chair
Contact Tel: (020) 8317 1309
Activities: Worship, resource, visits, youth, elderly, women, newsletters, books, inter-faith
Traditions: Sanatan
Movements: Swaminarayan
Other Languages: Gujarati, Hindi, Kutchi
Affiliations: Shree Swaminarayan Temple Bhuj Kutch India

South East Hindu Association Hindu Temple*
5 Anglesea Avenue, London SE18 6EH
Tel: (020) 8854 4906
Contact: R P Gupta
Position: Secretary
Traditions: Multi-Traditional
Other Languages: Hindi, Gujarati, Punjabi

HACKNEY

Hackney Hindu Council*
498 Kingsland Road, London E8 4AE
Tel: (020) 8254 3647
Contact: Mr B Singh
Position: Vice Chair
Contact Tel: (020) 8591 8994
Other Languages: Hindi, Punjabi, Gujarati

HAMMERSMITH AND FULHAM

Bharatiya Vidya Bhavan, Institute of Indian Art and Culture*
4a Castletown Road, West Kensington, London W14 9HE
Tel: (020) 7381 3086 **Fax:** (020) 7381 8758
Email: info@bhavan.net
Website: http://www.bhavan.net/
Contact: Dr H V S Shastry
Position: Academic Director
Activities: Practice/meditation, community centre, central body, youth, elderly, women, newsletter/journal, books, visits, inter-faith, resources.
Traditions: Multi-Traditional
Other Languages: Gujarati, Hindi, Tamil, Bengali
Affiliations: Bharatiya Vidya Bhavan, India; Inter Faith Network for the UK

London Sevashram Sangha*
99a Devonport Road, Shepherds Bush, London W12 8PB
Tel: (020) 8723 4257 **Fax:** (020) 8726 4257
Contact: Swami Nirliptananda
Position: Secretary
Activities: Worship, resource, visits, youth, newsletters, books, inter-faith
Traditions: Multi-Traditional
Movements: Bharat Sevashram Sangha
Other Languages: Hindi, Bengali, Gujarati
Affiliations: Bharat Sevashram Sangha

Mohyal Community Association (UK) London*
84b Telephone Place, London SW6 1TH
Tel: (020) 7385 8592
Contact: Mr S L Mehta
Position: Secretary
Activities: Youth, elderly, women, newsletters
Other Languages: Hindi, Punjabi, Urdu

HARINGEY

Brittania Hindu (Shiva) Temple Trust*
Highgate Hill Murugan Temple, 200a Archway
Road, Highgate, London N6 5BA
Tel: (020) 8348 9835 **Fax:** (020) 8482 6508
Contact: Mr Kanthiah Ranganathan
Position: Trustee
Contact Tel: (020) 8998 1703
Activities: Worship/practice/meditation,
community centre, central body, umbrella body,
youth, elderly, women, newsletter/journal, books,
radio, visits, inter-faith
Traditions: Shaiva
Movements: Veda Agama
Other Languages: Tamil
Affiliations: Federation of Hindu Temples in UK;
World Saiva Council

HARROW

Hindu Swayamsewak Sangh (UK)*
31 Devonshire Road, Harrow-on-Hill HA1 4LS
Tel: (020) 8863 1042
Contact: Mr Jayantibhai Patel
Position: Director/Trustee
Activities: Central body, youth, elderly, newsletter
Traditions: Sanatan
Other Languages: Hindi

Kingsbury Asian Elders Group*
305 Byron Road, Wealdstone, Harrow HA3 7TE
Tel: (020) 8863 3847 **Fax:** (020) 8861 5069
Email: lavingia@btinternet.com
Contact: Mr Dhirubhai Lavingia
Position: Secretary
Contact Tel: (020) 8863 3847
Other Languages: Gujarati, Hindi, Swahili
Affiliations: Hindu Council (Brent)

Kutch Leva Patel Community*
West End Road, Northholt UB5 6RE
Tel: (020) 8951 3405
Position: Secretary
Affiliations: Hindu Council (Brent)

Kutch Madhapar Karyalaya UK
31 Ruskin Gardens, Kenton, Harrow HA3 9PX
Contact: Mr Harilal Murji Halai
Position: Chairman
Affiliations: Hindu Council (Brent)

Malawi Hindu Association*
5 West Towers, Pinner, London HA5 1TZ
Tel: (020) 8868 3324 **Fax:** (020) 8868 3324

Email: usha@cwmail.net
Contact: Mrs Usha Radia
Position: President
Activities: Youth, elderly, women
Traditions: Sanatan
Other Languages: Gujarati
Affiliations: Brent Indian Association

Pushtimargiya Vaishnav - Mahila Samaj*
Charnwood, 147 Uxbridge Road, Harrow
HA3 6DG
Tel: (020) 8954 2142
Contact: Madhuben Somani
Position: President
Affiliations: Hindu Council (Brent)

Rajput Seva Samaj
3 D'arcy Gardens, Kenton, Harrow HA3 9JU
Contact: Rasik Vaghel
Position: President
Affiliations: Hindu Council (Brent)

HILLINGDON

Hindu Society*
37 Stowe Crescent, Ruislip HA4 7SR
Tel: (01895) 676939
Contact: Dr Bholanath Bhargava
Position: President
Activities: Worship/practice/meditation,
community centre, central body, umbrella body,
youth, elderly, women, newletter/journal, books,
newspapers, radio, television, visits, inter-faith,
resources
Traditions: Multi-Traditional
Other Languages: Hindi, Sanskrit

Shree Limbachia Gnati Mandal*
3 Strone Way, Hayes UB4 9RU
Email: solankee@ntlworld.com
Contact: Mr Mahendra Solankee
Position: Secretary
Affiliations: Hindu Council (Brent)

HOUNSLOW

Hindu Cultural Trust Centre*
55 Manor Avenue, Hounslow TW4 7JN
Tel: (020) 8230 0571
Contact: Gian Chand Gaur
Position: General Secretary
Activities: Worship, resource, umbrella body, visits,
youth, elderly women, newsletters, books, inter-
faith
Traditions: Sanatan

Movements: Vedic, Cultural or Sanatanic
Other Languages: Hindi, Punjabi, Gujarati

Sarvodaya Sangh*
17 Heath Court, Benham Gardens, Hounslow
TW4 5JY
Tel: (020) 8230 3691
Contact: Mr Damjibhai Limbachia
Position: Secretary
Activities: Resource, youth
Traditions: Sanatan
Movements: Sarvodaya
Other Languages: Gujarati, Hindi
Affiliations: Hindu Council (Brent)

Shree Sorathia Prajapati Youth Community*
12 Laburnam Road, Hounslow **Tel:** (020) 8577
0986

**Vishwa Hindu Parishad Sanatan International
(UK)***
55 Manor Avenue, London TW4 7JN
Tel: (020) 8230 057 **Fax:** (020) 8737 3677
Contact Tel: (020) 8737 3677
Activities: Umbrella body
Other Languages: Hindi, Punjabi, Gujarati
Affiliations: Hindu Cultural Trust Centre,
Hounslow

Visva Adhyatmik Sansthan*
48 Sutton Lane, Hounslow TW3 3BD
Tel: (020) 8556 4732 **Fax:** (020) 7629 5589
Contact: Gurdial Singh Sandhu
Position: Advisor
Contact Tel: (020) 8252 4224
Contact Email: spedding@easynet.co.uk
Activities: Worship/practice/meditation,
community centre, youth, elderly, women, books
Traditions: Multi-Traditional
Other Languages: Sanskrit
Affiliations: Adhyatmik Foundation Inc.

KENSINGTON AND CHELSEA

Shanti Sadan*
29 Chepstow Villas, Notting Hill Gate, London
W11 3DR
Tel: (020) 7727 7846 **Fax:** (020) 7792 9871
Website: http://www.shanti-sadan.org/
Contact: Anthony Collins
Position: Secretary
Activities: Newsletter/journal, books
Traditions: Yoga
Movements: Advaita Vedanta, Adhyatma Yoga

KINGSTON UPON THAMES

Sarvoday Hindu Association*
c/o 243 Raeburn Ave, Kingston-upon-Thames
KT5 3DF
Tel: (020) 8390 3646
Contact: Mr H Desai

National Association of Patidar Samaj*
77 Brockenhurst Avenue, Worcester Park
KT4 7RH
Fax: (020) 8404 7285
Email: pravinamin@aol.com
Contact: P N Amin
Position: President
Activities: Community centre, youth
Other Languages: Gujarati

LAMBETH

Caribbean Hindu Society*
16 Ostade Road, Brixton Hill, London SW2 2BB
Tel: (020) 8674 0755 **Fax:** (020) 8674 0755
Contact: Mr Sukhlal
Position: President
Activities: Worship/practice/meditation, youth,
elderly, newsletter/journal, visits, inter-faith
Traditions: Sanatan
Other Languages: Hindi

Hindu Resource Centre*
10 De Montfort Road, London SW16 1LZ
Tel: (020) 8675 6717 **Fax:** (020) 8675 6717
Contact: Mrs Saraswati Dave
Position: Chair
Activities: Resource, media, umbrella body, youth,
elderly, women, inter-faith
Traditions: Multi-Traditional
Other Languages: Gujarati, Punjabi, Hindi, Tamil
Affiliations: Vishwa Hindu Parishad

Shree Swaminarayan Temple*
72 Colmer Road, London SW16 5JZ
Tel: (020) 8679 8050 **Fax:** (020) 8679 8050
Contact: Kamal Patel
Position: President
Contact Tel: (07713) 654559
Contact Email: kpatel1550@hotmail.com
Activities: Worship/practice/meditation, youth
Other Languages: Gujarati, Hindi

Surrey Gujarati Hindu Society*
PO Box 7728, London SW2 3SG
Tel: (020) 8674 8902

Contact: Rajni Patel
Position: Secretary

MERTON

Karamsad Samaj*
12 Morden Gardens, Mitcham CR4 4DH
Tel: (020) 8646 5515
Email: karamsadsamaj@talk21.com
Website: http://www.karamsadsamaj.co.uk/
Contact: Mr Suresh M Patel
Position: Secretary
Activities: Community centre, youth, elderly,
women, newsletter/journal
Traditions: Multi-Traditional
Other Languages: Gujarati
Affiliations: Hindu Council (Brent)

Shree Ganapathy Temple*
125-133 Effra Road, Wimbledon, London
SW19 8PU
Tel: (020) 85427482 **Fax:** (020) 4042888
Email: info@ganapathy temple.org.uk.
Website: http://www.ganapathytemple.org.uk/
Contact: R M Ratnasinham
Position: Chief Co-ordinator
Contact Tel: (020) 8946 1140
Activities: Worship, resource, youth, elderly,
women
Traditions: Shaiva
Other Languages: Tamil, Hindi, French
Affiliations: National Council of Hindu Temples,
Federation Of Shaiva Hindu Temples

NEWHAM

Aarti Society*
37 Dunbar Road, Forest Gate, London E7 9HH
Tel: (020) 8472 2718
Contact: Mrs R J Patel
Position: President
Contact Tel: (020) 8472 3754
Activities: Worship/practice/meditation
Other Languages: Gujarati

Gujarat Hindu Welfare Association*
141 Plashet Road, Plaistow, London E13 0RA
Tel: (020) 8552 0525 **Fax:** (020) 8552 5125
Contact: Mr Bal Vantbhai Desai
Position: Secretary
Activities: Community centre, elderly, women,
visits

Traditions: Multi-Traditional
Other Languages: Gujarati, Hindi

Hindu Centre (East London) and Radha Krishna Temple*
5 Cedars Road, Stratford, London E15 4NE
Tel: (020) 8534 8879
Contact: Mr S R Mittal
Position: Joint Secretary
Contact Tel: (020) 8252 1261
Activities: Worship/practice/meditation, youth,
elderly, women, visits
Traditions: Sanatan
Other Languages: Hindi, Gujarati, Punjabi, Urdu

Lakshmi Narayana Trust*
272 High Street North, Manor Park, London
E12 6SA
Tel: (020) 8552 5082
Contact: Dr P Alagrajah
Position: Chairperson
Contact Tel: (020) 8502 6163
Traditions: Vaishnava
Other Languages: Tamil, Malayalam, Telugu

London Sri Murugan Temple*
78 Church Road, Manor Park, London E12 6AF
Tel: (020) 8478 8433
Position: Secretary

Mahalakshmi Temple*
272 High Street North, Manor Park, London
E12 6SA
Tel: (020) 8552 5082 **Fax:** (020) 8552 5315
Email: office@srimahalakshmitemple.org.uk
Website:
http://www.srimahalakshmitemple.org.uk/
Contact: Dr P A Alagrajah
Position: President
Activities: Worship
Traditions: Vaishnava
Other Languages: Tamil, Telugu

Newham Hindu Cultural Association*
106 Caistor Park Road, Stratford, London
E15 3PR
Tel: (020) 8471 3712
Contact: Mr Vyas
Position: Secretary
Activities: Youth, elderly, women, inter-faith
Traditions: Shaiva
Movements: Arya Samaj
Other Languages: Gujarati, Hindi, Sanskrit

Shiromani Bhagat Baba Namdev Ji Mission and Community Centre
2a Lucas Avenue, London E13 0RL

Shree Kutch Leva Patel Community UK (Newham)*
35 Heigham Road, East Ham, London E6 2JL
Tel: (020) 8471 4760
Contact: Mrs V Patel
Position: Secretary
Activities: Worship/practice/meditation, community centre, youth, elderly, women, visits, inter-faith, resources
Traditions: Vaishnava
Movements: Swaminarayan
Other Languages: Gujarati, Hindi,

Shree Kutch Satsang Swaminarayan Temple*
22-24 Shaftesbury Road, Forest Gate, London E7 8PD
Tel: (020) 8470 9375
Email: dkpatel@x.stream.com
Contact: Mr Shamji K Vekaria
Position: President
Contact Tel: (07957) 405955
Activities: Worship, visits, youth, elderly, women
Movements: Swaminarayan
Other Languages: Gujarati, Hindi

Shree Narayana Guru Mission of the UK*
16 Barking Road, East Ham, London E6 3BP
Tel: (020) 8471 0720
Email: guru.mission@sngm.org
Website: http://www.sngm.org/
Contact: Dr Parish K Bhasi
Position: Secretary
Activities: Worship/practice/meditation, community centre, central body, youth, elderly, women, newsletter/journal, visits, inter-faith, resources
Traditions: Yoga
Other Languages: Malayalam

Swaminarayan Hindu Mission, East London
Upton Centre, Claude Road, London E13 0QB
Tel: (020) 8552 8646

REDBRIDGE

Ilford Hindu Playscheme*
109 Auckland Road, Ilford IG1 4SQ
Tel: (020) 8518 5499

Samodya Samaj UK*
42 Breamore Road, Ilford
Tel: (020) 8599 4370
Contact: Mr Umesh Chaunan
Position: President

Shree Sanatam Dharam Mandal*
149 Henley Road, Ilford IG1 2NQ
Tel: (020) 8574 4781

Vishwa Hindu Parishad
Ilford Hindu Centre, 43 Cleveland Road, Ilford IG4 1EE
Tel: (020) 8553 5471 **Fax:** (020) 8518 5499

SOUTHWARK

Maha Lakshmi Satsang*
Honor Oak Park, Forest Hill, London SE23 3LE
Tel: (020) 8650 3728 **Fax:** (020) 8650 3728
Email: ramesh.charan@btinternet.com
Contact: Mr Ramesh Charan
Position: Secretary
Activities: Worship/practice/meditation, community centre, youth, women, books, visits, resources
Traditions: Sanatan
Other Languages: Hindi, Gujarati

Virsad Union UK*
4b Dulwich Wood Park, London SE19 1XQ
Email: virsad_union@hotmail.com
Website: http://www.virsad.com
Other Languages: Gujarati

TOWER HAMLETS

Hindu Pragati Sangha
33 Rhondda Grove, London E3 5AP
Tel: (020) 82211780

WALTHAM FOREST

Hindu Cultural Association*
129 New Road, Chingford, London E4 9EZ
Tel: (020) 8529 2346
Contact: Mr R Vasitha
Position: Chair
Activities: Youth, elderly, women
Traditions: Multi-Traditional
Other Languages: Hindi, Punjabi

Shree Vallabh Nidhi UK*
159/161 Whipps Cross Road, Leytonstone, London
E11 1NP
Tel: (020) 8989 2034
Contact: Rameshchandra Gordhambhai
Position: Secretary/Treasurer
Activities: Visits
Traditions: Sanatan
Movements: Pushtimargi
Other Languages: Gujarati, Hindi

WANDSWORTH

Gujarati Brahma Samaj*
9 Lingwell Road, Wandsworth, London
SW17 7NH
Tel: (020) 8672 1918
Contact: Mr J Thaker

Hindu Society*
664 Garratt Lane, Tooting, London SW17 0NP
Tel: (020) 8944 0251
Contact: Dr Rajendra Singh
Position: Secretary
Activities: Community centre, elderly, women,
visits
Traditions: Multi-Traditional
Other Languages: Hindi, Gujarati, Punjabi, Urdu

Radha-Krishna Temple*
33 Balham High Road, London SW12 9AL
Tel: (020) 8673 6437
Contact: Secretary

Rajput Dhobi Youth*
127 Hebdon Road, London SW17 7NL
Tel: (020) 8767 2975
Contact: Mr Umesh Solanki
Position: Secretary
Affiliations: Hindu Council (Brent)

Satyananda Yoga Centre*
70 Thurleigh Road, London SW12 8UD
Tel: (020) 8673 4869 **Fax:** (020) 8675 4080
Contact: Swami Pragyamurti Saraswati
Position: Director
Activities: Meditation, resource, umbrella body,
youth, elderly, women, newsletters, inter-faith
Traditions: Yoga
Movements: Bihar School of Yoga and Swami
Satyananda Saraswat
Affiliations: Bihar School of Yoga, India

Sivananda Yoga Vedanta Centre*
51 Felsham Road, Putney, London SW15 1AZ
Tel: (020) 8780 0160 **Fax:** (020) 8780 0128
Email: london@sivananda.org
Website: http://www.sivananda.org/
Contact: Swami Saradananda
Position: Director
Activities: Worship, umbrella body, visits, youth,
elderly, women, newsletter, books, inter-faith
Traditions: Yoga, Vedanta
Movements: Swami Sivananda
Affiliations: Sivananda Yoga Vedanta Centres
Headquarters, Quebec, Canada

Wandsworth Bengali Community Centre*
57-59 Trinity Road, Tooting Bec, London
SW17 7SD
Tel: (020) 8682 4934 **Fax:** (020) 8672 9308
Email: mislam8324@aol.com
Contact: Dr Misbah Islam
Position: Company Secretary
Contact Tel: (020) 8672 9308
Activities: Community centre, elderly, women
Other Languages: Urdu, Hindi, Gujarati

WESTMINSTER, CITY OF

Iyengar Yoga Institute*
223a Randolph Avenue, London W9 1NL
Tel: (020) 7624 3080 **Fax:** (020) 7372 2726
Email: office@iyi.org.uk
Website: http://www.iyi.org.uk/
Contact: Angus Fookes
Position: Manager
Activities: Resource
Traditions: Yoga
Movements: Iyengar Yoga

Radha Krishna Temple*
10 Soho Street, London W1D 3DL
Tel: (020) 7437 3662 **Fax:** (020) 7439 1127
Email: london@pamho.net
Website: http://www.iskcon-london.com/
Contact: Gaura Krsna das
Contact Tel: (020) 74373662
Contact Email:
gaurakrsnadas@iskcon.fsnet.co.uk.
Activities: Worship, visits, inter-faith
Traditions: Vaishnava
Movements: Chaitanya
Affiliations: National Council of Hindu Temples;
International Society for Krishna Consciousness

SOUTH EAST
City, Town or Local Bodies

Patanjali Centre for Classical Yoga*
The Cot (Kutiya), Marley Lane, Battle TN33 0RE
Tel: (01424) 870538 **Fax:** (01424) 870538
Email: patanjali.centre@talk.com
Website:
http://www.geocities.com/patanjaliyogacentre/
Contact: Sri Indar Nath
Position: Founder Director
Traditions: Yoga
Movements: Vedanta/Yoga

Hindu Association Hastings*
c/o 4 Collington Mansions, Collington Avenue,
Bexhill-on-Sea TN39 3PU
Fax: (01424) 022023
Contact: Mrs Jayshree S Patel
Position: President
Contact Tel: (01424) 220232
Activities: Resource, youth, women, newsletters
Traditions: Multi-Traditional
Other Languages: Gujarati

Hindu Women's Group
259 Preston Drove, Brighton BN1 7FN

Medway Hindu Centre*
71 Ernest Road, Chatham ME4 5PT
Tel: (01634) 402843 **Fax:** (01634) 291119
Email: rbpatel@dialstart.net
Contact: Mr Ramanbhai B Patel
Position: President
Contact Tel: (01634) 402843
Activities: Resource, visits, youth, elderly, women,
inter-faith
Traditions: Sanatan
Movements: Vedic Culture
Other Languages: Gujarati, Hindi, Punjabi,
Swahili
Affiliations: National Congress of Gujarati
Organisations

Gurjar Hindu Union (Crawley)*
110/112 Spencer Road, West Green, Crawley
RH11 7DA
Tel: (01737) 736464 **Fax:** (01737) 736020
Website: http://www.ghu-crawley.co.uk/
Contact: Mr Ashwin Soni
Position: Honorary Secretary

Contact Tel: (07801) 045481
Contact Email: asoni@kcc.com
Activities: Worship/practice/meditation,
community centre, youth, elderly, women,
newsletter/journal, visits, inter-faith, resources
Traditions: Sanatan
Other Languages: Gujarati, Hindi
Affiliations: National Council of Hindu Temples

Medway Hindu Sabha
361 Canterbury Street, Gillingham ME7 5XS
Tel: (01634) 576170

Hove Hindu Community
59 Addison Road, Hove BN3 1TQ

Southend and District Hindu Association*
10 Stonehill Close, Leigh-on-Sea SS9 4AZ
Contact: Mr M D Solanki
Position: Secretary
Contact Tel: (01702) 524851

Geeta Ashram*
147 Old Bedford Road, Luton LU2 7EF
Tel: (01582) 421990 **Fax:** (01582) 421990
Email: vbtailor@aol.com
Contact: Mr Vinod B Tailor
Activities: Books, inter-faith
Traditions: Sanatan
Other Languages: Hindi, Gujarati

Milton Keynes Hindu Association
8 Sandywell Drive, Downhead Park, Milton Keynes
MK15 9AJ
Contact: Mr Ashok Patel
Position: Secretary
Contact Tel: (01908) 674421
Other Languages: Gujarati, Hindi

Swaminarayan Hindu Temple
79a Trafalgar Road, Portslade by Sea BN41 1XD
Tel: (01273) 420200

Berkshire Mandir*
c/o St Bartholomew Church, 72 London Road,
Reading RG1 5AS
Tel: (0118) 9751291
Contact: Mr R Mall
Position: Secretary

Gujrat Samaj*
8 Willowside, Woodley, Reading RG5 4HJ

Contact: Mr T K Desai
Position: Committee member
Contact Tel: (0118) 9697722
Activities: Worship/practice/meditation, youth, elderly, women
Traditions: Multi-Traditional
Other Languages: Gujarati, Hindi

Reading Hindu Temple Educational, Cultural and Community Centre*
Whitley Hall, 112 Whitley Street, RG2 0EQ
Tel: (0118) 975 5612
Contact: Mr J M Malhotra
Activity: Worship, youth, elderly, women, inter-faith

Hindu Cultural Society of Slough*
Hindu Temple, Keele Drive, Chalvey, Slough
SL1 2XU
Tel: (01753) 790135
Contact: Dharm Jangra
Position: President
Contact Tel: (01753) 790135
Activities: Worship, visits, youth, elderly, women, inter-faith
Traditions: Sanatan
Movements: Sanatan
Other Languages: Hindi, Gujarati, Punjabi
Affiliations: National Council of Hindu Temples

Hindu Cultural Society Southall*
82 Saxon Road, Ealing, Southall UB1 1QJ
Tel: (020) 8574 6079
Contact: Mr Bal Dev Mohan
Position: Secretary
Activities: Youth, elderly, inter-faith, resources,
Traditions: Vedic (Satya Sanatan)
Movements: Arya Samaj
Other Languages: Hindi, Punjabi, Sanskrit

Vedic Society Hindu Temple*
75-195 Radcliffe Road, Northam, Southampton
SO14 0PS
Tel: (023) 8063 2275
Contact: Secretary
Activities: Worship, youth, elderly, women, newsletter, inter-faith
Traditions: Sanatan
Other Languages: Hindi, Punjabi, Gujarati
Affiliations: National Council of Hindu Temples

Vishwa Hindu Parishad*
6 Bassett Crescent West, Bassett, Southampton
SO16 7DZ
Tel: (023) 8079 0770
Contact: Mr Mahesh Sareen
Position: Honorary Secretary
Activities: Resource, umbrella body, youth, elderly, women, inter-faith
Traditions: Sanatan
Movements: Arya Samaj
Other Languages: Hindi, English
Affiliations: Vedic Society of Southampton; Vishwa Hindu Parishad UK

Paraskthi Hindu (Saiva) Temple Trust*
Sri Raja Rajeswary Amman Temple, Stoneleigh
Prayer Hall, 4 Dell Lane, Stoneleigh KT17 2NE
Tel: (020) 8393 8147
Contact: Mr R Kunasingam
Position: Chairman
Contact Tel: (020) 8542 5803
Activities: Worship/practice/meditation

SOUTH WEST
City, Town or Local Bodies

The Hindu Temple*
163b Church Road, Redfield, Bristol BS5 9LA
Tel: (0117) 9351007
Contact: Batook Pandya
Position: Chairperson
Activities: Worship, resource, visits, youth, elderly, women, newsletters, inter-faith
Traditions: Sanatan
Other Languages: Gujarati, Hindi, Punjabi
Affiliations: National Council of Hindu Temples

ISKCON Bristol*
c/o Oddfellows Hall, West Park, Clifton, Bristol
BS8 2LT
Website: http://www.iskcon.org.uk/
Contact: Minaketanarama dasa
Position: President
Contact Tel: (01275) 851178
Contact Email: mktamadasabcs_uk@yahoo.co.uk
Activities: Worship, resource, visits, youth, newsletters, books, inter-faith
Traditions: Vaishnava
Movements: Chaitanya
Other Languages: Hindi, Gujarati

Hindu Community Centre*
64 Swindon Road, Cheltenham GL50 4AY
Tel: (01242) 584250
Contact: President

Indian Association (Cheltenham)
Hindu Community Centre, 64 Swindon Road,
Cheltenham GL50 4AY
Tel: (01242) 584250
Contact: Secretary
Activities: Worship, resource, visits, youth, elderly,
women, inter-faith
Traditions: Sanatan
Other Languages: Gujarati, Hindi
Affiliations: National Council of Hindu Temples

Gloucester Hindu Centre*
15 Cherston Court, Barnwood, Gloucester GLA 3LE
Tel: (01452) 653314
Contact: Mr Lallu Patel
Position: Trustee
Contact Tel: (01452) 618753
Movements: Worship/practice/meditation
Other Languages: Gujarati
Affiliations: National Council Of Hindu Temples

Hindu Samaj*
Facechoice Pharmacy, Freshbrook Village Centre,
Swindon SN5 8LY
Tel: (01793) 870226
Contact: Mrs Sushma Patel
Position: President
Activities: Resource, visits, youth, elderly, women
Traditions: Multi-Traditional
Other Languages: Gujarati, Hindi, Punjabi

NORTHERN IRELAND

City, Town or Local Bodies

Hindu Mandir
86 Clifton Street, Belfast BT16 1AN

**International Society for Krishna
Consciousness (ISKCON)***
Brooklands, 140 Upper Dunmurry Lane, Belfast
BT17 0HE
Tel: (028) 9062 0530
Website: http://www.iskcon.org.uk/Belfast
Contact: Padma-malini devi dasi
Position: Interfaith Director
Contact Email: Padma_mdd@yahoo.com

Activities: Worship, visits, women, newsletter,
books, inter-faith
Traditions: Vaishnava
Movements: Chaitanya
Affiliations: National Council of Hindu Temples,
Northern Ireland Inter-Faith Forum

SCOTLAND

Scottish National Bodies

Gujarati Association of Scotland*
189 Harvie Avenue, Newton Mearns, Glasgow
G77 6LT
Tel: (0141) 639 6946
Email: agandhi@ukgateway.net
Contact: Mr Anant Gandhi
Traditions: Multi-Traditional

ISKCON (Scotland)*
Karuna Bhavan Bankhouse Road, Lesmahagow
ML11 0ES
Tel: (01555) 894790 Fax: (01555) 894526
Email: karuna.bhavan@virgin.net
Contact: Prabhupada Vani Das
Traditions: Vaishnava
Movements: Chaitanya

City, Town or Local Bodies

**Tayside Hindu Cultural and Community
Centre***
10 Taylors Lane, Dundee DD2 1AQ
Tel: (01382) 669652
Contact: Mr Chaman Lal Dogra
Position: Secretary
Contact Tel: (01382) 858254
Activities: Worship, visits
Other Languages: Tamil, Telugu, Punjabi,
Gujarati, Hindi, Kannada

Edinburgh Hindu Mandir and Cultural Centre*
St Andrew Place, Leith, Edinburgh EH6 7EG
Tel: (0131) 5550140
Contact: Mr Mukund B Joshi
Contact Tel: (0131) 4400084
Activities: Worship/practice/meditation,
community centre, youth, elderly, women,
newsletter, visits, inter-faith, resources

Traditions: Sanatan
Other Languages: Hindi, Punjabi, Gujarati, Sanskrit
Affiliations: National Council of Hindu Temples

Hindu Mandir*
1 La Belle Place, Glasgow G3 7LH
Tel: (0141) 3320482 **Fax:** (0141) 4201764
Contact: Mr J L Kale
Contact Tel: (0141) 9591727
Activities: Worship/practice/meditation,
community centre, elderly, women,
newletter/journal, visits, inter-faith
Traditions: Sanatan
Other Languages: Hindi, Punjabi, Gujarati
Affiliations: Council of Hindu Temples UK

WALES

City, Town or Local Bodies

Hindu Cultural Association*
India Centre, 4 Sanquahar Street, Roath, Cardiff
CF24 2AA
Tel: (01443) 201337 **Fax:** (01443) 400283
Contact: Mr S Purbey
Activities: Resource, umbrella body, visits, youth,
elderly, women, newsletters
Traditions: Multi-Traditional
Other Languages: Hindi

ISKCON West Wales*
Ger-y-nant Penrhiwpal, Llandysul, Newcastle
Emlyn SA44 5QQ
Tel: (01239) 851178 **Fax:** (01239) 851178
Email: mktandasabcs_uk@yahoo.co.uk
Website: http://www.iskcon.org.uk/
Contact: His Grace Minakgtanaramadasa
Position: President
Activities: Worship/practice/meditation,
newsletter/journal, inter faith
Traditions: Vaishnava
Movements: Chaitanya
Languages: Hindi, Gujarati, Bengali

Sanatan Dharma Mandal and Hindu
Community Centre*
22 The Parade, Roath, Cardiff CF2 3AB
Tel: (029) 2045 5564
Contact: Mrs Vimla

Contact Tel: (029) 2056 4242
Activities: Worship/practice/meditation,
community centre, youth, elderly, women, visits
Traditions: Sanatan
Other Languages: Gujarati

Shree Kutchi Leva Patel Samaj*
Mardy Street, Grangetown, Cardiff CF17 6QT
Tel: (029) 2037 2032
Contact: Mr Arvind Varsani
Position: Chairman
Contact Tel: (029) 2034 4932
Activities: Worship/practice/meditation,
community centre, youth
Movements: Arya Samaj
Other Languages: Gujarati

Shree Swaminarayan Temple*
4 Merches Place, Grangetown, Cardiff CF11 6RD
Tel: (029) 2037 1128
Contact: Naran B Patel
Activities: Worship/practice/meditation, youth,
elderly, women, visits
Traditions: Sanatan
Movements: Swaminarayan
Other Languages: Gujarati

Gwent Hindu Community*
6 Gaudi Walk, Rogerstone, Newport NP10 0AG
Tel: (01633) 893141
Contact: Mr D O Trivedi
Activities: Worship/practice/meditation, inter-faith
Traditions: Multi-Traditional
Other Languages: Gujarati

ISKCON Swansea*
Govinda's, 8 Cradock Street, Swansea SA1 3EN
Tel: (01792) 468469
Email: govin_das@hotmail.com
Website: http://www.iskcon.org.uk/swansea
Contact: Tarakanatha Dasa
Activities: Worship/practice/meditation, visits,
inter-faith, resources
Traditions: Vaishnava
Movements: Chaitanya

INTRODUCING JAINS IN THE UK

JAINS IN THE
UNITED KINGDOM   357

ORIGINS AND DEVELOPMENT
OF JAINISM   357

SOURCES OF JAIN BELIEFS
AND PRACTICES   358

KEY JAIN BELIEFS   359

TRADITIONS IN JAINISM   361

JAIN LIFE   362

JAIN WORSHIP   362

JAIN CALENDAR AND
FESTIVALS   363

JAIN ORGANISATIONS   364

JAINS IN THE UNITED KINGDOM

Migration

Most Jains now living in the United Kingdom can trace their historical and ethnic origins back to the Gujarat and Rajasthan areas of India. Some migrated directly from India in the 1950s; others came in the 1960s and 1970s from the East African countries in which they or their forebears had previously settled, such as Kenya, Uganda and Tanzania.

Distribution

Many of the Jains in the UK live in and around the Greater London area and in Leicester. Jain communities are also found in Coventry, Luton, Manchester, Northampton and Wellingborough. Jains have long been engaged in business and finance. In the UK, they are well-represented in the professions of accountancy, medicine and pharmacy.

Jain places of worship are not recorded as a separate category in the running totals of certified places of worship in England and Wales kept by the Registrar General.

There are four Jain places of worship of which three are in the Greater London area and one in Leicester, namely, the Oshwal Centre in Potters Bar, the Oshwal Association in Croydon, the Mahavir Foundation in Kenton, and the Jain Temple in Leicester.

ORIGINS AND DEVELOPMENT OF JAINISM

The Tirthankaras

The precise origins of Jainism cannot be traced, but it began in India. The term *Jain* means a follower of the *Jinas* (Spiritual Victors), a line of human teachers who are believed to have existed from time immemorial and to have attained *kevalajnana* (infinite knowledge) and perfect purity through their own spiritual efforts. The *Jinas* are also known as *Tirthankaras*, literally meaning *Ford-Makers*, those who help others to cross over the floods of *samsara* (the cycle of birth and death). Jains believe that in the present cosmic cycle there have been twenty-four *Tirthankaras* who have taught others the tenets of Jainism.

Mahavira

The twenty-fourth *Tirthankara*, Vardhamana, usually called *Mahavira* (the Great Hero), is traditionally said to have been born in 599 BCE into a *kshatriya* (noble) family in the area of what is now Bihar, in India, although some modern scholars have suggested a rather later date.

When he was thirty years old, with the permission of his family he left home on a spiritual quest. Jains affirm that after twelve years he attained *kevalajnana* (omniscience). Shortly after this, eleven learned men came to the place where *Mahavira* was in order to challenge him, but when he answered their doubts they became his disciples and later on the *Ganadharas* (leaders) of the fourfold order of *monks* and *nuns*, laymen and laywomen which he founded.

During the next thirty years, it is thought that his followers within this order grew to about 14,000 *sadhus* (male *ascetics*) and 36,000 *sadhvis* (female *ascetics*). There were also approximately 500,000 *shravakas* (lay men) and *shravikas* (lay women) associated with the order. At the age of seventy-two, *Mahavira* died at Pavapuri (Bihar) and is believed to have attained *moksha* or *nirvana*, the state of perfection beyond the cycle of birth and death.

Jainism in India

At first, Jainism flourished throughout the Ganges valley area of India. After the fall of the Mauryan dynasty of Emperor Ashoka (c200 BCE) many Jains, together with their *mendicant* leaders, migrated west to the city of Mathura on the Yamuna River, with others migrating further west to Rajasthan and Gujarat, and south to Maharashtra and Karnataka, where Jainism rapidly grew in popularity.

SOURCES OF JAIN BELIEFS AND PRACTICES

Scriptures

Jain scriptures are known as the *Shruta*, *Agamas* or *Siddhanta* (doctrine) which comprise the canonical literature containing the teachings of *Mahavira* and other *Tirthankaras*. This literature consists of some sixty texts and is divided into three main groups of writings. These three groups are the *Purvas* (Older Texts); the *Angas* (Limbs); and the *Angabahyas* (Subsidiary Canon). A majority of these texts are written in Ardhamagadhi, an ancient language of Maghadha.

Purvas

The *Purvas* are believed to constitute the teachings of the former *Tirthankaras* as handed down in oral tradition. Jains in the *Shvetambara* tradition (see below under "Traditions") believe that all this material was lost. Jains in the *Digambara* tradition (see below) claim that some of the material from these oral teachings is the basis for their early treatise, *Shat Khanda-Agama* (the Scripture in Six Parts).

Angas

The *Angas* consist of twelve books including such major texts as the *Acharanga Sutra*, which is the oldest, and the *Bhagavati Sutra*, which is the largest. Based on the teachings of *Mahavira*, they were compiled by the *Ganadharas* and contain materials about doctrinal matters, rules of discipline for *monks* and *nuns*, Jain cosmology, ecclesiastical law, and narratives for the instruction of the laity. *Digambaras* have traditionally maintained that these texts are no longer extant in their original form.

Angabahya

The *Angabahya* (Subsidiary Canon) texts were composed in a later period by *mendicant* authors. They mainly elucidate the material found in the *Angas*. The most well-known and popular of these is the *Kalpa Sutra* of the *Shvetambaras*, which contains the biography of *Mahavira* and also of other *Tirthankaras*.

Other Texts

In addition to the *canon* itself, there are extensive Sanskrit commentaries and independent treatises written in both prose and verse forms. The *Tattvartha Sutra*, written in the second century BCE by Acharya Umasvati, belongs to this group of texts. This text, together with its several commentaries, was the first significant Jain text written in Sanskrit and is viewed by contemporary Jains as being a fundamental text which provides the basis for Jain education. Its content summarises the key aspects of the whole of Jain teaching, including ethics, metaphysics, epistemology and cosmology.

KEY JAIN BELIEFS

Ahimsa

The cardinal principle of Jainism is *ahimsa*, generally translated as non-violence, although it goes far beyond that to encompass the avoidance of all physical or even mental harm to any living being, including the tiniest. Although they recognise that a completely harmless life is humanly impossible, Jains strive to the best of their ability to obey the precept of *ahimsa*.

Reality in Jain Perspective

Jainism is a religion without a belief in a creator god. According to its scriptures, there is *akasha* (infinite space) within which there is a finite area called *loka* (the universe). Within this universe there are an infinite number of *jiva* or *atmas* (sentient beings).

There are also what are called *pudgalas* (non-sentient material atoms) endowed with the qualities of palpability, such as softness/hardness, lightness/heaviness, as well as of taste, smell and colour.

In addition to matter and space, other *ajiva* (non-sentient existents) include the principles of *dharma* (motion), *adharma* (rest) and *kala* (time). These *dravyas* (existents) are all, like the universe itself, viewed as being uncreated, beginningless and eternal. It is only their appearances and surface attributes which are in a state of change, and these appearances and attributes are known as *paryayas* (modifications).

The attribution of two apparently opposite characteristics to the same entity (for example, eternal substance and changing modes) reflects the distinctive Jain view of *anekantavada* (the multi-faceted or pluralist nature of reality). According to this principle, Jains believe that all aspects of reality must be taken into account for a complete and true understanding of its nature. The study of the totality of these aspects, when considered in the context of *dravya* (existents), *kshetra* (place), *kala* (time) and *bhava* (condition), produces *naya* (a correct view of reality).

The idea of *syadvada* (qualified assertion) further underlines the Jain approach of *anekantavada* and is illustrated by the use of the term *syat* (literally, "in some specific sense only") which is employed in Jain discourses on reality as describing only one aspect of the totality.

Sentient Beings

Consciousness is understood as that which distinguishes *jiva* or *atmas* (sentient beings or souls) from all other existents, including material atoms. During the state of embodiment, this consciousness manifests through the senses and the mind, resulting in what is understood by sentient beings as knowledge of objects. The ability to know is understood as varying almost infinitely from one being to another. However, Jains broadly categorise all forms of sentient life in a hierarchy based upon the number of senses they possess.

The lowest forms of life are believed to have only the sense of touch through which they experience pleasure and pain. These forms of life include, for example, algae and plants. Next are those beings with two, three and four senses, for example, insects. Higher than these are animals with five senses and a mind which exhibits some developed means of rational thinking. The most highly developed are seen as being the "hell beings", the "heavenly beings" and humans.

In Jain cosmology, the heavens and hells are temporary abodes and are located, respectively, in the upper and lower parts of the universe. Human beings and animals that have five senses occupy the smallest area of the universe between the heavens and the hells. It should be noted, however, that in Jain thought human beings are distinguished from all other forms of life because of their capacity for a high degree of spiritual progress. Jains believe that it is only from the human state that *moksha* (release from the cycle of birth and death) is possible.

Karma

The variety of life-forms, like life itself, is seen as having no beginning. There is no original form of life from which the others have evolved. Jains believe that, in its transmigration from one body to another, it is likely that one soul will have gone through a wide variety of life-forms. Such variety in embodiment and levels of consciousness is explained by means of the doctrine of *karma*. The doctrine of *karma* maintains that the kind of body a soul may inhabit in its next life is determined primarily by the activities it undertakes in the present life. Unwholesome volitions, accompanied by attachment and aversion, necessarily produce evil acts such as hurting and lying, whilst wholesome volitions, accompanied by

equanimity and friendliness, generate acts of charity and kindness. The strength of the volition of the *soul* at the time of a given action is considered to be the most significant factor in shaping future lives and in perpetuating the cycle of birth and death.

In Jain understanding, all volitional acts attract a certain amount of a very subtle form of matter. This is drawn to the soul and binds with the already existing layer of *karmic* matter in a process known as *bandha* (bondage). An analogy used for this is of dust settling on a wet mirror. Just as a mirror's capacity to reflect perfectly is obstructed by accumulated dust, so the *soul's* capacity for *jnana* (knowledge) and *sukha* (the experience of happiness) is understood as being affected by varieties of *karmic* matter.

Jains categorise this *karmic* matter into eight main varieties according to their effects on the soul. The first four are seen as destructive to the nature of the *soul*. Of these, the first two are those that obscure the qualities of knowledge and perception. The next two are the *karmas* that obstruct the practice of right conduct and limit the energy required for that conduct. The remaining four *karmas* affect body structure, longevity of the body, social environment and, most importantly, the feeling of happiness and unhappiness which is experienced in proportion to one's past good and evil acts. As understood by Jains, the doctrine of *karma*, far from being pessimistic as is sometimes alleged, is a spur to endeavour: the individual soul is seen as responsible for its own spiritual progress.

Jain Path to Moksha

The beginningless bondage of the soul to *karmic* matter and the soul's ensuing embodiment is, however, not seen as being necessarily endless. Jains affirm that a *soul* can terminate this bondage by gaining *samyak-darshana* (true faith in the nature of reality as taught by the *Jinas*), by *samyak-jnana* (knowing thoroughly the distinction between the soul and *karmic* matter), and by *samyak-caritra* (following proper conduct as exemplified in the lives of the *Jinas*).

Right faith, right knowledge and right conduct are known collectively as *The Three Jewels of Jainism*. Together they constitute the Jain path to *moksha*. Right conduct involves refraining from evil actions, speech and thoughts which prevent the influx of new *karmic* matter. This development is gradual, the initial stages of which are viewed as being applicable to lay people and the advanced stages as being applicable to *mendicants*.

Through renunciation and the constant endeavour to follow their life-long vows (see below), a *mendicant monk* or *nun* effectively blocks the influx of all new *karmas* that will mature and, in the course of time, produce new births for the *soul*. The *mendicant* engages in *tapas* (austerities), mainly in the form of fasting and *dhyana* (sustained meditation), which are believed to bring about *nirjara* (exhaustion) of the mass of *karma* that has accumulated from the past.

It is believed that if one follows such a holy life over a long period of time, indeed over very many lifetimes, a *soul* may attain total emancipation from all destructive *karmic* matter and thus be freed from rebirth forever. Such a person is, at this stage, called an *arhat* (worthy of worship) or a *kevalin* (one who has attained omniscience), being a *soul* that has attained freedom from all residual *karmic* matter. At the end of life, such a *soul* rises instantaneously to the summit of the universe where, motionless, it abides forever in its omniscient glory and is called a *Siddha* (Perfected Being), being now free from all *karmic* matter.

TRADITIONS IN JAINISM

There are two main *monastic* groupings within Jainism, the *Shvetambara* and the *Digambara*. These terms are also used derivatively to describe their lay followers. The majority of Jains worldwide, and in the UK, are *Shvetambara*. The two groups, which emerged in the third and fifth centuries CE, differ in some of their beliefs and practices, but agree in their basic philosophy.

Shvetambara

The *Shvetambara* (white-robed) *monks* and *nuns* wear three pieces of white clothing and carry a set of begging bowls and a *rajoharana* (small woollen whisk-broom) used to avoid harm to insects. They travel on foot, do not stay in one place for more than four days except during the monsoon, and do not keep money or material possessions other than a walking stick and a blanket.

It is estimated that there are over 2,500 *Shvetambara* monks and 5,000 *Shvetambara nuns* living in India today. A group of the *Shvetambara*, known as the *Sthanakvasis*, and a sub-group of the latter called *Terapanthis*, additionally wear a *muhpatti* (piece of cloth) over the mouth to avoid harming minute living beings in the air when they breathe.

Mendicant leaders of the *Terapanthi* community have introduced a practice of new renunciants spending a few years in training to teach the Jain religion. These young novices, called *samanas* (male novices) and *samanis* (female novices) are, prior to their full initiation as *mendicants*, permitted to use transport for the purpose of visiting Jain communities in India and overseas. In recent years they have been very active in educational work.

Digambara

The *Digambara* (sky-clad) *monks* renounce all forms of property including clothes and begging bowls. They are allowed to carry only a peacock-feather whisk-broom and a gourd for washing water. *Digambara nuns* are clothed in a white sari. In all other matters the *nuns* obey the same regulations as *monks*, including eating and drinking only once a day in the home of a Jain lay person.

Due to the severity of their *mendicant* rules there are probably no more than a few hundred *Digambara monks* and *nuns* living in India today. Because of the restrictions on travel for these *ascetics*, the day-to-day leadership of the *Digambara* community in India and abroad rests upon lay scholars and advanced laymen.

JAIN LIFE

Anuvratas

A lay person who undertakes to refrain from all forms of intentional violence expresses this by assuming the *anuvratas* (five life-long minor vows).

As has been explained, the vow of *ahimsa* (not harming) is the cardinal principle of Jainism. It includes not hurting sentient beings, and is therefore expressed in a strictly vegetarian diet. Jain scriptures permit the consumption of dairy products such as milk, curds and ghee (clarified butter), but prohibit the eating of meat, eggs and honey (the latter because of the harm to bees which gathering honey involves).

They also prohibit the consumption of certain vegetables that grow underground and produce numerous sprouts, such as potatoes, or fruits with many seeds such as figs, as well as fermented products such as alcohol.

Some lay people, as well as all *mendicants*, observe the restriction of not eating after sunset or before sunrise, an ancient practice which was designed to avoid unintentional harm to insects that appear after dark.

The principle of *ahimsa* also underlies the remaining vows of *satya* (truthfulness), *asteya* (not stealing), *brahmacharya* (refraining from sexual activity outside of marriage) and *aparigraha* (placing limits on one's possessions). Employment is also restricted to occupations where there is only a minimal likelihood of harm to human or animal life.

Mahavratas

Jains consider that the true path of emancipation does not begin until one renounces the household altogether in order to lead the celibate life of a *sadhu* (male *mendicant*) or *sadhvi* (female *mendicant*) by taking the *mahavratas* (the great vows). The vows taken by a *mendicant* are the same as those taken by a lay person, but are much more restrictive.

For example, for *mendicants*, the vow of *ahimsa* includes not harming even the most minute of one-sense beings. The vow of *brahmacharya* means complete celibacy and *aparigraha* means renouncing all possessions except the few items deemed necessary to support a *mendicant* life.

A *mendicant*, therefore, subsists on the voluntary support of the lay people. Giving food and providing necessities to *mendicants* are considered to be the most meritorious acts. The initiation (*diksha*) of a new *monk* or *nun* is accompanied by much ceremony and rejoicing. The *mendicants* are treated with great respect and play an important part in the religious instruction of the laity.

JAIN WORSHIP

Personal Puja

Jains may offer *puja* (worship) at their home shrines three times a day, before dawn, at sunset and, at night, by chanting *mantras* (litanies). The most important of these mantras is the *Panca-namaskara-mantra* saying, "I pay homage to the *Arhats* (the living omniscient beings), *Siddhas* (the perfected beings), *Acharyas* (the Jain *mendicant* leaders), *Upadhyayas* (Jain *mendicant* teachers) and the *Sadhus* (all other Jain *ascetics*)". The second important ritual is *pratikramana*, a confession of transgressions against one's religious vows committed knowingly or unknowingly.

Mandirs

In areas of the country where there is no temple, Jains meet in homes and halls. In addition to worshipping in their home shrines, many Jains also worship at *Shvetambara* or *Digambara mandirs* (temples). These *mandirs* contain images of one or more *Tirthankaras* depicted in meditation, either standing or seated in the lotus posture. Devotion to the *Jinas* represented by these images inspires Jains to engage in meritorious activities.

Before coming into a place of worship Jains purify themselves with a bath. Shoes and all leather objects are left outside. At the entrance to the *mandir*, a worshipper puts sandalwood paste-mark on his or her brow to signify their intention to live a life according to the teachings of *Jina*. Using rice grains, a *swastika* design (not to be confused with the Nazi *swastika*) is made on a low table indicating a desire to be liberated from the four destinies of the world cycle. To the chant of *mantras*, worshippers bathe the images of the *Tirthankaras*, offer flowers and incense, and wave *arati* (lamps) in front of them.

While all *Digamabaras* and the majority of the *Shvetambaras* worship in *mandirs*, the *Shvetambara* groups called the *Sthanakvasis* and the *Terapanthis* do not participate in these temple rituals. Instead, they emphasise *bhava puja* (mental worship) and perform their religious rites in *upashraya* (meditation halls).

In India, *Shvetambaras* and *Digambaras* worship in separate *mandirs*, but in Leicester there is a purpose-built Jain *mandir* which provides places of worship for all Jains. Within this *mandir*, in addition to the main *Shvetambara* shrine, there is a also a *Digambara* shrine and a *Sthanakvasi upashraya* for *pratikramana* (the ritual of confession), as well as a meditation room dedicated to Shrimad Rajachandra (1868-1901), a great spiritual leader and counsellor to *Mahatma* Gandhi on religious matters. The *mandir* also contains a museum which displays the history, philosophy, architecture and way of life of the Jains. The Oshwal Centre in North London has a mandir located in a separate building from its community hall.

JAIN CALENDAR AND FESTIVALS

Calendar

Jains date the era of Mahavira, known as the *Vira-nirvana-samvat*, from the year of his death in 527 BCE. However, except for special events in Jain history, they have traditionally used the *Vikramasamvat* calendar which is also used among Hindus. Both calendars are lunar.

Festivals

The following are the most significant Jain festivals:

Mahavira Jayanti (March/April)
Marks the anniversary of the birth of *Mahavira*.

Akshaya-tiritiya (April/May)
Means "Immortal Third" and celebrates the first time that alms were given to Jina Rishabha, the first *Tirthankara* of this cosmic cycle.

Shruta-pancami (May/June)
Or *Guru-pancami*, meaning "Teacher's Fifth", is celebrated by the *Digambaras* on the fifth (*pancami*) day of May/June. Among the *Shvetambaras* this day is known as *Jnana-pancami* (Knowledge-Fifth) and is observed in October/November. It commemorates the day on which the Jain scriptures were first written down. At this time, copies of the scriptures are displayed in Jain *mandirs*.

Paryushana-parva (August/September)
A period of eight to ten days which marks the most important religious period during the four months of the rainy season in India. At this time, Jain *monks* and *nuns* find a fixed place of residence instead of moving from

place to place as they do at other times of the year. During this time, lay people often observe special vows of eating only one meal or of *fasting* from sunrise to sunrise. Among *Shvetambaras*, the portion of the sacred *Kalpa Sutra* which contains the life of *Mahavira* is recited.

The *Digambaras* call this season *Dasha-lakshana-parva*, meaning "the Period of Cultivating the Ten Virtues" which are asceticism, forgiveness, humility, honesty, purity, truthfulness, self-restraint, study, detachment, and celibacy. During the festival, each day is devoted to a discourse on one of these virtues. The final day is the holiest in the year and is marked by the celebration of *Samvatsari-pratikramana*. This is an annual ceremony of confession in which all Jains participate, requesting forgiveness from relatives and friends for offences of thought, word or deed by uttering the words *micchami dukkadam* (meaning "may my transgressions be forgiven").

Vira-Nirvana (November)
This coincides with the Indian festival of *Diwali*, when Jains mark the death and *nirvana* of *Mahavira*.

Karttika-purnima (December)
Is the day on which the rainy season retreat for *monks* and *nuns* comes to an end, and they resume their travels on foot. This marks the end of the Jain religious year.

JAIN ORGANISATIONS

Jain Organisations

There are both national and local Jain organisations in the UK and they are known by such common Indian terms as *mandal* (the Hindi word literally meaning "circle"), *samaj* (the Hindi word meaning "society") and *sangh* (the Hindi word for "group" or "gathering"). Local groups may be open to general Jain membership or may be specific to certain social groupings, popularly known

as *castes*, such as the *Oshwal* and *Navnat* who were originally Indian trading communities.

There are also interest groups which deal with issues of particular concern to Jains including, for example, the Young Indian Vegetarians. Some may be more specific in their membership as with the National Association of Vanik Associations. The Jain Academy, Jain Samaj Europe and the Institute of Jainology are three organisations which are concerned with the promotion of Jainism and Jain principles at both national and international levels. The Young Jains organisation is concerned with spreading the principles of Jainism among younger people, including the presentation of the relevance of Jain values to non-Jains. It does this, for example, amongst other things, through its promotion of vegetarianism.

Personnel

As explained earlier, the Jain community is composed of four groups of people: *sadhus* (male *ascetics* or *monks*), *sadhvis* (female *ascetics* or *nuns*), *shravakas* (lay men) and *shravikas* (lay women). *Sadhus* and *sadhvis* dedicate themselves exclusively to the pursuit of *moksha*. They renounce their family and all their possessions and take the *mahavratas* (Five Great Vows) at an initiation ceremony known as *diksha*. Jainism has no priesthood, although at the *mandirs* there are sometimes designated lay men (*pujaris*) who perform the religious rituals.

FURTHER READING

Acharya Bhuvanbhanusoorishwarji, *Handbook of Jainology*, Sri Vishvakalyan Prakashan Trust, Mehsana, 1987.

Banerjee, S R, *Chhotelal Jain's Jaina Bibliography* (2 volumes), Vir Sewa Mandir, New Delhi, 1982.

Banks, M, *Organising Jainism in India and England*, Clarendon Press, Oxford, 1992.

Bhargava, D, *Jain Ethics*, Motilal Banarsidass, Delhi, 1968.

Bhattacharya, B C, *The Jaina Iconography*, Motilal Banarsidass, Delhi, (2nd edition), 1974.

Bhattacharyya, N, *Jain Philosophy: Historical Outline*, Munshiram Manohalal, New Delhi, 1976.

Dundas, P, *The Jains*, Routledge, London, 1992.

Ghosh, A, *Jain Art and Architecture* (3 volumes), Bharatiya Jnanapith, New Delhi, 1974-1975.

Jain, J P, *Religion and Culture of the Jains*, Bharatiya Jnanpith, New Delhi, 1975.

Jain, M U K, *Jain Sects and Schools*, Concept Publishing, Delhi, 1975.

Jain Samaj Europe, *Mahavira Darshan and Rituals: Special Issue of The Jain*, April 1992.

Jaini, P S, *The Jaina Path of Purification*, University of California Press, Berkeley, 1979.

Jaini, P S, *Gender and Salvation: Jaina Debates on the Spiritual Liberation of Women*, University of California Press, Berkeley, California, 1991.

Johnson, W J, *Harmless Souls: Karmic Bondage and Religious Change in Early Jainism*, Motilal Banarsidass, Delhi, 1985.

Kapashi, V, *In Search of the Ultimate*, V K Publications, Harrow, 1984.

Laidlow, J, *Riches and Renunciation: Religion, Economy and Society among the Jains*, Clarendon Press, Oxford, 1995.

Marett, P, *Jainism Explained*, Jain Samaj Europe Publications, Leicester, 1985.

Nahar, P C and Ghosh, J C, *Encyclopaedia of Jainism*, Sri Satguru Publications, Delhi, 1986.

Sangave, V S, *Jaina Community: A Social Survey* (2nd edition), Popular Prakashan, Bombay, 1980.

Satyaprakash (ed), *Jainism: A Select Bibliography*, Indian Documentation Service, Gurgaon, 1984.

Shah, N K, *The World of the Conquerors* (2 Volumes), Sussex Academic Press, 1998.

Sogani, K C, *Ethical Doctrines in Jainism*, Jaina Samskrita Samrakshaka Sangha, Sholapur, 1967.

Umasvati/Umasvami, *Tattvartha Sutra: That Which Is*, translated by Nathmal Tatia, The Institute of Jainology, International Sacred Literature Trust Series, Harper Collins, London, 1994.

JAIN UNITED KINGDOM ORGANISATIONS

The organisations listed in this section include head offices of organisations with branches throughout the United Kingdom and organisations which aspire to serve the Jain community at a UK-wide level.

Aden Vanik Association of UK*
9 Cedar Wood Drive, Garston, Watford
WD25 0RR
Tel: (01923) 893421
Contact: Subhash Bakhai
Position: President

Ahimsa for Quality of Life*
20 James Close, London NW11 9QX
Tel: (020) 8455 5573 **Fax:** (020) 8922 7619
Email: natubhaishah@aol.com
Contact: Dr Natubhai Shah
Position: Chair
Affiliations: United Religions Initiative, San Francisco, USA
Promotion of quality of life by advancement of education; relief of poverty, sickness and distress; Yoga classes and stress relief counselling.

Digambar Jain Visa Mewada Association of UK*
10 St John's Villas, Friern Barnet Road, London N11 3BU
Tel: (020) 8368 7202
Contact: Mr Shah Mahesh

Institute of Jainology*
Unit 18, Silicon Business Centre, 26-28 Wandsworth Road, Greenford UB6 7JZ
Tel: (020) 8997 2300 **Fax:** (020) 8997 4964
Email: diple@compuserve.com
Contact: Mr Nemu Chandaria
Position: Co-ordinator
Contact Tel: (020) 8997 2300
Activities: Umbrella body, youth, newsletter/journal, inter-faith, resources
Traditions: Multi-Traditional
Other Languages: Gujarati, Hindi
Affiliations: Confederation of World Jain Organisations; Inter Faith Network for the UK
Founded in 1983 at the World Jain Conference held in London. It aims to promote greater understanding of the Jain faith and to render Jain philosophy and teachings more accessible to all by developing, translating and publishing Jain texts.

International Mahavir Jain Mission*
322 Hampstead Road, Handsworth Wood, Birmingham B20 2RA
Tel: (0121) 3841878
Contact: Mr Arvinder Jain
Position: Secretary
Contact Tel: (0121) 3841878
Contact Email: arvinderjain@hotmail.com

Activities: Worship/practice/meditation, inter-faith, resources
Traditions: Svetambara
Other Languages: Hindi, Punjabi

Jain Association of UK*
55 Tryfan Close, Redbridge, Ilford IG4 5JY
Tel: (020) 8551 2388
Email: jainjd@hotmail.com
Contact: Mr Jiwan Dhar Jain
Position: President
Contact Tel: (020) 8550 5794
Activities: Central body
Traditions: Multi-Traditional
Other Languages: Hindi, Punjabi
The oldest Jain association in the UK. It aims to promote Jainism in the community.

Jain Centre*
32 Oxford Street, Leicester LE1 5XU
Tel: (0116) 2543091
Contact: Dr Ramesh Mehta
Position: President
Activities: Worship/practice/meditation, visits, inter-faith
Traditions: Multi-Traditional
Other Languages: Gujarati, Hindi
Affiliations: National Council of Vanik Organisations; Jain Academy

Jain Samaj Europe*
Jain Centre, 32 Oxford Street, Leicester LE1 5XU
Tel: (0116) 2543091
Contact: Mr Haresh Shah
Position: President
Activities: Umbrella body, youth, elderly, women, newsletter/journal, books, inter-faith
Traditions: Multi-Traditional
Other Languages: Gujarati
Affiliations: Inter Faith Network for the UK

Jain Sangha of Europe*
20 James Close, London NW11 9QX
Tel: (020) 8455 5573 **Fax:** (020) 8922 7619
Email: natubhaishah@aol.com
Contact: Dr Natubhai Shah
Position: Chair
Affiliations: Jain Academy; Ahimsa Quality of Life
Involved in encouraging cooperation between different Jain organisations; promotion of Jain values in the western world; promotion of cordial relations with other communities and participation in inter-faith movements.

Mahavir Jain Temple*
1 The Broadway, Willesden, Harrow HA3 7EH
Tel: (020) 8428 3005 **Fax:** (020) 8961 9449
Contact: Laxmichand Shah
Position: Chairman
Activities: Worship, visits youth, elderly, women
Traditions: Digambara
Other Languages: Gujarati
Affiliations: Oshwal Association of the UK; Navnat Vanik Association of the UK; Shree Digamber Jain Swadhiyay Mandir Trust

National Council of Vanik Organisations (UK)
1 Elm Croft Gardens, London NW9 9QP
Tel: (020) 8206 1396
Contact: D R Shah
Position: General Secretary

Navnat Vanik Association of the UK*
Navnat Bhavan, 36 Masons Avenue, Wealdstone, Harrow HA3 5AR
Website: http://www.navnat.com/
Contact: Mr Subhash Bakhai
Position: President
Contact Tel: (01923) 893421
Contact Email: bakhai4@aol.com
Activities: Worship/practice/meditation, community centre, youth, elderly, women, newsletter/journal, inter-faith
Traditions: Multi-Traditional
Social Groups: Vanik
Other Languages: Gujarati
Affiliations: Hindu Council of Brent; National Council of Vanik Associations; Institute of Jainology,
Promotes understanding of the Jain and Hindu religions. Its principles are non-violence, human and animal welfare and the preservation of nature.

Oshwal Association of the UK*
Coopers Lane Road, Northaw EN6 4DG
Tel: (01707) 643838 **Fax:** (01707) 644562
Contact: Mr R J Shah
Position: President
Activities: Worship/practice/meditation, community centre, central body, youth, elderly, women, newsletter/journal, visits, resources
Traditions: Svetambara
Social Groups: Oshwal
Other Languages: Gujarati
Affiliations: Institute of Jainology
The largest Jain organisation in the UK.

World Council of Jain Academies*
20 St James Close, Woodlands, London
NW11 9QX
Tel: (020) 8455 5573 **Fax:** (020) 8922 7619
Email: natubhaishah@aol.com
Contact: Dr Natubhai Shah
Position: Secretary General
Activities: Resources
Traditions: Multi-Traditional
Other Languages: Gujarati, Hindi
We have established both Undergraduate and
Postgraduate Jain Study courses at De Montfort
University, Leicester; Jain Educational and Research
Centre at Mumbai University, India; and at SOAS.

Young Indian Vegetarians*
226 London Road, West Croydon CR0 2TF
Tel: (020) 8686 6931 **Fax:** (020) 8681 7143
Email: animalahimsa@yahoo.co.uk
Website: http://www.indian-vegetarians.org/
Contact: Mr Nitin Mehta
Position: Chair
Activities: Newsletter/journal
Traditions: Multi-Traditional
Other Languages: Gujarati, Hindi, Swahili,
Punjabi
Promoting vegetarianism and animal rights

Young Jains*
1 Colonial Way, PO Box 233, North Watford
WD2 4EW
Tel: (020) 8866 3296
Email: youngjains@yahoo.com
Website: http://www.youngjains.org.uk/
Contact: Mr Shaileen Shah
Position: President
Contact Tel: (020) 8959 5563
Activities: Youth, newsletter/journal, visits, inter-
faith
Traditions: Multi-Traditional
Social Groups: Oshwal, Navnat, Vanik
Other Languages: Gujarati

JAIN REGIONAL AND LOCAL ORGANISATIONS AND TEMPLES

There are a variety of forms of regional and local Jain organisations that are reflected in this directory. There are only three temples, but there are also a number of organisations which operate from premises that are either owned or hired, whilst other groups are run from and/or meet in the homes of members.

In the Greater London area, quite a number of the listed Jain organisations work at a geographical level beyond the local or even Borough boundaries. These are therefore listed in both the regional and/or area sections of Greater London and also under the Boroughs in which they are based.

ENGLAND 369

YORKSHIRE AND THE HUMBER 369

NORTH WEST 369

EAST MIDLANDS 369

WEST MIDLANDS 370

EAST OF ENGLAND 370

LONDON 370

SOUTH EAST 373

ENGLAND

YORKSHIRE AND THE HUMBER
City, Town or Local Bodies

Yorkshire Jain Foundation*
The Beeches, 14 Ancaster Road, West Park, Leeds LS16 5HH
Tel: (0113) 2751483 **Fax:** (0113) 2751483
Email: k.v.mardia@leeds.ac.uk
Contact: Professor Kanti V Mardia
Position: President
Activities: Resource, books, inter-faith
Traditions: Multi-Traditional
Other Languages: Hindi, Gujarati
Affiliations: Jain Academy, Jain Samaj Europe

NORTH WEST
Regional or County Bodies

Jain Social Group Midlands and North*
12 Cringle Drive, Cheadle SK8 1JJ
Tel: (0161) 4287617
Email: drnareshshah@hotmail.com
Other Languages: Gujarati, Hindi
Affiliations: The Jain Social Group of Bombay

City, Town or Local Bodies

Jain Samaj Manchester*
4 The Spinney, Cheadle SK8 1JA
Tel: (0161) 4287349 **Fax:** (0161) 6834280
Contact: Babubhai Kapadia
Position: President
Activities: Visits, youth, elderly, women, newsletters
Traditions: Multi-Traditional
Other Languages: Gujarati, Hindi
Affiliations: National Council of Vanik Associations

EAST MIDLANDS
Regional or County Bodies

Jain Social Group Midlands and North*
12 Cringle Drive, Cheadle SK8 1JJ
Tel: (0161) 4287617
Email: drnareshshah@hotmail.com
Other Languages: Gujarati, Hindi
Affiliations: The Jain Social Group of Bombay

City, Town or Local Bodies

Jain Centre*
32 Oxford Street, Leicester LE1 5XU
Tel: (0116) 2543091
Contact: Dr Ramesh Mehta
Position: President
Activities: Worship/practice/meditation, visits, inter-faith
Traditions: Multi-Traditional
Other Languages: Gujarati, Hindi
Affiliations: National Council of Vanik Organisations; Jain Academy

Oshwal Association of the UK - Leicester
102 Fairstone Hill, Oadby, Leicester LE2 5RH
Tel: (0116) 2810404
Contact: Rajesh Panachand Chandaria
Position: Chairperson

Oshwal Association of the UK - Northampton and Wellingborough
1 Hertford Court, Meadowfields, Northampton NN3 9TD
Tel: (01604) 416040
Contact: Mr Anil Shah
Position: Chairperson

WEST MIDLANDS
Regional or County Bodies

Jain Social Group Midlands and North*
12 Cringle Drive, Cheadle SK8 1JJ
Tel: (0161) 4287617
Email: drnareshshah@hotmail.com
Other Languages: Gujarati, Hindi
Affiliations: The Jain Social Group of Bombay

City, Town or Local Bodies

International Mahavir Jain Mission*
322 Hampstead Road, Handsworth Wood, Birmingham B20 2RA
Email: arvinderjain@hotmail.com
Contact: Mr Arvinder Jain
Position: Secretary
Contact Tel: (0121) 3841878
Activities: Worship/practice/meditation, youth, elderly, resources
Traditions: Multi-Traditional
Other Languages: Hindi, Punjabi, Gujarati

Jain Ashram*
322 Hampstead Road, Birmingham B20 2RA
Email: arvinderjain@hotmail.com
Contact: Mr A Jain
Position: Secretary
Contact Tel: (0121) 384 1878
Contact Email: arvinderjain@hotmail.com

Jain Sangh Birmingham*
53 Sunningdale Close, Birmingham B20 1LH
Tel: (0121) 5548253
Contact: Mr Vinod Mehta
Position: Secretary
Contact Tel: (0121) 5548253
Activities: Worship/practice/meditation
Traditions: Multi-Traditional
Other Languages: Gujarati, Hindi
Affiliations: Hindu Council of Birmingham

Vanik Samaj - Coventry
23 Moreall Meadows, Coventry CV4 7HL
Tel: (024) 7641 3142
Contact: Mr Kishore Shah
Position: Secretary

EAST OF ENGLAND
City, Town or Local Bodies

Oshwal Association of the UK - Luton
68 Overstone Road, Luton LU4 8QZ
Tel: (01582) 511782
Contact: Mr Chandra D Shah
Position: Chairperson

LONDON
Regional and Area Bodies

Bhakti Mandal, London*
14 Camrose Avenue, Edgware HA8 6EG
Tel: (020) 8952 6193
Contact: Miss Parfula Shah
Position: Secretary
Activities: Worship/practice/meditation, youth, elderly, women, visits, inter-faith, resources
Traditions: Multi-Traditional
Social Groups: Oshwal
Other Languages: Gujarati, Hindi

Jain Social Group London*
153 Chalklands, Wembley, London HA9 9DU
Tel: (020) 89080833 **Fax:** (020) 85379694
Email: pramod@cwcom.net
Contact: Pramod Punater

Position: President
Other Languages: Gujarati
Affiliations: JSG Federation Bombay

Jain Social Group - South London*
Hill Side, Bishops Walk, Croydon CR0 5BA
Tel: (020) 8655 1499 **Fax:** (020) 8656 0033
Contact: Mr Bharat Vora
Position: President
Contact Tel: (020) 8656 0011

Jain Vishwa Bharati, London*
148 Hendon Way, London NW2 2NE
Tel: (020) 8458 5653 **Fax:** (020) 8458 0120
Contact: Mr Mangi Lal Baid
Position: President
Activities: Community centre, youth, elderly,
women, visits, inter-faith, resources
Traditions: Svetambara
Other Languages: Hindi, Gujarati, Marwari
Affiliations: Jain Vishwa Bharati Institute,
Rajasthan, India
Affiliations: National Council Vanik Associations
A non-profit making society dedicated to the
promotion of Jainism in the western world.

**Oshwal Association of the UK - East London
and Essex**
52 Hall Road, Chadwell Road, Chadwell Heath,
Romford RM6 4LJ
Tel: (020) 8501 3730
Contact: Mrs Avni Shah McGeoch
Position: Chairperson
Traditions: Svetambara
Other Languages: Gujarati
Affiliations: Institute of Jainology; World Oshwal
Federation

**Oshwal Association of the United Kingdom -
North West London***
312 Whitton Avenue East, Greenford, Middlesex
UB6 0JP
Tel: (01701) 643838 **Fax:** (01707) 644562
Contact: Mr Laxmichand Shar
Position: Chairman
Contact Tel: (0208) 644562
Activities: Worship/practice/meditation, education
Other Languages: Gujarati

Oshwal Association of the UK - North London*
9 Lansdowne Road, London N3 1ET
Tel: (020) 8349 3817
Contact: Mr Kishor Bhimji Shah

Oshwal Association of the UK (South London)
44 Elliott Road, Thornton Heath CR7 7QA
Tel: (020) 7928 3271
Contact: Mr Hitesh Bhagwanji Shah
Position: Chairperson

Oshwal Association of the UK - West Area*
28 Elmsworth Avenue, Hounslow TW3 4DY
Tel: (020) 8737 7746
Contact: Kiran Shah
Position: Chairperson
Traditions: Svetambara
Other Languages: Gujarati

Shree Jain Sangh East London and Essex*
86 Elgin Road, Seven Kings, Ilford IG3 8LN
Tel: (020) 8252 6993
Contact: Mr Viryesh Shah
Position: Treasurer
Activities: Youth, elderly, women,
newsletter/journal
Traditions: Multi-Traditional
Other Languages: Gujarati, Hindi

Borough or Local Bodies

BARNET

Jain Samaj Europe - London Branch*
2 Mount Road, London NW4 3PU
Tel: (020) 8202 0469 **Fax:** (020) 8202 9089
Email: kc@jam69.freeserve.co.uk
Contact: Mr K C Jain
Position: Chairperson
Other Languages: Hindi

Jain Sangh Europe
49 Highfield Avenue, London NW11 9EU

Jain Social Group - London
12 Westchester Drive, London NW4 1RD
Tel: (020) 8203 1601
Contact: Rajni J Shah
Position: General Secretary
Activities: Umbrella body
Other Languages: Gujarati

Oshwal Association of the UK - North London*
9 Lansdowne Road, London N3 1ET
Tel: (020) 8349 3817
Contact: Mr Kishor Bhimji Shah
Position: Chairman

Veerayatan UK*
Garnett House, 4 Percy Road, Finchley, London
N12 8DQ
Tel: (020) 8445 6625 **Fax:** (020) 8445 0482
Email: mahendra@angergroup.com
Contact: Mr Mahendra Mehta
Position: Chairman
Activities: Youth, resources
Traditions: Multi-Traditional
Other Languages: Gujarati
Affiliations: Veerayatan India

BRENT

**Digambar Jain Visa Mewada Association of the
UK***
172 Carlton Avenue, Wembley HA0 3QX
Tel: (020) 8904 8297 **Fax:** (020) 8904 4949
Contact: Mr Nipon Shah
Position: President
Traditions: Digambara
Social Groups: Vanik
Other Languages: Gujarati

Jain Social Group London*
153 Chalklands, Wembley, London HA9 9DU
Tel: (020) 89080833 **Fax:** (020) 85379694
Email: pramod@cwcom.net
Contact: Pramod Punater
Position: President
Other Languages: Gujarati
Affiliations: JSG Federation Bombay

Jain Vishwa Bharati*
148 Hendon Way, London NW2 2NE
Tel: (020) 8458 5653 **Fax:** (020) 84580120
Contact: M Baid
Position: President
Contact Tel: (020) 84580441
Other Languages: Hindi, Gujarati,
Affiliations: Jain Vishwa Bharati Institute, Ladnun,
India

CITY OF LONDON

Jain Vishwa Bharati, London*
148 Hendon Way, London NW2 2NE
Tel: (020) 8458 5653 **Fax:** (020) 8458 0120
Contact: Mr Mangi Lal Baid
Position: President
Activities: Community centre, youth, elderly,
women, visits, inter-faith, resources
Traditions: Svetambara

Other Languages: Hindi, Gujarati, Marwari
Affiliations: Jain Vishwa Bharati Institute,
Rajasthan, India
Affiliations: National Council Vanik Associations

CROYDON

Jain Social Group - South London*
Hill Side, Bishops Walk, Croydon CR0 5BA
Tel: (020) 8655 1499 **Fax:** (020) 8656 0033
Contact: Mr Bharat Vora
Position: President
Contact Tel: (020) 8656 0011

HARROW

Bhakti Mandal, London*
14 Camrose Avenue, Edgware HA8 6EG
Tel: (020) 8952 6193
Contact: Miss Parfula Shah
Position: Secretary
Activities: Worship/practice/meditation, youth,
elderly, women, visits, inter-faith, resources
Traditions: Multi-Traditional
Social Groups: Oshwal
Other Languages: Gujarati, Hindi

Jain Social Group - Middlesex*
11 Lindsay Drive, Kenton, Harrow HA1 4RS
Tel: (020) 8863 5261
Email: krishah@brookdrive45.freeserve.co.uk
Contact: Mr C N Shah
Position: Secretary
Contact Tel: (020) 8863 5261
Traditions: Multi-Traditional
Other Languages: Gujarati

Mahavir Foundation Ltd*
11 Lindsay Drive, Kenton, Harrow HA3 0TA
Tel: (020) 8204 2871 **Fax:** (020) 8933 2353
Contact: Vinod Kapashi
Position: President
Activities: Worship, visits, elderly, books, inter-faith
Traditions: Multi-Traditional
Other Languages: Gujarati, Hindi

Mahavir Jain Temple*
1 The Broadway, Willesden, Harrow HA3 7EH
Tel: (020) 8428 3005 **Fax:** (020) 8961 9449
Contact: Laxmichand Shah
Position: Chairman
Activities: Worship, visits youth, elderly, women
Traditions: Digambara

Other Languages: Gujarati
Affiliations: Oshwal Association of the UK;
Navnat Vanik Association of the UK; Shree
Digamber Jain Swadhiyay Mandir Trust

Oshwal Association of the United Kingdom - North West London*
312 Whitton Avenue East, Greenford, Middlesex
UB6 OJP
Tel: (01701) 643838 **Fax:** (01707) 644562
Contact: Mr Laxmichand Shar
Position: Chairman
Contact Tel: (0208) 644562
Activities: Worship/practice/meditation,
Education
Other Languages: Gujarati

Shree Navyug Jain Pragati Mandal
241 Portland Crescent, Stanmore HA7 1LP
Tel: (020) 8930 9131 **Fax:** (020) 8206 1761
Contact: Mr Suman Shah
Position: President

HOUNSLOW

Oshwal Association of the UK - West Area*
28 Elmsworth Avenue, Hounslow TW3 4DY
Tel: (020) 8737 7746
Contact: Kiran Shah
Position: Chairperson
Traditions: Svetambara
Other Languages: Gujarati

LAMBETH

Oshwal Association of the UK (South London)
99 Briar Avenue, Norbury, London SW16 3AG
Tel: (020) 8683 0258
Contact: Miss Damyanti Shah
Position: Secretary
Activities: Worship, resource, umbrella body, visits,
youth, elderly
Traditions: Svetambara
Movements: Oshwal
Other Languages: Gujarati

Vanik Association of the UK*
71 Pretoria Road, London SW16 6RL
Tel: (020) 8677 0774 **Fax:** (0208) 6770434
Email: cashahpres@hotmail.com
Contact: Mr Mradula Shah
Position: Secretary
Activities: Worship/practice/meditation, education
Other Languages: Gujarati, Hindi

Affiliations: National Council Of Vanik
Association

REDBRIDGE

Shree Jain Sangh East London and Essex*
86 Elgin Road, Seven Kings, Ilford IG3 8LN
Tel: (020) 8252 6993
Contact: Mr Viryesh Shah
Position: Treasurer
Activities: Youth, elderly, women,
newsletter/journal
Traditions: Multi-Traditional
Other Languages: Gujarati, Hindi

SOUTH EAST
City, Town or Local Bodies

Vanik Samaj of the United Kingdom*
92 Osbourne Road, Brighton BN1 6LU
Tel: (01273) 555053
Contact: Mr B C Mehta
Position: Secretary

Jain Meditation Centre UK*
68 Chervil, Beanhill, Milton Keynes MK6 4LG
Tel: (01908) 240150
Contact: Mr S D Kothari
Position: Co-ordinator
Activities: Worship/practice/meditation
Traditions: Multi-Traditional
Other Languages: Gujarati

INTRODUCING JEWS IN THE UK

JEWS IN THE
UNITED KINGDOM   375

ORIGINS AND DEVELOPMENT
OF JUDAISM   376

SOURCES OF JEWISH BELIEFS
AND PRACTICES   377

KEY JEWISH BELIEFS   378

TRADITIONS IN JUDAISM   380

JEWISH LIFE   381

JEWISH WORSHIP   383

JEWISH CALENDAR AND
FESTIVALS   385

JEWISH ORGANISATIONS   387

FURTHER READING   389

JEWS IN THE UNITED KINGDOM

Jews have been present for many centuries in the territories which today make up the United Kingdom. The first settlers came after the Norman conquest but their descendants were expelled in 1290 by Edward I. Following the English Civil War, Menasseh ben Israel of Amsterdam successfully campaigned for their readmission.

Sephardi and Ashkenazi

The Jewish population in the UK is composed of both *Sephardi* and *Ashkenazi* Jews. *Sephardi* is the name given to Jews who came originally from Spain, Portugal and the Middle East. *Sephardi* Jews have the longest continuous communal history here, having been present in an organised form since the mid-seventeenth century.

However, the majority of Jews in the UK today are descendants of two waves of immigration by *Ashkenazi* Jews. *Ashkenazi* is the name given to the Jews of Central and East European origins. *Ashkenazi* Jews migrated to England in large numbers for economic reasons or fled from persecution in the Russian Empire between 1881-1914, and from 1933 onwards during the Nazi persecution in Germany and other European countries.

Since 1956 small numbers of Jewish immigrants have arrived from Arab and East European countries. There is also a significant Israeli Jewish community in the UK.

Geographical Spread

The densest concentrations of the British Jewish population are found in the Greater London area and the largest provincial Jewish populations are found in Manchester, Leeds and Glasgow. There are also other sizeable Jewish communities in Birmingham, Bournemouth, Brighton, Liverpool and Southend.

70 per cent of Jews are affiliated to a *synagogue*. Of these, about 60.7 per cent belong to *Orthodox* (see below) synagogues and 27.3 per cent to the *Progressive* sector (see below) of *Reform and Liberal* synagogues and 1.5 per cent to *Masorti* synagogues.

The Registrar General's list of certified places of worship records a total of 349 Jewish places of worship 1999 in England and Wales and this directory includes details of 184 *synagogues* in the UK of which 176 are in England and Wales.

Languages

English is used among UK Jews as the normal language for day-to-day communication, but Hebrew and Yiddish are also used. Ladino was the lingua franca of *Sephardi* Jews of Spanish origin and is based on Castilian Spanish. Judaeo-Arabic is spoken among some Jews originally from Arabic lands.

Hebrew is the language of the Bible, of prayer, and of modern Israel. It is the universal language which binds together all Jews in the *Diaspora*. It is the main language of worship and many children learn it in *Cheder* (*synagogue*-based religious instruction) or in Jewish day schools.

Yiddish is a Jewish language of Eastern European origin which was originally a Judaeo-German dialect with a number of Slavic and Hebrew words. Yiddish is used conversationally among a number of the *Haredim* (see "Traditions in Judaism" below).

The majority of Jews cannot, however, conduct conversations in Yiddish and in modern Jewish circles it is generally spoken only amongst the older generation of *Ashkenazi* Jews. More recently, though, there has been a concern to prevent the language dying out and organisations have been set up to propagate Yiddish language and literature.

ORIGINS AND DEVELOPMENT OF JUDAISM

Patriarchs

The origins of Judaism are set out in the *Tenakh* or Hebrew *Bible*. It is believed that God entered into a *Brit* (a *covenant* forming a permanent relationship) with the Jewish community, first through Abraham and then through Moses at Sinai. Where an idea of "chosenness" appears within Judaism, it is a reference to the belief that the Jews have been "chosen" for a particular task and to live within a *covenantal* relationship with God and its implications for living. Jews believe that this *covenantal* relationship gives them no advantage above others, but rather an extra responsibility to live in accordance with God's laws and to contribute to the world's moral order.

Abraham is traditionally considered to be the first of three *avot* (forefathers) of the kinship group who are seen as ancestors of the Jewish people. When Abraham died, the leadership of this growing community was passed on to his son Isaac who, in turn, passed it on to his son Jacob. The name Israel (meaning "one who struggles with God"), which was given to Jacob, is also used to describe the Jewish people as a whole.

Moses and the Israelites

Judaism centres on faith in one God and the belief that God made fundamental revelations to the Jewish people through Moses at Mount Sinai around 1300 BCE, after Moses had led them out of enslavement to the Pharaohs in Egypt. Following the death of Moses, Joshua became leader and led the conquest of the land of Canaan which the Israelites believed had been promised to them by God. After the conquest the land was divided into twelve areas for the twelve tribes of Israel descended from the sons and grandsons of Jacob (Reuben, Simeon, Judah, Issachar, Zebulun, Benjamin, Dan, Naphtali, Gad, Asher, Ephraim, and Menasseh). The terms Jew and

Judaism derive from the name Judah, one of the twelve sons of Jacob.

Kingdoms and Exile

In approximately 1030 BCE Saul was appointed to be King. He was later succeeded by King David, to be followed by King Solomon who erected the great temple in Jerusalem. In time, two kingdoms developed, the Southern Kingdom of Judah with Jerusalem as its capital and the Northern Kingdom of Israel. Both Kingdoms were eventually defeated and occupied by invading armies. In 586 BCE the Temple was destroyed during the Babylonian invasion and many Jews were exiled to Babylon. Eventually, some of the Jews returned to Jerusalem and rebuilt the Temple but it was again destroyed by the Romans in 70 CE, leading to a further *diaspora*, or dispersion, of the Jewish people throughout the Roman Empire.

A new *Torah* centre was set up at Yavneh, near Jerusalem, and the foundations were laid for a *rabbinic* form of Judaism, not dependent upon the continuation of the *Temple* rituals. The classical texts of *rabbinic* Judaism, such as the *Mishnah* (see below), were originally produced in first and second century Galilee. These were then taken up in the Jewish academies of Babylonia (contemporary Iraq) and Palestine where, by the sixth century, the *Talmud* (see below) was completed.

Rabbinic law, commentary and *Biblical* interpretation have been enriched in every generation. From philosophy to mysticism and religious poetry, a rich and diverse cultural tradition has been created and its development still continues in the contemporary world.

Diaspora, Holocaust and Israel

Today there are Jewish communities in many countries. Following the *Holocaust* of European Jewry in which six million Jews were systematically killed by the Nazis and those who collaborated with them, the modern State of Israel was founded in 1948. Jewish communities outside of Israel are collectively known as the *Diaspora*, and UK Jews are thus one of the many *Diaspora* communities.

SOURCES OF JEWISH BELIEFS AND PRACTICES

Tenakh

Judaism is derived from the Jewish scriptures as interpreted by the *rabbis* (teachers) past and present. These scriptures, traditionally referred to by Christians as the *Old Testament*, are known among Jews as the *Tenakh*. This is an acronym of the names of the initials of its three constituent sections: *Torah*, *Nevi'im* and *Ketuvim*.

The *Torah* (teaching) is referred to among Jews as the *Humash* (from the Hebrew word meaning five) because it consists of the five books of Moses (*Genesis*, *Exodus*, *Leviticus*, *Numbers* and *Deuteronomy*) which contain what are believed to be God's revelation to Moses on Mount Sinai. It includes six hundred and thirteen commandments dealing with questions of ethics, spirituality, diet, ritual and all other aspects of communal and social life.

The *Nevi'im* (plural of *navi* meaning prophet) consist of the books of the prophets, namely *Isaiah*, *Jeremiah*, *Ezekiel* and the twelve minor prophets, together with the related historical books of *Joshua*, *Judges*, *Samuel* and *Kings* covering the period up to the Babylonian exile.

The *Ketuvim* (writings) include such texts as the books of *Ruth* and *Esther*, as well as the *Psalms* and the *Song of Songs* which are major sources of Jewish liturgy and spiritual expression.

Talmud

The *Tenakh* is complemented by the *Talmud* (from the Hebrew root meaning "to study") which was compiled by *rabbinic* scholars in the centuries following the destruction of the second Temple by the Romans in 70CE.

Orthodox Jews believe that it includes material that was revealed at Sinai at the same time as the *Torah*, but which was then transmitted by oral tradition down the generations.

The *Talmud* has two components: the *Mishnah* (meaning learning or study) and the *Gemara* (from the Aramaic meaning "learning"). The *Mishnah* is primarily a summary of religious and civil law. It is divided into six *sedarim* (orders), each of which contains a varying number of volumes or tractates: *zera'im* (seeds), which contains materials on prayers and agricultural laws; *mo'ed* (festivals), which deals with matters related to the *Shabbat* or *Sabbath* (see below) and festivals; *nashim* (women), which includes laws on marriage and divorce; *nezikin* (damages), which contains civil and criminal law; *kodashim* (holy things), which includes laws of sacrifice and *Temple* ritual; and *tohorot* (purification), which contains laws relating to personal and religious purity.

The *Gemara* is a commentary on, and discussion of, the *Mishnah*. It comprises analysis, debate and clarification of legal source material. The text is an edited record of the argumentation and discussions of the scholars, retaining the thrust and parry of the *rabbinic* colleges. The *Gemara* also contains a wide range of narrative material, including historical anecdote, allegory, prayer, religious discussion and ethical guidance.

The non-legal material in the *Talmud* is known as the *Aggadah* (an Aramaic word derived from the Hebrew word for narrative). The legal material is known as *Halakhah* (see below), from a Hebrew root meaning "to go". *Halakhah* is the practice or "way" of the tradition.

Midrash

Another important literary genre of Jewish religious tradition is *Midrash*. The *Midrash* consists of *rabbinic* interpretation of the *Bible* and includes moral teachings, legends and parables from a variety of great *rabbis*. The earliest texts date perhaps from 400-500 CE,

but they reflect generations of literary development. The latest collections are from 1100-1200 CE and major anthologies were made between 1200-1500 CE.

Halakhah

The life of the Jewish community is focused around the interpretation and practice of the *Halakhah* (Jewish law). The wealth of texts used as a basis for legal decisions include Moses Maimonides' twelfth century *Code* and the sixteenth century *Shulhan Arukh* of Joseph Caro together with numerous commentaries from all periods including the present. A *Beth Din* is a court of law that rules according to *Halakhah*. Members of the Jewish community approach it for rulings on issues in personal and social life such as divorce and conversion to Judaism.

KEY JEWISH BELIEFS

Shema

The *Shema* (hear) is a daily prayer composed of three passages in the *Torah*. It contains the basic affirmation of the Jewish faith. Its first line is a clear injunction to absolute *monotheism*, stating that the Lord is one God (Deuteronomy 6 v4). The one God created the world, extending justice, compassion and love to all women and men. Whilst God's ways can be known, He is also awe-inspiring in His transcendence and His ultimate essence lies beyond human cognition. God is seen as both King and Father, worshipped in awe, yet close to His people in intimacy and devotion.

Torah and Mitzvot

The *Torah* is the revelation of God's will that includes the *mitzvot* (commandments) which encompass every aspect of life. The *mitzvot* enable men and women to sanctify their daily lives and bring holiness into the world. Jews emphasise the obligations of love and reverence for God who created heaven and earth. Study of the *Torah* is a passionate and sacred task that is central in the religious life.

Prayer is of great significance and the weekly *Shabbat* and festivals are set aside for celebration and devotion. *Torah*, prayer, the weekly *Shabbat* and festivals infuse the mundane with the transcendent and the eternal.

Humanity

The world is understood to be a creation of God and must be treated accordingly. Humanity is made in the Divine image and love of one's neighbour is the great principle of social life and the founding inspiration of the Jewish community. Justice and compassion are Divine attributes that Jewish people are obliged to realise in all aspects of their lives. Sin and spiritual estrangement are profound and ever-present and the *High Holy Days* of the Jewish year are devoted to penitence and prayer, but also to charity and forgiveness, since the compassion of God can restore broken relationships.

Kingdom of God

Jews have traditionally looked towards the establishment of God's kingdom on earth. Also, traditionally, this has been connected with a belief in a *Mashiach* (Anointed One), or *Messiah*. There are a variety of different Jewish understandings of the concept of *Mashiach*. In the original sense of "*anointed one*", the term covers Jewish kings such as David and Solomon.

The traditional belief is that a special person will reveal himself and the Jewish community will be gathered from its exile around the world and re-establish itself in the ancient land; the *Temple* will be rebuilt and never again be destroyed; and the *Kingdom of God* will be established on earth for everyone and the dead will be *resurrected*. Some understand this in a physical sense, whilst others think it refers to the spiritual continuity of the soul. Another perspective, often found among *Progressive* Jews, is that there will be no individual *Mashiach* but rather a new *Messianic* era without war and conflict.

Eretz Yisrael, Zionism and Attitudes Towards Israel

For the Jewish people as a whole, the land of Israel is of great importance. For centuries, Israel has been viewed by the Jewish people as the eternal homeland promised by God at the beginning of history. After centuries of exile, the foundation of the modern state of Israel has created a focus of Jewish life which is both religious and ethnic in its aspirations.

Jews everywhere tend to feel a common destiny with the Jews of Israel as well as with the diaspora throughout the world. When key events occur in Israel, Jews in the UK share in either the joy or the pain of these events. For the great majority of Jewish people, with the exception of some *Haredim* (or *Ultra-Orthodox* see below), the modern state of Israel is an integral part of their identity. It is of such paramount importance to the Jewish people that attempts to deny its right to exist are seen as veiled anti-semitism and there are few issues around which Jews unite as much as the defence and survival of Israel.

The term *Zionism* comes from Zion, another biblical name for Jerusalem and, by extension, for Israel. The concept of *Zionism* is found in both a religious and political sense. As a political movement, *Zionism* is understood by most Jews as a liberation movement of the Jewish people which is intended to end the centuries of exile and to secure a Jewish homeland in Palestine. This movement was officially begun at the end of the nineteenth century by Theodor Herzl who founded the World Zionist Organisation which is now based in Israel.

Some *Haredim* (mainly in Israel itself) oppose political *Zionism* on the basis of denying that a secular state can have religious significance. By contrast, religious *Zionists* see redemptive significance in the development of the State of Israel and view the ingathering of the Jewish exiles as a manifestation of Divine providence.

TRADITIONS IN JUDAISM

There are a number of different Jewish traditions present in the UK. Many Jews have moved between traditions. Some people brought up in *Orthodox* communities join *Progressive synagogues* in later life and vice versa.

Orthodox

The *Orthodox* Jewish tradition accords the *Bible* and its *rabbinical* interpretations full authority in determining law, life and religious practice. It believes both the *Torah* and the oral law contained in the *Talmud* to have been revealed by God and to contain God's unchanging words. *Orthodoxy* understands itself as representing the mainstream of Judaism in historical continuity with the Jewish inheritance.

Hasidic

Within the orbit of *Orthodoxy* is the *Hasidic* movement. The word *Hasidic* comes from *Hasid*, which literally means "pious". *Hasidic* groups originated in the *shtetls* (villages) of Central and Eastern Europe during the eighteenth and nineteenth centuries. They followed the teachings of Israel ben Eliezer also known as the Baal Shem Tov who lived in the eighteenth century in Poland, and took a mystical approach to Judaism. Today the term *Hasidic* generally refers to those *Orthodox* whose theology is influenced more by mystic spirituality than by an intellectual orientation.

Haredim

The *Haredim* (often popularly referred to by people outside this group as the *Ultra-Orthodox*), include many *Hasidic* Jews, although not all *Haredim* are *Hasidic*. The distinction between *Haredim*, whether *Hasidic* or not, and the more mainstream *Orthodox* is that the *Haredim* seek to exclude some aspects of modern culture from their lives and tend to reproduce in minute detail the cultural ways of previous generations.

Some groupings are influenced by the body of Jewish mystical philosophy known as the *Kabbalah* which consists of teachings that were transmitted within select circles of disciples. The most important *Kabbalistic* text is the *Zohar*, which is a commentary on the *Humash* and was composed in thirteenth century Spain.

Progressive

Progressive (which includes both *Liberal* and *Reform* Jews, see section on "Jewish Organisations" below) Jews believe that the *Torah* was inspired by God, but written down by humans according to God's will. Thus they see it as open to challenge and revision and subject to the need of reinterpretation. Revelation is viewed as progressive because God's will is seen to be constantly unfolding. *Progressive* Jews make a distinction between those parts of Judaism that have eternal significance and absolute value, for example, the *Shabbat* and the pursuit of justice, and those seen as temporary and relative, such as gender distinctions in Jewish law.

The *Reform* movement began in the early nineteenth century as an attempt to create a Judaism consistent with the modern world. The *Liberal* movement was first established in Germany and the USA as an offshoot of the *Reform* movement. Its adherents considered sincerity of heart to be paramount in Judaism and believed that rituals should be relatively unimportant. They therefore reformed the *synagogue* services and belief and practice in the light of modern knowledge and circumstances. In modern times, there has been a return to many of the traditional rituals.

Masorti (Conservative)

Established at the beginning of the twentieth century, what is known as *Masorti* in the UK and as *Conservative Judaism* in the United States, is sometimes characterised as half-way between *Orthodox* Judaism and *Progressive*

Judaism. *Masorti* Jews wish to maintain a commitment to the *Halakhah* whilst taking an historically contextual approach to its application. So, for example, the *Shabbat* liturgy may be very similar to that used in *Orthodox* congregations, but men and women may sit together in the *synagogue* during services. *Masorti* Jews attempt to comply with as much of the *Torah* as is practicable in modern society, but they may accept the inevitability, for example, of driving to *synagogue* on the *Sabbath* now that members may live further away.

JEWISH LIFE

In *Orthodox*, *Masorti* and *Reform* Judaism a Jew is traditionally understood to be any person born of a Jewish mother or a person who has converted to the Jewish faith. In *Liberal* Judaism and *Reform* Judaism in the United States, having a Jewish father may also be considered to qualify a child for membership of the community if the child has had a Jewish upbringing.

Circumcision

A number of ceremonies mark transitional points in Jewish life. As a sign of God's *covenant*, Abraham was required to *circumcise* himself and his two sons (Isaac and Ishmael). Because of this, Jewish law asserts that a male Jew should normally be *circumcised* on the eighth day of his life. This requirement is known as *Brit Milah* and is carried out by a trained *Mohel* (*circumciser*) usually in the home with family and friends present. There is no equivalent requirement for girls, although in some communities a baby-naming ceremony for babies of either gender takes place and they may be blessed in the *synagogue*.

Barmitzvah and Batmitzvah

Before the age of thirteen, male Jews are not expected to carry responsibility for *mitzvot* (the *commandments*), but at thirteen years old they take up a new position within the community. The ceremony which marks this is called *Barmitzvah* (son of commandment) and it involves the young man reading in Hebrew from the weekly portion of the *Torah* scroll, usually during the Saturday morning service in the *synagogue*. After the service the family of the boy who has become *Barmitzvah* may provide *Kiddush* (see below under "Jewish Worship") for the congregation, presents are given to the boy, and some families may have a party for family and friends.

In *Progressive* Judaism there is also a *Batmitzvah* (daughter of commandment ceremony) for thirteen year old females which is in the same form as the *Barmitzvah* ceremony. In some *Orthodox* circles girls celebrate a *Batmitzvah* at the age of twelve, the traditional coming of age for females, whereas others may participate in a communal *Bat Hayil* ceremony. This ceremony often takes place on a Sunday and involves the recitation of *Psalms* and special readings. In *Progressive* Judaism there is also a ceremony called *Kabbalat Torah*, which takes place at the age of sixteen and marks the culmination of the young person's religious education.

Shabbat

The *Shabbat* (or *Sabbath*) is central to the rhythm of Jewish individual, family and communal life. It is observed as a day of worship, rest and peace. Saturday, the day on which it is observed, is believed to correspond to the seventh day of the creation on which God rested from creating the earth.

Shabbat begins about half an hour before sunset on the Friday evening and ends at nightfall on the Saturday night because the description of creation in the scriptural *Book of Genesis* refers to "evening and morning", implying that a day is deemed to begin on its preceding night. The times therefore vary from week to week, starting later in summer and earlier in winter. Exact times are available in the Jewish press. *Shabbat* is concluded with *Havdalah*, a ceremony of separation marking the transition from the *Shabbat* to the working week, which is performed at home after the last *Shabbat* services.

During *Shabbat* it is forbidden for Jews to engage in any activities which are considered as work. This general rule has been variously interpreted by different Jewish traditions. For example, *Orthodox* Jews may not drive their cars on *Shabbat* as this entails making a spark in the engine. This is seen as synonymous with starting a fire which, in turn, is considered to be work. *Progressive* Jews, however, do not deem this as work and therefore do drive. The general exception to these *Shabbat* rules, as in other areas of Jewish life, is where there is danger to life, in which case the laws of the *Shabbat* are set aside and precedence is given to saving lives.

Kashrut

Judaism has a series of important food regulations known as *kashrut* (meaning "fitness"). Animals, birds and fish might be either *kosher* (permitted) or *treif* (forbidden). *Treif* is derived from the Hebrew *terephah*, which refers to an animal torn by a wild beast.

Acceptable animals for consumption are all those with split hooves which chew the cud, such as sheep, cows and deer. Pigs, rabbits and horses are unacceptable, as are birds of prey. Other birds are acceptable provided that there is a tradition that the bird is *kosher*. For example, chicken is acceptable but hawk is not. Eggs are considered *kosher* if they are from *kosher* fowl. Only fish which have both fins and scales are acceptable. So, for example, cod is acceptable but prawns are not.

Provided that they are clear of all insects, fruit and vegetables are all acceptable and are also considered *parve*, which means that they are neither milk nor meat products and can be eaten with both (see below). Food which contains, or has been cooked in, products from non-acceptable animals are also unacceptable. Thus, for example, chips cooked in non-*kosher* animal fat are not acceptable.

For meat to be *kosher* it must have been humanely slaughtered by a *shochet* (a qualified slaughterer) working under the supervision of the *Beth Din* (religious court). *Shechitah* (which is slaughter according to Jewish law) involves the draining of blood from the animal by slitting its throat.

Once killed, the meat from the animal must then be *kashered*. This involves the meat being soaked and salted or, in certain cases such as liver, broiled, in order to remove excess blood. The prohibition against consuming blood comes from the view that blood represents life. So, for example, eggs with blood spots may also not be eaten.

Jewish law prohibits the mixing of milk foods with meat foods. This derives from *biblical* prohibitions against boiling a kid in its mother's milk. Separate sets of kitchen utensils are used for the two types of food and a time lapse is observed between eating one type of food and the other. Glass (although not pyrex) can be used for both types of food. Fish may be served with milk but then it would not be eaten at the same meal as meat. The extent to which Jewish people are observant of these food laws varies from person to person. If intending to provide food for Jewish guests it is wise to check first about any requirements.

Israel

The majority of Jews identify with Israel and many become involved with its life in several ways. For many Jews, their identity revolves much more around Israel than around the *synagogue* and other "religious" matters. The means of identification and involvement include: taking regular holidays there; taking an interest in Israeli news, politics and culture; becoming involved in and/or giving money to Israeli charities; eating Israeli food, and so on.

Many Jews view Israel as their "spiritual homeland". It is a common practice amongst Jewish teenagers to participate in an Israel experience "tour" or "gap year" following their final examinations in order to learn Hebrew. These tours are often a key factor in developing a Jewish identity.

Women

Women, and especially mothers, are seen as having a key role in Jewish life because of their role in the family which is at the centre of the practice of Judaism and, in particular, of many of its festivals and celebrations. In *Progressive* Judaism the gender role distinctions specified in Jewish law are no longer recognised as binding. They are, however, still upheld in *Orthodox* Judaism. For example, when a marriage breaks down, in the *Orthodox* and *Reform* traditions a woman may not remarry in a *synagogue* until she has been given a *get* (religious divorce) by her husband and a man normally cannot remarry until a woman has accepted a bill of divorce from him.

Halachically, a woman is believed to become ritually unclean by the process of menstruation. According to *Halachah*, before marriage, after menstruation, and after childbirth, women should visit a *mikveh* or ritual bath. Married women in the *Orthodox* tradition observe this tradition, but many *Progressive* Jews view the practice of visiting the *mikveh* as an option rather than as obligatory.

In *Progressive* Judaism both women and men can form a *minyan* (see section on "Jewish Worship"), carry the *Torah*, and become rabbis. In the *Orthodox* sector women do not to take on these roles, but many *Orthodox* *synagogues* employ women as teachers and elect women to positions of *synagogal* and organisational management.

JEWISH WORSHIP

Traditionally, during worship (whether at home or in the *synagogue*) all males and married women cover their heads as a sign of respect when addressing God although some *Progressive* Jewish communities do not observe this practice. Some Jews keep their heads covered at all times in recognition of the continual presence of God. The traditional means for doing this is, for Jewish men, the small cap known as a *kippah* (in Hebrew) or a *yarmulkah* (in Yiddish). Among the *Orthodox*, many married women cover their heads at all times with a *sheitel* (wig). In principle, any form of headcovering is acceptable for either sex.

Shabbat Worship

Shabbat is the key occasion for Jewish communal worship. The most regular and well attended forms of communal worship on *Shabbat* are *Kabbalat Shabbat* (the first *Shabbat* service at dusk on Friday evening) and *Maariv* (the evening service said every day including Friday night), as well as *Shaharit* and *Musaf* on Saturday morning. In *Progressive synagogues* the Saturday morning service usually lasts one to two hours and in *Orthodox synagogues* for between two and three hours.

In the *Orthodox* tradition the entire service, except the *rabbi's* sermon and the prayer for the Royal Family, is conducted in Hebrew. *Progressive* Jewish *congregations* often say other prayers in English, although the extent of English usage varies from *congregation* to *congregation*. In *Progressive synagogues*, the service may be accompanied by musical instruments. In *Orthodox synagogues* there is no instrumental accompaniment although there may be unaccompanied singing by a male choir.

During the *Shabbat* morning service a portion of the *Torah* is read. The *Torah* is divided into the weekly *Sidrah* or *Parashah* (fifty-four weekly portions) to be read each consecutive Saturday in the *synagogue*. In an *Orthodox synagogue* a minimum of seven men are called to the reading of the *Torah*. Following this reading, the *Haftarah* (an excerpt from the *Nevi'im* which has some connection with the *Torah* portion) is read.

In many *congregations*, either regularly every week or occasionally, *Kiddush* is recited after the service in an adjoining room or hall. This is the prayer proclaiming the holiness of the *Shabbat* and festivals and on those days it is recited before meals over a cup of *kosher* wine. The congregation usually stays for biscuits, cake and a chat.

Other Communal Worship

Three daily prayers are stipulated. These are *Shaharit* (morning service), *Minhah* (afternoon prayers) and *Maariv* (evening prayers). In the *Orthodox* tradition, formal communal prayers can only be said when a *minyan* (group of ten or more Jewish males) has been convened. Communal worship can take place anywhere. An example of this is where collective prayers are said at the home of a bereaved person during the seven days of mourning immediately after a death. This is known as "*sitting Shivah*". It is not necessary for a *rabbi* to officiate at communal prayers and any person familiar with them may lead them.

The *Siddur* (prayer book - derived from the Hebrew word meaning "order") contains prayers for communal services, for private prayer, for special occasions and for travellers. The various Jewish traditions have different authorised prayer books for use in their *synagogues*. Prayers are mainly in Hebrew with the English translation given in prayer books on the opposite page. As with all Hebrew texts, prayer books open from right to left, since Hebrew is written from right to left. There are special prayer books for the *Pilgrim Festivals* and for the *High Holy Days*, known as *Mahzorim* (from the Hebrew word meaning cycle).

Special services for children are held in many larger *synagogues* to encourage them to be able to take an active role in the service when they are older. Above all, *Shabbat* is a family-orientated time with special meals and time for the whole family.

Synagogue

The principal place of Jewish communal worship is the *synagogue*, which *Ashkenazi* Jews usually refer to by the Yiddish word *shul*. Due to the *Orthodox* rule of walking to the *synagogue* on *Shabbat* and at festivals, *Orthodox synagogue* buildings have moved from inner city areas, where Jews first settled, to the suburbs of towns and cities where the main Jewish communities are now established.

The *synagogue* is a building where worship takes place, but it is also a central place of administration, cultural and social activities and education programmes. *Synagogues* are self-financing and may have a *Heder* (room) which is a school for Jewish education where children can gain religious knowledge and learn Hebrew. The *synagogue* might also offer adult Jewish education. In the larger *synagogues* services are held every morning and evening.

In *Orthodox synagogues* men and women are separated for reasons of propriety and women usually sit in a gallery above the section where the men conduct the service. Sometimes, where there is no gallery, the women are seated behind the men with a short curtain or partition separating the two. In some very small house *synagogues*, women and men worship in different rooms.

Inside the *synagogue*, a range of symbols and objects may be seen. The *Magen David* (Shield of David) is a six pointed star which is a Jewish symbol of no particular religious significance. The *Menorah* is an seven-branched candlestick of a type dating back to the *Temple* in Jerusalem prior to its destruction by the Romans.

The *Bimah* is a raised platform, usually in the centre of the *synagogue*, from which the *Torah* is read. Most *synagogues* also have a pulpit from which the sermon is preached. A *Chazzan* (see section on "Personnel") leads *congregational* prayer. The *Aron Kodesh* (*Holy Ark*) is an alcove or cupboard with wooden or ornate door panels which contains the *Torah* scrolls. In Western countries it is usually on the East wall of the *synagogue* which is the direction of Jerusalem. It has an embroidered curtain across it, known as a *Parochet*. A *Ner Tamid* (everlasting light) is a lamp hung in front of the *Aron Kodesh*, reminding the congregation of the eternal presence of God.

The *Sefer Torah* is a hand-written scroll of the *Torah*. In *Orthodox* synagogues, it is read four times a week, on Monday and Thursday mornings, Saturday mornings and Saturday afternoons. It is also read on other distinctive days such as the holy days. The *Torah* scroll is kept inside a velvet cover and is usually decorated with metal breastplates and adornments. It has an honoured place in Jewish worship, especially at the festival of *Simchat Torah* (see below). The sanctity of the *Sefer Torah* is underlined by the use of a *Yad* which is a long pointer in the shape of a hand used by the reader so that the place may be kept without touching the parchment which, if smudged, is no longer holy.

A *mezuzah* (literally meaning door post) is a parchment scroll containing two sections of scripture (Deuteronomy 6 v. 4-9 and Deuteronomy 11 v. 13-21) which constitute the first paragraphs of the *Shema*, placed in a small, hollow box. These may be found on the doors of *synagogue* buildings and are also found on the doorposts of most Jewish homes. They are placed slanting in the top third of the right hand doorpost of every room except the toilet and the bathroom and they signify the sanctity of home and communal life.

Clothing and Prayer

Tephilin (*phylacteries*) are worn on the forehead and left arm by male *Orthodox* Jews over thirteen years old. They consist of two strap-on leather boxes which enclose parchment sections of the scriptures, the wearing of which is believed by the *Orthodox* to be in accordance with scriptural commandment. *Tephilin* are worn for morning prayers, but not for *Shabbat* or festival prayers.

Tallitot (the singular being *tallit* or *tallis*) are traditional prayer shawls, often with black or blue stripes. *Tzitzit* are the fringes which are attached to the four corners, they contain 613 knots acting as a reminder of the 613 commandments. Traditional style prayer shawls are usually made of wool.

Some *Orthodox* Jewish men may wear the fringes, known as *Arba Kanfot* (meaning "four corners"), at all times on a vest under their clothes. In *Progressive* Jewish communities women are often encouraged to wear a prayer

shawl if they take a leading role in corporate worship, but they are not obliged to do so.

JEWISH CALENDAR AND FESTIVALS

Calendar

According to the Jewish calendar, which counts from what is traditionally believed to have been the year of the world's creation, the *Common Era* year 2001 is the Jewish year 5761. The relevant year appears on Jewish legal documents such as marriage certificates, on Jewish periodicals and on grave stones.

Jews use a combined lunar and solar calendar, where each month is equivalent to twenty-nine or thirty days, and a year is usually three hundred and fifty-four days. In a nineteen solar year cycle an extra month is inserted into years three, six, eight, eleven, fourteen, seventeen and nineteen.

Festivals

Because months are based on the moon, no fixed date for Jewish festivals can be given in the *Gregorian* calendar. With regard to the festivals mentioned below, the period of duration given is that followed by *Orthodox* Jews. *Progressive* Jews may celebrate the main festivals for a day less. The reason for this is that prior to mathematical calculation of the new moon, festivals were originally given an extra day in order to ensure their observance on the correct date, since a new moon could fall on one of two days. *Progressive* Jews believe that now the new moon can accurately be calculated the addition of an extra day is no longer needed and this has always been the practice in the State of Israel, except in the case of *Rosh Hashanah* (see below) which is observed for two days.

Jewish festivals always begin in the evening and are grouped into three types. These are: the *Yamim Noraim* (Days of Awe); the *Shalosh Regalim* (Hebrew literally meaning "three foot festivals") which are the three festivals that have an agricultural and historical significance and in which it was traditional for every Jew to go to Jerusalem; and the minor festivals.

The Yamim Noraim

Rosh Hashanah (September/October)
Rosh Hashanah is the Jewish New Year. It involves two days of judgement and penitence. The *Shofar* (ram's horn) is blown in the *synagogue* to remind people of their sins and to call them to spiritual awareness. It begins the Jewish year and the ten days of repentance which culminate in *Yom Kippur*. *Rosh Hashanah* and *Yom Kippur* are days during which no work may be done.

Yom Kippur (Day of Atonement)
A twenty-five hour *fast* devoted to prayer and worship, recollecting the sins of the past year and seeking forgiveness for them from one another and from God.

The Shalosh Regalim

Sukkot (September/October)
This is the festival of *Tabernacles* which commemorates the wandering of the children of Israel between Egypt and Canaan and God's protection during this period. There is a practice of building *sukkot* (temporary huts) onto the sides of houses or in gardens. This practice is intended to recall how the Jewish ancestors lived in the wilderness. Normally, the UK climate prevents Jews living in the *sukkot* for the entirety of the festival, but Jewish families may have their meals in them. *Sukkot* can often be seen on the sides of *synagogue* and Jewish communal buildings.

The festival has a *harvest* connection which is acknowledged by taking four types of plant which are carried in procession around the *synagogue*: a *lulav* (palm branch), an *etrog* (citron), two *aravot* (willow branches) and three *hadassim* (myrtle branches). In the *Diaspora*, *Sukkot* is a nine day period with the first two and last two days as festival days. The final day is *Simchat Torah*.

Simchat Torah (The Rejoicing of the Torah)
A day of great festivities to celebrate the completion and recommencement of the annual cycle of readings from the *Torah* in the *synagogue*.

Pesach (March/April)
Pesach (often known in the English language as *Passover*) occurs at a time when the first fruits of barley would have been offered as sacrifice in the *Temple* when the barley harvest was gathered. It is an eight day period of which the first two and last two days are celebrated as festivals. It commemorates the *Exodus* from Egypt and God's *redemption* of the Hebrew people.

As a reminder that the Hebrews had no time to wait for bread to rise before they had to leave Egypt, no *hametz* (leavened products) are consumed at this time. Such foods must be removed from the home, either by eating them beforehand or by giving them away. Prior to the festival the house is scrupulously cleaned in order to remove any crumbs of *hametz*. *Matzah* (meaning unleavened bread) is consumed during the festival period. A spare set of kitchen utensils, cutlery and crockery are usually used for the duration of the festival.

The home ceremony centres around the *seder* meal which, in the *Diaspora*, takes place on the first two nights of the festival. The order of service surrounding this meal is found in the *Haggadah* (*Seder* service book) which utilises verses from the *Torah* and from *Midrashic* commentaries in order to tell the story of the *Exodus*. The *Seder* is an important family occasion, in which all present, including young children, are encouraged to participate.

Shavuot (Pentecost) (May/June)
This festival commemorates the Israelites' reception of the *Torah* at Mount Sinai and their pledging of allegiance to God. On the night before the festival many Jews stay awake all night studying the *Torah* in preparation for the anniversary of the revelation on the next day. The *Book of Ruth* is read during *Shavuot*.

This festival lasts for two days and is the harvest festival of Mediterannean first fruits such as olives, dates, grapes, and figs. Traditionally, dairy foods are eaten on *Shavuot*.

Minor festivals and additional fast days

There are other festivals which form a part of Jewish life but which are without restrictions on work:

Hanukah (December)
This festival commemorates the rededication of the *Second Temple* in Jerusalem by the Maccabees in 168 BCE after it had been desecrated by the Hellenists. *Rabbinic* legend recounts that only one jar of oil with the *High Priest's* seal on it was found which was fit for use to light the Temple *menorah* (seven-branched candlestick), but by a miracle the little jar lasted for eight whole days.

Hanukah lasts for eight days, and for each day one more candle on the *Hanukiah* (a nine-branched candelabrum) is lit at home and in the synagogue. It has a lamp for each of the eight days with an additional serving light. Sometimes large *Hanukiyyot* are erected outside the *synagogue* and in city squares. Some families give gifts to children at this time.

Purim (February/March)
Is the day which commemorates the story found in the *Book of Esther* about the saving of the Jews of the Persian empire from the evil government minister Haman. On this day children dress up and the *synagogue* services include the reading of the *Book of Esther*, with the worshippers booing and hissing whenever Haman's name is mentioned. Presents are given to friends as well as gifts to the poor. It is a time marked by fancy dress parties and general merry-making.

Yom Hashoa (April/May)
Holocaust Remembrance Day, marked by the lighting of candles and by communal services or meetings.

Yom Haatzma'ut (May)
Israeli Independence day is celebrated by a service in many *synagogues*.

Tishah Be-Av (July/August)
This day commemorates the destruction of the *First Temple* in 586BCE and the *Second Temple* in 70CE as well as other calamities affecting the Jewish people. It is widely observed as a fast day.

There are also a number of other fasts which are observed by Jews to varying degrees. For example, the day before *Purim* is the *Fast of Esther*.

JEWISH ORGANISATIONS

General Organisations

The main national representative organisation for British Jews is the Board of Deputies of British Jews which was founded in 1760. Every *synagogue* and national communal organisation is entitled to elect delegates to the Board which meets most months. The Board deals with secular matters affecting the status and rights of British Jews including such topics as communal defence, group relations, inter-faith matters, education, relations with Israel and foreign affairs. It also has a Community Research Unit and a Jewish Community Information helpline.

There are several other national representative organisations which are more specific in nature, such as the League of Jewish Women and the Anglo-Jewish Association. Local *Jewish Representative Councils* are found in areas of sizeable Jewish population and include both religious and community organisations. In terms of specifically religious organisations, there are national *synagogue* groupings which have local *synagogues* affiliated to them and are described below.

There are other national religious organisations of a more specific nature, for example the Initiation Society which trains and authorises people to *circumcise* in the

Orthodox tradition, and the National Council of Shechita Boards which deals with issues concerning *shechita*. In addition there are many local religious organisations including local *shechita* boards and *kosher* meals-on-wheels services.

There is a range of national and local organisations which are particular to the Jewish community but do not as such serve a religious function. These include various welfare organisations such as Jewish Care and the Jewish Marriage Guidance Council. There are political organisations and also *Zionist* cultural groups and charitable refugee support groups.

There are several communal educational organisations and *Yeshivot* (plural of *Yeshiva*, a place of advanced Jewish learning, primarily concerned with *Talmudic* study). Whilst *Yeshivot* offer ordination to those studying within them who wish to serve in the *Rabbinate*, there are also academic Colleges which specifically serve this need. In *Orthodox* Judaism there is the London School of Jewish Studies and, in *Progressive* Judaism, the Leo Baeck College. In addition, there are many local and national organisations promoting Jewish education and culture in general, including historical societies, musical groups, youth groups and *Holocaust* remembrance organisations.

There is a whole range of multi-national Jewish organisations. For example, there is a Conference of European Rabbis to which all *Orthodox rabbis* are entitled to belong. The Reform Synagogues of Great Britain and the Union of Liberal and Progressive Synagogues are constituent members of the World Union of Progressive Judaism which aims to foster the growth and practice of *Progressive* Judaism. Further details of all Jewish organisations can be found in *The Jewish Year Book*, an annual publication.

Orthodox Organisations

There are a number of organised groupings of *Orthodox synagogues*, the largest of which is the United Synagogue, established in 1870. The spiritual leader of many *Orthodox Ashkenazi* Jews is the *Chief Rabbi* of the Hebrew Congregations of the Commonwealth, who is appointed by the *Chief Rabbinate Council* consisting of representatives of the *Orthodox* United Synagogue. Other *Orthodox* groupings include the smaller Federation of Synagogues and the Union of Orthodox Hebrew Congregations. There are also Spanish and Portuguese *Sephardi* congregations. The oldest *Orthodox synagogue* still in use in the UK is the Bevis Marks Sephardi synagogue in London, which was built in 1701.

The best known *Hasidic* group in Britain is part of a world movement known as *Lubavitch*. The *Lubavitch* feel a particular obligation to persuade Jewish people to become religiously observant and to prevent the assimilation of Jews into secular culture. *Hasidic* Jews are concentrated in London and Greater Manchester with smaller numbers in other places where there are large Jewish communities.

Reform and Liberal Organisations

There are two *Progressive* Jewish traditions in the UK: *Reform* Judaism and *Liberal* Judaism. *Reform* Judaism is the larger of the two traditions and originally the *Liberal* movement was more radically different from the *Orthodox* community than was *Reform* Judaism. Now, however, the initial distinction between *Liberal* and *Reform* Judaism has diminished and the communities have, to a significant degree, converged in their practice. *Rabbis* for both communities are given the same training at Leo Baeck College in London. Most UK *Progressive* Jews live in London, the South of England, Manchester and Leeds.

The *Reform* movement has its own *Beth Din* (established in 1948), cemeteries, day school and a major cultural centre in North London and is organised nationally in the Reform Synagogues of Great Britain. The first *Reform synagogue* in the UK was the West London Synagogue opened in 1840.

The *Liberal* movement began in the UK in 1902 with the foundation of the Jewish Religious Union. The first *Liberal* Jewish congregation was set up in 1910 in London and was called the Liberal Jewish Synagogue. Since 1944 the name of the national representative organisation of the *Liberal* movement's has been the Union of Liberal and Progressive Synagogues.

Masorti

The *Masorti* grouping is a relatively small one, whose congregations are affiliated to the Assembly of Masorti Synagogues which was founded in 1985.

Independent Synagogues

In addition to the formal groupings, there are a number of independent *synagogues* of both *Orthodox* and *Progressive* traditions.

Personnel

The *rabbi's* role within the Jewish community is to teach and to preach, to take on pastoral duties and to advise on Jewish law. All *rabbis* in the *Orthodox* sector are male whilst the *Progressive* sector has both male and female *rabbis*. *Rabbis* are often, but not always, salaried by the congregation. A *synagogue minister* can sometimes be referred to as *Reverend* which often implies that the minister does not have *rabbinic* ordination. *Hasidic* groupings are led by *Rebbes*. The *Rebbe* is a charismatic spiritual leader. The office of *Rebbe* is hereditary, often, but not always, being passed down to the eldest son.

A *Hazzan/Cantor* is a singer who leads the *synagogue* services and, in *Orthodox synagogues*, is male. *Progressive synagogues* tend not to have *Hazzanim* (plural of *Hazzan*), preferring to have a choir to assist the rabbi during services. A *sofer* (scribe) is a person who writes *Torah* scrolls, *tephillin*, and *mezuzot* by hand, using a quill pen on parchments.

A *dayan* is a judge in Jewish law who serves on the *Beth Din* and administers Jewish law in the cases brought before it. In an *Orthodox Beth Din*, *dayanim* are permanent salaried members, whilst in the *Reform Beth Din*, *rabbis* serve in rotation as *dayanim*. The *Hevra Kaddisha* (holy brotherhood) is a Jewish burial society responsible for washing and shrouding Jewish corpses and for looking after the needs of the bereaved.

Many *synagogues* have a committee structure. Some medium sized *synagogues* have part-time Secretaries and some large *synagogues* have full time Secretaries or Executive Directors who can be approached as a first point of contact with the community.

FURTHER READING

Alexander, P S (ed), *Textual Sources for the Study of Judaism*, Manchester University Press, Manchester, 1987.

Close, B E, *Judaism*, Hodder and Stoughton, London, 1991.

Cohn-Sherbok, D, *The Jewish Heritage*, Blackwell, Oxford, 1988.

Cohn-Sherbok, D, "Judaism in Modern Britain: A New Orientation", in Badham, P (ed), *Religion, State and Society in Modern Britain*, Edwin Mellen Press, Lampeter, 1989, pp 209-224.

Cohn-Sherbok, D, *Jewish Mysticism*, Oneworld, Oxford, 1995.

Commission on Representation of the Interests of the British Jewish Community, *A Community of Communities: Report of the Commission on Representation of the Interests of the British Jewish Community*, Institute for Jewish Policy Research, London, 2000

Cooper, H and Morrison, P, *A Sense of Belonging: Dilemmas of British Jewish Identity*, Weidenfeld and Nicolson, London, 1991.

de Lange, N, *Judaism*, Oxford University Press, Oxford, 1987.

Englander, D, "Integrated But Insecure: A Portrait of Anglo-Jewry at the Close of the

Twentieth Century" in Parsons, G (ed), *The Growth of Religious Diversity: Britain from 1945, Volume 1, Traditions*, Routledge, London, pp 95-132.

Friesel, E, *Atlas of Modern Jewish History*, Oxford University Press, Oxford, 1990.

Gilbert, M, *Jewish History Atlas*, Weidenfeld and Nicholson, London, 1969.

Gilbert, M, *Holocaust Atlas*, Board of Deputies of British Jews, London, 1978.

Glatzer, N N (ed), *The Judaic Tradition*, Behrman, New York, 1969.

Goldberg, D and Rayner, J, *The Jewish People*, Viking Penguin, 1989.

Goodkin, J and Citran, J, *Women in the Jewish Community: Review and Recommendations*, Women in the Community, London, 1994.

Gubbay, L and Levy A, *Ages of Man: A Plain Guide to Traditional Jewish Custom, Practice and Belief in Modern Times*, DLT, London 1985.

Katz, R, *Pastoral Care and the Jewish Tradition*, Fortress Press, Philadelphia, 1985

Halfpenny, P and Reid, M, *The Financial Resources of the UK Jewish Voluntary Sector*, Institute for Jewish Policy Research, London, 2000

Kushner, T (ed), *The Jewish Heritage in British History: Englishness and Jewishness*, Frank Cass and Company, London, 1992.

Lawton, C, *The Jewish People: Some Questions Answered*, Board of Deputies of British Jews (Central Jewish Lecture and Information Centre), London, 1983.

Mayonet, J, *The Explorer's Guide to Judaism*, Holder and Stoughton, London, 1998.

Massil, S W (ed), *The Jewish Year Book*, Vallentine Mitchell, London, 1997.

Neusner, J, *Between Time and Eternity: The Essentials of Judaism*, Dickenson Publishing Company, Californnia, 1975.

Pearl, C and Brookes, R S, *A Guide to Jewish Knowledge*, Jewish Chronicle Publications. London, 1965.

Pilkington, C, *Teach Yourself Judaism*, Hodder, 1995.

Reform Synagogues of Great Britain, *Faith and Practice: A Guide to Reform Judaism*, Reform Synagogues of Great Britain, London, 1991.

Schmool, M and Cohen, F, *British Synagogue Membership in 1990*, Board of Deputies of British Jews (Community Research Unit), London, 1991.

Schmool, M and Miller, S, *Women in the Jewish Community: Survey Report, Women in the Community*, London, 1994.

Schmool, M and Cohen, F, *A Profile of British Jewry: Patterns and Trends at the Turn of the Century*, Board of Deputies of British Jews, London 1998.

Seltzer, R M, *Jewish People, Jewish Thought*, Collier Macmillan, London, 1980.

Turner, R, *Jewish Living*, Jewish Chronicle Publications, London, 1982.

Union of Liberal and Progressive Synagogues, *Affirmations of Liberal Judaism*, London, 1992.

Unterman, A, *The Wisdom of the Jewish Mystics*, Sheldon Press, London, 1976.

Waterman, S and Kosmin, B, *British Jewry in the Eighties*, Board of Deputies of British Jews (Community Research Unit), London, 1986.

Williams, B, *The Making of Manchester Jewry: 1740-1875*, Manchester University Press, Manchester, 1976.

JEWISH UNITED KINGDOM ORGANISATIONS

The Jewish community has an extensive range of organisations operating at a United Kingdom level. This directory has prioritised the inclusion of those with a specifically religious focus or basis, although a number of more broadly communal organisations are also included. There are, however, a wider number of communal groups and bodies, contact details of which can be obtained from the annual publication, *The Jewish Year Book*.

45 Aid Society Holocaust Survivors*
46 Amery Road, Harrow HA1 3UQ
Tel: (020) 8422 1512 **Fax:** (020) 8422 1512
Website: http://www.45 aid society. org/
Other Languages: Polish, Hungarian, Czech, German, Hebrew, Yiddish
Affiliations: Board Of Deputies Of British Jews

Agudath Hashochtim V'Hashomrim of Great Britain (Cattle Section)*
33 Elm Park Avenue, London N15 6AR
Contact: S B Spitzer
Position: Honorary Secretary

Agudath Hashochtim V'Hashomrim of Great Britain (Poultry Section)*
25 Rostrevor Avenue, London N15 6LA
Contact: S Leaman
Position: Honorary Secretary

Anglo-Jewish Association*
Commonwealth House, 1/19 New Oxford Street, London WC1A 1NU
Tel: (020) 7404 2111 **Fax:** (020) 7404 2611
Email: anglojewish@netscapeonline.co.uk
Contact: Cythnia Steuer
Position: Secretary
Traditions: Cross–community
We offer grants and loans to Jewish students at UK Universities. We also hold gatherings on general topical events.

Assembly of Masorti Synagogues*
1097 Finchley Road, London NW11 0PU
Tel: (020) 8201 8772 **Fax:** (020) 8201 8917
Email: masorti.uk@ort.org
Contact: Michael Gluckman
Position: Director
Activities: Resource, umbrella body, newsletters, books
Traditions: Masorti
Masorti Judaism is traditional, halachically observant Judaism that considers the tools of modern critical scholarship and an awareness of historical development to be essential components of Jewish understanding.

Assembly of Rabbis*
c/o Sternberg Centre for Judaism, 80 East End Road, London N3 2SY
Tel: (020) 8349 4731 **Fax:** (020) 8343 0901
Website: http://www.reformjudaism.org.uk/
Contact: Rabbi Sylvia Rothschild
Position: Chair

Activities: Central body, women, newsletter/journal, books, inter-faith, resources
Traditions: Reform
Other Languages: Hebrew
Affiliations: Reform Synagogues of Great Britain; World Union for Progressive Judaism

Association of Jewish Ex-Berliners*
45 Brockley Avenue, Stanmore HA7 4LT
Tel: (020) 8958 8814 **Fax:** (020) 8958 9703
Email: alf-ella@netcomuk.co.uk
Contact: A Silverman
Position: Vice Chairman
Activities: Central body, elderly, newsletter/journal, inter-faith
Traditions: Cross-community
Other Languages: German

Association of Jewish Ex-Servicemen and Women*
Ajex House, East Bank, Stamford Hill, London N16 5RT
Tel: (020) 8800 2844 **Fax:** (020) 8880 1117
Contact: Mr Jacques Weisser
Position: General Secretary

Association of Jewish Ex-Servicemen and Women*
26 Clifton Road, Ilford IG2 7DF
Tel: (020) 8554 8738
Contact: Mr Harry Cohen
Position: Chairman

Association of Jewish Friendship Clubs*
26 Enford Street, London WC1 2DD
Tel: (020) 7724 8100 **Fax:** (020) 7724 8203
Contact: Mrs Irene Glausiusz
Position: Adminstrator
Activities: Central body, umbrella body, elderly
Traditions: Cross-community
Other Languages: Yiddish
Affiliations: League of Jewish Women, United Synagogue
The Association of Jewish Friendship clubs is an umbrella organisation for a network of friendship clubs within the Jewish community in London and the provinces.

Association of Jewish Refugees in GB (AJR Charitable Trust)*
1 Hampstead Gate, 1a Frognal, London NW3 6AL
Tel: (020) 7431 6161
Contact: Mr Ronald Channing

Day centre, meals on wheels, financial assistance, welfare advice, sheltered housing.

Association of Jewish Sixth Formers*
Hillel House, 1-2 Endsleigh Street, London WC1H 0DS
Tel: (020) 7387 3384 **Fax:** (020) 7387 3392
Email: office@aj6.org
Website: http://www.aj6.org/
Activities: Youth, newsletter/journal, resources
Traditions: Cross-community
AJ6 is an organisation that offers Jewish educational activities for its members and information and training services for the entire sixth form Jewish community.

Association of Jewish Teachers*
c/o 44a Albert Road, Hendon, London NW4 2SJ
Tel: (020) 8457 9700 **Fax:** (020) 8457 9707
Email: aj6.hq@ort.org
Contact: Administrator
Position: Administrator
Activities: Newsletters
Traditions: Cross-community
Other Languages: German
Affiliations: Board of Deputies of British Jews
AJT is a professional educational association for Jewish teachers. Most, but not all, of our members work in non-Jewish schools.

Association of Jewish Women's Organisations in the UK*
4th Floor, 24-32 Stephenson Way, London NW1 2JW
Tel: (020) 7387 7688 **Fax:** (020) 7387 2110
Contact: Mrs Sandra Harris
Position: Chairman
Contact Tel: (020) 8958 7140
Activities: Umbrella body, women, inter-faith
Traditions: Cross-community
Affiliations: London Civic Forum; Women's National Commission; National Council of Women; International Council of Jewish Women
We are also associates of the Women's National Commission.

Association of Ministers (Chazanim) of Great Britain*
9 Marlborough Mansions, Hampstead, London NW6 1JP
Tel: (020) 7431 0575
Contact: Revd Stanley Ivan Brickman
Position: Chairman
Activities: Worship, visits, youth, elderly, inter-faith

Traditions: Orthodox
Affiliations: United Synagogue

Association of Orthodox Jewish Professionals of GB*
53 Wentworth Road, London NW11 0RT
Tel: (020) 8455 2349

Association of Reform and Liberal Mohelim*
Sternberg Centre for Judaism, 80 East End Road, London N3 2SY
Tel: (020) 8343 2568 **Fax:** (020) 8343 0901
Contact: Mrs Sylvia Morris
Position: Administrator
Traditions: Cross-community
Affiliations: Reform Synagogues of Great Britain; Union of Liberal and Progressive Synagogues
The Association lays down required standards of religious and medical practice for its members (currently 14 nationwide) and has produced an explanatory leaflet which is available from the office.

Association of United Synagogue Women*
735 High Road, Finchley, London N12 0US
Tel: (020) 8343 8989 **Fax:** (020) 8343 6262
Contact: Josephine Wayne
Position: Liaison
Activities: Worship, resource, umbrella body, elderly, women
Traditions: Orthodox
Affiliations: United Synagogue

B'nai B'rith Hillel Foundation*
Hillel House, 1-2 Endsleigh Street, London WC1H 0DS
Tel: (020) 7388 0801 **Fax:** (020) 7383 0390
Activities: Inter-faith

B'nai B'rith Youth Organisation*
Hillel House, 1/2 Endsleigh Street, London WC1H 0DS
Tel: (020) 7387 3115 **Fax:** (020) 7387 8014
Email: bbyo@anjy.org
Contact: Dani Pearlman
Position: Youth Director
Activities: Central body, youth, resources
Traditions: Cross-community
Run by the youth for the youth: a pluralist, apolitical Zionist movement which offers social and educational programmes for 13-18 year olds.

Board of Deputies of British Jews*
Commonwealth House, 1-19 New Oxford Street, London WC1A 1NU
Tel: (020) 7543 5400 **Fax:** (020) 7543 0010

Email: info@bod.org.uk
Website: http://www.bod.org.uk/
Contact: Neville Nagler
Position: Director General
Activities: Umbrella body, inter-faith, resources
Traditions: Cross-community
Other Languages: Hebrew
Affiliations: Inter Faith Network for the UK; European Jewish Congress; World Jewish Congress
The Board of Deputies is the elected body for British Jewry, with representatives from synagogues and communal organisations throughout Britain. The Board represents the interests of the British Jewish community.

Campaign for the Protection of Shechita*
c/o London Board of Shechita, 401 Nether Street, London N3 1YR
Tel: (020) 8349 9160
Contact: M Kester

Centre for Jewish Education*
Montagu Centre, 21 Maple Street, London W1T 4BE
Tel: (020) 7580 0214 **Fax:** (020) 7486 4184
Email: cjeuk@compuserve.com
Website: http://www.knowledge.co.uk/cje
Contact: Judy Thwaites
Position: Kesher Co-ordinator
Activities: Resource, media, umbrella body, visits, newsletters, books
Traditions: Reform, Liberal, Masorti
Other Languages: Hebrew
Affiliations: Reform Synagogues of Great Britain; Union of Liberal and Progressive Synagogues

Chai-Lifeline (Cancer Care)*
Shield House, Harmony Way, off Victoria Road, Hendon, London NW4 2BZ
Tel: (020) 8202 2211 **Fax:** (020) 8202 2111
Email: info@chai-lifeline.org.uk
Contact: Barbara Levin
Position: Director of Services
Other Languages: Hebrew
Affiliations: Cancer BACUP
Supports Jewish cancer patients regardless of orthodoxy. Encompasses total Jewish community and provides psychological therapies and a range of complementary therapies. Lectures by experts, medical and advisory panel available.

Commonwealth Jewish Council and Trust*
BCM Box 6871, London WC1N 3XX
Tel: (020) 7222 2120 **Fax:** (020) 7222 1781
Email: jo_silverman@yahoo.com

Contact: Maureen Gold
Position: Administrative Director
Activities: Resource, umbrella body, newsletters
Traditions: Cross-community
Other Languages: Hebrew, French
Affiliations: Commonwealth Institute; World Jewish Congress

Council of Reform and Liberal Rabbis*
Manor House, 80 East End Road, London N3 2SY
Contact: Rabbi John Rayner
Position: Chair
Activities: Central body, umbrella body, inter-faith, resources
Traditions: Cross-community
Other Languages: Hebrew
Affiliations: World Union of Progressive Judaism

Federation of Synagogues*
65 Watford Way, Hendon, London NW4 3AQ
Contact: Gordon Coleman
Position: Chief Executive
Activities: Worship, resource, umbrella body, newsletters
Traditions: Orthodox
Other Languages: Yiddish, Ivrit
Affiliations: Conference of European Rabbis
The Federation operates Synagogues, Beth Din (Court of Jewish Law), Kashrut Authority, Educational Establishments, Ritualarium and Jewish Cemeteries.

GET (Religious Divorce) Advisory Service*
23 Ravenhurst Avenue, Hendon, London NW4 4EE
Tel: (020) 8203 6313 **Fax:** (020) 8203 8727
Email: info@jmc-uk.org
Website: http://www.jmc-uk.org/
Contact: Jeffery Blumenfield
Position: Director
Traditions: Cross-community
Other Languages: Hebrew
Affiliations: Jewish Marriage Council

Guild of Jewish Journalists*
103 Highfield Avenue, London NW11 9TU
Tel: (020) 8455 9425
Contact: John Lewis
Position: Honorary Secretary

Holocaust Educational Trust*
BCM Box 7892, London WC1N 3XX
Tel: (020) 7222 6822 **Fax:** (020) 7233 0161
Email: hetrust@compuserve.com

Website: http://www.het.org.uk/
Contact: Tamar Burman
Position: Press and Info Officer
Activities: Youth, books, inter-faith, resources
Other Languages: French, Italian, Hebrew
The Holocaust Educational Trust (HET) produces cross-curricular resources, research and teacher training. HET promotes awareness and understanding of the Holocaust and the universal lessons that can be learnt.

Initiation Society*
47 The Ridgeway, London NW11 8QP
Tel: (020) 8455 2008
Contact: Dr M Sifman
Position: Medical Officer

Institute for Jewish Policy Research*
79 Wimpole Street, London W1G 9RY
Tel: (020) 7935 8266 **Fax:** (020) 7935 3252
Email: jpr@jpr.org.uk
Website: http://www.jpr.org.uk
Position: Director
Activities: Umbrella body, newsletter/journal, inter-faith, resources
Traditions: Cross-community
JRP informs and influences policy, opinion and decision-making on social, political and cultural issues affecting Jewish life particularly in the UK and Europe through research, analysis and policy development.

Institute of Jewish Studies*
University College, London, Gower Street, London WC1E 6BT
Tel: (020) 7679 3520
Established in 1954 to promote the academic study of all branches of Jewish civilisation. Its activities include public lectures, seminars, research projects and international conferences. Inclusion in the mailing list and admission to programmes is free.

Institute of Higher Rabbinical Studies*
22 Claremont Place, Gateshead NE8 1TL
Tel: (0191) 4772189
Contact: Mr S Ehrentrev
Position: Secretary
Activities: Worship/practice/meditation, resources
Traditions: Cross-community
Other Languages: Hebrew, Yiddish
Also know as Kolel Harabbonim

International Jewish Vegetarian Society*

Bet Teva, 853-855 Finchley Road, Golders Green,
London NW11 8LX
Tel: (020) 8455 0692
Contact: Shirley Labelda
Position: Editor/Secretary
The Jewish Vegetarian Society is an international
movement and membership is open to everyone.
There are two types of membership, practising
vegetarians and non-vegetarians who are
sympathetic to our cause.

Jewish Aids Trust*

Walsingham House, 133 High Road, Whetstone,
London N20 9HR
Tel: (020) 8446 8228 **Fax:** (020) 8446 8227
Email: admin@jat-uk.org
Website: http://www.jat-uk.org/
Contact: Rosalind Collin
Position: Director
Traditions: Cross-community
The Jewish Aids Trust provides face-to-face
counselling for people affected by HIV; financial
support for people with Aids; and HIV educational
programmes for the entire community.

Jewish Association for the Mentally Ill (JAMI)*

169 North End Road, London NW11 7PH
Tel: (020) 8458 2223 **Fax:** (020) 8458 1117
Email: ruth.jami@btclick.com
Website: http://www.mentalhealth-jami.org.uk/
Contact: Mrs Ruth Coleman
Position: Administrator
Activities: Youth, newsletter/journal, visits
Traditions: Cross-community
Other Languages: Hebrew, French
JAMI provides solely for younger (18-55) members
of the community suffering mental health problems,
and their carers. We have a Day Centre, support
groups and volunteer training.

Jewish Blind and Disabled*

118 Seymour Place, London W1H 1NP
Tel: (020) 8883 1000 **Fax:** (020) 8444 6729
Email: jbphs@jaysoft.compulink.co.uk
Contact: Jason J Ozin
Position: Executive Director
Activities: Visits
Traditions: Cross-community
Provides caring, sheltered housing for the Jewish
blind, partially sighted or disabled persons or families
with a disabled member.

Jewish Book Council*

PO Box 20513, London NW8 6ZS
Tel: (020) 7483 2092
Contact: Marion Cohen
Position: Chair
Activities: Resource
Traditions: Cross-community
Other Languages: Hebrew
The main focus is the setting up and organisation of
Jewish Book Week - the largest Jewish Book Fair in
Europe. Alongside the book fair we organise a series
of literary events featuring local, national and
international figures plus a schools programme.

Jewish Care*

Stuart Young House, 221 Golders Green Road,
London NW11 9DQ
Tel: (020) 8922 2000 **Fax:** (020) 8922 1998
Email: info@jcare.org
Website: http://www.jewishcare.org/
Contact: Joanna Selwyn
Position: Communications
Activities: Elderly
Traditions: Cross-community
Offers services for the elderly, visually impaired
people and people with mental health problems and
unemployed people. It also meets the needs of
Holocaust survivors and provides youth and
community services.

Jewish Committee for H M Forces*

25-26 Enford Street, London W1H 1DW
Tel: (020) 7724 7778 **Fax:** (020) 7706 1710
Contact: Revd Michael Weisman
Position: Senior Chaplain
Activities: Resource, inter-faith
Traditions: Cross-community
Other Languages: French, German, Hebrew

Jewish Council for Racial Equality*

33 Seymour Place, London W1N 6AT
Tel: (020) 8455 0896 **Fax:** (020) 8458 4700
Email: jcore@btinternet.com
Contact: Dr Edie Friedman
Position: Director
Activities: Resource, newsletters, books, inter-faith
Traditions: Cross-community
The Jewish Council for Racial Equality was set up
to encourage the Jewish community to play a more
active role in combatting racism and developing
Britain's multi-racial society.

Jewish Crisis Helpline (Miyad)*

23 Ravenshurst Avenue, Hendon, London
NW4 4EE
Tel: (020) 8203 6311 **Fax:** (020) 8203 8727
Email: info@jmc-uk.org
Website: http://www.jmc-uk.org/
Contact: Mr Jeffery Blumenfeld
Position: Director
Traditions: Cross-community
Other Languages: Hebrew
Affiliations: Jewish Marriage Council
The lines (020-8203-6211 and 0345-581999) are
open Sunday to Thursday 12 noon to midnight,
Friday 12 noon till 1 hour before sunset and on
Saturdays we open 1 hour after sunset till midnight.

Jewish Deaf Association*

90 Cazenove Road, Julius Newman House,
London N16 6AB
Tel: (020) 8446 0502 **Fax:** (020) 8445 7451
Email: mail@jda.dircon.co.uk
Website: http://www.jda.dircon.co.uk/
Contact: Ms Susan Lipin
Position: Executive Director
Activities: Community centre, youth, elderly,
newsletter/journal, resources
Traditions: Orthodox - Central Ashkenazi
Other Languages: Sign Language
Affiliations: United Synagogue

Jewish Education Bureau*

8 Westcombe Avenue, Leeds LS8 2BS
Tel: (0870) 8008532 **Fax:** (0870) 8008533
Email: charing@cwctv.net
Contact: Rabbi Douglas S Charing
Position: Director
Activities: Inter-faith, resources
Traditions: Cross-community
Other Languages: German, Hebrew

Jewish Guide Advisory Council*

23 Wentworth Close, Watford WD17 4LW
Tel: (01923) 255426
Contact: Mrs L Myers
Position: National Chairman

Jewish Lads' and Girls' Brigade*

Camperdown, 3 Beechcroft Road, South
Woodford, London E18 1LA
Tel: (020) 8989 8990
Email: jlgb@ort.org
Contact: Richard S Weber
Position: Secretary
Activities: Youth
Traditions: Orthodox - Central Ashkenazi

The JLGB is the longest established Jewish youth
movement in the UK. It provides activities through
uniformed groups throughout the UK and, through
the Outreach-Kiruv project in Jewish state schools,
clubs and other movements.

Jewish Lesbian and Gay Helpline*

BM Jewish Helpline, London WC1N 3XX
Tel: (020) 7706 3123
Contact: David Marks
Position: Secretary
Activities: Resources
Traditions: Liberal, Reform
Affiliations: Central Council for Jewish
Community Services; World Congress of Jewish
Gay and Lesbian Organisations
We provide information, support and counselling to
Jewish lesbians and gay men, their families and
friends.

Jewish Marriage Council*

23 Ravenhurst Avenue, Hendon, London
NW4 4EE
Tel: (020) 8203 6311 **Fax:** (020) 8203 8727
Email: info@jmc-uk.org
Website: http://www.jmc-uk.org/
Contact: Mr Jeffery Blumenfeld
Position: Director
Activities: Visits
Traditions: Cross-community
Other Languages: Hebrew
We offer a counselling and mediation service for
marital, personal or relationship problems to both
individuals and couples. Groups are run for those
undergoing change in their lives: ie divorce support
and pre-marriage, and we also help those who have
problems with Jewish divorce.

Jewish Memorial Council*

25 Enford Street, London W1H 1DW
Tel: (020) 7724 7778 **Fax:** (020) 7706 1710
Contact: Mr J Zaltzman
Position: General Manager
Activities: Worship, resource, youth, books, inter-
faith
Traditions: All Traditions
Other Languages: Hebrew, Yiddish
Rev Malcolm Weisman is Religious Adviser to the
Small Communities both in the British Isles and the
Commonwealth.

Jewish Museum, The - Camden Town*

Raymond Burton House, 129-131 Albert Street,
London NW1 7NB
Tel: (020) 7284 1997 **Fax:** (020) 7267 9008
Contact: Ms Rickie Burman

Position: Director
Activities: Resource, visits, youth, elderly, women, newsletter
Traditions: Cross-community
Other Languages: French
The museum has permanent displays and collections on Jewish history and religion in Britain and one of the world's finest collections of Jewish ceremonial art. Changing exhibitions, cultural events and educational programmes on Judaism and Jewish history.

Jewish Museum, The*
80 East End Road, Finchley, London N3 2SY
Tel: (020) 8349 1143 **Fax:** (020) 8343 2162
Email: jml.finchley@lineone.net
Website: http://www.jewsusm.ort.org/
Contact: Ms Carol Seigel
Position: Curator
Activities: Youth, elderly, books, visits, resources
Traditions: Cross-community
The Jewish Museum, Finchley, is based within a vibrant Jewish community centre in North London, and houses the museum's social history collections and holocaust education gallery.

Jewish Refugees Committee, World Jewish Relief*
The Forum, 74/80 Camden Street, London WC1H 0AN
Tel: (020) 7691 1781 **Fax:** (020) 7691 1780
Email: wjr@wjr.org.uk
Contact: L S Montague
Other Languages: Russian, German, French, Italian
The Jewish Refugees Committee assists Jewish refugees and asylum seekers in the UK. We are part of a registered charity.

Jewish Scout Advisory Council (JSAC)*
103 Kenton Lane, Kenton, Harrow HA3 8UJ
Tel: (020) 8907 3446
Contact: R Simmons
Position: Honorary Secretary
Activities: Umbrella body, youth
Traditions: Cross-community
Affiliations: Makor - Association of Jewish Youth
JSAC is an umbrella organisation to which Jewish Scout groups in England and Wales are affiliated. Activities are arranged in which groups take part. Affiliated to the Scout Association.

Jewish Woman's Network*
41 Dorset Drive, Edgware HA8 7NT
Tel: (020) 8896 2050

Email: avril@easynet.co.uk
Website: http://www.jwn.ort.org/
Contact: Vicky Grosser
Position: Chair

Jewish Womens' Aid*
P O Box 2670, London WC1N 3XX
Tel: (020) 8445 8060 **Fax:** (020) 8445 0305
Email: jwa@dircon.co.uk
Contact: Ms Stephanie Barnett
Activities: Community centre, elderly
Traditions: Cross Community
Other Languages: Hebrew
Affiliations: National Network of Jewish Housing Associations
JWA is run by Jewish women for Jewish women who have experienced domestic abuse. JWA manages the only Jewish refuge in Europe, a confidential freephone helpline and drop-in groups.

League of Jewish Women*
24–32 Stephenson Way, London NW1 2JW
Tel: (020) 7387 7688 **Fax:** (020) 7387 2110
Email: office@leagueofjewishwomen.org.uk
Website: http://www.leagueofjewishwomen.org.uk/
Contact: Jackie Baines
Position: Head of Development
Contact Email: jackieb@leagueofjewishwomen.org.uk
A non-fundraising voluntary welfare organisation with 70 groups throughout Great Britain. Its members care for all communities irrespective of race, religion, creed, colour, able or disabled. The organisation will also give opinion on social issues.

Leo Baeck College*
The Manor House, 80 East End Road, Finchley, London N3 2SY
Tel: (020) 8349 5600 **Fax:** (020) 8343 2558
Email: info@lbc.ac.uk
Website: http://www.lbc.ac.uk/
Contact: John Olbrich
Position: Registrar
Contact Email: jolbrich@lbc.ac.uk
Activities: Inter-faith

London Beth Din*
Adler House, 735 High Road, London N12 0US
Tel: (020) 8343 6270 **Fax:** (020) 8343 6257
Contact: David Frei
Position: Registrar
Traditions: Orthodox
Other Languages: Hebrew, Yiddish, French

Affiliations: United Synagogue
The London Beth Din is divided into three divisions; Family, which supervises divorces, adoptions and conversions; Judicial, which resolves legal disputes; and Kashrut, which supervises most of London's restaurants, bakers, caterers and issues food certificates.

London Jewish Cultural Centre*
The Old House, c/o Kings College, Kidderpore Avenue, London NW3 7ST
Tel: (020) 7431 0345
Email: admin@ljcc.org.uk
Website: http://www.ljcc.org.uk/
Contact: Dr Joanna Newman
Position: Director of Adult Ed
Activities: Community centre, umbrella body, youth, elderly, newsletter/journal, inter-faith, resources
Traditions: Cross-community
Other Languages: Hebrew, Yiddish, German
Founded in 1978, Spiro is an educational body which aims to bring a knowledge and understanding of Jewish history, culture and language to Jews and non-Jews through courses, cultural events and tours.

London School of Jewish Studies*
Schaller House, Albert Road, Hendon, London NW4 1TE
Tel: (020) 8203 6427 **Fax:** (020) 8203 6420
Email: enquiries@lsjs.ac.uk
Website: http://www.lsjs.ac.uk/
Contact: Dr I I Rabinowitz
Position: Director
Contact Email: director@lsjs.ac.uk
Activities: Youth, women, resources
Traditions: Orthodox
Other Languages: Hebrew
Affiliations: United Synagogue; Office of the Chief Rabbi
LSJJ has four centres; Training; Lifelong Learning; Academic; Library (large collection of Judaica and Hebraica).

Lubavitch Foundation*
2 Dovedale Road, Liverpool L18 3ER
Tel: (0151) 7290443
Email: info@lubavitchliverpool.com
Website: http://www.lubavitchliverpool.com/
Contact: Rabbi Kievman
Position: Director
Contact Tel: (0151) 729 0443
Contact Email: rabbi@lubavitchliverpool.com

Activities: Worship/practice/meditation, community centre, central body, youth, elderly, women, newsletter/journal, visits, resources
Traditions: Chassidic
Other Languages: Yiddish, Hebrew

Lubavitch Foundation*
107-115 Stamford Hill, London N16 5RP
Tel: (020) 8800 0022 **Fax:** (020) 8809 7324
Contact: Rabbi S F Vogel
Position: Director
Activities: Worship/practice/meditation, community centre, central body, youth, elderly, women, newsletter/journal, books, visits
Traditions: Charedi
Other Languages: Yiddish, Hebrew
Affiliations: Chabad - Lubavitch

MAKOR (Formally JPMP)*
Marlock House, 142 Bury Old Road, Manchester M8 6HD
Tel: (0161) 7214205 **Fax:** (0161) 7206483
Email: infomanchester@makor.org.uk
Contact: Director
Position: Director
Contact Tel: (07939) 118008
Activities: Central body, umbrella body, youth, newsletter/journal, resources
Traditions: Cross-community
Other Languages: Hebrew

Makor - AJY*
Balfour House, 741 High Road, London N12 0BQ
Tel: (020) 8446 8020
Contact: Roy Graham
Position: Director
Activities: Resource, umbrella body, newsletters
Traditions: Cross-Community

Manor House Centre for Psychotherapy and Counselling, The*
The Sternberg Centre, 80 East End Road, London N3 2SY
Tel: (020) 8371 0180
Contact: Judith Dell
Position: Course Director

Mazal Tov: The Progressive Jewish Marriage Bureau*
28 St Johns Wood Road, London NW8 7HA
Tel: (020) 7289 8591
Email: mazaltov@ulps.org
Contact: Ms Ruth Green
Position: Administrator

Traditions: Liberal
Affiliations: Union of Liberal and Progressive
Synagogues
All applicants are offered confidential and individual
interviews before acceptance as members.

National Council of Shechita Boards*
PO Box 579, Adastra Suite, 401 Nether Street,
London N3 1YR
Tel: (020) 8349 9160 **Fax:** (020) 8346 2209

National Network of Jewish Social Housing*
c/o Harmony Close, Princes Park Avenue, London
NW11 0JJ
Tel: (020) 8381 4901 **Fax:** (020) 8458 1772
Contact: Sara Clarke
Position: Administrator
Contact Email: sclarke@bnaibrithjbg.org.uk

Noam Masorti Youth*
97 Leeside Crescent, Golders Green, London
NW11 0JL
Tel: (020) 8201 8773 **Fax:** (020) 8458 4027
Email: noam@masorti.ort.uk
Contact: Mr Jonathon Whine
Position: Director
Activities: Worship/practice/meditation,
community centre, youth, newsletter/journal,
resources
Traditions: Masorti
Other Languages: Hebrew
Affiliations: Assembly of Masorti Synagogues;
Zionist Federation
Noam is the Zionist Youth Movement of Masorti
Synagogues. We are a democratic youth movement
run by members for members. We run clubs, camps
and courses for 9-22 year olds.

Office of the Chief Rabbi*
Adler House, 735 High Road, North Finchley,
London N12 0US
Tel: (020) 8343 6301 **Fax:** (020) 8343 6310
Email: info@chiefrabbi.org
Website: http://www.chiefrabbi.org/
Contact: Lilian Isaacs
Activities: Umbrella body, books, inter-faith,
resources
Traditions: Orthodox
Other Languages: Hebrew, French
Affiliations: United Synagogue; European
Council of Rabbis

Operation Judaism*
95 Willows Road, Birmingham B12 9QF
Tel: (0121) 4406673
Contact: Rabbi Shmuel Arkush

Position: Director
Activities: Resource, media, books
Traditions: Cross-community

Rabbinical Commission for the Licensing of Shochetim*
Office of the Chief Rabbi, 735 High Road, North
Finchley, London N12 0US
Tel: (020) 8343 6301 **Fax:** (020) 8343 6310
Email: info@chiefrabbi.org
Contact: Revd Alan Greenbat
Position: Secretary
Activities: Umbrella body
Traditions: Orthodox
Other Languages: Hebrew, Yiddish, French

Rabbinical Council of the United Synagogue*
Adler House, 735 High Road, Finchley, London
N12 0US
Tel: (020) 8343 6313 **Fax:** (020) 8343 6310
Contact: Rabbi Dr Julian Shindler
Position: Executive Director

Reform Synagogues of Great Britain*
The Sternberg Centre for Judaism, 80 East End
Road, Finchley, London N3 2SY
Tel: (020) 8349 5700 **Fax:** (020) 8343 5699
Email: admin@reformjudaism.org.uk
Website: http://www.reformjudaism.org.uk/
Contact: Mrs N Landau
Position: Director of HR
Activities: Umbrella body
Traditions: Reform
Other Languages: Hebrew
Affiliations: Board of Deputies of British Jews;
London Civic Forum; World Union for Progressive
Judaism
The Reform Movement seeks, through a
partnership between its synagogues and the
Movement infrastructure (volunteers and staff, lay
leaders and rabbis) to articulate, teach and live out
the faith and values of Reform Judaism.

Reform Synagogues of Great Britain Youth and Students Division*
The Sternberg Centre, 80 East End Road, Finchley,
London N3 2SY
Tel: (020) 8349 4731 **Fax:** (020) 8343 4972
Email: rsy.rsgb@ort.org
Contact: Mr Daren Gordon
Position: Director of Youth
Activities: Resource, youth
Traditions: Reform
Other Languages: Hebrew
Affiliations: World Union for Progressive Judaism
Reform Judaism is an informed and questioning,
compassionate and egalitarian expression of a unique

faith and culture, rooted in the tradition of Torah yet in dialogue with modernity.

RSGB/ULPS Social Action*

c/o Reform Synagogues of GB, The Sternberg Centre for Judaism, 80 East End Road, London N3 2SY
Tel: (020) 8349 5653 **Fax:** (020) 8349 5699
Website: http://www.refsyn.org.uk/
Contact: Vicky Joseph
Position: Co-ordinator
Contact Email:
vicky.joseph@reformjudaism.org.uk
Activities: Inter-faith, resources
Traditions: Reform/Liberal
Affiliations: Reform Synagogues of Great Britain; Union of Liberal and Progressive Synagogues
Social Action is a joint initiative of the Reform and Liberal Synagogues that offers a practical Jewish response to current events and issues of social and ethical concern.

Sternberg Centre for Judaism*

The Manor House, 80 East End Road, Finchley, London N3 2SY
Tel: (020) 8349 5640 **Fax:** (020) 8349 5699
Email: admin@reformjudaism.org.uk
Website: http://www.refsyn.org.uk/
Contact: Rabbi Tony Bayfield
Position: Director
Activities: Umbrella body
A national centre for the promotion of Jewish religious, educational, cultural and intellectual matters. The Centre also houses an Interfaith Dialogue Centre and Library.

Society for Jewish Study*

1a Church Mount, London N2 0RW
Contact: Mrs Rosemary Goldstein
Position: Secretary
Activities: Resources
Traditions: Cross-community

Tay-Sachs Screening Centre, Clinical Genetics*

7th Floor, New Guy's House, Guy's Hospital, St Thomas Street, London SE1 9RT
Tel: (020) 7955 4648 **Fax:** (020) 7955 2550
Contact: Sara Levene
Position: Genetic Counsellor

Tzedek*

25 Kings Close, London NW4 2JU
Tel: (020) 8202 4744
Email: tzedekuk@aol.com

Website: http://www.tzedek.org.uk/
Contact: Steven Derby
Position: Development Officer
Contact Email: tzedekuk@aol.com
Activities: Newsletter/journal, inter-faith, resources
Traditions: Cross-community
Tzedek is a Jewish overseas development and educational charity. We provide grants to development projects for poverty relief programmes and arrange educational activities. We also send volunteers overseas.

Union of Jewish Students*

Hillel House, 1-2 Endsleigh Street, London WC1H 0DS
Tel: (020) 7387 4644 **Fax:** (020) 7383 0390

Union of Liberal and Progressive Synagogues*

The Montagu Centre, 21 Maple Street, London W1T 4BE
Tel: (020) 7580 1663 **Fax:** (020) 7436 4184
Email: montagu@ulps.org
Website: ww.ulps.org
Contact: Michael A Burman
Position: Administrative Director
Activities: Umbrella body, youth, elderly, women, newsletter/journal, books, inter-faith, resources
Traditions: Liberal

Union of Maccabi Associations*

Prestige House, Station Road, Boreham WD5 1DF
Tel: (020) 8207 0700
Contact: Richard Feldman
Position: Chair
Activities: Resource, umbrella body, youth, newsletters, inter-faith
Traditions: Cross-community
Other Languages: Hebrew
Affiliations: Maccabi World Union

Union of Orthodox Hebrew Congregations*

140 Stamford Hill, London N16 6QT
Tel: (020) 8802 6226 **Fax:** (020) 8809 7092
Contact: A Klein
Position: Administrator
Activities: Resource, umbrella body, newsletters
Traditions: Charedi
Other Languages: Yiddish, Hebrew
Established in 1926 as a congregational association for Orthodox Jews of primarily Central and Eastern European origin, including many of the Hasidic Congregations.

United Synagogue Agency for Jewish Education*
Bet Meir, 44A Albert Road, Hendon, London NW4 2JS
Tel: (020) 8457 9700 **Fax:** (020) 8457 9700
Email: info@aje.org.uk
Website: http://www.aje.org.uk/
Contact: Simon Goulden
Position: Chief Executive
Contact Email: simon@aje.org.uk
Activities: Umbrella body, youth, newsletter/journal, books, resources
Traditions: Orthodox – Central Ashkenazi
Other Languages: Hebrew, French, Yiddish
Affiliations: United Synagogue

United Synagogue*
735 High Road, London N12 0US
Tel: (020) 8343 8989 **Fax:** (020) 8343 6262
Email: info@unitedsynagogue.co.uk
Website: http://www.unitedsynagogue.co.uk/
Contact: Peter Sheldon
Position: Chief Executive
Traditions: Orthodox
Other Languages: Hebrew, French

Yakar Educational Foundation*
2 Egerton Gardens, London NW4 4BA
Tel: (020) 8202 5551 **Fax:** (020) 8202 9653
Website: http://www.yakar.org.uk/
Contact: Rabbi Jeremy Rosen
Position: Director
Contact Email: jeremyrosen@msn.com

JEWISH REGIONAL AND LOCAL ORGANISATIONS AND SYNAGOGUES

A variety of forms of local Jewish organisations are listed in this directory. These include synagogues; welfare bodies; representative bodies; student societies and houses; *yeshivot*; and other educational institutions with the general exception of Jewish schools.

ENGLAND	402
NORTH EAST	402
YORKSHIRE AND THE HUMBER	403
NORTH WEST	406
EAST MIDLANDS	410
WEST MIDLANDS	411
EAST OF ENGLAND	412
LONDON	413
SOUTH EAST	425
SOUTH WEST	429
NORTHERN IRELAND	430
SCOTLAND	430
WALES	431

ENGLAND

NORTH EAST
Regional or County Bodies

Gateshead Jewish Family Service*
7 Oxford Terrace, Bensham, Gateshead NE8 1RQ
Tel: (0191) 4775677 **Fax:** (0191) 4772241
Contact: Mrs R Hirsch
Position: Scheme Manager
Activities: Youth, elderly
Traditions: Charedi
Other Languages: Yiddish, Hebrew, French
Affiliations: Gateshead Jewish Community

Jewish Students' Society in the North East*
Tel: (0191) 213 0919
Email: susan.olsburgh@unn.ac.uk
Contact: Susan Olsburgh
Position: Students Liaison Officer

North East Jewish Community Service*
Lionel Jacobson House, Graham Park Road, Gosforth, Newcastle-upon-Tyne, Tyne and Wear, NE3 4BH
Tel: (0191) 285 1968
Contact: Mr Bernard Shaffer
Position: Community Care Officer

Representative Council of North East Jewry*
56 Southwood Gardens, Newcastle-upon-Tyne NE3 3BX
Tel: (0191) 2854043 **Fax:** (0191) 2848941
Contact: Henry Ross
Position: Honorary Secretary
Activities: Umbrella body, newsletters, inter-faith, resources
Traditions: Cross-community
Affiliations: Board of Deputies; Northern Representative Council

City, Town or Local Bodies

Darlington Hebrew Congregation*
Bloomfield Road, Darlington DL3
Contact: Mr L J Starr
Position: Secretary
Contact Tel: (01325) 333736
Activities: Worship/practice/meditation, community centre, visits, inter-faith
Traditions: Reform
Affiliations: Newcastle Reform Synagogues;

Reform Synagogues of Great Britain; World Union of Progressive Judaism

Gateshead Jewish Family Service*
7 Oxford Terrace, Bensham, Gateshead NE8 1RQ
Tel: (0191) 4775677 **Fax:** (0191) 4772241
Contact: Mrs R Hirsch
Position: Scheme Manager
Activities: Youth, elderly
Traditions: Charedi
Other Languages: Yiddish, Hebrew, French
Affiliations: Gateshead Jewish Community

Sunderland Talmudical College and Yeshiva*
Prince Consort Road, Gateshead NE3 4DS

YORKSHIRE AND THE HUMBER
Regional or County Bodies

Leeds Jewish Representative Council*
151 Shadwell Lane, Moortown, Leeds LS17 8DW
Contact: Kenneth Shendery
Position: President
Contact Tel: (0113) 2697520
Activities: Umbrella body, newsletter/journal, inter-faith
Traditions: Orthodox - Central Ashkenazi

Leeds Jewish Welfare Board*
311 Stonegate Road, Moortown, Leeds LS17 6AZ
Tel: (0113) 2684211 **Fax:** (0113) 2664754
Email: ijwb@dial.pipex.com
Contact: Ms Sheila Saunders
Position: Chief Executive
Activities: Community centre, youth, elderly, newsletter/journal, inter-faith, resources
Traditions: Cross-community
Affiliations: Leeds Jewish Housing Association

City, Town or Local Bodies

B'nai B'rith*
26 Thorndale Rise, Poplars Farm, Kings Road, Bradford BD2 1NU
Contact: Mrs K Fabian
Position: Secretary
Contact Tel: (01274) 390783

Bradford Jewish Benevolent Society*
11 Staveley Road, Shipley, Bradford BD18 4HD
Tel: (01274) 504468
Contact: M Levi
Position: Treasurer

Bradford Reform Synagogue*
Bowland Street, Bradford BD1 3BW
Contact: Mrs Clare Chapman
Position: Secretary
Contact Tel: (01274) 575993
Activities: Worship/practice/meditation, newsletter/journal, visits, inter-faith, resources
Traditions: Reform
Other Languages: German
Affiliations: Reform Synagogues of Great Britain; Board of Deputies of British Jews

Sir Moses Montefiore Synagogue*
Holme Hill, Heneage Road, Grimsby DN32 9DZ
Tel: (01472) 351404
Contact: Bernard Greenberg
Position: Secretary
Activities: Worship
Traditions: Orthodox
Affiliations: United Synagogue

Harrogate Hebrew Congregation*
St Mary's Walk, Harrogate HG2 0LW
Contact: Philip Morris
Position: Secretary
Contact Tel: (01423) 879143
Contact Email: philipmorris@ukgateway.net
Activities: Worship
Traditions: Orthodox
Affiliations: Leeds Jewish Representative Council; United Synagogues

Hull Hebrew Congregation*
c/o 37 Redlands Drive, Kirk Ella, Hull HU10 7UX
Tel: (01482) 651599 **Fax:** (01482) 651599
Contact: Howard J Levy
Position: Hon Secretary
Activities: Worship/practice/meditation, community centre, youth, women, newsletter/journal, visits, inter-faith
Traditions: Orthodox

Hull Jewish Representative Council*
251 Beverley Road, Kirkella, Hull HU10 7AG
Tel: (01482) 650288
Contact: Mrs A Segelman
Position: Honorary Secretary

Hull Reform Synagogue*
Great Gutter Lane West, Willerby, Hull HU10 6DP
Tel: (01482) 658312 **Fax:** (01482) 342836
Email: iansugarman@isa.karoo.co.uk
Website:
http://beehive.thisishull.co.uk/hullreformsynagogue

Contact: Mr Ian Sugarman
Position: Chair
Activities: Worship/practice/meditation, community centre, youth, newsletter/journal, visits, inter-faith
Traditions: Reform
Affiliations: Hull Jewish Representative Council; Reform Synagogues of Great Britain;

University of Hull Jewish Society*

c/o Union of Jewish Students, Hillel House, London WC1H 0DS
Tel: (020) 7387 4644 **Fax:** (020) 7383 0390
Activities: Youth, visits
Traditions: Cross-community
Affiliations: The "Yorkie" Regional Union of Jewish Students; The Union of Jewish Students; World Union of Jewish Students

B'nai B'rith Lodge of Leeds*

c/o Beth Hamedrash Hagadol Synagogue, Street Lane Gardens, Leeds LS17 6HQ
Tel: (0113) 2692181 **Fax:** (0113) 2370113
Email: office@bhhs.freeserve.co.uk
Contact: President
Affiliations: B'nai B'rith, London

B'nai Brith Hillel Foundation*

Hillel House, 2 Springfield Mount, Leeds LS2 9NE
Tel: (0113) 266 6346
Email: colinsive@mcmail.com
Contact: Sheila Sive

Beth Hamedrash Hagadol Synagogue*

399 Street Lane, Leeds LS17 6HQ
Tel: (0113) 2692181 **Fax:** (0113) 2370113
Email: office@bhhs.freeserve.co.uk
Contact: June Mathieson
Position: Executive Officer
Activities: Worship/practice/meditation, community centre, youth, elderly, women, newsletter/journal, visits, inter-faith
Traditions: Orthodox - Central Ashkenazi
Other Languages: Hebrew
Affiliations: Leeds Jewish Representative Council; Chief Rabbinate Council

Chevra Kadisha - Leeds Joint*

28 Primley Park View, Leeds LS17 7JA

Council of Orthodox Synagogues*

4 Wellhouse Road, Leeds LS8 4BS

Donisthorpe Hall*

Shadwell Lane, Leeds LS17 6AW
Tel: (0113) 2684248 **Fax:** (0113) 2370502
Contact: Mrs Sue Ullmann
Position: Support Services Manager
Contact Email: sue_ullmann@donisthorpe.org
Activities: Worship/practice/meditation, elderly, newsletter/journal
Traditions: Cross-community
Other Languages: Hebrew, Yiddish
Affiliations: Leeds Representative Council

Etz Chaim Synagogue*

411 Harrogate Road, Leeds LS17 7TT
Tel: (0113) 266 2214 **Fax:** (0113) 237 1183
Tradition: Orthodox

Jewish Day Centre*

26 Queenshill Avenue, Moor Town, Leeds LS17 6AX
Tel: (0113) 2692018
Contact: Naomi Caplin
Position: Manager
Contact Tel: (0113) 2692018

Jewish Students' Association*

c/o Hillel House, 2 Springfield Mount, Leeds LS2 9NE
Tel: (0113) 2433211

Leeds Jewish Education Authority (Talmud Torah)*

2 Sand Hill Lane, Leeds LS17 6AQ
Tel: (0113) 217 2533
Contact: Mrs Shoshana Anoyalfi
Position: Head Teacher
Activities: Resources

Leeds Kashrut Authority*

151 Shadwell Lane, Leeds LS17 8DW
Tel: (0113) 288 8151
Contact: Mrs B Cline
Position: Administrator
Affiliations: Leeds Jewish Representative Council; National Council of Shechita Boards

Leeds Jewish Representative Council*

151 Shadwell Lane, Moortown, Leeds LS17 8DW
Contact: Kenneth Shendery
Position: President
Contact Tel: (0113) 2697520

Activities: Umbrella body, newsletter/journal, inter-faith
Traditions: Orthodox - Central Ashkenazi

Leeds Jewish Welfare Board*
311 Stonegate Road, Moortown, Leeds LS17 6AZ
Tel: (0113) 2684211 **Fax:** (0113) 2664754
Email: ijwb@dial.pipex.com
Contact: Ms Sheila Saunders
Position: Chief Executive
Activities: Community centre, youth, elderly, newsletter/journal, inter-faith, resources
Traditions: Cross-community
Affiliations: Leeds Jewish Housing Association

Queenshill Synagogue*
49 Queenshill Drive, Moortown, Leeds LS17 6BG
Tel: (0113) 2687364
Contact: Mrs Louise Natalie Diamond
Position: Secretary
Activities: Worship/practice/meditation, elderly
Traditions: Orthodox - Central Ashkenazi
Affiliations: Leeds Beth Din

Shomrei Hadass Congregation*
368 Harrogate Road, Leeds LS17 6QB
Traditions: Orthodox
Other Languages: Hebrew, Yiddish

Sinai Synagogue*
Roman Avenue, Roundhay, Leeds LS8 2AN
Tel: (0113) 2665256 **Fax:** (0113) 2661539
Email: synagogue@sinaileeds.freeserve.co.uk
Contact: Rabbi Ian Morris
Position: Rabbi
Activities: Worship, resource, visits, youth, elderly, newsletter
Traditions: Reform
Other Languages: Hebrew
Affiliations: Leeds Jewish Representative Council; Reform Synagogues of Great Britain; World Union for Progressive Judaism

United Hebrew Congregation*
151 Shadwell Lane, Alwoodley, Leeds LS17 8DW
Tel: (0113) 2696141 **Fax:** (0113) 2696141
Email: minyan@uhcleeds.fsnet.co.uk
Contact: Mrs Tolkin
Position: Administrator
Activities: Worship/practice/meditation, community centre, youth, elderly, women, newsletter/journal
Traditions: Orthodox - Central Ashkenazi

Other Languages: Hebrew, Yiddish
Affiliations: Office of the Chief Rabbi

Zionist Council*
411a Harrogate Road, Leeds LS17 7YY
Tel: (0113) 2680899 **Fax:** (0113) 2370568
Contact: Mr P Margolis
Position: Chairman
Activities: Umbrella body
Traditions: Cross-community
Other Languages: Hebrew
Affiliations: Zionist Federation of Great Britain and Northern Ireland; World Zionist Organisation

Jewish Welfare Organisation*
2 Balmoral Court, Hill Turrets Close, Sheffield S11 9RF
Tel: (0114) 236 7958
Email: tony@kaddish.freeserve.co.uk
Contact: Anthony Kaddish

Representative Council of Sheffield and District Jews*
Sheffield
Tel: (0114) 2360984 **Fax:** (0114) 2353045
Contact: Mr Michael Rose
Position: Honorary Secretary
Contact Tel: (0114) 2301125
Contact Email: mjrose@clara.net
Activities: Umbrella body
Traditions: Reform and Orthodox
Affiliations: Northern Representative Councils' Forum

Sheffield and District Reform Jewish Congregation*
PO Box 675, Eccleshall, Sheffield S11 8TE
Tel: (07719) 209259
Website: http://www.shef-ref.co.uk/
Position: Chair
Activities: Worship, newsletter/journal
Traditions: Reform
Affiliations: Northern Reform Synagogues of Great Britain; Reform Synagogues of Great Britain

Sheffield Jewish Congregation and Centre*
Kingfield Synagogue, Brincliffe Crescent, Sheffield S11 8UX
Tel: (0114) 2552996
Contact: Rabbi Y Golomb
Position: Rabbi

NORTH WEST
Regional or County Bodies

Jewish Marriage Council*
85 Middleton Road, Crumpsall, Manchester
M8 4JY
Tel: (0161) 7405764 **Fax:** (0161) 7927406
Contact: Mr Alan Wellins
Position: Chair
Traditions: Cross-Community
Other Languages: German
Affiliations: Office of the Chief Rabbi

Jewish Representative Council of Greater Manchester and Region*
Jewish Cultural Centre, Bury Old Road,
Manchester M8 6FY
Tel: (0161) 7208721 **Fax:** (0161) 7208721
Email: jewishmanchester@anjy.org
Website: http://www.anjy.org/jewishmanchester
Contact: Mrs B Austell
Position: President
Activities: Umbrella body, inter-faith

Merseyside Jewish Representative Council*
Shifrin House, 433 Smithdown Road, Liverpool
L15 3JL
Tel: (0151) 7332292
Contact: Julia Bracey
Position: Contact
Activities: Central body, umbrella body, youth,
elderly, women, newsletter/journal, visits, resources
Traditions: Cross-community
Affiliations: Northern Jewish Representative
Councils; British Board of Deputies

City, Town or Local Bodies

Blackpool Reform Synagogue*
40 Raikes Parade, Blackpool FY1 4EX
Tel: (01253) 23687
Contact: L.Firth
Position: Chairman -
Contact Tel: (01253) 713619
Affiliations: Reform Synagogues Of Great Britain

Yeshurun Hebrew Congregation*
Coniston Road, Gatley, Cheadle SK8 4AP
Tel: (0161) 4288242 **Fax:** (0161) 4915265
Email: yeshurun@btinternet.com
Contact: Mr Leonard Kaufman
Position: Adminstrator
Activities: Worship/practice/meditation,

community centre, youth, elderly, women,
newsletter/journal, visits
Traditions: Orthodox - Central Ashkenazi
Other Languages: Hebrew
Affiliations: United Synagogues of Manchester;
Chief Rabbi's Office

Allerton Hebrew Congregation*
Corner Booker Avenue, Mather Avenue, Allerton,
Liverpool L18 9TB
Tel: (0151) 4276848
Email: allerton.syn@virgin.net
Contact: Paul Fisher
Position: Administrator
Activities: Worship
Traditions: Orthodox

Greenbank Drive Hebrew Synagogue*
Greenbank Chambers, Greenbank Drive, Liverpool
L17 1AF
Tel: (0151) 7331417 **Fax:** (0151) 7333862
Contact: Mr Philip Ettinger
Position: Senior Warden
Activities: Worship/practice/meditation, youth,
elderly, women, visits

Liverpool Jewish Resource Centre - MAKOR*
Liverpool Jewish Youth and Community Centre,
Harold House, Dunbabin Road, Liverpool
L15 6XL
Tel: (0151) 7223514 **Fax:** (0151) 4752212
Contact: Avril Lewis
Position: Administrator
Activities: Visits, inter-faith, resources
Traditions: Cross-community
Other Languages: Hebrew
Affiliations: Merseyside Jewish Representative
Council; Makor United Jewish Israel Appeal

Liverpool Jewish Youth and Community Centre*
Harold House, Dunbabin Road, Liverpool
L15 6XL
Tel: (0151) 4755671 **Fax:** (0151) 4752212
Email: harold.house@ort.org
Contact: Esmond Sidney Rosen
Position: Director
Activities: Resource, umbrella body, visits, youth,
elderly, women
Traditions: Cross-community
Other Languages: Ivrit, Yiddish
Affiliations: Merseyside Jewish Representative
Council; Maccabi; Association of Jewish Youth;
World Confederation

Liverpool Old Hebrew Congregation*
Synagogue Chambers, Princess Road, Liverpool
L8 1TQ
Tel: (0151) 7093431
Contact: Mrs Petula Nevitt
Position: Administrator
Activities: Worship, visits
Traditions: Orthodox
Other Languages: Hebrew
Affiliations: Merseyside Jewish Representative
Council; United Synagogue

Liverpool Progressive Synagogue*
28 Church Road North, Wavertree, Liverpool
L15 6TF
Tel: (0151) 7335871
Contact: Rabbi Normon Zalud
Position: Rabbi
Activities: Worship/practice/meditation, resources
Other Languages: Hebrew
Affiliations: Union Of Liberal And Progresive
Synagogues

Merseyside Jewish Community Care*
Shifrin House, 433 Smithdown Road, Liverpool
L15 3JL
Tel: (0151) 7332292 **Fax:** (0151) 7340212
Email: mjccshifrin@hotmail.com
Contact: Ms Lisa Dolan
Position: Chief Executive
Activities: Elderly
Traditions: Cross-community
Affiliations: Merseyside Jewish Representative
Council

Merseyside Jewish Representative Council*
Shifrin House, 433 Smithdown Road, Liverpool
L15 3JL
Tel: (0151) 7332292
Contact: Julia Bracey
Position: Contact
Activities: Central body, umbrella body, youth,
elderly, women, newsletter/journal, visits, resources
Traditions: Cross-community
Affiliations: Northern Jewish Representative
Councils; British Board of Deputies

Cheetham Hebrew Congregation*
The Jewish Cultural Centre, Bury Old Road,
Manchester M8 6FY
Contact: Mr Stone
Position: President

**Cheshire Reform Congregation, Menorah
Synagogue***
198 Altrincham Road, Sharston, Manchester
M22 4RZ
Tel: (0161) 4287746 **Fax:** (0161) 4270937
Email: office@menorah.org.uk
Contact: Rabbi Brian Fox
Position: Rabbi
Activities: Worship/practice/meditation, youth,
elderly, newsletter/journal, visits, inter-faith,
resources
Traditions: Reform
Other Languages: Hebrew
Affiliations: Reform Synagogues of Great Britain

Higher Prestwich Hebrew Congregation*
Highbury House, 445 Bury Old Road, Prestwick,
Manchester M25 1QP
Tel: (0161) 7334800 **Fax:** (0161) 733 4800
Contact: Phil Reed
Position: President
Activities: Worship
Traditions: Orthodox
Other Languages: Hebrew
Affiliations: Manchester Jewish Representative
Council

Hillock Hebrew Congregation*
Beverley Close, Ribble Drive, Whitefield,
Manchester M45 8BB
Tel: (0161) 9595663
Contact: Mr Richard Walker
Position: Secretary
Activities: Worship/practice/meditation,
newsletter/journal, visits
Traditions: Orthodox - Central Ashkenazi
Affiliations: Jewish Representative Council;
British Board of Deputies

Holy Law and South Broughton Congregation*
Bury Old Road, Prestwich, Manchester M25 0EX
Tel: (0161) 7401634 **Fax:** (0161) 720 6623
Email: ostice@holylaw.freeserve.co.uk

Jewish Cultural Centre*
Jubilee School, Bury Old Road, Manchester
M7 4QY
Tel: (0161) 7954000 **Fax:** (0161) 7926222
Contact: Rabbi C Farro
Position: Director
Activities: Worship, resource, visits, youth, elderly,
women
Traditions: Lubavitch
Other Languages: Ivrit, Yiddish

Jewish Representative Council of Greater Manchester and Region*
Jewish Cultural Centre, Bury Old Road, Manchester M8 6FY
Tel: (0161) 7208721 **Fax:** (0161) 7208721
Email: jewishmanchester@anjy.org
Website: http://www.anjy.org/jewishmanchester
Contact: Mrs B Austell
Position: President
Activities: Umbrella body, inter-faith

Manchester Central Board for Hebrew Education and Talmud Torah*
24a Bury New Road, Prestwich, Manchester M25 OLD
Tel: (0161) 7985577 **Fax:** (0161) 798 5577
Contact: Mr J M Nathan
Position: Chairman
Activities: Umbrella body, youth, provision of academic/educational resources
Traditions: Orthodox
Other Languages: Hebrew

Manchester Jewish Community Care*
85 Middleton Road, Manchester M8 4JY
Tel: (0161) 7400111 **Fax:** (0161) 7214273
Contact: Michael Galley
Position: Chief Executive
Activities: Elderly, newsletters
Traditions: Cross-community
Affiliations: Manchester Jewish Representative Council

Manchester Jewish Federation*
12 Holland Road, Higher Crumpsall, Manchester M8 4NP
Tel: (0161) 7950024 **Fax:** (0161) 7953688
Email: thefed@charity.vfree.com
Website: http://www.charity.vfree.com\thefed
Contact: Mr Mark Cunningham
Position: Adult Team Manager
Activities: Community centre
Traditions: Cross-community
Other Languages: Hebrew, Spanish

Manchester Jewish Homes For Aged*
c/o Heathlands Drive, Prestwich, Manchester M25 9SB
Tel: (0161) 7724800 **Fax:** (0161) 7724934
Contact: Mr R B Farrar
Position: General Manager

Manchester Reform Synagogue*
Jackson's Row, Manchester M2 5NH

Tel: (0161) 8340415
Contact: Mrs F Morris
Position: Administrator
Activities: Worship/practice/meditation, community centre, youth, elderly, newsletter/journal, visits, inter-faith, resources
Traditions: Reform
Affiliations: Reform Synagogues of Great Britain

Morris Feinmann Home Trust*
178 Palatine Road, Didsbury, Manchester M20 2YW
Tel: (0161) 4453533 **Fax:** (0161) 4481755
Contact: Mrs Tracey Paine
Position: General Manager
Traditions: Cross-community
Other Languages: German
Affiliations: Manchester Jewish Representative Council

Outreach Residential and Community*
1 Delaunays Road, Crumpsall Green, Manchester M8 4QS
Tel: (0161) 7403456 **Fax:** (0161) 7405678
Email: out.reach@dial.pipex.com
Website: http://www.outreach.co.uk/
Contact: Ms Sandra Bitaye
Position: Chief Executive
Traditions: Cross-community

Prestwich Hebrew Congregation*
The Shrubbery, Bury New Road, Prestwich, Manchester M25 9WN
Tel: (0161)773 1978 **Fax:** (0161) 733 7015
Contact: Rabbi Y Landes
Position: 1st Minister

Sha'arei Shalom North Manchester Reform Synagogue*
Elms Street, Whitefield, Manchester M45 8GQ
Tel: (0161) 7966736 **Fax:** (0161) 7966736
Contact: Mr Brian Fink
Position: Co-Chairman
Contact Tel: (0161) 7968018
Contact Email: finkandwood@cwctv.net
Activities: Worship/practice, community centre, elderly, newsletter/journal, visits
Traditions: Reform
Affiliations: Reform Synagogues of Great Britain; World Union for Progressive Judaism

Shechita Board*
435 Cheetham Hill Road, Manchester M8 7PF
Tel: (0161) 7409711 **Fax:** (0161) 721 4249

Email: bethdon@a.o.l
Contact: Y Brodie
Position: Administrator

South Manchester Synagogue*
Wilbraham Road, Manchester M14 6JS
Tel: (0161) 2241366 **Fax:** (0161) 2258033
Contact: Mrs T. M. Hyams
Position: Administrator
Traditions: Orthodox

United Synagogue*
Meade Hill Road, Manchester M8 4LP
Tel: (0161) 7409586
Contact: Mr Sidney Huller
Position: President
Activities: Worship, visits
Traditions: Orthodox
Affiliations: Manchester Jewish Representative
Council; United Synagogues

Whitefield Hebrew Congregation*
Park Lane, Whitefield, Manchester M45 7PB
Tel: (0161) 7663732

Sale and District Hebrew Congregation*
14 Hesketh Road, Sale M33 5AA
Tel: (0161) 962 1882
Contact: Mrs Iris Gould
Position: Honorary Secretary
Activities: Worship, resource, visits, youth, women,
newsletter
Traditions: Orthodox – Central Ashkenazi
Other Languages: Hebrew
Affiliations: Manchester Jewish Representative
Council

Academy for Rabbinical Research (Kolel)*
134 Leicester Road, Salford M7 4GB
Tel: (0161) 7401960
Contact: Revd J Freedman
Position: Secretary

Central and North Manchester Synagogue*
Leicester Road, Salford M7 4EP
Contact: Mr Melvyn Green
Position: Secretary
Contact Tel: (0161) 740 4830
Activities: Worship/practice/meditation, youth
Traditions: Orthodox – Central Ashkenazi

Kahal Chassidim Synagogue (Lubavitch)*
62 Singleton Road, Salford M7 0LU
Tel: (0161) 7403632

Contact: D Lipsidge
Position: Secretary

Lubavitch Foundation*
62 Singleton Road, Salford M7 0LU
Tel: (0161) 7209514 **Fax:** (0161) 7409514
Contact: Rabbi Levi Wineberg
Position: Youth Director
Activities: Worship, resource, youth, elderly,
women
Traditions: Charedi
Other Languages: Yiddish, Hebrew
Affiliations: Lubavitch England

Lubavitch Yeshiva*
62 Singleton Road, Salford M7 0LU
Tel: (0161) 7409264
Contact: Rabbi A Cohen
Position: Dean

Manchester Congregation of Spanish and Portuguese Jews*
10 Rutland Drive, Salford M7 4WJ
Tel: (0161) 7927406
Contact: David Salem
Position: Chair
Activities: Worship, resource
Traditions: Sephardi
Other Languages: Spanish
Affiliations: Manchester Jewish Representative
Council

Manchester Great and New Synagogue*
Stenecourt Road, Holden Road, Salford M7 4LN
Tel: (0161) 7928399
Contact: E Levene
Position: Secretary

Reshet Torah Education Network*
4 Hanover Gardens, Broughton Park, Salford
M7 4FQ
Tel: (0161) 7405735 **Fax:** (0161) 7954295
Contact: Rabbi S M Kupetz
Position: Executive Director
Activities: Youth, elderly, women, resources
Traditions: Charedi
Other Languages: Yiddish

Preston Synagogue*
c/o 31 Avondale Road, Southport PR9 0NH
Tel: (01704) 538276
Contact: Dr C E Nelson
Position: Honorary Secretary

Southport Jewish Representative Council*
65 Beach Priory Gardens, Southport PR9 9AB
Contact: Mrs Abrahamson
Position: President
Activities: Central body, umbrella body
Traditions: Orthodox - Central Ashkenazi
Affiliations: Board of Deputies of British Jews

Southport New Synagogue*
Portland Street, Southport PR9 9LQ
Tel: (01704) 535950 **Fax:** (01704) 535950
Contact: Mrs Eileen Lippa
Position: Administrator
Activities: Worship, inter-faith
Traditions: Reform
Affiliations: Southport Jewish Representative
Council; Reform Synagogues of Great Britain

St Annes Hebrew Congregation*
The Synagogue, Orchard Road, St Annes-on-Sea
FY8 1PJ
Tel: (01253) 721831
Contact: Peter Davidson
Position: President
Activities: Worship, resource, visits, youth, women
Traditions: Orthodox
Affiliations: Manchester Jewish Representative
Council

EAST MIDLANDS
City, Town or Local Bodies

Jewish Communal Centre*
Highfield Street, Leicester LE2 1AD
Tel: (0116) 2540477

Leicester Hebrew Congregation*
Synagogue, Highfield Street, Leicester LE2 1AD
Tel: (0116) 2470733
Contact: Honorary Secretary
Activities: Worship, umbrella body, visits,
newsletter, inter-faith
Traditions: Orthodox

Leicester Progressive Jewish Congregation*
24 Avenue Road, Stoneygate, Leicester LE2 3EA
Tel: (0116) 2448968 **Fax:** (0116) 2715584
Contact: Jeffrey Kaufman
Position: Honorary Secretary
Activities: Worship, resource, visits, youth, elderly,
women
Other Languages: Hebrew
Affiliations: Union of Liberal and Progressive
Synagogues

University of Leicester, Jewish Society*
c/o Students Union, Leicester University, Leicester
LE1 7RH
Activities: Youth
Traditions: Cross-community
Other Languages: Hebrew
Affiliations: Union of Jewish Students

Northampton Hebrew Congregation*
95-97 Overstone Road, Northampton NN1 3JW
Tel: (01604) 33345
Contact: Graham Goldcrown
Position: Honorary Secretary
Activities: Worship, visits, elderly, women,
newsletter
Traditions: Orthodox
Affiliations: United Synagogue

Nottingham Hebrew Congregation*
Shakespeare Villas, Shakespeare Street, Nottingham
NG1 4FQ
Tel: (0115) 9472004
Email: officenhc@aol.com
Contact: Mrs Gilda Hyman
Position: Secretary
Activities: Worship/practice/meditation
Traditions: Orthodox - Central Ashkenazi
Other Languages: French
Affiliations: Nottingham Jewish Representative
Council; United Synagogue

Nottingham Jewish Welfare Board*
35 Arnot Hill Road, Nottingham NG5 6LN
Tel: (0115) 9260245
Contact: Dr M Caplan
Position: Chair

**Nottingham Jewish Women's Benevolent
Society***
c/o Nottingham Hebrew Congregation,
Shakespeare Villas, Nottingham NG1 4FQ
Tel: (0115) 9476663
Contact: Hilary Markson
Position: Chair
Activities: Elderly, women
Traditions: Orthodox, Liberal/Reform/Cross-
Affiliations: Nottingham Representative Council,
National League Of Hospitals And Friends

Nottingham Progressive Jewish Congregation*
Nottingham Progressive Synagogue, Lloyd Street,
Mansfield Road, Sherwood, Nottingham NG5 4BP
Tel: (0115) 9624761
Email: npjc@ulps.org

Website: http://www.npjc.org.uk
Contact: Natalie Bogod

Nottingham University Jewish and Israel Society*

Clubs and Societies Office, Portland Building, University Park, Nottingham NG7 2RD
Tel: (0115) 9351100 **Fax:** (0115) 9351100
Email: jsoc@nottingham.ac.uk
Website: http://www.unu.nottingham.ac.uk/~jsoc/
Contact: Mr Danny Stone
Contact Email: jsocchair@hotmail.com
Activities: Youth
Traditions: Cross-community
Affiliations: Union of Jewish Students; World Union of Jewish Students

WEST MIDLANDS
Regional or County Bodies

Representative Council of Birmingham and Midlands Jewry*

Singers Hill, Blucher Street, Birmingham B1 1QL
Tel: (0121) 6432688 **Fax:** (0121) 6432688
Email: bjrepco@dircon.co.uk
Website: http://www.brijnet.org/birmingham
Contact: Mrs Ruth Jacobs
Position: Administrator
Activities: Umbrella body
Traditions: Cross-community

City, Town or Local Bodies

Birmingham Central Synagogue*

133 Pershore Road, Edgbaston, Birmingham B5 7PA
Tel: (0121) 4404044 **Fax:** (0121) 4404044
Contact: Mr S Cohen
Position: Hon. Secretary
Activities: Worship/practice/meditation
Traditions: Orthodox - Central Ashkenazi

Birmingham Hebrew Congregation*

Singers Hill, Ellis Street, City Centre, Birmingham B1 1HL
Contact: Mr Bernard Gingold
Position: Administrator
Contact Tel: (0121) 6430884
Contact Email: office@singershill.freeserve.co.uk
Activities: Worship/practice/meditation, visits
Traditions: Orthodox - Central Ashkenazi

Affiliations: Birmingham Jewish Representative Council; London Beth Din

Birmingham Progressive Synagogue*

4 Sheepcote Street, off Broad Street, Birmingham B16 8AA
Tel: (0121) 6435640 **Fax:** (0121) 6338372
Website: bps@ulps.org
Contact: Mrs Rosa Plotnek
Position: Administrator
Activities: Worship/practice/meditation, community centre, umbrella body, youth, elderly, women, newsletter/journal, visits, inter-faith, resources
Traditions: Liberal
Other Languages: German, Hebrew
Affiliations: Union of Liberal and Progressive Synagogues; The World Union of Progressive Jewry

Hillel House*

26 Somerset Road, Edgbaston, Birmingham B15 2QD
Tel: (0121) 4545684

Leamington and District Progressive Jewish Group*

c/o Birmingham Progressive Synagogue, 4 Sheepcote Street, Birmingham B16 8AA
Traditions: Liberal
Affiliations: Union of Liberal and Progressive Synagogues; World Union of Progressive Judaism

Lubavitch in the Midlands*

Birmingham Lubavitch Centre, 95 Willows Road, Birmingham B12 9QF
Tel: (0121) 4406673
Contact: Rabbi Shmuel Arkush
Position: Director
Activities: Resource, youth, elderly, women
Traditions: Cross-community
Affiliations: Lubavitch UK; Lubavitch International

Representative Council of Birmingham and Midlands Jewry*

Singers Hill, Blucher Street, Birmingham B1 1QL
Tel: (0121) 6432688 **Fax:** (0121) 6432688
Email: bjrepco@dircon.co.uk
Website: http://www.brijnet.org/birmingham
Contact: Mrs Ruth Jacobs
Position: Administrator
Activities: Umbrella body
Traditions: Cross-community

Solihull and District Hebrew Congregation*
3 Monastery Drive, Solihull, Birmingham B92 7DP
Tel: (0121) 7075199 **Fax:** (0121) 7068736
Website: http://www.solihulshul.org/
Activities: Worship/practice/meditation
Traditions: Orthodox
Affiliations: Office of the Chief Rabbi

Coventry Hebrew Congregation*
Barrass Lane, Coventry CV1 3BU
Tel: (01926) 747691
Email: laurence.benjamin@ntlworld.com
Contact: Dr Benjamin
Position: Secretary
Traditions: Orthodox - Central Ashkenazi
Affiliations: Office of the Chief Rabbi

Coventry Jewish Reform Community*
Coventry
Tel: (024) 7667 2027

Stoke-on-Trent Hebrew Congregation*
The Synagogue, Birch Terrace, Hanley, Stoke-on-Trent ST1 3JN
Contact: Harold Sydney Morris
Position: President
Contact Tel: (01782) 616417
Activities: Worship/practice/meditation, visits, inter faith
Traditions: Orthodox - Central Ashkenazi
Affiliations: Board of Deputies of British Jews, UJIA

EAST OF ENGLAND
City, Town or Local Bodies

Basildon Hebrew Congregation*
3 Furlongs, Basildon SS16 4BW
Tel: (01268) 524947
Contact: M M Kochmann
Position: Chair

Bushey and District United Synagogue*
177-189 Sparrows Herne, Bushey WD23 1AJ
Tel: (020) 8950 7340 **Fax:** (020) 8421 8267
Email: rabbi.salasnik@bushey-community.org
Contact: Rabbi Z M Salasnik
Position: Rabbi
Activities: Worship/practice/meditation, community centre, youth, elderly, women, newsletter/journal, visits
Traditions: Orthodox - Central Ashkenazi
Affiliations: United Synagogue

Beth Shalom Reform Synagogue*
Cambridge
Email: info@beth-shalom.org.uk
Website: www.beth-shalom.org.uk

Cambridge Traditional Jewish Congregation*
3 Thompsons Lane, Cambridge CR5 8AU
Tel: (01223) 354783
Website: http://www.cam.ac.uk/societies/cvjs and folcon links
Contact: Simon Goldhill
Position: Chairperson
Activities: Worship, resource
Traditions: Orthodox

Cambridge University Jewish Society*
3 Thompson's Lane, Cambridge CB5 8AQ
Tel: (01223) 354783
Email: soc-cajs@lists.cam.ac.uk
Contact: Mr Alon Zieve
Position: Development Officer
Contact Email: ajz23@cam.ac.uk
Activities: Worship/practice/meditation, community centre, youth, newsletter/journal, resources
Traditions: Cross-community
Other Languages: Hebrew, French , Italian
Affiliations: Union of Jewish Students

Cambridge University Progressive Jewish Group*
c/o Cambridge University Jewish Society, 3 Thompson's Lane, Cambridge CB5 8AQ
Tel: (01223) 354783

Colchester and District Jewish Community*
The Synagogue, Fennings Chase, Priory Street, Colchester CO1 2QG
Tel: (01206) 545992
Email: tanenb@essex.ac.uk
Contact: Ms N Stevenson
Position: Secretary
Activities: Worship/practice/meditation, youth, elderly, women, visits, inter-faith, resources
Traditions: Cross-community
Other Languages: Ivrit
Affiliations: United Synagogue

Spec Jewish Youth and Community Centre*
87 Brookside South, East Barnet EN4 8LL
Tel: (020) 8368 5117
Website: http://www.speconline.org.uk/
Contact: Mr Matthew Lent
Position: Centre Director

Activities: Community centre, youth, resources
Traditions: Cross-community
Affiliations: Association of Jewish Youth

Potters Bar and Brookmans Park District Synagogue*
Meadowcroft, Great North Road, Bell Bar, Hatfield
AL9 6DB
Tel: (01707) 656202 **Fax:** (01707) 656202
Email: office@pottersbarshul.org.uk
Website: http://www.pottersbarshul.org.uk/
Contact: Rabbi Zvi Solomons
Position: Rabbi
Contact Tel: (01707) 656202
Contact Email: rabbi@pottersbarshul.org.uk
Activities: Worship/practice/meditation, youth,
women, newsletter/journal
Traditions: Orthodox – Central Ashkenazi
Affiliations: United Synagogue

Hemel Hempstead United Synagogue*
Lady Sarah Cohen Community Centre, Midland
Road, Hemel Hempstead HP2
Tel: (01923) 32007
Contact: H Nathan
Position: Honorary Secretary

Luton Hebrew Congregation Synagogue*
P O Box 215, Luton LU1 1HW
Tel: (01582) 725032
Contact: The Hon Secretary

Jewish Ladies' Society*
Norwich Synagogue, 3a Earlham Road, Norwich
NR2 3RA
Tel: (01603) 623948
Contact: Mrs E Griffiths
Position: Secretary

Norwich Hebrew Congregation*
Norwich Synagogue, 3a Earlham Road, Norwich
NR2 3RA
Tel: (01603) 623948
Contact: Mr P Prinsley
Position: Honorary Secretary
Contact Tel: (01603) 506482
Activities: Worship/practice/meditation
Traditions: Orthodox – Central Ashkenazi

Peterborough Hebrew Congregation*
142 Cobden Avenue, Peterborough PE1 2NU
Tel: (01733) 264151
Contact: C. Salamon
Position: Administrator

Peterborough Liberal Jewish Community*
525 Lincoln Road, Peterborough PE1 2PB
Activities: Worship
Traditions: Liberal
Affiliations: Union of Liberal and Progressive
Synagogues

St Alban's Synagogue*
Oswald Road, St Albans AL1 3AQ
Tel: (01727) 825295
Contact: H Turner
Position: Secretary
Activities: Worship
Traditions: Orthodox – Central Ashkenazi
Affiliations: United Synagogue

LONDON
Regional and Area Bodies

Chabad Lubavitch Centre*
395 Eastern Avenue, Gants Hill, Ilford IG2 6LR
Tel: (020) 8554 1624 **Fax:** (020) 8518 2126
Email: clcams@aol.com
Website: http://www.chabadlubavitchilford.com/
Contact: Rabbi A M Sufrin
Position: Director
Activities: Worship/practice/meditation,
community centre, youth, elderly, women,
newsletter/journal
Traditions: Orthodox – Central Ashkenazi
Other Languages: Yiddish, Hebrew
Affiliations: Lubavitch Foundation UK, Central
Lubavitch

London Board for Shechita*
Elscot House, Arcadia Avenue, Finchley, London
N3 2JU
Tel: (020) 8349 9160 **Fax:** (020) 8346 2209
Email: shechita@FreeNet.co.uk
Contact: Michael Kester
Position: Executive Director

London Jewish Cultural Centre*
The Old House, c/o Kings College, Kidderpore
Avenue, London NW3 7ST
Tel: (020) 7431 0345
Email: admin@ljcc.org.uk
Website: http://www.ljcc.org.uk/
Contact: Dr Joanna Newman
Position: Director of Adult Ed
Activities: Community centre, umbrella body,
youth, elderly, newsletter/journal, inter-faith

Traditions: Cross-community
Other Languages: Hebrew, Yiddish, German

Borough and Local Bodies

BARKING AND DAGENHAM

Barking and Becontree United Synagogue*
200 Becontree Avenue, Becontree, Dagenham
RM8 2TR
Tel: (020) 8594 4604
Contact: Mrs B Berman
Position: Secretary

BARNET

Beth Shmuel Synagogue*
171 Golders Green Road, Golders Green, London
NW11 9BY
Tel: (020) 8458 7511
Contact: Rabbi E Halpern

Beth Yissochor Dov Beth Hamedrash*
2/4 Highfield Avenue, London NW11 9ET
Contact: Rabbi G Hager

Brady-Maccabi Youth and Community Centre*
4 Manor Park Crescent, Edgware HA8 7NL
Tel: (020) 8952 2948

Edgware Adath Yisroel Synagogue*
261 Hale Lane, Edgware HA8 8NX
Fax: (020) 8958 8121
Email: rabbi@eayc.demon.co.uk
Contact: Rabbi Z Lieberman
Position: Minister
Activities: Worship, youth, elderly, women,
newsletter
Traditions: Traditional Orthodox
Other Languages: Hebrew, Yidish

Edgware and District Reform Synagogue*
118 Stonegrove, Edgware HA8 8AB
Tel: (020) 8958 9782 **Fax:** (020) 8905 4710
Email: admin@edrs.org.uk
Website: http://www.edrs.org.uk/
Contact: Synagogue Administrator
Activities: Worship, community centre, youth,
elderly, women, newsletter/journal, visits, inter-faith
Traditions: Reform
Other Languages: Hebrew
Affiliations: Reform Synagogues of Great Britain;
World Union of Progressive Judaism

Edgware Masorti Synagogue*
Stream Lane, Edgware HA8 7YA
Tel: (020) 8905 4096 **Fax:** (020) 8905 4333
Email: masorti.edgware@virgin.net
Contact: Linda Lassman
Position: Administrator
Activities: Worship, resource, visits, youth, women,
newsletter
Traditions: Masorti
Other Languages: Hebrew
Affiliations: Association of Masorti Synagogues;
World Council of Synagogues

Edgware United Synagogue*
Parnell Close, Edgware HA8 8YE
Tel: (020) 8958 7508
Contact: Administrator

Finchley Progressive Synagogue*
54a Hutton Grove, Finchley, London N12 8DR
Tel: (020) 8446 4063 **Fax:** (020) 8446 4063
Email: roz@thefps.free-online.co.uk
Website:
http://www.thesynagogue.freeserve.co.uk/
Contact: Roz Lests
Position: Administrator
Activities: Worship, visits, youth, elderly,
newsletter, inter-faith
Traditions: Liberal
Other Languages: German, French, Hebrew
Affiliations: Union of Liberal and Progressive
Synagogues; World Union of Progressive Judaism

Finchley Reform Synagogue*
Fallow Court Avenue, Finchley, London N12 0BE
Tel: (020) 8446 3244 **Fax:** (020) 8446 5980
Email: frs@frs.demon.co.uk
Contact: Rabbi Sheila Shulman
Position: Rabbi
Activities: Worship
Affiliations: Reform Synagogues of Great Britain

Finchley Synagogue*
Kinloss Gardens, Finchley, London N3 3DU
Tel: (020) 8346 8551 **Fax:** (020) 8349 1579
Email: admin@kinloss1.freeserve.co.uk
Contact: Beryl Fireman
Position: Administrator
Activities: Worship, resource, visits, youth, elderly,
women
Traditions: Orthodox
Other Languages: Ivrit
Affiliations: United Synagogue

Golders Green Synagogue*
41 Dunstan Road, London NW11 8AE
Tel: (020) 8455 2460 **Fax:** (020) 8731 9296
Contact: Mrs Stella Alexander
Position: Administrator
Activities: Worship, resource, visits, youth, elderly, women
Traditions: Orthodox - Central Ashkenazi

Hampstead Garden Suburb (United) Synagogue*
Norrice Lea, Hampstead Garden Suburb, London N2 0RE
Tel: (020) 8455 8126 **Fax:** (020) 8201 9247
Contact: Mrs M S Wolff
Position: Administrator
Activities: Worship, youth, elderly, women
Traditions: Orthodox
Other Languages: Hebrew
Affiliations: United Synagogue

Hendon Adath Yisroel Synagogue*
11 Brent Street, London NW4 2EU
Tel: (020) 8202 9183
Contact: N Hammond
Position: Secretary

Hendon Reform Synagogue*
Danescroft Avenue, Hendon, London NW4 2NA
Tel: (020) 8203 4168
Contact: Mrs R Bloom
Position: Administrator
Activities: Worship, visits, youth, elderly, women, newsletter
Traditions: Reform
Affiliations: The Reform Synagogues of Great Britain; World Union of Progressive Judaism

Hendon Synagogue*
Raleigh Close, Wykeham Road, Hendon, London NW4 2TA
Tel: (020) 8202 6924 **Fax:** (020) 8202 1720
Email: peryyburns@aol.com
Contact: Jonathan Benson
Position: Executive Secretary
Activities: Worship, visits, youth, elderly, women, newsletter
Traditions: Orthodox
Other Languages: Hebrew, French, German
Affiliations: United Synagogue

Holocaust Survivors' Centre*
Corner of Parson Street, Church Road, London

NW4 1QA
Tel: (020) 8202 2404

Jewish Bereavement Counselling Service*
PO Box 6748, London N3 3BX
Tel: (020) 8349 0839 **Fax:** (020) 8349 0839
Contact: Rae Adler
Position: Co-ordinator
Activities: Resource
Traditions: Cross-community
Affiliations: Visitation Committee; Central Council of Jewish Social Services

Jewish Museum, The*
80 East End Road, Finchley, London N3 2SY
Tel: (020) 8349 1143 **Fax:** (020) 8343 2162
Email: jml.finchley@lineone.net
Website: http://www.jewsusm.ort.org/
Contact: Ms Carol Seigel
Position: Curator
Activities: Youth, elderly, books, visits, resources
Traditions: Cross-community

Link Psychotherapy Trust*
31 Coleridge Walk, London NW11 6AT
Tel: (020) 8349 0111
Contact: Mrs Judith Elkan
Position: Chair
Contact Tel: (020) 8455 8845
Activities: Resources
Other Languages: Hebrew, Portuguese, French

London Board for Shechita*
Elscot House, Arcadia Avenue, Finchley, London N3 2JU
Tel: (020) 8349 9160 **Fax:** (020) 8346 2209
Email: shechita@FreeNet.co.uk
Contact: Michael Kester
Position: Executive Director

Machzikei Hadath Synagogue*
Highfields Road, London NW11 9LU
Tel: (020) 8204 1887
Contact: R Shaw
Position: Honorary Secretary

Manor House Society - Sternberg Centre*
Sternberg Centre for Judaism, 80 East End Road, London N3 2SY
Tel: (020) 8349 5654 **Fax:** (020) 8349 5659
Email: pam.lewis@reformjudaism.org.uk
Website: http://www.reformjudaism.org.uk/
Contact: Pam Lewis
Position: Administrator

Activities: Worship/practice/meditation, community centre, umbrella body, youth, elderly, women, newsletter/journal, books, visits, inter-faith, resources
Traditions: Cross-community
Other Languages: Hebrew
Affiliations: Reform Synagogues of Great Britain; World Union for Progressive Judaism

New North London Synagogue*
The Manor House, 80 East Road, Finchley, London N3 2SY
Contact: Bette Rabie
Activities: Worship/practice/meditation, youth, elderly, women, newsletter/journal, resources
Traditions: Masorti
Affiliations: Association of Masorti Synagogues

New Whetstone Masorti Synagogue*
All Saints Arts Centre, 122 Oakleigh Road, North London N20 9EZ
Tel: (020) 8455 6054 **Fax:** (020) 8455 6054
Email: office@glent.co.uk

North Hendon Adath Yisroel Synagogue*
Holders Hill Road, Hendon, London NW4 1NA
Tel: (020) 8203 0797
Contact: Mr A H Ehreich
Position: Secretary
Contact Tel: (020) 7405 0739
Activities: Worship/practice/meditation, newsletter/journal
Traditions: Charedi
Other Languages: Hebrew, Yiddish, Arabic
Affiliations: Union of Orthodox Hebrew Congregations

North Western Reform Synagogue*
Alyth Gardens, Golders Green, London NW11 7EN
Tel: (020) 8455 6763 **Fax:** (020) 8458 2469
Email: mail@alyth.org
Contact: Mrs Lynette Chazen-Hart
Position: Community Director
Activities: Worship/practice/meditation, community centre, youth, elderly, women, newsletter/journal, visits, inter-faith, resources
Traditions: Reform
Other Languages: Hebrew, Yiddish
Affiliations: Reform Synagogues of Great Britain

Otto Schiff Housing Association (Osha)*
63-67 The Bishop's Avenue, London N2 0BG
Tel: (020) 8209 0022 **Fax:** (020) 8201 8089

Contact: Gaby Wills
Position: Group Manager

Society of Friends of Jewish Refugees*
Balfour House, 741 High Road, London N12 0BQ
Tel: (020) 8446 1477 **Fax:** (020) 8446 1180

Southgate and District Reform Synagogue*
120 Oakleigh Road North, Whetstone, London N20 9EZ
Tel: (020) 8445 3400 **Fax:** (020) 8445 3737
Website: http://www.our-shul.com/
Contact: Mrs Minsky
Position: Adminstrator
Activities: Worship/practice/meditation, community centre, youth, elderly, women, newsletter/journal, visits, inter-faith, resources
Traditions: Reform
Other Languages: Hebrew
Affiliations: Reform Synagogues of Great Britain

United Synagogue Visitation Committee*
Adler House, 735 High Road, London N12 0US
Tel: (020) 8343 8989 **Fax:** (020) 8343 6262
Website: http://www.unitedsynagogue.co.uk/
Contact: J Wayne
Position: Admin Director

Woodside Park Synagogue*
Woodside Park Road, Finchley, London N12 8RZ
Tel: (020) 8445 4236 **Fax:** (020) 8446 5515
Email: admin@woodsidepark.org.uk
Contact: Deanna Bruce
Position: Administrator
Activities: Worship, youth, newsletter
Traditions: Orthodox
Affiliations: United Synagogue

BRENT

Dollis Hill United Synagogue*
Parkside, Dollis Hill Lane, London NW2 6RJ
Contact: Warren Land
Position: Administrator
Contact Tel: (020) 8958 6777

Harrow and Wembley Progressive Synagogue*
326 Preston Road, Harrow HA3 0QH
Tel: (020) 8904 8581 **Fax:** (020) 8904 6540
Website: http://www.hwps.org/
Contact: H C Sanderson
Position: President
Activities: Worship/practice/meditation, community centre, elderly, newsletter/journal, visits

Traditions: Liberal
Affiliations: Union of Liberal and Progressive Synagogues

Wembley Synagogue*
8-10 Forty Avenue, Wembley HA9 8JW
Tel: (020) 8904 6565 **Fax:** (020) 8908 2740
Email: 100346.260@compuserve.com
Contact: Mrs Rita Garfield
Position: Administrator
Activities: Worship, visits, youth, elderly, women, newsletter
Traditions: Orthodox
Other Languages: Hebrew, Yiddish, German
Affiliations: United Synagogue

Willesden and Brondesbury United Synagogue*
143-145 Brondesbury Park, London NW2 5JL
Tel: (020) 8459 1083
Contact: Mrs J Questle
Position: Administrator

BROMLEY

Bromley and District Reform Synagogue*
28 Highland Road, Bromley BR1 4AD
Tel: (020) 8460 5460 **Fax:** (020) 8460 5460
Email: bromleyshul@fsmail.net
Website: http://www.bromleyshul.org.uk/
Contact: Janet Burlem
Position: Administrator
Activities: Worship/practice/meditation, community centre, youth, elderly, women, newsletter/journal, visits, inter-faith, resources
Traditions: Reform
Affiliations: Reform Synagogues of Great Britain

CAMDEN

Belsize Square Synagogue*
51 Belsize Square, London NW3 4HX
Tel: (020) 7794 3949 **Fax:** (020) 7431 4559
Email: belsqsyn@aol.com
Website: http://www.synagogue.org.uk/
Contact: Judith Berman
Position: Synagogue Secretary
Activities: Worship/practice, community centre, youth, newsletter/journal, visits, inter-faith
Traditions: Independent-Progressive
Other Languages: German
Affiliations: World Union of Progressive Judaism

Hampstead Synagogue*
1 Dennington Park Road, West Hampstead,

London NW6 1AX
Tel: (020) 7435 1518 **Fax:** (020) 8431 8369
Contact: Mr I Nadel
Position: Administrator
Activities: Worship, visits, elderly, newsletter, inter-faith
Traditions: Orthodox - Central Ashkenazi
Other Languages: Hebrew, Yiddish
Affiliations: United Synagogue

Jewish Museum, The - Camden Town*
Raymond Burton House, 129-131 Albert Street, London NW1 7NB
Tel: (020) 7284 1997 **Fax:** (020) 7267 9008
Contact: Ms Rickie Burman
Position: Director
Activities: Resource, visits, youth, elderly, women, newsletter
Traditions: Cross-community
Other Languages: French
The museum has permanent displays and collections on Jewish history and religion in Britain and one of the world's finest collections of Jewish ceremonial art. Changing exhibitions, cultural events and educational programmes on Judaism and Jewish history.

London Jewish Cultural Centre*
The Old House, c/o Kings College, Kidderpore Avenue, London NW3 7ST
Tel: (020) 7431 0345
Email: admin@ljcc.org.uk
Website: http://www.ljcc.org.uk/
Contact: Dr Joanna Newman
Position: Director of Adult Ed
Activities: Community centre, umbrella body, youth, elderly, newsletter/journal, inter-faith, resources
Traditions: Cross-community
Other Languages: Hebrew, Yiddish, German

Shir Hayim - Hampstead Reform Jewish Community*
37a Broadhurst Gardens, London NW6 3BN
Tel: (020) 7794 8488
Email: mail@shirhayim.org.uk
Contact: Mr Michael Teper
Position: Chairman
Contact Email: michael@shirhayim.org.uk
Activities: Worship/practice/meditation, community centre, newsletter/journal, visits, inter-faith
Traditions: Reform
Other Languages: Hebrew, German, Yiddish
Affiliations: Reform Synagogues of Great Britain

South Hampstead Synagogue*
21-22 Eton Villas, Eton Road, London NW3 4SP
Tel: (020) 7722 1807
Contact: Muriel Spector
Position: Administrator

CITY OF LONDON

Bevis Marks Synagogue*
Bevis Marks, London EC3A 5DQ
Tel: (020) 7626 1274 **Fax:** (020) 7283 8825
Email: bevismarks@first-step.demon.co.uk
Contact: Maurice Bitton
Position: Shamash
Activities: Worship
Traditions: Sephardi
Other Languages: Spanish, Hebrew, Portuguese, French
Affiliations: Spanish and Portugese Jews Congregation

EALING

Ealing Liberal Jewish Congregation*
Ealing Liberal Synagogue, Lynton Avenue, Drayton Green, West Ealing W13 0EB
Tel: (020) 8997 0528 **Fax:** (020) 8997 0528
Contact: Mr Arnold Aarons
Position: Administrator
Activities: Worship/practice/meditation, community centre, newsletter/journal, visits
Traditions: Liberal
Other Languages: German, Hebrew
Affiliations: Union of Liberal and Progressive Synagogues

Ealing Synagogue*
15 Grange Road, Ealing, London W5 5QN
Tel: (020) 8579 4894
Contact: Mrs S Hayman
Position: Administrator
Activities: Worship, visits, youth, elderly, women, newsletter, books, inter-faith
Traditions: Orthodox
Affiliations: United Synagogue

ENFIELD

Cockfosters and North Southgate Synagogue*
Old Farm Avenue, Southgate, London N14 5QR
Tel: (020) 8886 8225

Enfield and Winchmore Hill Synagogue*
53 Wellington Road, Bushill Park, Enfield EN1 2PG

Tel: (020) 8363 2697
Contact: S Marco
Position: Administrator
Traditions: Orthodox
Affiliations: United Synagogue

Palmer's Green and Southgate Synagogue*
Brownlow Road, New Southgate, London N11 2BN
Tel: (020) 8881 0037
Contact: Mr Martin M Lewis
Position: Administrator
Activities: Worship/practice/meditation, community centre, youth, women, newsletter/journal, visits
Traditions: Orthodox - Central Ashkenazi
Affiliations: United Synagogue

Southgate and District Reform Synagogue*
120 Oakleigh Road, North Whetstone, London N20 9EL
Tel: (020) 8882 6828 **Fax:** (020) 8882 7539
Contact: Mrs C Z Elf
Position: Administrator
Activities: Worship, women, newsletter
Traditions: Reform
Other Languages: Hebrew, Yiddish
Affiliations: Reform Synagogues of Great Britain; World Union for Progressive Judaism

Southgate Progressive Synagogue*
75 Chase Road, London N14 4QY
Tel: (020) 8886 0977 **Fax:** (020) 8882 5394
Contact: Rabbi Stephen Howard

HACKNEY

Aden Jews' Congregation*
17 Clapton Common, London E5 9AB
Tel: (020) 8806 1320
Contact: M A Solomon
Position: Chairman and Honorary Secretary

Beth Hamedrash Beis Nadvorna*
43-45 Darenth Road, London N16 6ES
Tel: (020) 8806 2030
Contact: Rabbi Mordechai Leifer
Position: Rabbi
Activities: Worship, elderly
Traditions: Orthodox, Charedi
Other Languages: Yiddish, Hebrew
Affiliations: Union of Orthodox Hebrew Congregations

Beth Hamedrash D'Chasidey Gur*
2 Lampard Grove, London N16 6UZ
Tel: (020) 8806 4333

Beth Hamedrash D'Chasidey Ryzin*
33 Paget Road, London N16 5ND
Tel: (020) 8800 7979

Beth Hamedrash D'Chasidey Square*
47 East Bank, London N16 5PS

Beth Hamedrash Torah Chaim Liege*
145 Upper Clapton Road, London E5 9DB
Contact: Rabbi Y Meisels

Clapton Federation Synagogue*
47 Lea Bridge Road, London E5 9QE
Tel: (020) 8806 4369
Contact: W Jacobs
Position: Secretary

College for Higher Rabbinical Studies Tiferes Sholom*
37 Craven Walk, Stamford Hill, London N16 6BS
Tel: (020) 8800 3868
Contact: Rabbi E Schwartz
Position: Principal
Contact Tel: (07970) 07158
Activities: Worship/practice/meditation, resources
Traditions: Charedi
Other Languages: Yiddish
Affiliations: Union of Orthodox Hebrew Congregations

Commercial Road Talmud Torah Synagogue*
153 Stamford Hill, London N16 5LG
Tel: (020) 8800 1618 **Fax:** (020) 8800 1618
Contact: Tova Mordechai
Position: Secretary
Activities: Elderly
Traditions: Orthodox – Central Ashkenazi
Affiliations: Adath Yisroel

Hackney United Synagogue*
Brenthouse Road, Mare Street, London E9 6QG
Tel: (020) 8985 4600
Contact: Mrs B Heumann
Position: Administrator

Hatzola Trust*
The Knoll, Fountayne Road, London N16 7EA
Tel: (020) 8806 7947
Contact: Rabbi Eli Kernkraut
Position: Trustee

Traditions: Orthodox
Other Languages: Yiddish, Hebrew

Lubavitch Synagogue*
107-115 Stamford Hill, London N16 5RP
Tel: (020) 8800 0022
Position: Rabbi N Sudak

New Synagogue*
Egerton Road, London N16 6UD
Tel: (020) 8800 6003
Contact: J Yeshooa
Position: Administrator
Activities: Worship/practice/meditation
Affiliations: United Synagogues

North London Bikur Cholim Ltd*
11 Ashtead Road, Hackney, London E5 9BJ
Tel: (020) 8806 1844 **Fax:** (020) 8806 1844
Contact: Mrs Caroline Joseph
Position: Honorary Organiser
Contact Tel: (020) 8802 5032
Traditions: Charedi
Other Languages: Yiddish, German, Hebrew

North London Progressive Synagogue*
100 Amhurst Park, London N16 5AR
Tel: (020) 8800 8931 **Fax:** (020) 8800 0416
Email: nlps@ulps.org
Contact: The Administrator
Activities: Worship/practice/meditation, community centre, newsletter/journal, visits, inter-faith
Traditions: Liberal
Affiliations: Union of Liberal and Progressive Synagogues

Springfield Synagogue*
202 Upper Clapton Road, London E5 9DH
Tel: (01702) 340762
Contact: L Blackman
Position: President and Honorary Secretary

Walford Road Synagogue*
99 Walford Road, London N16 8EF

Yesodey Hatorah Synagogue*
2/4 Amhurst Park, London N16 5AE

HAMMERSMITH AND FULHAM

Hammersmith and West Kensington Synagogue*
71 Brook Green, Hammersmith, London W6 7BE

Tel: (020) 7602 1405
Contact: Mr D Arram
Position: Hon Officer
Contact Tel: (07836) 350388
Contact Email: darram@mcmail.com
Activities: Worship/practice/meditation
Traditions: Orthodox - Central Ashkenazi
Affiliations: United Synagogue

HARINGEY

Highgate United Synagogue*
Grimshaw Close, 57 North Road, London N6 4BJ
Tel: (020) 8340 7655 **Fax:** (020) 8340 7655
Contact: Mr Charles Loeb
Position: Secretary

Muswell Hill Synagogue*
31 Tetherdown, Muswell Hill, London N10 1ND
Tel: (020) 8833 5925 **Fax:** (020) 8833 5925
Contact: L Leighton
Position: Administrator
Traditions: Orthodox

HARROW

Belmont United Synagogue*
101 Vernon Drive, Stanmore HA7 2BW
Tel: (020) 8426 0104
Contact: Mrs C Fletcher
Position: Administrator

Kenton Synagogue*
Shaftesbury Avenue, Kenton, Harrow HA3 0RD
Tel: (020) 8907 5959
Contact: A Primhak
Position: Secretary
Activities: Worship, resource, youth, elderly,
women, newsletter
Traditions: Orthodox
Affiliations: United Synagogue

Middlesex New Synagogue*
39 Bessborough Road, Harrow HA1 3BS
Tel: (020) 8864 0133
Contact: Mrs Simon
Position: Adminstrator
Activities: Worship/practice/meditation,
community centre, youth, elderly, women,
newsletter/journal, visits, inter-faith, resources.
Traditions: Reform
Affiliations: Reform Synagogues of Great Britain

Norwood Ravenswood*
80-82 The Broadway, Stanmore HA7 4HB
Tel: (020) 8954 4555 **Fax:** (020) 8420 6800
Contact: Ront Shebson
Position: Communications Officer
Traditions: Cross-community

Pinner Synagogue*
1 Cecil Park, Pinner HA5 5HJ
Tel: (020) 8868 7204 **Fax:** (020) 8868 7011
Activities: Worship, visits, youth, elderly,
newsletter, inter-faith
Traditions: Orthodox
Affiliations: United Synagogue

Stanmore and Canons Park United Synagogue*
London Road, Stanmore HA7 4NS
Tel: (020) 8954 2210 **Fax:** (020) 8954 4369
Email: stanmoresynagogue@cwcom.net
Contact: Mrs B S Dresner
Position: Administrator
Activities: Worship, resource, youth, elderly,
women, newsletter
Traditions: Orthodox - Central Ashkenazi
Affiliations: United Synagogue

HAVERING

Harold Hill and District Affiliated Synagogue*
Trowbridge Road, Harold Hill RM3 8YW
Tel: (01708) 348904
Contact: Honorary Secretary

Romford and District Synagogue*
25 Eastern Road, Romford RM1 3NH
Tel: (01708) 746190
Contact: J R Rose
Position: Hon Secretary
Contact Tel: (01708) 748199
Activities: Worship/practice/meditation,
community centrem umbrella body, elderly, visits,
inter-faith
Traditions: Orthodox - Central Ashkenazi
Affiliations: United Synagogue

HILLINGDON

Northwood and Pinner Liberal Synagogue*
Oaklands Gate, Northwood HA6 3AA
Tel: (01923) 822592 **Fax:** (01923) 824454
Email: admin@npls.org.uk
Contact: Ingrid Squires
Position: Adminstrator

Activities: Worship, resource, visits, youth, elderly, newsletter
Traditions: Liberal
Affiliations: Union of Liberal and Progressive Synagogues

Ruislip and District Affiliated Synagogue*
Shenley Avenue, Ruislip Manor HA4 6BP
Tel: (01895) 622059
Contact: Mrs Sheryl Green
Position: Secretary
Activities: Worship/practice/meditation, youth, elderly, women, newsletter/journal, visits, inter-faith, resources
Traditions: Orthodox - Central Ashkenazi
Affiliations: United Synagogue

HOUNSLOW

Hounslow and Heathrow Synagogue*
100 Staines Road, Hounslow TW3 2LF
Tel: (020) 8572 2100
Contact: Louis Gilbert
Position: Financial Representative
Contact Tel: (020) 8894 4020
Activities: Worship/practice/meditation
Traditions: Orthodox - Central Ashkenazi
Other Languages: Hebrew
Affiliations: United Synagogue

KENSINGTON AND CHELSEA

Beit Klal Yisrael*
North Kensington Reform Synagogue, PO Box 1828, London W10 5RT
Tel: (020) 8960 5750
Contact: Mr Michael Hornsby
Position: Membership Secretary
Activities: Worship/practice/meditation, women, newsletter/journal
Traditions: Reform
Affiliations: Reform Synagogues of Great Britain; World Congress of Jewish Gay and Lesbian Organisations

North Kensington Reform Synagogue*
PO Box 1828, London W10 5RT
Tel: (020) 8960 5750
Contact: Rabbi Sheila Shulman
Position: Rabbi
Activities: Worship/practice/meditation
Traditions: Reform
Affiliations: World Congress of Gay and Lesbians

Spanish and Portugese Synagogue*
8 St James Gardens, Holland Park, London W11 4RB
Tel: (020) 7603 7961 **Fax:** (020) 7603 9471
Contact: Mrs Ruth Lynton
Position: Secretary
Activities: Worship/practice/meditation, youth, newsletter/journal, visits
Traditions: Sephardi
Affiliations: Sephardi Synagogues

Westminster Synagogue*
Rutland Gardens, Knightsbridge, London SW7 1BX
Tel: (020) 7584 3953
Contact: Mrs E V Atkins
Position: Secretary
Traditions: Reform

KINGSTON UPON THAMES

Kingston and Surbiton District Synagogue*
33-35 Uxbridge Road, Kingston-upon-Thames KT1 2LL
Tel: (020) 8546 9370
Contact: Rabbi Stanley Coten
Position: Minister
Activities: Worship
Traditions: Orthodox - Central Ashkenazi
Affiliations: United Synagogue

LAMBETH

South London Liberal Synagogue*
Prentis Road, Streatham, London SW16 1QB
Tel: (020) 8769 4787
Contact: Mrs Ruth Edwards
Position: Administrator
Activities: Worship/practice, youth, women, newsletter/journal, visits, inter-faith, resources
Traditions: Liberal
Other Languages: Hebrew
Affiliations: Union of Liberal and Progressive Synagogues; World Union of Progressive Judaism

South London United Synagogue*
45 Leigham Court Road, London SW16 2NF
Tel: (020) 7677 0234
Contact: Mr D Saul
Position: Administrator

MERTON

Wimbledon and District Reform Synagogue*
1 Queensmere Road, Wimbledon, London
SW19 5QD
Tel: (020) 8946 4836 **Fax:** (020) 8944 7790
Contact: Miss Anita Wilson
Position: Administrator
Activities: Worship, newsletters, inter-faith
Traditions: Reform
Affiliations: Reform Synagogues of Great Britain

NEWHAM

West Ham and Upton Park Synagogue*
93-95 Earlham Grove, Forest Gate, London
E7 9AN
Tel: (020) 8522 1917
Contact: Mrs E Benjamin
Position: Secretary
Activities: Worship/practice/meditation,
community centre, newsletter/journal
Traditions: Orthodox - Central Ashkenazi
Affiliations: United Synagogue

REDBRIDGE

Achdut Youth Centre*
7 Parham Drive, Gants Hill, Ilford, IG2 6LZ
Tel: (020) 8554 8587 **Fax:** (020) 8554 2545
Contact: Rabbi Godlewsky

Barkingside Jewish Youth Centre*
Carlton Drive, Barkingside, Ilford IG6 1LZ
Contact: Mrs Karen Burns
Position: Centre Director
Affiliations: Association of Jewish Youth

Barkingside Progressive Synagogue*
129 Perryman's Farm Road, Ilford IG2 7LX
Tel: (020) 8554 9682
Email: bps.synagogue@virgin.net
Website: http://freespace.virgin.net/bps.synagogue
Contact: Mr David Forbes
Position: Chair
Activities: Worship/practice/meditation,
community centre, youth, elderly,
newsletter/journal, visits, inter-faith, resources
Traditions: Liberal
Affiliations: Union of Liberal and Progressive
Synagogues, World Union of Progressive Judaism

Chabad Lubavitch Centre*
395 Eastern Avenue, Gants Hill, Ilford, Ilford
IG2 6LR
Tel: (020) 8554 1624 **Fax:** (020) 8518 2126
Email: Rabbi@chabadlubavitch.ilford.com.
Contact: Rabbi A M Sufrin
Position: Director
Activities: Worship/practice/meditation, resources
Traditions: Orthodox
Other Languages: Hebrew, Yiddish

Clayhall United Synagogue*
Sinclair House, Woodford Bridge Road, Redbridge
IG4 5LN
Tel: (020) 8551 6533 **Fax:** (020) 8551 9803
Email: clayhalluynagogue@hotmail.com
Website: http://www.clayhallsynagogue.org.uk./
Contact: Mrs M Mervish
Position: Administrator

Ilford Federation Synagogue*
14/16 Coventry Road, Ilford IG1 4QR
Tel: (020) 8554 5289
Contact: The Secretary

Newbury Park Synagogue*
23 Wessex Close, Newbury Park, Ilford IG3 8JU
Tel: (020) 8597 0958
Contact: Mrs Elizabeth Benjamin
Position: Secretary
Activities: Worship/practice, community centre,
elderly, women, newsletter/journal, visits, resources
Traditions: Orthodox - Central Ashkenazi
Affiliations: North East London Region
Orthodox Synagogues; United Synagogue

Ohel Jacob Beth Hamedrash*
1st Floor, 478 Cranbrook Road, Ilford IG2 6EW
Tel: (020) 8554 8587
Contact: D Grant
Position: Honorary Secretary

Redbridge Jewish Youth and Community
Centre*
Sinclair House, Woodford Bridge Road, Ilford
IG4 5LN
Tel: (020) 8551 0017 **Fax:** (020) 8551 9027
Contact: Ms Myra Topper
Position: Centre Manager
Activities: Worship, resource, umbrella body, visits,
youth, elderly
Traditions: Cross-community
Other Languages: Hebrew, Yiddish
Affiliations: Jewish Care

South West Essex Settlement and Reform Synagogue*
Oaks Lane, Newbury Park, Ilford IG2 7PL
Tel: (020) 8599 0956 **Fax:** (020) 8597 9164
Email: admin@swesrs.fasnet.co.uk
Contact: Rabbi Henry Goldstein
Activities: Worship/practice/meditation, community centre, youth, elderly, women, newsletter/journal, visits, inter-faith, resources
Traditions: Reform
Affiliations: Eastern Counties Association of Progressive Synagogues; Reform Synagogues of Great Britain; World Union of Progressive Judaism

Sukkat Shalom Reform Synagogue*
1 Victory Road, Hermon Hill, Wanstead, London E11 1UL
Tel: (020) 8530 3345
Email: it@sukkatshalom.co.uk
Website: http://www.sukkatshalom.co.uk/
Contact: David Hulbert
Position: Rabbi
Contact Tel: (020) 8559 2235
Activities: Worship/practice, community centre, youth, newsletter/journal, visits, inter-faith, resources
Traditions: Reform
Affiliations: Eastern Communities Associated Progressive Synagogues; Reform Synagogues of Great Britain

Wanstead and Woodford United Synagogue*
20 Churchfields, South Woodford, London E18 2QZ
Tel: (020) 8504 1990
Contact: Mrs S Braude
Position: Administrator

Woodford Progressive Synagogue*
Marlborough Road, South Woodford, London E18 1AR
Tel: (020) 8989 7619
Email: woodfordprogressive@synagogue.demon.co.uk
Website: http://www.synagogue.demon.co.uk/
Contact: The Administrator
Activities: Worship/practice, youth, elderly, newsletter/journal, visits, resources
Traditions: Liberal
Affiliations: Union of Liberal and Progressive Synagogues

TOWER HAMLETS

East London Central Synagogue*
30-40 Nelson Street, London E1 2DE
Tel: (020) 7790 9809
Contact: L.Gayer
Position: Secretary

Fieldgate Street Great Synagogue*
41 Fieldgate Street, Whitechapel, London E1 1JU
Tel: (020) 7247 2644
Contact: Mrs D Jacobson
Position: Secretary
Activities: Worship
Traditions: Orthodox
Affiliations: Federation of Synagogues

Sandy's Row Synagogue*
Sandy's Row, Middlesex Street, London E1 7HW
Tel: (020) 7253 8311
Contact: E Wilder
Position: Secretary

Stepney Jewish Community Centre*
Beaumont Hall, 2/8 Beaumont Grove, Stepney, London E1 4NQ
Tel: (020) 7790 6441 **Fax:** (020) 7265 8342
Email: ppaine@jcare.org
Contact: Philippa Paine
Position: Manager
Activities: Elderly

WALTHAM FOREST

Highams Park and Chingford United Synagogue*
Marlborough Road, Highams Park, London E4 9AJ
Tel: (020) 8527 0937
Contact: Mr Charles Loeb
Position: Administrator

Leytonstone and Wanstead Synagogue*
2 Fillebrook Road, London E11 4AT
Tel: (020) 8924 7505
Contact: Cllr Laurie Braham
Position: Secretary
Contact Tel: (020) 8539 0088
Contact Email: cllr.l.braham@lbwf.gov.uk
Activities: Worship
Traditions: Orthodox - Central Ashkenazi
Affiliations: Federation of Synagogues

Waltham Forest Hebrew Congregation*
140 Boundary Road, Walthamstow, London
E17 8LA
Tel: (020) 8509 0775 **Fax:** (020) 8518 8200
Contact: A Wolpert
Position: Secretary
Contact Tel: (0831) 577482
Traditions: Orthodox

WANDSWORTH

**New Wimbledon and Putney District
Synagogue***
The Clubroom, Toland Square, Eastwood Estate,
Roehampton, London SW15
Tel: (020) 8788 0176
Contact: J Leigh
Position: Honorary Secretary

Wimbledon and District Synagogue*
1 Queensmere Road, off Wimbledon Parkside,
London SW19 5QD
Tel: (020) 8946 4836 **Fax:** (020) 8944 7790
Contact: Rabbi William Wolff

WESTMINSTER, CITY OF

Central Synagogue*
36-40 Hallam Street, London W1N 6NN
Tel: (020) 7580 1355 **Fax:** (020) 7636 3831
Email: centralsyn@brisnet.org
Contact: Mrs C Jowell
Position: Secretary
Contact Tel: (020) 7580 1355
Activities: Worship/practice/meditation,
community centre, youth, elderly, women,
newsletter/journal, visits, inter-faith
Traditions: Orthodox - Central Ashkenazi
Affiliations: United Synagogue

Centre for Jewish Education*
Montagu Centre, 21 Maple Street, London
W1T 4BE
Tel: (020) 7580 0214 **Fax:** (020) 7486 4184
Email: cjeuk@compuserve.com
Website: http://www.knowledge.co.uk/cje
Contact: Judy Thwaites
Position: Kesher Co-ordinator
Activities: Resource, media, umbrella body, visits,
newsletters, books
Traditions: Reform, Liberal, Masorti
Other Languages: Hebrew
Affiliations: Reform Synagogues of Great Britain;
Union of Liberal and Progressive Synagogues

Liberal Jewish Synagogue*
28 St John's Wood Road, St Johns Wood, London
NW8 4HA
Tel: (020) 7286 5181 **Fax:** (020) 7266 3591
Email: ljs@ljs.org
Website: www@ljs.org
Contact: Ms Joyce Whitman
Position: Administrative Director
Contact Tel: (020) 7432 1288
Contact Email: j.whitman@ljs.org
Activities: Worship/practice/meditation,
community centre, youth, elderly,
newsletter/journal, visits, inter-faith, resources
Traditions: Liberal
Other Languages: Hebrew
Affiliations: Union of Liberal and Progressive
Synagogues

New London Synagogue*
33 Abbey Road, London NW8 0AT
Tel: (020) 7328 1026 **Fax:** (020) 7372 3142
Email: nls@masorti.org
Contact: Rabbi Chaim Weiner
Position: Rabbi
Contact Email: weiner@masorti.org.uk
Traditions: Masorti
Other Languages: Hebrew
Affiliations: World Council of Synagogues;
Assembly of Masorti Synagogues

New West End Synagogue*
St Petersburgh Place, Bayswater Road, London
W2 4JT
Tel: (020) 7229 2631 **Fax:** (020) 7229 2355
Website: Newwest End.org.uk
Contact: Mrs S Hayman
Activities: Worship, visits, youth, elderly, newsletter
Traditions: Orthodox - Central Ashkenazi
Affiliations: United Synagogue

Sephardi Centre, The*
2 Ashworth Road, Maida Vale, London W9 1JY
Tel: (020) 7266 3682 **Fax:** (020) 7289 5957
Email: sephardicentre@easynet.co.uk
Contact: Rabbi Saul Djanogly
Position: Director
Activities: Community centre, youth, books, visits,
resources
Traditions: Sephardi
Other Languages: Hebrew Arabic
Affiliations: Spanish and Portugese Jews
Congregation

Spanish and Portuguese Jews' Congregation*
2 Ashworth Road, London W9 1JY

Tel: (020) 7289 2573 Fax: (020) 7289 2709
Contact: Mr Howard Miller
Position: Chief Administrator
Activities: Worship/practice/meditation,
community centre, central body, youth, elderly,
women, newsletter/journal, books, visits, resources
Traditions: Sephardi
Other Languages: Hebrew

St John's Wood Synagogue*
37/41 Grove End Road, St Johns Wood, London
NW8 9NG
Tel: (020) 7286 3838 Fax: (020) 7266 2123
Email: sjwsyn@dircon.co.uk
Website: http://www.bigshul.com/
Contact: Mrs L Young
Position: Administrator
Activities: Worship, visits, youth, elderly, women,
newsletter
Traditions: Orthodox
Affiliations: United Synagogue

West Central Liberal Synagogue*
The Montagu Centre, 21 Maple Street, London
W1T 4BE
Tel: (020) 7636 7627
Contact: Henry J Berman
Position: Honorary Secretary
Activities: Worship, visits, newsletter, inter-faith
Traditions: Liberal
Affiliations: Union of Liberal and Progressive
Synagogues

West End Great Synagogue*
32 Great Cumberland Place, London W1H 7DJ
Tel: (020) 7724 8121 Fax: (020 7723 4413

West London Synagogue of British Jews*
33 Seymour Place, London W1H 6AT
Tel: (020) 7723 4404 Fax: (020) 7224 8258
Email: admin@wls.org.uk
Website: http://www.wls.org.uk/
Contact: Maurice Ross
Position: Executive Director
Contact Email: m.ross@wls.org.uk
Activities: Worship/practice/meditation,
community centre, youth, elderly, women,
newsletter/journal, visits, inter-faith, resources
Traditions: Reform
Other Languages: Hebrew
Affiliations: Reform Synagogues of Great Britain;
World Union of Progressive Judaism

Western Charitable Foundation*
32 Great Cumberland Place, London W1H 7DJ
Tel: (020) 7723 9333
Contact: Sidney Jaque
Position: Chair
Contact Tel: (020) 7722 3671
Traditions: Orthodox – Central Ashkenazi

Western Marble Arch United Synagogue*
32 Great Cumberland Place, London W1H 7TN
Tel: (020) 7723 9333 Fax: (020) 7224 8065
Email: stephen@westernmarblearchsynagogue.com
Contact: Stephen Garcia
Position: Community Administrator
Tradition: Independent Orthodox

SOUTH EAST
City, Town or Local Bodies

South Bucks Jewish Community*
Zion Hall, c/o 15 The Willows, Chesham Bois,
Amersham HP6 5NT
Tel: (01494) 431885 Fax: (01494) 431884
Email: info@sbjc.org.uk
Website: http://www.sbjc.org.uk/
Contact: Dr Sacker
Position: Secretary
Contact Email: sacker@nildram.co.uk
Activities: Worship/practice/meditation,
community centre, youth, elderly, women,
newsletter/journal, visits, inter-faith, resources
Traditions: Liberal
Affiliations: Union of Liberal and Progressive
Synagogues

Hastings and District Jewish Society*
PO Box 74, Bexhill on Sea TN39 4ZZ
Contact: Mr Alfred Ross
Position: Secretary
Contact Tel: (01424) 848344
Activities: Worship/practice/meditation, inter-
faith
Traditions: Reform
Affiliations: Brighton and Hove Representative
Council; Board of Deputies of British Jews

Bognor Regis and District Hebrew
Congregation*
Elm Lodge, Sylvan Way, Bognor Regis PO21 2RS
Tel: (01243) 823006 Fax: (01243) 866859
Contact: Mr J S Jacobs
Position: Honorary Secretary

Contact Email: bjacobs571@aol.com
Activities: Worship/practice/meditation,
newsletter/journal
Traditions: Cross-community
Affiliations: Jewish Memorial Council

Borehamwood and Elstree Synagogue*
PO Box 47, Croxdale Road, Borehamwood
WD6 4QF
Tel: (020) 8386 5227 **Fax:** (020) 8386 3303
Email: admin@bwoodshul.demon.co.uk
Website: http://www.bwoodshul.demon.co.uk/
Contact: Barry Winterman Position
Position: Administrator
Activities: Worship/practice/meditation,
community centre
Traditions: Orthodox - Central Ashkenazi
Affiliations: United Synagogue

Cheltenham Hebrew Congregation*
Synagogue Chambers, St James Square,
Cheltenham GL50 3PU
Tel: (01242) 578893 **Fax:** (01242) 578893
Contact: Mr Michel Webber
Position: Chairman
Activities: Worship/practice
Traditions: Orthodox - Central Ashkenazi
Other Languages: Hebrew
Affiliations: Jewish Ladies Guild

Crawley Progressive Jewish Congregation*
44 Brighton Road, Crawley RH10 6AT
Tel: (01293) 34294
Contact: Mrs L Bloom
Position: Honorary Secretary

Eastbourne Hebrew Congregation*
22 Susans Road, Eastbourne BN21 3TJ
Tel: (01435) 866928 **Fax:** (01435) 865783
Contact: Margaret Mindell
Position: Honorary Secretary
Activities: Worship/practice/meditation,
community centre, elderly
Traditions: Orthodox - Central Ashkenazi
Other Languages: Hebrew
Affiliations: Brighton Representative Council

Hertsmere Progressive Synagogue*
High Street, Elstree WD6 3BY
Tel: (020) 8953 8889
Email: hps@ulps.org
Website: http://www.hpselstree.org.uk/
Contact: Mrs Penny Beral
Position: Honorary Secretary
Contact Tel: (01923) 855367

Contact Email: penny@beral.clara.net
Activities: Worship/practice/meditation,
community centre, youth, elderly,
newsletter/journal, visits, inter-faith, resources
Traditions: Liberal
Affiliations: Union of Liberal and Progressive
Synagogues

Brighton and Hove Hebrew Congregation*
The Synagogue, 31 New Church Road, Hove
BN3 4AD
Tel: (01273) 888855 **Fax:** (01273) 888810
Email: office@bhhc-shul.org
Website: http://www.bhhc-shul.org/
Contact: Mrs Lesley Shaw
Position: Administrator
Activities: Worship, visits, youth, elderly, newsletter
Traditions: Orthodox
Other Languages: Hebrew, French, Yiddish
Affiliations: Brighton and Hove Representative
Council

Brighton and Hove Progressive Synagogue*
6 Lansdowne Road, Hove BN3 1FF
Tel: (01273) 737223 **Fax:** (01273) 737223
Email: bhps@freenetname.co.uk
Website:
http://www.brightonandhoveprosynagogue.org.uk/
Contact: Mrs Goldman
Position: Adminstrator
Activities: Worship/practice/meditation,
community centre, elderly, newsletter/journal,
inter-faith, resources
Traditions: Liberal
Affiliations: Union of Liberal and Progressive
Synagogues; World Union of Progressive Judaism

Brighton and Hove Jewish Centre*
Ralli Hall, 81 Denmark Villas, Hove BN3 3TH
Tel: (01273) 202254 **Fax:** (01273) 202254
Contact: Mrs Norina Duke
Position: Administrator
Activities: Community centre, umbrella body,
youth, elderly, visits, inter-faith
Traditions: Cross-community
Other Languages: Yiddish, Hebrew, German
Affiliations: Friendship Clubs UK, B'nai Brith
Youth Organisation, Maccabi Youth Organisation

Brighton and Hove Jewish Representative
Council*
11 Hove Manor, Hove Street, Hove BN3 2DF
Tel: (01273) 732732
Email: goldslippers60@aol.com
Contact: Mrs Beryl Sharpe

Position: Chair
Activities: Community centre, umbrella body, visits, inter-faith
Traditions: Cross-community
Other Languages: Hebrew
Affiliations: Board of Deputies of British Jews

Brighton and Hove Jewish Welfare Board*
76 Marmion Road, Hove BN3 5FT
Tel: (01273) 722523
Contact: Mrs J Markham
Position: Honorary Secretary

Hove Hebrew Congregation*
79 Holland Road, Hove BN3 1JN
Tel: (01273) 732035
Contact: Mrs C Sweid
Position: Administrator
Activities: Worship, elderly, women, visits
Traditions: Orthodox
Affiliations: Brighton and Hove Jewish Representative Council; Board of Deputies of British Jews

Torah Academy*
31 New Church Road, Hove BN3 4AD
Tel: (01273) 28675

Milton Keynes and District Reform Synagogue*
214 Grasmere Way, Linslade, Leighton Buzzard LU7 7QH
Tel: (01908) 569661
Contact: Len Sharpstone
Position: Chair
Contact Tel: (01525) 373010
Contact Email: leonardsharpsonte@tpsco.net
Activities: Worship, visits, youth, newsletter, inter-faith
Traditions: Reform
Other Languages: Hebrew
Affiliations: Reform Synagogues of Great Britain

South Hampshire Reform Jewish Community*
61 Newfield Road, Liss Forest GW33 7BW
Tel: (01730) 892155 **Fax:** (01730) 891096
Email: fran@liss-online.co.uk
Contact: Mrs Frances Dowty
Position: Secretary
Contact Tel: (01730) 894563
Activities: Worship/practice/meditation, youth, elderly, women, newsletter/journal, visits, inter-faith, resources.
Traditions: Reform
Other Languages: Hebrew
Affiliations: Reform Synagogues of Great Britain

Kingston Liberal Synagogue*
Rushett Road, Long Ditton KT7 0UX
Tel: (020) 8398 7400 **Fax:** (020) 8873 2405
Email: kls@kingstonls.freeserve.co.uk
Contact: Mrs B Dombey
Position: Adminstrator
Activities: Worship/practice/meditation, community centre, youth, elderly, newsletter/journal, visits, inter-faith, resources
Traditions: Liberal
Affiliations: The Dittons CCJ; Union of Liberal and Progressive Synagogues; World Union of Progressive Judaism

Maidenhead Synagogue*
Grenfell Lodge, Ray Park Road, Maidenhead SL6 8QX
Tel: (01628) 673012
Contact: Rabbi Dr Jonathan Romain
Position: Minister
Activities: Worship, resource, visits, youth, elderly, women
Traditions: Reform
Affiliations: Reform Synagogues of Great Britain

Margate Hebrew Congregation*
Margate Synagogue, Albion Road, Cliftonville, Margate CT9 2HT
Tel: (01843) 228550
Contact: Mr Denis Coberman
Position: Life President
Contact Email: denis@dcobermas.freeserve.co.uk
Activities: Worship/practice/meditation, community centre, elderly, newsletter/journal, visits, inter-faith
Traditions: Orthodox - Central Ashkenazi
Affiliations: United Synagogue; Bnai Brith

Oxford Jewish Congregation*
The Synagogue, 21 Richmond Road, Oxford OX1 2JL
Tel: (01865) 53042
Contact: Elaine Lyons
Position: Administrator
Activities: Worship, resource, visits, youth, elderly, newsletter
Traditions: Orthodox (Progressive and Liberal)

Radlett and Bushey Reform Synagogue*
118 Watling Street, Radlett WD7 7AA
Tel: (01923) 856110 **Fax:** (01923) 858444
Email: office@r-brs.freeserve.co.uk
Contact: Sandra Denby
Position: Secretary
Activities: Worship, community centre, resource,

visits, youth, elderly, newsletter
Traditions: Reform
Other Languages: Hebrew
Affiliations: Reform Synagogues of Great Britain;
World Union of Progressive Judaism

Thanet and District Reform Synagogue*
239a Margate Road, Ramsgate CT12 6TE
Tel: (01843) 851164
Contact: David Mirsky
Position: Chairman
Activities: Worship, visits, newsletter, inter-faith
Traditions: Reform
Affiliations: Reform Synagogues of Great Britain

Reading Hebrew Congregation*
Goldsmid Road, Reading RG1 7YB
Tel: (0118) 9571018
Email: secretary@rhc.datanet.co.uk
Website: http://www.rhc.org.uk/
Contact: Mrs Louise Créme
Position: Secretary
Activities: Worship/practice, community centre,
youth, elderly, newsletter/journal, visits, inter-faith,
resources
Traditions: Orthodox - Central Ashkenazi

Reading University Jewish Society*
Reading, c/o 1/2 Endsleigh Drive, London
WC1H 0DS
Tel: (020) 7387 4644 **Fax:** (020) 7383 0390
Email: jsoc@reading.ac.uk
Contact: Mr David Cowan
Position: Hillel House Warden
Contact Email: ujs@ujs.org.uk
Activities: Youth, newsletter/journal, inter-faith,
resources
Traditions: Cross-community
Affiliations: Union of Jewish Students

Romford and District Synagogue*
25 Eastern Road, Romford RM1 3NH
Tel: (01708) 746190
Contact: J R Rose
Position: Hon Secretary
Contact Tel: (01708) 748199
Activities: Worship/practice/meditation,
community centre, umbrella body, elderly, visits,
inter-faith
Traditions: Orthodox - Central Ashkenazi
Affiliations: United Synagogue

Southampton Synagogue*
Mordaunt Road, Inner Avenue, Southampton
SO3 0GP
Tel: (023) 8022 0129
Contact: Mr Martyn Rose
Position: President
Activities: Worship, visits, inter-faith
Traditions: Orthodox
Affiliations: Bournemouth Representative
Council

Staines and District United Synagogue*
Westbrook Road, South Street, Staines TW18 4PR
Tel: (01784) 254604
Email: staines.synagogue@btinternet.com
Website:
http://www.btinternet.com/~staines.synagogue
Contact: Phyllis Fellman
Position: Honorary Secretary
Contact Tel: (01784) 254604
Activities: Worship, visits, women, newsletter,
inter-faith
Traditions: Orthodox
Affiliations: United Synagogue

Welwyn Garden City Hebrew Congregation*
Barn Close, Handside Lane, Welwyn Garden City
AL8 6ST
Tel: (01438) 715686
Email: floradora@hotmail.com
Contact: Mr G Tuch
Position: Chairman
Contact Tel: (01707) 890575
Activities: Worship/practice/meditation,
community centre, newsletter/journal, visits
Traditions: Orthodox - Central Ashkenazi
Movements: United Synagogue
Affiliations: United Synagogue

Coleman Levene Talmud Torah (Orthodox)*
Synagogue Office, Finchley Road, Westcliff-on-Sea
SS0 8AD
Tel: (01702) 344900
Contact: Principal

Southend and District Reform Synagogue*
851 London Road, Westcliff-on-Sea SS0 9SZ
Tel: (01702) 711663
Email: shul@sdrs.co.uk
Contact: Philip Freeman
Position: Chairman
Activities: Worship/practice/meditation,
community centre, youth, elderly, women,

newsletter/journal, visits, inter-faith, resources
Traditions: Reform
Affiliations: Reform Synagogues of Great Britain

Southend and Westcliff Hebrew Congregation*
Synagogue Office, Finchley Road, Westcliff-on-Sea
SS20 8AD
Tel: (01702) 344900 **Fax:** (01702) 391131
Email: swhc@btclick.com
Contact: Mr Ashley Kalms
Position: Treasurer
Activities: Worship/practice/meditation,
community centre, youth, elderly, women,
newsletter/journal, visits, inter-faith, resources
Traditions: Orthodox - Central Ashkenazi
Other Languages: Hebrew
Affiliations: United Synagogues

Southend Jewish Youth Centre (SJYC)*
38 Ceylon Road, Westcliff-on-Sea SS0 7HP
Tel: (01702) 346545
Contact: David Jay
Position: Secretary
Activities: Visits, youth
Traditions: Orthodox - Central Ashkenazi
Affiliations: Southend and Westcliff Hebrew
Congregation; Maccabi Union; Association of
Jewish Youth

Youth Centre (Orthodox)*
38 Ceylon Road, Westcliff-on-Sea SS0 7HP
Tel: (01702) 346545
Contact: D Jay
Position: Secretary

North West Surrey Synagogue*
Horvath Close, Rosslyn Park, Weybridge
KT13 9QZ
Tel: (01932) 855400 **Fax:** (01932) 855400
Email: admin@nwss.freeserve.co.uk
Website: http://www.nwss.org.uk/
Contact: Rabbi J Tabick
Position: Rabbi
Contact Email: rabbi@nwss.freeserve.co.uk
Activities: Worship/practice/meditation,
community centre, youth, elderly, women,
newsletter/journal, visits, inter-faith, resources
Traditions: Reform
Other Languages: Hebrew
Affiliations: Reform Synagogues of Great Britain;
World Union of Progressive Synagogues

SOUTH WEST
City, Town or Local Bodies

Bristol Hebrew Congregation*
9 Park Row, Bristol BS1 5LP
Tel: (0117) 9246031
Contact: Rabbi Hillel Simon
Position: Rabbi
Contact Email: simon77@aol.com
Activities: Worship/practice/meditation
Traditions: Orthodox
Other Languages: Hebrew
Affiliations: Bristol Jewish Representative
Council; Chief Rabbinate

Bristol Jewish Representative Council*
42 Vicarage Road, Bristol BS3 1PD
Tel: (0117) 9636171 **Fax:** (0117) 9231835
Email: eleonardglynn@aol.com
Contact: Leonard Glynn
Position: Chair
Traditions: Orthodox

Exeter Hebrew Congregation*
Synagogue Place, Mary Arches Street, Exeter
EX4 3BA
Tel: (01392) 251529
Email: exeshul@eclipse.co.uk
Website: http://www.eclipse.co.uk/exeshul
Contact: Mrs Sonia Fodor
Position: President
Activities: Worship/practice/meditation,
newsletter/journal, visits, inter-faith
Traditions: Cross-community

Jersey Jewish Congregation*
The Synagogue, Petite Route des Mielles, St
Brelade, Jersey JE3 8FY
Tel: (01534) 744946 **Fax:** (01534) 861431
Email: stever@jerseymail.co.uk
Contact: Mr Stephen Regal
Position: President
Contact Tel: (01534) 482 429
Activities: Worship/practice/meditation,
community centre, women, visits
Traditions: Orthodox - Central Ashkenazi
Affiliations: Board of Deputies of British Jews

Plymouth Hebrew Congregation*
Synagogue Chambers, Catherine Street, Plymouth
PL1 2AD
Tel: (01752) 301955
Email: info@plymouthsynagogue.co.uk

Website: http://www.plymouthsynagogue.co.uk/
Contact: Dr Peter Lee
Position: Honorary Secretary
Affiliations: Independent Orthodox Community

Swindon Jewish Community*

Swindon
Email:
swindonjewishcommunity@btinternet.com
Activities: Worship/practice/meditation
Traditions: Reform
Affiliations: Reform Synagogues of Great
Britain

NORTHERN IRELAND

City, Town or Local Bodies

Belfast Hebrew Congregation*

49 Somerton Road, Belfast BT15 4DD
Tel: (028) 9077 9794
Contact: Cyril Rosenberg
Position: Deputy Chairman
Contact Tel: (028) 9077 8609
Activities: Worship/practice/meditation,
community centre, umbrella body, youth, elderly,
women, newsletter/journal, visitor, inter-faith
Traditions: Orthodox - Central Ashkenazi
Affiliations: United Synagogues

SCOTLAND

Scottish National Bodies

Jewish Blind Society (Scotland)*

May Terrace, Giffnock, Glasgow G46 6LD
Tel: (0141) 6201800 **Fax:** (0141) 6201088
Contact: Mrs Carole Blake
Position: Secretary
Traditions: Orthodox
Affiliations: Glasgow Jewish Representative
Council

Jewish Care Scotland*

May Terrace, Giffnock, Glasgow G46 6LD
Tel: (0141) 6201800 **Fax:** (0141) 6202409
Email: admin@jcarescot.org.uk
Contact: Mrs Ethne Woldman
Position: Chief Executive
Activities: Visits, elderly
Traditions: Cross-Community

Affiliations: Glasgow Jewish Representative
Council

Scottish Council of Synagogues*

28 Field Road, Busby, Glasgow G76 8SE
Tel: (0141) 6443611 **Fax:** (0141) 6444430
Contact: Bernard Mann
Position: Secretary
Activities: Umbrella body
Traditions: Orthodox

Scottish Jewish Archives Centre*

Garnethill Synagogue, 129 Hill Street, Glasgow G3
6UB
Tel: (0141) 3324911 **Fax:** (0141) 3324911
Email: archives@sjac.fsbusiness.co.uk
Website: http://www.sjac.org.uk/
Contact: Harvey L Kaplan
Position: Director

Regional or County Bodies

Glasgow Jewish Representative Council*

222 Fenwick Road, Giffnock, Glasgow G46 6UE
Tel: (0141) 5778200 **Fax:** (0141) 5778202
Email: glasgow@j-scot.org
Contact: Beverley Taylor
Position: Secretary
Activities: Umbrella body, inter-faith, newsletter
Traditions: Cross-community
Affiliations: European Council of Jewish
Communities

City, Town or Local Bodies

Edinburgh Hebrew Congregation*

4 Salisbury Road, Edinburgh EH16 5AB
Tel: (0131) 6673144
Email: ray.taylor@lineone.net
Contact: Dr Ian Leifer
Position: President
Activities: Worship, umbrella body, visits, youth,
elderly, women
Traditions: Orthodox Central Ashkenazi
Other Languages: Hebrew
Affiliations: Scottish Standing Jewish Conference;
Office of the Chief Rabbi

Garnethill Hebrew Congregation*

129 Hill Street, Glasgow G3 6UG
Tel: (0141) 3324151
Contact: Rhoda Livingston
Position: Secretary

Activities: Worship, resource, visits, newsletters, inter-faith
Traditions: Orthodox
Other Languages: Hebrew
Affiliations: Scottish Representative Council; United Synagogue

Giffnock and Newlands Synagogue*
Maryville Avenue, Giffnock, Glasgow G46 7NE
Tel: (0141) 5778250 **Fax:** (0141) 5778252
Email: giffnock@j-scot.org
Website: http://www.j-scot.org/giffnock
Contact: Mrs Gardner
Position: Office Secretary
Activities: Worship/practice/meditation, community centre
Traditions: Orthodox - Central Ashkenazi
Other Languages: Hebrew, Yiddish
Affiliations: Glasgow Jewish Representative Council, Board of Deputies of British Jews

Glasgow Jewish Community Centre*
222 Fenwick Road, Giffnock, Glasgow G46 6UE
Tel: (0141) 5778228 **Fax:** (0141) 5778202
Email: glasgow@j-scot.org
Contact: Beverley Taylor
Position: Secretary
Activities: Community centre, youth, elderly, women, resources
Traditions: Cross-community
Other Languages: Hebrew
Affiliations: Glasgow Jewish Representative Council

Glasgow Jewish Representative Council*
222 Fenwick Road, Giffnock, Glasgow G46 6UE
Tel: (0141) 5778200 **Fax:** (0141) 5778202
Email: glasgow@j-scot.org
Contact: Beverley Taylor
Position: Secretary
Activities: Umbrella body, inter-faith, newsletter
Traditions: Cross-community
Affiliations: European Council of Jewish Communities

Glasgow New Synagogue*
147 Ayr Road, Newton Mearns, Glasgow G77 6RE
Tel: (0141) 6394083
Email: shul@gns.org.uk
Website: http://www.gns.org.uk/
Contact: Pete Tobias
Position: Minister/Rabbi
Activities: Worship, resource, visits, youth, women, newsletter
Traditions: Reform
Affiliations: Glasgow Jewish Representative Council; Reform Movement (RSGB)

Glasgow Yeshiva*
Giffnock Synagogue, Maryville Avenue, Glasgow G46 7NF
Tel: (0141) 5778260
Contact: Rabbi N Leslie
Position: Organiser
Activities: Youth
Traditions: Charedi

Netherlee and Clarkston Hebrew Congregation*
Clarkston Road, Clarkston, Glasgow G76 8NE
Tel: (0141) 6378206
Contact: Mrs Pamela Livingston
Position: Secretary
Contact Tel: (0141) 6397194
Activities: Worship
Traditions: Orthodox - Central Ashkenazi
Affiliations: Glasgow Jewish Representative Council

WALES

City, Town or Local Bodies

Cardiff New Synagogue (Reform)*
Moira Terrace, Cardiff CF24 0EJ
Tel: (029) 2049 1689
Website: http://www.cardiffnewsyn.org/
Contact: Mr Stanley Soffa
Position: Chairman
Activities: Worship/practice/meditation
Traditions: Reform
Affiliations: Reform Synagogues of Great Britain

Swansea Hebrew Congregation*
17 Mayals Green, Mayals, Swansea SA3 5JR
Tel: (01792) 401205 **Fax:** (01792) 405948
Contact: H M Sherman
Position: Chair

INTRODUCING MUSLIMS IN THE UK

MUSLIMS IN THE UNITED KINGDOM   433

ORIGINS AND DEVELOPMENT OF ISLAM   434

SOURCES OF MUSLIM BELIEFS AND PRACTICES   435

KEY MUSLIM BELIEFS   437

TRADITIONS IN ISLAM   437

MUSLIM LIFE   439

MUSLIM WORSHIP   441

MUSLIM CALENDAR AND FESTIVALS   442

MUSLIM ORGANISATIONS   444

FURTHER READING   446

MUSLIMS IN THE UNITED KINGDOM

Migration and Patterns of Settlement

There has been a significant Muslim presence in the United Kingdom since the early nineteenth century when Muslim seamen and traders from the Middle East and the Indian subcontinent began to settle around major ports. For example, Yemeni Muslims settled in South Shields and established a Muslim community there and similar communities grew up around the ports of Liverpool and Cardiff. Some of the seamen later moved inland after failing to secure employment in the ports or on the ships and the pattern of settlement thus widened. After the First World War there was further settlement by Muslims who had been demobilised from military service in the British army.

The size of the Muslim population increased significantly with the arrival in the 1950s and 1960s of workers from the Indo-Pakistani subcontinent who had been recruited for, or were seeking employment, in the mills and factories due to a shortage of workers in the aftermath of the Second World War. As a direct result of the implementation of Africanisation policies in the newly independent African states, the early 1970's saw the arrival from Kenya and Uganda of a large number of Muslims of Asian ethnic origins. Recently, some Muslim refugees have arrived from countries such as Somalia and Bosnia.

The largest local communities are found in the West Midlands, West Yorkshire, Lancashire, Greater London and in Scotland's central belt, but Muslim communities are also found in most major towns and cities. The first *mosques* in the UK were established in Liverpool and Woking around the end of the nineteenth century. In England and Wales the Registrar General lists 584 *mosques* for 1999 which are certified as places of worship and this directory includes records of 486 places of worship in the UK of which 443 are in England and Wales.

Ethnic Backgrounds and Languages

Approximately two thirds of the Muslims in the UK have ancestral origins in the Indo-Pakistani subcontinent, coming to Britain either directly or via earlier migrations to East Africa and the Caribbean. The remaining one third have their ethnic and national origins in a variety of other countries and regions, such as Cyprus, Malaysia, Iran and the Middle East. There are also indigenous Britons who have embraced Islam.

Because the ethnic background of the UK Muslim population is quite diverse, a number of different languages are spoken in addition to English. Arabic, Bengali, Farsi, Gujarati, Hausa, Malay, Punjabi, Pushto, Turkish, and Urdu are among the most commonly used of these. Among Muslims, a reading knowledge of Arabic is considered very important since this is the language of the *Qur'an* (see below).

ORIGINS AND DEVELOPMENT OF ISLAM

Revelation

According to Muslim belief, the last *Prophet* of Islam was the *Prophet* Muhammad (570-632CE). He was born in the Arabian city of Makka and from the age of forty received a series of revelations from God (in Arabic, Allah). The revelations are believed to have come to Muhammad through the Angel Jibreel (Gabriel) over a period of twenty-three years.

It is stressed by Muslims that Muhammad did not bring a new faith. As the "seal of the *prophets*" he is understood to complete the succession of *prophets*, renewing and completing the teachings of Abraham, Moses and Jesus who are seen as being among the greatest of the *prophets*.

Muslims believe that essentially the same message, guiding people to the right path, was communicated by God through all the *prophets*. Because people kept disobeying and corrupting the code of guidance which the *prophets* preached, other *prophets* were sent to restate the original message. Muslims therefore affirm the *Torah* brought by Moses and the *Gospel* or *Injil* of Jesus, although they believe that these have been corrupted from their original purity. Muhammad is thus seen as the last of the *prophets*, correcting error and calling people back to Islam or submission to the ways of God.

The Prophet Muhammad and the 'Ummah

All those who believed in Muhammad as the last of the *prophets* and in the revelation to him which forms the *Qur'an*, were welcomed into the *'Ummah* (world Muslim community) irrespective of their place of origin, language or colour of skin. With this newly established Muslim community, in 622CE Muhammad migrated from Makka to Madina, five hundred kilometres away.

This migration is known as the *Hijra*. The formative significance of this event in Islamic history can be seen from the fact that the Muslim dating system begins from the *Hijra* and that therefore, in English, dates in the Muslim calendar are expressed as "AH" (after *Hijra*).

Caliphate and Imamate.

After the death of the Prophet Muhammad, the *Caliphate* (from *khalifa* meaning viceroy) was established to provide leadership for the Muslim community. Among *Sunni* Muslims (see below) Abu Bakr, 'Umar, 'Uthman and 'Ali are recognised as the first four *Caliphs* and are often called *al-khulafa ar-rashidun* (the rightly guided *Caliphs*) because their exemplary lives are viewed as role models for the community.

However, following the death of Muhammad there was a serious dispute within the

Muslim community concerning the location of authority. This led to the development of the distinctive *Sunni* and *Shi'a* traditions of Islam (see below), with a different line of authority emerging within the *Shi'a* tradition. The word *Sunni* comes from "one who adheres to the *sunna*", the *sunna* (see below) being one of the four sources of Islamic law which relates to the actions and sayings of the *Prophet* Muhammad. The name *Shi'ite* comes from *shiat 'Ali* (the follower of 'Ali).

The *Shi'a* advocated the appointment of 'Ali ibn Abu Talib as successor to the *Prophet* instead of Abu Bakr. After 'Umar's death and following his appointment by Abu Bakr, 'Ali the son-in-law of the Prophet Muhammad was offered the *Caliphate* on certain conditions, but an arbiter awarded the function to 'Uthman. Following 'Uthman's assassination 'Ali was elected as the Fourth *Caliph*, but was then himself assassinated. Following a series of disputes and a civil war, his son Hasan was elected *Caliph* but gave up the office for the sake of reconciliation.

Upon Hasan's death his brother Husayn led a revolt to re-establish the legitimacy of the *Caliphate* against those who violated the reconciliation agreement of his brother. Husayn was betrayed and killed at Karbala in confrontation with the armies of the *Caliph* Yazid. This event became the foundation of the developing themes of suffering and persecution to be found in the *Shi'a* tradition of Islam, and so Husayn is seen by *Shi'a* Muslims as an inspiration to all who suffer and struggle against injustice. Reverence for 'Ali and his successors led to the development of the *Shi'a* idea of the *Imamate* in which descendants of Ali have a special sanctity and role in the spiritual leadership of the community.

In *Sunni* Islam, the idea of the *Caliphate* continued under a succession of Muslim dynasties, beginning with the Umayyad dynasty (661–750CE), centred upon the geographical region known today as Syria.

Following the Abbasid dynasty centred upon Baghdad, rival *Caliphates* were established with Cordoba in Spain being ruled by a second Umayyad dynasty from 929CE and Cairo becoming the capital of the Fatimid dynasty from 969CE. The concept of the *Caliphate* survived into modern times with the Ottoman Empire.

Development and Diversity

From its origins in Arabia, Islam spread towards the Indian sub-continent after 750CE, and also into Africa and Europe. In Europe the history of Islam is at its longest in the Balkans, Sicily and Spain. In Spain, after its initial establishment by military force in the early eighth century, Islamic culture spread through the land influencing many aspects of life and thought, developing peacefully alongside Christian and Jewish culture, until the Muslims were finally expelled by the Christian monarchs of the early sixteenth century.

During the Moghul empire (1516–1707CE) Islam made deep inroads into India, from where it spread to Malaysia, Indonesia and the Philippines. The partition of the Indian sub-continent in 1947, following the end of British colonial rule, resulted in the creation of the Muslim majority state of Pakistan. Following a civil war, in 1971 the eastern part of Pakistan became the independent country of Bangladesh.

SOURCES OF MUSLIM BELIEFS AND PRACTICES

Qur'an

The *Qur'an* is the fundamental source of guidance for Muslims. They regard it as the pre-eminent "sign" or "miracle" of God and as the final and ultimate source of guidance which is for all places and all times. It can be applied in each age in the way most suitable to the conditions of that age and is a guide to ethics, human relationships, social justice, political principles, law, trade and commerce.

The text of the *Qur'an* is divided into *surahs* (or chapters) which are of varying lengths and are not in chronological order but are believed to be in this order under divine instruction. The opening *surah*, called the *Fatiha*, is a key prayer of Muslims and a summary of Islamic belief which must be read in Arabic during the observance of every *salat* (Muslim obligatory daily prayers – see below).

Because the *surahs* of the *Qur'an* are viewed as the actual words of God, the learning and recitation of the *Qur'an* is a central duty and joy for believers. The language in which the *Qur'an* was revealed was Arabic, and an understanding of this is therefore seen as essential for penetrating its true meaning. It is thus considered preferable to read it in its original Arabic version although translations (or more strictly, in Islamic understanding, interpretations) are available in English and many other languages.

Shari'ah

The framework within which Muslim life has evolved is the *Shari'ah* (law). The sources of *Shari'ah* are the Qur'an, the *Sunna*, *Ijma*, *Ijtihad* and *Qiyas*.

The *Sunna* is the example of the *Prophet* and his way of life which acts as a model for Muslims to emulate. It is whatever the Prophet said, did or approved of. It therefore also includes the *Hadith*. The *Hadith* are the traditions which contain accounts of the words and actions of Muhammad and his companions and they have been gathered into generally recognised collections of material.

Ijma is the practice of reaching consensus of approval for particular aspects of *Shari'ah*. Where Islamic legislation is unclear about a situation, experts who are knowledgeable about the holy texts propose clarifications which must gain their consensus agreement for it to become an accepted principle.

Ijtihad (Sunni term) or *'aql* (*Shi'a* term) is the concept of independent reasoning or intelligence. Rational discussion and debate is very much at the heart of Islam. One form of reasoning which is often employed is that of *Qiyas* (or analogy). In the use of *Qiyas*, analogies are drawn between situations in the *Qur'an*, *Sunna* and *Hadith* and contemporary circumstances in order to determine the application of the *Shari'ah* to novel situations. However, among *Sunni* Muslims many have argued that, following the development of classical Islamic jurisprudence, the "gates of *ijtihad*" became closed in the tenth century CE.

Schools

Among the *Sunni* Muslims there are four recognised *madhahib* or *madhhabs* (schools of law) whose scholars have the task of discerning the way of applying the *Shari'ah* in various contexts. These are named after their founders: the *Hanafi*, the *Hanbali*, the *Maliki* and the *Shafi'i* schools. They are all recognised as having developed out of the *usul al-fiqh* (the principles of Islamic jurisprudence), and each school therefore recognises the other as being truly Muslim.

Different schools have come to predominate in various areas of the world. The *Hanafi* school is predominant in India and most parts of the former Ottoman Empire, the *Maliki* school in West Africa and the Arab West, and the *Shafi'i* in Indonesia, Malaysia and the Philippines. The *Shafi'i* is also important in Egypt where the first two schools can also be found. The *Hanbali* school is found in Saudi Arabia and Qatar. Muslims in Britain with ethnic or ancestral backgrounds in these various areas of the world might therefore be expected to follow the relevant predominant school. The *Shi'a* tradition of Islam also has a number of schools, the most widespread of which is the *Ja'fari* school of the *Twelvers* (see below).

KEY MUSLIM BELIEFS

The Key Beliefs and Five Pillars of Islam

Islam rests upon six basic beliefs. It affirms the oneness of God *(Allah),* the books revealed by God, belief in the *prophets,* the angels, the *Day of Judgement* and life after death. The essentials of Muslim practice are summarised in the *Five Pillars of Islam.* The five pillars are:

Shahadah

The declaration of faith which states that there is no god except God and Muhammad is his messenger.

Salat

Ritual prayer carried out five times a day (see section on "Muslim Worship" below).

Zakat

A welfare due which should consist of two and a half per cent of a Muslim's untouched annual savings over a specified amount in order to help the service of the needy. An additional charity is due at the end of *Sawm* (fasting) during the month of *Ramadan,* and this is known as *Sadaqa al-Fitr.*

Ramadan

A month of fasting and spiritual discipline (for details see section on "Muslim Calendar and Festivals").

Hajj

This is the Pilgrimage to Makka which involves visiting the *Ka'bah* (the *House of God*), believed to have been built around four thousand years ago by Abraham, and performing certain prescribed rituals in and around Makka. For those who can afford it, the *Hajj* is a requirement at least once in a lifetime.

Monotheism

Islam is strictly *monotheistic.* God, *Allah,* is believed to be one and unique and is spoken of in masculine terms although the Divine Reality is affirmed as being beyond the limitations of human gender. He is merciful and powerful, omniscient and omnipresent. He is in control of events in history and of the *Day of Judgement.* He created the universe and sustains it and has prescribed Islam (submission to God) as the correct way of life for the people he has created. It is also believed that, although humans have a choice as to whether they follow this way or not, all will eventually return to God to whom they will be accountable for their deeds in this world.

Goal and Purpose of Human Life

The purpose of human life is to exercise *khilafa* (authority and trust) to manage the world in a responsible way and to live in accordance with God's creative will. Human beings are called back to a life in submission to God's will as expressed in the revelations of *Torah, Injil* (*Gospel* of Jesus), of all the other *prophets* of God and, finally, through the revelation of the *Qur'an.* How each person individually responds to the will and revelation of God is believed to determine their eternal destiny. Muslims expect the coming of a descendant of the *Prophet* before the end of time, in order to establish justice on the earth.

Belief in the *Day of Judgement,* when an individual's actions will be placed on the scales of good and evil, acts as a powerful reinforcement for the personal responsibility of each human being.

TRADITIONS IN ISLAM

There are two principal traditions within Islam – *Sunni* and *Shi'ia.* There is also an aspect of Islam known as *Sufism* (see below) which either *Sunni* or *Shi'a* Muslims might embrace.

Sunni

Ninety per cent of the world's Muslims are *Sunni.* They recognise the first four "rightly guided" *Caliphs* and understand the *Qur'an*, *Sunna*, *Ijma* and *Qiyas* to be the four sources of the law. Within the *Sunni* branch of Islam there are a range of movements and groupings which have particular emphases or concerns. They are not, however, as organisationally clear-cut as, for example, Christian denominations and there may well be cross-membership of the various tendencies. In the UK, the majority of these groupings are of South Asian origin and are organised in a variety of *Sunni* Muslim traditions:

Barelwis

Barelwi is the term commonly used to denote a devotional style of Islam found among some groups of Muslims with origins in the Indian subcontinent. It holds in high esteem the teachings of Maulana Ahmad Raza Khan (1856-1921) of Bareilly, Uttar Pradesh, in India who was a member of the *Qadiri Sufi* order and a great *Mufti* (Jurist) of the *Hanafi* school of interpretation.

Barelwis celebrate the *milad* (birthday) of the *Prophet* Muhammad as a major festival, giving a particularly high respect to the person of the *Prophet* Muhammad as a model and inspiration for Muslim life but also affirming that he had access to knowledge of "the unseen". A key concept of *Barelwi* thought is that the *Divine Light* which existed from the beginning of time can be seen in Muhammad.

They look to *sayyids* (descendants of the Prophet) and to *pirs* (spiritual guides) for spiritual authority, teaching, guidance and intercession with God and they defend the Islamic legitimacy of popular devotional practice at the shrines of *pirs*.

Deobandis

The *Deobandi* movement was founded in India by Maulana Muhammad Qasim. It is named after a *daral'ulum* (training college) for Indian Muslim religious scholars founded in 1867 in the Indian town of Deoband.

Established in the context of British colonial power in India its scholars were concerned to defend a clear Islamic identity against the influence of non-Islamic ideas.

Its curriculum, and that of the many colleges which came to be modelled upon it, promotes an interpretation of Islam in which the emphasis is on textual scholarship, with pre-eminence given to study of the *Qur'an*, *Hadith* and *Shari'ah* (interpreted through the *Hanafi* school). Although its scholars were, like the *Barelwi* movement, within the *Sufi* tradition, the *Deobandi* movement emphasised the role of spiritual guides as exemplars, not accepting the legitimacy of any intercessory role for *pirs*.

Tablighi Jamaat

Tablighi Jamaat was founded in India in 1927 by *Maulana* Muhammad Ilyas (1885-1944), a *Sufi* and a student of *Deoband*. The movement is broadly within the *Deobandi* tradition and is usually non-political. It attempts to encourage other Muslims to practise the ritual aspects of Islam on a more fervent and regular basis and its committed members travel widely to spread its message.

Ahl-e-Hadith

Ahl-e-Hadith is a movement whose followers accept only the teachings of the *Qur'an* itself and the earliest teachings in the *Hadith*. It rejects any regulations which are not from these sources. This movement is sometimes known as *ghayr muqallidun* (not attached to any school of thought).

Jamaat-i-Islami

Jamaat-i-Islami operates as a religious movement in India and Sri Lanka, but as a religio-political party in Pakistan and Bangladesh. It was founded in India in 1941 by Sayyid Abul A' la Mawdudi (1903-1979). It favours a return to the following of traditional Muslim doctrine in the face of the secular influences of Western civilisation and, more specifically, is committed to seeing Islamic ideology enshrined in an Islamic state.

Shi'a

About ten per cent of Muslims worldwide are *Shi'a*, an Arabic word which literally means follower or associate. The *Shi'a* believe that Muhammad instituted from within his family (the descendants of Ali and Fatima, the Prophet's youngest daughter) a succession of individual *Imams* (spiritual leaders) to guide the community. The *Shi'a* concept of the *Imam* should not be confused with the general use of the term by Muslims to describe their local prayer leaders (see section below on "Personnel").

In common with other Muslims, *Shi'as* believe that the process of revelation was completed with the coming of Muhammad, but they differ from other Muslims in believing that *Imams* or *Hujjah* (*Proofs of God*) are specially selected by God and have the authority to interpret the *Qur'an* and to provide guidance to believers.

Shi'as observe more festivals than *Sunnis* (see section on festivals). In addition, they value pilgrimages to the shrines of their *Imams* and saints - in particular those of *Imam* Ali (in Najaf) and *Imam* Husayn (in Karbala) in Southern Iraq.

Twelvers and Seveners

All *Shi'a* Muslims agree that Ali was the first *Imam*, but thereafter there are differences of view concerning the succession. A minority are known as the *Seveners*, whilst the majority are known as the *Twelvers* (or *'Ithna Asherites*). The *Twelvers* believe in a series of twelve *Imams*, the last of whom, Muhammad Al-Muntazar, was last seen in 873CE and is believed to have been the *Mahdi* (*Guided One*). He is believed to be still alive but is now hidden and waiting for God's command to reappear.

Ismailis are a *Shi'a* Muslim group who accept the leadership of the first six *Imams*, but thereafter claim the primacy of the elder son of the sixth *Imam*, Ismail and therefore are known as *Seveners*. Among the *Ismailis* are the *Nizaris* who are also known as the *Agha*

Khanis. They believe in the *Aga Khan* as their living *Imam* and expect that he will, in turn, choose a member of his family to succeed him. The *Nizari* and the *Musta'lian Ismailis* disagreed over two opposing claimants to the *Imamate*. The *Bohras* are a group which emerged out of the *Musta'lian Ismailis*.

Tasawwuf

Tasawwuf (Sufism) is the name for the mystical strand of Islam which can be found in both the *Sunni* and *Shi'a* traditions of Islam. The word is thought to derive from the Arabic *suf* (wool) which characterised the simple clothing worn by early *ascetics*. *Sufism* traces its origins back through *silsilahs* (lines of spiritual initiation) and is led by spiritual authorities known as *shaykhs* or *pirs* who advise the initiates of the *Sufi Orders* in their quest for an intimately spiritual relationship with God.

Sufism involves a commitment to the practical and readily accessible aspects of Islam based on the *Shari'ah*, but also emphasises the inner or *esoteric* aspects of Islam. As aids to their spiritual development, the members of *Sufi Orders* may engage in various practices such as meditation, chanting the names of God, or ritual dancing. There are many worldwide *Sufi Orders* including, for example, the *Naqshbandi*, the *Qadiri*, the *Chishti* and the *Suhrawardi*.

MUSLIM LIFE

Becoming a Muslim

In order to become a Muslim a person must accept and declare that there is "no god except God" and that "Muhammad is his *messenger*" (*Shi'a* Muslims adding "and Ali is the seal on the will of the *Prophet*"). This declaration of faith is known as the *Shahada*.

Shari'ah

The basic Muslim beliefs are put into practice by means of the way of life given by God, revealed through the *Prophet* Muhammad, and known as the *Shari'ah* (pathway). The *Shari'ah* is not only concerned with prayer and ritual matters but also governs and regulates conduct of all kinds, for example attitudes to economics, family life, and the behaviour of rulers, thus codifying Islamic values as they apply to the whole of life.

Jihad

Jihad, the striving to protect, promote and live by the message of the *Qur'an* through words and actions, is central to Islam. It involves *da'wah*, which is the task of spreading the message of Islam through invitation issued by means of words and deeds; creating satisfactory social conditions for Islam to be practised freely; increasing the self-discipline of people who are already Muslims so that they become better Muslims; and, in limited circumstances, defending Islam by force of arms if necessary. This last aspect is only one dimension of *jihad* although outside the Muslim community *jihad* is often mistakenly assumed to mean only this. *Jihad* does not include imposing Islam by force on non-Muslims because the *Qur'an* forbids compulsion in matters of religion.

Halal

The term *halal* simply means permitted, and refers to a wide range of things which are allowed to Muslims. In popular usage in the UK, however, it is often identified with food laws which are also an important part of Muslim values and ethics. The *Qur'an* does not allow consumption of the meat of pigs and carnivorous animals. This includes pork products and foods which contain the by-products of pigs or carnivorous animals. They are *haram* (unlawful). Other meats are also *haram* unless the animal has been ritually slaughtered. Ritual slaughter involves prayers during slaughter, and a method of butchery which allows the blood to flow from the animal's body. Fish is permitted.

When *halal* meat is not available for consumption by Muslims, *kosher* meat (slaughtered according to the Jewish *shechita* method) is permissible for *Sunni* Muslims (although not for *Shi'a 'Ithna Asherites*) or a vegetarian meal will suffice. Foods which contain the by-products of non-*halal* meat are also considered unlawful, for example cheese which contains an animal product such as rennet. Also unlawful for Muslims is any food or drink perceived by Muslims to have been offered to an idol or to a false god. Alcohol of any kind is also prohibited under Islamic law and any drinks or foods which contain alcohol in any amount are unacceptable.

Gender and Family

According to Muslim understanding the *Shari'ah* confers equal dignity on both women and men. Men and women generally have the same religious duties, and in most cases the same legal rights, as in the possibility of owning property in their own right. However, women are not obliged to participate in congregational prayers. There are also gender differentiations of rights and responsibilities with regard to social and legal roles, some of which are believed by many Muslims to have been divinely revealed in the *Qur'an*.

In Islam, marriage and procreation are viewed very positively and celibacy is discouraged. Traditionally, the role of a man is believed to involve financial support of his wife and family (irrespective of his wife's wealth), and the protection of female family members including wife, daughters and, if his father is deceased, his mother as well.

Muslims believe that it is a duty to marry, and the ideal family structure is based on *monogamy* which is the normal practice among Muslims in the UK. However, under the terms of the *Shari'ah*, *polygamy* (although not *polyandry*) is considered lawful in certain circumstances. These include infertility of the first wife, or permanent physical or mental infirmity of the first wife.

Under Islamic law a man may take up to four wives at any one time, although the regulations regarding such marriages are such that *polygamy* is often a practical impossibility. These regulations include that a man must have the means to provide for each wife and that he must treat each wife absolutely equally, in both financial and social terms. The contracting of a *polygamous* marriage is not allowed in law in this country, but recognition can be accorded to *polygamous* marriages that have been contracted in overseas countries where this is permitted.

Modesty is an important concept in Islam. For men, modest dress should cover, at a minimum, the area from the navel to the knees. For women, it involves covering the full body and this is interpreted variously. Traditionally, in most Islamic societies this has involved the wearing of a *hijab* or veil of varying kinds. In some Islamic societies, including a number from which people have come to the UK, there may be an expectation that women will cover their faces from the sight of men other than their husbands and family members and avoid the company of such men by remaining primarily within the home and in female company. This practice is referred to as *purdah*. In mixed contexts it can take the form of the two sexes sitting separately.

MUSLIM WORSHIP

Salat

The main form of *'ibadah* (worship) is that of *salat* (Arabic for the five times a day obligatory prayers) or *namaz* (Urdu). The exact times at which prayer takes place vary throughout the year. Prayer time-tables are published with details of the times, and can often be found on display in *mosques*.

Generally speaking, prayer takes place at around the following periods of the day: *Fajr* (dawn), *Zuhr* (midday), *Asr* (late afternoon), *Maghrib* (after sunset), and *Isha* (late evening).

Prayers are obligatory from puberty onwards, except for women who are menstruating or in the post-natal period. People who are not fully conscious are also exempted from prayers.

Friday is the day for congregational prayers. Most male Muslims attend the *mosque* for this *Salat al-Jum'ah* which is mandatory for them. *Wudu* (ablutions or ritual washing) must take place prior to all prayers. This includes washing hands, face, hair, mouth, nose, arms (up to the elbows), and the feet (up to the ankles).

During prayer, worshippers face Makka, the *qiblah* (direction) of which is marked by the *mihrab*, a small niche in the wall of the *mosque*. In the UK, this direction is towards the south-east. A Muslim can pray in any clean place and use a prayer mat if he or she cannot reasonably attend a *mosque*. Muslim employees, school children and students should have the opportunity to conduct their obligatory prayers while at work or in school or college.

Mosques

The English word *mosque* comes from the Arabic word *masjid*, meaning a place of prostration. Within the Muslim community *mosques* are known by a number of terms, the most common being *masjid*. *Jami* is used to refer to the "central *mosque*".

The first *mosques* in the UK were established and financed by the personal efforts of individuals living in the area. For example, the first *mosque* in Birmingham was established in 1941 by two Yemeni Muslims who were concerned to make arrangements for Muslim prayers, burial rites, and religious education for children.

At present many *mosques* are buildings which were formerly private residences, or even rooms in houses which are still used as private residences. Others are in public buildings which had former uses, for example as warehouses or, occasionally, as Christian *churches*. Recently, however, a number of purpose built *mosques* have been constructed.

No images, paintings or decorations which represent living beings are to be found inside *mosques*. In some *mosques*, however, Arabic calligraphy may be observed on the walls and perhaps some geometrical patterns. There are no seats in a *mosque* but the floor is carpeted. Music is not played although in some *mosques* there may be congregational chanting. There is a *minbar* (*pulpit* or raised steps) to one side of the *mihrab* from which the *imam* delivers sermons on Fridays and at festival times. There may also be a symbol of the crescent moon and star which has come to be associated with Islam.

Although every *mosque* is, in principle, open to all Muslims, the management committees of particular *mosques* may, in practice, reflect specific Muslim tendencies or national or regional groupings. As a result, specific dominant languages are used for instruction and general communication, although the language of the prayers themselves is always Arabic. *Mosques* of different types do, however, sometimes join together to form councils of *mosques*, such as the Bradford Council of Mosques.

Mosques provide a number of services like the channelling of *Zakat* to the poor; providing *imams* to visit Muslims who are sick in hospital or who are inmates in prison; offering educational facilities (see below) and instruction in the Urdu and Arabic languages. In addition to this, many *mosques* are now registered for the solemnisation of marriages, and some *mosques* have installed morgues ensuring that Muslims can perform Islamic burial rites for their fellow Muslims.

Attendance at the *mosque* is not obligatory for Muslim women and, in practice, many *mosques* do not cater for their attendance. Where provision is made for women to pray at the same time as men they usually sit separately, for example in a room upstairs which is also considered as part of the *mosque*, although in some *mosques* women worship behind the men on the same floor. In some cases women are discouraged from worshipping in *mosques* and are only expected to attend for cultural events and special occasions.

MUSLIM CALENDAR AND FESTIVALS

Calendar

The Muslim calendar is a lunar one, with each year composed of twelve months and each month of twenty-nine or thirty days. As such, the Muslim year is eleven days shorter than a solar year. This means that festival dates move through the solar year and cannot be conclusively dated a long way in advance since they depend upon the sighting of the new moon for the start of a new month.

Al Hijrah

The first day of the Muslim year is the anniversary of the *Hijra* with which the Muslim calendar begins. This marks the *Prophet* Muhammad's original migration from Makka to Madina which led to the creation of the Muslim community. The year 2001CE is therefore, according to the Muslim calendar, the year 1421/1422AH.

'Ashurah

Is a *Shi'a* commemoration marking the martyrdom of *Imam* Husayn, the grandson of the *Prophet* Muhammad. This is the tenth day of the month of Muharram in the Islamic calendar. It is the occasion for "passion plays" and ritual mourning through which *Shi'as* express their sense of identity with the suffering of Husayn's martyrdom. Some *Sunni* Muslims also celebrate this but for other reasons.

Milad al-Nabi

Is a celebration of the birthday of the *Prophet* on the twelfth day of Rabi 'al-Awwal, the third month of the Muslim calendar. It is particularly important among *Barelwis* in view of their special veneration of the *Prophet*.

Lailat al-Baraat

Takes place fifteen days before *Ramadan* and celebrates the popular belief that on this night the fate of humankind is ordained for the next year.

Ramadan

Ramadan is the name of the ninth month (which is either twenty-nine or thirty days long) of the lunar year. During this time Muslims should abstain, from before dawn to sunset, from eating, drinking and sexual intercourse. These daylight abstentions are deemed by Muslims to reflect devotion to God as the person abstains for God alone. *Fasting* is also seen as increasing self-discipline and patience, decreasing selfishness and lending a sense of solidarity between Muslims and equality before God.

There are, however, some categories of people who can be exempt from the requirements of *fasting*. These include children who are below the age of puberty and people who are mentally unfit. They do not have to *fast* nor do they have to compensate in any way for missing the *fast*. People travelling long distances may temporarily break the *fast* but should make up for this by *fasting* at another time for each day they have missed. People whose health would be severely affected by *fasting* may *fast* in compensation at another point in the year for an equivalent length of time.

Those who will not recover from the risk of ill health or are very old may offer a poor Muslim a meal or the financial equivalent for each day of *fasting* missed. Menstruating women, pregnant women, and women who are breast feeding, are also not bound to *fast*. However, they must make up for each day they do not fast by *fasting* at another point in the year.

Lailat al-Qadr (Night of Power)

This marks the time when it is believed that the *Qur'an* began its descent to earth and was first revealed to the *Prophet* Muhammad. It occurs as one of the odd numbered nights of *fasting* in the last third of the month of *Ramadan*. The *Shi'as* regard *Lailat al-Qadr* as being the twenty third night of *fasting* in *Ramadan*. *Sunnis* look for it in the last ten nights of *fasting*, especially on the odd-numbered nights. The night belongs to the day following it, rather than to the one preceeding it.

Eid al-Fitr

This a festival marking the breaking of the *Ramadan fast* which occurs on the first day of the following month, Shawwal. It is one of the major festivals in the Muslim calendar. Between one and two days leave from work is usually taken to participate in this festival. Presents are given and charitable donations are encouraged. The festival emphasises unity and togetherness. An atmosphere of celebration is promoted, with gatherings held at *mosques* that often overflow outside.

Eid al-Adha

This is the *Festival of Sacrifice* which is a three day festival that marks the end of the *Hajj* to Makka and occurs on the tenth day of the Dhu'l Hijjah month. It celebrates the supreme example of sacrifice and submission exhibited by Abraham and his son Ishmael. It is celebrated not just in Mecca but throughout the Muslim world. In Muslim countries all Muslim families who can afford to do so sacrifice an animal as Abraham is believed to have done in substitution for his son, Ishmael. To mark the festival a third of this meat is then distributed to the poor, with the rest being shared with one third to charity, one third to family and one third to friends. In the UK this slaughter is usually carried out centrally on behalf of the community rather than by individuals.

MUSLIM ORGANISATIONS

The composition of the Muslim population in the UK is varied and can be considered from a number of different perspectives including groupings with an ethnic/national component and movements within the two main traditions within Islam, the *Sunni* and the *Shi'a*. Individual Muslims might identify themselves with one or more of these groupings at the same time. The *Barelwis*, *Deobandis* and *Tablighi Jamaat* are numerically the strongest of the Muslim movements in the UK and there is some overlap between them. The general background to the various Muslim movements has already been described in the earlier section on "Traditions in Islam".

Barelwis

This tendency is particularly numerous amongst communities with rural origins. Two national organisations linked to the *Barelwi* movement are the Jamaat Ahl-e-Sunnat and the World Islamic Mission.

Deobandi

In the UK, the *Deobandi* movement is found in many areas, but it is at its strongest in Lancashire, West Yorkshire and the Midlands. Two organisations with links to this movement are the Jamiat-e-Ulama of Britain and Dar-ul-Uloom seminary in Bury.

Tablighi Jamaat

The *Tablighi Jamaat* movement in the UK is centred in Dewsbury but is also very active elsewhere in West Yorkshire, Lancashire and the Midlands. Its organisations can also be found elsewhere in Britain. The movement is closely related to the *Deobandi* movement.

Ahl-e-Hadith

Within the UK this movement is mainly concentrated in Birmingham and London.

Jamaat-i-Islami

There are several organisations which have a relationship to the idealist, thinker and founder of *Jamaat-i-Islami*, Abul A'la Mawdudi (1903-1979). Such organisations include the UK Islamic Mission, which has several branches throughout the UK. The movement was originally found mainly amongst migrants from Pakistan. After the emergence of Bangladesh, Bengali Muslims established their own *Dawat-ul-Islam* movement in 1976. Later, the Islamic Forum of Europe was also formed by young Bangladeshis to serve the intellectual needs of Bangladeshi youth throughout Europe.

Sufi Orders

Sufi Orders have branches in most UK towns and cities with a substantial Muslim presence. There are also a number of *Sufi* centres associated with specific *Orders*. These *Orders* are generally *Sunni* rather than *Shi'a*. There are also a number of western *Sufi* organisations.

Other National and Regional Organisations

Several organisations with an international membership have a presence in the UK, such as the Muslim World League, which was established in Makka in 1962 and has an office, library and prayer hall in London.

The Muslim Council of Britain was formally launched in 1997 following a number of years of preparatory consultation across the community. It includes a wide range of Islamic organisations and *mosques* and seeks to represent the Muslim community as a whole in its contact with Government, other public bodies, and the media.

There are a number of other federations and councils of Islamic organisations at both regional and national levels. Such bodies can often have a degree of overlap in terms of membership. Regionally, these include the Lancashire Council of Mosques, the West

Midlands Council of Mosques, and the Federation of Muslim Organisations in Leicestershire. Nationally, they include the Imams and Mosques Council and the Union of Muslim Organisations (established in 1970).

In addition to the general organisations, which are related to particular movements within Islam, there are also a number of Muslim organisations which campaign on specific concerns for the Muslims. For example, the UK Action Committee on Islamic Affairs was formed in 1988 in the wake of the controversy over Salman Rushdie's book *The Satanic Verses*. It has a particular interest in the law, having campaigned for the withdrawal of the book and for the introduction of legal provision to protect against religious discrimination and has gone on to campaign on other issues. The Islamic Society of Britain was formed in 1990 with the aim of projecting Islam's image in the UK not as an "immigrant religion", but as a global tradition developing appropriate national traditions, priorities and policies to meet the challenges facing Islam and Muslims.

Educational Organisations

There is a range of educational bodies which operate on a national level and serve a variety of functions. For example, the Muslim College in London, which trains *imams*; the Islamic Foundation in Leicester, whic is an educational, research and training organisation founded in 1973 that produces literature and runs courses on Muslim belief and practice for non-Muslim professionals working in a multi-cultural context; the Muslim Community Studies Institute in Leicester, which carries out research and produces publications on Muslim life in both Muslim societies and Western societies; the Muslim Education Co-ordinating Council UK in London, which monitors and advises on the teaching of Muslim children in local education authority schools; the Muslim Educational Trust, which caters for the educational needs of Muslim children; the Islamic Academy in Cambridge, which is an educational research organisation; and the Muslim Education Forum, which brings together a number of these bodies in an informal network designed to co-ordinate their activities.

Madrassahs are *Qur'anic* schools which are local in nature and are usually attached to a *mosque* and many Muslim children attend them during the weekends or in the evening after day school. Both boys and girls attend such lessons where they read and learn sections of the *Qur'an* which in turn necessitates the learning of Arabic. They also learn the rituals and practices of Islam. There are also a few private Muslim day schools which provide a full time educational service for Muslim children. Three Muslim schools have been granted voluntary aided status.

Dawah

Dawah literally means invitation – the invitation to people to embrace Islam. There are a number of organised *dawah* initiatives which aim to spread the message of Islam throughout the UK. Some are local independent organisations. Others are affiliates of national organisations such as the UK Islamic Mission, which has branches and affiliated *mosques* throughout the UK. Some *missionary* groups aim to spread the word of Islam to non-Muslims, whilst others focus on drawing back Muslims who have drifted away from their faith.

Youth

Muslim youth organisations include local independent groups of Muslims and local groups affiliated to national organisations such as Young Muslims UK and the Federation of Student Islamic Societies (FOSIS), both of which organise workshops and "camps" for Muslim youth. In recent times radical Islamic revival groups such as Hizb-ut-Tahrir and Al Muhajiroun have been active in many institutions of higher education.

Women

Muslim women's groups have begun to emerge in various localities, both to represent the experience and to address the needs of Muslim women. The Muslim women's organisation An-Nisa provides a service of this kind.

Community Groups

Local Muslim community groups are usually attached to the *mosque* and are also normally loosely related to particular Muslim movements, or are composed of a group with the same ethnic origins and languages, such as the various Pakistan Muslim Welfare Associations. They have a welfare and cultural role and may be eclectic with sub-groups for certain sectors of the Muslim population, for example youth groups and women's groups.

Personnel

Individual *mosques* are usually controlled by *mosque* committees which generally include the offices of president and secretary. Committee membership elections are normally held annually. The *mosque* committee co-ordinates funding for the *mosque* and Muslim organisations connected with *mosques* and is also responsible for appointing an *imam*.

The *imam* is the leader of the prayers. *Imam* is an Arabic word meaning "the one who stands in front". In principle, this can be any Muslim who is well versed in the *Qur'an* and the liturgy for prayer. There is no hierarchy of ordained clergy although the *imam* may act as a spokesperson for the community.

Although *imams* are now being trained in the UK, frequently they will have arrived in adulthood from an area of the world where the majority of the members of a *mosque* community have their ethnic origins, and may therefore only have a poor command of the English language. In these circumstances, the chairperson or secretary of the *mosque* Committee might more usually represent the community to the outside world.

Fuqaha are experts in Islamic law. *Pirs* or *shaykhs* are spiritual guides from the *Sufi* orders. *Ulama* is a term denoting religious scholars in general.

FURTHER READING

Abdalati, H, *Islam in Focus*, American Trust Publications, Indianapolis, 1975.

Abul-Fadl, M, *Introducing Islam from Within*, Islamic Foundation, Leicester, 1991.

Ahmad, K, *Family Life in Islam*, Islamic Foundation, Leicester, 1981.

Ahsan, M and Kidwai, A (eds), *Sacrilege Versus Civility: Muslim Perspectives on The Satanic Verses Affair*, Islamic Foundation, Leicester, 1993 (revised and enlarged edition).

Ahsan, M, "Islam and Muslims in Britain", in Mutalib, H and Hashmi, T (eds), *Islam, Muslims and the Modern State*, Macmillan, Basingstoke, 1994, pp 339-361.

Andrews, A, "Sociological Analysis of Jamaat-i-Islami in the United Kingdom", in Barot, R (ed), *Religion and Ethnicity: Ethnic Minorities and Social Change in the Metropolis*, Kok Pharos, Kampen, The Netherlands, 1993, pp 68-79.

Anwar, M, *Muslims in Britain: 1991 Census and Other Statistical Sources*, Centre for the Study of Islam and Christian-Muslim Relations, Selly Oak Colleges, Birmingham, 1993.

Anwar, M, *Young Muslims in Britain: Attitudes, Educational Needs and Policy Implications*, Islamic Foundation, Leicester, 1994.

Awan, B A, "Islam", in Tiptaft, N, *Religion in Birmingham*, Norman Tiptaft Ltd, Warley, 1972.

Badawi, Z, *Islam in Britain*, Ta-Ha Publishers Ltd, London, 1981.

Barton, S W, *The Bengali Muslims of Bradford*, Community Religions Project, University of Leeds, Leeds, 1986.

Bowker, J, *What Muslims Believe*, Oneworld, Oxford, 1998.

Coulson, N J, *A History of Islamic Law*, Edinburgh University Press, Edinburgh, 1964.

Daftari, F, *The Ismailis: Their History and Doctrine*, Cambridge University Press, Cambridge, 1990.

Darsh, S M, *Muslims in Europe*, Ta-Ha Publishers, London, 1987.

Geaves, R, *Sectarian Influences within Islam in Britain: with Reference to the Concepts of 'Ummah' and 'Community'*, Community Religions Project Monograph Series, Department of Theology and Religious Studies, University of Leeds, Leeds, 1996.

Glassé, C, *The Concise Encylopaedia of Islam*, Stacey International, London, (2nd edition), 1991.

Henley, A, *Caring for Muslims and their Families: Religious Aspects of Care*, National Extension College, Cambridge, 1982.

Islamic Foundation, *Islam: The Essentials*, Islamic Foundation, Leicester, 1974.

Joly, D, "Making a place for Islam in British Society: Muslims in Birmingham", in Gerholm, T and Lithman, Y F (eds), *The New Islamic Presence in Western Europe*, Mansell, London, 1990, pp 32-52.

Joly, D and Nielsen, J S, *Muslims in Britain: An Annotated Bibliography, 1960-1984*, Centre for Research in Ethnic Relations, University of Warwick, Coventry, 1985.

Kucukcan, T, *Politics of Ethnicity, Identity and Religion: Turkish Muslims in Britain*, Ashgate Publishing, Aldershot.

Lemu, A and Heeren, F, *Women in Islam*, Islamic Foundation, Leicester, 1978.

Lewis, P, *Islamic Britain: Religion, Politics and Identity Among British Muslims*, I B Tauris, London, 1994.

Lewis, P, *The Function, Education and Influence of the Ulama in Bradford's Muslim Communities*, Community Religions Project Monograph Series, Department of Theology and Religious Studies, University of Leeds, Leeds, 1996.

Lings, M, *What is Sufism?*, Unwin Paperbacks, London, 1975.

Matar, N, *Islam in Britain: 1558-1685*, Cambridge University Press, Cambridge, 1998.

McDermott, M Y and Ahsan, M M, *The Muslim Guide: For Teachers, Employers, Community Workers and Social Administrators in Britain*, Islamic Foundation, Leicester, 1992 (revised edition).

Mawdudi, A, *Towards Understanding Islam*, Islamic Foundation, Leicester, 1981.

Nadwi, S A H A, *Muslims in the West: Message and Mission*, Islamic Foundation, Leicester, 1983.

Nasr, S H, *Ideals and Realities of Islam*, George Allen and Unwin, London, 1966.

Nasr, S H, *Living Sufism*, Unwin Paperbacks, London, 1980.

Nielsen, J S, *A Survey of British Local Authority Response to Muslim Needs*, Research Papers on Muslims in Europe No 30/31, June/September, 1986.

Nielsen, J S, "Muslims in Britain: searching for an identity", in *New Community*, Volume XIII, No 3, Spring 1987, pp 384-394.

Nielsen, J S, *Muslims in Western Europe*, Edinburgh University Press, Edinburgh, 1995 (2nd edition).

Nielsen, J S, "Muslims in Britain: Ethnic Minorities, Community or Ummah?", in Coward, H, Hinnells, J and Williams, R, *The South Asian Religious Diaspora in Britain, Canada and the United States*, State University of New York Press, New York, 2000, pp 109-125.

Jacobsen, J, *Islam in Transition: Religion and Identity Among British Pakistani Youth*, Routledge, London, 1998.

Padwick, C, *Muslim Devotions*, SPCK, London, 1961.

Peach, C, "The Muslim population of Great Britain", in *Ethnic and Racial Studies*, Volume XIII, No 3, 1990, pp 415-419.

Rahman, F, *Islam*, University of Chicago Press, Chicago (2nd edition), 1979.

Rahman, T, *A Code of Muslim Personal Law*, Volumes I & II, Islamic Publishers, Karachi, 1978 and 1980.

Raza, M S, *Islam in Britain: Past Present and Future*, Volcano Press Ltd, Leicester (2nd edition), 1992.

Rex, J, "The Urban Sociology of Religion and Islam in Birmingham", in Gerholm, T and Lithman, Y G, *The New Islamic Presence in Western Europe*, Mansell, London, 1990, pp 206-218.

Robinson, F, *Varieties of South Asian Islam*, Research Paper No.8, Centre for Research in Ethnic Relations, University of Warwick, Coventry, 1988.

Schimmel, A, *Islamic Names*, Edinburgh University Press, Edinburgh, 1989.

Shaykh Haeri, F, *The Elements of Sufism*, Element Books, Dorset, 1990.

Trimingham, J S, *The Sufi Orders in Islam*, Oxford University Press, Oxford, 1971.

UK Action Committee on Islamic Affairs, *Need for Reform: Muslims and the Law in Multi-Faith Britain*, UK Action Committee on Islamic Affairs, London, 1993.

Vertovec, S, *Annotated Bibliography of Academic Publications Regarding Islam and Muslims in the United Kingdom, 1985-1992*, Centre for Research in Ethnic Relations, University of Warwick, Coventry, 1993.

Vertovec, S, *Local Contexts and the Development of Muslim Communities in Britain: Observations in Keighley, West Yorkshire*, University of Warwick Centre for Research in Ethnic Relations, Coventry, n.d.

Wahab, I, *Muslims in Britain: Profile of a Community*, The Runnymede Trust, London, 1989.

Wolffe, J, "Fragmented Universality: Islam and Muslims", in Parsons, G (ed), *The Growth of Religious Diversity: Britain from 1945, Volume 1: Traditions*, Routledge, London, 1993, pp 133-172.

Yawar, T, *Caring About Faith: Muslim Children and Young Persons in Care*, Islamic Foundation, Leicester, 1992.

MUSLIM UNITED KINGDOM ORGANISATIONS

The organisations listed in this section include both head offices of organisations with branches throughout the country and organisations which aspire to serve the Muslim community on a UK-wide level.

Al Khoei Foundation*
Imam Khoei Islamic Centre, Brondsbury Park, London NW6 6TN
Tel: (020) 7372 4049 **Fax:** (020) 7372 0694
Contact: Mr Yousif Al-Khoei
Position: Director
Activities: Worship/practice/meditation, community centre, central body, youth, newsletter/journal, books, newspapers, visits, inter-faith
Traditions: Ithna Asheri
Other Languages: Arabic, Persian, Urdu
The Foundation runs schools in both London and New York. It has consultative status with the United Nations and is active in the field of inter and intra-faith dialogue.

Al Muntada Al Islami Trust*
7 Bridges Place, off Parson's Green Lane, Fulham, London SW6 4HW
Tel: (020) 7736 9060 **Fax:** (020) 7736 4255
Email: muntada@almuntada-alislami.org
Contact: Mr A H Montague
Position: Secretary
Contact Tel: (020) 7471 8269
Activities: Worship/practice/meditation, community centre, women, newsletter/journal, books, resources
Traditions: Sunni
Other Languages: Arabic
An independent provider of quality primary school education including Arabic language and Islamic studies to boys and girls from the ages of 4-10 years.

Al-Furqan Charity Trust*
1 Wynne Road, London SW9 0BB
Tel: (020) 7737 7266 **Fax:** (020) 7737 7266
Contact: A Siddiqui
Position: Secretary
Activities: Visits, women, newsletters
Traditions: Sunni
Other Languages: Urdu, Arabic, French

Al-Hoda Limited*
76-78 Charing Cross Road, London WC2H 0BD
Tel: (020) 7240 8381 **Fax:** (020) 7497 0180
Email: alhoda@alhoda.com
Website: http://www.alhoda.com/
Contact: The Manager
Activities: Books
Other Languages: Persian, Arabic, Urdu
We are publishers, booksellers and distributors.

Al-Hurau Schools Trust*
Midland House, 71 Hob Moor Road, Small Heath,
Birmingham B10 9AZ
Tel: (0121) 7665454 **Fax:** (0121) 7668556
Contact: Mohammad Abdul Karim Saqib
Position: Chairman
Activities: Worship, resource, youth, elderly,
newsletters, books
Traditions: Sunni
Other Languages: Urdu, Punjabi, Bengali, Arabic
Established Islamic School. Aims to provide Islamic
knowledge and subjects of the National Curriculum
for boys and girls in a segregated Islamic
environment.

Al-Muhajiroun*
PO Box 349, Edmonton, London N9 7RR
Tel: (020) 8884 0074 **Fax:** (020) 8803 4541
Email: almuhajiroun@hotmail.com
Website: http://www.almuhajiroun.org/
Contact: Sheik Omar Bakri Muhammad
Position: The Leader
Contact Email: obm@mail.com
Activities: Worship/practice/meditation,
community centre, central body, umbrella body,
youth, elderly, women, newsletter/journal, books,
newspapers, radio, television, visits, inter-faith,
resources
Traditions: Sunni
Movements: Usuli
Other Languages: Urdu, Arabic, French, Turkish
Affiliations: Khilafah Movement; The London
School of Shari'ah and The Shari'ah Court of the
UK; The International Islamic Front
An Islamic political party and cultural body which is
equipped with the Islamic culture based solely on
the Qur'an, Sunnah, Ijma'al-Sahabah and al-qiyas.

Al-Muttaqiin*
62 West Avenue, Wallington SM6 8PH
Tel: (020) 8686 1637 **Fax:** (020) 8686 1637
Email: almuttaqiin@btinternet.com
Contact: Brother Shafi Chowdhury
Position: Chairman
Contact Tel: (020) 8404 3717
Activities: Worship, resource, youth, inter-faith
Movements: Al-Muttaqiin
Other Languages: Bangla, Arabic
Affiliations: Muslim Council of Britain; UK
Action Committee on Islamic Affairs
Al-Muttaqiin (Allah-Conscious Careful Ones
Keeping Safe from the Shaitan) is also engaged in
refugee and school activities and in prison visits, as
well as English/Arabic Qur'an lessons.

AMANA*
PO Box 2842, London W6 9ZH
Tel: (020) 8748 2424
Contact: Umar Hegedus and Khadijah Knight
Activities: Resource
AMANA exists to promote an understanding of
Islam and its followers. It addresses both Muslims and
non-Muslims providing well-grounded advice and
information. It offers resources for training to
schools, colleges, social service departments and
employers.

Association for British Muslims*
47 Davis Road, London W3 7SE
Tel: (020) 8932 4081 **Fax:** (020) 8932 4081
Email: a-b-m@cwcom.net
Website: http://www.british-islam.org/
Contact: Amir Daoud Rosser-Owen
Position: Amir-President
Contact Email: rosser-owen@cwcom.net
Activities: Community centre, central body,
youth, elderly, women, newsletter/journal, books,
inter-faith, resources
Traditions: Sunni
Other Languages: Malay, Arabic, Urdu, Turkish
Affiliations: Union of Muslim Organisations of
UK and Eire
The senior Muslim organisation in the British Isles,
established in 1889. A social body working for all
British Muslims in social welfare, media monitoring
and consultation, and a prisoner correspondence
scheme.

Association of Muslim Lawyers*
PO Box 148, High Wycombe HP13 5WJ
Tel: (01494) 526955 **Fax:** (01494) 526955
Email: aml@aml.org.uk
Website: http://www.aml.org.uk/
Contact: Mrs Ifath Nawar
Position: Secretary
Activities: Newsletter/journal, resources
Other Languages: Urdu, Punjabi, Arabic
The organisation's main aim is to provide a platform
where issues of importance to Muslims in the UK
can be introduced, debated and then procedures set
in place.

Association of Muslim Professionals*
62 Whitchurch Road, Heath, Cardiff CF14 3LX
Tel: (029) 2022 4466 **Fax:** (029) 2022 2550
Website: http://www.ampwales.co.uk/
Contact: Mr Saleem Kidwai
Position: Secretary
Contact Email: saleemkidwai@compuserve.com

Activities: Community centre, youth, elderly, women, newsletter/journal, radio, inter-faith, resources
Traditions: Sunni
Movements: Ahl-e-Hadith, Barelwi, Deobandi, Jamati-I-Islami, Tablighi Jamaat, Tassawuf

Association of Muslim Researchers*
PO Box 8715, London SE23 3ZB
Tel: (020) 8699 1887 **Fax:** (020) 8699 1887
Email: amr@amrnet.demon.co.uk
Website: http://www.amrnet.demon.co.uk/
Contact: Miss S Sheriff
Position: Development Officer
Affiliations: Muslim Council of Britain
Generation, dissemination and application of knowledge, networking. Societies: Economic, Education and Humanities inclusive of Philosophy of Islam.

Association of Muslim Scholars of Islamics in Britain
Jamiat-e Ulama of Britain, 54 Sheldon Road, Nether Edge, Sheffield S7 1GW
Tel: (0114) 2550318
Contact: Mr M Ismail
Position: Secretary

Association of Muslim Schools of UK and Eire (AMS)*
1 Evington Lane, Leicester LE5 5PQ
Tel: (0116) 2738666 **Fax:** (0116) 2738777
Email: ams@webstar.co.uk
Contact: Ibrahim Hewitt
Position: Spokesman
Activities: Resource, umbrella body, newsletters
Affiliations: Muslim Council of Britain
Umbrella body for Britain's full-time Muslim schools - offers in-service training for teachers, curriculum development and management advice. School centred initial teacher training.

Astana Aliya Naqeebiya*
Naqeebi Building, Richmond Road, Bradford BD7 1DR
Tel: (01274) 724998 **Fax:** (01274) 742736
Contact: Mohammed Afsar
Position: Co-ordinator
Contact Tel: (07930) 363642
Activities: Worship/practice/meditation, youth, women, inter-faith
Traditions: Sunni
Movements: Barelwi, Tassawuf
Other Languages: Punjabi, Urdu, Hindi, Pushto

Azeemia Foundation (UK)*
Azeemi House, 92b Hampton Road, Forest Gate, London E7 0NU
Tel: (020) 8555 4786 **Fax:** (020) 8555 4786
Contact: Mrs A Azeemi
Position: Spiritual Teacher
Activities: Worship/practice/meditation, central body, youth, elderly, women, newsletter/journal, books, radio, television, visits, inter-faith, resources
Other Languages: Urdu, Hindi, Punjabi, Sindhi
Affiliations: Markazi Muraqba Hall, Surjani Town, Karachi, Pakistan
The Azeemia Spiritual Order has more than seventy-two Azeemia Centres throughout the world.

Central Jamiat Ulama UK*
International K N Mission, 183 St Georges Road, Bolton BL1 2PG
Tel: (01204) 361759 **Fax:** (01204) 361759
Contact: Dr Allama Musa Qasmi
Position: Secretary General
Activities: Worship, resource, visits, women, newsletters, inter-faith
Traditions: Sunni
Other Languages: Urdu, Gujarati, Punjabi
Affiliations: UK Action Committee on Islamic Affairs; The Muslim World League

Central Moonsighting Committee of Great Britain*
98 Ferham Road, Rotherham S61 1BN
Tel: (01709) 563677
Contact: Mufti Muhammas Aslam
Position: Chairman

Council of European Jamaats*
PO Box 196, Bretton, Peterborough PE3 9DE
Tel: (01733) 340261
Contact: Yasin Rahim
Position: Secretary
Links Shi'a Khoja 'Ithna Asheri mosques across Europe.

Dar al-Hekma Trust*
45 Chalton Street, London NW1 1HY
Tel: (020) 7383 2058 **Fax:** (020) 7383 3601
Email: al-hekma@al-hekma.org
Website: http://www.al-hekma.org/
Contact: Dr M Al-Jamri
Position: Secretary
Activities: Community centre, newsletter/journal
Traditions: Ithna Asheri
Other Languages: Arabic

Dar al-Islam Foundation*
61 Anson Road, Cricklewood, London NW2 3UY
Tel: (020) 8452 3220 **Fax:** (020) 8208 4354
Contact: Mr F Shareef
Position: Admin/Community Officer
Activities: Visits, youth, women, inter-faith
Traditions: Ithna Asheri
Other Languages: Arabic

Darul Uloom Muslim Training College
Holcombe Hall, Holcombe Brook, Ramsbottom,
Bury BL8 4NG
Tel: (01706) 825160
Contact: Mufti Shabbir

Dar-ul-Ehsan Publications*
252 Almondbury Bank, Almondbury, Huddersfield
HD5 8EL
Tel: (01484) 309852
Email: m.iqbal@hud.ac.uk
Contact: Dr Muhammad Iqbal
Position: Secretary/Treasurer
Activities: Books
Traditions: Sunni
Aims to promote better understanding of Muslims
and Islam by all, especially non-Muslims, through
publications on all aspects of Islam, particularly the
spiritual dimensions of the Faith.

Dawatul Islam Youth Group*
56 Bigland Street, London E1 2ND
Tel: (020) 7790 5166
Contact: Youth Secretary
Activities: Youth

Dawatul Islam UK and Eire*
56 Bigland Street, London E1 2ND
Tel: (020) 7790 5166
Contact: President

Discover Islam Centre*
2 Glynrhondda Street, Cardiff CF24 4AN
Tel: (029) 2039 0414 **Fax:** (029) 2022 6650
Email: discover.a@uklonline.co.uk
Website: http://www.almanarcentre.org/
Contact: Abu 'abdurrahmaan
Position: Director
Activities: Worship/practice/meditation,
community centre, youth, women, visits, resources
Other Languages: Arabic
Cultural and Information centre.

Edhi International Foundation UK*
69 Bell Street, London NW1 6SX

Tel: (020) 7723 7677
Contact: Mr Abdul Sattar Edhi
Position: Chairman
Other Languages: Urdu, Gujarati, Punjabi

European Islamic Mission*
22 Roberts Road, Balby, Doncaster DN4 0JW
Tel: (01302) 819470
Contact: Muhammed Shafi Chaudhary
Position: Chairman
Activities: Worship, resource, visits, youth, elderly,
newsletter
Traditions: Sunni
Other Languages: English, Urdu, Arabic

**Federation of Islamic Organisations in Europe
(FIOE)***
PO Box MAR005, Markfield LE67 9RY
Tel: (01530) 245919 **Fax:** (01530) 245913
Email: hq@fioe.org
Website: http://www.fioe.org/
Contact: Mr Ahmad K Al-Rawi
Position: President
Activities: Central body, umbrella body,
newsletter/journal
Traditions: Sunni
Other Languages: Arabic, French, German
Affiliations: Muslim Council of Britain

**Federation of Students Islamic Societies of the
UK and Eire (FOSIS)***
38 Mapesbury Road, London NW2 4JD
Tel: (020) 8452 4493 **Fax:** (020) 8208 4161
Email: info@fosis.org.uk
Website: http://www.fosis.org.uk/
Contact: President
Activities: Resources, umbrella body, visits, youth,
women, newsletter
Other Languages: Urdu, Arabic
Affiliations: FEMYSO – Forum of European
Muslim Youth and Student Organisations, WAMY
– World Assembly of Muslim Youth
FOSIS aims to: unite student Islamic societies on
Islamic principles; encourage formation of new
Islamic societies and support existing ones; promote
the interests of Muslim students; invite others to
Islam.

Guyana United Sad'r Islamic Anjuman*
8 Hazledean Road, Craven Road, London
NW10 8QU
Tel: (020) 8961 3814 **Fax:** (020) 8961 3814
Contact: Haji Abdool Hafiz Rahaman
Position: Vice President

A branch of an organisation in Georgetown, Guyana, which represents Muslims, founded in 1936. Its aim is to spread Islam in Guyana, where approximately ten per cent of the population are Muslim.

Halal Food Authority, The*
109 Fulham Palace Road, London W6 8JA
Tel: (020) 8563 1995 **Fax:** (020) 8563 1993
Email: hfa.khawaja@talk21.com
Website: http://www.halalfoodauthority.com/
Contact: Mr Masood Khawaja
Position: President
Contact Tel: (07860) 635537
Other Languages: Urdu, Arabic
Authentic endorsement of foodstuffs and pharmaceuticals for Halal purposes. Consultations on Halal regulatory matters.

Hijaz College*
Watling Street, Nuneaton CV11 6BE
Tel: (024) 7664 1333 **Fax:** (024) 7635 3345
Contact: Hazrat Moulana Noor Siddiqi
Position: Vice Principal
Activities: Worship, resource, umbrella body, visits, youth, elderly
Traditions: Sunni
Movements: Barelwi, Tassawuf
Other Languages: Urdu, Arabic, Punjabi, Dutch
The College aims to become a centre of excellence that offers Muslims the opportunity to acquire higher education within the spiritual and intellectual framework of Islam.

Idara Isha'at al Islam (Masjid-e-Imdadia)*
PO Box 36, Blackburn Street, Old Trafford, Manchester M16 7AN
Tel: (0161) 2329845 **Fax:** (0161) 2329845
Email: idarauk@hotmail.com
Contact: Ebraheem Yoosuf Bawa
Position: Founder
Activities: Worship/practice/meditation, community centre, central body, youth, elderly, women, newsletter/journal, books, radio, visits, inter-faith, resources
Traditions: Sunni
Movements: Deobandi, Tablighi Jamaat, Tassawuf
Other Languages: Urdu, Gujarati, Burmese
Affiliations: Darul Uloom Deoband
Mr Bawa is a Tablighi and founder of the first full-time Islamic Madrassa (1977). All his sons and daughters are Hafiz-ul-Qur'an. Sons are also famous Alim.

Imams and Mosques Council*
20-22 Creffield Road, London W5 3RP
Tel: (020) 8992 6636 **Fax:** (020) 8993 3946
Email: zbadawi@aol.com
Contact: Moulana Mohammad Shahid Raza
Position: Executive Director
Activities: Umbrella body, inter-faith
Other Languages: Urdu, Arabic
Affiliations: Inter Faith Network for the UK
The Council offers in-service training to the Imams to enhance their ability to work as religious leaders in the UK; operates a private pension scheme for Imams, contributing on a pound for pound basis. It is an organisation of affiliated mosques.

Indian Muslim Federation (UK)*
Trinity Close, Leytonstone, London E11 4RP
Tel: (020) 8558 6399 **Fax:** (020) 7278 4792
Contact: R Anwar Sharif
Position: Co-ordinator
Activities: Youth, elderly, women, inter-faith
Traditions: Sunni
Other Languages: Urdu, Punjabi, Hindi, Bengali
Affiliations: Leytonstone Islamic Association; Union of Muslim Organisations of UK and Eire; UK Action Committee on Islamic Affairs; The Muslim World League
Strives to promote educational, social, cultural, economical, political and religious activities and equality of opportunities for the Muslims in India.

Institute of Islamic Banking and Insurance*
ICIS House, 144-146 Kings Cross Road, London WC1X 9DH
Tel: (020) 7833 8275 **Fax:** (020) 7278 4797
Email: icisibi@demon.co.uk
Its aims and objectives include the promotion of the Islamic financial system through banking and insurance through conference seminars, lectures and publications. Education of prospective personnel in Islamic banking and insurance and developing Islamic financial instruments.

Institute of Islamic Studies*
34 Kinver Croft, High Gate, Birmingham B12 9HE
Tel: (0121) 4466428 **Fax:** (0121) 4466426
Contact: Dr Khalid Alavi
Position: Secretary
Activities: Books, inter-faith
Traditions: Sunni
Other Languages: Urdu, Punjabi, Arabic
Affiliations: UK Action Committee on Islamic Affairs; Educational Forum

Institute of Muslim Minority Affairs*
46 Goodge Street, London W1P 1FJ
The primary purpose of the Institute is to encourage, support and pursue research in, and to extend the study and knowledge of, the conditions of life of Muslim minority communities wherever they reside.

International College of Islamic Sciences (ICIS)*
Crusader House, 289 Cricklewood Broadway, Cricklewood, London NW2 6NX
Tel: (020) 8450 8383 **Fax:** (020) 8452 3366
Email: regicis@yahoo.com
Website: http://www.islamiccolleges.com/
Contact: Dr Ehsan Shahrestani
Position: Director
Activities: Resources
Traditions: Ithna Asheri
Other Languages: Arabic
Affiliations: World Ahl ul Bayt Islamic League

International Council for Islamic Information*
Markfield Conference Centre, Ratby Lane, Markfield LE67 9SY
Tel: (01530) 249928 **Fax:** (01530) 244946
Email: daudicii@aol.com
Contact: Mr Daud R Matthews
Position: Executive Director
Activities: Inter-faith, resources
Traditions: Sunni

International Thinkers Forum*
52 Pennington Road, Bolton BL3 3BR
Tel: (07946) 854644 **Fax:** (01204) 650681
Email: ghulam_ashraf@yahoo.com
Contact: Mr G Ashraf
Position: Chair
Activities: Inter-faith, resources
Traditions: Sunni
Other Languages: Urdu

IQRA Trust*
24 Culross Street, London W1Y 3HE
Tel: (020) 7491 1572 **Fax:** (020) 7493 7899
Email: info@iqratrust.org
Website: http://www.iqratrust.org/
Contact: Mr Faisal Osman
Position: Trustee
Activities: Newsletter/journal, books, radio, visits, inter-faith, resources
Traditions: Sunni
Other Languages: Arabic
Affiliations: IQRA Charitable Society, Jeddah

IQRA Trust, a registered charity, aims to promote a better understanding of Islam in Britain. It provides clear, accurate and reliable information about Islam and the Muslim way of life.

Islamia Girls High School*
Thornton Lodge Road, Huddersfield HD1 3JQ
Tel: (01484) 432928 **Fax:** (01484) 432928
Contact: Miss Farzana Alyas
Position: Secretary
Traditions: Sunni
Other Languages: Urdu, Punjabi, Arabic

Islamia Schools Trust*
129 Salusbury Road, Queen's Park, London NW6 6PE
Tel: (020) 7372 2171
Contact: Zafar Ashraf
Position: Administrator
Activities: Worship, resource, visits, youth, elderly, women
Traditions: Sunni
Other Languages: Arabic, Bengali, Urdu
Affiliations: Association of Muslim Schools of UK and Eire
Islamia Schools Trust runs two schools in North London. Islamia primary school admits both boys and girls and is state funded. The secondary school is for girls only and consistently tops the league table for the second year in succession among Brent schools.

Islamic Academy, The*
205 Gilbert Road, Cambridge CB4 3PA
Tel: (01223) 350976 **Fax:** (01223) 350976
Email: info@islamicacademy.ac.uk
Contact: Dr Shaikh Abdul Mabud
Position: Director General
Other Languages: Arabic, Bengali, Urdu
A religious education charity research orientated international organisation established in 1983 in order to make religious values as derived from Islam the basis for education.

Islamic Book Club (UK)*
Chashtiah Bookcentre, 49 Milkstone Road, Rochdale OL11 1EB
Tel: (01706) 350786 **Fax:** (01706) 350140
Contact: Mr Jamil Chishti
Position: Manager
Activities: Books
The bookshop offers free catalogues, translations of the Qu'ran and children's books with first orders.

The book centre houses a large selection of Islamic literature, materials, artefacts and gifts.

Islamic Book Service*
505-527 Coventry Road, Small Heath,
Birmingham B10 0LL
Tel: (0121) 7737706 **Fax:** (0121) 7734340
Contact: Dr A Rahim
Position: Director
Contact Tel: (0121) 7726408
Activities: Worship/practice/meditation
Other Languages: Arabic, Bangla, Urdu

Islamic Centre of England*
140 Maida Vale, London W9 1QB
Tel: (020) 7604 5500 **Fax:** (020) 7723 9629
Email: icel@ic-el.org
Contact: Hyder Shirazi
Position: Secretary
Traditions: Shi'a 'Ithna Asheri
Other Languages: Arabic, Farsi, Urdu, French
Answering questions on Islamic affairs via the Internet, Fax, telephone etc. Homepage in three languages showing prayer times and Adhan. Supplies books in Arabic, Persian, English, Urdu, French, Turkish and German.

Islamic College London
16 Settles Street, London E1 1JP
Tel: (020) 7377 1595 **Fax:** (020) 7377 1595
Contact: Abu Syed
Position: Principal
Activities: Worship, resource
Traditions: Sunni
Other Languages: Bengali
Affiliations: Dawatul Islam UK and Eire;
Association of Muslim Schools of UK and Eire

Islamic Council on Palestine
46 Goodge Street, London W1P 11FJ

Islamic Education and Training Centre*
26 Tividale Road, Oldbury B69 2LG
Tel: (0121) 5324783
Contact: Nasiruddin
Position: Chief Organiser
Contact Tel: (07801) 015142
Activities: Youth
Traditions: Sunni
Other Languages: Urdu, Punjabi, Mirpuri

Islamic Education Board*
Dar Al Tableegh, Jackets Lane, Harefield UB9 6PZ
Tel: (01923) 823606 **Fax:** (01923) 823132
Email: ieb@tableegh.org.uk

Contact: Muhsin Jaffer
Position: Chairman
Activities: Central body, umbrella body, books, radio, inter-faith, resources
Traditions: Ithna Asheri
Other Languages: Gujarati, Urdu, Farsi, Arabic
Affiliations: World Federation of Khoja Shi'a 'Ithna-Asheri Muslim Communities

Islamic Educational Trust*
138 Northgate Road, Edgeley, Stockport SK3 9NL
Tel: (0161) 4771595
Contact: Mr M I Kashmiri
Position: Chairman
Activities: Youth, newsletter/journal, books, visits, inter-faith, resources
Traditions: Sunni
Movements: Barelwi, Tassawuf
Other Languages: Urdu, Arabic, Punjabi, Gujarati
The trust was established in 2000 to educate Muslims about the Islamic faith and to help other communities to understand Islam.

Islamic Forum Europe*
169 Mile End Road, London E1 4AQ
Tel: (020) 7423 9766 **Fax:** (020) 7702 7254
Contact: Dr Muhammad Abdul Bari
Position: President
Activities: Central body, umbrella body, youth, elderly, women, newsletter/journal, radio, inter-faith, resources
Traditions: Sunni
Other Languages: Bengali
Affiliations: Muslim Council of Britain
Voluntary organisation catering for the social, cultural and educational needs of the Muslim community whilst raising awareness and promoting better understanding to non-Muslims.

Islamic Foundation*
Ratby Lane, Markfield, Leicester LE67 9SY
Tel: (01530) 244944 **Fax:** (01530) 244944
Email: ifoundation@islamic-foundation.org.uk
Website: http://www.islamic-foundation.org.uk/
Contact: Mr Mohammad Sadiq
Position: Administrative Officer
Activities: Worship, youth, women, newsletter/journal, books,
Traditions: Sunni
Other Languages: Arabic, Urdu
Affiliations: Inter Faith Network for the UK

Islamic Foundation for Ecology and Environmental Sciences (IFEES)*
93 Court Road, Balsall Heath, Birmingham
B12 9LQ
Tel: (0121) 4403500 **Fax:** (0121) 4408144
Email: ahlan@ifees.org
Website: http://www.ifees.org/
Contact: Mr Fazlun Khalid
Position: Director
Activities: Books, resources
Traditions: Sunni
Other Languages: Arabic, Urdu
IFEES is an Islam focussed environmental organisation, networked internationally and collaborating with non-governmental organisations, universities and grass roots organisations world wide to produce books and resource materials.

Islamic Human Rights Commission*
PO Box 598, Wembley HA9 7XH
Tel: (020) 8902 0888 **Fax:** (020) 8902 0889
Email: ihrc@dial.pipex.com

Islamic Information Centre (London)*
99 Uxbridge Road, Shepherds Bush, London
W12 8NL
Tel: (020) 8749 3877
Contact: Ayhan Ogretici
Position: Secretary
Activities: Worship, resource, visits, youth, inter-faith
Traditions: Sunni
Other Languages: Urdu, Hindi, Punjabi, Arabic

Islamic Jihad of Europe*
116a Whalley New Road, Blackburn BB1 6LB
Tel: (07759) 449294
Contact: Mr Tasaddiq Rehman
Position: Chairman
Contact Tel: (01254) 665354
Activities: Central body, newsletter/journal
Traditions: Sunni
Other Languages: Urdu, Punjabi, Arabic

Islamic Men and Women's Association*
52 Oulton Terrace, Bradford BD7 1QF
Tel: (01274) 744568
Contact: Ms Mubarik Iqbal
Position: Chairperson
Activities: Community centre
This organisation is set up to unite Muslims and work for the welfare of the community. It forbids personal attack and welcomes Muslims from all sects and from all communities.

Islamic Museum In London and Cultural Centre*
c/o 44 Crofton Road, Camberwell, London
SE5 8NB
Tel: (020) 7701 3670 **Fax:** (020) 7701 3670
Contact: Dr H Alsaigh
Position: Secretary to Board
Activities: Resources
Traditions: Multi-Traditional
The Islamic Museum aims to provide a major forum for information on all aspects of the culture that is Islam, together with its social, geographical, political and religious importance.

Islamic Prayer Group (IPG)*
PO Box 4268, London SE11 4BD
Tel: (07956) 964258 **Fax:** (020) 7582 6295
Contact: Maroof Abedye
Position: Secretary General
Activities: Visits, youth, inter-faith
Traditions: Sunni
Other Languages: Yoruba

Islamic Propagation Centre International*
434 Coventry Road, Small Heath, Birmingham
B10 0UG
Tel: (0121) 7730137 **Fax:** (0121) 7668577
Email: info@ipci-iv.co.uk
Website: http://www.ipci-iv.co.uk/
Contact: Mr S M Khan
Position: Chairman
Activities: Books, visits, inter-faith
Movements: Ahl-e-Hadith, Barelwi, Deobandi, Jamati-i-Islami, Tablighi Jamaat, Tassawuf
Other Languages: Urdu, Arabic, Bengali, Punjabi
Devoted to supplying information and literature on Islam. The Group works to gain new members of the faith and engages in daw'ah, in other words, presenting and preaching the message of Islam.

Islamic Relief UK/World-Wide (National Office)*
151b Park Road, London NW8 7HT
Tel: (0870) 4443135 **Fax:** (020) 7722 3228
Email: iruk@islamic-relief.org.uk
Website: http://www.islamic_relief.org.uk/
Contact: Mr Imran Madden
Position: UK Manager
Other Languages: Arabic, Urdu, French
Affiliations: Economic and Social Council of UN; International Red Cross and Red Crescent Code of Conduct
Islamic Relief is dedicated to alleviating the poverty and suffering of the world's poorest people.

Islamic Relief World-Wide (International Office)*
19 Rea Street South, Digbeth, Birmingham
B5 6LB
Tel: (0121) 6055555 **Fax:** (0121) 6225003
Email: 100667.130@compuserve.com
Contact: Dr Hany El Banna
Position: Managing Director
Other Languages: Arabic, French, Dutch, German
International office of Islamic Relief which aims to alleviate poverty by providing humanitarian aid during emergencies and promoting sustainable and appropriate development through working with local communities and partners overseas.

Islamic Research Academy (IRAP)*
PO Box 15002, Dunblane FK15 0ZA
Tel: (01786) 821670 **Fax:** (01786) 824370
Contact: Dr Abd al-Fattah El-Awaisi
Position: Secretary General
Activities: Resource, newsletters, books, inter-faith
Other Languages: Arabic
The object of the Academy's establishment is to advance Islamic education and research with special reference to the promotion of studies and research into Islamic Jerusalem.

Islamic Research Institute of GB*
34 Warren Street, Savile Town, Dewsbury WF12 9LX
Tel: (01924) 464523 **Fax:** (01924) 464523
Contact: Mr Munshi Yakub
Position: Chair
Activities: Books, inter-faith, resources
Traditions: Sunni
Movements: Deobandi, Tablighi Jamaat
Other Languages: Gujarati, Urdu, Arabic

Islamic Rights Movement*
PO Box 139, Leicester LE2 2YH
Contact: Mr A Hussain
Position: Chairperson
Activities: Resource, inter-faith
The Islamic Rights Movement takes an interfaith approach to human rights. It believes all religions must unite to exert pressure on governments and raise the social consciousness of the people to safeguard human life, freedom of thought and from torture.

Islamic Sharia Council of UK and Eire*
34 Francis Road, London E10 6PW
Tel: (020) 8558 0581 **Fax:** (020) 8881 3984

Email: shariacouncil@hotmail.com
Website: http://www.islamic-sharia.co.uk
Contact: Dr Suhaib Hasfan
Contact Tel: (020) 9250673
Email: suhaib@hotmail.com
Position: General Secretary
Traditions: Sunni
Other Languages: Urdu, Arabic
Semi-legal court, established in 1980 to cater for families in dispute in order to effect reconciliation and, failing this, to dissolve the marriage Islamically. It also deals with issues related to access to minors and inheritance.

Islamic Society for the Promotion of Religious Tolerance in the UK*
121 Harley Street, London W1N 1DH
Tel: (020) 7935 3330
Contact: Dr H El-Essawy
Position: Chairman
Activities: Resource, media, visits, youth, elderly, women, inter-faith
Traditions: Sunni
Other Languages: Arabic, French, Italian
The Society is dedicated to the promotion of tolerance through promoting of understanding.

Islamic Society of Britain*
PO Box 7539, Birmingham B10 9AU
Tel: (0845) 0878766 **Fax:** (0845) 0878766
Email: info@isb.org.uk
Website: http://www.isb.org.uk/
Contact: General Secretary
Activities: Central body, youth, women, newsletter/journal, books, visits, inter-faith, resources
Traditions: Sunni
The Society is committed to creating greater understanding and awareness of Islam.

Islamic Society of Britain*
Markfield Conference Centre, Ratby Lane, Markfield LE67 9RN
Tel: (01902) 711892 **Fax:** (01902) 711892
Email: dilwarslamf@demon.co.uk
Contact: Mr Zahid Parvez
Position: President
Activities: Resource, umbrella body, visits, youth, elderly, women,
Other Languages: Urdu, Punjabi, Bengali

Islamic Texts Society*
22a Brooklands Avenue, Cambridge CB2 2DQ
Tel: (01223) 314387 **Fax:** (01223) 324342

Email: mail@its.org.uk
Website: http://www.its.org.uk/
Contact: Miss Fatima Azzam
Position: Director
Activities: Books
ITS is a publishing house founded in 1981 also registered as an educational charity. ITS produces translations of works important to Islamic faith and culture.

Islamic Vision Limited*
434 Coventry Road, Birmingham B10 0UG
Tel: (0121) 7730137 **Fax:** (0121) 7668577
Email: info@ipci-iv.co.uk
Website: http://www.ipci-iv.co.uk/
Contact: Mr Mohsin Beg
Position: Director
Activities: Books
Traditions: Sunni
Movements: Ahl-e-Hadith, Barelwi, Deobandi, Jamati-i-Islami, Tablighi Jamaat, Tassawuf
Other Languages: Urdu, Arabic, Bengali, Punjabi

Ismaili Centre*
1 Cromwell Gardens, London SW7 2SL
Tel: (020) 7581 2071 **Fax:** (020) 7589 3246
Contact: Mr Zaher Lalani
Position: Chief Executive Officer
Traditions: Ismaili
A multi-purpose meeting place established by the Ismaili Muslim community for cultural, educational, religious and social activities. The conference rooms, exhibition and lecture facilities are used by public and private secular institutions.

Jama't Ahl-e-Sunnat UK (Association of Sunni Muslims, UK)
106 Leslie Road, Nottingham NG7 6PR
Tel: (0115) 9790956
Contact: Maulana Syed Zahid Hussain
Position: President
Movements: Barelwi
An organisation of imams and Ulama of the Sunni Muslim tradition, representing the Barelwi movement. It mainly acts to liaise between mosques and Sufi organisations within the Barelwi circle and organises national conferences on issues affecting Muslims.

Jameah Islameah*
Cattshill, Mark Cross, Crowborough TN6 3NJ
Tel: (01892) 853051
Website: http://www.islamicjameah.com/
Contact: Imran Mulla

Position: Secretary
Activities: Resource, visits, youth
Traditions: Sunni
Other Languages: Urdu, Gujarati, Bengali, Arabic
Affiliations: Union of Muslim Organisations, UK and Eire; Association of Muslim Schools, UK and Eire

Jamiat-e-Ulama of Britain*
12 Leeds Old Road, Bradford BD3 8HT
Tel: (01274) 660688 **Fax:** (01274) 660928
Contact: Haji M Ayub Laher
Contact Tel: (07973) 661441
Movements: Deobandi
Affiliations: Inter Faith Network for the UK
A national organisation of Muslim scholars, with links to the Deobandi movement. It conducts educational activities, provides advice to Muslims on Islamic observance and plays a role in building up relationships with other communities.

Kafel Fund International
6 Oakhurst Grove, East Dulwich, London SE22 9AQ
Email: htnbetkf@netcomuk.co.uk
Contact: Hawk Savas
Position: Trustee
Activities: Worship, inter-faith
Traditions: Sunni
Other Languages: Turkish, Urdu, Bengali, Arabic
Affiliations: Indirect Affiliation to Saudi Groups

Khaniqahi Nimatullahi*
41 Chepstow Place, Bayswater, London W2 4TS
Tel: (020) 7229 0769 **Fax:** (020) 7229 0769
Email: darvish@nimatullahi.org
Website: http://www.nimatullahi.org/
Contact: Dr Alireza Nurbakhsh
Activities: Worship/practice/meditation
Traditions: Tassawuf
Movements: Sufism
Other Languages: French, Persian, German, Italian

Khilafah Movement*
PO Box 349, Edmonton, London N9 7RR
Tel: (07956) 920006 **Fax:** (020) 8803 4541
Email: khilafah@2fs.com
Website: http://www.obm.clara.net/
Contact: Sheikh Abdullah Abu Al-Farouq
Position: Leader
Contact Tel: (07956) 920006
Activities: Worship/practice/meditation, community centre, central body, umbrella body, young, elderly, women, newsletter/journal, books,

newspapers, radio, television, visits, resources
Traditions: Sunni
Movements: Usuli
Other Languages: Arabic, Urdu, Bengali, Turkish
Affiliations: London School of Shari'ah; Shari'ah Court of the UK; Al-Muhajiroun
The Khilafah movement is a world-wide party based on the divine ideology of Al-Islam and is working to establish the global Islamic order by establishing the Khilafah, ie Islamic State.

Kokani Muslim World Foundation*
28 West Avenue Road, London E17 9SE
Tel: (020) 8521 0907
Contact: Mr Abdulla Mukadam
Position: Secretary
Activities: Youth, elderly, women, newsletter/journal, resources
Traditions: Sunni
Other Languages: Urdu, Hindi, Kokani, Marathi

League of British Muslims UK*
Ilford Muslim Community Centre, Eton Road, Ilford IG1 2UE
Tel: (020) 8514 0706
Contact: Mr B A Chaudhry
Position: Chairperson
Activities: Worship/practice/meditation, community centre, umbrella body, youth, elderly, women, visits, inter-faith, resources
Traditions: Sunni
Other Languages: Urdu, Bengali, Gujarati, Arabic
Affiliations: Regents Park Mosque
We are active in the 3 Faiths Forum of Christians, Jews and Muslims to work closely for the benefit and harmony of communities within the UK and abroad.

London Central Mosque and Islamic Cultural Centre, The*
146 Park Road, London NW8 7RG
Tel: (020) 7724 3363 **Fax:** (020) 7724 0493
Email: islamic200@aol.com
Website: http://www.islamicculturalcentre.co.uk/
Contact: Mr Nizar Boga
Position: Advisor
Contact Tel: (020) 7706 4432
Activities: Worship/practice/meditation, community centre, youth, elderly, books, radio, television, visits, inter-faith, resources
Traditions: Sunni
Other Languages: Arabic, Punjabi, Urdu, Bengali
Affiliations: Inter Faith Network for the UK
Undertaking Health Education programmes; co-ordinating and providing service to Muslims in

prisons throughout the UK; running nursery classes; providing library service; preparing for a permanent Art and Heritage Gallery.

Madrasah-e-Darul Qirat Majidiah (UK)*
46/48 Cannon Street, London E1 0BH
Tel: (020) 7790 9315 **Fax:** (020) 7790 9315
Contact: Mufti M I Hussain
Position: Secretary
Contact Tel: (020) 7702 2587
Activities: Worship/practice/meditation, community centre, youth, elderly, resources
Traditions: Sunni
Movements: Barelwi, Tassawuf
Other Languages: Bengali, Urdu, Arabic
An independent Islamic Secondary school as well as a weekend and evening study support.

Malaysian Islamic Study Group - UK and Eire*
90 St Thomas Road, Finsbury Park, London N4 2WQ

Markazi Jamiat Ahl-e-Hadith (UK)*
20 Green Lane, Small Heath, Birmingham B9 5DB
Tel: (0121) 7730019 **Fax:** (0121) 7668779
Website: http://www.ahlehadith.co.uk/
Contact: Shouaib Ahmed
Position: General Secretary
Activities: Worship/practice/meditation, community centre, central body, youth, elderly, women, newsletter/journal, books, visits, resources
Movements: Ahl-e-Hadith
Other Languages: Urdu, Punajbi, Arabic
Affiliations: Ittehad-ul-Ulema (UK); Muslim Unity of Britain; Muslim Council of Britain; Over 40 branches in the UK. Headquarters in this country of Jamiat Ahl-e-Hadith.

Medical Aid for Palestinians
33a Islington Park Street, London, N1 1QB
Tel: (020) 72264114
Contact: Mrs Saida Nusseibeh
Position: Chief Executive

Medina Islamic Mission*
7 Dawn Close Road, Martindale Road, Hounslow West TW4 7EN
Tel: (020) 8577 0647
Contact: Khawaja Mahmood Ahmed
Position: President
Activities: Resource
Traditions: Sunni
Other Languages: Urdu, Arabic, Punjabi

Memon Association UK*

3 Weir Road, Balham, London SW12 8UW
Tel: (020) 8743 3233 **Fax:** (020) 8743 3233
Contact: Mr A A Yousuf
Position: Hon Gen Secretary
Works towards the advancement of Islam and the education of Muslim children in accordance with the tenets of the Sunni school of thought. It aims to give financial assistance to members of the Muslim community, and others, who are poor and needy.

Muhammadi Trust*

17 Beverley Way, London SW20 0AW
Tel: (020) 8336 1018 **Fax:** (020) 8336 1017
Email: muhammaditrust@aol.com
Website:
http://www.al-islam.org/publishers/mtrust
Contact: Mr Syed Shabbar
Position: Managing Trustee
Activities: Community centre, youth, books, television, visits, inter-faith, resources
Traditions: Ithna Asheri
Other Languages: Urdu, Arabic, Farsi
Affiliations: Majlis Muhammadi
Our television channel is 'The Pakistan Channel TV'.

Muslim Advisory and Community Welfare Council*

317 Markhouse Road, Walthamstow, London E17 8EE
Tel: (020) 8925 9050
Contact: M Salah-ud-Din
Position: Secretary
Activities: Resource, media, youth, elderly, inter-faith
Traditions: Sunni
Other Languages: Urdu, Punjabi
The object of this organisation is to promote social welfare, advise and render charitable services for the benefit of the Muslim Community and to improve unity amonst the Muslims and also to promote and to encourage fellowship through religion.

Muslim Aid*

PO Box 3, London NW1 7UB
Tel: (020) 7387 7171 **Fax:** (020) 7387 7474
Email: mail@muslimaid.org.uk
Website: http://www.muslimaid.org.uk/
Contact: Mr E Mohamed
Position: Co-ordinator
Other Languages: Urdu, Punjabi, Arabic, Malay
Works in 48 countries across Africa, Asia, Europe and the Middle East providing education, healthcare, skills training, safe clean water, emergency relief and shelter.

Muslim Association of Nigeria (UK)*

365 Old Kent Road, London SE1 5JH
Tel: (020) 7231 0100 **Fax:** (020) 7237 0009
Contact: Alhaji Tajudeen A Salami
Position: Head Missioner
Contact Tel: (0956) 962195
Activities: Worship
Traditions: Sunni
Other Languages: Yoruba, Hausa, Arabic
Affiliations: Nigerian Muslims Organisations; Union of Muslim Organisations, UK and Eire; Muslim World League, Saudi Arabia.

Muslim College*

20-22 Creffield Road, London W5 3RP
Tel: (020) 8992 6636 **Fax:** (020) 8993 3946
Email: badawi@muslimcollege.ac.uk
Website: http://www.muslimcollege.ac.uk/
Contact: Dr M A Zaki Badawi
Position: Principal
Activities: Resource, visits, women
Other Languages: Arabic
The College offers: a 3 year post-graduate Diploma course in Islamic Studies for the training of those who wish to work as an imam in the West; courses in Arabic.

Muslim Community Studies Institute*

PO Box 139, Leicester LE2 2YH
Tel: (0116) 706714 **Fax:** (0116) 706714
Contact: Asaf Hussain
Activities: Resource, youth, women, books, inter-faith
A research and consultancy organisation which also publishes; mobilises Muslim youth and women for active participation in community affairs; and raises the consciousness of Muslims by educating them in Islamic Human Rights.

Muslim Council of Britain*

PO Box 52, Wembley HA9 0XW
Tel: (020) 8903 9024 **Fax:** (020) 8903 9026
Email: admin@mcb.org.uk
Website: http://www.mcb.org.uk
Contact: Mr Yousuf Bhailok
Position: Secretary General
Activities: Umbrella body, newsletter/journal, inter-faith
Other Languages: Urdu, Bengali, Arabic
Affiliations: Inter Faith Network for the UK
Established in November 1997, MCB has rapidly expanded to become a significant umbrella body for

British Muslims, representing over 300 organisations nationally.

Muslim Education Consultative Committee*
93 Court Road, Balsall Heath, Birmingham B12 9LQ
Tel: (0121) 4403500 **Fax:** (0121) 4408144
Contact: Dr S Qureshi
Position: Treasurer
Activities: Resource, women
Other Languages: Arabic, Punjabi, Urdu, Mirpuri

Muslim Education Forum*
50 Oakwood Drive, Bingley BD16 4SJ
Tel: (01274) 569387
Contact: Mr Mohammed Akram Khan Cheema
Position: Amir

Muslim Educational Co-ordinating Council (UK)*
7 Paul Gardens, East Croydon CR0 5QL
Tel: (020) 8681 6087
Contact: Mr Nazar-e Mustafa
Position: Chair
Activities: Resource
Other Languages: Arabic, Bengali, Urdu
Affiliations: The Islamic Cultural Centre; Muslim College
Helps refugees to go through exams in various fields; helps students to re-sit exams to improve grades; helps students in research work; asks examination boards to use a roll number and centre number rather than names on examination papers.

Muslim Educational Trust*
130 Stroud Green Road, London N4 3RZ
Tel: (020) 7272 8502 **Fax:** (020) 7281 3457
Email: info@muslim-ed-trust.org.uk
Website: http://www.muslim-ed-trust.org.uk/
Contact: Mr Ghulam Sarwar
Position: Director
Activities: Resource, books
Traditions: Sunni
Other Languages: Urdu, Bengali, Punjabi
The Muslim Educational Trust advises on the educational needs of British Muslim children, and on educational issues in general.

Muslim Food Board*
PO Box 1786, Leicester LE5 5ZE
Tel: (0116) 2738228 **Fax:** (0116) 2738228
Email: mfb@halaal.org
Website: http://www.halaal.org/
Contact: Mr Muhammad Shahid Raza

Position: Director
Activities: Resources
Traditions: Sunni
Other Languages: Urdu
Provides consultancy on the preparation of food products according to the dietary laws of Islam; research into available food products; authentication and issue of Halal certification for food products; and information on food products suitable for Muslims.

Muslim Hands*
148-164 Gregory Boulevard, Nottingham NG7 5JE
Tel: (0115) 9117222 **Fax:** (0115) 9117220
Email: contact@muslimhands.org
Website: http://www.muslimhands.org/
Contact: Mr Amjad Shah
Position: Manager
Contact Email: shah@muslimhands.org
Traditions: Sunni
Other Languages: Urdu, Punjabi, Arabic
We are an international relief organisation.

Muslim Information Centre*
233 Seven Sisters Road, London N4 2DA
Tel: (020) 7272 5170 **Fax:** (020) 7272 3214
Contact: Mohammed Tameem
Position: Secretary
Activities: Books, inter-faith, resources
Traditions: Sunni
Other Languages: Arabic, Urdu, Somali
Affiliations: Muslim Welfare House; Muslim Council of Britain; Islamic Propagation Organisation
Will also give information over the telephone, and supply short courses free to students and advise the media on different issues.

Muslim Institute for Research and Planning*
109 Fulham Palace Road, London W6 8JA
Tel: (020) 8563 1995 **Fax:** (020) 8563 1993
Website: http://www.musliminstitute.com/
Contact: Dr Ghayasuddin Siddiqui
Position: Director
Contact Tel: (07860) 259289
Contact Email: drsiddiqui@talk21.com
Activities: Resources, media, youth, elderly, women, newsletter
Other Languages: Urdu, Punjabi, Arabic, Farsi
Affiliations: The Muslim Parliament; The Muslim Institute Trust; Halal Food Authority; Bait al-Mal al-Islam
Undertakes research on Islam; organises seminars and conferences, lectures, Arabic language courses;

study of the life of the Prophet; issues in the Islamic movement.

Muslim Ladies Hostel (FOSIS)*
Staverton Lodge, 122 Brondesbury Park, Willesden Green, London NW2 5JR
Tel: (020) 8451 0033
Email: ladieshostel.@fosis.demon.co.uk
Position: Hostel Warden
Activities: Resource, youth, newsletters, books
Other Languages: Urdu, Arabic
Student services provided.

Muslim Law (Shariah) Council*
20-22 Creffield Road, London W5 3RP
Tel: (020) 8992 6636 **Fax:** (020) 8993 3946
Contact: Moulana Mohammad Shahid Raza
Position: Executive Secretary
Other Languages: Urdu, Arabic
Operates an information desk on Islam; provides services to the Muslims concerned with questions of marriage, divorce, inheritance etc; gives Islamic legal opinion on questions put to it; offers expert information on Islamic law to non-Muslims.

Muslim Men's Hostel (FOSIS)
38 Mapesbury Road, London NW2 4JD
Tel: (020) 8438 0190
Contact: Hostel Warden

Muslim Parliament of Britain (Head Office)*
458 Cheetham Hill Road, Manchester M8 9JW
Tel: (0161) 7209959 **Fax:** (0161) 7209959
Contact: Mohammed Khan
Position: Secretary

Muslim Parliament of Great Britain*
109 Fulham Palace Road, London W6 8JA
Tel: (020) 8563 1995 **Fax:** (020) 8563 1993
Contact: Dr Muhammad Ghayasuddin Siddiqui
Position: Leader
Contact Tel: (07860) 259289
Contact Email: drsiddiqui@talk21.com
Activities: Media, youth, women, newsletters
Other Languages: Urdu/Punjabi, French, Farsi, Arabic
Affiliations: Bait Al-Mal Al-Islami; Halal Food Authority; Halal Food Consumers Association; Human Rights Committee, Muslim Institute
We seek to promote human rights through lobbying and campaigning.

Muslim Scholars Movement of Europe*
40 Albion Road, Wellgate, Rotherham S60 2NF
Tel: (01709) 560038

Contact: Mr Mumtaz Hussain
Activities: Worship, resource, media, umbrella body, visits, youth
Other Languages: English, Urdu, Punjabi, Arabic

Muslim Ummah Solidarity Movement*
64 Somerville Road, Small Heath, Birmingham B10 9EL
Tel: (0121) 3288466
Contact: Malik Fazal Hussain
Position: General Secretary
Activities: Media, umbrella body, books, inter-faith
Traditions: Sunni
Other Languages: Urdu, Arabic
Affiliations: Urdu Forum (UK) Birmingham; Jamiate Nizame Islam; Pakistan Community Centre; Pakistan Workers Association

Muslim Welfare House*
233 Seven Sisters Road, Islington, London N4 2DA
Tel: (020) 7263 3071 **Fax:** (020) 7281 2687
Contact: Mr Fadi Itani
Position: Director
Activities: Community centre
Traditions: Sunni
Other Languages: Arabic, French, Eritrean
Affiliations: Muslim Council of Britain
Gives careers advice and guidance, IT courses, English courses, supplementary schools, dress-making, counselling, social advice, life-skills courses, drop-in translation, library, prayer facilities.

Muslim Women's Helpline*
11 Main Drive, East Lane Business Park, Wembley HA9 7NA
Tel: (020) 8908 3205 **Fax:** (020) 8291 2005
Email: mwhl@amr.net.demon.co.uk
Website:
http://www.amrnet.demon.co.uk/related/mwhl
Contact: Ms N Ebrahim
Position: Co-ordinator
Activities: Newsletter/journal, visits, inter-faith
Other Languages: Urdu, Gujarati, Punjabi, Arabic
Affiliations: Muslim Council of Britain
We are a telephone counselling service for Muslim women of any ethnicity. We support, advise and refer to other organisations, Muslim and non-Muslim.

Muslim World League*
46 Goode Street, London W1T 4LU
Tel: (020) 7636 7568 **Fax:** (020) 7637 5034
Email: mwl@webstar.co.uk
Contact: G Rahman
Position: Deputy Director

Activities: Worship/practice/meditation, youth, elderly, visits
Traditions: Sunni
Other Languages: Arabic, Urdu, Bengali, Hindi
Affiliations: Muslim Council of Britain; Muslim World League, Makkah, Saudi Arabia

Naqshbandi Haqqani Trust
St Mary's Priory, 277 St Anne's Road, Tottenham, London N15 5RG
Position: Secretary
Activities: Resource, youth, books
Traditions: Sunni
Movements: Tassawuf
Other Languages: Urdu, Arabic, Bengali, Gujarati
The name Naqshbandi means "he who works to make a design" ie, the person who imprints the name of God on his or her heart. We encourage participation of young people and women and welcome people who are not of the Muslim faith for discussions.

National Muslim Education Council of UK*
109 Campden Hill Road, London W8 7TL
Tel: (020) 7229 0538
Contact: Dr S A Pasha
Position: Secretary
Contact Tel: (020) 7221 6608
Activities: Central body, youth, books, inter-faith
Traditions: Sunni
Other Languages: Urdu, Bengali, Turkish, Arabic
Co-ordinate work with the DFES to ensure Islamic teaching to Muslim children in state schools. Holds biennial National Educational conferences to assess the problems faced by Muslim children in state schools.

Organisation of British Muslims
7 Penner Close, Wimbledon, London SW19 6QA
Tel: (020) 8944 5859 **Fax:** (020) 8944 5697
Contact: Abdul Latif Bahalim
Position: National Secretary
Activities: Resource, umbrella body
Traditions: Sunni, Ismaili, Ithna Asheri, Shi'a
Other Languages: Urdu, Punjabi, Arabic, Persian
Affiliations: Organisation of European Muslims; Organisation of World Muslims
OBM seeks proper representation of the largest minority of the British Muslims in the British and European Parliaments. The British and European Muslims can contribute towards a better understanding and better relations between UK/EU and 52 Muslim Countries.

Pakistan Muslim League UK*
32 Malmesbury Road, Small Heath, Birmingham B10 0JQ
Tel: (0121) 7724253 **Fax:** (0121) 2477777
Contact: Dr S A Khan
Position: President
Activities: Central body
Traditions: Sunni
Movements: Barelwi
Other Languages: Urdu, Punjabi, Pushto, Sindhi

Pashtoon Association UK*
253 Bordesley Green, Birmingham B9 5EX
Tel: (0121) 7735996
Contact: Mr Hawas Khan
Position: President
Activities: Community centre
Traditions: Sunni
Movements: Ahl-e-Hadith, Barelwi, Deobandi, Jamati-I-Islami, Tablighi Jamaat, Tassawuf
Other Languages: Pushto

Quranic Mission UK*
6 Ridley Avenue, Acklam, Middlesbrough TS5 7AN
Tel: (01642) 822125 **Fax:** (01642) 288412
Email: quranicmissionuk@hotmail.com
Website: http://www.toluislam.com/
Contact: Mohammed Hanif
Position: Facilitator
Contact Tel: (01642) 828182
Activities: Central body, youth, women, newsletter/journal, books
Movements: Tolu-e-Islam
Other Languages: Urdu
Affiliations: Muslim Discussion Group, Middlesbrough; Bazm Tolu-e-Islam, London; Idara Tolu-e-Islam, Pakistan
To challenge and remove all non-Qur'anic ideologies, beliefs, rigid interpretations and practices prevalent in present day Islam and replace them with dynamic Qur'anic concepts based upon reason and rationale.

Raza Academy*
138 Northgate Road, Edgeley, Stockport SK3 9NL
Tel: (0161) 4771595 **Fax:** (0161) 2911390
Contact: Mr M I Kashmiri
Position: Chairman
Activities: Youth, newsletter/journal, books, newspapers, radio, visits
Traditions: Sunni
Movements: Barelwi, Tassawuf
Other Languages: Urdu, Arabic, Gujarati, Punjabi

Affiliations: Jamiat Tabligh ul Islam, Bradford; World Islamic Mission

Founded in 1985, the Raza Academy publishes a monthly journal. Since 1985 The Academy has published over 80 books on Islam written in English.

S I Education Society*

133 Rowan Road, London SW16 5HU
Tel: (020) 8241 0222 **Fax:** (020) 8241 2214
Contact: Moulana Syed Shamim-us Sibtan Rizvi
Position: Managing Trustee
Activities: Worship, resource, media, visits, youth, elderly
Traditions: Muslim Shi'a, Ithna Asheri
Other Languages: Urdu, Gujarati, Punjabi

Has an Islamic bookshop; Islamic library; weekly religious gathering; marriage bureau. There are also monthly magazines "The Minister" (English). "Al-Moballigh" (Urdu) and audio magazine "The Voice" (English); recorded religious messages (English) (020-8241-2212) and for religious guidance (07956-129188).

Seerah Foundation*

78 Gillespie Road, London N5 1LN
Tel: (020) 8478 3156 **Fax:** (020) 8478 3156
Contact: Ms Yasmin Hassan
Position: Secretary
Activities: Books
Traditions: Sunni
Other Languages: Urdu, Punjabi

Society of Muslim Lawyers*

PO Box 349, Edmonton, London N9 7RR
Tel: (0956) 600569 **Fax:** (020) 8803 4541
Email: obm@clara.net
Website: http://www.sml.f2s.com/
Contact: Mr Choudary
Position: Chairman
Contact Tel: (07956) 920006
Contact Email: anjem@hotmail.com
Activities: Umbrella body, youth, elderly, women, newsletter/journal, books, visits, resources
Traditions: Sunni
Movements: Usulis (Juristic Scholars)
Other Languages: Arabic, Urdu, Bengali
Affiliations: London School of Shari'ah; Shari'ah Court of the UK; Al-Muhajiroun (The Khiladaf Movement)

One of the most active bodies for the defence of the Muslim Community against discrimination and conflict between secular law and divine Islamic laws; well equipped with civil English law and Islamic Shariah law.

Sri Lanka Islamic Association/Sri Lanka Islamic Cultural Home (UK)*

7 Broadway Buildings, Boston Road, London W7 3TT
Tel: (020) 8952 2105 **Fax:** (020) 8962 2105
Contact: A Azahim Mohamed
Position: General Secretary
Activities: Resource, visits, youth, women, newsletters, inter-faith
Traditions: Sunni (Sunath Jamath)
Other Languages: Sinhalese, Arabic, Tamil
Affiliations: Union of Muslim Organisations UK and Eire; Muslim Communities Development Project; Muslim World League

The organisation has children's Qur'an classes at the weekends and classes for adults on Saturdays. It holds youth activities on Fridays and plays cricket during the Summer months. It also celebrates the Muslim festival of Eid and has a library service.

Sri Lanka Islamic UK Association*

Position: General Secretary

The organisation was formed in 1973 to get Sri Lankan Muslims together. Today its membership covers over five hundred families and it is the only representative body for Sri Lankan Muslims in the UK.

Sri Lanka Muslim Refugee Assistance (UK)*

60 Cumberland Road, Harwell, London W7 2EB
Tel: (020) 8840 5819 **Fax:** (020) 8959 5189
Contact: Mr Nuski Mohammed
Position: President
Other Languages: Tamil

Ta Ha Publishers Ltd*

1 Wynne Road, London SW9 0BB
Tel: (020) 7737 7266 **Fax:** (020) 7737 7266
Contact: Afsar Siddiqui
Position: Director
Activities: Books
Traditions: Sunni
Other Languages: Urdu, Arabic
Affiliations: Islamic Publishers Association

We have published over 230 titles for both adults and children. Our publications are of high quality but at very low prices. Catalogue and price list can be obtained on request.

UK Action Committee on Islamic Affairs*
PO Box 157, New Malden KT3 3YJ
Tel: (020) 8974 2780 **Fax:** (020) 8974 2781
Email: info@uxacia.com
Contact: Iqbal Sacranie
Position: Joint Convenor
Activities: Umbrella body, inter-faith
Other Languages: Urdu, Arabic, Bengali, Gujarati
Affiliations: Muslim Council of Britain
UKACIA was formed in October 1988. It is an umbrella body representing Muslim organisations and mosques throughout the country. Activities have particularly been on issues relating to the community and law in Britain, especially religious discrimination.

UK Islamic Mission*
202 North Gower Street, London NW1 2LY
Tel: (020) 7387 2157 **Fax:** (020) 7383 0867
Contact: Maulana Syed Sherif Ahmed
Position: President
Activities: Umbrella body, inter-faith
A charitable organisation which aims to help the Muslim community in the UK to project its cultural identity and to promote and encourage mutual appreciation and friendly relations between Muslims and non-Muslims, as well as unity among Muslims.

UK Turkish Islamic Cultural Centre and Suleymaniye Mosque*
212-216 Kingsland Road, Shoreditch, London E2 8AX
Tel: (020) 7684 9900 **Fax:** (020) 7684 9992
Email: suleymaniye.mosque@which.net
Website: http://www.ukturkislam.co.uk/
Contact: Mr Hakan Ozgul
Position: Secretary
Contact Tel: (020) 7684 7566
Contact Email: h_ozgul@hotmail.com
Activities: Worship/practice/meditation, community centre, central body, youth, elderly, women, resources
Traditions: Sunni
Movements: Naqshbandi
Other Languages: Turkish, Arabic
Affiliations: The Union of Turkish Islamic Cultural Centres

Union of Muslim Families (UK)*
46 Goodge Street, London W1T 4LU
Tel: (020) 7637 1971
Contact: Mr Naz Usmani
Position: Assistant Secretary
Activities: Resource, media, umbrella body, visits, youth, elderly
Traditions: Sunni

Union of Muslim Organisations of UK and Eire (UMO)*
109 Campden Hill Road, London W8 7TL
Tel: (020) 7229 0538 **Fax:** (020) 7792 2130
Contact: Dr Sayid Aziz Pasha
Position: General Secretary
Contact Tel: (020) 7221 6608
Activities: Central body, umbrella body, youth, inter-faith, resources
Other Languages: Urdu, Arabic, Bengali, Turkish
The Union of Muslim Organisations is a democratically-elected national representative body of British Muslims.

Universal Sufism - Sufi Movement*
Arama, Hawthorn Road, Highfield, Southampton SO17 1PX
Tel: (023) 8055 8357
Contact: Miss V H Best
Activities: Worship/practice/meditation
Affiliations: Sufi Movement, The Hague, Holland

WAQF Al-Birr Educational Trust*
2 Digswell Street, London N7 8JX
Tel: (020) 7607 8839
Activities: Resource
Other Languages: Urdu, Arabic

World Ahl Ul-Bayt Islamic League*
19 Chelmsford Square, London NW10 3AP
Tel: (020) 8459 8475 **Fax:** (020) 8451 7059
Email: wabil@wabil.com
Contact: His Eminence Sayyed Musawi
Position: Chair
Contact Tel: (020) 8459 6051
Contact Email: musawi@wabil.com
Activities: Umbrella body, youth, women, newsletter/journal, books, radio, inter-faith, resources
Traditions: Ithna Asheri
Other Languages: Arabic, Urdu, French
Affiliations: Inter Faith Network for the UK
Worldwide organisation with affiliates of Shi'a organisations and carrying out welfare activities for the upliftment of the poor, financially, educationally and morally. Open to Shi'a personalities well-known for their interest and endeavour in Islamic affairs. It aims to co-ordinate activities of Shi'a organisations throughout the world and to create better understanding between Shi'as and other Muslims and non-Muslims.

World Assembly of Muslim Youth (WAMY) Western Europe Office*
46 Goodge Street, London W1T 4LU
Tel: (020) 7636 7010 **Fax:** (020) 7636 7080
Contact: Mr Noureddin Miladi
Position: Executive Director
Activities: Resource, umbrella body, visits, youth, elderly, women,
WAMY is an independent, international Islamic organisation working to improve the Islamic awareness among Muslim youth and introducing Islam to people of other faiths. Founded in 1972 in Riyadh, Saudi Arabia.

World Federation of Khoja Shi'a 'Ithna-Asheri Muslim Communities*
Islamic Centre, Wood Lane, Stanmore HA7 4LQ
Tel: (020) 8954 9881 **Fax:** (020) 8954 9034
Email: secretariat@world-federation.org
Website: http://www.world-federation.org/
Contact: Mustafa Jaffer
Position: Admin Secretary
Activities: Worship, resource, umbrella body, visits, books, inter-faith
Traditions: Shi'a

World Islamic Mission (UK)*
4th Floor, 53-56 Great Sutton Street, London EC1V 0DG
Tel: (020) 7608 3799 **Fax:** (020) 7608 3792
Contact: Mr S G Syedain
Position: Senior Vice President
Activities: Youth, women, books, inter-faith
Traditions: Sunni
Other Languages: Urdu, Arabic
Affiliations: Imams and Mosques Council UK; World Islamic Mission International; Inter Faith Network for the UK

World Islamic Propagation Establishment (UK)*
359 Rayners Lane, Pinner HA5 5EN
Tel: (020) 8426 2216 **Fax:** (020) 8426 2217
Contact: Mr Shahid Akmal
Position: Chair
Activities: Resource, youth, inter-faith
Traditions: Sunni
Other Languages: Urdu, Punjabi, Gujarati, Swahili
We specialise in comparative religions, especially Christianity and Islam. We are the official London distributors of literature, video and audio products by Sheikh Ahmed Deedat (S.Africa), Dr Khalid Al-Mansour (USA) and Dr. Zakir Naik (India)

World of Islam Trust (ALTAJLR)*
33 Thurloe Place, London SW13 9QZ
Tel: (020) 7581 3522 **Fax:** (020) 7584 1977
Contact: Alistair Duncan
Position: Director
Activities: Resource, books, inter-faith
The Trust helps towards understanding and appreciating the contribution of Islamic culture and civilisation to the Family Of Nations.

Young Muslim Organisation UK*
94 Whitechapel Road, London E1 1JE
Tel: (020) 7247 7918 **Fax:** (020) 7247 7918
Contact: Janahid Akhmed
Position: President
Activities: Resource, media, umbrella body, youth, women, inter-faith
Traditions: Sunni
Other Languages: Urdu, Turkish, Arabic, French
Affiliations: East London Mosque; Islamic Forum Europe; UK Action Committee on Islamic Affairs
YMO UK caters mainly for the young in providing for their moral, spiritual and recreational needs. The organisation also plays a significant role in the community in tackling issues such as drugs, racism and violence.

Youth Muslim Organisation*
18 Nags Head Road, Ponders End, London EN3 7AJ
Tel: (020) 8443 2140
Email: abdul1@mdx.ac.uk
Contact: Haji Abdul Sattar
Position: President
Activities: Central body, youth, women, radio, visits, inter-faith, resources
Traditions: Sunni
Movements: Ahl-e-Hadith, Jamati-i-Islami
Other Languages: Bangla, Arabic, Urdu
Increase religious awareness and give educational support to youth.

MUSLIM REGIONAL AND LOCAL ORGANISATIONS AND MOSQUES

A variety of forms of Muslim regional and local organisation are listed in this directory. These include *mosques*, schools, welfare bodies and student societies. In some cases there are separate entries at the same address where a welfare association owns a *mosque* but receives a separate entry because its objectives and activities are wider than the *mosque* activities alone. There are also some entries that reflect where a number of organisations with a particular sectoral remit, such as women's or youth work, are based at the same address and are sometimes different parts of the same organisation.

ENGLAND 467

NORTH EAST 467

YORKSHIRE AND THE HUMBER 469

NORTH WEST 482

EAST MIDLANDS 496

WEST MIDLANDS 501

EAST OF ENGLAND 514

LONDON 517

SOUTH EAST 533

SOUTH WEST 539

NORTHERN IRELAND 542

SCOTLAND 542

WALES 545

ENGLAND

NORTH EAST
City, Town or Local Bodies

Mosque*
4 Mayorswell Close, Durham City DH1 1JU
Tel: (0191) 3867972
Activities: Education
Other Languages: Arabic
Affiliations: Muslim Welfare House

Dar ul Islam Central Mosque and Islamic Education Centre*
30 Southfield Road, Middlesbrough TS1 3EX
Tel: (01642) 884224 **Fax:** (01642) 254585
Email: waleid.allam@ntlworld.com
Contact: Allah Ditta
Position: Chairman
Activities: Worship/practice/meditation, youth
Other Languages: Urdu, Arabic

Islamic Cultural Association*
3 South Terrace, South Bank, Middlesbrough TS6 6HW
Tel: (01642) 462598
Contact: M Rauf
Position: Chairman
Activities: Worship, resource, visits
Traditions: Sunni
Movements: Ahl-e-Hadith
Other Languages: Urdu, Arabic
Affiliations: Cleveland Mosques

Madrassa-Zia-ul-Qur'an*
2a Bow Street, Middlesbrough TS1 4BS
Tel: (01642) 230408
Contact: H Zaman
Position: Secretary

Masjide-e Jamia Al Madina
133a Waterloo Road, Middlesbrough TS1 3JB
Tel: (01642) 245855

Muslim Federation, Cleveland*
9 Park Road North, Middlesbrough TS1 3LF
Tel: (01642) 873305 **Fax:** (01642) 873307
Contact: Mr Ali Luft
Position: Chair
Activities: Worship, resource, visits, youth, women, education
Traditions: Sunni
Other Languages: Arabic, Urdu, Somali, French

Heaton Mosque*
1 Rothbury Terrace, Heaton, Newcastle-upon-Tyne NE6 5XH
Tel: (0191) 2654083
Contact: Mohammad Ahmad
Position: Secretary

Islamic Society - University of Newcastle-upon-Tyne*
King George VI Building, Kings Walk off Thomas Street, Newcastle-upon-Tyne NE 1 7RU
Tel: (0191) 2326889 **Fax:** (0191) 2228811
Email: 150c@ncl.ac.uk
Website:
http://www.societies.ncl.ac.uk/islamic.society
Contact: Lotfy Az Az
Position: General Secretary
Contact Tel: (07900) 560250
Contact Email: irwanprasetyo@newcastle.ac.uk
Activities: Worship, resource, visits, youth, women
Other Languages: Arabic, Malay, Turkish, Farsi, Urdu, Bengali
Affiliations: Muslim Welfare House; Federation of Students Islamic Society

Muslim Welfare House*
6 North Terrace, Spital Tongues, Newcastle-upon-Tyne NE2 4AD
Tel: (0191) 2323055
Email: mwh@mwhouse.freeserve.co.uk
Contact: Mr Mahmoud Kurdi
Position: Secretary
Activities: Worship/practice/meditation, community centre, youth, resources
Traditions: Sunni
Movements: Jamati-i-Islami
Other Languages: Arabic, Urdu
Affiliations: Muslim Welfare House, London

Newcastle Mosque and Islamic Centre*
Malvern Street, off Elswick Road, Newcastle-upon-Tyne NE4 6SU
Tel: (0191) 2260562
Contact: Zafar Jung Khan
Position: President
Activities: Worship, resource, youth, inter-faith
Traditions: Sunni
Movements: Barelwi
Other Languages: Punjabi, Urdu

Pakistan Muslim Association*
Malvern Street, Newcastle-upon-Tyne NE4 6SU
Tel: (0191) 2260562

Contact: Mr Z J Khan
Position: Chairperson

Turkish Community Association - Kotku Mosque*
35 Grainger Park Road, Newcastle-upon-Tyne NE4 8SA
Tel: (0191) 2739000
Email: turkishcommunitycentre@yahoo.com
Website:
http://www.turkishcommunitycentre.cjb.net/
Contact: Mr Saim Kayadibi
Position: Chair
Contact Tel: (07950) 430821
Contact Email: skayadibi@yahoo.com
Activities: Worship/practice/meditation, community centre, youth, elderly, women, newsletter/journal, resources
Traditions: Sunni
Other Languages: Turkish, Arabic, Urdu

UWAIS Foundation*
113/115 Fenham Hall Drive, Fenham, Newcastle-upon-Tyne NE4 9XB
Tel: (0191) 2747540
Contact: Mr Mohammed Mushtaq Ahmed
Position: Chair/Trustee
Activities: Resource, youth, women
Other Languages: Urdu, Punjabi, Arabic

Alazhar Mosque
Laygate Lane, South Shields
Tel: (0191) 5450738

South Tyneside Bangladesh Muslim Cultural Association*
3-5 Baring Street, off Ocean Road, South Shields NE33 2DR
Tel: (0191) 4542501
Email: abbyg@banglaplace.fsnet.co.uk
Contact: Mohammed Rana Rahman
Position: Secretary
Contact Tel: (0191) 4275163
Activities: Worship/practice/meditation, resources
Traditions: Sunni
Movements: Jamati-i-Islami
Other Languages: Bengali, Arabic
Affiliations: Central Mosque, London

Muslim Welfare Trust*
16 Northcote Street, Stockton-on-Tees TS18 3JB
Contact: Imam

Thornaby Muslim Association*
127-129 West Bury Street, Thornaby, Stockton-on-Tees TS17 6LW
Tel: (01642) 650104 **Fax:** (01642) 650104
Email: ziauddin@hotmail.com
Contact: Mr M Anwar
Contact Tel: (01642) 612982
Activities: Worship/practice/meditation, visits
Traditions: Sunni
Movements: Deobandi
Other Languages: Punjabi, Urdu

UK Islamic Mission*
9 Kenley Gardens, Norton, Stockton-on-Tees TS20 1QF
Tel: (01642) 556512 **Fax:** (01642) 552232
Contact: Dr S Irfan-Haque
Position: President
Activities: Resource, visits, youth, elderly, inter-faith
Traditions: Sunni
Movements: Jamati-i-Islami
Other Languages: Urdu, Punjabi

Sunderland Mosque*
73-77 Chester Road, Sunderland SR2 7PN
Tel: (0191) 5658708
Contact: Imamuddin

Ali Taj Prayer Room*
1st Floor, 34-35 Tangier Street, Whitehaven CA28 7UZ
Tel: (01946) 592679
Contact: Mr Jomiar Ali
Position: Secretary

YORKSHIRE AND THE HUMBER
Regional or County Bodies

Huddersfield Islamic Library*
18 St Steven Road, Lockwood, Huddersfield HD1 3QY
Tel: (01484) 452786
Email: info@islamiclibrary.co.uk
Website: http://www.islamiclibrary.co.uk/
Contact: Mr Mohammad Imran
Position: Secretary
Contact Tel: (07931) 730439
Contact Email: ashigemadinah@hotmail.com
Activities: Community centre, youth, women, radio, visits, inter-faith, resources
Traditions: Sunni
Other Languages: Urdu, Punjabi, Arabic

Sheffield and Rotherham District Council of Muslims*
1 Derriman Glen, Silverdale Road, Sheffield S11
Tel: (0114) 2360465 **Fax:** (0114) 2360532

City, Town or Local Bodies

Anwar-ul-Islam*
90 Dark Lane, Clark Green, Batley WF17 7RN
Tel: (07810) 746526
Contact: Hasan Loonat
Position: General Secretary
Contact Tel: (01924) 503317
Other Languages: Gujarati, Urdu

Dabhel-Simlak Muslim Welfare Society*
1 Whitaker Street, Batley WF17 5AQ
Tel: (01924) 472215

Indian Muslim Welfare Society*
28 Track Road, Batley WF17 7AA
Tel: (01924) 500555 **Fax:** (01924) 500556
Email: imws@hotmail.com
Contact: Masa Kazi
Position: Administration Officer
Contact Email: masakazi@hotmail.com

Jama Masjid Mosque*
1 Whitaker Street, Batley WF17 5AQ
Tel: (01924) 472215
Contact: Akhtar Ali
Position: General Secretary
Contact Tel: (01924) 472215
Other Languages: Urdu

Masjid and Madrassa Noor ul Islam*
Snowden Street, Batley WF17 7RS
Tel: (01924) 472919
Contact: Mr Akooji Badat
Position: Chairman
Contact Tel: (01924) 503411
Contact Email: akooji.badat@ntlworld.com
Activities: Worship/practice/meditation, community centre
Movements: Deobandi
Other Languages: Hindi, Urdu, Arabic,

Masjid-e-Zinatul Islam*
Taylor Street, Batley WF17 5BA
Contact: Mr Mohammad Pandoor
Position: General Secretary
Contact Tel: (0778) 8975140

Mount Pleasant Islamic Trust*
Purlwell Lane, Batley WF17 7NQ

Tel: (01924) 472378 **Fax:** (01924) 420786
Contact: Mr Ismail Y Lunat
Position: General Secretary
Activities: Worship/practice/meditation,
community centre, youth, elderly, women, visits,
inter-faith, resources
Traditions: Sunni
Movements: Deobandi, Tablighi Jamaat, Tassawuf
Other Languages: Gujarati, Urdu, Arabic
Affiliations: Indian Muslim Welfare Society,
Muslim Council of Britain, Rabtah al Alam la
Islamiyya

Muslim Elderly and Disabled Organisation*
18 Woodsome Estate, Batley WF17 7EB
Tel: (01924) 503640
Contact: Ahmed Patel
Position: Chair
Activities: Visits, youth, elderly, women
Traditions: Sunni
Other Languages: Gujarati, Urdu

Warwick Road Women's Group*
c/o Warwick Road School, Batley WF17 7AN
Tel: (01924) 325344
Contact: Mrs Zulekha Loonat
Position: Co-opted member
Activities: Community centre, women
Traditions: Sunni
Other Languages: Gujarat, Punjabi, Urdu

Islamic Cultural and Welfare Association*
Henry Street, Batley Carr, Batley Carr WF17 6JJ
Tel: (01924) 463275 **Fax:** (01924) 463275
Contact: Ismail Ebrahim Dajz
Position: President
Activities: Worship, resource, visits, youth, elderly,
women
Traditions: Sunni
Movements: Deobandi, Tablighi Jamaat
Other Languages: Gujarati, Urdu
Affiliations: Indian Muslim Welfare Society

Abu Bakar Mosque*
38 Steadman Terrace, Bradford BD3 9NB
Contact: Mr Amanullah Khan
Position: President
Contact Tel: (01274) 668343
Activities: Worship/practice/meditation
Traditions: Sunni
Movements: Deobandi
Other Languages: Urdu, Pushto, Punjabi
Affiliations: Council of Mosques Bradford

Anjuman-e-Haideria*
47/48 Southfield Square, Bradford BD8 7SL
Tel: (07880) 880628
Contact: Syed Zulfiqat Naqvi
Position: General Secretary
Activities: Worship, resource, youth, women, inter-
faith
Traditions: Ithna Asheri
Other Languages: Punjabi, Urdu
Affiliations: Council of Mosques

Bait ul Aman Jamia Mosque and Madrassah*
6 Maudsley Street, Bradford BD3 9JT
Contact: Mr Sunna Ullah
Position: President
Activities: Youth, elderly
Traditions: Sunni
Movements: Tassawuf
Other Languages: Bengali

Bradford Council of Mosques*
6 Claremont, Bradford BD7 1BG
Tel: (01274) 732479
Contact: Sher Azam
Position: President
Contact Tel: (01274) 578081

Bradford Eid Committee*
5 Hallfield Road, Bradford BD1 3RP
Tel: (01274) 736000 **Fax:** (01274) 736555
Contact: Mohammad Abbas
Position: Treasurer
Activities: Resource, inter-faith
Traditions: Sunni
Other Languages: Urdu, Punjabi

Bradford Sunni Muslim Khalifa Society*
57 Upper Seymour Street, Bradford BD3 9LJ
Tel: (01274) 403295
Contact: Mrs Kareem

Council for Mosques*
378-380 Great Horton Road, Bradford BD7 3HS
Tel: (01274) 521792 **Fax:** (01274) 521792
Contact: M Saleem Khan
Position: Centre Co-ordinator
Activities: Community centre, central body,
umbrella body, elderly, women, inter-faith, resources
Other Languages: Urdu, Punjabi, Hindi, Gujarati

Dar-al-Argam*
16 Neal Street, Bradford BD5 0BX
Tel: (01274) 392727
Contact: Dr N Al'ramadhani
Position: Director

East African Muslim Association (EAMA)*
17 Daleside Walk, Bradford BD5 8PP
Tel: (01274) 400206
Contact: Mr K A Hafeez
Position: Secretary
Activities: Elderly, resources
Traditions: Sunni
Movements: Barelwi, Deobandi
Other Languages: Urdu, Punjabi, Kiswahili,
Gujarati

Feversham College*
Radcliffe Avenue, Bradford BD2 1JL
Tel: (01274) 559500 **Fax:** (01274) 559509
Contact: Mohammed Ibrahim
Position: Chairperson
Activities: Resource, visits, inter-faith
Traditions: Sunni
Other Languages: Urdu, Punjabi, Pushto,
Bengali, Arabic
Affiliations: Muslim Association of Bradford;
Muslim Education Forum; Muslim Teachers
Association

Frankri Centre
47 Elizabeth Street, Bradford BD5 0SD

Human Relief Foundation*
PO Box 194, Bradford BD7 1YW
Tel: (01274) 392727
Contact: Dr Al'Ramadhani
Position: Chairperson

Hussainia Islamic Mission*
All Saints Road, Bradford BD7 3AY
Tel: (01274) 306291
Contact: Tufail H Kazhi
Position: Treasurer
Contact Tel: (01274) 306291
Activities: Worship, youth
Traditions: 'Ithna Asheri
Other Languages: Urdu, Punjabi, Persian, Arabic
Affiliations: Bradford Council for Mosques

Islamic Cultural and Educational Association*
101 Thornbury Road, Thornbury, Bradford
BD3 8SA
Contact: Mr Munsaf Dad Saddiq
Position: Secretary
Activities: Worship/practice/meditation, youth,
elderly, women
Traditions: Sunni
Movements: Barelwi
Other Languages: Urdu, Punjabi

Islamic Cultural Educational Centre
190 Toller Lane, Heaton, Bradford BD9 5JB

Islamic Missionary College
28 Shearbridge Road, Bradford BD7 3AF
Tel: (01274) 305654
Contact: Mohammed Yousaf
Position: President
Activities: Worship, resource, visits
Traditions: Sunni
Movements: Barelwi
Other Languages: Punjabi, Urdu

Islamic Relief*
47-51 Carlisle Road, Bradford BD8
Tel: (01274) 481123 **Fax:** (01274) 481123
Contact: Manager
Activities: Resource, visits
Other Languages: Urdu, Punjabi

Jame Masjid Ahl-e-Hadith
49 Hastings Street, Bradford BD5 9PR

**Jamia Masjid and Muslim Association of
Bradford***
30 Howard Street, Bradford BD5 0BP
Tel: (01274) 724819 **Fax:** (01274) 729173
Email: nawaz@khan129.fsnet.co.uk
Website: http://www.muslimab.org/
Contact: Nawaz Khan
Position: Secretary
Contact Tel: (01274) 740274
Activities: Worship/practice/meditation,
community centre, central body, youth, elderly,
women, inter-faith, resources
Movements: Deobandi, Tablighi Jamaat
Other Languages: Urdu, Punjabi, Hindko,
Pushto
Affiliations: Council for Mosques; Muslim
Council of Britain

Jamia Masjid Hanfia*
Carlisle Road, Bradford BD8 8AD
Tel: (01274) 492539
Contact: Mr M Sahawad
Position: Secretary

Jamia Mosque Tabligh-Ul-Islam
Woodhead Road, Bradford BD7 1NX

Jamiat Tabligh ul-Islam*
1-3 Burnett Place, Marshfield, Bradford BD5 9LX
Tel: (01274) 729087
Contact: Mr Ali Shankat

Position: Caretaker
Activities: Worship/practice/meditation
Traditions: Sunni
Other Languages: Urdu

Jamiyat Tabligh-ul-Islam*
St Lukes Church Hall, Victor Street, Bradford
BD8 8NG
Tel: (01274) 548232
Contact: Mr Hussain
Position: Chairperson

Jamiyat Tabligh-ul-Islam Mosque*
133 Toller Lane, Bradford BD8 9HL
Tel: (01274) 543132
Contact: Mr Mohammad Ashraf
Position: Secretary
Contact Tel: (01274) 547372
Activities: Worship, resource, visits, inter-faith
Traditions: Sunni
Movements: Barelwi, Tassawuf
Other Languages: Punjabi, Urdu
Affiliations: Bradford Council for Mosques

Jamiyat Tabligh-ul-Islam*
68-69 Salt Field Square, Nr Lumb Lane, Bradford
BD8
Tel: (01274) 729087
Contact: Mr L Hussain
Position: Trustee

Jamiyat Tabligh-ul-Islam*
23 Cleveland Road, Heaton, Bradford B9 4PB
Tel: (01274) 548232 **Fax:** (01274) 496096
Contact: Mr Khadim Hussain
Position: President
Activities: Worship
Traditions: Sunni
Movements: Barelwi
Other Languages: Arabic, Urdu

Jamiyat Tabligh-ul-Islam*
68-69 Southfield Square, Manningham, Bradford
BD8 7SN
Tel: (01274) 729087
Contact: Mr Liaqat Hussain
Position: Trustee
Activities: Worship, umbrella body, visits, youth,
inter-faith
Traditions: Sunni
Movements: Barelwi
Other Languages: Punjabi, Urdu
Affiliations: Bradford Council of Mosques

Madinatul Uloom Mosque and Islamic Centre*
14 Nesfield Street, Manningham Lane, Bradford
BD1 3ET
Tel: (01274) 729418

Madina Masjid Mosque*
133 Newton Street, Bradford BD5 7BJ
Tel: (01274) 722744
Email: m.a.s.arif@takzi.com
Contact: Mr M A Samad
Position: Secretary
Contact Tel: (01274) 306785
Activities: Worship
Other Languages: Bengali, Urdu, Arabic

Madrassah and Mosque Tarteel-ul-Quran
42 Woodview Terrace, Manningham, Bradford
BD9 7AJ
Tel: (01274) 775723
Contact: Maulana Zafar Iqbal Ahmed
Position: Imam
Activities: Worship, resource, youth, inter-faith
Traditions: Sunni
Movements: Deobandi, Tablighi Jamaat/Hanafi
Other Languages: Punjabi, Hindko, Pushto, Urdu

Madressa Islam Talimuddin Society - Masjid-e-Quba*
20 Bundria Court, off Church Street, Bradford
BD8 7PD
Tel: (01274) 542027
Contact: Secretary

Millat-e-Islamia Cultural Centre*
Ivanhoe Road, off Great Horton Road, Bradford
BD7 3HY
Tel: (01274) 577469
Position: Secretary
Other Languages: Urdu, Arabic

Minhaj-ul-Qur'an Centre*
187 Manningham Lane, Bradford BD8 7HP
Tel: (01274) 720760
Contact: Muhammed Afzel Saeedi
Position: Principal

Mosque and Bradford Muslim Welfare Society*
62 St Margarets Road, Bradford BD7 3AE
Tel: (01274) 575919
Contact: A H Pandor
Position: Secretary

Mosque (Jamiyat-ahl-e-Hadith)*

5 Camden Terrace, Bradford BD8 7HX
Tel: (01274) 728993 **Fax:** (01274) 660928
Contact: Habib Ur Rehnan
Position: Secretary
Contact Tel: (0774) 8653346
Activities: Education, youth
Other Languages: Urdu, Arabic
Affiliations: Marhazi Jamiat Ahl-e-Hadith (UK)

Muslim Association of Bradford Elderly Day Centre*

24 Howard Street, Bradford BD5 0BP
Tel: (01274) 740274 **Fax:** (01274) 729173
Contact: Nawaz Khan
Position: Secretary
Contact Tel: (01274) 740274
Other Languages: Urdu, Punjabi, Pushto

Nimrah Mosque*

10 Hanover Square, Manningham, Bradford
BD1 3BY
Tel: (01274) 733439
Contact: Mohammad Younas
Position: Secretary
Contact Tel: (01274) 724668
Other Languages: Urdu, Pushto

Noor-e-Islam Mosque*

62 Margaret's Road, Bradford BD7 3AE
Tel: (01274) 575919

Shahjalal Islamic Society*

149a Little Horton Lane, Bradford BD5 0HS
Tel: (01274) 304092
Contact: Mr Konuhar Ali
Position: Development Worker
Activities: Worship/practice/meditation,
community centre, youth, elderly, resources
Traditions: Sunni
Other Languages: Bengali, Urdu

Sufat-ul-Islam UK Association*

154 Sunbridge Road, Bradford BD1 2HF
Tel: (01274) 732497
Contact: Mr M Ayub
Activities: Worship/practice/meditation,
community centre, central body, newsletter/journal,
resources
Traditions: Sunni
Other Languages: Punjabi

Sultan Bahu Educational Trust*

466 Great Horton Road, Bradford BD7 3HS
Tel: (01274) 501622
Contact: M Aslam Baig
Position: Convenor
Activities: Worship, resource, youth, elderly,
women
Traditions: Sunni
Other Languages: Punjabi, Urdu
Affiliations: Council for Mosques

Surti Muslim Khalifa Society*

32 Bertram Road, Khalifa House, Manningham,
Bradford BD8 7LN
Contact: Abdusattar Khalifa
Position: Chairman
Activities: Worship, resource, visits, youth, elderly,
women
Traditions: Sunni
Movements: Deobandi
Other Languages: Gujarati, Urdu
Affiliations: Bradford Council of Mosques; The
Foundation of UK Khalifa Societies; UK Council
of Mosques

Tabligh-ul-Islam Madrassa*

45 Coventry Street (off Wakefield Road), Bradford
BD4
Tel: (01274) 732958
Contact: Mr Pirsayyed Mahroof

Tawakkulia Islamic Society*

48 Cornwall Road, Bradford BD8 7JN
Tel: (01274) 734563
Contact: Ajijur Rahman
Position: President
Activities: Worship, resource
Traditions: Sunni
Movements: All Movements
Other Languages: Bangla

UK Islamic Mission*

3 Byron Street, Bradford BD3 0AD
Tel: (01274) 306299
Contact: Mr M Rashid
Position: President
Contact Tel: (01274) 597531
Activities: Worship/practice/meditation, youth,
women, visits
Traditions: Sunni
Movements: Jamati-i-Islami
Other Languages: Urdu, Punjabi, Gujarati,
Bangla

Affiliations: The Council For Mosques, Bradford; Muslim Council of Britain

West Bowling Islamic Society*
133 Newton Street, West Bowling, Bradford
BD5 7BJ
Tel: (01274) 722744
Contact: M Farid
Position: Secretary
Activities: Resources
Other Languages: Arabic, Urdu, Punjabi

Dewsbury Moor Muslim Association*
Pilgrim Avenue, Kirklees M C, Dewsbury
WF13 3NL
Tel: (01924) 430612
Contact: Mr Jebar Khaliq
Position: Chairman
Activities: Worship/practice/meditation, community centre, central body, umbrella body, youth, elderly, women, newspapers, visits, inter-faith, resources
Other Languages: Punjabi, Urdu, Gujarati

Dewsbury Muslim Association*
25 South Street, Savile Town, Dewsbury
WF12 9NB
Tel: (01924) 454178
Contact: Mr Mohamed Musa Patel
Activities: Worship
Other Languages: Gujarati, Urdu

Gulzar-e-Madina Mosque*
3 High Street, West Town, Dewsbury WF13
Tel: (01924) 430338
Contact: Mr M Bashir

Ilaahi Masjid and Madressa*
2 Hope Street, Dewsbury WF13 2BT
Tel: (01924) 460761
Contact: Mr Ahmed Akudi
Position: Chairman
Activities: Worship, resource, visits, youth,
Traditions: Sunni
Movements: Tablighi Jamaat
Other Languages: Gujarati, Urdu
Affiliations: Indian Muslim Welfare Society

Madni Jamia Masjid and Pakistan Muslim Association*
North Gate, Dewsbury WF13 1DZ
Tel: (01924) 461700 **Fax:** (01924) 451857
Contact: Moulana Abdul Rashid Rabbani
Activities: Worship, resource

Traditions: Sunni
Movements: Deobandi
Other Languages: Urdu, Punjabi
Affiliations: Education Centre; Jamiat-e-Ulana, Britain

Madrassah-e-Islamiyah*
53 Headfield Road, Dewsbury WF12 9JQ
Tel: (01924) 466696
Contact: Mr Mohammad Ejaz
Position: Secretary

Madresa Noor-ul-Islam*
Snowdon Street, Dewsbury WF17 7RS
Tel: (01924) 472919
Contact: Akooji Badat
Position: Chairman
Other Languages: Arabic, English, Urdu

Makki Madani Masjid
33 Kertland Street, Saville Town, Dewsbury
WF12 9PU
Tel: (01924) 458388
Contact: Safdar Ali
Position: Secretary
Activities: Worship, resource, visits, inter-faith
Traditions: Sunni
Movements: Barelwi, Tassawuf
Other Languages: Urdu, Punjabi
Affiliations: Jamaat-e-Ahl-e-Summat

Markazi Jamia Masjid Anwar-e-Madina
Crawshaw Street, Ravensthorpe, Dewsbury
WF13 3ER
Tel: (01924) 459554
Contact: Abdul Qayum Khan
Position: Imam
Activities: Worship, resource
Traditions: Sunni
Movements: Barelwi
Other Languages: Urdu, Punjabi

Markazi Mosque and Mosque Committee*
South Street, Savile Town, Dewsbury WF12 9NG
Contact Tel: (01924) 430338

Masjid-Al-Tawheed*
25 Netherfield Road, Ravensthorpe, Dewsbury
WF13 3JY
Tel: (01924) 458485
Contact: Abdul Haque Sheikh
Position: Religious Secretary
Activities: Worship/practice/meditation
Other Languages: Arabic, Urdu

Masjid-e-Umar and Madressa-e-Talimuddin*
North View, Savile Town, Dewsbury WF12 9LF
Tel: (07974) 782369 **Fax:** (07974) 147342
Email: mdeedatuk@yahoo.co.uk
Contact: Mr Muhammad Dedat
Position: Joint Secretary
Contact Email: mdeedatuk@hotmail.com
Activities: Worship, resource, inter-faith
Traditions: Sunni
Movements: Tablighi Jamaat
Other Languages: Urdu, Gujarati

Mosque
Huddersfield Road, Raventhorpe, Dewsbury
W13 3EP

Mosque*
North Road, Ravensthorpe, Dewsbury WF13
Tel: (01924) 461089

Mosque*
1 Stoney Bank Street, Scout Hill, Dewsbury
WF13 3RJ
Tel: (01924) 451085
Contact: Mr Mohammad Razaq
Position: Secretary

Mosque*
1 Whittaker Street, Dewsbury WF17 5AQ
Tel: (01924) 472215

Mosque*
206 Bradford Road, Dewsbury WF13 2HD
Tel: (01924) 462873

Zakaria Mosque/Indian Muslim Patel Society
2 Chapel Street, Savile Town, Dewsbury
WF12 9NQ

Doncaster Mosque Trust*
Bentinck Close, St James Street, Hyde Park,
Doncaster DN 3ST
Tel: (01302) 368336
Contact: M M Mufti
Position: Secretary
Activities: Worship, resource, visits
Traditions: Sunni
Movements: Deobandi
Other Languages: Arabic, Urdu, Punjabi

Pakistani Cultural Centre and Mosque*
12 Thoresby Avenue, Belle Vue, Doncaster
DN4 5BJ
Contact: Mr M Shabir
Position: General Secretary

Contact Tel: (01302) 810077
Activities: Worship/practice/meditation,
community centre, elderly, women, resources
Traditions: Sunni
Movements: Barelwi
Other Languages: Urdu, Punjabi, Mirpuri

Pakistani Cultural Centre and Mosque*
8 St Helens Road, Belle Vue, Doncaster DN4 5EH
Tel: (01302) 326136 **Fax:** (01302) 326199
Contact: Ali Asghar
Position: Assistant Secretary
Contact Tel: (01302) 326136
Activities: Worship, resource, visits
Traditions: Sunni
Other Languages: Urdu, Arabic

Sulthainia Mosque
Lime Tree Court (off Lime Tree Avenue),
Doncaster DN4 5DH

Islamic Association of South Humberside*
204 Stanley Street, Grimsby DN32 7LH
Tel: (01472) 362600
Contact: Soab Mohamed Nawab
Position: Imam
Activities: Worship, visits, women
Traditions: Sunni
Movements: Tablighi Jamaat
Other Languages: Arabic, Urdu, Bengali

Anjuman Islah-ul-Muslemeen*
18 Rothwell Road, Halifax HX1 2HA
Tel: (01422) 380934 **Fax:** (01422) 340096
Contact: Dr Rahmat A Chaudhry
Position: President
Contact Tel: (01422) 340096
Other Languages: Urdu, French

Bain-ul-Aqwami Anjuman Tabligh-ul-Islam*
Vincent Street, Hopwood Lane, Halifax HX1 4EN
Tel: (01422) 342366 **Fax:** (01422) 342366
Contact: Mohammad Tariq Chaudhry
Position: Chief Organiser
Contact Tel: (01422) 342366
Activities: Worship, resource, youth, elderly,
women
Traditions: Sunni
Movements: Barelwi
Other Languages: Urdu, Punjabi

British Muslim Association*
Victoria House, 86 Hopwood Lane, Halifax HX1
4EJ

Tel: (01422) 362276 **Fax:** (01422) 366995
Contact: Mohammed Rahoof
Position: Chair
Activities: Worship, resource, umbrella body, youth, elderly, women
Traditions: Sunni
Movements: Jamaat-i-Islami
Other Languages: Urdu, Punjabi, Arabic
Affiliations: Calderdale Racial Equality Council; Calderdale Council of Mosques

Calderdale Islamic Youth/Dawat-e-Islami*

372 Queens Road, Halifax HX1 4PH
Tel: (01422) 344732
Contact: Mohammed Rahoof
Position: Chairman
Activities: Youth, inter-faith
Traditions: Sunni
Movements: Jamaat-i-Islami
Other Languages: Urdu, Punjabi
Affiliations: Dawat-e-Islami-Karachi Pakistan

Central Jamia Mosque Madni*

Education Centre, Gibbet Street, St John's, Halifax HX1 5XS
Tel: (01422) 365645
Contact: Mr M Sultan
Position: General Secretary
Other Languages: Urdu, Arabic

Elland Mosque Association*

26/34 Elizabeth Street, Elland, Halifax HX5 0JH
Tel: (01422) 378808
Contact: Fazal-ur-Rehman Tariq
Position: Chairman
Contact Tel: (01484) 515311
Activities: Worship/practice/meditation, visits, inter-faith
Traditions: Sunni
Movements: Imam Abu Hanifa
Other Languages: Urdu, Gujarati, Punjabi
Affiliations: Huddersfield Muslim Burial Council

Jamiat Ahl-e-Hadith Mosque*

97 Hopwood Lane, Halifax HX1 4ET
Tel: (01422) 356843
Contact: Mr Iqbal
Position: Secretary

Makki Masjid and Anjuman Islah-ul-Muslemeen*

Thornley Works, Hermon Avenue, Halifax HX1 3XN
Tel: (01422) 380934

Contact: M S Bashir
Position: Secretary
Other Languages: Urdu, Punjabi

Markazi Jamia Masjid*

49 Rhodes Street, Halifax HX1 5DE
Tel: (01422) 330041
Contact: Haji Ayub
Position: Treasurer
Contact Tel: (01422) 330041
Contact Email: akeelayub@hotmail.com
Activities: Provision of academic/educational resources, youth
Traditions: Sunni
Other Languages: Urdu, Punjabi, Arabic

Markazi Jame Mosque Riza and Islamic Centre*

129 Halifax Old Road, Birkby, Huddersfield HD22 2RP
Tel: (01484) 540449
Contact: Mr M Anwar- Ul-Haque
Position: Secretary
Contact Tel: (01484) 518501
Activities: Worship, resource, visits, youth, elderly, women
Traditions: Sunni
Movements: Barelwi
Other Languages: Urdu, Arabic, Punjabi

Abu Bakkr Mosque*

169 Church Street, Paddock, Huddersfield HD1 4UJ
Tel: (01484) 450183
Contact: Mr Quari
Position: Imam

Huddersfield Council of Islamic Affairs Charitable Trust (HCIACT)*

c/o Muslim Community Centre, Clare Hill, off Cambridge Road, Huddersfield HD1 5BU
Tel: (01484) 515311 **Fax:** (01484) 517985
Contact: Fazul-ur-Rehman Tariq
Position: Secretary General
Activities: Umbrella body, visits, youth, elderly, women, inter-faith
Other Languages: Urdu, Punjabi

Huddersfield Islamic Library*

18 St Steven Road, Lockwood, Huddersfield HD1 3QY
Tel: (01484) 452786
Email: info@islamiclibrary.co.uk
Website: http://www.islamiclibrary.co.uk/
Contact: Mr Mohammad Imran

Position: Secretary
Contact Tel: (07931) 730439
Contact Email: ashigemadinah@hotmail.com
Activities: Community centre, youth, women, radio, visits, inter-faith, resources
Traditions: Sunni
Other Languages: Urdu, Punjabi, Arabic

Jamia Masjid*
32 Upper George Street, Huddersfield HD1 4AW
Tel: (01484) 420029
Contact: Z Ali
Position: Secretary

Jamia Salfia*
62 Halifax Old Road, Birkby, Huddersfield HD1 6HG
Tel: (01484) 547808
Contact: Mr Azhar
Position: Secretary
Activities: Worship/practice/meditation
Traditions: Sunni
Movements: Ahl-e-Hadith
Other Languages: Urdu
Affiliations: Jamiat Ahle Hadith

Jamiat Ahle Hadith*
62 Old Halifax Road, Birkby, Huddersfield HD1 6HG
Tel: (01484) 547808 **Fax:** (01484) 462892
Traditions: Sunni
Movements: Ahl-e-Hadith
Other Languages: Punjabi, Urdu, Arabic, Farsi
Affiliations: Jamiat Ahl-e-Hadith, Birmingham

Jamiat Salfia*
68 Halifax Old Road, Birkby, Huddersfield HD1 6HG
Tel: (01484) 547808
Email: ahlehadith@hotmail.com
Contact: Brother Mohammed Hanif Asad
Position: Chair
Activities: Worship, resource, youth, women, inter-faith
Other Languages: Urdu, Arabic, Kurdish
Affiliations: Jamiat Ahl-e-Hadith UK

Madani Jamia Masjid Association*
73 Victoria Road, Lockwood, Huddersfield HD1 3RT
Tel: (01484) 513248
Contact: Mr Mohammad Saeed
Position: Secretary

Madni Jamia Masjid*
Mamchan Street, Lockwood, Huddersfield HD1 3QZ
Tel: (01484) 301103
Contact: Mr Mohammed Shafie
Position: President
Activities: Worship
Other Languages: Arabic, Urdu, Punjabi
Affiliations: Muslim Council of Britain

Masjid Anwar-e-Madina*
8-10 Clara Street, Fartown, Huddersfield HD1 6EN
Tel: (01484) 421236
Contact: Mr M Shazad Hussan
Position: Co-optee
Contact Tel: (07788) 998801
Contact Email: shazad286@usa.net
Activities: Worship/practice/meditation, community centre, youth, elderly, women, visits, resources
Traditions: Sunni
Movements: Jamiat Ahl-e-Sunnat
Other Languages: Urdu, Punjabi, Puthwari

Masjid Omar*
32 Blacker Road, Birkby, Huddersfield HD1 5HT
Tel: (01484) 541634

Muslim Community Centre (Huddersfield Council Of Islamic Affairs Charitable Trust)*
Clare Hill, off Cambridge Road, Kirklees, Huddersfield HD1 5BU
Tel: (01484) 435839 **Fax:** (01484) 435839
Contact: F R Tariq
Position: Honorary Advisor
Contact Tel: (01484) 515311
Contact Email: frtariq@hotmail.com
Other Languages: Urdu, Arabic, Persian

Muslim Funeral Association*
112 Halifax Old Road, Fartown, Huddersfield HD2 2RW
Tel: (01484) 309850
Contact: Mr Habib Ullah
Position: Treasurer
Traditions: Sunni
Other Languages: Urdu

Shah Jalal Mosque and Madrassa*
85 Fenton Street, Lockwood, Huddersfield HD1 3RA
Tel: (01484) 513388
Contact: Mr Moklis Ali
Position: Secretary

Contact Tel: (01484) 513746
Activities: Community centre
Traditions: Sunni
Movements: Barelwi
Other Languages: Bengali, Urdu

Hull Mosque and Islamic Centre
Berkeley Street, Hull HU3 1PR
Tel: (01482) 24833

Mosque
153 Boulevard, Hull HU3 3EJ

Pearson Park Mosque and Islamic Centre*
20 Pearson Park, Hull HU5 2TD
Tel: (01482) 473867
Contact: Farouk Chrundry
Position: Chairman

Al-Amin Talimul Islamic Society*
33 Victoria Road, Keighley BD21 1HD
Tel: (01535) 607620
Contact: Afruj Ali Ruf
Position: Secretary
Activities: Worship, resource, inter-faith
Traditions: Sunni,
Other Languages: Bengali, Urdu

Keighley Jamia Mosque and Muslim Association*
75 Emily Street, Keighley BD21 3EG
Tel: (01535) 607039
Contact: Mahdood Alam
Position: General Secretary
Activities: Worship, umbrella body, visits, youth, elderly, women
Traditions: Sunni,
Other Languages: Punjabi, Urdu, Arabic,
Affiliations: Bradford Council of Mosques; Imams and Mosques Council

Mosque
70 Marlborough Road, Keighley

Sangat Day Centre*
Keighley Muslim Community Centre, Keighley BD21 3EG
Tel: (01535) 610263 **Fax:** (01535) 600087
Contact: Khadim Hussain
Position: Manager
Activities: Community centre
Other Languages: Bengali, Urdu

Shahjalal Mosque and Bangladesh Islamic Organisation*
Temple Row, Keighley BD21 2AH
Tel: (01535) 603444

UKIM Jamia Madinah Masjid*
Spencer Street, Keighley BD212QQ
Email: ukimkeighley@hotmail.com
Website: http://www.ukim.org/
Contact: Ghufran Mehmood
Position: Secretary
Contact Tel: (07977) 431196
Contact Email: ghufran25@hotmail.com
Activities:
Worship/practice/meditation,youth,elderly,women, education
Other Languages: Urdu, Punjabi

Ahlul Bayt Islamic Centre*
35 Hanover Square, Leeds LS3 1BQ
Tel: (0113) 2443419 **Fax:** (0113) 2443419
Contact: Mr Mudhafar Ridha
Position: Office Co-ordinator
Contact Tel: (0113) 2720405
Activities: Worship/practice/meditation, community centre, youth, women, visits, inter-faith
Traditions: 'Ithna Asheri
Other Languages: Arabic, Farsi

Almadina Jamia Mosque
33 Brundell Grove, Leeds LS6 1HR
Tel: (0113) 2758615

Jamia Tul Batool Mir Tul Islam Trust*
7 Beck Road, Leeds LS8 4EJ
Tel: (0113) 2485067
Contact: Sahibzadh M D Hussain
Position: Chairman
Contact Tel: (07980) 745386
Movements: Worship/practice/meditation
Other Languages: Urdu

Kashmir Muslim Community Centre and Mosque
1 Hardy Street, Beeston, Leeds LS11 6BJ
Tel: (0113) 2774
Contact: Mohammed Kaman Bhatti
Position: Chairman
Activities: Worship, inter-faith
Traditions: Sunni,
Other Languages: Punjabi, Urdu

Khoja Sh'ia Ithna Asheri Muslim Community*
168 Beeston Road, Beeston, Leeds LS11 8BD

Tel: (0113) 2765558 **Fax:** (0113) 2267212
Email: secretary@bhamani.demon.co.uk
Website: http://www.baabulilm.org/
Contact: Mr Rashid Bhaman
Position: Secretary
Contact Tel: (0113) 2713066
Activities: Worship/practice/meditation,
community centre, youth, elderly, women, visits
Traditions: 'Ithna Asheri
Other Languages: Urdu, Gujarati
Affiliations: Council of European Jamats; World
Federation of KSIM Communities

Leeds Grand Mosque*
9 Woodsley Road, Leeds LS6 1SN
Tel: (0113) 2445400 **Fax:** (0113) 2445400
Contact: Mr Zaher Birawi
Position: Chairman
Contact Tel: (0113) 2674374
Contact Email: zaher.birawi@lineone.net
Activities: Worship/practice/meditation, youth,
women, visits
Traditions: Sunni
Other Languages: Arabic
Affiliations: Muslim Council of Britain

Leeds Islamic Centre*
44-48 Spencer Place, Leeds LS7 4BR
Tel: (0113) 2621300
Email: myounis@onetel.net.uk
Website: http://www.leeds-islamic-centre.co.uk/
Contact: Mr Muhammad Khan Chaudhary
Position: Secretary
Contact Tel: (0113) 2468640
Contact Email: khan1426@netscapeonline.co.uk
Activities: Worship, resource, media, umbrella
body, visits, youth, elderly
Traditions: Sunni
Movements: Deobandi
Other Languages: Urdu, Punjabi, Bangla, Pahari
Affiliations: Yorkshire Council of Mosques; Union
of Muslim Organisations; Muslim World League

Leeds Muslim Council*
31-33 Brudenell Grove, Leeds LS6 1HR
Tel: (0113) 2752535
Contact: Dr Jameel Malik
Position: Secretary
Activities: Worship/practice/meditation, resources
Traditions: Sunni
Movements: Barelwi
Other Languages: Urdu, Mirpuri

Leeds Student Islamic Society*
Leeds Metropolitan University, City Campus,
Claverly Street, Leeds LS1 3HE
Tel: (07979) 457172
Email: z.clane70@hotmail.com
Contact: Mr Khuram Majid
Position: President
Contact Email: z.dan1@talk21.com
Activities: Worship/practice/meditation, central
body, visits, inter-faith
Traditions: Sunni
Other Languages: Punjabi, Urdu, Arabic, Malay
Affiliations: Federation of Student Islamic
Societies (FOSIS)

Masjid-e-Bilal and Muslim Community Centre
Harehills Place, Harehills Road, Leeds LS14 3DZ
Tel: (0113) 2480711

Masjid-e-Umar and Muslim Association*
29 Stratford Street, off Dewsbury Road, Leeds
LS11 6JG
Tel: (0113) 2709536
Email: nolchocc@hotmail.com
Contact: Abdur Razzaque
Position: Secretary General
Other Languages: Bengali, Urdu, Arabic
Affiliations: Local Charities

**Mosque and Muslim Welfare Centre and Jamia
Masjid Ghosia***
7 Brooklyn Terrace, Armley, Leeds LS12 2BX
Tel: (01132) 790172
Contact: M Naseem
Position: President
Other Languages: Urdu, Arabic

Mosque and Madrassah*
29 Stratford Street, Beeston, Leeds LS11 6JG
Contact: Abdur Razzaque
Position: General Secretary
Activities: Worship/practice/meditation,
community centre, youth, elderly, visits, resources
Traditions: Sunni
Other Languages: Urdu, Bengali, Arabic, Gujarati

Pakistani Community Centre*
Conway Road, Leeds LS8 5JH
Tel: (0113) 2143128 **Fax:** (0114) 2143131
Movements: ESOL, Arabic and Urdu Classes
Other Languages: Urdu, Arabic, Punjabi

Jamia Mosque*
84 Gerard Road, Wellgate, Rotherham S6 2PP
Tel: (01709) 838949

Contact: Karamat Hussain
Position: Chair
Contact Tel: (01709) 375141
Activities: Worship/practice/meditation
Traditions: Sunni
Movements: Barelwi

Jamiah Mosque and Community Centre*
114a College Road, Rotherham S60 1JF
Tel: (01709) 563631
Contact: Mr Jamia

Jamiat-ahl-e-Hadith*
Moorgate Street, Rotherham S60 2EY
Tel: (01709) 369715
Contact: M Rashid
Position: Secretary
Activities: Worship, resource, visits, youth, elderly, women
Traditions: Sunni
Movements: Ahl-e-Hadith
Other Languages: Urdu, Arabic, Punjabi
Affiliations: Jamiat Ahl-e-Hadith UK Birmingham

Markazul Uloom Al-Islamia*
33-35 Ridge Road, Rotherham S65 1NS
Tel: (01709) 835675 **Fax:** (01709) 835675
Contact: Hussain
Position: Chairman

Mosque
46 Milton Road, Eastwood, Rotherham S65 1QS

Mosque*
Chapel Walk, Rotherham S60 1EP
Tel: (01709) 560038
Contact: Mr Mumtaz Hussain
Position: Imam
Activities: Worship, resource, visits, youth, elderly, women
Movements: Deobandi, Tablighi Jamaat
Other Languages: Urdu, Punjabi, Gujarati,
Affiliations: United Muslim Organisation

Bangladeshi Mosque
29 Gilliatt Street, Scunthorpe DN15 6EY

Madni Mosque and Madrassa*
44 Percival Street, Scunthorpe DN15 6JD
Tel: (01724) 864810
Contact: Raziur Rahman
Position: Caretaker
Contact Tel: (07961) 420191

Contact Email: rojrahman01.hotmail.com
Activities: Worship/practice/meditation, youth, elderly, women, radio, resources
Traditions: Sunni
Movements: Deobandi, Tablighi Jamaat
Other Languages: Bengali, Urdu, Arabic, Gujarati

Pakistan Islamic Centre*
4 Parkinson Avenue, Scunthorpe DN15 7JX

Scunthorpe Mosque and Committee
107 West Street, Scunthorpe DN15 6EQ

Anjuman-e-Haideria*
140 Steade Road, Nether Edge, Sheffield S7 1DU
Tel: (0114) 2501158
Contact: M Khan Malik
Position: President
Activities: Youth, elderly, women, radio
Traditions: 'Ithna Asheri
Other Languages: Urdu, Persian

Dar ul Aloom Siddiqia Mosque
24 Burngreave Road, Sheffield S9 3FA
Tel: (0114) 2701034

Elahi Mosque and Islamic Cultural Centre*
305 Staniforth Road, Darnall, Sheffield S9 3FP

Haqqani House Sufi Centre*
Former Christian Science Buildings, Vincent Road, Nether Edge, Sheffield S7 1DE
Tel: (0114) 2589408
Contact: Noah Nazir
Position: Trustee
Activities: Worship, visits, youth, women, newsletter, inter-faith
Traditions: Sunni,
Movements: Tassawuf,
Other Languages: Urdu, Arabic, Turkish, Spanish

Ittehad Committee*
8 Briar Road, Nether Edge, Sheffield S9 1SA
Tel: (0114) 2588106
Contact: Mr S Khan
Activities: Elderly
Traditions: 'Ithna Asheri
Other Languages: Urdu
Affiliations: Anjuman-e-Haidria

Jamia Masjid Hanifa and Islamic Cultural Centre*
372 Sheffield Road, Sheffield S9 1RQ
Contact: Mr M Riaz

Position: Secretary
Activities: Worship/practice/meditation, community centre, women, inter-faith, resources
Traditions: Sunni
Other Languages: Urdu, Arabic

Jamia Mosque Ghosia*
Firth Park Road, Sheffield S5 6WN
Tel: (0114) 2610551
Contact: Imam
Activities: Worship/practice/meditation, community centre, youth, elderly, women, visits, inter-faith, resources
Traditions: Sunni
Other Languages: Urdu, Punjabi, Arabic

Jamia Mosque Gulzar-e-Habib and Education Centre*
46-48 Ribston Road, Darnall, Sheffield S9 3AY
Tel: (0114) 2449801

Jamiyate Tablighe Islam*
Bodmin Street, Sheffield S9 3TA
Tel: (0114) 2445618
Contact: Mr Hafiz M Rafique

Madni Islamic Community Association and Mosque*
22 Wincobank Lane, Sheffield S4 8AA
Tel: (0114) 2442998
Contact: Mr Tariq Khan

Makki Mosque Organisation*
Plantation Road, Sheffield S8 9TH
Contact: Mr M Rafique
Position: Secretary
Contact Tel: (0114) 2582348
Activities: Worship/practice/meditation, community centre, youth, elderly, books, radio, visits, inter-faith
Traditions: Sunni
Movements: Deobandi, Tablighi Jamaat
Other Languages: Urdu
Affiliations: Jamat Ulma Birtina; Aalami Majlise Tahaffuze Khatme Nu Buwwat

Markazi Mosque Trust*
13 Industry Road, Sheffield S9 5SP
Tel: (0114) 2441500
Contact: Haji Mohammed Siddique
Position: Chair/Secretary
Activities: Worship, resource, umbrella body, visits, youth, elderly
Other Languages: Arabic, Urdu

Muslim Welfare House of Sheffield*
10 Severn Road, Broomhill, Sheffield S10 2SU
Tel: (0114) 2671969 **Fax:** (0114) 2671969
Website: http://www.mwhs.freeseerve.co.uk/
Contact: Dr Omer El-Hamdoon
Position: Assistant Director
Contact Tel: (07971) 038958
Activities: Worship/practice/meditation, community centre, youth, women, visits, resources
Traditions: Sunni
Other Languages: Arabic, Somali, Urdu

Noor-al-Hadi
275 Staniforth Road, Sheffield S9 3FP

Sheffield Allyah Jame Mosque and Islamic Cultural Centre*
Roundall Street, Darnall, Sheffield S9 3LE
Tel: (0114) 2618162
Contact: Moulana Amin
Position: First Imam
Traditions: Sunni
Other Languages: Bengali, Urdu
Affiliations: Imams and Mosques Council; Muslim World League

Sheffield Islamic Centre and Madina Mosque
24-32 Wolseley Road, Sheffield S8 0ZU
Tel: (0114) 2585021

Sheffield and Rotherham District Council of Muslims*
1 Derriman Glen, Silverdale Road, Sheffield S11
Tel: (0114) 2360465 **Fax:** (0114) 2360532

Sufi Islamic Centre*
Haqqani House Sufi Centre, Vincent Road, Nether Edge, Sheffield S7 1DE
Tel: (0114) 2589408
Contact: Noah Nazir
Position: Trustee
Activities: Worship, resource, visits, youth, elderly, women
Traditions: Sunni
Movements: Ahle Sunnatwat Jamaat
Other Languages: Urdu, Arabic, Spanish, Italian

Tinsley Islamic Cultural Centre*
372 Sheffield Road, Tinsley, Sheffield S9 1RQ
Tel: (0114) 2433519
Contact: Mr Mohammed Riaz
Position: Secretary
Activities: Worship, resource, umbrella body, visits, youth, elderly

Other Languages: Urdu, Punjabi, Arabic
Affiliations: Sheffield Council of Mosques

Jamiat Ahl-e-Hadith*
23-25 Midland Street, Skipton BD23 1SE
Tel: (01758) 790374
Contact: Mr Sana Ullah
Position: Imam
Activities: Worship, resource, inter-faith
Traditions: Sunni
Movements: Ahl-e-Hadith
Other Languages: Urdu
Affiliations: Jamiat Ahl-e-Hadith UK, Muslim
World League

Agbrigg Muslim Association*
26 St Catherine Street, Wakefield WF1 5BW
Tel: (01924) 256635
Contact: Rashid Ahmed Mughal
Position: President
Activities: Worship, resource, visits, youth, elderly,
women
Traditions: Sunni
Movements: Deobandi, Tablighi Jamaat
Other Languages: Urdu, Arabic

Central Jamia Masjid Madrassah Arabiyah Islamia*
South Street, off Charles Street, Wakefield
WF1 4PG
Tel: (01924) 215053
Contact: Mr Islam Ali Shah
Position: Secretary
Contact Tel: (01924) 215053
Activities: Worship/practice/meditation, youth,
elderly, inter-faith, resources
Traditions: Sunni
Movements: Deobandi, Tablighi Jamaat
Other Languages: Urdu, Arabic, Punjabi
Affiliations: Tablighi Markaz, Dewsbury

Ghousia Mosque*
Duke of York Street, Wakefield WF1 3DA
Tel: (01924) 376555

Jamia Sawfia Mosque
Park Hill Lane, Eastmoor, Wakefield SF1 2NJ

Markazi Jamia Mosque*
12 Grange Street, Wakefield WF2 8TF
Tel: (01924)376555

UK Islamic Mission and York Mosque and Islamic Centre*
Bull Lane, Lawrence Street, York YO10 3EN

Tel: (01904) 413123
Contact: Zubair Ahmad
Position: Imam and Teacher
Contact Email:
zahmad@zapublish.freeserve.co.uk
Activities: Worship, umbrella body, visits, inter-
faith, youth
Traditions: Sunni
Other Languages: Arabic, Urdu, French
Affiliations: UK Islamic Mission

York Muslim Association*
76 Fourth Avenue, York YO3 0UA
Tel: (01904) 413081
Contact: Aziz Suleman Karbani
Position: Secretary
Contact Tel: (01904) 426261
Activities: Worship, resource, inter-faith
Other Languages: Urdu, Bengali, Katchi, Gujarati

NORTH WEST
Regional or County Bodies

Lancashire Council of Mosques*
Bangor Street Community Centre, Norwich Street,
Blackburn BB1 6NZ
Tel: (01254) 692289 **Fax:** (01254) 660074
Email: info@lancashiremosques.org.uk
Website: http://www.lancashiremosques.org.uk/
Contact: Dr M Chandia
Position: Director
Activities: Umbrella body, visits, youth, elderly,
women
Other Languages: Urdu, Gujarati, Bengali,
Pushto
Affiliations: Muslim Council of Britain

North British Muslim Trust*
19 Lancaster Place, Blackburn BB2 6JT
Tel: (01254) 676618
Contact: Mr Sardar Khan
Position: Trustee
Activities: Worship/practice/meditation
Traditions: Sunni
Other Languages: Urdu, Punjabi, Arabic

UK Islamic Mission*
425 Cheetham Hill Road, Cheetham Hill,
Manchester M8 0PF
Contact: M Abdus Salam
Position: Chairman
Contact Tel: (0161) 2056662
Activities: Worship/practice/meditation,

community centre, youth, elderly, women, books, visits, inter-faith, resources
Other Languages: Urdu, Punjabi
Affiliations: UK Islamic Mission

City, Town or Local Bodies

Ghosia Razvia Jamia Mosque and Islamic Centre*
Higher Antley Street, Accrington BB5 0QB
Tel: (01254) 397398
Contact: Munsif Dad
Position: Secretary
Contact Tel: (07971) 389395
Traditions: Sunni
Other Languages: Punjabi, Urdu

Madressah Talim-ul-Islam*
50 Fountain Street, Central, Accrington BB5 0QP
Tel: (01254) 388599
Contact: Mr M S Bhatti
Position: Chairperson
Traditions: Sunni
Other Languages: Urdu, Punjabi, Arabic

Raza Jamia Mosque and Islamic Centre*
229 Blackburn Road, Accrington BB5 0AL
Tel: (01254) 393454
Contact: Mr Haji Zadar
Position: Chairman

United Muslim Mothers Association*
12 Charter Street, Hyndburn, Accrington BB5 0SG
Tel: (01254) 388886 **Fax:** (01254) 388886
Contact: Faizur Rahman
Position: Development Worker
Other Languages: Bengali

Darul-Uloom Qadiria Jilania*
95 Burlington Street, Ashton-under-Lyne OL6 6HJ
Contact: Mohammed Zafar Iqbal Qazi
Position: Secretary
Contact Tel: (0161) 3083510
Activities: Worship/practice/meditation, community centre, youth, elderly, visits, resources
Traditions: Sunni
Movements: Barelwi
Other Languages: Urdu, Punjabi
Affiliations: Darul -Uloom Qadira Jilania, Walthamstow, London

Jamia Masjid*
Newton Street, Penny Meadow, Ashton-under-

Lyne 0L6 6EJ
Tel: (0161) 3300617
Contact: Mr M Azhar
Position: Trustee
Activities: Worship
Traditions: Sunni
Movements: Deobandi
Other Languages: Urdu

Madrassa Arbia Taleemul Qur'an and Mosque
Richmond Hill, Katherine Street, Ashton-under-Lyne OL7 0AL
Tel: (0161) 3309837

Wirral Islamic Centre and Shah Jahal Mosque*
309 Borough Road, Birkenhead CH41 2UZ
Tel: (0151) 6662089
Contact: Mr Khan
Position: Secretary

Bilal Mosque*
71-73 Cedar Street, Blackburn BB1 9TT
Contact: M Farooq
Position: Secretary
Contact Tel: (07714) 306391
Contact Email: farooq_m786@hotmail.com

Blackburn Council of Mosques*
108 Audley Range, Blackburn BB1 1TF
Tel: (01254) 261573
Contact: Mr Nizam Makda
Position: Chairman
Activities: Central body, visits, inter-faith
Traditions: Sunni
Movements: Barelwi, Deobandi, Jamati-I-Islami, Tablighi Jamaat
Other Languages: Gujarati, Punjabi, Urdu, Bengali
Affiliations: Lancashire Council of Mosques; Muslim Council of Britain

Hanfi Sunni Jamia Masjid and Hanfi Sunni Muslim Association*
33a Randall Street, Blackburn BB1 7LG
Tel: (01254) 52170
Contact: Mr G Haji

Hanfi-Sunni Circle and Mosque*
48 Altom Street, Blackburn BB1 7NE
Tel: (01254) 681563
Email: masjideraza@hotmail.com
Contact: Mr Yunus
Position: Secretary
Other Languages: Gujarati, Urdu, Arabic

Hanfia Muslim Raza Mosque
40 Balaclava Street, Blackburn BB1 7HW

Hazrat Sultan Bahu Trust, Blackburn, UK*
300 Whalley Range, Blackburn BB1 6NL
Tel: (01254) 673395
Contact: Mr Khaliq Hussain
Activities: Resource
Traditions: Sunni
Movements: Barelwi, Tassawuf
Other Languages: Punjabi, Urdu
Affiliations: Lancashire Council of Mosques

Islamic Academy UK
c/o 2 Blackburn Street, Blackburn BB1 7NG

Islamic Book Centre*
Frame House, 286 Whalley Range, Blackburn
BB1 6NL
Tel: (01254)265944
Contact: Mr M Yousuf
Position: Director

Islamic Centre and Mosque
2 Kendal Street, Blackburn BB1 7LH

Islamic Community Centre and Mosque
100 Rigby Road, Blackburn
Tel: (01253) 291967

Islamic Cultural Centre and Jaame Mosque*
Cumberland Street, Blackburn BB1 1JP
Tel: (01254) 608683
Contact: Moulana Ahmed Suleman Sidat JP
Position: Chairman
Contact Tel: (01254) 583345
Activities: Worship/practice/meditation
Traditions: Sunni
Movements: Ahl-e-Hadith
Other Languages: Gujarati, Urdu, Arabic

Islamic Education Centre*
44 Devonport Road, Blackburn BB2 1HW
Tel: (01254) 670079
Contact: Mr Mohammed Sabir

Islamic Education Society*
108 Audley Road, Blackburn BB1 1TF
Tel: (01254) 261573
Contact: Mr N I Makda
Position: Secretary
Activities: Worship/practice/meditation, resources
Traditions: Sunni
Movements: Deobandi, Tablighi Jamaat

Other Languages: Gujarati, Punjabi, Urdu
Affiliations: Blackburn Council of Mosques;
Lancashire Council of Mosques; Muslim Council
of Britain

Islamic Religious Centre and Mosque*
209 Preston New Road, Blackburn BB2 6BN
Tel: (01254) 698384
Contact: Sabir Patel
Position: President
Contact Tel: (01254) 673938
Traditions: Sunni
Other Languages: Gujarati, Urdu

Jame Masjid e Noor*
71 Saunders Road, Blackburn BB2 6LS
Tel: (01254) 698609
Contact: Mohammad Younus
Position: General Secretary
Contact Tel: (01254) 664613
Other Languages: Urdu, Arabic

Jamia Ghosia Mosque*
98-99 Chester Street, Blackburn BB1 1DQ
Tel: (01254) 51080
Contact: Mr Mire Zaman
Position: Chairman

Kokni Muslim Association
Newton Street, Blackburn BB1 1NE

Lancashire Council of Mosques*
Bangor Street Community Centre, Norwich Street,
Blackburn BB1 6NZ
Tel: (01254) 692289 **Fax:** (01254) 660074
Email: info@lancashiremosques.org.uk
Website: http://www.lancashiremosques.org.uk/
Contact: Dr M Chandia
Position: Director
Activities: Umbrella body, visits, youth, elderly,
women
Other Languages: Urdu, Gujarati, Bengali,
Pushto
Affiliations: Muslim Council of Britain

Madressa Islamia
Segar Street, Great Harwood, Blackburn BB6 7DR
Contact: M Anwar
Activities: Worship, resource, visits
Traditions: Sunni
Movements: Tablighi Jamaat
Other Languages: Punjabi, Urdu
Affiliations: Lancashire Council of Mosques

Madressa e Talimul-Islam
86 Stansfield Street, Blackburn BB2 2NG

Makki Masjid*
Wimberley Street, Blackburn BB1 8HX
Tel: (01254) 676884
Contact: Ismail Master
Position: Secretary

Masjid-e-Alhidayah
22-36 Whalley Street, Blackburn BB1 7NB

Masjid-e-Aneesul Islam*
Troy Street, off Whalley Range, Blackburn
BB1 6NY
Tel: (01254) 583245
Contact: Mr A Patel

Masjid-e-Hidayah
50 Millham Street, Blackburn BB1 6EU
Contact: Imam Patel
Position: Imam

Masjid-e-Rizwan*
Newton Street, Blackburn BB1 1NE
Tel: (01254) 679466
Contact: Mr Jamal Patel
Position: President

Masjid-e-Sajedeen and Madressa-e-Islamiah*
Plane Tree Road, Little Harwood, Blackburn
BB1 5PA
Tel: (01254) 54313 **Fax:** (01254) 54313
Contact: Mr Mohammed E Marda
Position: General Secretary
Activities: Worship, resource, visits
Traditions: Sunni (Imam Hanafi)
Movements: Tablighi Jamaat, Deobandi
Other Languages: Arabic, Gujarati, Urdu
Affiliations: Blackburn Council of Mosques;
Lancashire Council of Mosques; Muslim World
League

Masjid-e-Saliheen*
Didsbury Street, Blackburn BB1 3JL
Contact: Moulana Osman Khan
Position: President/Principal
Contact Tel: (07050) 105351
Contact Email: athmankhan@hotmail.com
Other Languages: Urdu, Arabic

Masjid-e-Tauheedul Islam Mosque*
31 Bicknell Street, Blackburn BB1 7EY
Tel: (01254) 54318

Activities: Worship/practice/meditation
Traditions: Sunni
Other Languages: Urdu, Gujarati

Masjid-e-Zainabia*
25 Logwood Street, Blackburn BB1 9TU
Contact: Mr Mohammed Hussain
Position: General Secretary
Contact Tel: (01254) 582621
Activities: Education
Traditions: Ithna Asheri
Other Languages: Urdu

Masjidul-Momineen and Kokni Muslim Welfare Society
Ash Street, Little Harwood, Blackburn BB1 6LX
Contact: Secretary

Muslim Welfare Institute*
35 Wellington Street, St John's, Blackburn BB1 8AF
Tel: (01254) 694015 **Fax:** (01254) 694015
Email: mwinstitute@talk21.com
Contact: Moulana Hanif
Position: Secretary
Activities: Youth, newsletter/journal
Traditions: Sunni
Other Languages: Urdu, Gujarati, Punjabi, Arabic
Affiliations: Muslim Council of Britain

Naqshbandia Aslamiyya Spiritual Centre
78 Pringle Street, Blackburn BB1 ISA

New Madina Mosque
19-21 Oak Street, Blackburn BB1 6NT
Tel: (01254) 677448

Rawdhatul-Uloom*
19 Dock Street, Blackburn BB1 3AT
Tel: (01254) 670017
Traditions: Sunni
Other Languages: Urdu, Gujarati, Hindi, Bengali

Shi'a Islamic Centre (Mosque)*
143 Preston New Road, Blackburn BB2 6BJ
Tel: (01254) 265592
Contact: Imtiaz Ali Nazir
Position: Secretary
Activities: Worship, resource, visits, youth, elderly, women
Traditions: Ithna Asheri
Other Languages: Urdu, Punjabi, Gujarati
Affiliations: Lancashire Council of Mosques;
Majlis Ulama-e-Europe, Harrow; World Federation
of Khoja Ithna Asheri Jamaat, Stanmore

A R Rehman Mosque*
2 Randal Street, Bolton BL3
Contact: The Secretary

Al Jamiah al Islamiyah Darul Uloom Lancashire, UK*
Hospital Road (Former Blair Hospital), Bromley Cross, Bolton BL7 9PY
Tel: (01204) 301550 **Fax:** (01204) 308519
Contact: Qaari Yakub Nanji
Position: Principal
Activities: Worship, resource, visits
Traditions: Sunni
Movements: Deobandi, Tablighi Jamaat
Other Languages: Gujarati, Urdu, Bengali, Arabic
Affiliations: UK Action Committee on Islamic Affairs; Muslim Council of Britain; Muslim World League

All Aazad Indian's Anjuman*
c/o 4 Henrylee Street, Bolton BLT 3BT
Tel: (01204) 652761
Contact: Yaqub Babu

Ashrafia Mosque*
Cannon Street North, Bolton BL3 5DN
Tel: (01204) 384713
Contact: Mr Gulam Hussain Mohamed
Position: Secretary
Activities: Worship
Traditions: Sunni
Movements: Deobandi
Other Languages: Gujarati, Urdu, Bengali, Arabic

Bolton Central Islamic Society*
Taiyabah Mosque and Community Centre, 31a Draycott Street, Bolton BL1 8HD
Tel: (01204) 335997
Contact: Mr A Aziz
Position: Spokesperson
Activities: Worship, resource, umbrella body, visits, youth, newsletter
Traditions: Sunni
Movements: Deobandi, Tablighi Jamaat
Other Languages: Gujarati, Arabic, Urdu
Affiliations: Lancashire Council of Mosques

Bolton Muslim Welfare Trust*
Swan Lane, Bolton BL3 6TQ
Tel: (01204) 361103 **Fax:** (01204) 533220
Contact: Yakoob M Patel
Position: Secretary
Activities: Resource, visits, youth, elderly, women, books, inter-faith, education

Traditions: Sunni
Other Languages: Gujarati, Urdu
Affiliations: Association of Muslim Schools UK

Bolton Surti Sunni Vohra Muslim Centre
Bankfield Works, Bankfield Street, Bolton BL3

Daubhill Muslim Society and Al Rahman Mosque*
2-14 Randal Street, Daubhill, Bolton BL3 4AQ
Tel: (01204) 660177
Contact: Rashid Ahmed Nadat
Position: Secretary
Activities: Worship, resource, visits
Traditions: Sunni
Movements: Deobandi
Other Languages: Gujarati, Urdu

Farnworth Cultural Centre*
118 Market Street, Farnworth, Bolton BL4 9AE
Contact: Mr Iftikhar Khan

Farnworth Mosque*
Granville Street, Farnworth, Bolton BL4 7LD
Tel: (01204) 574601
Contact: Bashir Ahmed
Position: Secretary

Great Lever Muslim Society*
35 Sheringham Place, Daubhill, Bolton BL3 5EX
Tel: (01204) 385780
Contact: Mr Haroon Ibrahim
Position: Coordinator
Activities: Worship, resource
Traditions: Sunni
Movements: Deobandi
Other Languages: Gujarati, Urdu, Hindi

Kamboli Muslim Welfare Association
101 Mancroft Avenue, Bolton BL3 3AA

Madina Mosque
128 St Georges Road, Bolton BL1 2BX

Makkah Mosque*
Rishton Lane, Great Lever, Bolton BL3 6QU
Tel: (01204) 524200
Contact: Mr Sarwar
Position: General Secretary
Activities: Worship/practice/meditation, inter-faith, resources
Traditions: Sunni
Other Languages: Urdu, Punjabi

Masjeed-e-Ghosia*
81/83 Auburn Street, Bolton BL3 6TQ
Tel: (01204) 650583
Contact: Mohammed Sahid Akuji
Position: Secretary
Contact Tel: (01204) 656324
Contact Email: wady_I@hotmail.com
Activities: Worship, resource
Traditions: Sunni
Movements: Hanfi
Other Languages: Gujarati, Urdu

Masjid-e-Noor-ul-Islam
Prospect Street, off Halliwell Road, Halliwell,
Bolton BL1 3QH
Tel: (01204) 535738

Sugra Mosque
24 Egerton Street, Farnworth, Bolton B14 7LE

Zakaria Mosque*
20 Peace Street, Bolton BL3 5LJ
Tel: (01204) 535002
Contact: Mr Ayoob Limbada

Anjaman-e-Muhibban-e-Ahel-e-Bait Hussainia Mosque*
37 Grey Street, Burnley BB10 1BA
Tel: (01282) 412279
Contact: Riaz Ahmed
Position: President
Contact Tel: (01282) 435402
Activities: Worship/practice/meditation
Other Languages: Urdu, Punjabi

Central Jamia Masjid-e-Farooq-i-Acam
North Street, Burnley BB10 1LU
Tel: (01282) 422321

Darul Uloom
141 Leyland Road, Burnley BB11 3DN
Tel: (01282) 412082
Contact: Secretary
Activities: Resource, youth
Traditions: Sunni
Movements: Barelwi
Other Languages: Urdu
Affiliations: Lancashire Council of Mosques

Ghausia Girls High School*
1-5 Cross Street, Burnley BB9 7EN
Contact: Mrs Mirza
Position: Secretary
Other Languages: Punjabi, Urdu

Ghausiah Mosque*
66-68 Colne Road, Burnley BB10 1LG
Tel: (01282) 424999
Contact: Mr Hassani
Position: Imam
Contact Tel: (01282) 414206

Jamia Masjid Abu-Baker*
56 Brougham Street, Burnley BB12 0AT
Tel: (01282) 422358 **Fax:** (01282) 701062
Contact: Mohammad Bashir
Position: President
Activities: Worship, resource, umbrella body, visits, youth, elderly
Traditions: Sunni
Movements: Barelwi, Deobandi/Jamati-i-Islami
Other Languages: Arabic, Urdu, Bengali
Affiliations: Lancashire Council of Mosques

Jamia Masjid-e-Farooq-e-Azam
North St (off Colne Rd), Duke Bar, Burnley BB10 1LU
Tel: (01282) 422321
Contact: Mr Izat Khan
Position: General Secretary

Masjid Ibrahim*
25 Elm Street, Burnley BB10 1PD
Tel: (01282) 436101
Contact: M S Qadri
Position: President
Contact Tel: (01282) 438152

Shah Jalal Mosque and Madrassa*
112-114 Burns Street, Burnley BB12 0AJ
Tel: (01282) 709360 **Fax:** (01282) 720270
Email: administration@bill.appeal.org.uk
Contact: Councillor Mozaquir Ali
Position: President
Contact Tel: (07977) 205357
Activities: Worship, resource, visits, youth, elderly, women
Traditions: Sunni
Movements: Ahl-e-Hadith
Other Languages: Bangladeshi
Affiliations: Lancashire Council of Mosques

Darul Uloom Muslim Training College
Holcombe Hall, Holcombe Brook, Ramsbottom,
Bury BL8 4NG
Tel: (01706) 825160
Contact: Mufti Shabbir

Islamic Centre*
Church Street, Bury BL9 6AZ
Tel: (0161) 7647306
Email: islamic_786@hotmail.com
Contact: Mr Liaqat Ali
Position: Trustee
Other Languages: Arabic, Urdu
Affiliations: BM REC

Jamia Mosque*
23-25 Parker Street, Bury BL9 0RJ
Tel: (0161) 7636884
Contact: Hafiz Shokat
Position: Imam
Contact Tel: (07977) 2121490
Other Languages: Urdu, Punjabi, Pushto

Jinnah Youth
65 Shepard Street, Bury BL9 0RT

Khizra Mosque*
85 Warmersley Road, Bury BL9 5AN
Tel: (0161) 7641638 **Fax:** (0161) 7636884
Contact: Moulana Muhammad Bilal
Position: Imam
Activities: Worship
Traditions: Sunni
Movements: Deobandi, Tablighi Jamaat
Other Languages: Urdu, Punjabi, Pushto

Mosque and Dar-ul-Uloom*
Holcombe Hall, Holcombe, Bury BL8 4NG
Tel: (01706) 826106 **Fax:** (01706) 827907
Contact: Ali
Position: Secretary
Activities: Worship/practice/meditation
Other Languages: Urdu

Noor-ul-Islam Mosque*
2/4 Yarwood Street, Bury BL9 7AU
Contact: Muzamil Khan
Position: President
Activities: Worship/practice/meditation,
community centre, youth, elderly, women, visits,
inter-faith, resources
Traditions: Sunni
Movements: Barelwi, Tassawuf
Other Languages: Punjabi, Urdu, Arabic, Farsi

Shah-Jalal Mosque*
45 Egerton Street, Chester CH1 3NP
Tel: (01244) 316356
Contact: Al Haj Mohammad Mubarak Ali
Position: Trustee

Contact Tel: (01244) 313424
Activities: Worship, visits
Traditions: Sunni
Movements: Ahl-e-Hadith
Other Languages: Bengali, Hindi

Chorley Muslim Welfare Society*
142 Lyons Lane, Chorley PR6 0PJ
Tel: (01257) 268644
Contact: Mohammed Sajid
Position: Secretary
Activities: Worship, resource, youth
Traditions: Sunni
Movements: Deobandi, Tablighi Jamaat
Other Languages: Urdu, Gujarati, Bengali
Affiliations: Racial Equality Council, Preston;
Lancashire Council of Mosques

Shajalal Mosque*
145 Walthall Street, Crewe CW2 7LD
Tel: (01270) 651432
Contact: Mr Lotis
Position: Imam

Madina Mosque*
21-23 Victoria Street, Darwen BB1 5JJ
Contact: Mahmood Dalvi
Position: Secretary
Contact Tel: (07780) 733022
Activities: Worship/practice/meditation,
community centre, resources
Traditions: Sunni
Movements: Tablighi Jamaat
Other Languages: Urdu

Masjid-e-Bilal and Islamic Centre*
2-4 Beaconsfield Street, Haslingden BB4 5TD
Tel: (01706) 218830
Contact: Muhammad Rahman
Position: Secretary
Activities: Worship, resource, visits, youth, elderly
Traditions: Sunni
Movements: Deobandi, Tablighi Jamaat
Other Languages: Urdu, Pushto, Punjabi, Hindi
Affiliations: Lancashire Council of Mosques

Jamee Mosque*
16-18 Grenfield Street, Hyde SK14 1BX
Tel: (0161) 3661551
Contact: The Chairman
Activities: Worship, resource
Traditions: Sunni
Movements: Ahle-Sunnah Wal Jamaat
Other Languages: Bengali, Urdu, Arabic

Lancaster Islamic Society and Mosque*
Fenton Street, Lancaster LA1 1LA
Tel: (01524) 64131
Contact: The President
Activities: Worship, visits
Traditions: Sunni
Movements: Deobandi, Tablighi Jamaat
Other Languages: Urdu, Arabic, Gujarati
Affiliations: Lancashire Council of Mosques;
Markaji Masjid Dewsbury; Darool Uloom
Deoband

Muslim Welfare Society and Raza Mosque
71 Blade Street, Lancaster LA1 1TS
Tel: (01524) 32087
Contact: Mr I Sulliman
Position: Secretary

**Al-Rahma Mosque and Liverpool Muslim
Society***
29-31 Hathersley Street, Toxteth, Liverpool L8 2TJ
Tel: (0151) 7092560 **Fax:** (0151) 7092560
Email: anwar_rahim@yahoo.com
Contact: Mr Anwar Rahim
Position: General Secretary
Activities: Worship/practice/meditation,
community centre, umbrella body, youth, elderly,
women, visits, inter-faith, resources
Traditions: Sunni
Other Languages: Arabic, Urdu, Somali, Malay

Liverpool Islamic Institute and Mosque*
8 Cramond Avenue, Penny Lane, Liverpool
L18 1EQ
Tel: (0151) 7341222 **Fax:** (0151) 2918144
Contact: Mr M A Akbar
Position: Chairman
Contact Tel: (0151) 4274489
Activities: Worship/practice/meditation, youth,
elderly, women
Traditions: Sunni
Movements: Deobandi
Other Languages: Urdu, Arabic
Affiliations: Muslim Council of Britain

Quranic Study Circle*
119 Queen's Drive, Mossley Hill, Liverpool
L18 1JL
Tel: (0151) 7332940 **Fax:** (0151) 2918144
Contact: Dr A Z Khan
Position: Ameer
Activities: Youth, elderly, women, inter-faith
Traditions: Sunni
Movements: Deobandi, Jamati-I-Islami

Other Languages: Urdu, Arabic
Affiliations: UK Islamic Mission; Muslim Council
of Britain; World Islamic Movement

University of Liverpool Islamic Society*
Guild of Students, Mount Pleasant, Liverpool
L69 7BR
Tel: (0151) 7086515
Email: livisoc@yahoo.co.uk
Website: http://www.liv.ac.uk/
Contact: Mr Rafay Siddiqui
Position: Chair
Contact Email: md0u812a@liv.ac.uk
Activities: Worship/practice/meditation, youth,
women, inter-faith, resources
Traditions: Sunni

Al Falah Islamic Centre*
79 Heywood Street, Cheetham Hill, Manchester
M8 0PD
Tel: (0161) 7089108
Contact: Abdul
Position: Trustee

Al-Karima Trust*
200 Platt Lane, Rusholme, Manchester M14 7DE
Tel: (0161) 2251378 **Fax:** (0161) 2251378
Contact: Imam Zafar Mahmod
Position: Chairman
Contact Tel: (0161) 2562909
Activities: Worship/practice/meditation, youth,
elderly, women, resources
Traditions: Sunni
Other Languages: Arabic, Urdu, Bengali

Al-Markazi Al-Najmi*
5-9 Woodfold Avenue, Levenshulme, Manchester
M19 3AP
Tel: (0161) 2255307 **Fax:** (0161) 2255307
Contact: Dr M Abdulhussin/ Dr Z A Husain
Position: Vice President/Secretary

**Al-Quba Mosque and Sahcorn Islamic and
Education Centre***
109 Beresford Road, Longsight, Manchester
M13 0TB
Tel: (0161) 2490307

Dar Al-Islam Foundation*
2a Higher Ardwick, Ardwick, Manchester
M12 6BZ
Tel: (0161) 2744534 **Fax:** (0161) 2744534
Email: daralislam@yahoo.com
Contact: Mr Lukman Faily

Position: General Manager
Contact Tel: (07879) 602659
Activities: Worship/practice/meditation, community centre, youth, elderly, women
Other Languages: Arabic

Dar-Ul-Uloom Islamia Education and Cultural Centre*

1 Hawkhurst Road, Longsight, Manchester M13 0SJ
Tel: (0161) 2562812
Contact: Khalil Hussain
Position: Trustee
Activities: Worship, resources
Other Languages: Urdu
Affiliations: Manchester Council of Mosques

Dar-Us- Salam Mosque*

47 Slade Lane, Longsight, Manchester M13 0QJ
Tel: (0161)2257129

Didsbury Mosque and Islamic Centre*

271 Burton Road, off Barlow Moor Road, West Didsbury, Manchester M20 2WA
Tel: (0161) 4342254 **Fax:** (0161) 4480324
Contact: Asim Suleman
Position: Secretary
Contact Tel: (07989) 039579
Contact Email: noordwijk7@hotmail.com
Activities: Worship, visits, youth, elderly, women, newsletter
Traditions: Sunni
Other Languages: Arabic, Dutch, Spanish

Eccles and Salford Islamic Mosque*

5 Liverpool Road, Eccles, Manchester M30 0WB
Tel: (0161) 7892609
Contact: Mr Mohamed Kader
Position: Treasurer
Activities: Worship/practice/meditation, visits, resources
Movements: Jamati-i-Islami

Idara Isha'at Ul Islam*

52 Milner Street, Manchester M16 7GG
Tel: (07787) 526801

Islamic Academy of Manchester*

19 Chorlton Terrace, Brunswick, Manchester M13 9TD
Tel: (0161) 2731145
Contact: Maulana Hafiz Muhammad Iqbal Rangooni
Position: Imam
Activities: Worship, resource, visits, youth, elderly, women

Traditions: Sunni
Movements: Deobandi
Other Languages: Punjabi, Urdu, Arabic, Gujarati
Affiliations: Deoband, India

Islamic Centre and Madrassa Arabia*

52 Bury Old Road, Prestwich, Manchester M25 0ER
Tel: (0161) 7402125
Contact: Anwar Nayeer
Position: Secretary

Islamic Welfare Circle

c/o 28 Henley Avenue, Stretford, Manchester M16 0EW
Position: Mr A Ghandi Choudhury

Islamic Youth Movement*

425 Cheetham Hill Road, Cheetham Hill, Manchester M8 0PF
Tel: (0161) 2056662 **Fax:** (0161) 2056663
Contact: Mr M A Salam
Position: Chairman
Contact Tel: (0161) 7401665
Activities: Worship/practice/meditation, youth, elderly, women, visits, inter-faith, resources
Traditions: Sunni
Movements: Jamati-i-Islami
Other Languages: Urdu, Punjabi, Arabic, Malay

Itehad-ul-Muslimeen*

92 Duncan Road, Manchester M13 0GU
Tel: (0161) 2485817
Email: itehad_ul_muslimeen@hotmail.com
Contact: Mr Mohammad Akram
Position: Chairman
Contact Tel: (0161) 8810371
Activities: Worship/practice/meditation, youth, resources
Traditions: Sunni
Movements: Barelwi
Other Languages: Urdu, Punjabi

Jaffaria Islamic Centre

404 Moss Lane East, Rusholme, Manchester M14

Jamia Mosque and Ibadur Rahman Cultural Society*

3 Woodlands Road, off Cheetham Hill Road, Cheetham Hill, Manchester M8 7LF
Tel: (0161) 7403696
Contact: Dr Bashir Ahmad
Position: Trustee

Jamiat Ahle Hadith (Makki Mosque)*
125 Beresford Road, Longsight, Manchester
M13 0TA
Tel: (0161) 2572491 **Fax:** (0161) 2365518
Contact: A Sattar
Position: Secretary
Contact Tel: (0161) 4853152
Activities: Worship/practice/meditation, youth
Other Languages: Urdu, Punjabi, Arabic
Affiliations: Jamat Ahle Hadith Centre,
Birmingham

Khanka Naqshabandia Mosque*
181a Mauldeth Road, Burnage, Manchester M19 1BA
Tel: (0161) 2572424

Madina Masjid and Islamic Centre*
2 Barlow Road, off Stockport Road, Levenshulme,
Manchester M19 3DJ
Tel: (0161) 2245143 **Fax:** (0161) 2249674
Website: http://www.ukim.org/
Contact: Hafiz Saleem
Position: President
Activities: Worship, resource, visits, youth, elderly,
inter-faith
Traditions: Sunni
Movements: Deobandi, Jamati-i-Islami
Other Languages: Urdu, Punjabi, Bengali, Arabic
Affiliations: Muslim Educational Trust, London;
UK Action Committee on Islamic Affairs

**Manchester Central Mosque and Islamic
Cultural Centre***
20 Upper Park Road, Manchester M14 5RU
Tel: (0161) 2244119
Contact: Mr I Khan
Position: Treasurer
Activities: Worship, visits
Traditions: Sunni
Other Languages: Urdu, Punjabi
Affiliations: Greater Manchester Council of
Mosques; Ahl-e-Sunnat

Manchester Council of Mosques*
c/o North Manchester Mosque, 3 Woodlands
Road, Manchester M8 7LF
Tel: (0161) 6435499
Contact: Dr Bashir Ahmed
Position: Chairman

Manchester Islamic High School For Girls*
55 High Lane, Chorlton, Manchester M21 9FA
Tel: (0161) 8812127 **Fax:** (0161) 8610534

Contact: Mrs Mona Mohamed
Position: Headteacher
Activities: Resources
Traditions: Sunni
Movements: Ahl-e-Hadith
Other Languages: Urdu, Arabic

Masjid Imdadiah*
Blackburn Street, Old Trafford, Manchester
M16 9LJ
Tel: (0161) 2329851
Contact: Mr Iqbal
Position: Secretary
Activities: Worship, resource, visits, youth, elderly,
newsletter
Traditions: Sunni
Movements: Deobandi
Other Languages: Urdu, Gujarati, Hindi/Punjabi,
Burmese

Masjid-e-Noor*
115-117 Stamford Street, Old Trafford, Manchester
M16 9PY
Contact: A Chunara
Position: Chairman
Contact Tel: (0161) 2263163
Activities: Worship/practice/meditation
Traditions: Sunni
Movements: Deobandi, Tablighi Jamaat
Other Languages: Gujarati, Urdu

Mosque*
Burton Road, West Didsbury, Manchester M20
Tel: (0161) 434 2254
Contact: Mr Soliman
Position: Secretary

Mosque and Darul Uloom*
1 Hawkhurst Street, Longsight, Manchester M13 0SJ
Tel: (0161) 2562812

Muslim Parents Association*
13 Hazel Avenue, Whalley Range, Manchester
M16 8DY
Tel: (0161) 8607869 **Fax:** (0161) 8607869
Contact: Mr Ahmad Nazir
Position: Co-ordinator
Activities: Umbrella body, youth, elderly, women,
inter-faith
Traditions: Sunni
Movements: All groups
Other Languages: Punjabi, Urdu
Affiliations: Manchester Council of Mosques

Muslim Society and Community Advisory Service
76 Moss Park Road, Stretford, Manchester
M32 9HQ

Muslim Youth Foundation*
Clydesdale House, 27 Turner Street, Manchester
M4 1DY
Tel: (0161) 8325352 **Fax:** (0161) 8325454
Contact: Mohammad Hafiz
Position: Trustee
Contact Tel: (0161) 2364001
Other Languages: Urdu, Arabic, Bengali

Noor-Ul-Quran*
4 Newton Avenue, Longsight, Manchester
M12 4EW
Tel: (0161) 2240774
Contact: Mr Shahzada
Position: Chairman
Contact Tel: (07811) 738159
Activities: Resource, media, umbrella body, visits, youth, elderly
Traditions: Sunni
Other Languages: Urdu, Arabic, Bengali

Shah Jalal Mosque and Islamic Society
1a Eileen Grove, Off Platt Lane, Rusholme, Manchester M1 5WE
Tel: (0161) 2242165
Contact: The Chair
Activities: Worship
Traditions: Sunni
Other Languages: Bengali

Shere Rabbani Mosque*
11a Bedford Avenue, Whalley Range, Manchester
M16 8JS
Tel: (0161) 9619778
Contact: Mr M Bashir
Position: Secretary

Sunni Muslim Association*
Dada Hall, 20 Brideoak Street, Cheetham, Manchester M8 7PN
Tel: (0161) 2034631
Email: talatzeria@hotmail.com.
Contact: Talat M Zeria
Contact Tel: (0161) 7986249
Activities: Resource, youth, elderly, women, newsletter
Traditions: Sunni
Movements: Barelwi
Other Languages: Kutch, Gujarati, Urdu, Punjabi

University of Manchester Islamic Society*
Steve Biko Building, Students' Union, Oxford Road, Manchester M13 9PR
Tel: (07801) 573015
Email: isoc_net@hotmail.com
Website: http://www.manchesterisoc.org.uk/
Contact: Mr Bilal Al-Khaffaf
Position: President
Contact Email: mailbilal@breathemail.net
Activities: Worship/practice/meditation, central body, youth, women, newsletter/journal, visits, inter-faith, resources
Traditions: Sunni
Other Languages: Arabic, Urdu, Punjabi

Young Muslim Sports Club*
258 Barlow Moor Road, Chorlton-Cum-Hardy, Manchester M21 8HA
Tel: (0161) 8818269 **Fax:** (0161) 8811245
Contact: Mr Azim Khan
Position: Co-ordinator
Other Languages: Urdu, Punjabi

Zakariyya Mosque and Madrassa*
22-24 Clarendon Road, Whalley Range, Manchester M16 8LD
Tel: (0161) 881 9860
Contact: Imam

Mossley Community Mosque
81 Egmont Street, Mossley OL5 9NB
Tel: (01457) 55507

Idara Minhaj-Ul-Quran*
15 Cross Street, Pendle, Nelson BB9 7LE
Tel: (01282) 616466 **Fax:** (01282) 616466
Email: imq-nelson@cwcom.net
Website: http://www.minhaj.org/
Contact: M A Alam
Position: Director
Contact Tel: (01282) 604719
Contact Email: rafiqhabib@cwcom.net
Other Languages: Urdu, Arabic, Punjabi
Affiliations: Lancashire Council of Mosques; Minhaj-ul-Quran International

Ilm-o-Adab Mission
155 Every Street, Nelson BB9 7HG

Ithaad*
5 Cross Street, Nelson BB9 7EN
Tel: (01282) 694700 **Fax:** (01282) 611104
Contact: Najir Mehmood
Position: Community Officer

Contact Tel: (01282) 661996
Other Languages: Urdu, Punjabi

Ithaad Advice Centre*
5 Cross Street, Nelson BB9 7EN
Tel: (01282) 694700
Contact: Abdul Hazif Malik
Position: General Secretary
Activities: Youth, elderly, women, inter-faith
Traditions: Sunni
Movements: Jamati-i-Islami
Other Languages: Urdu, Punjabi

Jamiah Sultania Mosque*
3-7 Bridge Street, Brierfield, Nelson BB9 5LR
Tel: (01254) 692764
Contact: Mr Mohanmmed Arif
Position: Secretary
Contact Tel: (07785) 514914
Activities: Worship/practice/meditation
Traditions: Sunni
Movements: Barelwi

Jamiat Ahl-e-Hadith*
Mohammadi Masjid, Netherfield Road, Nelson
BB9 9QL
Tel: (01282) 698229
Contact: Mohammad Aslam
Position: President
Contact Tel: (07713) 006465
Activities: Worship, resource, visits
Traditions: Sunni
Movements: Ahl-e-Hadith
Other Languages: Punjabi, Urdu, Arabic
Affiliations: Jamiat Ahl-e-Hadith

**Al Madina Jamia Mosque And Islamic
Educational Centre***
230-240 Waterloo Street, Oldham OL4 1ES
Tel: (0161) 6271431
Contact: A Aziz
Position: Secretary
Activities: Worship/practice/meditation, education
Other Languages: Arabic, Urdu, Punjabi

Al-Khazra Markazi Masjid*
53 Chadderton Way, Oldham OL9 6DP
Tel: (0161) 6242626

Hussania Islamic Mission*
102 Greengate Street, Oldham OL4 1EB
Tel: (0161) 6272155
Contact: Sam
Position: Imam

Activities: Worship/practice/meditation
Other Languages: Urdu, Persian, Arabic

Jamia Mosque
2 Derby Street, Werneth, Oldham OL9 7BH

Jamiat Ahle Hadith Mosque*
11 Ross Street, Oldham OL8 1UA
Tel: (0161) 6208548 **Fax:** (0161) 6208548
Email: ahlehadees@hotmail.com
Contact: Mr S Rehman
Position: Priest
Contact Tel: (0161) 7858069
Contact Email: shafiq@rehmans.fsbusiness.co.uk
Activities: Worship/practice/meditation, umbrella
body, youth, newsletter/journal, books, visits, inter-
faith, resources
Traditions: Sunni
Movements: Ahl-e-Hadith
Other Languages: Urdu, Arabic
Affiliations: Markzi Jamiat Ahle Hadith UK

Madina Mosque and Islamic Centre*
29 Stansfield Street, Oldham OL1 2HA
Tel: (0161) 6786862
Contact: Haji Sabur Miah
Position: Chairman
Activities: Worship/practice/meditation
Other Languages: Bengali

Minhaj-ul-Quran Islamic Educational Centre*
138 Werneth Hall Road, Coppice, Oldham OL8 1QZ
Tel: (0161) 633 2837
Contact: Mr Zafer
Position: President

Nagina Mosque and Urdu School*
74 -76 Werneth Hall Road, Coppice, Oldham OL8
1QZ
Tel: (0161) 6265194
Contact: Bashir Bhatti
Position: Vice President

Nusrat-ul-Islam*
Pitt Street, Glodwick, Oldham OL4 1AN
Tel: (0161) 2840087
Contact: Mohammed Tufail
Contact Tel: (0161) 6204765
Activities: Worship/practice/meditation,
community centre, youth, elderly, television, visits,
inter-faith
Traditions: Sunni
Movements: Deobandi, Tablighi Jamaat
Other Languages: Urdu, Punjabi, Pushto

Oldham Mosque and Islamic Centre
156-158 Middleton Road, Oldham OL9 6BG

Tabligh-ul-Islam Mosque
87 Greengate Street, Oldham OL4 1DH

UK Islamic Mission*
44/46 Manchester Road, Werneth, Oldham
OL9 7AP
Tel: (0161) 2845913 **Fax:** (0161) 6204472
Website: http://www.ukim.com/
Contact: Mr Feroz Din
Position: President
Activities: Worship/practice/meditation,
community centre, youth, elderly, women,
newsletter/journal, visits, inter-faith
Traditions: Sunni
Movements: Jamati-i-Islami

Gujarat Sunni Muslim Community Centre
15 Eldon Street, Preston PR1 7YD

Gujarati Sunni Muslim Society - Masjid-e-Noor*
Noor Street, Preston PR1 1QS
Tel: (01772) 881786 **Fax:** (01772) 881786
Contact: Secretary
Activities: Worship/practice/meditation
Other Languages: Gujarati

Hanfi Sunni Raza Mosque*
103-105 St Paul's Road, Preston PR1 1UH
Tel: (01772) 203578
Contact: Mr Khan
Position: Secretary

Madrassa-e-Noorul-Islam Mosque*
Noor Hall, Noor Street, Preston PR1 1QS
Tel: (01772) 881786
Contact: Hajji Ibrahim

Masjed Quba
190 New Hall Lane, Preston PR1 4DX

Masjeed-e-Quba*
17 Lex Street, Preston PR1 4XL
Tel: (01772) 701970
Contact: Bashir Ahmed
Position: Secretary

Masjid-e-Aqsa Preston Hanfi Sunni Muslim Society*
95-99 Fishwick Parade, Preston PR1 4XR
Tel: (01772) 797758
Position: General Secretary

Activities: Worship, resource
Traditions: Sunni
Movements: Barelwi
Other Languages: Urdu, Gujarati, Punjabi, Arabic
Affiliations: Lancashire Council of Mosques;
Imams and Mosques Council; Muslim World
League, Charity Commission

Masjid-e-Falah
135-137 Kent Street, Preston PR1 1PE

Masjid-e-Salam*
49 Watling Street, Fulwood, Preston PR2 8EA
Tel: (01772) 788447
Contact: Mr F Assenjee
Position: Joint Secretary
Activities: Worship/practice/meditation, youth,
women, visits, inter-faith, resources
Traditions: Sunni
Movements: Deobandi, Tablighi Jamaat
Other Languages: Gujarati, Urdu
Affiliations: Lancashire Council of Mosques;
Muslim Council of Britain

Medina Mosque*
26-28 Fishwick Parade, Preston PR1 4XQ
Tel: (01772) 788847
Contact: Musa Roked
Position: Secretary
Contact Tel: (01772) 798847
Activities: Worship/practice/meditation
Other Languages: Gujarati, Urdu

Preston Muslim Cultural Centre*
21 Fishergate Hill, Preston PR1 8JB
Tel: (01772) 824357
Contact: Ismail Tagari
Position: Secretary
Activities: Worship, resource
Traditions: Sunni
Movements: Tablighi Jamaat
Other Languages: Gujarati, Urdu
Affiliations: Lancashire Council of Mosques

Preston Muslim Forum*
17 Holmrook Road, Preston PR1 6SR
Tel: (01772) 889000
Contact: Mr Iqbal Mulla
Position: Senior Officer
Activities: Women, resources
Other Languages: Gujarati, Urdu

Preston Muslim Society*
18 Clarendon Street, Preston PR1 3YN

Tel: (01772) 257127
Contact: The Secretary
Contact Tel: (01772) 906422
Activities: Worship
Other Languages: Gujarati, Urdu

Quwwatul Islam Mosque and Preston Muslim Society*
Peel Hall Street, Deepdale, Preston PR1 6QX
Tel: (01772) 254578
Contact: Secretary

Roza Mosque
103-105 St Paul's Road, Preston PR1 1MH

Masjed Noor and Islamic Education Centre*
72 Eton Hill Road, Radcliffe M26 2XT
Tel: (0161) 7234536 **Fax:** (0161) 7231395
Contact: Mr M Muneer
Position: Chairman
Activities: Worship/practice/meditation, youth, elderly, women
Traditions: Sunni
Movements: Barelwi, Deobandi
Other Languages: Urdu, Punjabi

Al-Amin (Islamic Teaching Centre) Mosque*
40 Corbett Street, Wardleworth, Rochdale
OL16 2EX
Tel: (01706) 356990
Email: alaminmasjid@yahoo.com
Contact: Mr Alhaj M Miah
Position: Trustee
Contact Tel: (07720) 721265
Contact Email: mamiah@femail.com
Activities: Worship/practice/meditation, youth, elderly, visits, resources
Traditions: Sunni
Movements: Tablighi Jamaat
Other Languages: Bengali, Urdu, Punjabi, Arabic

Astana Mujadaddia Haidaria
5 James Street, Rochdale OL12 0DX

Bilal Mosque*
Bulwer Street, Rochdale OL16 2EU
Tel: (01706) 861 853
Contact: Mr Ahmed
Position: Imam

Dar-ul-Uloom Jamia Chashtiah Monir Ul-Islam*
Multi Purpose Community and Worship Centre, 49/53a Milkstone Road, Rochdale OL11 1EB
Tel: (01706) 650487

Contact: Hafiz Abdul Haq Chishti
Position: General Secretary
Activities: Worship, visits, youth, elderly, women, inter-faith
Traditions: Sunni
Affiliations: Rochdale Council Of Mosques; Imam and Mosques Council London; Jama'at Ahle Sunnat; World Islamic Mission

Jalalia Jame Mosque
66 Trafalgar Street, Rochdale OL1 6JL
Tel: (01706) 46822

Jamia Masjid Al-Furqhan*
17 Philip Street, off Deeplish Road, Rochdale
OL11 1PJ
Tel: (01706) 523370
Contact: Mr Riaz ul-Haq
Position: President
Contact Tel: (01706) 633487
Contact Email: abu.saffiyah@mcmail.com
Activities: Worship, youth
Traditions: Sunni
Movements: Ahl-e-Hadith
Other Languages: Urdu, Punjabi
Affiliations: Markazi Jamiat Ahle-Hadith, Birmingham

Madrassa Dar-Ul-Monawar
1 Derby Street, Rochdale OL11 1LT

Madrassa Islamia (Urdu Centre)*
58 Morley Street, Rochdale OL16 2LG
Contact: Imam M Ismail Khan
Position: Director
Contact Tel: (01706) 343551
Activities: Worship/practice/meditation, youth, elderly, women, visits, resources
Traditions: Sunni
Movements: Barelwi, Tassawuf

Markazi Jamia Masjid*
Mere Street, Rochdale OL11 1HJ
Tel: (01706) 645135 **Fax:** (01706) 645771
Email: hafizmalik@yahoo.com
Website: http://www.masjid.org.uk/
Contact: Abdul Malik
Contact Tel: (01706) 645200
Activities: Worship/practice/meditation, community centre, central body, youth, elderly, women, resources
Traditions: Sunni
Movements: Deobandi, Tablighi Jamaat
Other Languages: Punjabi, Urdu, Bengali, Arabic

Neelie Mosque and Islamic Centre*
34-36 Durham Street, Rochdale OL11 1JJ
Tel: (01706) 648094 **Fax:** (01706) 648094
Contact: Mohammed Sharif Baleem
Position: Chairman
Activities: Worship, visits, youth, elderly, women
Traditions: Sunni
Other Languages: Urdu, Punjabi

Rochdale Muslim Society*
47 Norford Way, Bamford, Rochdale OL11 5QS
Tel: (01706) 526036
Contact: Dr A Rauf
Traditions: Sunni
Other Languages: Urdu, Punjabi

UK Islamic Mission*
34-36 Durham Street, Rochdale OL11 IJJ
Tel: (01706) 648094 **Fax:** (01706) 648094
Contact: Zamir Ahmed
Position: President
Activities: Resource, visits, youth, elderly, women, inter-faith
Traditions: Sunni
Other Languages: Urdu, Punjabi
Affiliations: UK Islamic Mission

Southport Muslim Society*
102a Sussex Road, Southport PR9 0SL
Tel: (01704) 539859
Contact: Mr Yusuf Muquiz
Position: Imam
Contact Tel: (01704) 510131
Activities: Worship/practice/meditation
Traditions: Sunni
Other Languages: Bengali, Arabic

Muslim Welfare Centre*
69 Fox Street, Edgeley, Stockport SK3 9AR
Contact: Mr A Khaliq
Position: Chairman
Contact Tel: (0161) 2827059
Activities: Youth, elderly
Traditions: Sunni
Other Languages: Urdu, Punjabi

Muslim Society and Masjid-e-Hamza*
Eagle Street Mosque, Eagle Street, Todmorden
OL14 5HQ
Tel: (01706) 816310
Contact: Mubarak Ali
Position: Imam
Activities: Worship
Traditions: Sunni

Movements: Tablighi Jamaat
Other Languages: Urdu, Punjabi, Bengali

Jamait-ul-Muslemeen*
19-21 Arpley Street, Warrington WA1 1NZ
Tel: (01925) 637912
Contact: Mr Javad
Position: Secretary
Contact Tel: (01925) 637033

Prayer Room*
Ist Floor, 34/35 Tangir Street, Whitehaven
LA28 7UZ
Contact: Ali Taq

Wigan Islamic Centre*
Poolstock, Clifton Street, Worsley Menses, Wigan
WN3 5GJ
Tel: (01942) 495038
Contact: A Nasir
Position: Secretary
Activities: Worship, visits, youth, elderly
Traditions: Sunni
Movements: Ahl-e-Hadith
Other Languages: Urdu, Arabic

EAST MIDLANDS
Regional or County Bodies

Federation of Muslim Organisations in Leicestershire*
Muslim Community Resource Centre, Melbourne
Centre, Melbourne Road, Leicester LE2 0GU
Tel: (0116) 2125250 **Fax:** (0116) 212250
Contact: Mr Suleman Nagdi
Position: Executive Member
Contact Tel: (07759) 446555
Contact Email: s.nagdi@ntlworld.com
Activities: Community centre, umbrella body,
youth, elderly, women, newsletter/journal, radio,
inter-faith
Affiliations: Muslim Council of Britain

City, Town or Local Bodies

Islamic Deen and Dawah Centre*
29 Newbold Road, Chesterfield S41 7PG
Tel: (01246) 277284 **Fax:** (01246) 220728
Contact: Mr Mushtaq Sharif
Position: Chair
Activities: Worship/practice/meditation,
community centre, youth, visits

Traditions: Sunni
Other Languages: Mirpuri

Derby Jamia Mosque*
6 Rose Hill Street, Derby DE23 8HL
Tel: (01332) 344838
Contact: Rehmat Khan
Position: Treasurer
Activities: Worship, resource, visits, inter-faith
Traditions: Sunni
Movements: Barelwi
Other Languages: Urdu, Punjabi
Affiliations: Council of Sunni Mosques

Islamic Centre Derby*
The Central Mosque, Sacheveral Street, Derby
DE1 2JR
Tel: (01332) 292021
Contact: Rafaqat Ali
Position: Treasurer
Activities: Worship, resource, media, visits, youth,
elderly
Traditions: Sunni
Other Languages: Urdu, Punjabi, Arabic

Jamia Hanfia-Taleem-ul-Islam*
26 Western Road, Derby DE23 6SE
Tel: (01332) 204187
Contact: Abdullah Abdusshakur
Activities: Worship, resource, youth, elderly,
women
Traditions: Sunni
Other Languages: Urdu, Bengali, Arabic, Serbo-
Croat

Jamiat-Ahl-e-Hadith*
7a Hastings Street, Normanton, Derby DE3 6QQ
Tel: (01332) 766237
Contact: Ghazanfer Yousaf Khan
Position: Public Relations
Activities: Worship, resource, youth, elderly,
women
Movements: Ahl-e-Hadith
Other Languages: Urdu, Punjabi
Affiliations: Muslim World League

Masjid-e-khulfa-e-Rashedeen*
144 Cameron Road, Cavendish, Derby DE23 8RU
Tel: (01332) 773421

Mosque*
54 Dairyhouse Road, Normanton, Derby
DE3 8HL
Position: Caretaker
Activities: Youth, elderly, women

Pakistan Muslim Welfare Association*
9 Madeley Street, Derby DE3 8EX
Tel: (01332) 365845

Hinckley Muslim Association*
1 Manor Close, Burbage, Hinckley LE10 2NL
Tel: (01455) 611480
Contact: Mr Manzoor E Moghal
Position: President
Activities: Worship/practice/meditation,
community centre
Traditions: Sunni
Movements: Deobandi
Other Languages: Urdu, Punjabi, Bengali
Affiliations: Federation of Muslim Organisations,
Leicester; Muslim Council of Britain

Al Hilal Muslim Youth Association*
18 Morley Road, Leicester LE5 3HP
Tel: (0116) 2514500 **Fax:** (0116) 2122730
Contact: Khalid Rashid
Position: Chairman
Activities: Umbrella body, youth
Traditions: Sunni
Other Languages: Gujarati, Urdu, Punjabi
Affiliations: Federation of Muslim Organisations;
Union of Muslim Organisations

Al-Taqwa Islamic Education Centre*
1 Harewood Street, Leicester LE5 3LX
Tel: (0116) 2125802
Contact: Mr M Amjad
Position: Secretary

Anjumman-E-Saifee*
74 Overdale Road, Leicester LE2 3YH
Tel: (0116) 2664668
Contact: Mr J A Kapasi
Position: Trustee
Affiliations: Dawoodi Bohra Jammat

Baitul Mukaram Mosque
22-24 St Stephens Road, Leicester LE2 1DQ

Bangledesh Association
23 Melbourne Road, Leicester LE2 0GT

**Belgrave Muslim Education Welfare
Association***
38 Glendon Street, Leicester LE4 6JR
Tel: (0116) 2680943
Contact: Mr Abdul Jamal
Position: Secretary
Activities: Resource
Traditions: Sunni

Other Languages: Gujarati, Urdu
Affiliations: Federation of Muslim Organisations in Leicestershire

Dar-us-Salam Mosque*
55-57 Upper Tichbourne Street, Leicester
LE2 1GL
Tel: (0116) 2543887 **Fax:** (0116) 2545050
Email: n.chowdhury@iccda.co.uk
Contact: Nizam Chowdhury
Position: General Secretary
Contact Tel: (07944) 838960
Activities: Worship, resource, visits, elderly, inter-faith, education
Traditions: Sunni
Other Languages: Bengali

Darul Uloom Leicester*
119 Loughborough Road, Leicester LE4 5LN
Tel: (0116) 2668922 **Fax:** (0116) 2992458
Contact: Mr Mohammed Patel
Position: Headmaster
Contact Tel: (07730) 437517
Activities: Youth, resources
Traditions: Sunni
Movements: Deobandi
Other Languages: Urdu, Arabic

Darus Salam Trust*
55-57 Upper Tichbourne Street, Leicester
LE2 1DR
Tel: (0116) 2543887
Contact: Nizam Chowdhury
Position: General Secretary
Contact Tel: (0116) 2101190
Contact Email: n.chowdhury@lccda.uk
Activities: Worship/practice/meditation, community centre, youth, elderly, women, newsletter/journal, visits, inter-faith, resources
Traditions: Sunni
Other Languages: Bengali, Urdu, Hindi

Dawoodi Bohra Welfare Society*
1b Royal Road, Leicester LE4 5DP
Tel: (0116) 2660866
Contact: Mr Mohsin Sulemanji
Position: Committee Member
Activities: Worship
Traditions: Dawoodi Bohra
Other Languages: Gujarati
Affiliations: Dawoodi Bohra Welfare Society GB; Federation of Muslim Organisations, Leicester

De Montfort University Islamic Society*
Students Union, The Gateway, Leicester LE1 9BH

Email: dmuslim@hotmail.com
Contact: Mr Akbar Sameja
Position: President
Contact Tel: (07931) 362402
Contact Email: akbarsameja@yahoo.co.uk
Activities: Worship/practice/meditation, community centre, youth, women
Traditions: Sunni
Other Languages: Urdu, Gujarati, Punjabi, Arabic
Affiliations: FOSIS (Federation of Student Islamic Societies)

Evington Muslim Centre, Masjid Umar*
1-3 Evington Drive, Leicester LE5 5PF
Tel: (0116) 2735529
Contact: Ibrahim Fulat
Position: Chairman
Contact Tel: (0116) 2434184

Islamic Centre and Mosque*
2a Sutherland Street, Leicester LE2 1DS
Tel: (0116) 2854052
Contact: Mr Murawat Hussein
Position: Secretary
Activities: Worship, resource, visits, youth, elderly, women,
Traditions: Sunni
Movements: Barelwi, Tassawuf
Other Languages: Urdu, Gujarati, Punjabi, Bengali
Affiliations: Federation of Leicester Mosques; Imams and Mosques Council; Union of Muslim Organisations

Islamic Centre*
2a Sutherland Street, Leicester LE4 6PN
Tel: (0116) 2854052
Contact: Mohammed Hussain
Position: Chairman
Activities: Youth, elderly, women
Traditions: Sunni
Movements: Barelwi
Other Languages: Kutchee, Gujarati, Kishwahili, Urdu

Islamic Dawah Academy
120 Melbourne Road, Leicester LE2 0GU

Islamic Education Trust
3-11 Keythorpe Street, Highfields, Leicester
LE2 0AL
Tel: (0116) 2511833

Jame Mosque*
51 Asfordby Street, Leicester LE5 3QJ

Tel: (0116) 2621963
Contact: Mr I Omarji
Position: Secretary
Other Languages: Gujarati, Urdu, Arabic

Leicester Central Mosque, Conduit Street*
2A Sutherland Street, Leicester LE2 0JN
Tel: (0116) 2544459 **Fax:** (0116) 2544459
Contact: Mr M H Khan
Position: Chairman
Activities: Worship, resources, youth, women, inter-faith
Traditions: Sunni
Movements: Barelwi
Other Languages: Urdu

Leicester University Islamic Society*
University of Leicester, Percy Gee Building,
Leicester LE1 7RH
Tel: (07779) 329104
Email: tiub1@le.ac.uk
Contact: Mr Bhuiya
Position: President
Activities: Worship/practice/meditation, youth, women, inter-faith, resources
Traditions: Sunni
Other Languages: Urdu, Arabic, Gujarati, Turkish
Affiliations: Leicester University Students Union; Federation of Students Islamic Societies (FOSIS)

Majlis-E-Dawat-ul-Haq (UK)
126 Earl Howe Street, Leicester LE2 0DG

Masjid al Bukhari and Muslim Education Centre*
159 Loughborough Road, Leicester LE4 5LR
Tel: (0116) 2665506
Contact: Gulam Omarji Makadam
Position: Chairperson
Movements: Worship/practice/meditation
Other Languages: Gujarati, Urdu

Muslim Khoja Shia Ithna-Asheri Community*
127 Loughborough Road, Belgrave, Leicester
LE4 5LQ
Tel: (0116) 2682828
Contact: Mr Rajani
Position: Chairman
Contact Tel: (07973) 195136
Activities: Worship/practice/meditation, community centre, youth, elderly, women, newsletter/journal
Traditions: 'Ithna Asheri
Other Languages: Urdu, Gujarati, Kutch, Swahili

Muslim Ladies' Association*
117 Twycross Street, Oadby, Leicester LE2 ODX
Contact: Tabaffum
Position: Secretary
Contact Tel: (0116) 2554427
Activities: Resource, youth, women
Traditions: Sunni
Other Languages: Urdu, Punjabi

Muslim Welfare Trust*
c/o 24 Wilson Street, Leicester LE2 0BB
Tel: (0116) 2517948

Narborough Road Islamic Centre
55 Barclay Street, Leicester LE3 0JD
Tel: (0116) 2545552 **Fax:** (0116) 2555540

Pakistan Association Muslim Community*
Muslim Community Centre, Old Boys School,
Melbourne Road, Leicester LE2 0GU
Tel: (0116) 254 3718
Contact: Mr R T Khan
Position: Chairperson

Surati Muslim Khalifa Society*
127 Mere Road, Leicester LE5 5GQ
Tel: (0116) 2511120
Contact: Mr Abdul Kader Ismail Daud
Position: President
Activities: Community centre, youth, women, elderly, inter-faith, resources
Traditions: Sunni
Movements: Ahl-e-Hadith, Deobandi
Other Languages: Gujarati, Urdu, Arabic
Affiliations: Federation of Gujarati Muslim Khalifa Societies of UK

UK Islamic Mission Leicester*
41 Gwendolen Road, Leicester LE5 5FL
Contact: Mr Sadiq Khokhar
Position: Secretary
Activities: Resource, women, books, inter-faith
Other Languages: Urdu
Affiliations: Muslim Council of Britain

Lincoln Islamic Association*
Orchard Street, Lincoln LN1 1XX
Tel: (0116) 2425943
Contact: Farouq Mullah
Position: Secretary
Activities: Worship, youth
Traditions: Sunni
Other Languages: Urdu, Arabic, Bengali

Loughborough Mosque and Islamic Cultural Association*
83-85 King Street, Loughborough LE11 1BS
Tel: (01509) 214500
Contact: M I Miah
Position: General Secretary
Other Languages: Bengali

Loughborough Students Union Islamic Society
Loughborough Students Union, Loughborough LE11 3TU
Affiliations: FOSIS (Federation of Student Islamic Societies)

Shahjala Centre
Rendell Street, Loughborough
Contact: Mr M T Chowdary
Activities: Women
Other Languages: Bengali

Al Jamat-ul-Muslimin of Bangladesh
8 St George's Street, off Regent Square, Northampton NN1 2TR
Tel: (01604) 24930

Islamic Pakistani Community Centre*
98a Colwyn Road, Northampton NN1 3PX
Tel: (01604) 621125
Contact: Mr S Khan
Position: Co-ordinator
Activities: Worship, resource, media, visits, youth, elderly
Other Languages: Punjabi, Urdu, Bengali

Mosque*
43 Argyle Street, Northampton NN5 5LJ
Tel: (01604) 754085
Contact: Secretary

Islamic Centre*
3 Curzon Street, St Anns Road, Nottingham NG3 1DG
Tel: (0115) 9590001
Contact: Mr R Azam
Position: Chairman

Jameah Fatimah*
118a Berridge Road, Forest Fields, Nottingham NG7 6HT
Tel: (0115) 9244004
Contact: Amed
Position: Teacher/Priest

Jamiah Fatimia*
c/o 18 Austen Avenue, Forest Fields, Nottingham
NG7 6PE
Tel: (0115) 9786006
Contact: A H Bhatti
Position: Secretary
Activities: Worship, resource, inter-faith
Traditions: Sunni
Movements: Barelwi
Other Languages: Urdu

Karima Institute*
512-514 Berridge Road West, Forest Fields, Nottingham NG7 5JU
Tel: (0115) 8415806 **Fax:** (0115) 8415807
Email: musharraf3@hotmail.com
Contact: Mrs K Yusef
Position: Office Manageress
Contact Tel: (0116) 2745191
Contact Email: akyusef@btinternet.com
Activities: Resources
Other Languages: Urdu, Punjabi, Arabic
Affiliations: Muslim Council Of Britain

Madni Masjid and Muslims Education Centre*
289 Gladstone Street, Forest Fields, Nottingham NG7 6HX
Tel: (0115) 96908000
Contact: R Haq
Position: Principal
Activities: Worship, resource, visits, youth, elderly, women,
Other Languages: Urdu, Punjabi, Arabic

Madrassa-e-Islamia*
58 Thurgarten Street, Sneinton, Nottingham NG2 4AG
Tel: (0115) 9117601
Contact: Aurangzeb Khan
Position: Chair
Activities: Worship, resource, youth, elderly, women
Traditions: Sunni
Movements: Barelwi
Other Languages: Urdu,Punjabi

Masjid Bilaal Mosque*
3-5 Lenton Boulevard, Lenton, Nottingham NG7 2ET
Tel: (0786) 6734943
Contact: Mr M Saddique
Position: Chairman
Activities: Worship/practice/meditation
Other Languages: Arabic

Mosque
65 Belper Avenue, Carlton, Nottingham NG4 3SE

Muslim Women Organisation*
165a Ilkeston Road, The Lodge, Lenton,
Nottingham NG7 3HF
Tel: (0115) 9420590
Contact: Mrs Shanaz Mahmood
Position: Admin Worker
Activities: Education
Traditions: Sunni
Other Languages: Urdu, Punjabi

Nottingham University Islamic Society
Students Union, Nottingham NG7 2RD

Pakistan Community Centre*
163 Woodborough Road, Nottingham NG3 1AX
Tel: (0115) 9582973
Contact: Mr Idris
Position: Manager

Pakistan Muslim Association
10 Radford Road, Hyson Green, Nottingham
NG7 5FS

Sneinton Muslim Centre
5 Kingsley Road, Sneinton, Nottingham
NG2 4AR

Jamia Al-Karam*
Eaton Hall, Retford DN22 0PR
Tel: (01777) 706441 **Fax:** (01777) 711538
Contact: Mr Pirzada Mohd Imdad Hussain
Position: Principal
Activities: Worship/practice/meditation, youth
Traditions: Sunni
Other Languages: Urdu

*Islah-ul-Muslimeen Mosque and Islamic
Centre**
Winstanley/Strode Road, Wellingborough
NN8 1EL
Tel: (01933) 275541
Contact: Community Officer
Activities: Worship/practice/meditation,
community centre, youth, elderly, women, visits
Traditions: Sunni
Movements: Ahl-e-Hadith

WEST MIDLANDS
Regional or County Bodies

Ahl-e-Sunnat-wal-Jamaat Ulema Sangsad*
108 Reginald Road, Saltley, Birmingham B8 1LU
Tel: (0121) 3285473
Contact: Mr Mohammed Monsur Alam
Position: Secretary General
Contact Tel: (0121) 356 8955
Activities: Worship/practice/meditation, central
body, youth, elderly, visits
Traditions: Sunni
Movements: Barelwi
Other Languages: Bengali, Urdu, Hindi, Arabic
Affiliations: Shahjalal Marifati - Zikir Mission

Confederation of Sunni Mosques Midlands*
107 Golden Hillock Road, Small Heath,
Birmingham B10 0DP
Tel: (0121) 6221369
Contact: Raja M Saleem Akhtar
Position: Chairman

City, Town or Local Bodies

Ahl-e-Sunnat-wal-Jamaat Ulema Sangsad*
108 Reginald Road, Saltley, Birmingham B8 1LU
Tel: (0121) 3285473
Contact: Mr Mohammed Monsur Alam
Position: Secretary General
Contact Tel: (0121) 356 8955
Activities: Worship/practice/meditation, central
body, youth, elderly, visits
Traditions: Sunni
Movements: Barelwi
Other Languages: Bengali, Urdu, Hindi, Arabic
Affiliations: Shahjalal Marifati - Zikir Mission

Al-Hijrah Mosque*
59 Hobmoor Road, Small Heath, Birmingham
B10 9AZ
Tel: (0121) 7665454 **Fax:** (0121) 7668556
Contact: M A K Saqib
Position: President
Activities: Worship, resource, visits
Traditions: Sunni
Other Languages: Urdu, Arabic, Punjabi, Bengali

All Muslim Welfare Society*
7 Park Avenue, Hockley, Birmingham B18 5ND
Tel: (0121) 5546717
Contact: Mohammed Sadiq
Position: Chairman

Amina Trust*
56 Dolphin Road, Sparkhill, Birmingham
B11 1AR
Tel: (0121) 2477405
Email: aminatrust@hotmail.com
Contact: Hamid Lea
Position: Secretary
Activities: Resource, visits, youth, women, books,
inter-faith
Traditions: Sunni
Movements: Tassawuf (Sufi)
Other Languages: Urdu, Arabic, Bengali, Punjabi

Amir-e-Millat Mosque and Community Centre*
144 Stoney Lane, Spark Hill, Birmingham B12 8AJ
Tel: (0121) 4495695
Contact: Mr Mohammed Omar
Position: President

An-Noor Islamic Welfare Society UK*
61 Wills street, Lozells, Birmingham B19 1QR
Tel: (07980) 020801
Contact: President
Other Languages: Urdu, Bangladeshi

Anjuman-e-Naqeebul Islam Mosque*
82 Washwood Heath Road, Satley, Birmingham
B8 1RD
Tel: (0121) 3284930
Contact: Ziauddin
Position: Secretary
Contact Tel: (0121) 3284930
Activities: Worship/practice/meditation
Other Languages: Urdu

Anjuman-eTabligh-ul-Islam*
6 Wyecliffe Road, Handsworth, Birmingham
B20 3TB
Tel: (0121) 5237529
Contact: Mr Masam Khan
Position: Secretary
Activities: Worship
Traditions: Sunni
Movements: Deobandi, Tablighi Jamaat
Other Languages: Urdu, Hindi, Punjabi

Anjumane Islam
23 Arden Road, Aston, Birmingham B6 6AP

Anwar-ul-Madina*
762 Washwood Heath Road, Ward End,
Birmingham B8 2JY
Contact: Mr Safdar Hussian
Position: Trustee

Bangladesh Islamic Centre and Mosque*
88 Wills Street, Birmingham B19 1QT

Bangladesh Islamic Centre*
64 Osborn Road, Sparkbrook, Birmingham
B11 1PS
Tel: (0121) 7731298
Contact: F Choudhury
Position: General Secretary
Contact Tel: (07961) 332850
Other Languages: Bengali, Sylheti

Bangladesh Welfare Association and Mosque*
19-21 Alum Rock Road, Saltley, Birmingham
B8 1LL
Tel: (0121) 3284746
Contact: Mr A Rahman
Position: Vice President

Birmingham Anjumane Islam Mosque Trust*
Saddam Hussein Mosque, 2 Trinity Road,
Birchfield, Birmingham B6 6AG
Tel: (0121) 5549157 **Fax:** (0121) 5549157
Contact: Hazratmian Kazi
Position: Chairman
Activities: Worship, visits, youth, elderly, women,
inter-faith
Traditions: Sunni
Movements: Ahl-e-Hadith, Deobandi
Other Languages: Urdu
Affiliations: Council of Mosques; Union of
Muslim Organisation UK and Ireland; The Muslim
World League UK

Birmingham Jami Masjid and Islamic Centre*
517-527 Coventry Road, Small Heath,
Birmingham B10 0LL
Tel: (0121) 7726408 **Fax:** (0121) 7734340
Email: darul2000@hotmail.com
Contact: Dr Abu SMA Rahim
Position: Chairman
Activities: Worship/practice/meditation,
community centre, umbrella body, youth, elderly,
women, radio, resources
Traditions: Sunni
Movements: Ahl-e-Hadith, Deobandi, Jamati-I-
Islami, Tablighi Jamaat
Other Languages: Bengali, Urdu, Arabic

**Blackheath Islamic and Community Centre/UK
Islamic Mission***
314-318 Long Lane, Halesowen, Birmingham
B62 9LQ
Tel: (0121) 5597314

Central Mosque Birmingham*
180 Belgrave Middleway, Highgate, Birmingham
B12 0XS
Tel: (0121) 4405355 **Fax:** (0121) 4464410
Contact: Dost Mohammad Khan
Position: General Secretary
Activities: Worship, resource, visits, youth,
newsletters, inter-faith
Movements: Ahle Sunnah wa Jamaat
Other Languages: Urdu, Punjabi, Arabic, Bengali

Dar-ul-Uloom Islamia Ghamkol Sharif*
107-113 Golden Hillock Road, Small Heath,
Birmingham B10 0DP
Tel: (0121) 7714533/4 **Fax:** (0121) 7530778
Contact: Mohammad Saleem Akhtar
Position: Chairperson
Contact Tel: (0121) 6221369
Activities: Worship, resource, umbrella body, visits,
youth, elderly
Traditions: Sunni
Movements: Barelwi
Other Languages: Mirpuri, Urdu, Punjabi
Affiliations: Confederation of Sunni Mosques

Darul Uloom Islamic High School*
521 Coventry Road, Small Heath, Birmingham
B10 0LL
Tel: (0121) 7726408 **Fax:** (0121) 7734340
Contact: Mr M Noar
Position: Head Of School Division
Activities: Resources
Other Languages: Bangladeshi, Urdu, Arabic

Darwel Uloom Jamian Arabian Islamiah
Islamic Centre, 221-223 Cotterills Lane,
Birmingham B8 3RS

East African Muslim Association*
265 Golden Hillock Road, Sparkbrook,
Birmingham B11 2PY
Tel: (0121) 7714511
Contact: Ahmed Minhas

Ghamkol Sharif Central Jamia Mosque*
150 Golden Hillock Road, Small Heath,
Birmingham B10 0DX
Tel: (0121) 7738120
Contact: Sufi Mohammad Abdullah Khan
Activities: Worship
Traditions: Sunni
Movements: Barelwi

**Ghausia Mosque Trust And Islamic Community
Centre**
232 Slade Road, Erdington, Birmingham
B23 7RH
Tel: (0836) 607608 **Fax:** (0121) 3260847
Contact: Khalid Mahmood
Position: President
Activities: Worship, resource, visits, youth
Traditions: Sunni
Movements: Barelwi
Other Languages: Urdu, Punjabi
Affiliations: Confederation of Sunni Mosques,
Midlands

Handsworth Islamic Centre*
27 Putney Road, Handsworth, Birmingham
B20 3PY
Tel: (0121) 5519012
Contact: Quari A Wafi
Position: Chairperson

Handsworth Mosque and Islamic Centre
23 Booth Street, Handsworth, Birmingham
B21 0NX

Hazarat Sultan Bahu Trust*
17 Ombersley Road, Balsall Heath, Birmingham
B12 8UT
Tel: (0121) 4404096 **Fax:** (0121) 4465682
Email: alhiraschool@aol.com.
Contact: Muhammad Amin Qadri
Position: Finance Director
Activities: Worship, resource, visits, youth, elderly,
women
Traditions: Sunni
Movements: Barelwi, Tassawuf
Other Languages: Arabic, Urdu

**Idara Maarif-e-Islam Hussainia Mosque and
Community Centre***
Herbert Road (Corner of Regent Park Road),
Birmingham B10 0PP
Tel: (0121) 7736212

Imams and Mosques Council Birmingham*
5 Shooters Close, Edgbaston, Birmingham B5 7LN
Tel: (0121) 4401580 **Fax:** (0121) 4402785

Islamic Cultural and Educational Centre*
98 Greswolde Road, Sparkhill, Birmingham
B11 4DL
Tel: (0121) 7022969 **Fax:** (0121) 7022969
Contact: Mr Khan
Position: Chairman

Contact Tel: (07930) 560537
Activities: Worship/practice/meditation,
community centre, youth, resources
Traditions: Sunni
Movements: Deobandi, Tablighi Jamaat
Other Languages: Urdu, Punjabi, Arabic

Islamic Cultural Study Centre*

262 Washwood Heath Road, Birmingham B8 1RJ
Tel: (0121) 3260966 **Fax:** (0121) 3260966
Website: http://www.islamicstudy.org/
Contact: Sheikh Mahmood H Rashid
Position: Chairman
Contact Tel: (0121) 2407268
Activities: Worship/practice/meditation,
newsletter/journal, resources
Traditions: Sunni
Movements: Tassawuf
Other Languages: Urdu, Arabic

Islamic Education and Cultural Centre*

14 Linwood Road, Handsworth, Birmingham
B21 9HT
Tel: (0121) 5152110
Contact: Enam-Ur-Rahman
Position: Secretary
Contact Tel: (0121) 5511575
Activities: Worship, visits
Traditions: Sunni
Movements: Jamati-i-Islami
Other Languages: Bengali, Urdu, Pushto

Islamic Education Centre and Mosque Razar*

9 Serpentine Road, Ashton, Birmingham B6 6SB
Tel: (0121) 3281297
Contact: Mr Mohammed Saeed
Position: Treasurer

Islamic Education Centre*

174 Havelock Road, Birmingham B8 1RX
Tel: (0121) 7731973
Contact: Niaz Muhammed
Position: General Secretary

Islamic Education Centre*

232 Witton Road, Aston, Birmingham B6 6LB
Contact: Mr A Sabur Choudhury
Position: Chairperson
Contact Tel: (0121) 5234265
Activities: Worship/practice/meditation
Traditions: Sunni
Movements: Tablighi Jamaat
Other Languages: Bengali, Urdu
Affiliations: Tablighi Markaz

Islamic Educational Cultural Centre*

2 Yewtree Road, Aston, Birmingham B6 6RT
Contact: Moulana Bostan Qadri
Position: President
Contact Tel: (0121) 3274204
Traditions: Sunni
Movements: Barelwi, Tassawuf
Other Languages: Urdu, Punjabi, Mirpuri
Affiliations: Confederation of Sunni Mosques,
Midlands; Muslim Council of Britain

Islamic Educational Cultural Centre*

9 Serpentine Road, Aston, Birmingham B6 6SB
Tel: (0121) 3274204
Contact: Maulana Bostan Qadri
Position: President
Contact Tel: (0121) 3280837
Activities: Worship/practice/meditation,
community centre
Traditions: Sunni
Movements: Barelwi
Other Languages: Urdu, Punjabi, Arabic
Affiliations: Confederation of Sunni Mosques,
Midlands; Muslim Council of Britain

Islamic Library and Central Hanafiyah Mosque*

28 Tennyson Road, Small Heath, Birmingham
B10 0HA
Tel: (0121) 7736094
Contact: Adil al-Farooqi
Position: Imam

Islamic Mosque and Teaching Centre

141 Nechells Park Road, Nechells, Birmingham
B7 5PH
Contact: Mr M Bashir

Islamic Resource Centre*

93 Court Road, Balsall Heath, Birmingham
B12 9LQ
Tel: (0121) 4403500 **Fax:** (0121) 4408144
Email: islamiccentre@hotmail.com
Website: http://www.islamiccentre.co.uk/
Contact: Mr Mohamed Khalid
Position: Manager
Activities: Community centre, resources
Traditions: Sunni
Other Languages: Urdu, Arabic, Punjabi
Affiliations: Muslim Education Forum

Islamic Shariah Institute*

PO Box 6008, Birmingham B10 0UW
Tel: (0121) 7735191
Email: enquiries@shariah/institute.org

Website: http://www.shariah/institute.org
Contact: Mr Abdul Razzaq
Position: Secretary

ISRA Islamic Relief Agency*
PO Box 1301, Camp Hill, Birmingham B11 1QP
Tel: (0121) 7668771 **Fax:** (0121) 7665058
Email: ukisra@aol.com
Website: http://www.isra-uk.org/
Contact: Mr Abdal Samad
Position: Director

Jalalabad Association*
12 Pugh Road, Aston, Birmingham B6 5LL
Tel: (0121) 3284662 **Fax:** (0121) 3284662
Contact: M A Islam
Position: General Secretary
Other Languages: Bengali

Jalalabad Bangladesh Islamic and Language Centre
267 Malmesbury Road, Small Heath, Birmingham B10 0JE

Jalalabad Mosque and Islamic Centre
24-26 Dartmouth Road, Selly Oak, Birmingham B29 6EA
Tel: (0121) 4711556
Contact: Hira Miah
Position: Secretary

Jamiat Ulma-e-Islam*
34 Farndon Road, Alum Rock, Birmingham B8 3HS

Jamatia Islamic Centre
179-181 Woodland Road, Sparkhill, Birmingham B11 4ER
Tel: (0121) 7786612

Jamia Islamia (Naqshbandia)
1 Willow Crescent, Cannon Hill, Birmingham B14 7TA

Jamia Mosque and Community Centre*
62 Wills Street, Lozells, Birmingham B19 1QR
Tel: (0121) 5230810
Contact: Mr Mohammed Siddique Baig
Position: Secretary
Contact Tel: (07944) 730399
Activities: Worship, resource, visits
Traditions: Sunni
Other Languages: Mirpuri, Punjabi, Urdu
Affiliations: Sunni Confederation of Mosques

Jamia Mosque Hamza Islamic Centre*
90 Church Road, Moseley, Birmingham B13 9AE
Tel: (0121) 4494385 **Fax:** (0121) 4494385
Contact: Saifur Rehman
Position: Committee Member
Contact Tel: (07939) 067727
Activities: Worship, elderly, youth, radio, umbrella body, visits
Traditions: Sunni
Movements: Deobandi, Tablighi Jamaat
Other Languages: Urdu, Punjabi, Hindko
Affiliations: Birmingham Council of Mosques

Jamia Naqshbandia Newabia*
108 Bordesley Green, Birmingham B9 4TS
Tel: (0121) 766 6845
Contact: Mr Ali
Position: Imam

Jamiat-ul-Muslimin*
28 Tennyson Road, Small Heath, Birmingham B10 9AR
Tel: (0121) 7736094

Jamiate Nizame Islam
64 Somerville Road, Small Heath, Birmingham B10 9EL
Tel: (0121) 3288466
Contact: Malik Fazal Hussain
Position: Nazim
Activities: Worship, youth, newsletter
Traditions: Sunni
Other Languages: Urdu, Arabic
Affiliations: Pakistan Community Centre; Urdu Forum (UK), Birmingham

Jono Sova Jono Seba Employment Resource Centre Ltd*
196 Ash Road, Saltley, Birmingham B8 1DG
Tel: (0121) 3273446 **Fax:** (0121) 3285540
Email: jsjscentre@aol.com
Contact: Monawwar Ahmed
Position: Centre Manager
Other Languages: Bengali

Khoja Shi'a 'Ithna Asheri Muslim Community of Birmingham*
17 Clifton Road, Balsall Heath, Birmingham B12 8SX
Tel: (0121) 4466437 **Fax:** (0121) 4466437
Email: ksimc@talk21.com
Contact: Mr Hassan Naqvi
Position: Hon Secretary
Contact Tel: (0121) 2461299

Contact Email: hnaqvi@iname.com
Activities: Worship/practice/meditation, community centre, youth, elderly, women, newsletter/journal, visits, resources
Traditions: 'Ithna Asheri
Movements: Ahl-e-Hadith
Other Languages: Gujarati, Urdu
Affiliations: World Federation of Khoja Shi'a 'Ithna-Asheri Muslim Communities

King's Heath Mosque
113 Station Road, Birmingham B14 7TA

Madina Masjid*
Corner of Adderley Road and Ash Road, Saltley, Birmingham B8 1EG
Tel: (0121) 3271123

Madrasa-Islamia Taaleem-Ul Quran
147 Kyrwicks Lane, Birmingham B11 1SS

Madrassa Islamia*
219-221 Alexander Road, Acocks Green, Birmingham B27 6EH
Contact: Abdil Malik
Position: General Secretary
Contact Tel: (0121) 707 5820
Activities: Worship, resource, umbrella body, youth, women
Traditions: Sunni
Movements: Barelwi
Other Languages: Urdu, English, Arabic
Affiliations: Sunni Confederation

Madrassa Naim-ul-Qur'an
37 Whitehall Road, Small Heath, Birmingham B9 5EL

Madressa Islamia Talimuddin Society*
113 Station Road, King's Heath, Birmingham B14 7TA
Tel: (0121) 4448988
Contact: Mohammed Saeed Esakjee
Position: Chairperson
Contact Tel: (0121) 4413175
Activities: Worship/practice/meditation, youth, education
Other Languages: Urdu, Arabic

Makki Madrassa*
75 Stafford Road, Handsworth, Birmingham B21 9DU
Tel: (0121) 5517417
Email: makkimadrassa@hotmail.com

Contact: Mohammed Ashraf
Position: Chairman
Contact Tel: (0121) 5541530
Activities: Worship/practice/meditation
Traditions: Sunni
Movements: Deobandi
Other Languages: Mirpur, Henkor, Urdu, Bengali

Masjid and Madrassah Faiz-ul-Qur'an*
298 Dudley Road, Edgbaston, Birmingham B18 4HL
Tel: (0121) 4556581
Contact: Mr Mohammed Nawaz
Position: Secretary
Contact Tel: (07968) 702152
Activities: Worship, visits, youth, elderly
Movements: Ahl-e-Sunnat Jamaat
Other Languages: Urdu, Punjabi, Bengali, Mirpiri

Masjid Muhammadi and Madrassa Salafiah*
23-26 Hartopp Road, Saltley, Birmingham B8 1TE
Tel: (0121) 3280019
Contact: Mr Arabi
Position: Secretary

Masjid-e-Noor*
257 Victoria Road, Aston, Birmingham B6 5HP
Tel: (0121) 3280156
Contact: F U Ahmed
Position: Secretary

Maulana Nisar Dawah Trust*
33 Dolobran Road, Sparkbrook, Birmingham B11 1HL
Tel: (0121) 7666147 **Fax:** (0121) 7734340
Contact: M Noor
Position: Secretary
Activities: Resource, media, visits, youth, elderly, women, newsletter
Traditions: Sunni
Movements: Jamati-i-Islami
Other Languages: Urdu, Arabic
Affiliations: Jami Mosque, 521 Coventry Road, Birmingham; Sharia Council

Medina Mosque*
7 Park Avenue, Hockley, Birmingham B18 5ND
Tel: (0121) 5546717
Contact: Mohammad Sadiq
Position: President

Mehr-ul-Millat Mosque*
21 Shakespeare Street, Sparkhill, Birmingham
B11 4RU
Tel: (0121) 7735966
Contact: Ameere Millat
Position: President
Other Languages: Urdu, Punjabi

Mohammedi Islamic Centre*
171 Walford Road, Sparkbrook, Birmingham
B11 1QJ
Tel: (0121) 7079353
Contact: M D Abdul Malik
Position: Secretary/Trustee
Contact Tel: (07811) 126959
Activities: Worship/practice/meditation, youth,
elderly
Traditions: Sunni
Other Languages: Bengali, Sylheti, Urdu, Arabic

Mosque Farooq Azam and Madrassah Ghosia*
74 College Road, Alum Rock, Birmingham
B8 3TB
Tel: (0121) 3284100

Muath Welfare Trust*
The Bordesley Centre, Statford Road, Camp Hill,
Birmingham B11 1AR
Tel: (0121) 7530297 **Fax:** (0121) 7666853
Email: mwt@amaneh.org.uk
Website: http://www.amanah.org.uk./
Contact: Salem Ahmed
Position: Director
Activities: Worship, resource, visits, youth, elderly,
women, education
Traditions: Sunni
Other Languages: Arabic, Urdu

Muslim Education Trust*
55 Portland Road, Edgbaston, Birmingham
B16 9HS
Tel: (0121) 4540671
Contact: Ali Mohammad Rajput
Position: Director
Activities: Education
Other Languages: Urdu, Persian, Arabic

Muslim Foundation Mosque*
122 Stamford Road, Handsworth, Birmingham
B20 3PS
Tel: (0121) 3444907
Contact: Mr Toqir ul Islam
Position: Secretary
Activities: Worship/practice/meditation, youth,
elderly, radio, visits, inter-faith, resources

Traditions: Sunni
Movements: Jamati-i-Islami
Other Languages: Urdu, Arabic

Muslim Liaison Committee*
Central Jamia Mosque, 180 Belgrave Road,
Birmingham B12 0XS
Tel: (0121) 4405355
Contact: Mr M Y Qamar/ Malik Fazal Hussain
Position: Chairman/ Secretary
Activities: Resources
Other Languages: Urdu

**Muslim Welfare Society and Parents
Association***
38 Greenland Road, Selly Park, Birmingham
B29 7PN
Tel: (0121) 4155686
Contact: Mohammad Rafique
Position: Chairman
Contact Tel: (0121) 4720949
Activities: Youth, inter-faith, resources
Traditions: Sunni
Other Languages: Urdu
Affiliations: Pakistan Welfare Society/Pakistan
Forum

Noor-ul-Uloom Mosque*
85 St Oswald Road, Small Heath, Birmingham
B10 9RB
Tel: (0121) 7737036
Position: M Sadiq

Paigham-e-Islam Trust*
423 Stratford Road, Sparkhill, Birmingham
B11 4LB
Tel: (0121) 7738301 **Fax:** (0121) 7731735
Email: islamic.info@btclick.com
Contact: Mr T Rahim
Position: Secretary
Activities: Worship, resource, visits, youth, elderly,
women
Traditions: Sunni
Other Languages: Urdu, Punjabi, Pushto
Affiliations: UK Islamic Mission

**Qamar-Ul-Islam Mosque and Education
Centre***
168-170 Fosbrooke Road, Hobmoor, Birmingham
B10 9JP
Tel: (0121) 7530273 **Fax:** (0121) 7737786
Contact: Rasaqat Hussain
Position: Chairman

Selly Park Muslim Welfare Society*
15 Selly Park Road, Selly Park, Birmingham
B29 7PX
Tel: (0121) 4712168 **Fax:** (0121)4712168
Contact: Mr S A Malik
Position: Chairperson
Contact Tel: (0121) 4712168
Other Languages: Urdu, Punjabi
Affiliations: BVO

*Shah Jahal Jami Masjid Jame Qur'ania
Madressa**
1-3 Ralph Road (off Alum Rock Road), Saltley,
Birmingham B8 1NA

*Shah Jalal Bengali School and Islamic Centre
Jami Masjid**
61 Poplar Road and 111 Medlicott Road,
Sparkhill, Birmingham B11 1UH
Tel: (0121) 7721933
Contact: Dewan Abdulla Harun
Position: President
Activities: Worship, youth, elderly
Traditions: Sunni
Movements: Ahl-e-Hadith; Barelwi/Deobandi/
Tablighi
Other Languages: Bengali, Urdu, English
Affiliations: Birmingham Jami Masjid and Islamic
Centre; Darul Uloom Islamic School and College

Small Heath Mosque*
20 Green Lane, Small Heath, Birmingham B10
Tel: (0121) 7730019
Contact: Mr Abdul Hadir
Position: President

Sparkbrook Islamic Centre*
179-187 Anderton Road, Sparkbrook, Birmingham
B11 1ND
Tel: (0121) 7738651 **Fax:** (0121) 7724965
Email: sicamasjid@totalise.co.uk
Contact: Mohammad Afzal
Position: Centre Manager
Activities: Worship/practice/meditation,
community centre, youth, elderly, women, visits,
inter-faith
Traditions: Sunni
Movements: Jamati-i-Islami
Other Languages: Punjabi, Urdu, Bengali, Arabic
Affiliations: UK Islamic Mission

*Washwood Heath Muslim Centre and
Madrassah Qasim Ul-Uloom**
790 Washwood Heath Road, Washwood Heath,
Birmingham B8 2JG
Tel: (0121) 3277434 **Fax:** (0121) 3277434

Contact: Qari Tassawar Ul-Haq
Position: Director
Other Languages: Urdu, Punjabi, Arabic

Witton Islamic Centre*
311-313 Witton Road, Witton, Birmingham
B6 6NJ
Tel: (0121) 328 1088
Contact: Mr Shaffrat Ali
Position: Secretary

Woodstock Girls School*
11-15 Woodstock Road, Mosely, Birmingham
B13 9BB
Tel: (0121) 4496690
Contact: Mrs T Anees
Position: Headteacher
Contact Tel: (0121) 4496690
Other Languages: Urdu, Arabic, Punjabi

Young Muslim Organisation*
523 Coventry Road, Small Heath, Birmingham
B10 0LL
Tel: (0121) 7726408
Contact: Dr Abdur-Rahim
Position: President

Young Muslims (UK)
194 St Saviour's Road, Saltley, Birmingham
B8 1HA
Contact: Shakila Begum
Position: Secretary

Zakariya Mosque and Islamic Welfare Centre
259 Percy Road, cnr Hillfield Road, Birmingham
B11 3LG

Zawiya Islamic Centre*
126 Pershore Road, Edgbaston, Birmingham
B5 7NY
Tel: (0121) 4401347
Contact: S Abdi
Position: Chairman

Zawiya Mosque*
294 Edward Road, Edgbaston, Birmingham
B5 7PH
Tel: (0121) 4405746
Contact: Sheikh Mohamed Kassam
Position: Sheikh

Zia-ul-Qur'an Mosque
233 St Saviours Road, Alum Rock, Birmingham
B8 1EP
Tel: (0121) 3281584

Burton Muslim Mosque, Hanfia*
18-23 Princess Street, Burton-on-Trent
DE14 2NW
Tel: (01283) 510935 **Fax:** (01283) 510935
Email: mosque@shaid.co.uk
Contact: Shaid Hussain
Position: Secretary
Contact Tel: (07970) 196376
Activities: Worship/practice/meditation,
community centre, visits, resources
Movements: Ahle Sunnat Al Janmmat
Other Languages: Urdu, Mirpuri, Punjabi

Darul-Uloom Islamic Ghousia*
23a Parker Street, Burton-on-Trent DE14 2QL
Tel: (01283) 569862
Email: ghousiainstitute@hotmail.com
Contact: M Ashraf
Position: Trustee
Contact Email: mashraf46@hotmail.com
Other Languages: Urdu, Punjabi

Jamiat Ahl Hadith*
7-10 York Street, Burton-on-Trent DE14 2XL
Contact: Mohammed Sadiq
Position: Chairman
Activities: Worship/practice/meditation, inter-
faith, resources
Movements: Ahl-e-Hadith
Other Languages: Urdu, Punjabi, Mirpuri

Coventry Muslim Community Association Ltd*
Coventry Muslim Resource Centre, Red Lane,
Foleshill, Coventry CV6 5EE
Tel: (024) 7663 7933 **Fax:** (024) 7663 8234
Contact: Mr Osman Sheikh
Position: Development Officer
Activities: Community centre, central body,
youth, elderly, women, visits, inter-faith, resources
Traditions: Sunni
Other Languages: Urdu, Gujarati, Punjabi,
Bengali

Hazrat Dewan-e-Hazoori Educational Centre*
130 Station Street West, Foleshill, Coventry
CV6 5ND
Tel: (024) 7658 1219 **Fax:** (024) 7658 1667
Contact: Mohammed Iqbal Khan
Position: President
Activities: Worship, resource
Traditions: Sunni
Other Languages: Punjabi, Urdu

Hillfields Muslim Association*
1-5 Berry Street, Hillfields, Coventry CV1 5JT
Tel: (024) 7625 1184
Contact: Mr Shabbir A Usmani
Position: Hon Gen Secretary
Contact Tel: (024) 7655 5497
Activities: Worship, resource
Traditions: Sunni
Movements: Deobandi, Ehle Sunnat Val Jamaat
Other Languages: Gujarati, Urdu, Bengali

Islamic Society*
University of Warwick, Coventry CV4 7AL
Email: suaaf@warwick.ac.uk
Contact: Asim Khan
Position: President
Other Languages: Malay, Arabic, Urdu,
Bangladeshi
Affiliations: Al-Nasr Trust

Jalalabad Masjid and Education Centre
237 Harnall Lane East, Coventry CV1 5AX

Jamia Mosque*
Eagle Street, Foleshill, Coventry CV1 4GY
Tel: (024) 7622 2169

Masjid-e-Zeenat-ul-Islam*
283-287 Stoney Stanton Road, Coventry
CV1 4FR
Tel: (024) 7622 2774
Contact: Mr Khalifa
Position: Secretary

Muslim Advice and Support Service (MASS)*
242 Stoney Stanton Road, Coventry CV1 5AY
Tel: (024) 7627 2878
Contact: Mrs Zakia Butt
Position: Chairperson

Tazeem-e-Banatul Islam*
148 Westmorland Road, Wyken, Coventry
CV2 5BU
Contact: Mrs Hamida Shah
Position: Chairperson
Contact Tel: (024) 7626 5722
Activities: Community centre
Traditions: Sunni
Movements: Barelwi
Other Languages: Urdu, Gujarati

Bangladesh Ahle Hadith Society*
43 Highgate Street, Sandwell, Cradley Heath
B64 5RY

Tel: (01384) 566203 **Fax:** (01384) 566203
Contact: Ataur Rahman
Position: President
Activities: Worship/practice/meditation,
community centre
Traditions: Sunni
Movements: Ahl-e-Hadith
Other Languages: Bengali, Urdu

Dudley Mosque and Muslim Community Centre*
Birmingham Street, Castle Hill, Dudley DY2 7AJ
Tel: (01384) 253951 **Fax:** (01384) 253951
Email: hashni223@hotmail.com
Contact: Mr M Hanif
Position: General Secretary
Activities: Worship/practice/meditation
Traditions: Sunni
Movements: Tassawuf
Other Languages: Urdu, Arabic

Jamia Masjid and Islamic School Ahl-e-Hadith*
29 Queen's Cross, Dudley DY1 1QN
Tel: (01384) 258479
Contact: Mr M Shabir
Position: Secretary
Activities: Worship, visits, elderly, women
Movements: Ahl-e-Hadith
Other Languages: Urdu

Muslim Community Association*
10-12 New Street, Leamington Spa CV31 1HP
Tel: (01926) 429100
Contact: Chand Mubarak
Position: Secretary
Activities: Worship, resource, visits, youth, elderly,
women
Traditions: Sunni
Other Languages: Urdu, Punjabi

Nuneaton Muslim Society*
The Mosque, Frank Street, Nuneaton CV11 5RB
Tel: (024) 7638 2372
Contact: Mr Mahmood C Mamoojee
Position: Honorary Secretary
Activities: Worship, resource, umbrella body, visits,
youth, inter-faith
Traditions: Sunni
Other Languages: Urdu, Gujarati
Affiliations: Union of Muslim Organisations

Mosque*
28 Easemore Street, Redditch B98 8HA
Tel: (01527) 63834
Contact: Mohammed Akram

Rugby Mosque
65 King Edward Road, Rugby CV11 4BQ

Sandwell Muslim Organisation*
52 Birmingham Street, Oldbury, Sandwell
B69 4DZ
Tel: (0121) 5442425 **Fax:** (0121) 5447864
Contact: Mr Javed Iqbal
Position: Project Manager
Contact Tel: (0121) 5522000
Activities: Community centre, umbrella body,
youth, elderly, women
Traditions: Sunni
Other Languages: Mirpuri

Bangladesh Islamic Centre*
67 Dartmouth Street, West Bromwich, Sandwell
B70 8BZ
Tel: (0121) 5535598
Contact: Mr A Jalil
Position: Secretary

Cradley Heath Mosque and Islamic Centre
Building 1-5, Plant Street, Sandwell B64

Darbar Unique Centre
Oldfield Street, Fenton, Stoke-on-Trent ST4 3PQ

Gilani Noor Mosque*
2 Chaplin Road, Longton, Stoke-on-Trent
ST3 4QS
Tel: (01782) 335606
Contact: K Hussain

Islamic Cultural Centre*
16 York Street, Hanley, Stoke-on-Trent ST1 5EH
Tel: (01782) 268122
Contact: Abdul Matin
Position: Secretary
Activities: Worship
Traditions: Sunni
Movements: Ahl-e-Hadith
Other Languages: Bengali, Urdu
Affiliations: Federation of Mosques, Stoke-on-
Trent

Muslim Welfare Community Association and Islamic Centre*
Bedford Road, Shelton, Stoke-on-Trent ST1 4PJ
Tel: (01782) 280364
Contact: Mr Rana Muhammad Tufail
Position: Trustee/Director
Contact Tel: (01782) 610548
Activities: Worship/practice/meditation, resources
Traditions: Sunni, Hanafi

Movements: Barelwi
Other Languages: Urdu, Punjabi

Tunstall Mosque*
2a Keele Street, Tunstall, Stoke-on-Trent ST6 5AR
Tel: (01782) 813617
Contact: Mr B Ali
Position: President

Blackheath Jamia Mosque Trust
143-150 Maltmill Lane, Blackheath, Stourbridge
B62 8J

Jamia Ghausia Mosque and Welfare Association*
2a High Street, Lye, Stourbridge DY9 8AU
Tel: (01384) 893110
Contact: Mr K Dad
Position: Chairman
Activities: Worship
Traditions: Sunni
Movements: Barelwi
Other Languages: Urdu, Punjabi

Mosque
1 Valley Road, Lye, Stourbridge DY9

Telford Central Mosque*
41 Tan Bank, Wellington, Telford TF1 1HJ
Tel: (01952) 242933
Activities: Worship, visits
Traditions: Sunni
Movements: Deobandi, Tablighi Jamaat
Other Languages: Punjabi, Urdu, Arabic

Al-Islah Community Trust*
93 Park Lane East, Tipton DY4 8RD
Tel: (0121) 5579174 **Fax:** (0121) 5576789
Contact: Ahmadul Haque
Position: President
Activities: Worship, resource, visits, youth, elderly, women
Traditions: Sunni
Movements: Tassawuf
Other Languages: Bengali, Urdu
Affiliations: Muslim World Aid

Kanz-ul-Iman Muslim Welfare Association and Central Jamia Mosque*
Binfield Street, Tipton DY4 8RG
Tel: (0121) 5207864
Contact: Mr M Arif
Position: Chairman
Other Languages: Urdu

Mosque and Tipton Muslim Trust Association*
17 Wellington Road, Tipton DY4 8RS
Tel: (07092) 098967 **Fax:** (07092) 098968
Email: tmta@mail.com
Contact: Hurmuz Ali
Position: Chairman
Activities: Worship, resource
Traditions: Sunni
Movements: Ahl-e-Sunnat
Other Languages: Bengali
Affiliations: Sandwell Confederation of Bangladeshi Muslim Organisations

Tipton and Tividale Muslim Welfare Association*
10 Gate Street, Tipton DY4 7SP
Tel: (0121) 5205832
Contact: Abdul Qayyum
Position: Chair
Activities: Worship, resource, youth, elderly, women
Traditions: Sunni
Other Languages: Urdu, Arabic
Affiliations: Confederation of Sunni Mosques

Bangladesh Mosque (Bangladesh Islamic Cultural Association)*
74 Wednesbury Road, Walsall WS1 3RR
Tel: (01922) 641073
Contact: Mr Kaisor Ali
Position: President
Contact Tel: (01922) 723715
Activities: Worship/practice/meditation
Other Languages: Bangladeshi
Affiliations: U.M.O (UK and Ireland), WCVS, SREP, NCRA.

Central Mosque*
41 Selborne Street, Walsall WS1 2JN
Tel: (01922) 636132
Contact: Mr A Khaliq
Position: President

Ghausia Qasmia Trust
28 Little London, Walsall WS1 3EW
Contact: M Yasin

Ghosia Qasmia Mosque and Darul Uloom
34-35 Mount Street, Walsall WS6 7AG
Tel: (01922) 34862

Jamia Qadria Educational Centre
24 Charlotte Street, Walsall WS1 2BD

Masjid-al-Farouq*
Milton Street, Palfrey, Walsall WS1 4JS
Tel: (01922) 645786
Contact: Dr Habibkhan Pathan
Activities: Worship, resource, umbrella body, visits, youth, elderly
Traditions: Sunni
Movements: Deobandi, Tablighi Jamaat
Other Languages: Urdu, Gujarati, Bengali, Punjabi
Affiliations: Federation of Indian Muslim Organisations; Union of Muslim Organisations (UK and Eire)

Masjid-e-Abu Bakr*
156 Wednesbury Road, Walsall WS1 4JJ
Tel: (01922) 20618 **Fax:** (01922) 646175
Contact: Mr Luqman
Position: President
Contact Tel: (01922) 620618

Mosque and Butts Muslim Community*
22 Cannon Street, Butts, Walsall WS2 8AY
Contact: Mohammed Ayub
Position: Secretary
Contact Tel: (07900) 131400
Activities: Worship, resource
Traditions: Sunni
Movements: Deobandi, Tablighi Jamaat
Other Languages: Urdu, Punjabi

Mosque and Education and Cultural Centre*
51 Cobden Street, Darlaston, Walsall WS10 9SW
Contact: I A Mohammed
Position: Secretary
Contact Tel: (0121) 5265830
Activities: Worship/practice/meditation, education
Traditions: Sunni, Hanafi
Other Languages: Urdu, Bengali, Gujarati

Mosque and Islamic Centre*
4 Rutter Street, Walsall WS1 4HN
Tel: (01922) 620982
Contact: Imam U R Saeed
Position: Imam
Contact Tel: (01922) 624515
Activities: Worship/practice/meditation, community centre, youth, elderly, women, visits, inter-faith, resources
Traditions: Sunni
Movements: Ahl-e-Hadith, Barelwi, Deobandi, Jamati-I-Islami, Tablighi Jamaat, Tassawuf
Other Languages: Urdu, Arabic, Bengali
Affiliations: Muslim Council of Britain

Pakistan Muslim Welfare Association*
4 Raleigh Street, Birchill, Walsall
Tel: (01922) 640787
Contact: Mohammed Khan/Mr Haq
Position: General Secretary

Popda Society, The*
Camden Centre, Camden Street, Walsall WS1
Email: popdasociety@hotmail.com
Contact: Ali Adam Mohammed
Position: Secretary
Contact Tel: (01922) 441318
Activities: Community centre, youth, elderly, women, newsletter/journal, visits, inter-faith, resources
Traditions: Sunni
Movements: Deobandi
Other Languages: Gujarati

Shah Jalal Jami Masjid and Madrasha
32-33 Hart Street, Walsall WS1 3PJ

Union of Muslim Organisations, Walsall*
90a Wednesbury Road, Walsall WS1 4JH
Tel: (01922) 628111 **Fax:** (01922) 721211
Email: info@umo-walsall.co.uk.
Contact: Mohammed Gora
Position: Development Worker
Activities: Resource, umbrella body, inter-faith
Traditions: Sunni
Movements: Barelwi
Other Languages: Urdu, Punjabi, Gujarati, Bengali

Bangladesh Islamic Association*
10-11 Lewisham Road, Smethwick, Warley B66 2BP
Tel: (0121) 5588204 **Fax:** (0121) 5588204
Contact: Mr Musleh Uddin
Position: Centre Manager
Activities: Worship, resource, visits, youth, women
Traditions: Sunni
Other Languages: Bengali

Oldbury Mosque and Muslim Welfare Association
Formerly Oldbury Labour Club, Oldbury Road, Smethwick, Warley B66 1HN
Tel: (0121) 5652666

Pakistani Muslim Islamic Community Centre*
1-7 Corbett Street, Smethwick, Warley B66 3PY
Tel: (0121) 5556047
Contact: Zahoor Ahmed

Sandwell Pakistan Muslim Welfare Association*
95 Beeches Road, Warley B65 0BB
Tel: (0121) 5614250
Contact: Mr R G Khan

Smethwick Bangladeshi Muslim Welfare Association*
253 Halfords Lane, Smethwick, Warley B66 1BD
Tel: (0121) 5589449
Contact: Mr Asad Uddin
Position: Secretary
Contact Tel: (0121) 5695594/5
Activities: Worship/practice/meditation, youth
Traditions: Sunni
Other Languages: Bengali

Smethwick Pakistani Muslims Association*
1-7 Corbett Street, Smethwick, Warley B66 3PY
Tel: (0121) 5556047
Contact: Nazreen Suleman
Position: Manager

Young Muslim Organisation (Smethwick)*
2 Kimberley Road, Smethwick, Warley B66 2DA
Tel: (0121) 5588204
Contact: Abdul Hannan
Position: Chairman
Contact Tel: (07930) 423155
Activities: Worship/practice/meditation, youth, inter-faith, resources
Traditions: Sunni
Other Languages: Bengali
Affiliations: Bangladeshi Islamic Association

Bangladesh Islamic Society*
48 Cook Street, Darlaston, Wednesbury
WS10 9RH
Tel: (0121) 5266790
Contact: Bashir Ahmed
Position: Trustee
Activities: Worship, youth
Traditions: Sunni
Movements: Jamati-i-Islami
Other Languages: Bengali
Affiliations: Union of Muslim Organisations

Bangladesh Muslim Association*
93 Vicarage Road, Wednesbury WS10 9DP
Tel: (0121) 5560491
Contact: Mr Gous Ahmed
Position: Chairman
Contact Tel: (0121) 5022137
Activities: Worship/practice/meditation
Other Languages: Bengali

Muslim Education and Cultural Trust*
51 Cobden Street, Darlaston, Wednesbury
WS10 9RL
Contact: Mr I A Mohammed
Position: Secretary
Contact Tel: (0121) 5265830
Activities: Worship
Traditions: Sunni
Movements: Ahl-e-Hadith
Other Languages: Bangladeshi, Urdu

Muslim Welfare Society*
Masjid-e-Umar, Bills Street, Darlaston, Wednesbury
WS10 8BB
Tel: (0121) 5266596
Contact: Yusuf M Patel
Position: Honorary Secretary
Contact Email: yusufpatel@blueyonder.co.uk
Activities: Worship, resource, visits, youth, women
Traditions: Sunni
Movements: Deobandi
Other Languages: Gujarati, Urdu
Affiliations: Union of Muslim Organisations

Wednesbury Bangladesh Islamic Centre and Mosque
Rear of 22 Market Place, Wednesbury WS10 7AY

Wednesbury Bangladesh Muslim Welfare Association*
22 Market Place, Wednesbury
Tel: (0121) 502 0479
Contact: Mr Arju Miah
Position: Chairman
Activities: Worship, youth, elderly
Traditions: Sunni
Other Languages: Bengali
Affiliations: Confederation of Bangladeshi Muslim Organisations, Sandwell

Wednesbury Jami Masjid and Islamic Community Centre
7-8 Spring Head, Wednesbury WS10 9AD

Al-Dharam Brotherhood Wolverhampton UK*
71 Park Street South, Blackenhall, Wolverhampton
WV2 3JG
Tel: (01902) 345271 **Fax:** (01902) 345271
Contact: Mr Janak Raj
Position: General Secretary
Contact Tel: (0956) 166099
Activities: Worship/practice/meditation, youth, elderly, women, newsletter/journal

Other Languages: Punjabi, Hindi
Affiliations: Wolverhampton Inter Faith

Anjuman-e-Arian*
42 Austin Street, Whitmore Reans, Wolverhampton
WV6 0NW
Tel: (01902) 711042
Email: manzoor_42@hotmail.com
Contact: M Hussand
Position: General Secretary
Contact Tel: (07902) 711042
Other Languages: Urdu

**Bilal Jamia Mosque and Muslim Community
Centre***
58 Newhampton Road West, Whitmore Reans,
Wolverhampton WV6 0RU
Tel: (01902) 771980
Contact: Mr Choudry
Position: Chairman

East African Muslim Association*
14 Albert Road, Tettenham, Wolverhampton
WV6 0AE
Tel: (01902) 711293
Contact: A A Malik
Position: Secretary
Contact Tel: (01902) 715440
Other Languages: Urdu, Punjabi

Pakistan Muslim Welfare Association*
197 Waterloo Road, Wolverhampton WV1 4RA
Tel: (01902) 312232 **Fax:** (01902) 312232
Contact: Mr Qudrat Ullah
Position: Secretary
Activities: Visits, youth, elderly, women
Traditions: Sunni
Movements: Deobandi, Tablighi Jamaat
Other Languages: Urdu, Punjabi

Sahara Centre*
18 Leicester Street, Wolverhampton WV6 0PR
Tel: (01902) 560039 **Fax:** (01902) 833695
Contact: Mr M U Qazi
Position: Secretary
Activities: Resource, youth, newsletters
Traditions: Sunni
Other Languages: Urdu, Punjabi

Wolverhampton Mosque Trust*
197 Waterloo Road, Wolverhampton WV1 4RA
Tel: (01902) 312232 **Fax:** (01902) 312232
Email: jamiamassjid@hotmail.com
Contact: Shah Ali

Position: Vice Chairman
Contact Tel: (01902) 312232
Activities: Worship, resource, visits, youth, elderly,
inter-faith
Traditions: Sunni
Movements: Deobandi, Tablighi Jamaat
Other Languages: Urdu, Bengali, Punjabi,
Gujarati, Arabic, English

Al-Medina Islamic Centre*
20 Middle Street, Worcester WR1 1NQ
Tel: (01905) 29532
Contact: Muhammed M Haque
Position: Secretary
Contact Tel: (07974) 751614
Activities: Worship/practice/meditation
Traditions: Sunni
Movements: Tablighi Jamaat
Other Languages: Bengali, Urdu

EAST OF ENGLAND
City, Town or Local Bodies

Basildon Muslim Association*
36 Gordons, Pitsea, Basildon SS13 3DZ
Tel: (01268) 554234 **Fax:** (01268) 554234
Contact: Sister Safina
Position: Secretary
Activities: Worship/practice/meditation,
community centre
Traditions: Sunni
Other Languages: Urdu, Punjabi, Swahili, Arabic

Jamah Masjid Gulshane Baghdad*
97a Ford End Road, Queens Park, Bedford
MK40 4LA
Tel: (01234) 351770
Contact: Mr Saddiqi
Position: Manager
Contact Tel: (01234) 350392

Mosque and Cultural Centre
34 Alexandra Road, Bedford MK40 1JB
Tel: (01234) 47032

Pakistan Mosque Committee*
97 Ford End Road, Queens Park, Bedford
MK40 4JU
Tel: (01234) 351770
Contact: Muhammad Siddiq Khan
Position: Chair Person
Contact Tel: (01234) 350392
Activities: Worship/practice/meditation

Traditions: Sunni
Movements: Barelwi
Other Languages: Urdu, Punjabi, Bengali

Cambridge Muslim Welfare Society and Abu Bakar Siddiq Mosque
Mawson Road, off Mill Hill, Cambridge CB1 2BZ
Tel: (01223) 350134

Chelmsford Mosque*
13a Molsham Street, Chelmsford CM2 0HU
Tel: (01245) 261563
Contact: Mr Raja
Position: Chairman
Contact Tel: (01245) 355195
Other Languages: Urdu, Bengali

Mosque
6 Baddow Road, Chelmsford CM2 0DG

Colchester Islamic Cultural Association*
2 Priory Street, Colchester CO1 2PY
Tel: (01206) 794919
Contact: M Z A Muquit
Position: Imam
Activities: Worship, resource, visits, youth, elderly
Traditions: Sunni
Other Languages: Bengali, Arabic, Urdu, Creole

Islamic Society*
University of Essex, Wivenhoe Park, Colchester CO4 3SQ
Tel: (01206) 872019
Email: islamic@essex.ac.uk
Website: http://www.essex.ac.uk/~islamic

Muslim Women's Association*
38 Seamons Close, Dunstable LU6 3EQ
Tel: (01582) 606672
Contact: Mrs Nasyer Sultana Jaffari JP
Position: Director
Activities: Resource, media, visits, youth, elderly, women, inter-faith
Traditions: Sunni, 'Ithna Asheri
Movements: Ahl-e-Hadith
Other Languages: Urdu, Bengali, Hindi, Gujarati
Affiliations: Anjumane-Haideria, Luton; Adare-e-Jafria, London

Quwwatul Islam Mehira Ghousia Mosque*
150 St Albans Hill, Bennet End, Hemel Hempstead HP3 9NH
Tel: (01422) 243785
Contact: Syed Asad Ali Shah
Position: Imam

Activities: Worship, resource, visits, youth, elderly
Traditions: Sunni
Movements: Barelwi
Other Languages: Urdu
Affiliations: Sunnat Wal Jamat UK, Daraloom Quadiria Jilania

St Ives Mosque
22 Needlingworth Road, Huntingdon PE17 4JN

Ipswich Bangledesh Mosque and Community Centre*
32-36 Bond Street, Ipswich IP4 1JE
Tel: (01473) 226879

Jamiat Ilhya Minhaj al-Sunnah*
PO Box 24, Ipswich LP3 8EN
Tel: (01473) 251578 **Fax:** (01473) 251578
Email: mail@jimas.org
Website: http://www.jimas.org/

Shahjalal islamic Centre and Masjid*
110/112 St Helen's Street, Ipswich IP4 2LB
Tel: (01473) 412983
Contact: S G Robbani
Contact Tel: (01473) 257712

West Norfolk Islamic Association*
1 Barsham Drive, Southwooden, Kings Lynn PE30 3TT
Tel: (01553) 671198
Contact: Mr A Karim
Position: President

Al Jalal Jame Masjid*
314 Biscot Road, Luton LU3 1AE
Tel: (01582) 411744
Contact: Mr Abdul Hoque
Position: Treasurer
Activities: Worship/practice/meditation, resources
Traditions: Sunni
Other Languages: Bengali, Urdu

Islamic Cultural Centre*
23 Westbourne Road, Luton LU4 8JD
Tel: (01582) 410704 **Fax:** (01582) 410704
Contact: Abdul Aziz Qazi
Position: Managing Trustee
Activities: Worship, resource, media, visits, youth, elderly
Traditions: Sunni
Movements: Barelwi
Other Languages: Punjabi, Urdu, Kashmiri
Affiliations: Markazi Jamat Ahle Sunnat (UK)

Jalalabad Islamic Cultural Centre and Education Centre Jame Masjid*
36-38 Leagreave Road, Luton
Tel: (01582) 483581
Contact: Ibrahim
Position: President

Jamia Al Akbaria*
241 Selbourne Road, Luton LU4 8NP
Tel: (01582) 561452
Contact: Mr Mohammed
Position: Chairman

Lewsey Muslim Cultural Society*
24 Sussex Close, Luton LU4 0UE
Tel: (01582) 608500
Contact: Abdul-Khaleq Vazifdar

Luton Central Mosque*
2 Westbourne Road, Luton LU4 8JD
Tel: (01582) 734988 **Fax:** (01582) 704538
Contact: Haji Sulaiman
Position: Chairman
Contact Tel: (07943) 648752
Activities: Worship/practice/meditation
Traditions: Sunni
Other Languages: Urdu,Punjabi,Arabic
Affiliations: Islamic Cultural Society

Maarifful-Uloom Al-Islamia Al-Arabia and Baitul Abrar Jame Masjid*
364-366 Leagreave Road, Luton
Tel: (01582) 595535
Contact: Mr Sadek Mirh
Position: President

Masjid-e-Ali*
1a Beech Road, Luton LU1 1DW
Tel: (01582) 486841

Mosque (UK Islamic Mission)
128-130 Oak Road, Luton LU4 8AD
Tel: (01582) 27734

Young Muslims*
368 Dunstable Road, Luton LU4 8JT
Tel: (01582) 753845
Contact: Rashid Nazar
Position: President
Activities: Resource, visits, youth, newsletters, inter-faith
Traditions: Sunni
Movements: Jamati-i-Islami

Other Languages: Urdu, Bengali
Affiliations: Medina Masjid, Luton

Zakariya Mosque and Madressa-r-Furqaniah
c/o 21a Drayton Road, Luton LU4 0PG
Tel: (01582) 608500
Contact: Abdul-Khaleq Vazifdar

Ihsan Mosque and Islamic Centre*
17 Chapel Field East, Norwich NR2 1SF
Tel: (0870) 7300027
Contact: I Mears
Position: Chairman
Activities: Worship/practice/meditation, visits
Other Languages: Arabic

Husaini Islamic Centre*
2-4 Burton Street, Peterborough PE2 5HD
Tel: (01733) 231429 **Fax:** (01733) 390050
Email: hic@peterborough.fsnet.co.uk
Contact: Mr Sajjad Panjwani
Position: Honorary Secretary
Activities: Worship/practice/meditation, community centre, youth, elderly, women, visits, resources
Traditions: 'Ithna Asheri
Other Languages: Urdu, Gujarati
Affiliations: World Federation of Shi'a 'Ithna Asheri Muslim Communities; Council of European Jamaats

Islamia Jamatkhana
Craig Street, Peterborough PE1 2EJ

Mosque
406 Gladstone Street, Peterborough PE1 2BY

Sunni Mosque
60 Cromwell Road, Peterborough PE1 2EB

UK Islamic Mission Peterborough*
311 Cromwell Road, Peterborough PE1 2HP
Tel: (01733) 554425 **Fax:** (01733) 554425
Email: ukim_peterborough@hotmail.com
Contact: Muzaffar Hussain
Position: Secretary
Contact Tel: (01733) 346503
Contact Email: hussainmuzaffar@hotmail.com
Activities: Worship, resource, visits, youth, women
Traditions: Sunni
Movements: Jamati-i-Islami
Other Languages: Punjabi, Urdu
Affiliations: UK Islamic Mission

Hertfordshire Muslim Education Council*
70 Mount Pleasant Lane, Bricketwood, St. Albans
AL2 3XB
Tel: (01932) 673820
Contact: Khalil ur Rehman Moghul
Position: Chairman
Activities: Resource, umbrella body, youth, inter-
faith
Traditions: Sunni
Other Languages: Urdu, Punjabi, Bengali

Islamic Centre*
141 Hatfield Road, St Albans AL1 4JX
Tel: (01727) 836272
Contact: Mr Khalil Urehman
Position: Chairman
Contact Tel: (01727) 761409
Activities: Worship/practice/meditation, youth,
women, visits
Traditions: Sunni
Movements: Ahl-e-Hadith, Barelwi, Deobandi,
Tablighi Jamaat
Other Languages: Urdu, Arabic

Jame Mosque and Bangladesh Islamic Centre
77 Hatfield Road, St Albans AL1 4JL

Southend Mosque and Southend Islamic Trust*
191-197 West Road, Westcliff-on-Sea, Southend-
on-Sea SS0 9DH
Tel: (01702) 347265 **Fax:** (01702) 344165
Contact: Dr M A Pasha
Position: Honorary Secretary
Contact Tel: (01702) 586610
Activities: Worship/practice/meditation,
community centre, youth, elderly, women,
newsletter/journal
Traditions: Sunni, Shi'a
Other Languages: Urdu, Bengali, Punjabi, Arabic

Anjuman-e-Jaafariyah*
Al-Zahra Centre, Merton Road, Watford
WD1 7BY
Tel: (01923) 231257
Contact: Sayyid Zakar Hussain Shah
Position: Secretary
Contact Tel: (07956) 598824
Contact Email: zakshah@innocent.com
Activities: Worship, resource, youth
Traditions: Shi'a 'Ithna Asheri
Other Languages: Urdu, Punjabi
Affiliations: World Federation of Khoja Shi'a
'Ithna Asheri Muslim Communities

Dar-ul-Ehsan*
8 Bruce Grove, Watford WD24 4DR
Tel: (01923) 245376
Contact: Mohammed Ramzan
Position: Amir
Other Languages: Urdu, Punjabi

Mosque
Addiscombe Road Annexe, Addiscombe Road,
Watford WD18

Watford Arabic School*
492 Wippendell Road, Watford WD1 7QJ
Tel: (01923) 245670 **Fax:** (01923) 213377
Contact: Dr A Ghany Saleh
Position: Founder and Director

**Watford Mosque and Welfare Association for
the Muslim Community***
Watford Jamia Mosque, Cambridge Road, Watford
WD1 8AJ
Tel: (01923) 245367
Contact: Mohammed Aslam Khan
Position: Secretary/Chairman
Activities: Worship, resource, visits, youth, elderly,
women
Traditions: Sunni
Movements: Barelwi
Other Languages: Urdu, Bengali, Arabic

Watford Muslim Community Project*
15 Harwoods Road, Watford WD1 7RB
Tel: (01923) 223466 **Fax:** (01923) 228388
Contact: Zakia Iftikhar
Position: Project Co-ordinator
Activities: Elderly
Other Languages: Urdu, Paharri, Punjabi
Affiliations: Watford Council; Citizens Advice
Bureau; Shelter; CPAG, CVS, WREC, Herts
Constabulary

LONDON
Regional or Area Bodies

British Muslim Council*
22 Lynmouth Road, London N16 6XL
Tel: (020) 8806 2898 **Fax:** (020) 8806 2898
Contact: Shuja Shaikh
Position: Chair
Activities: Worship, umbrella body, youth, elderly,
women, newsletter
Other Languages: Urdu, Turkish, Bengali

Council of Mosques for North East London*
c/o Noor-ul-Islam, 711 High Road, Leyton,
London E10 6RA
Tel: (020) 8923 7860
Activities: Worship, umbrella body, inter-faith
Traditions: Sunni
Other Languages: Urdu, Arabic

Islamic Association of North London*
685 High Road, North Finchley, London
N12 0DA
Tel: (020) 8492 0028
Contact: Mr Abdullah O'Toole
Position: Honorary Secretary
Contact Tel: (020) 8203 4553
Contact Email: francisotoole@hotmail.com
Activities: Worship/practice/meditation,
community centre, youth, elderly, women,
newsletter/journal, inter-faith, resources
Traditions: Sunni
Other Languages: Arabic, Urdu, Punjabi, Hindi
Affiliations: Muslim Council of Britain

**Khoja Shi'a 'Ithna-Asheri Muslim Community
of London***
Islamic Centre, Wood Lane, Stanmore HA7 4LQ
Tel: (020) 8954 6247 **Fax:** (020) 8954 8028
Contact: Fadhl Tharoo
Position: Honorary Secretary
Activities: Worship, resource, umbrella body, visits,
youth, elderly
Traditions: Shi'a 'Ithna Asheri
Other Languages: Urdu, Arabic, Gujarati,
Kutchi/Swahili
Affiliations: World Federation of Khoja Shi'a
'Ithna-Asheri Muslim Communities

London Islamic Turkish Association*
16 Green Lanes, Newington Green, London
N16 9ND
Tel: (020) 8249 5417 **Fax:** (020) 7690 4214
Email: lita@aol.com
Website: http://www.litaocagi.com/
Contact: Mr Harlin Akyol
Position: General Secretary
Contact Tel: (020) 7249 5417
Contact Email: hakyo76@hotmail.com
Activities: Resources
Traditions: Sunni
Other Languages: Turkish

North London Muslim Welfare Association*
51 Northfield Road, Enfield, London EN3 4BP

Tel: (020) 8804 1762
Contact: Mr Qureshi
Position: Secretary
Activities: Youth, elderly, women,
newsletter/journal, visits, inter-faith, resources
Traditions: Sunni
Other Languages: Urdu, Punjabi

South London Islamic Centre*
8 Mitcham Lane, Streatham, London SW16 6NN
Tel: (020) 8677 0588
Contact: Mohammed Aslam Ijaz
Position: Hon Gen Secretary
Activities: Worship, resource, visits, youth, elderly,
women
Traditions: Sunni
Other Languages: Urdu, Gujarati, Bengali, Arabic

UK Islamic Centre West London*
Brownlow Road, West Ealing, London W13 0SQ
Tel: (020)088404140 **Fax:** (020) 8567 2877
Contact: Mr S M Ali
Position: Secretary
Activities: Worship

Borough or Local Bodies

BARKING AND DAGENHAM

Barking Muslims Association*
2 Victoria Road, Barking IG11 8PY
Tel: (020) 8478 8526
Contact: Mr Nemat Ali
Position: Secretary
Activities: Worship, resource, umbrella body, visits,
youth, elderly
Traditions: Sunni
Other Languages: Urdu, Punjabi, Bengali, Pushto

BARNET

Help the Humanity*
14 Harcourt Avenue, Edgware HA8 8XN
Tel: (020) 8958 4697 **Fax:** (020) 8958 4697
Email: nhmir@aol.com
Contact: Naseem Haider Mir
Position: Secretary
Activities: Worship, resource
Traditions: Sunni
Movements: Jamati-i-Islami
Other Languages: Urdu, Punjabi

Hendon Mosque and Islamic Centre*
Brent View Road, West Hendon, London
NW9 7EL
Tel: (020) 8202 3236 **Fax:** (020) 8201 5904
Contact: Mr S M Kadri
Position: Secretary
Activities: Worship/practice/meditation,
community centre
Traditions: Sunni
Other Languages: Urdu, Arabic
Affiliations: Union of Muslim Organisations

Imam Khoei Islamic Centre*
Chevening Road, London NW6 6TN
Tel: (020) 8960 6378 **Fax:** (020) 8960 6398
Website: http://www.al-khoei.org/
Contact: S M S Mousavi-Khalkhali
Position: Director
Contact Email: gmousari@hotmail.com
Activities: Worship
Other Languages: Arabic, Persian
Affiliations: Al-Khoei Foundation

Khawateen*
40 Church Crescent, Whetstone, London N20 0JP
Tel: (020) 8368 2120
Contact: Mrs Shahida Parveen Rehman
Position: Secretary
Activities: Youth, elderly, women, inter-faith
Other Languages: Urdu, Punjabi

Muslim Educational and Literary Sevices*
61 Alexandra Road, Hendon, London NW4 2BX
Tel: (020) 8202 1799 **Fax:** (020) 8201 5924
Contact: Mr Abdulwahid Hamid
Position: Director
Activities: Resource, books

BRENT

Central Mosque of Brent*
Station Parade, Willesden Green, London
NW2 4NX
Tel: (020) 8450 1987
Contact: Raja Mohammad Riaz
Position: Chairman
Contact Tel: (020) 8451 0009
Activities: Worship
Traditions: Sunni
Movements: Barelwi
Other Languages: Arabic, Urdu, Punjabi, English

Ghana Muslim Union*
77 Fawood Avenue, Stonebridge, London

Tel: (020) 8965 5464
Contact: Ahmed Jimbah
Position: Head

Jame Mosque and Community Centre
106 Harrowdene Road, London HA0 2JF

Masjid At-Taqwa*
Willesden Library, 95 High Road, Willesden,
London NW10 2SF
Contact: Mr Dawud Abdul Malik
Position: Welfare Officer
Contact Tel: (020) 8961 9734
Activities: Worship/practice/meditation,
community centre
Traditions: Sunni
Other Languages: Arabic, Somali, Urdu, Sudanese

Mosque and Islamic Centre of Brent*
33a Howard Road, London NW2 6DS
Tel: (020) 8450 1986 **Fax:** (020) 8452 7403
Contact: Mr Sadiq
Position: Secretary
Activities: Worship

Sudbury Muslim Community Centre*
24a District Road, Sudbury, Wembley HA0 2LD

Wembley Mosque and Islamic Centre*
5 Stanley Avenue, Alperton, Wembley HA0 4JA
Tel: (020) 8902 3258 **Fax:** (020) 8902 3258
Contact: Dr Abdul Ghaffar
Position: Director
Activities: Worship/practice/meditation,
community centre, inter-faith, resources
Traditions: Sunni
Other Languages: Arabic, Punjabi, Gujarati, Urdu

Wembley Mosque Muslim Welfare Association*
35-37 Ealing Road, London HA0 4AE
Tel: (020) 8900 9673 **Fax:** (020) 8903 7256
Contact: Sajjad Ahmed
Position: General Secretary
Contact Tel: (020) 7245 0404
Activities: Resources

BROMLEY

Bromley Muslim Council*
Empire House, 11 High Street, London SE20 7HJ
Tel: (020) 8659 0640
Email: dr.khalid@sharif786.freeserve.co.uk
Contact: Dr Khalid Sharif
Position: Chair

Activities: Elderly
Traditions: Sunni
Other Languages: Urdu, Punjabi
Affiliations: British Muslim Council

CAMDEN

Imam Hussain Mosque (IHM)*
14 Brondesbury Road, Kilburn, London
NW6 6AS

Islamic Book Centre*
120 Drummond Street, London NW1 2HL
Tel: (020) 7388 0710
Contact: Mr Watsi
Position: General Secretary

Shah Jalal Masjid*
204a Start Cross Street (off Drummond Street),
Euston, London NW1
Tel: (020) 7387 0046
Contact: Mr M Allay

CROYDON

Croydon Mosque and Islamic Centre*
525 London Road, Thornton Heath, Croydon
CR7 6AR
Tel: (020) 8684 8200
Contact: Imran Khan
Position: Caretaker
Activities: Worship, resource, visits, youth, elderly,
women
Traditions: Sunni
Other Languages: Urdu, Punjabi, Bengali, Arabic
Affiliations: South London Mosques

Muslim Association of Croydon*
82 Virginia Road, Thornton Heath, Croydon
CR7 8EJ
Tel: (020) 8405 1299 **Fax:** (0870) 1331389
Email: sultansabri@cablenet.co.uk
Contact: Sultan Sabri
Position: General Secretary

EALING

Acton Muslim Welfare Association*
2-5 Oldham Terrace, Ealing, London W3 6LS
Tel: (020) 8993 8073
Contact: Mr Aizulhaq
Position: General Secretary

Anjuman-e-Burhani*
Mohamedi-Park Masjid Complex, Rowdell Road,
Northolt, Ealing UB5 6AG
Tel: (020) 7229 6404 **Fax:** (020) 7221 2691
Contact: Sheikh Walijee Hassanali
Activities: Worship
Traditions: Shi'a Imami Ismalia Talybi Dawoodi
Bohra
Movements: Dawoodi Bohras
Other Languages: Gujarati, Hindi, Urdu, Arabic

Central Jamia Masjid*
Montague Way, Southall UB2 5PA
Tel: (020) 8813 9218 **Fax:** (020) 8813 9218
Contact: Mohammad Bashir
Position: Chairman
Activities: Worship, visits, women
Traditions: Sunni
Movements: Tablighi Jamaat
Other Languages: Urdu, Punjabi, Somali, Arabic

Islamic Educational and Recreational Institute (Abu Bakr Mosque)*
165-69 The Broadway, Southall UB1 1LR
Tel: (020) 8571 6839 **Fax:** (020) 8571 0241
Email: info@abubakrmosque-southall.org.uk
Website: http://www.abubakrmosque-
southall.org.uk/
Contact: A S Shahid
Position: General Secretary
Activities: Worship/practice/meditation

Jamia Masjid*
Brownlow House, Brownlow Road, West Ealing,
London W13 0SQ
Tel: (020) 8840 4140
Contact: Syed Mohammed Ali
Position: Secretary
Activities: Worship, resource, umbrella body, visits,
youth, elderly
Traditions: Sunni
Movements: Jamati-i-Islami
Other Languages: Urdu, Gujarati, Punjabi,
Pushto
Affiliations: UK Islamic Mission

Mercy Universal*
PO Box 81, Greenford UB6 9YW
Tel: (020) 8575 5999 **Fax:** (020) 8575 3666
Contact: Dr Ayyub Dhakur
Position: Chairman

Muslim Welfare Centre*
4 Eccleston Road, West Ealing, London W13

Tel: (020) 8579 2369
Contact: Mr Bashir
Position: Chair Person

UK Islamic Centre West London*
Brownlow Road, West Ealing, London W13 0SQ
Tel: (020)088404140 Fax: (020) 8567 2877
Contact: Mr S M Ali
Position: Secretary
Activities: Worship

ENFIELD

Edmonton Islamic Centre*
198 Upper Fore Street, London N18 2JD
Tel: (020) 8807 5151
Contact: Nasim Siddiqi
Position: Chairman
Activities: Worship, resource, visits, youth, elderly,
women
Traditions: Sunni
Movements: Practice of Qur'an/Hadith
Other Languages: Urdu, Punjabi, Bengali,
Arabic/Turkish
Affiliations: Union of Muslim Organisations, UK
and Ireland

Muslim Community and Education Centre*
c/o 2 Doveridge Gardens, Palmers Green, London
N13 5BL
Tel: (020) 8886 3097
Contact: Mr S Sharikh
Position: Treasurer

North London Muslim Welfare Association*
51 Northfield Road, Enfield, London EN3 4BP
Tel: (020) 8804 1762
Contact: Mr Qureshi
Position: Secretary
Activities: Youth, elderly, women,
newsletter/journal, visits, inter-faith, resources
Traditions: Sunni
Other Languages: Urdu, Punjabi

Sisters in Islam (Muslim Girls Club)*
Ponders End Youth Centre, 129 South Street,
Ponders End, London EN3 4PX
Tel: (020) 8804 5908 Fax: (020) 8804 7426
Contact: Mrs R Hassan
Contact Tel: (020) 8372 0423
Activities: Youth, women, newsletter, visits, inter-
faith, resources
Traditions: Sunni
Other Languages: Bengali

GREENWICH

Asian Youth and Social Club*
6 Tuam Road, Plumstead Common, London
SE18 2QU
Tel: (020) 8855 8877 Fax: (020) 8855 8877
Contact: Saeed Ahmad
Position: Chairman
Activities: Resource, visits, youth, elderly, inter-
faith, education
Traditions: Sunni
Other Languages: Urdu, Punjabi, Hindi, Gujarati
Affiliations: Muslim Education Coordinating
Council-London

Charlton Mosque*
30-32 Ransome Road, Charlton, London
SE7 8SR
Tel: (020) 8858 4479
Contact: Mr M Anwar
Position: Chair
Activities: Worship

Greenwich Islamic Centre*
Woolwich Mosque, 131 Plumstead Road, London
SE18 7DW
Tel: (020) 8855 0786
Contact: Abdul Hamid Ismail
Activities: Worship, resource, visits, youth, elderly,
women
Other Languages: Urdu, Bengali, Somali
Affiliations: Central London Mosque; Muslim
World League

University of Greenwich Islamic Society
Student's Union, 17 Thomas Street, Woolwich,
London SE18 6HU

HACKNEY

**Aziziye Mosque and UK Turkish Islamic
Association***
117-119 Stoke Newington Road, London
N16 8BU
Tel: (020) 7254 0046
Contact: Mehmet Fatih
Position: Imam
Contact Tel: (07876) 214349
Contact Email: serenli@yahoo.com
Activities: Worship/practice/meditation, youth,
women, resources
Traditions: Sunni
Other Languages: Turkish, Urdu, Bengali, Arabic

British Muslim Council*
22 Lynmouth Road, London N16 6XL
Tel: (020) 8806 2898 **Fax:** (020) 8806 2898
Contact: Shuja Shaikh
Position: Chair
Activities: Worship, umbrella body, youth, elderly, women, newsletter
Other Languages: Urdu, Turkish, Bengali

Dalston Mosque*
160 Dalston Lane, Hackney, London E8 1NG
Contact: Mr M Ashraf
Position: President
Contact Tel: (020) 7241 4829
Activities: Worship/practice/meditation
Traditions: Sunni
Movements: Tablighi Jamaat
Other Languages: Urdu, Bangali, Gujarati, Nigerian
Affiliations: Anjuman Islamul Muslimeen

Hackney Muslim Council*
14 Warneford Street, London E9 7NG
Tel: (020) 8985 3258
Contact: A G Mulla
Position: Trustee

Hackney Muslim Women's Council*
101 Clapton Common, London E5 9AB
Tel: (020) 8809 0993 **Fax:** (020) 8809 0993
Activities: Community centre, elderly, women, resources
Traditions: Sunni
Other Languages: Urdu, Gujarati

London Islamic Turkish Association*
16 Green Lanes, Newington Green, London N16 9ND
Tel: (020) 8249 5417 **Fax:** (020) 7690 4214
Email: lita@aol.com
Website: http://www.litaocagi.com/
Contact: Mr Harlin Akyol
Position: General Secretary
Contact Tel: (020) 7249 5417
Contact Email: hakyo76@hotmail.com
Activities: Resources
Traditions: Sunni
Other Languages: Turkish

Madina Mosque Trust*
2a Leabridge Road, Clapton, London E5 9QD
Tel: (020) 8985 8204
Contact: M S Pirbhai
Position: Trustee

Contact Tel: (020) 8986 1568
Activities: Worship, community centre
Traditions: Sunni
Movements: Deobandi, Tablighi Jamaat
Other Languages: Gujarati, Urdu

Markuzul Uloom London*
1 Sandringham Road, Dalston, London E8 2LR
Tel: (020) 7241 5737 **Fax:** (020) 7249 3824
Contact: Mr Shuyeb Ahmed
Position: Principal
Contact Tel: (0795) 6245232

North London Muslim Housing Association*
62 Cazenove Road, Stamford Hill, London N16 6BJ
Tel: (020) 8806 9696
Contact: Ms Tiffany Mcdonald
Position: Personal Assistant

Tayyibah Girls School*
88 Filey Avenue, Stamford Hill, London N16 6JJ
Tel: (020) 8880 0085 **Fax:** (020) 8880 0085
Contact: Mrs N B Qureshi
Position: Head Teacher
Traditions: Sunni

UK Turkish Islamic Trust Mosque and Cultural Centre and Funeral Services*
203 Green Lanes, Hackney, London N16 9NH
Tel: (020) 359 1222 **Fax:** (020) 7923 2554
Contact: Ramadan Houssein Guney
Contact Tel: (01483) 472222
Position: Chair
Activities: Worship, resource, youth, elderly, women
Traditions: Sunni
Other Languages: Turkish, Arabic, Urdu

Union of Muslims in Hackney*
14 Warneford Street, London E9 7NG
Tel: (020) 8985 3258
Contact: A G Mulla
Position: President
Contact Tel: (020) 8985 8901

Upper Clapton Muslim Welfare and Womens Association
66 Detmold Road, London E5 9NJ

Validesultan Mosque*
1a Clissold Road, London N16 9EX
Tel: (020) 7241 5425 **Fax:** (020) 8518 2861
Contact: Mehmet Bolukbasi

Position: President
Activities: Worship, resource, umbrella body, visits, youth, elderly
Traditions: Sunni
Movements: Ahl-e-Hadith, Jamati-i-Islami
Other Languages: Turkish, Arabic

HAMMERSMITH AND FULHAM

Burhani Community Centre*
354 Lillie Road, London SW6 7PL
Tel: (020) 7229 6404
Contact: Dr Idris Zainuddin
Position: Chairperson

Hammersmith Imamwada
30-32 Southerton Road, London W6 0PH

Holy Party*
62 St Stephens Avenue, Shepherd's Bush, London W12 8JD
Tel: (020) 8743 9699
Contact: Mr S B Khawaja
Position: Chair

Kanoon Tawheed Islamic Centre*
30-32 Southerton Road, Hammersmith, London W6 0PH
Tel: (020) 8746 3158 **Fax:** (020) 8746 3158
Email: isa@tawheed.org.uk
Website: http://www.tawheed.org.uk/
Contact: H Mazaherian
Position: Director
Activities: Worship, resources
Traditions: Shi'a 'Ithna Asheri
Other Languages: Farsi (Iranian)
Affiliations: Al-Tawhid Charity

Mosque*
69 Tunis Road, London W12 7EY
Activities: Worship

Mosque*
302 Oxbridge Road, London W12 7LJ
Tel: (020) 8740 0463
Activities: Worship

Muslim Womens Association*
66 Rosebury Road, London SW6 2NG
Tel: (020) 7731 5455
Contact: Mrs Mussarrat Aftab
Position: Chair
Activities: Resource, visits, youth, elderly, women,

inter-faith
Traditions: Sunni, Shi'a
Other Languages: Urdu, Punjabi, Turkish, Bengali/Hindi

Shepherds Bush Mosque and Muslim Cultural Centre*
302 Uxbridge Road, Shepherds Bush, London W12 7LJ
Tel: (020) 8740 0463 **Fax:** (020) 8742 9070
Contact: Dr Ahmed Adam Badat
Position: President
Contact Tel: (020) 8743 5153
Contact Email: ahmedbadat@aol.com
Activities: Worship, resource, visits, youth
Traditions: Sunni
Other Languages: Urdu, Bengali, Arabic

HARINGEY

Bangladesh Muslim Organisation
90 Sydney Road, London N8 0EX

Fatih Mosque*
10 Caxton Road, London N22 6TB
Activities: Worship/practice/meditation

Hornsey Mosque and Islamic Centre*
389-395 Hampden Road, Hornsey, London N8 0NA
Tel: (020) 8348 0353
Contact: Mr Ali
Position: President
Contact Tel: (020) 8372 3023
Other Languages: Arabic

Islamic Community Centre*
115 Clyde Road, London N15 4JS
Tel: (020) 8809 2137 **Fax:** (020) 8211 7019
Contact: Mr Ahad Ali
Position: Director
Contact Tel: (07932) 667313
Activities: Youth
Other Languages: Arabic, Bengali, Urdu, Somali

Islamic Computer Centre*
73 St Thomas's Road, London N4 2QJ
Tel: (020) 7359 6233 **Fax:** (020) 7226 2924
Email: islamicsoft@webstar.co.uk
Website: http://www.salaam.co.uk/icc
Contact: A K Barkatulla
Position: Director
Contact Tel: (020) 8922 0859

Contact Email: barkatulla@webstar.co.uk
Other Languages: Urdu, Arabic

London Islamic Cultural Society*
389-395 Wightman Road, Hornsey, London
N8 0NA
Tel: (020) 8348 0353
Contact: Mr Abdool Alli
Position: President
Activities: Worship, resource, visits, youth, elderly,
women
Traditions: Sunni
Other Languages: Bengali, Urdu, Turkish

Young Muslim Organisation UK*
Haringey Branch, 115 Clyde Road, London
N15 4JS
Tel: (020) 8809 2137 **Fax:** (020) 8211 7019
Contact: Mr Ahad Ali
Position: Youth Leader
Contact Tel: (07932) 667313
Activities: Youth
Other Languages: Bengali, Urdu,

HARROW

Harrow Central Mosque*
36-38 Station Road, Harrow HA1 2SQ
Tel: (020) 8861 2071
Email: 8h.mosque@bigbluesky.uk.net
Contact: Ghulam Rabani
Position: Secretary
Contact Tel: (020) 8861 2071
Activities: Worship, resource, visits, youth, elderly,
women
Traditions: Sunni
Other Languages: Urdu, Punjabi, Bengali, Arabic
Affiliations: Union of Muslim Organisations;
Islamic Cultural Centre, London

Harrow Muslim Education Society*
417 Pinner Road, Harrow HA1 4HN
Tel: (020) 8427 1481 **Fax:** (020) 8427 6892
Contact: Mr Syed Khalid Mahmood
Position: Chairperson
Contact Tel: (020) 8427 1481
Other Languages: Urdu, Arabic

Islamic and Cultural Society of Harrow*
27 Northolt Road, South Harrow, Harrow
HA2 7NW
Tel: (020) 8204 5514
Contact: Mr Rizvi

Position: Chairman
Other Languages: Urdu, Punjabi, Bengali, Sindhi

**_Khoja Shi'a 'Ithna-Asheri Muslim Community
of London*_**
Islamic Centre, Wood Lane, Stanmore HA7 4LQ
Tel: (020) 8954 6247 **Fax:** (020) 8954 8028
Contact: Fadhl Tharoo
Position: Honorary Secretary
Activities: Worship, resource, umbrella body, visits,
youth, elderly
Traditions: Shi'a 'Ithna Asheri
Other Languages: Urdu, Arabic, Gujarati,
Kutchi/Swahili
Affiliations: World Federation of Khoja Shi'a
'Ithna-Asheri Muslim Communities

HAVERING

Havering Islamic Cultural Centre*
Century Community Centre, Albert Road,
Romford RM1 2PS
Tel: (01708) 763954 **Fax:** (01708) 700190
Contact: Mr M Saleem
Position: Treasurer
Activities: Worship/practice/meditation
Other Languages: Urdu, Arabic
Affiliations: U.M.O

Romford Mosque - Essex Islamic Trust*
29 Lessington Avenue, Romford RM7 9EB
Tel: (01708) 705293 **Fax:** (01708) 705293
Contact: Mr Kamal Siddiqui
Position: Chair
Activities: Worship/practice/meditation,
community centre, youth, elderly, women,
newsletter/journal, resources
Traditions: Sunni
Movements: Ahle-Sunnat ul Jamat
Other Languages: Urdu, Arabic, Hindi
Affiliations: Union of Muslim Organisations

HILLINGDON

Hidayah Centre*
Old L B of Hillingdon Library, Bedwell Gardens
(off Station Road), Hayes UB3 4EF
Tel: (020) 8756 0406
Contact: Mr Hassam
Position: General Secretary
Contact Tel: (07931) 333611

Islamic Education and Cultural Society*
Hayes Civic Hall, 3 Pump Lane, Hayes UB3 3NB
Tel: (020) 8561 4654
Contact: Obaid R Siddiqui
Position: Chairman
Activities: Worship, resource, visits, youth, elderly, women
Traditions: Sunni
Other Languages: Urdu, Punjabi, Arabic, Somalian

HOUNSLOW

Anjuman-e-Khwateen*
28 Lansdowne Road, Hounslow TW3 1LQ
Tel: (020) 8570 1394
Position: c/o Mrs Ahsan Shah
Other Languages: Urdu
Affiliations: Islamic Women's Movement of Great Britain

Hounslow Islamic Relief Association*
97 Midsummer Avenue, Hounslow TW4 5AY
Tel: (020) 8330 6686 **Fax:** (0870) 139 0739
Contact: Mr Hussain Sultan
Contact Email: hussain_sultan@hotmail.com
Other Languages: Arabic

Hounslow Jamia Masjid and Islamic Centre*
457 Wellington Road South, Hounslow TW4 5JH
Tel: (020) 8570 0938 **Fax:** (020) 8572 3445
Email: gshjmic@hotmail.com
Website: http://www.hounslowmosque.co.uk/
Contact: Mr Tahir Aslam
Position: General Secretary
Contact Tel: (07798) 893629
Activities: Worship/practice/meditation, community centre, newsletter/journal, visits, inter-faith, resources
Traditions: Sunni
Movements: Barelwi
Other Languages: Urdu, Arabic, Somali, Bengali
Affiliations: Union of Muslim Organisations

Hussaini Islamic Mission*
19 Thornbury Road, Isleworth TW7 4LQ
Tel: (020) 8569 8823 **Fax:** (020) 8568 1721
Contact: Hojjatol Islam M Hasan (Maroofi)
Position: Resident Alim
Contact Tel: (020) 8579 0365
Other Languages: Urdu, Punjabi

Isleworth Muslim Women's Association*
1 Witham Road, Isleworth, Hounslow TW7 4AJ
Tel: (020) 8560 6702
Contact: Mrs Naseem Yousef
Position: Organiser
Contact Email: naseemyousef@hotmail.com
Activities: Women, visits, inter-faith, resources
Traditions: Sunni
Movements: Ahl-e-Hadith
Other Languages: Urdu, Punjabi

ISLINGTON

Mosque*
67 Westbourne Road, Bayswater, London N7 8AD
Tel: (020) 7727 0729
Position: General Secretary
Activities: Worship

North London Central Mosque
7-11 St Thomas' Road, London N4 2GH

Union of Muslim Families UK*
55 Balfour Road, Islington, London N5 2HD
Tel: (020) 7226 0934 **Fax:** (020) 7226 0934
Contact: Chair
Position: Chair
Contact Tel: (020) 7226 0934
Activities: Resource, visits, youth
Traditions: Sunni
Movements: Ahl-e-Hadith
Other Languages: Urdu, Bengali, Arabic, French
Affiliations: The Muslim World League

KENSINGTON AND CHELSEA

Islamic Museum and Cultural Centre*
44 Crofton Road, London SE5 8NB
Tel: (020) 7701 3670
Contact: Dr Hani Alsaigh
Position: Secretary

Islamic Universal Association*
20 Penzance Place, London W11 4PG
Tel: (020) 7602 5273
Contact: Mr A Alemi
Position: Imam

Muslim Cultural Heritage Centre*
244 Acklam Road, London W10 5YG
Tel: (020) 8964 1496 **Fax:** (020) 8969 2928
Email: info@mchc.org.uk
Website: http://www.mchc.org.uk/
Contact: Dr Abdulkarim Khalil

Position: Director
Activities: Worship/practice/meditation, community centre, youth, elderly, women, visits, inter-faith
Traditions: Sunni
Other Languages: Arabic, Urdu, Bengali, Somali

KINGSTON UPON THAMES

Kingston Mosque and Muslim Association*
55/55a East Road, Kingston-upon-Thames KT2 6EJ
Tel: (020) 8549 5315
Contact: Mohammed Anwar Malik
Position: Secretary
Activities: Worship, resource, visits, youth, women, inter-faith
Traditions: Sunni
Movements: Sunni Jamati
Other Languages: Arabic, Urdu, Bengali

Kingston Muslim Womens Welfare and Cultural Association*
38 Gainsborough Road, New Malden KT3 5NU
Tel: (020) 8330 1247
Contact: Mrs Hamida Syed Rizvi
Position: General Secretary
Contact Tel: (020) 8715 2227
Activities: Youth, women, resources
Traditions: Sunni
Movements: Deobandi
Other Languages: Urdu, Punjabi, Gujarati

LAMBETH

Ahl-ul-Bayt Islamic Centre*
11-13 Edgeley Road, London SW4 6EH
Tel: (020) 7627 0709
Contact: Dr M Bahraluloom
Position: Chair

Brixton Mosque and Islamic Cultural Centre*
1 Gresham Road, London SW9 7PH
Tel: (020) 7326 4098 **Fax:** (020) 7326 4098
Contact: Abdul Haqq Baker
Position: Chairman/Ameer
Activities: Worship, resource, umbrella body, visits, youth, women
Traditions: Sunni
Movements: Salafee
Other Languages: Arabic, French, Somali
Affiliations: South London Council of Mosques

Jamaat Hyderi Islamic Centre*
26 Estreham Road, Streatham, London SW16 5PQ
Tel: (020) 8769 7553 **Fax:** (020) 8696 0104
Email: admin@hyderi.org
Website: http://www.hyderi.org/
Contact: Secretary
Activities: Worship
Other Languages: Urdu, Gujarati

South London Islamic Centre*
8 Mitcham Lane, Streatham, London SW16 6NN
Tel: (020) 8677 0588
Contact: Mohammed Aslam Ijaz
Activities: Worship, resource, visits, youth, elderly, women
Traditions: Sunni
Other Languages: Urdu Gujarati, Bengali, Arabic

UK Islamic Mission*
202 North Gower Street, London NW1 2LY
Tel: (020) 7387 2157 **Fax:** (020) 7383 0867
Position: Secretary

LEWISHAM

Lewisham and Kent Islamic Centre*
363-365 Lewisham High Street, Catford, London SE13 6NZ
Tel: (020) 8690 5090 **Fax:** (020) 8690 5090
Contact: Mr Ghulam Shabbin
Position: Chairman
Contact Tel: (020) 8691 2942
Activities: Worship, visits, youth, women, inter-faith
Traditions: Sunni
Other Languages: Urdu, Punjabi, Bengali, Arabic
Affiliations: South London Mosques; Union of Muslim Organisations

MERTON

Al-Furqan Islamic Heritage Foundation*
Eagle House, High Street, Wimbledon, London SW19 5EF
Tel: (020) 8944 1233 **Fax:** (020) 8944 1633
Email: info@alfurqan.com
Website: http://www.alfurqan.org/
Contact: Dr Hamilton
Position: Executive Officer
Activities: Newsletter/journal, books, visits, resources
Other Languages: Arabic

Darul Amaan Islamic Centre*
54 High Street, Merton, London SW19 1DH
Tel: (020) 8543 5687

Madina House Trust*
63 Coombe Lane, London SW20 0BD
Tel: (020) 8946 1052 **Fax:** (020) 8946 0641
Email: ask.hass@supanet.com.
Contact: Mrs Khanum Hassan
Position: President
Activities: Women,youth
Other Languages: Urdu, Arabic, French
Affiliations: Other womens groups and childrens homes

Wimbledon Mosque*
262-270 Durnsford Road, Wimbledon, London
SW19 8DS
Tel: (020) 8946 3350 **Fax:** (020) 8542 1408
Email: qasim7@yahoo.com
Contact: Mr Mohammad Hassan
Position: Secretary
Contact Tel: (020) 8542 6829
Activities: Worship/practice/meditation,
community centre, women, visits, inter-faith
Traditions: Sunni
Other Languages: Urdu, Arabic, Bengali
Affiliations: Council of Mosques; Muslim
Council of Britain

NEWHAM

Al-Tawhid Mosque and Madrasah Ahl-e-Hadith*
80 High Road, Leyton, London E15 2BP
Tel: (020) 8519 6655
Contact: Mohammed Idrees Sethi
Position: Secretary
Activities: Worship, resource, youth, women
Traditions: Sunni
Movements: Ahl-e-Hadith
Other Languages: Urdu, Punjabi, Arabic
Affiliations: Walthamstow Islamic Sharia Council;
Al Qur'an Society; World League League; Call to
Islam

Anjuman-e-Islamia (Newham) and Mosque*
266-268 High St North, Manor Park, London
E12 6SB
Tel: (020) 8472 5663
Contact: Chairman

Canning Town Mosque and Welfare Association*
Muslim Community Centre, 269 Barking Road,
Canning Town E13 8EQ
Tel: (020) 8472 5096
Contact: Mr S Ali
Position: Secretary

Forest Gate Mosque*
451 Romford Road, Forest Gate, London E7 8AB
Tel: (020) 8534 8672

Ibrahim Mosque*
721-723 Barking Road, Plaistow, London
E13 9EQ
Tel: (020) 8548 8196
Contact: Hasiz Saheb
Position: Imam

Idara Minhal-ul-Quran (London)*
292-296 Romford Road, Forest Gate, London
E7 9HD
Tel: (020) 8257 1786 **Fax:** (020) 8534 4247

Imamia Mission Mosque*
328 Romford Road, Forest Gate, London E7 8BS
Tel: (020) 8555 5363 **Fax:** (020) 8555 5363
Contact: Mr S A Shah
Position: President
Contact Tel: (07956) 363574
Activities: Worship/practice/meditation
Other Languages: Urdu, Punjabi

Islamic Association East Ham Muslim Cultural Centre*
Madina Masjid, 225 High Street North, East Ham,
London E6 1JG
Tel: (020) 8472 3069
Contact: Abdul Rahman Sheikh
Position: President
Activities: Worship, resource
Traditions: Sunni
Movements: Deobandi
Other Languages: Urdu, Gujarati, Bengali

Islamic Centre (Upton Park)*
175-177 Plashet Grove, Upton Park, London
E6 1BX
Tel: (020) 8552 6133
Contact: Mr Iqbal
Position: Secretary

Islamic Centre*
72 Selwyn Road, Upton Park, London E13 0PY

Tel: (020) 8472 2745
Contact: Mr Naeem Khan
Position: Chairperson

Islamic Dawah Centre*
381 High Street North, Manor Park, London
E12 6PG
Tel: (020) 8503 4323
Email: abu@aysha3b.freeserve.co.uk.
Contact: S Mubalak
Position: Secretary
Activities: Resources
Other Languages: Tamil

**Manor Park Islamic Cultural Centre and
Shajalal Mosque***
722-726 Romford Road, Manor Park, London
E12 6BT
Tel: (020) 8514 7772
Contact: Mr Foyzur Rahman
Position: General Secretary
Activities: Worship, visits
Traditions: Sunni
Movements: Ahl-e-Hadith
Other Languages: Bengali, Urdu
Affiliations: Muslim World League

**Markaz-ud-Dawat-Wal Irshad Muslim
Community Centre**
177-179 Plashet Grove, East Ham, London E6 1BX

**Masjid-e-Bilal and East London Islamic
Centre***
295 Barking Road, East Ham, London E6 1LB
Tel: (020) 8471 9355
Contact: Mr Afzal
Position: President

Masjid-e-Falah*
510 Barking Road, Plaistow, London E13 8QE
Tel: (020) 8470 1031 **Fax:** (020) 8472 1215
Contact: Mr K Khan
Position: Secretary
Contact Tel: (07930) 754910
Other Languages: Urdu, Punjabi, Hindi

Medina Mosque and Muslim Cultural Centre*
225 High Street North, East Ham, London E6 1JG
Contact: Mr M Tusaddaq
Position: Secretary
Activities: Worship/practice/meditation, resources
Traditions: Sunni
Other Languages: Urdu, Gujarati, Punjabi,
Bengali

Newham Islamic Association*
88 Greenstreet, Farsgate, London E7
Tel: (020) 8472 6887

Newham Muslim Citizens Association*
112 Katherine Road, East Ham, London E6 1EW
Tel: (07931) 351559
Contact: Mr M M Farhat
Position: President
Contact Tel: (020) 8553 1896
Contact Email: maqbool.farhat@virgin.net
Activities: Community centre, youth, women,
newsletter/journal, inter-faith
Other Languages: Urdu, Punjabi, Gujarati,
Bengali
Affiliations: Tolu-e-Islam Movement

**Newham North Islamic Association Mosque
and Community Centre***
88 Green Street, London E7 8JG
Tel: (020) 8472 6887
Contact: Mr Shahan H Hussain
Position: General Secretary

Quwwat-ul-Islam Mosque and Islam Society
62-66 Upton Lane, London E7 9LN
Tel: (020) 8472 1072
Contact: Maulana Osman Adam

Stratford Islamic Association*
3 Brydges Road, Stratford, London E13 1NA
Tel: (020) 8519 6367
Contact: Secretary

REDBRIDGE

Bazme Tolu-e-Islam*
76 Park Road, Ilford IG1 1SF
Tel: (020) 8553 1896 **Fax:** (020) 8553 1896
Email: bazm.london@virgin.net
Website: http://www.toluislam.com/
Contact: Mr Maqbool Mahmood Farhat
Position: Chairman
Contact Email: maqbool.farhat@virgin.net
Activities: Central body, women,
newsletter/journal, books
Other Languages: Urdu
Affiliations: Idara Tolu-e-Islam, Lahore, Pakistan

**Gujarati Senior Citizens Welfare Association
Redbridge***
91 Elgin Road, Seven Kings, Ilford IG1 8LW
Contact: Mr B V Sudra
Position: Secretary

Contact Tel: (020) 8599 9855
Contact Email: gscwr@supanet.com

Ilford Islamic Centre Ltd*
52-56 Albert Road, Ilford IG1 1HW
Tel: (020) 8553 5739
Contact: Mr Ghulam Hussain
Position: Secretary
Activities: Worship/practice/meditation
Traditions: Sunni
Other Languages: Urdu, Punjabi, Bengali,
Gujarati

Ilford Muslim Society*
112 Balfour Road, Ilford IG1 4JE
Tel: (020) 8478 0347
Position: Secretary
Activities: Worship, resource, visits, inter-faith
Traditions: Sunni
Movements: Deobandi, Tablighi Jamaat
Other Languages: Gujarati, Hindi, Urdu

Muslim Defence Council UK*
17 Natal Road, Ilford IG1 2HA
Tel: (020) 8514 4436
Contact: Mr Raja Adalat Khan
Position: General Secretary
Contact Tel: (07957) 164544
Other Languages: Urdu
Affiliations: World Islamic Mission

Qurani Murkuz*
10-12 Mulberry Way, South Woodford, London
E18 1ED
Tel: (020) 8989 4759

Rafique Foundation*
Rafique House, 72 Herent Drive, Clayhall, Ilford
IG5 0HG
Tel: (020) 8550 3893
Email: rafiquefoundation@tinyworld.co.uk
Contact: Mr M I Khawaja
Position: General Secretary
Activities: Worship/practice/meditation, youth,
newletter/journal, books
Other Languages: Urdu, Punjabi
Affiliations: Tolu-e-Islam

Redbridge and Chigwell Muslim Association*
36 Woodford Avenue, Gants Hill, Ilford IG2 6XQ
Tel: (020) 8551 6189 **Fax:** (020) 8551 9819
Contact: Mr Ali M Qureshi
Position: Chairperson
Activities: Visits, youth, women, inter-faith
Traditions: Sunni

Movements: Unity of Muslims
Other Languages: Arabic, Bengali, Urdu, Sindhi
Affiliations: Union of Muslim Organisations UK
and Eire; The Council of Mosques and Muslim
Organisations (UK)

Seven Kings Mosque*
645-647 High Road, Seven Kings, Ilford IG3 8RA
Tel: (020) 8599 1800
Contact: Mr Yousuf Seth
Position: President

SOUTHWARK

Aaina Women's Group*
c/o Thomas Calton Centre, Alpha Street, London
SE15 4NX
Tel: (020) 7358 0697 **Fax:** (020) 7358 0697
Contact: Maliha Bashir
Position: Support Worker
Other Languages: Urdu, Hindi, Arabic

Baitul Aziz Masjid and Madrassa*
1 Dickens Square, off Harper Road, London
SE1 4JL
Tel: (020) 7378 7764

Dulwich Islamic Centre*
23 North Cross Road, London SE22 9ET
Tel: (020) 8299 1046
Contact: Hussain Malik
Position: Chairman
Activities: Worship, resource, youth, elderly,
women
Traditions: Sunni
Other Languages: Urdu, Bengali, Arabic
Affiliations: South London Mosques

Muslim Association of Nigeria (UK)*
MAN's Building, 365 Old Kent Road, London
SE1 5JH
Tel: (020) 7231 0100 **Fax:** (020) 7237 0009
Email: manuk@aol.com
Contact: Miss Amina Ellis
Position: Administrator
Contact Tel: (020) 7237 0009
Activities: Worship, resource, media, visits, youth
Movements: Ahl-e-Hadith
Other Languages: Nigerian Languages, Arabic
Affiliations: Union of Muslim Organisations UK
and Eire; Council of Nigerian Muslim
Organisations (UK)
Other Languages: Nigerian languages, Arabic

Southwark Muslim Women's Association*
Bellenden Old School, Bellenden Road, London
SE15 4DG
Tel: (020) 7732 8053 **Fax:** (020) 7732 3310
Email: smwa@compuserve.com
Website: http://www.smwa.org.uk/
Contact: Zafar Iqbal
Position: Centre Manager
Contact Tel: (020) 2777 7320
Activities: Resource, visits, youth, elderly, women
Traditions: Sunni, Ismaili
Other Languages: Urdu, Bengali, Turkish, Patwa,
Arabic, Persian

SUTTON

Bangladesh Welfare Association*
10a Clifton Rise, Wallington, Sutton SE14
Tel: (020) 8691 4491
Contact: Mr Shelim Rahman
Position: Secretary
Contact Tel: (020) 8691 9171
Activities: Youth, women

**Muslim Cultural and Welfare Association of
Sutton***
Wentworth Hall, 80 Ruskin Road, Carshalton
SM5 3DH
Tel: (020) 8647 9041 **Fax:** (020) 8395 6113
Contact: Councillor Lal Hussain
Position: Secretary
Activities: Worship/practice/meditation,
community centre, youth, elderly, women,
newsletter/journal, radio, inter-faith, resources
Traditions: Sunni
Other Languages: Urdu, Bengali
Affiliations: British Muslim Association

Sutton Islamic Centre*
62 Oakhill Road, Sutton SM1 3AG
Tel: (020) 8641 6869
Contact: Misdiq Zaidi
Position: Chair
Contact Tel: (020) 8767 2300
Other Languages: Urdu
Affiliations: Muslim Council of Britain

TOWER HAMLETS

Al-Huda Cultural Centre and Mosque*
91 Mile End Road, London E1 4UJ
Tel: (020) 7780 9495

Assembly of Muslim Youth*
6 Rudestone House, London E3 3AT
Tel: (020) 8980 2604
Contact: Hafiz Abdullah Mohammad
Position: Chief Organiser
Activities: Resource, youth, books, inter-faith
Traditions: Sunni,
Other Languages: Bengali

**Burdett Estate Mosque and Islamic Community
Centre***
Wallwood Street, London E14 7AW
Tel: (020) 75362572
Contact: K Jaman
Position: General Secretary
Contact Tel: (07960) 340454
Activities: Worship/practice/meditation, education
Other Languages: Bangladeshi

Darul Ummah Jame Mosque*
56 Bigland Street, London E1 2ND
Tel: (020) 7790 5166 **Fax:** (020) 7790 2005
Website: http://www.dawatul-islam.org/
Contact: Burhan Uddin
Position: Secretary
Activities: Worship/practice/meditation,
community centre, youth
Other Languages: Bengali

**Dockland Darul Amanat Mosque and Islamic
Centre***
23 Farnworth House, Manchester Road, London
E14 3HY
Tel: (020) 7537 2705
Email: shoeb_ahammad@hotmail.com
Contact: Mr M S Ahammad
Position: Chair
Activities: Worship/practice/meditation,
community centre
Traditions: Sunni
Movements: Deobandi, Tablighi Jamaat, Tassawuf
Other Languages: Bengali

East London Mosque*
82/92 Whitechapel Road, London E1 1JE
Tel: (020) 7247 1357 **Fax:** (020) 7377 9879
Contact: M A R Khan
Position: Caretaker
Activities: Worship, resource, visits, youth, elderly,
women
Traditions: Sunni
Other Languages: Bengali, Urdu,
Nigerian/Somalian, Arabic

Esha 'atul Islam*
18-22 Damien Street, Tower Hamlets, London
E1 2HX

Esha'atul Islam Mosque*
16 Ford Square, London E1 2HS
Tel: (020) 7790 3966 **Fax:** (020) 7790 5536
Contact: Maulana Shamsul Haque
Position: Imam/General Secretary
Contact Tel: (020) 7265 1890
Activities: Worship, resource, youth, elderly,
women, inter-faith
Traditions: Sunni
Other Languages: Bengali, Urdu, Arabic
Affiliations: Council of Mosques; Muslim World
League

Jamia Masjid*
59 Brick Lane, Aldgate East, London E1 6QL
Tel: (020) 7247 6052
Contact: Mdzillul Hoque
Contact Tel: (020) 7247 6052
Traditions: Sunni
Other Languages: Bengali

Markazi Mosque*
9-11 Christian Street, off Commercial Road,
London E1 1SE
Tel: (020) 7481 1294

Medina Jame Masjid
248 Westferry Road, Tower Hamlets, London
E14 3AG

Muslim Care*
206-208 Brick Lane, London E1 6SA
Tel: (020) 7613 0772 **Fax:** (020) 7729 0904
Contact: Mr Faizullah Khan
Position: Director
Contact Email: khanfaizullah@hotmail.com
Other Languages: Urdu, Punjabi
Affiliations: Muslim Council of Britain

Shadwell Jame Masjid and Madrasah
143-145 Shadwell Place, Tower Hamlets, London
E1 2QB

Shahporan Masjid and Islamic Centre
444 Hackney Road, Tower Hamlets, London
E2 9DY

Shoreditch Masjid Trust
53-55 Red Church Street, Tower Hamlets, London
E2 7DP
Tel: (020) 7739 5530

**UK Turkish Islamic Cultural Centre and
Suleymaniye Mosque***
212-216 Kingsland Road, Shoreditch, London
E2 8AX
Tel: (020) 7684 9900 **Fax:** (020) 7684 9992
Email: suleymaniye.mosque@which.net
Website: http://www.ukturkislam.co.uk/
Contact: Mr Hakan Ozgul
Position: Secretary
Contact Tel: (020) 7684 7566
Contact Email: h_ozgul@hotmail.com
Activities: Worship/practice/meditation,
community centre, central body, youth, elderly,
women, resources
Traditions: Sunni
Movements: Nakshebande
Other Languages: Turkish, Arabic
Affiliations: The Union of Turkish Islamic
Cultural Centres

WALTHAM FOREST

Al-Qur'an Society*
34 Francis Road, Leyton, London E10 6PW
Tel: (020) 8556 4490 **Fax:** (020) 8558 0581
Contact: Dr Suhaib Hasan
Position: Chairperson
Contact Email: suhaib@hotmail.com
Activities: Resource, books
Traditions: Sunni
Other Languages: Urdu, Arabic

Ashville Jamia Masjid Mosque*
134a Ashville Road, Leyton Stone, London
E11 4DU
Tel: (020) 8926 2314
Contact: Maulana Sharif Pathan
Position: Imam
Activities: Worship
Traditions: Sunni
Movements: Deobandi, Tablighi Jamaat
Other Languages: Urdu, Gujarati, Arabic, French

Chingford Islamic Society and Mosque*
92 Chingford Mount Road, Chingford, London
E4 8SD
Contact: Mr Keshad Beekhun
Position: Secretary
Contact Tel: (020) 8375 4089
Activities: Worship/practice/meditation,
community centre, youth, women, visits
Traditions: Sunni
Movements: Tablighi Jamaat
Other Languages: Urdu, Gujarati

Council of Mosques for North East London*
c/o Noor-ul-Islam, 711 High Road, Leyton,
London E10 6RA
Tel: (020) 8923 7860
Activities: Worship, umbrella body, inter-faith
Traditions: Sunni
Other Languages: Urdu, Arabic

International Muslim Movement*
12 East Avenue, Walthamstow, London E17
Tel: (020) 8520 4121
Contact: A Hussain
Position: Secretary
Contact Tel: (020) 8558 9324
Activities: Worship/practice/meditation, books,
resources
Traditions: Sunni
Movements: Barelwi
Other Languages: Urdu
Affiliations: Waltham Forest Islamic Association;
Jamat-e-Ahle-Sunnat

Leyton Muslim Cultural Society*
715 High Road, London E10 5AB
Tel: (020) 8539 0769
Contact: Yusuf Hansa
Position: Chair
Activities: Worship, resource, youth, elderly,
women, newsletters
Traditions: Sunni
Other Languages: Creole or Patois, French, Urdu
Affiliations: Noor ul Islam; Council of Mosques
for North East London

Leytonstone Mosque and Islamic Association*
Dacre Road, London E11 3AG
Tel: (020) 8539 7251
Contact: Mr Iqbal Patel
Position: General Secretary

Masjid-e-Vmer*
79 Queens Road, Walthamstow, London E17 8QR
Tel: (020) 8520 2658
Contact: Mr A Vawda
Position: Secretary
Other Languages: Hindi, Urdu, Gujarati

Mauritian Islamic Welfare Association (MIWA)*
715 High Road, Leyton, London E10 5AB
Tel: (020) 8539 0769
Email: miwatis@aol.com
Contact: Mr Swaley Assam
Position: Chair
Activities: Youth, elderly, women, newsletters

Traditions: Sunni
Other Languages: Patois, Urdu
Affiliations: Noor ul Islam

Muslim Parents Association
c/o 13c Hoe Street, London E17

Noor-ul-Islam*
711 High Road, Leyton, London E10 6RA
Tel: (020) 8923 7860
Contact: Mr Yusuf Hansa
Position: Chairman
Activities: Worship, visits, youth, elderly, women,
inter-faith
Traditions: Sunni
Other Languages: English, French, Urdu, Arabic
Affiliations: Council of Mosques for North East
London

**Waltham Forest Islamic Association and
Leabridge Road Mosque***
439-451 Lea Bridge Road, Leyton, London
E10 7EA
Tel: (020) 8539 4282 **Fax:** (020) 8558 3117
Contact: Mr T H Chaudhury
Position: President
Activities: Worship, resource, visits, youth, elderly,
inter-faith
Traditions: Sunni
Movements: Barelwi
Other Languages: Urdu, Punjabi, Bengali,
Gujarati

WANDSWORTH

Balham Mosque*
47a Balham High Road, London SW12 9AW
Tel: (020) 8675 7912 **Fax:** (020) 8675 2731
Contact: Mr Aniz Jussab
Position: Secretary
Contact Tel: (020) 8674 5750
Contact Email: ali.mayfair@btinternet.com
Activities: Worship, resource, visits, youth, elderly,
women
Traditions: Sunni
Other Languages: Urdu, Gujarati, Punjabi, Arabic
Affiliations: Council of Mosques in South
London and Surrey; Muslim Council of Britain

**Battersea Mosque/Islamic Cultural and
Education Centre/Islamic Youth Group**
73/75 Falcon Road, Battersea, London SW11 2PG
Tel: (020) 7228 4267

Idara-e-Jaaferiya Mosque*
18 Church Lane, Tooting, London SW17 9PP
Tel: (020) 8672 5373
Contact: Maulana Raza Haider Rizvi
Position: Resident Alim
Activities: Worship, resources, youth, women, newsletter
Traditions: Shi'a 'Ithna Asheri
Movements: Ahl-e-Bayt
Other Languages: Urdu, Arabic, Punjabi, Persian

Mosque*
49 Lower Richmond Road, Putney, London SW15
Tel: (020) 8788 5554
Activities: Worship

Muslim Womans Association*
425 Leabridge Road, Leyton, London E10 7EA
Tel: (020) 8539 7478 **Fax:** (020) 8539 7478
Contact: Co-ordinator
Activities: Women

Muslim Women's Prisoner Support Group*
P O Box 6001, London SW15 4XA
Tel: (020) 8876 1375
Contact: Mrs K Adam
Position: Founder

Tooting Islamic Centre*
145 Upper Tooting Road, London SW17 7TJ
Tel: (020) 8767 2344 **Fax:** (020) 8767 2544
Contact: Mr M A Jussab
Position: Secretary
Activities: Worship, resource, umbrella body, visits, youth, women
Traditions: Sunni
Movements: Salafee
Other Languages: Arabic, French, Somali
Affiliations: South London Council of Mosques

WESTMINSTER, CITY OF

Gretra Mosque*
32 Page Street, London SW1P 4EN
Tel: (020) 7828 4531
Contact: Mr Sabur
Position: Secretary

Islamic Universal Association*
20 Penzance Place, Holland Park Avenue, London W1 4PG
Tel: (020) 7602 5273 **Fax:** (020) 7603 0525
Email: i.u.a@.totalise.co.uk
Contact: Mr Alemi
Position: Chairman

Contact Tel: (020) 7602 5273
Contact Email: i.u.a.@totalise.co.uk
Activities: Worship, resource, media, umbrella body, visits, youth
Traditions: Sh 'ia 'Ithna Asheri
Other Languages: Farsi, Arabic

London Central Mosque and Islamic Cultural Centre, The*
146 Park Road, London NW8 7RG
Tel: (020) 7724 3363 **Fax:** (020) 7724 0493
Email: islamic200@aol.com
Website: http://www.islamicculturalcentre.co.uk/
Contact: Mr Nizar Boga
Position: Advisor
Contact Tel: (020) 7706 4432
Activities: Worship/practice/meditation, community centre, youth, elderly, books, radio, television, visits, inter-faith, resources
Traditions: Sunni
Other Languages: Arabic, Punjabi, Urdu, Bengali
Affiliations: Inter Faith Network for the UK

Madina House (Children's Home)*
146 Gloucester Place, London NW1 6DT
Tel: (020) 7262 5314
Contact: Khanam Hassan
Position: Chair of Trustees
Contact Tel: (020) 8946 1052
Other Languages: Urdu, Arabic, French

Mayfair Islamic Centre*
19 Hertford Street, Mayfair, London W1J 7RU
Tel: (020) 7495 8283
Contact: Dr H Aikarmi
Position: President

Muslim Advice Centre*
46 Goodge Street, London W1T 4LU
Tel: (020) 7637 1971
Other Languages: Urdu, French, Arabic, Bangladeshi

SOUTH EAST
Regional or County Bodies

Sussex Muslim Society Trust UK*
8 Caburn Road, Hove BN3 6EF
Tel: (01273) 722438 **Fax:** (01273) 722438
Contact: Imam Dr Abdul Jalil Sajid
Position: Director
Contact Email: ajsajid@ibelieve.co.uk
Activities: Umbrella body, youth, women, newsletter/journal, books, radio, inter-faith,

resources
Traditions: Sunni
Other Languages: Arabic, Urdu, Bengali
Affiliations: Brighton and Hove Inter-faith
Contact Group; The Muslim Council of Europe;
World Muslim League

City, Town or Local Bodies

Banbury Madina Mosque*
Merton Street, Banbury OX16
Tel: (01295) 276662
Contact: Mr Gul Bahar
Position: Chair
Activities: Worship, resource, umbrella body, visits,
youth, elderly
Traditions: Sunni
Other Languages: Urdu, Punjabi, Arabic

Basingstoke Muslim Welfare Association*
26 Alexandra Road, Basingstoke RG21 7RG
Tel: (01256) 816758
Contact: Mukhtar Hamid Siddiqui
Position: Chairman
Contact Tel: (01256) 816758
Activities: Youth, elderly, women
Traditions: Sunni
Other Languages: Urdu, Bengali, French,
Turkish, Gujarati and Arabic

Brighton Mosque and Community Centre*
150 Dyke Road, Brighton BN1 5PA
Tel: (01273) 505247 **Fax:** (01273) 729438
Contact: Abduljalil Sajid
Position: Director
Activities: Worship, resource, media, youth,
women, newsletter
Other Languages: Arabic, Urdu, Bengali, Punjabi
Affiliations: Sussex Muslim Society; British
Muslim Council; Union of Muslim Organisations;
Imams and Mosques Council

Madina Masjid Al-Medina Mosque*
24 Bedford Place, Brighton BN1 2PT
Tel: (01273) 737721

Students Islamic Society and Mosque*
c/o Students Union, University of Sussex, Falmer,
Brighton BN 9QF
Tel: (01273) 606755
Contact: Theresa Davis
Contact Tel: (01273) 678217

Camberley Islamic Centre*
282 London Road, Camberley GU15
Tel: (01276) 670717
Contact: Mr L Kareen
Position: Chairperson
Contact Tel: (01252) 334084

Kent Islamic Centre Mosque*
22a Chatham Hill, Chatham ME5 7AA
Tel: (01634) 831673
Contact: Mr Nural Haque
Position: Chairman

Anjuman ul Muslameen Limited*
163 Bellingdon Road, Chesham HP5 2NN
Tel: (01494) 772065
Contact: Zafar Ali Raja
Position: Chairman
Activities: Worship, resource
Traditions: Sunni
Other Languages: Punjabi, Urdu
Affiliations: Chesham Mosque

Crawley Islamic Centre and Mosque*
157 London Road, Langley Green, Crawley
RH10 9TA
Tel: (01293) 528488
Activities: Worship
Traditions: Sunni
Other Languages: Punjabi, Urdu

Crawley Mosque (Jamiat-ul-muslemeen)*
Broadwood Rise, Broadfield, Crawley RH11 9SE
Tel: (01293) 553070 **Fax:** (01293) 518713
Contact: Mohammed Kadri
Position: Chairman
Contact Tel: (01293) 518713
Activities: Worship/practice/meditation, education
Traditions: Sunni
Other Languages: Urdu, Gujarati, Arabic, Pushto

Eastbourne Islamic Cultural Centre*
Ashford Square, Eastbourne BN21 3TX
Tel: (01323) 638755 Fax: (01323) 638755
Contact: Dr Taleb Dugahee
Position: Secretary
Activities: Worship, resource, visits, youth, elderly,
women
Traditions: Sunni
Movements: Tablighi Jamaat
Other Languages: French, Urdu, Bengali, Arabic

Wessex Shi'a 'Ithna Asheri Jamaat*
Al Mahdi, Wickham Road, Fareham PO17 5BU
Tel: (01329) 832537 **Fax:** (023) 9286 4872
Email: info@almahdi.org.uk
Website: http://www.almahdi.org.uk/
Contact: Mr Versi
Position: President
Contact Tel: (023) 9229 1728
Contact Email: sibtain@versi.co.uk
Activities: Worship/practice/meditation, youth,
elderly, women, newsletter/journal, books, visits,
inter-faith, resources
Traditions: 'Ithna Asheri
Other Languages: Swahili, Farsi, Arabic, Gujarati
Affiliations: Council of European Jamaats; World
Federation of Khoja Shi'a 'Ithna Asheri Muslim
Communities

Folkstone Mosque*
8a Ford Road South, Folkstone
Tel: (01303) 254562
Contact: M M Alam
Position: Secretary

Gillingham Mosque*
114 Canterbury Street, Gillingham ME7 5UH
Tel: (01634) 850878
Contact: Khilzar Hayat Khan-Lodhi
Position: Secretary General
Activities: Worship, resource, visits, youth, elderly,
women
Traditions: Sunni
Other Languages: Urdu, Arabic, Punjabi,
Kiswahili

Kent Muslim Welfare Association (KMWA)*
114 Canterbury Street, Gillingham ME7 5UH
Tel: (01634) 850878
Contact: Syed Ikram Ali
Position: Chief Spokesman
Activities: Worship, youth, elderly, women
Traditions: Sunni

Gravesend and Dartford Muslim Association*
11 Albion Terrace, Gravesend DA12 2SX
Tel: (01474) 351336
Contact: Mr M E Aslam
Position: Chairman
Contact Tel: (01474) 364899
Activities: Community centre
Traditions: Sunni
Movements: Barelwi
Other Languages: Urdu

**Jamia Rehmania Educational and Cultural
Trust***
103 Rutland Avenue, Castlefield, High Wycombe
HP12 3JQ
Tel: (01494) 539406 **Fax:** (01494) 539406
Contact: Mr K B Rehman
Position: Chairman
Contact Tel: (01494) 523881
Activities: Worship/practice/meditation
Other Languages: Urdu, Arabic
Affiliations: W.D.C, B.C. Council.

**Wycombe Islamic Mission and Mosque Trust
Ltd**
34 Jubilee Road, High Wycombe HP11 2PG
Tel: (01494) 520807
Contact: Mr Mohammed Hanif
Position: Secretary
Activities: Worship, resource, inter-faith
Traditions: Sunni
Movements: Barelwi
Other Languages: Urdu, Punjabi, Arabic
Affiliations: Union of Muslim Organisations

Wycombe Islamic Society*
16-17 Portland House, Arnison Avenue, Totteridge,
High Wycombe HP13 6DQ
Tel: (01494) 539693
Email: inform-wise@mail.com
Website: http://www.wise-web.org.uk/
Contact: Mr Amjad Iqbal
Position: Secretary
Contact Email: abushuait@hotmail.com
Activities: Worship/practice/meditation, youth,
women, resources
Traditions: Sunni
Other Languages: Urdu, Arabic, Punjabi

Hitchin Mosque and Islamic Centre*
28 Florence Street, Hitchin SG5 1QZ
Tel: (01462) 456478
Contact: Rashid Ali
Position: President
Contact Tel: (01462) 433927
Activities: Worship/practice/meditation
Traditions: Sunni

Brighton Islamic Mission*
8 Caburn Road, Hove BN3 6EF
Tel: (01273) 722438 **Fax:** (01273) 722438
Email: ajsajid@hotmail.com
Contact: Dr Imam Abduljalil Sajid
Position: Director
Contact Tel: (07971) 861972

Contact Email: ajsajid@ibelieve.co.uk
Activities: Youth, women, newsletters, books,
inter-faith
Other Languages: Arabic, Urdu, Bengali, Punjabi
Affiliations: Muslim Council of Britain; Union of
Muslim Organisations; Imams and Mosques
Council; World Muslim League

Muslim Ladies Circle*
Sussex Muslim Society, 8 Caburn Road, Hove
BN3 6EF
Tel: (01273) 722438 **Fax:** (01273) 722438
Email: ajsajid@hotmail.com
Contact: Mrs Jamila Sajid
Position: Chair
Activities: Resource, women, books, inter-faith
Traditions: Sunni
Movements: Ahl-e-Hadith, Deobandi/Jamati-i-
Islami
Other Languages: Urdu, Bengali, Arabic, Punjabi
Affiliations: The Sussex Muslim Society; Council
of British Muslims; Union of Muslim
Organisations; World Muslim League

Muslim Marriage Guidance Council
8 Caburn Road, Hove BN3 6EF
Tel: (01275) 722438

Shahjalal Masjid*
252 Portland Road, Hove BN3 5QT
Tel: (01273) 323990
Contact: Abdulla Al Mahmood
Position: Imam
Contact Tel: (01273) 418172
Traditions: Sunni
Other Languages: Bengali

Islamic Trust (Maidenhead)*
The Mosque and Islamic Centre, Holmanleaze,
Maidenhead SL6 8AW
Tel: (01628) 629423
Contact: Mr Fazal Awan
Position: Chairman
Contact Tel: (01753) 822880
Activities: Worship/practice/meditation,
community centre, youth, visits, inter-faith,
resources
Traditions: Sunni
Other Languages: Punjabi, Urdu
Affiliations: Union of Muslim Organisations

Mosque and Meeting Hall*
Holmaneaze, Maidenhead SL6 8AW
Contact: Fazal Awan

Position: Chairman
Contact Tel: (01753) 822880
Activities: Worship/practice/meditation
Other Languages: Urdu, Punjabi
Affiliations: Union Of Muslim Organisations,
National Association Of British Pakistanis

Community and Islamic Centre*
20-28 Mote Road, Maidstone ME15 6ES
Tel: (01622) 759973
Contact: M S Usmani

Margate Mosque*
14-20 Athelstan Road, Cliftonville, Margate
CT9 2BA
Tel: (01843) 220862 **Fax:** (01843) 220862
Email: margatemosque@yahoo.com
Contact: Mr Ijaz
Position: Khadim
Activities: Worship/practice/meditation
Other Languages: Arabic, Urdu, Persian

Central Jamia Mosque and Islamic Educational and Pakistani Community Centre*
14-16 Church Street, Wolverton, Milton Keynes
MK12 5JN
Tel: (01908) 221341
Contact: Mr Raja Sarfraz Hussain
Position: General Secretary
Contact Tel: (07730) 825062
Activities: Worship/practice/meditation,
community centre, visits
Traditions: Sunni
Other Languages: Urdu, Punjabi, Arabic

Milton Keynes Granby (Shi'a) Mosque*
Peverel Drive, Granby, Bletchley, Milton Keynes
MK1 1NL
Tel: (01908) 502568 **Fax:** (01908) 660699
Contact: Mr Dalal

Milton Keynes Jamee Masjid*
48-52 Duncombe Street, Bletchley, Milton Keynes
MK2 2LY
Tel: (01908) 367758
Contact: Mr Kalamdar Ali
Position: Secretary
Activities: Worship/practice/meditation, youth,
elderly
Traditions: Sunni
Movements: Deobandi, Tablighi Jamaat, Tassawuf
Other Languages: Bengali, Arabic, Urdu

Bangladeshi Islamic Education Centre and Mosque*
57 Cowley Road, Oxford OX4 1HR
Tel: (01865) 793118
Contact: Mr L Rahman

Islamic Books*
62 Kelburn Road, Oxford OX4 2SH
Tel: (01865) 777951
Contact: Sheikh Ahmad Bullock

Madina Mosque and Muslim Welfare House*
2 Stanley Road, Cowley, Oxford OX4 1QZ
Tel: (01865) 243142
Contact: Secretary
Activities: Worship, resource, visits, youth, elderly, women
Traditions: Sunni
Other Languages: Arabic, Urdu, Pushto, Punjabi

Oxford Centre for Islamic Studies*
George Street, Oxford OX1 2AR
Tel: (01865) 278730 **Fax:** (01865) 248942
Email: islamic.studies@oxcis.ac.uk
Website: http://www.oxcis.ac.uk
Contact: Dr Basil Mustafa
Position: Bursar
Other Languages: Arabic, Urdu, French, Latin

Oxford Mosque Society*
10-11 Bath Street, St Clements, Oxford OX4 1AY
Tel: (01865) 245547
Contact: Chairman
Traditions: Sunni
Other Languages: Punjabi, Urdu, Pushto

Portsmouth Jamia Mosque and Islamic Centre*
73-75 Marmion Road, Southsea, Portsmouth PO5 2AX
Tel: (023) 9283 2541
Contact: Secretary
Activities: Worship, youth, women

Masjidu Allah and Muslim Association Thanet
44 Grange Road, Ramsgate CT11 9LP

Anjuman Muhibban-e-Rasool*
15 Bulmershe Road, Reading RG1 5RH
Tel: (0118) 9012313
Contact: Raja Mohammed Banaras
Position: Trustee
Contact Tel: (07788) 728382
Activities: Worship, resource, visits, youth, elderly
Traditions: Sunni

Movements: Barelwi
Other Languages: Urdu, Punjabi

Central Jamme Mosque*
18a Waylen Street, Reading RG1 7UR
Tel: (0118) 9508860 **Fax:** (0118) 9507335
Email: harunur@zoom.co.uk
Contact: Rashid Harunur
Position: Community Officer
Contact Tel: (07867) 792238
Contact Email: rashid61@fsnet.co.uk
Activities: Worship/practice/meditation, youth, elderly, resources
Traditions: Sunni
Other Languages: Bangladeshi, Urdu, Gujarati

Jamia Khulafa-e-Rashidin and Haq Char-yar Islamic Centre*
2a Valentia Road, Reading RG30 1DL
Tel: (0118) 956618
Contact: Iman M A Qari
Position: Chair and Trustee
Activities: Worship, resource, media, visits, youth, elderly
Traditions: Sunni
Movements: Deobandi, Tablighi Jamaat, Tassawuf
Other Languages: Urdu, English, Arabic, Punjabi

Jamiat Ahl-e-Hadith (Reading Branch)*
31 Cumberland Road, Reading RG1 3LB
Tel: (0118) 9669247
Contact: Mr R A Mir
Position: Chair
Activities: Worship/practice/meditation, community centre, youth, elderly, women, visits, resources
Traditions: Sunni
Movements: Ahl-e-Hadith
Other Languages: Urdu, Punjabi, Arabic
Affiliations: Reading Council for Racial Equality

Masjid Committee*
46 Alexandra Road, Reading RG1 5PF
Tel: (0118) 9261565
Contact: Mr A Q Khan
Position: Chairman
Contact Tel: (0118) 9267767
Activities: Worship/practice/meditation, central body, visits, inter-faith
Traditions: Sunni
Movements: Tablighi Jamaat
Other Languages: Punjabi, Urdu

Reading Islamic Centre and I M Ghausia*
50/52 South Street, Reading RG1 4QU
Tel: (0118) 9504756 **Fax:** (01189) 560262
Contact: Haji M Banaras
Position: General Secretary
Contact Tel: (01189) 560262
Activities: Worship, resource
Traditions: Sunni
Movements: Barelwi, Ahl-e-Sunnat-Wal-Jamat
Other Languages: Urdu, Punjabi, Bengali, Arabic

Islamic Centre Redhill*
30 Earlswood Road, Redhill RH1 6HW
Contact: Zulfiqar Khan Noon
Position: President
Contact Tel: (01737) 763578
Activities: Worship/practice/meditation,
community centre, visits, inter-faith
Traditions: Sunni
Movements: Barelwi
Other Languages: Urdu
Affiliations: Union of Muslims Organisations

East Sussex Islamic Association*
Masjid-Al-Haque, Mercatoria, St Leonards-on-Sea
TN38 0EB
Tel: (01424) 426232
Contact: Dr Tariq Yusuf Rajbee
Position: Founder Trustee
Contact Tel: (01424) 744355
Activities: Worship/practice/meditation,
community centre, women, visits
Traditions: Sunni
Movements: Ahle Jama' Wal Sunnah
Other Languages: Arabic, Bengali, Urdu

Islamic Information Centre*
38 Little Ridge Avenue, St Leonards-on-Sea
TN37 7LS
Tel: (01424) 755355 **Fax:** (01424) 755560
Email: tariqrajbee@hotmail.com
Contact: Ayhan Ogretici
Position: Chairman
Contact Tel: (01424) 812727
Activities: Visits, inter-faith, resources
Traditions: Sunni
Movements: Ahle-Sunnah wal Jamaa
Other Languages: Hindi
Affiliations: Al Qur'an Society, London;
International Council of Islamic Information

Jamia Masjid and Islamic Centre*
83 Stoke Poges Lane, Slough SL1 3NY
Tel: (01753) 522561

Contact: Muhammad Latif Khan
Position: Secretary
Activities: Worship, resource, visits
Traditions: Sunni
Other Languages: Urdu, Punjabi

Slough Islamic Trust*
78 Diamond Road, Slough SL1 1RX
Tel: (01753) 521179
Contact: Mr Abdel
Position: Trustee
Activities: Worship, resource, visits, inter-faith
Traditions: Sunni
Movements: Barelwi
Other Languages: Punjabi, Urdu

Slough Mosque Committee*
35 Ragstone Road, Slough SL1 2PP

UK Islamic Mission*
106 St Pauls Avenue, Slough SL2 5ER
Tel: (01753) 520607
Contact: M Asghar
Position: Vice President
Other Languages: Urdu

**Southampton Medina Mosque Trust and
Community Centre***
Compton Walk, off St Mary's Road, Southampton
S014 0BH
Tel: (023) 8023 2101
Contact: Rashid Brora
Position: Secretary
Activities: Worship, resource, visits, youth, elderly,
women
Other Languages: Urdu, Punjabi

Southampton Mosque Trust*
189 Northumberland Road, Southampton
S014 0EP
Tel: (023) 8063 5941 **Fax:** (023) 8022 6500
Email: zahmed5280@aol.com
Contact: Zahir Ahmed
Position: Secretary
Contact Tel: (023) 8033 1560
Activities: Worship, visits, youth
Traditions: Sunni
Other Languages: Urdu, Punjabi, Bangladeshi,
Arabic

UK Islamic Mission, Southampton*
186 Priory Road, St Denys, Southampton
S017 2HS
Tel: (023) 8058 4798

Contact: Wasim Darr
Position: President
Activities: Central body, youth, visits, inter-faith, resources
Traditions: Sunni
Movements: Jamaat-i-Islami
Other Languages: Urdu, Punjabi

Tunbridge Wells Islamic Cultural Centre*
99 Camden Road, Tunbridge Wells TN1 2QR
Tel: (01892) 532420
Contact: Mr Paracha
Position: Secretary

Southend Muslim Association*
The Mosque, Westborough Road, Westcliff-on-Sea SS0 7JP
Tel: (01582) 347265 **Fax:** (01702) 344165
Contact: Abdul Hasanayn
Position: Secretary
Contact Tel: (01702) 347265
Activities: Resources
Other Languages: Urdu

Southend Young Muslim Organisation*
c/o Southend Islamic Trust, 191-197 West Road, Westcliff-on-Sea SS0 9DH
Tel: (01702) 347265 **Fax:** (01702) 344165
Contact: Iqbal Awan
Position: Co-ordinator
Contact Tel: (01702) 347265
Activities: Resources
Other Languages: Urdu

Mosque
14 Wick Drive, Wickford SS12 9AS

Muslim Community Centre*
117 Walton Road, Woking GU21 5DW
Tel: (01483) 771944
Contact: Mr K Razaq
Position: Administrator
Contact Tel: (07950) 975395
Contact Email: khalilrazaq@yahoo.com
Activities: Worship/practice/meditation, community centre, youth
Other Languages: Urdu, Arabic

Shahjahan Mosque*
149 Oriental Road, Guildford, Woking GU22 7BA
Tel: (01483) 721743
Contact: Pir M Ijaz Qadri
Position: Imam and Director

Contact Tel: (07957) 271363
Activities: Worship, resource, visits, youth, elderly
Traditions: Sunni
Movements: Razvi-Qadri
Other Languages: English, Urdu, Punjabi, Arabic, Persian, Pushto

Worthing Islamic Social and Welfare Society*
Worthing Islamic Cultural Centre, Ivy Arch Road, Worthing BN14 8BX
Tel: (01903) 215163
Contact: Ali Abdul Rahman
Position: Chairman
Contact Tel: (01903) 210192
Activities: Worship, visitors, youth, elderly
Traditions: Sunni
Other Languages: Bengali, Urdu, Arabic

SOUTH WEST
Regional or County Bodies

Aashyana Housing Association Ltd*
429 Stapleton Road, Eastville, Bristol BS5 6NA
Tel: (0117) 9393911 **Fax:** (0117) 9393922
Email: housingenquiries@aashyana.fednet.org.uk
Website: http://www.aashyanahousing.com/
Contact: Mr Saeed Anwar
Position: Director
Contact Email:
saeed.anwar@aashyana.fednet.org.uk
Other Languages: Urdu, Punjabi, Bangla
Affiliations: National Housing Federation

City, Town or Local Bodies

Bath Islamic Centre and Mosque*
8 Pierrepont Street, Bath BA1 1LA
Tel: (01225) 460922
Email: bath_islamic_centre@yahoo.com
Contact: Rashad Ahmad Azami
Position: Director and Imam
Activities: Worship, resource, visits, youth
Other Languages: Arabic, Malay, Urdu, Bengali

Bath University Islamic Society*
Students Union, Bath University, Claverton Down, Bath BA2 8AY
Tel: (01225) 826826
Contact: Charlie Slack
Position: Administrator
Contact Tel: (01225) 323994

Bournemouth Islamic Centre and Central Mosque*
4 St Stephen's Road, Bournemouth BH8 8LF
Tel: (01202) 557072 **Fax:** (01202) 298681
Email: biccm@talk21.com
Contact: Mr Majid Yasin
Position: Director
Activities: Worship/practice/meditation, community centre, youth, women, visits, resources
Traditions: Sunni
Other Languages: Arabic, Turkish, Urdu, Bengali

Bristol Islamic Schools Trust*
31 Banner Road, Montpelier, Bristol BS6 5NA
Tel: (0117) 9523215 **Fax:** (0117) 9523215
Contact: Dr G Nounnu
Position: Chairman
Contact Tel: (07980) 843642
Activities: Resources
Affiliations: ACT, MCB, BREC

Bristol Jamia Mosque*
Green Street, Totterdown, Bristol BS3 4UB
Tel: (0117) 9770944
Contact: Secretary
Activities: Worship/practice/meditation, inter-faith
Traditions: Sunni
Other Languages: Urdu, Punjabi, Bengali, Gujarati
Affiliations: Union of Muslim Organisations

Bristol Muslim Cultural Society*
Unit 10, 42 Chelsea Road, Easton, Bristol BS6 6HY
Tel: (0117) 9392559 **Fax:** (0117) 9392559
Email: bmcs@bmcs.org.uk
Website: http://www.bmcs.org.uk/
Contact: Javaid Sarwar
Position: Link Officer
Activities: Resource, visits, inter-faith
Traditions: Sunni
Other Languages: Urdu, Punjabi
Affiliations: Bristol Council of Mosques; UK Council of Mosques

Bristol University Islamic Society*
c/o Students Union, Queen's Road, Bristol BS8 1LN
Email: islamicsoc_bristol@hotmail.com
Contact: Mr Naveed Mohammed
Position: Chair
Contact Tel: (0117) 3177484

Contact Email: nameon@yahoo.com
Activities: Worship/practice/meditation, youth, resources
Traditions: Sunni
Movements: Ahl-e-Hadith
Other Languages: Arabic, Urdu
Affiliations: FOSIS (Federation of Student Islamic Societies)

Easton Islami Darasoah*
2 Roman Road, Easton, Bristol BS5 6DA
Tel: (0117) 9510156
Contact: Malik Ahmad Khan
Position: President
Contact Tel: (0117) 9793996
Activities: Worship/practice/meditation
Traditions: Sunni
Other Languages: Urdu

Easton Masjid*
St Marks Road, Easton, Bristol BS5 6JH
Tel: (0117) 9510317
Contact: Khizar Hayat Malik
Position: Secretary
Contact Tel: (0117) 9522062
Activities: Worship, visits, inter-faith
Traditions: Sunni
Movements: Jamati-i-Islami
Other Languages: Urdu, Punjabi

Islami Darasgah Bristol*
109 Lower Cheltenham Place, Montpelier, Bristol BS6 5LA
Contact: Mr Tahir Mahmood
Position: Gen Secretary
Activities: Worship/practice/meditation
Traditions: Sunni
Movements: Barelwi
Other Languages: Punjabi, Urdu

Islamic Information Centre*
460 Stapleton Road, Eastville, Bristol BS5 6PA
Tel: (0117) 902 0037
Email: info@islamicinformationcentre.co.uk.
Website: http://www.islamicinformationcentre.co.uk./
Contact: Mr Majeed Kari
Position: Priest
Activities: Resources
Other Languages: Urdu, Bengali

Taleem-ul-Islam Trust*
28 Chelsea Park, Easton, Bristol BS5 6AG

Tel: (0117) 9558155
Contact: Javed Yousuf
Position: Trustee
Activities: Youth
Traditions: Sunni
Movements: Ahl-e-Hadith
Other Languages: Urdu, Punjabi, Bengali, Somalian

Masjid Al Madina - Bangladeshi Community Centre*
25 Sherbourne Place, Cheltenham GL52 2RP
Tel: (01242) 237992
Contact: S Shamsul
Position: Imam

Mosque and Muslim Association*
416-418 High Street, Cheltenham GL50 3JA
Tel: (01242) 695410
Contact: Mr Hasib Bakawala
Position: Secretary
Contact Tel: (01242) 695410
Contact Email: hasib@cablenet.co.uk
Activities: Worship/practice/meditation, community centre, youth, women, resources
Traditions: Sunni
Other Languages: Gujarati, Urdu

Mosque and Islamic Centre*
12-13 York Road, Exeter EX4 6PG
Tel: (01392) 250597
Activities: Worship/practice/meditation

Gloucester Muslim Welfare Association Ltd*
Masjid-e-Noor, 44-46 Ryecroft Street, Tredworth, Gloucester GL1 4LY
Tel: (01452) 416830
Contact: Mr Yakub Patel
Position: Honorary President
Activities: Worship, resource, visits, youth, elderly, women
Traditions: Sunni
Movements: Deobandi, Tablighi Jamaat
Other Languages: Gujarati, Urdu, Bengali
Affiliations: Union of Muslim Organisations; Muslim World League

Jamia Mosque and Gloucester Islamic Trust
All Saints Road, Gloucester GL1 4EE
Tel: (01452) 506870

Khoja Shi'a Muslim Community of Gloucester*
Wainsbridge, 69 Bristol Road, Quedgeley, Gloucester GL2 6NE

Tel: (01452) 530337
Contact: Mr Gulam Musa
Position: Vice President
Traditions: Shi'a 'Ithna Asheri
Other Languages: Urdu, Gujarati

Mosque and Muslim Welfare Association*
44-46 Ryecroft Street, Tredworth, Gloucester GL1 4LY
Tel: (01452) 416830 **Fax:** (01452) 396002
Email: info@gmwa.org.uk
Contact: Ismail Y Ginwalla
Position: Honorary Secretary
Contact Tel: (01452) 416830
Contact Email: ismailg@glos-city.gov.uk
Activities: Worship, visits, newsletter, inter-faith
Traditions: Sunni
Other Languages: Gujarati, Urdu, Punjabi, Bengali, Arabic, Hindi
Affiliations: Union of Muslim Organisations in UK and Eire; Muslim World League

Hazrat Shah Jabl Mosque and Bangladesh Islamic Centre
Swindon
Tel: (01793) 511051

Islamic Awareness and Education Project*
Bentley Centre, Stratton Road, Swindon SN1 2SH
Tel: (01793) 511520 **Fax:** (01793) 513002
Email: iaep@dial.pipex.com
Website: http://www.islam4schools.com/
Contact: Mr Hassan Morrison
Position: Education Officer
Activities: Worship/practice/meditation, resources

Mosque*
124-125 Broad Street, Swindon SN1 2DR
Tel: (01793) 523831
Activities: Worship

Thamesdown Islamic Association*
12 Don Close, Green Meadow, Swindon SN25 3LS
Tel: (01793) 523831
Contact: Khan Ahmad Nawaz
Position: Secretary
Contact Tel: (01793) 693569
Activities: Worship, resource, visits, youth, inter-faith
Traditions: Sunni
Other Languages: Urdu, Punjabi, Bangali
Affiliations: Union of Muslim Organisations; Islamic Cultural Centre, London; Muslim World League

Torbay Islamic Centre and Mosque*
130 Avenue Road, Torquay TQ2 5LQ
Tel: (01803) 211818 **Fax:** (01803) 200522
Email: yainassar@talk21.com
Website: http://www.torbayislamiccentre.co.uk/
Contact: Mr Y A Al-Nassar
Position: Trustee
Contact Tel: (01803) 215135
Activities: Worship/practice/meditation
Traditions: Sunni
Other Languages: Arabic, Bangladeshi

South Somerset Muslim Cultural Association*
Hillside Syed House, Mudford, Yeovil BA21 5SD
Tel: (01935) 479086
Contact: Mr S T Ali
Position: President
Activities: Worship/practice/meditation, youth, women
Traditions: Sunni
Other Languages: Bengali, Urdu, Farsi, Arabic

NORTHERN IRELAND

Regional or County Bodies

Belfast Islamic Centre*
38 Wellington Park, Belfast BT9 6DN
Tel: (028) 9066 4465 **Fax:** (028) 9066 4465
Email: jamaliweida@hotmail.com
Contact: Jamal Iweida
Position: President
Contact Tel: (028) 9020 5371
Activities: Worship/practice/meditation, community centre, youth, women, visits, inter-faith, resources
Other Languages: Urdu, Arabic, Bengali, Punjabi

SCOTLAND

Scottish National Bodies

United Muslim Organisations of Scotland*
26 Bank Street, Glasgow G12 8ND
Tel: (0141) 3395513 **Fax:** (0141) 3575554
Contact: Dr M.S.Kausar
Position: General Secretary
Activities: Resource, umbrella body, inter-faith
Other Languages: Urdu, Punjabi, Bengali

Central Scotland Islamic Centre*
Burghmuir Road, Stirling FK7 7NZ
Tel: (01786) 474324
Contact: Mr Mohammed Azad
Position: General Secretary
Contact Tel: (07973) 846334
Activities: Worship/practice/meditation, community centre, youth, visits
Traditions: Sunni
Movements: Ahl-e-Hadith, Barelwi, Deobandi, Jamati-i-Islami, Tablighi Jamaat, Tassawuf
Other Languages: Urdu

City, Town or Local Bodies

Mosque and Islamic Association of Aberdeen*
164 Spital, Aberdeen AB24 3JD
Tel: (01224) 493764 **Fax:** (01224) 403764
Contact: Dr Ruhul Amin
Position: Imam
Activities: Resource, visits, youth, women, newsletters, inter-faith
Traditions: Sunni
Other Languages: Urdu, Arabic, Malay, Bengali

Jamia Masjid Tajdar-e-Madina*
96A Victoria Street, Tayside, Dundee DD1 2NR
Tel: (01382) 24817
Contact: Mr Mohammed Arshad
Position: Chairman
Contact Email: m_hajee@hotmail.com
Activities: Worship/practice/meditation, youth, elderly, visits, resources
Traditions: Sunni
Other Languages: Urdu, Punjabi

Sunni Razvi Mosque and Islamic Centre*
125 Wood Mill Road, Dunfermline KY11
Tel: (01383) 739816
Contact: Mr M Ahmed
Position: Chairman

Heriot-Watt Islamic Society*
Heriot-Watt University, Room 1.11, LLB, Riccarton, Edinburgh EH14 4AS
Tel: (0131) 449 5111 **Fax:** (0131) 4495153
Contact: Hamayun Ahmad
Position: President
Activities: Worship
Traditions: Sunni
Other Languages: Urdu, Arabic

Idara Taleem-ul-Quran Trust*
8-10 Temple Park Crescent, Polwarth, Edinburgh
EH11 1HT
Tel: (0131) 2293844 **Fax:** (0131) 2290329
Email: idara@skybiz.com
Website: http://www.idaratrust.com/
Contact: Hafiz Abdul Hamid
Position: Director
Activities: Worship, resource, visits, youth, women,
inter-faith
Traditions: Sunni
Movements: Deobandi
Other Languages: Urdu, Punjabi, Bengali

Mosque and Islamic Centre*
50 Potter Row, Edinburgh EH8 9BT
Tel: (0131) 6670140 **Fax:** (0151) 6684245
Website: http://www.edmosque.com
Contact: Abdul Rahman Al Matrodi
Position: Director
Contact Tel: (0131) 6671777
Activities: Worship/practice/meditation

**Sarajia Islamic Studies And Community
Centre***
5 Whitburn Road, Bathgate, Edinburgh EH48 1HE
Tel: (01506) 635380 **Fax:** (01506) 635305
Contact: Mohammad Ajmal Tariq
Position: Secretary

Falkirk Islamic Centre*
8 Burnhad Lane, Falkirk FK1 1UG
Tel: (01324) 611018
Contact: Mr A Farooqi

Ahl Al-Bait Society*
25 Woodside Place, Glasgow G3 7QL
Tel: (0141) 5641105 **Fax:** (0141) 5641105
Email: ahlalbaitglasgow@hotmail.com
Contact: Director
Traditions: 'Ithna Asheri
Other Languages: Arabic

Dawat-ul-Islam Mosque*
31 Oakfield Avenue, Glasgow G12 8LL
Tel: (0141) 3573733
Contact: President
Activities: Resources
Other Languages: Bengali, Urdu

**Glasgow University Muslim Students
Association***
c/o SRC Glasgow University, University Avenue,
Glasgow G12 8QQ

Tel: (0141) 379 8541
Contact: Zakariyya Abdel-Hady
Position: President
Activities: Resource, youth, women, newsletters,
inter-faith
Traditions: Sunni
Other Languages: Urdu, Arabic, Malay

Islamic Society of Britain (Glasgow)*
16 Queens Crescent, Woodlands, Glasgow G4 9BL
Tel: (0141) 3572610 **Fax:** (0141) 3396261
Email: zakariya@hotmail.com
Contact: Dr Zakariyya Abdel-Hady
Position: President
Activities: Resource, media, visits, youth, women,
newsletters
Traditions: Sunni
Other Languages: Urdu, Arabic, Punjabi, Bengali
Affiliations: Islamic Society of Britain (Scotland);
Islamic Society Of Britain

**Jamiat Ittihad-ul-Muslimin, Glasgow Islamic
Centre and Central Mosque***
Mosque Avenue, Gorbals, Glasgow G5 9TX
Tel: (0141) 4293132 **Fax:** (0141) 4297171
Contact: Mr M T Shaheem
Position: President
Activities: Worship, resource, visits, youth, elderly,
women
Traditions: Sunni
Movements: Deobandi
Other Languages: Urdu, Punjabi, Arabic

**Khazra Central Mosque and World Islamic
Mission***
138 Butter Biggins Road, Glasgow G42 7AF
Tel: (0141) 4221154
Contact: Maulana Mohammad F Quadri
Position: Director
Activities: Worship/practice/meditation,
community centre, central body, youth, elderly,
women, newsletter/journal, visits, inter-faith,
resources
Traditions: Sunni
Movements: Barelwi, Tassawuf
Other Languages: Arabic, Urdu, Punjabi

Madrasa Alarabia al-Islamia*
490 Paisley Road West, Ibrox, Glasgow G51 1PY
Tel: (0141) 4272152
Contact: Mohammed Arif
Position: Trustee
Contact Tel: (0141) 429 7741
Other Languages: Urdu

Madrasa Taleem-ul-Islam*

161 Nithsdale Road, Pollokshields, Glasgow
G41 5QS
Tel: (0141) 4240787
Contact: Mr Mohammad Ashraf
Position: Secretary
Activities: Worship, resource, visits
Traditions: Sunni
Other Languages: Urdu, Arabic

Madrassa Zia-ul-Quran*

257 Kenmure Street, Pollockshields, Glasgow
G41 2NN
Tel: (0141) 4238001
Contact: Mr S H Rabbani
Position: Chair
Contact Tel: (0141) 4292483
Activities: Worship/practice/meditation
Traditions: Sunni
Movements: Barelwi
Other Languages: Urdu, Punjabi

Masjid al Furqan*

19 Carrington Street, Glasgow G4 9AJ
Tel: (0141) 3322811 **Fax:** (0141) 3322811
Contact: Haq Mawaz Ghani
Position: President

Masjid Noor*

79 Forth Street, Pollockshield, Glasgow G41 2TA
Tel: (0141) 4293383 **Fax:** (0141) 4180632
Contact: Khaliq-uz-Zaman Ansari
Position: Secretary
Activities: Worship, resource
Traditions: Sunni
Movements: Tablighi Jamaat
Other Languages: Urdu, Punjabi
Affiliations: Islamic Reform Centre; Anjuman-e-
Islamul Muslimeen of UK

Masjid Wal Madrassa Al-Farooq Glasgow*

32-38 Dixon Avenue, Crosshill, Glasgow G42 8EJ
Tel: (0141) 4332686
Contact: Mohmmad Idrees
Position: Imam

Muslim House*

16 Queen Crescent, Glasgow G4 9BL
Tel: (0141) 3310373 **Fax:** (0141) 3310373
Website: http://www.muslimhouse.org.uk/
Contact: Mr Bashir Elmedhem
Position: President
Contact Tel: (0141) 5748987
Contact Email: elmedhem@hotmail.com

Activities: Worship/practice/meditation
Other Languages: Arabic, Urdu
Affiliations: Muslim Association Of Britain

Strathclyde University Muslim Students Association (SUMSA)*

c/o The Union, 90 John Street, Glasgow G1 1XQ
Tel: (0141) 5484375
Email: sumsa@strath.ac.uk
Website: http://www.sumsa. co.uk/
Contact: Ibrahim El Farargy
Position: Imam
Contact Tel: (0141) 5484375
Contact Email: ibrahimaf44@hotmail.com
Activities: Worship, resource, youth, women,
newsletter
Other Languages: Arabic, Urdu
Affiliations: Federation of Students Islamic
Societies

UK Islamic Mission (Ladies Section)*

19 Carrington Street, Glasgow G4 9AJ
Tel: (0141) 3311119 **Fax:** (0141) 3322316
Contact: Mrs Shabbir
Position: In Charge of Ladies
Contact Tel: (0141) 5876792
Activities: Worship, resource, media, umbrella
body, visits, youth
Other Languages: Urdu, Punjabi
Affiliations: UK Islamic Mission Branch; Islamic
Society for Britain; Imams and Mosque Council

UK Islamic Mission*

19 Carrington Street, Glasgow G4 9AJ
Tel: (0141) 3311119 **Fax:** (0141) 3322811
Contact: Mr Aziz Khan
Position: General Secretary
Contact Tel: (0141) 5876990
Activities: Worship, resource, visits, youth, women,
inter-faith
Traditions: Sunni
Movements: Jamati-i-Islami
Other Languages: Urdu, English, Arabic

United Muslim Organisation, Strathclyde*

26 Bank Street, Hillhead, Glasgow G12 8ND
Tel: (0141) 3395573 **Fax:** (0141) 3575554
Contact: Dr M S Kauser
Position: Chairperson
Other Languages: Urdu, Punjabi

Young Muslims - Glasgow Branch*

19 Carrington Street, Glasgow G4 9AJ
Tel: (0141) 3322811 **Fax:** (0141) 3322811

Email: sqna@enterprise.net
Contact: Osama
Position: In Charge of Branch
Activities: Youth, women, inter-faith
Other Languages: Urdu, Punjabi
Affiliations: Islamic Society of Britain(Glasgow Branch);Young Muslims UK; Islamic Society of Britain

Fife Islamic Centre (Methil)*
786 Poplar Road, Central, Glenrothes KY7 4AA
Tel: (01592) 612970 **Fax:** (01592) 651920
Contact: Mr Saeed Ahmed
Position: Secretary
Activities: Worship/practice/meditation, youth, elderly, women, newsletter/journal, inter-faith, resources
Traditions: Sunni
Movements: Barelwi
Other Languages: Punjabi, Urdu, Bengali, Sindhi

Fife Islamic Centre (Kirkcaldy)*
Cumbrae Terrace, Kirkcaldy KY2
Tel: (01592) 641057
Contact:
Mohammad Sebir
Position: Secretary

Kirkcaldy Islamic Education and Cultural Society*
24 Boreland Road, Kirkcaldy KY1 2YG
Tel: (01592) 597888
Contact: Panch Bsaya

Livingstone Mosque and Community Centre
1 Craig's Hill, East Road, Livingstone EH5 5DD
Tel: (01506) 31936

Dundee Islamic Centre*
114 Hilltown, Dundee, Tayside DD3
Tel: (01382) 228374
Contact: Mr Ibrahim Okhai
Position: Chairman
Contact Tel: (01382) 622122
Activities: Worship
Traditions: Tablighi Jamaat
Other Languages: Urdu, Punjabi

Dundee Islamic Society*
Miln Street, Dundee, Tayside DD1 5DD
Tel: (01382) 622122 **Fax:** (01382) 622122
Email: iho@rockwell solutions.com
Contact: Mr Ibrahim Okhai
Position: Chairman

Activities: Worship/practice/meditation
Other Languages: Arabic, Urdu

WALES
Regional or County Bodies

South Wales Islamic Centre*
Alice Street, Butetown, Cardiff CF10 5LB
Tel: (02920) 460243 **Fax:** (02920) 460243
Contact: Sheikh Said Hassan Ismail
Position: Secretary
Contact Tel: (029) 2046 0998
Activities: Worship, resource, visits
Traditions: Sunni
Movements: Shafai
Other Languages: Arabic

City, Town or Local Bodies

Islamic Students Society*
University of Wales, Aberystwyth SY23 2AX
Email: scty49@aber.ac.uk
Contact: Mr Al-Huthali
Position: Chair
Contact Tel: (07979) 746894
Activities: Worship/practice/meditation, community centre, youth, inter-faith, resources
Movements: Ahlussunnah wal-jama'ah
Other Languages: Arabic, Urdu

Bangor Islamic Centre*
61 High Street, Bangor LL57 1NR
Tel: (01248) 354612
Contact: Mr Mirwaz Khan
Position: Chairman
Activities: Worship, resource, visits, youth, elderly, women
Traditions: Sunni
Other Languages: Arabic, Urdu, Bangladeshi, Turkish
Affiliations: Muslim Welfare House

Madrassah Ta'leem al-Qur'ann Wal-Sunnah*
3 Vere Street, Barry CF63 2HX
Tel: (01446) 410718 **Fax:** (01446) 411504
Email: sufyan@ntlworld.com
Contact: Mr S Sufyan
Position: Secretary
Activities: Worship/practice/meditation, youth, elderly, women, newsletter/journal
Traditions: Sunni

Other Languages: Urdu, Punjabi, Bangladeshi, Gujarati

Al-Manar Centre Trust and Mosque*
2 Glynrhondda Street, Cardiff CF24 4AN
Tel: (029) 2022 6607 **Fax:** (029) 2022 6650
Email: almanar.a@ukonline.co.uk
Contact: Abdel
Position: Secretary
Activities: Worship/practice/meditation, community centre, youth, women, visits, resources
Other Languages: Arabic

Bilal Mosque*
63 Severn Road, Canton, Cardiff CF11 9EA
Tel: (029) 2039 7640
Contact: Mr M Ishaq
Position: General Secretary
Activities: Worship/practice/meditation, visits, resources
Traditions: Sunni
Movements: Deobandi
Other Languages: Urdu, Punjabi, Pushto, Arabic
Affiliations: UK Racial Equality Council

Canton Mosque and Madresa Talimul Quran*
61-63 Severn Road, off Cowbridge Road, Canton, Cardiff CF11 9EA
Tel: (029) 2039 7640
Contact: Mr Mohammed Is'haq
Position: Secretary
Activities: Worship, resource
Traditions: Sunni
Movements: Deobandi, Tablighi Jamaat
Other Languages: Urdu, Bengali, Arabic
Affiliations: South Wales Council of Mosques; UK Council of Mosques

Cardiff University Islamic Society*
Student Union, Park Place, Cardiff CF10 3QN
Tel: (029) 2078 1400
Email: cuis@cardiff.ac.uk
Website: www.cf.ac.uk/suon/islam
Contact: General Secretary

Dar-ul-Isra, Islamic Ecucation and Welfare Society*
21-23 Wyverne Road, Cathays, Cardiff CF2 3GB
Tel: (029) 2034 4073
Contact: Imam Mushtaq
Position: Imam
Activities: Worship/practice/meditation, community centre, youth, elderly, women
Traditions: Sunni

Other Languages: Urdu, Arabic, Malay
Affiliations: UK Islamic Mission; Muslim Association of Britain

Dar-ul-Isra Mosque*
21 Wyverne Road, Cathays, Cardiff CF24 4BG
Tel: (0292) 0344073
Position: Imam
Contact Tel: (029) 2034 4073
Activities: Worship/practice/meditation
Other Languages: Urdu, Arabic
Affiliations: The UK Islamic Mission

Islamic Shikka Pratisthan*
19 Dulwich Gardens, Llandaff, Cardiff CF5 1SE
Contact: Mr Siraj Ali
Position: President and Treasurer
Activities: Worship/practice/meditation, youth
Traditions: Sunni
Other Languages: Bengali

Madina Mosque
163-167 Woodville Road, Cathays, Cardiff CF24 4NW

Mosque (Islamic Shikka Prophieshtan)*
37 Plantagenet Street, off Tudor Road, Cardiff CF1 8RF
Tel: (01222) 221309
Contact: Mr Liakath Ali
Position: Secretary
Contact Tel: (029) 2022 1309

Muslim Ladies Mosque
Lucas Street, Cardiff CF2 4NZ

Noor-El-Islam Mosque*
17 Maria Street, Butetown, Cardiff CF10 5HH
Tel: (029) 20498435 **Fax:** (029) 20498435
Email: nurel Islam@btinternet.com
Website: http://www.nurelislam.com/
Contact: A Ahmed
Position: Admin/Fundraiser
Contact Tel: (0777) 3494859
Activities: Worship/practice/meditation
Traditions: Sunni
Other Languages: Somali, Arabic

Shah Jalal Mosque and Islamic Cultural Centre*
124 Mynachdy Road, Gabalfa, Cardiff CF4 6HA
Tel: (029) 20480217
Contact: Mr Ali Akbar

UK Islamic Mission*
21 Wyverne Road, Cathays, Cardiff CF24 4BG
Tel: (029) 2387 2157 **Fax:** (029) 2383 1867
Contact: Mr G Raiz
Position: Secretary
Contact Tel: (029) 2041 8164
Activities: Worship/practice/meditation,
community centre, youth, elderly, women,
newsletter/journal, books, visits, resources
Traditions: Sunni
Movements: Jamati-i-Islami
Other Languages: Urdu, Arabic, Punjabi, Pushto

Centre for Islamic Studies*
University of Wales, Lampeter SA48 7YG
Tel: (01570) 424748
Contact: Marlene Ablett
Position: Administrator

Al-Noor Mosque
23a Harrow Road, Newport NP19 0BU
Tel: (01633) 244395
Contact: Mr A R Mujahid

Anjuman Raza-e-Mustafa*
15 Methuen Road, Newport NP19 0BN
Tel: (01633) 665021 **Fax:** (01633) 264803
Contact: Mr A R Mujahid
Position: Chair
Contact Tel: (07970) 856007
Activities: Resource, youth, elderly, women
Traditions: Sunni
Movements: Barelwi
Other Languages: Urdu, Punjabi

East Newport Islamic Cultural Centre*
12 Cedar Road, Mainsee, Newport NP9 0BA
Tel: (01633) 212254
Contact: Maulana Farid Khan
Position: Imam
Activities: Worship/practice/meditation
Other Languages: Bengali, Arabic, Urdu, Parsi

Hussaini Mosque
183-186 Commercial Road, Newport N9 2PF

Islamic Society for Gwent
63 Stow Hill, Newport NP20 4DX

Shahporan Bangladeshi Jam-e Mosque*
51-52 Hereford Street, Newport NP19 8DT
Contact: Alhaj Tahir Ullah
Position: Chairman
Contact Tel: (01633) 243413

Activities: Worship/practice/meditation, youth,
elderly, women, resources
Traditions: Sunni
Other Languages: Bengali, Arabic, Urdu

Imam Khoei Islamic Centre*
88a St Helen's Road, Swansea SA1 4BQ
Tel: (01792) 458372 **Fax:** (01792) 458372
Email: qjalali@yahoo.co.uk
Website: http://www.khoei.org.uk
Contact: Sayyed Qassim Al-Jalali
Position: Imam
Activities: Worship, visits, women
Other Languages: Arabic, Persian
Affiliations: Imam Khoei Foundation

Mosque and Islamic Community Centre
14 St Helens Road, Swansea SA1 4AW
Tel: (01792) 654532

Wrexham Muslim Association*
North East Wales Institute, Wrexham
Tel: (01978) 290606
Email: newimosque@hotmail.com
Contact: Dr F Jishi
Position: Secretary
Contact Tel: (01978) 852691
Contact Email: jishif@hotmail.com
Activities: Worship/practice/meditation
Traditions: Sunni

INTRODUCING SIKHS IN THE UK

SIKHS IN THE UNITED KINGDOM 549

ORIGINS AND DEVELOPMENT OF SIKHISM 550

SOURCES OF SIKH BELIEFS AND PRACTICES 551

KEY SIKH BELIEFS 552

TRADITIONS IN SIKHISM 553

SIKH LIFE 554

SIKH WORSHIP 556

SIKH CALENDAR AND FESTIVALS 558

SIKH ORGANISATIONS 559

FURTHER READING 560

SIKHS IN THE UNITED KINGDOM

Beginnings in the UK

Over eighty per cent of the world's Sikhs live in the Punjab, in the Indian subcontinent. The older Punjab Province was partitioned in 1947 with the end of British rule in the sub-continent, when West Punjab became part of Pakistan and East Punjab part of India. Most Sikhs living in the UK are of Punjabi ethnic origin.

A young Sikh prince called Maharaja Dalip Singh, the son of Maharaja Ranjit Singh, was exiled to the UK and was one of the first Sikhs to reside here. He acquired the Elveden Estate in Norfolk and this place is now frequently visited by Sikhs marking their early connections with the UK. Although a number of Sikhs settled in the UK between the 1920s and the 1940s, the vast majority of Sikh migrants arrived in the 1950s and 1960s.

Many of these came directly to the UK from the Punjab, although a significant minority came from East Africa and other former British colonies to which members of their families had initially migrated. Many Sikhs served in the British Indian armies in the First and Second World Wars and a number of ex-servicemen migrated to Britain, particularly after the Second World War. A few Sikhs in the UK are converts, but conversion to the Sikh religion is not common because Sikhism is not an actively proselytising faith and accords respect to all other faiths.

The Sikh population in the UK is the largest outside the Indian subcontinent. The most substantial communities are to be found in Birmingham, Bradford, Cardiff, Coventry, Glasgow, Leeds, Leicester, Greater London (especially in Southall) and Wolverhampton.

The first *gurdwara* in the UK was opened in Shepherd's Bush in 1911 at the initiative of Sant Teja Singh, and with funding from Maharaja Bhupinder Singh of Patiala. As the size of the UK Sikh population grew, the number of *gurdwaras* increased. The Registrar General's 1999 list of certified places of worship gives 170 *gurdwaras* in England and Wales and this directory records 202 *gurdwaras* in the UK of which 159 are in England and Wales.

Community Languages

Most Sikhs in the UK speak Punjabi and English, with almost all *gurdwaras* running Punjabi classes. *Gurmukhi* is the script of the Sikh Scriptures, which is also used for writing the modern Punjabi language.

Punjabi is held in great esteem and respect by Sikhs who have gone to great efforts to transmit it to second and third generation children. Punjabi speakers can communicate to some degree with Urdu and Hindi speakers as the three languages have some common vocabulary and grammar.

ORIGINS AND DEVELOPMENT OF SIKHISM

The Ten Gurus

Sikhs understand the Sikh *dharam* (the Sikh way of life), also known as *Gurmat* and *Khalsa Panth* (from *Khalsa* meaning "pure ones" and *panth* meaning "community") to be an original, revealed religion. It is based upon the teachings of the ten *Gurus* of Sikhism. The first *Guru* and founder of the faith, *Guru* Nanak Dev (1469-1539) was born in the Punjab at a place called Talwandi, renamed *Nankana Sahib* in his honour, which is now within the territory of the state of Pakistan.

Sikhs believe that *Guru* Nanak Dev was born in an enlightened state. Accounts of his early life illustrate that not only was he a precocious child, but that he also possessed divine charisma. When he was about thirty years old, he received the call to preach God's *Word* and over the next twenty-two years undertook four great journeys called *Udasis*. He is believed to have travelled extensively within and beyond the Indian subcontinent, as far as Assam in the east, Sri Lanka in the south, and the Middle East in the west, including Baghdad and the Muslim holy places of Makka and Madina.

He preached a message of universal love, peace and brotherhood and emphasised worship of the one God. He taught that the worship of God, in whatever tradition one practised it, should be sincere and honest and not clouded by hypocrisy or ritualism. He eventually settled at Kartarpur in the Punjab and founded a community who became known as *Sikhs* (meaning *disciples*, or learners).

Guru Nanak Dev was succeeded by nine other *Gurus*: *Guru* Angad Dev (1504-1552); *Guru* Amar Das (1479-1574); *Guru* Ram Das (1534-1581); *Guru* Arjan Dev (1563-1606); *Guru* Hargobind (1595-1644); *Guru* Har Rai (1631-1661); *Guru* Har Krishan (1656-1664); *Guru* Tegh Bahadur (1622-1675); and *Guru* Gobind Singh (1666-1708). Sikhs believe that the *Gurus* who conveyed God's *Word* were all spiritually one.

In an Indian context, the word *guru* usually refers to a spiritual leader. But among the Sikhs, when applied to their ten *Gurus*, its significance is much greater. The Sikh *Gurus* are seen as the divine teachers and exemplars who conveyed God's *Word*. They are not, however, objects of worship since the *Word* they convey is itself the *Guru*.

After the line of the ten *Gurus*, Sikhism acknowledges no more human *Gurus*. The tenth *Guru*, Guru Gobind Singh, vested spiritual authority in the *Guru Granth Sahib* (the Sikh scripture) and temporal authority in the *Khalsa Panth*. Henceforth, the living *Guru*, the *Guru Granth Sahib*, was to be the eternal *Guru* embodying the Divine word.

In 1699, Guru Gobind Singh instituted *Amrit Pahul* (see below) for both men and women, and in doing so completed the spiritual and temporal structure of the Sikh faith in the form of the *Khalsa Panth*. [See also the section on "the Namdhari Sikhs" in the Chapter on "Some Other Religious Traditions and Groups"].

History

Sikhism has distinctive religious beliefs and institutions together with its own language, literature, tradition and conventions. The early Sikhs faced considerable persecution in the Mughal Empire and later many Sikhs were martyred for their faith. However, the Sikhs in the Punjab eventually emerged as a temporal as well as spiritual community with its own military, economic and governmental structures. It was established as a sovereign nation in 1799 under Maharaja Ranjit Singh and remained so until the advent of the British Raj in the Punjab in 1849.

The Sikh *Gurus* founded several towns including Amritsar and its *Darbar Sahib* (commonly known among non-Sikhs as the Golden Temple) which was developed by *Guru* Arjan Dev who installed the *Guru Granth Sahib* at its centre. *Guru* Hargobind built the *Akal Takhat* (seat of the immortal) in front of the *Darbar Sahib*, declaring it to be the seat of temporal authority. The Sikh sovereign, Maharaja Ranjit Singh, spent lavishly on buildings within its precincts, donating gold and other precious gifts.

SOURCES OF SIKH BELIEFS AND PRACTICES

The Guru Granth Sahib

Sikhs believe that God has revealed himself continuously since before the advent of the ten *Gurus* and since their departure continues to do so by means of the scriptures. The *Guru Granth Sahib* is the most revered of the Sikh scriptures. This is the honorific title for those Sikh scriptures which, in academic usage, are often called *Adi Granth*. *Adi Granth* is also the name of an earlier version of the present scriptures, compiled by *Guru* Arjan Dev and installed by him at Amritsar in 1604. *Ad* or *adi* means "first", in importance, and *Granth* means volume.

This original manuscript version of the *Adi Granth* is often referred to as the *Kartarpuri Birh* (*Birh* meaning version), after the place name of Kartarpur in the Punjab where it is kept. In this manuscript version there are 5551 *shabads* (hymns) set to 30 *rag* (musical compositions) laid out over 975 pages. The *Adi Granth* contains the teaching of the first five *Gurus* and the Bhagat Bani, which contains verses from Hindu and Muslim *saints* which were found to be compatible with Sikh teachings. These were included to underline that divine truth could be perceived by anyone from any nation, creed or caste.

In 1706, at Damdama Sahib, *Guru* Gobind Singh added Guru Tegh Bahadur's *shabads*. In 1708, Guru Gobind Singh bestowed the status of *Guru* upon this *Damdama Birh*. The current *canonical* version of the *Guru Granth Sahib* in its standard modern print version now contains 5817 *shabads* set to 31 *rags*, in 1430 pages.

Dasam Granth

The *Dasam Granth* contains numerous writings of *Guru* Gobind Singh, together with the work of some poets. It was compiled by *Bhai* Mani Singh, who was the *granthi* (reader of the *Granth*) of the *Darbar Sahib* and it was completed in 1734. Both the *Guru Granth Sahib* and the *Dasam Granth* are written in the *Gurmukhi* script.

Rahit Nama

The *Rahit Nama* (*Code of Discipline*) consists of a set of principles according to which a Sikh's way of life should be conducted. They cover spiritual, moral and social discipline, and are reputed to be based on the injunctions of *Guru* Gobind Singh and compiled by various Sikh theologians from the late seventeenth to the late nineteenth century. However, the *Gurbani* (teaching of the *Gurus* - see further below) provides the fundamental guidelines and takes precedence in interpreting and following the *Rahit Nama*.

Rahit Maryada

Rahit Maryada is the *Sikh Code of Conduct* which is published by the Shromani Gurdwara Parbandhak Committee in Amritsar, established in 1920 in the wake of the Gurdwara Reform Movement. Amongst its responsibilities are the organisation and administration (in accordance with Sikh tenets) of a large number of *gurdwaras* in the Punjab, as well as hospitals and educational institutions. The *Code of Conduct* was first drawn up in 1936, but was formally approved and adopted with some amendments in 1945.

Works of Bhai Gurdas and Bhai Nandlal

Although they do not have the same status as the *Guru Granth Sahib* and the *Dasam Granth*, expositions by *Bhai* Gurdas and *Bhai* Nandlal are also highly regarded and are approved for reading and discourse in *gurdwaras*.

Bhai Gurdas (1551-1637CE) was a Sikh scholar and theologian of distinction to whom the fifth *Guru*, Arjan Dev, dictated the *Adi Granth* when it was first compiled. His own thirty-nine *vars* (theological and historical expositions in verse form) were held in very high esteem by the fifth *Guru* who declared that these writings would be a key to the proper understanding of the *Guru Granth Sahib*. Bhai Nandlal (1633-1713) was an eminent scholar and poet who worked in the Mughal Court of the Emperor Aurangzeb. He was a follower of *Guru* Gobind Singh and his writings, which were largely in the Persian language, were on Sikh philosophy.

KEY SIKH BELIEFS

Definitions

In the *Rahit Maryada* (see above) a Sikh is defined as one who believes in *Akal Purakh* (the one immortal God), the ten *Gurus*, the *Guru Granth Sahib* and the *Gurbani* (the teaching of the ten *Gurus* considered as a unity and incorporated in the *Guru Granth Sahib*). The *Gurbani* is also known as *Gurshabad* (or word of the *Guru*) and is believed by Sikhs to be divine guidance. A Sikh also believes in the *Amrit Pahul* (the Sikh form of initiation) of the tenth *Guru* and adheres to no other religion.

God

Sikhs are strictly *monotheistic* (believing in only one God). This one God is known among Sikhs by many names including Ram, Mohan, Gobind, Hari, Nirankar, and others. However, the two names traditionally used in worship, and especially in *Nam Japna* (the recitation of God's name), are *Satnam* (*sat* meaning "true", "real" or "existential" and *nam* meaning "name" or "radiance of the Reality") and *Waheguru* (translated as "Wonderful Lord").

Sikhs believe that God is *nirgun* (transcendent) and also *sargun* (immanent) but that God never becomes incarnate. It is believed that God can be experienced but is beyond human comprehension. The *Mul Mantar*, with which every section of the *Guru Granth Sahib* begins, is a distillation of the fundamental belief of Sikhism that there is only one God: "There is but One God, the Eternal Truth, the Creator, without fear, without enmity, timeless, immanent, beyond birth and death, self-existent: by the grace of the Guru, made known."

Sikhs believe that creation evolved slowly as a result of the creative will of God, developing from lower to higher forms of life: that from air came water, from water came the lower forms of life, leading to plants, birds and animals and culminating in humans as the supreme form of created life on earth.

Goal of Life

Guru Nanak Dev taught that everything which exists or happens ultimately does so within God's will and that nothing exists or occurs outside of it. This concept of the divine order or will is known as *hukam*. The purpose of a human life is understood as being to seek its creator and to merge with God, thus breaking the cycle of birth and death. The highest form of life on this earth is the human one.

Since human beings are conscious of their actions and the consequences of them, a human life is therefore the time when the cycle of transmigration can potentially be broken. The *karam* (actions and their consequences) of this life partly determine whether a person will achieve union with God. Failure to do so leads to the cycle of *rebirth* which may include lower forms of life than human. Liberation from rebirth is known as *mukti*.

Barriers to the liberation of the soul are believed to include *maya* which is seen as an illusory, materialistic view of the world, producing ignorance of one's own true nature and destiny and of God's will. This results in *haumai* (self-centredness), giving rise to *kam* (lust), *karodh* (anger), *lobh* (greed), *moh* (worldly attachment/obsessions) and *hankar* (pride), all of which block union with God. One must therefore overcome these barriers, developing instead *santokh* (contentment), *dan* (charity), *daya* (kindness), *parsanta* (happiness) and *nimarta* (humility).

The path to union with God is seen as having five stages: *Dharam Khand* (the region of realising one's social and spiritual duty), *Gian Khand* (region of divine knowledge), *Saram Khand* (region of wisdom and effort), *Karam Khand* (region of divine grace) and *Sach Khand* (region of truth or existential reality).

Khalsa Panth

Sikhs believe in the collective identity of the *Khalsa Panth* as a society of equals irrespective of their background. The first five people to be initiated in it are known as the *Panj Pyare* (the five beloved ones). These five, from a variety of caste-groups, volunteered from the crowd of around 80,000 Sikhs who had been summoned by *Guru* Gobind Singh to Anandpur Sahib on 30th March 1699 when the *Guru* asked who would offer sacrifice to the *Guru*.

Prior to their initiation, the *Panj Pyare* had the original names of Daya Ram, Dharam Das, Mohkam Chand, Himmat Rai, and Sahib Chand. They were all given the name *Singh* as a substitute for their original caste names, in order to signify that Sikhism recognises no castes. *Guru* Gobind Singh knelt before the *Panj Pare* and requested them to give the *Amrit Pahul* to him thus emphasising the importance of the *Khalsa Panth*.

TRADITIONS IN SIKHISM

Sikhs do not acknowledge internal groupings on the basis of doctrinal schools. Organisations do, however, exist within the *Panth* to cater for various interests or to reflect particular aspects of Sikh life. An example is that of the Sewa Panthis, a group devoted to the service of humanity founded in memory of Bhai Kanhaya. He was a Sikh who cared for the wounded without any discrimination whether they were the "enemies" or Sikh soldiers, and was highly praised for this by *Guru* Gobind Singh. When, in reply to a question, he stated that he saw no distinction between friend and foe but saw the *Guru* residing in all, the *Guru* warmly embraced him.

There are also groups whose origins can be found in the revivalist movements which have developed throughout Sikh history. These have generally been founded by Sikh individuals who are often given the honorific titles of *Sant*, *Bhai* or *Baba* on the basis of their reputation for spiritual guidance and teaching. They are expounders of the *Gurbani* and may hold significant influence within particular *gurdwaras* or Sikh organisations.

SIKH LIFE

Nam Japna

Nam Japna involves meditating on God and his attributes, reading and contemplating *bani* (passages) from the *Guru Granth Sahib*. It is said by Sikhs to result in being *gurmukh* (God-filled and God-centred) as opposed to being *manmukh* (self-centred). *Nam Japna* can be an individual or a group activity. In congregational worship it can be facilitated by *kirtan*, the singing of hymns from the *Guru Granth Sahib*, accompanied by music played on tablas (drums), harmoniums and other instruments. Although prayers can be said either individually or as a family, *sadh sangat* (congregational worship) is very important to Sikhs since it is believed that being in the company of enlightened *souls* helps purify one's own *soul*.

Birth, Marriage and Death

Soon after the birth of a child, a naming ceremony may be held in the *gurdwara*. After a prayer from the family, the name of the child is taken from the first letter of the *vak* or "word/order of the day", which is a passage of the *Guru Granth Sahib* read after its random opening.

Sikh marriage is known as *Anand Karaj* (ceremony of bliss). It is not viewed simply as a social or civil contract, but is seen as a spiritual state since living in this world and discharging family duties are advocated as the Sikh way of life. The marriage service involves the recitation of four stanzas, called *Lavan*, from the *Guru Granth Sahib*, in the presence of the bride, the bridegroom and their relatives and friends. After the recitation of each *Lav*, the bride and bridegroom usually walk around the *Guru Granth Sahib*.

The ceremony concludes with *Gurmat*, advice on the institution of marriage and its importance and then, as is usual with all Sikh ceremonies, with *ardas*, a collective prayer said in the presence of relatives and friends.

At death, Sikhs normally cremate the body. At the crematorium the *granthi* leads the mourners in the reading of *Kirtan Sohila* from the *Guru Granth Sahib*, and this is followed by a prayer. The family and friends then return to the *gurdwara* where relevant passages are read and sung from the *Guru Granth Sahib* and, following *ardas*, *langar* is taken before all leave for home. The family may also have a *sehaj path* (a reading, with breaks, of the entire *Guru Granth Sahib* over several days) or *akhand path* (a continuous reading for forty-eight hours) in memory of the departed soul as well as to console the immediate family and friends.

Ethics

Sikhs believe that God should always be remembered in the course of everyday life. *Guru* Nanak Dev taught that truth is above everything, but that truthful living is higher than truth. There are certain ethical principles which are intrinsic to Sikh belief and practice. Foremost amongst these are: *nam japna* (reciting the name), *kirat karna* (earning a living by honest and approved means) and *vand chhakna* (sharing with the needy). *Sewa* (service) to the community at large, or in helping to meet a particular need for the benefit of others, is also an essential part of Sikh life.

The concept of equality was of central importance to *Guru* Nanak Dev. He taught that all people are born with the opportunity to attain *mukti*, regardless of *caste* or creed and of whether they are rich or poor, male or female, high or low, educated or uneducated. What influences *mukti* is the *karam*, *maya* and *haumai* of individuals and the grace of the *Guru* in overcoming *haumai* and *maya*. The ten Sikh *Gurus* did not believe in any *caste* or professional distinctions and taught that every person is equal before God.

Equality

The Sikh concept of equality embraces women as well as men in both secular and religious life and was enjoined in the teachings and practices of the *Gurus*. Women have played a significant role in Sikhism, for instance at the first *Amrit Pahul* ceremony in Anandpur in 1699 in which *Guru* Gobind Singh's wife added sugar to the water. Both women and men can be fully initiated into the Sikh religion and can act as a *granthi* (see section below) in a *gurdwara*. However, in practice social and cultural conventions may influence gender roles.

Amrit Pahul

Amrit Pahul is the Sikh name for initiation into the *Khalsa Panth*. *Amrit* (the nectar of everlasting life or immortality) refers to the sweetened water used in *Amrit Pahul*. When coupled with adherence to the ethical principles of Sikhism this initiation is seen as the way to spiritual development and hence to the realisation of God's *grace*. The ceremony is for women as well as men and takes place at an age when the person can understand its significance.

The ceremony, called *Khande ki Pahul* and commonly referred to as the *amrit* ceremony, and can take place anywhere, providing that it is held in the presence of the *Guru Granth Sahib* and that five members of the *Khalsa Panth*, who have themselves received *amrit* and for this purpose constitute the *Panj Pyare*, are present to officiate. The ceremony follows the same practice as the original *amrit* ceremony carried out by *Guru* Gobind Singh in 1699.

Amrit is prepared by adding sugar to water in an iron or steel bowl and stirring the ingredients with a *khanda* (double-edged sword) and reciting five prayers: the *Japji, Jap*, the ten *Swayas*, *Chaupai* and the *Anand*. The initiate is also inducted into the Sikh code of discipline, takes the vows of the *Khalsa* and is then offered *amrit* and has some of it sprinkled on the eyes and hair.

The receiving of *amrit* is an expression of commitment as a Sikh and a Sikh who has received *amrit* is known as an *Amritdhari* Sikh. Sikhs who have not yet received *amrit* and who do not wear the long hair and other outward symbols of Sikhism are sometimes referred to as *Sahajdhari* (literally meaning "slow adopters") Sikhs. They include those who believe in Sikhism but have deferred the commitment involved in taking *amrit* and those who have lapsed and would need to take *amrit* again if they were to return to the status of an *Amritdhari*. The term *Keshdhari* is often used for those Sikhs who keep a beard, uncut hair and turban whether or not they have taken *amrit*.

Five Ks

Many Sikhs expect to be initiated at some stage in their life. Belonging to the *Khalsa* involves taking *amrit* and wearing the five articles of faith which distinguish individual men and women as members of the *Khalsa*, commonly known as "the five Ks" because the Punjabi word for each begins with the sound of "k". The "five Ks" are:

Kesh (uncut hair)

Kesh refers to the uncut hair which is required of Sikhs as one of the outwardly distinctive signs of Sikh identity. Men usually tie up and cover their hair with a *turban* and some women may also choose to wear a *turban*. *Turbans* may be of any colour and tied in a variety of styles. Usually the style and colour of a *turban* signify personal preference only.

As well as the "*five Ks*", the *turban* is seen as an essential and complementary adjunct to maintain the sanctity of the *kesh* and is treated by Sikhs with utmost respect. Historically, it is also a symbol of identity linked with royalty and responsibility. *Kesh* applies not only to the hair on the head and face: *Khalsa* Sikhs are enjoined not to cut or remove hair from any part of the body.

Kangha

A small wooden comb which should be worn in the hair. It is used to keep the hair clean and symbolises orderly spirituality.

Kara

An iron or steel bracelet worn by Sikhs, which is understood as a reminder of the universality of God and a symbol of spiritual allegiance, of brotherhood and sisterhood, as well as being a reminder of the covenant with the *Guru* to do good.

Kachhera

A knee length garment, tailored in a special manner, and usually worn under other clothes. It symbolises modesty and moral restraint.

Kirpan

A curved sword which is a reminder of the dignity and self-respect which Sikhs are called upon to uphold. It represents a readiness to fight for the protection of the weak and oppressed.

In short, the "*five ks*" have not only a moral and practical significance, but also a deep spiritual importance and the wearing of them is, for Sikhs, a sign of obedience to the will of God and of care for, and obedience to, the *Gurus* and their teachings.

Singh and Kaur

As instituted by *Guru* Gobind Singh, all Sikh men take the religious name *Singh* (meaning lion) and all Sikh women have *Kaur* (meaning princess) as their second name, for example, Paramjit Kaur (female), Mohinder Singh (male). This practice relates to Guru Gobind Singh's abolition of the *caste* system which was reflected in the surnames used by people.

It must, however, be noted that the name Singh does not necessarily mean that a person is a Sikh, since this name was common in India before the rise of Sikhism. In addition, in the UK, some Sikh wives use their husband's name of *Singh* as a surname following *Kaur*.

Sikhs will also often have a third name which may be derived from a place or a *got* (patrilinear clan) name. Some Sikhs use this third name as a surname, whilst others use only *Singh* or *Kaur*.

Diet

Sikhs are enjoined to avoid tobacco, alcohol and other intoxicants. Meat is only permitted for consumption if it is *jhatka*, where the animal is killed with only one stroke and instantaneously. Those Sikhs who eat meat must not eat *halal* meat (meat from animals killed according to Muslim law). Many Sikhs are, however, vegetarians and meat is never served in the *langar* (see below) in *gurdwaras*.

Pilgrimage

Although *pilgrimage* is not a religious duty for Sikhs, places associated with the Sikh *Gurus* are treated as places of *pilgrimage*. Many Sikhs going to the Punjab will visit the *Darbar Sahib* and some may also visit other sites, particularly Anandpur Sahib. A visit to the birthplace of *Guru* Nanak Dev at Nankana Sahib in Pakistan usually takes place in October/November each year when several hundred Sikhs from the UK join their fellow Sikhs from the Punjab in India and from other countries.

SIKH WORSHIP

Gurdwara

The Sikh place of congregational worship is called the *gurdwara*, meaning "doorway of the *Guru*". The *gurdwara* is not only a place for formal worship, but it is also a centre for religious education. Other activities also take place in *gurdwaras*, such as Punjabi classes, social activities such as youth clubs, women's groups, welfare provision and elderly day centres. In keeping with the Sikh tradition of service, *gurdwaras* often provide temporary accommodation for the needy.

A *gurdwara* is usually recognisable from the outside by the *Nishan Sahib* (*Nishan* meaning "flag" whilst *Sahib* is an honorific title of respect). This is a triangular saffron coloured flag with the *khanda* (*Khalsa* emblem) depicted in black. The emblem consists of a symbolic two-edged sword surrounded by a circle outside of which are two further swords, which symbolise the temporal and spiritual sovereignty of God.

Before entering the hall of worship, as a mark of respect, shoes must be removed and heads must be covered. Visitors should ensure that they are dressed modestly. No smoking or drinking of alcohol is permitted anywhere in a *gurdwara* and nor should tobacco or alcohol be taken into the *gurdwara*. On entering the foyer of the *gurdwara*, visitors may see pictures of the Sikh *Gurus* and of Sikh martyrs.

On entering the prayer hall, Sikh worshippers kneel, touching the floor with their foreheads before the *Guru Granth Sahib*. This should not be mistaken for regarding the *Guru Granth Sahib* as an object of worship since this is prohibited within Sikhism but rather as the respect shown to the revealed word of God believed to be within the scripture. At this time a worshipper also usually make a voluntary offering of money or fruit, milk or sugar.

As a social tradition, men and women tend to sit separately on opposite sides of the prayer hall. Worshippers sit on the carpeted floor, with their legs crossed. In the prayer hall, the focal point is the *Guru Granth Sahib* which is placed upon a dais. The dais is a raised platform with a canopy above it. The *Guru Granth Sahib* is placed on cushions and covered by *rumalas* (cloths).

Daily Prayers

A Sikh is called upon to rise early and after a bath or shower to meditate on one God. The daily prayer routine consists in the morning of the *Jap* or *Japji Sahib*, a prayer composed by *Guru* Nanak Dev, the *Jaap* and the ten *Swayas*

(compositions of the tenth *Guru*). It is the custom of some Sikhs also to recite other additional prayers in the morning. In the evening, the *Sodar Rehras* is recited and, before retiring to bed, the *Sohila*. These are both compilations of verses by different *Gurus*.

Sadh Sangat

No single day of the week is holy for Sikhs. In the UK, for convenience, the *gurdwara* is usually visited for *sadh sangat* on a Saturday or Sunday. The *gurdwara* is usually open daily and some Sikhs visit it every morning and evening. *Diwan* usually lasts between two and four hours.

A typical Sikh religious service consists of *Gurbani kirtan* (hymn-singing), a discourse on the divine name, followed by *Ardas* (a final corporate prayer) and is concluded by *Karah Prashad* (see below) and the sharing of *langar* (see below). The *Ardas* ends with the invocation of God's blessing on everyone and not just on the followers of the faith. In the morning service *Asa di Var* is followed by *Anand Sahib* and a collective prayer by the congregation. In the evening service, *Rehras* is usually followed by *Kirtan* and at the end of the service *Kirtan Sohila* is recited when the *Guru Granth Sahib* is laid to rest, usually in a separate room.

Path

The *Path* is the liturgical reading of the *Guru Granth Sahib*. On special occasions it is read from cover to cover by relays of readers. This form of reading is known as *Akhand Path* (meaing "continuous reading") totalling forty-eight hours. It occurs at most Sikh festivals, when the *path* begins in the morning two days prior to the festival, and also at weddings. *Saptah Path* is a form of *path* which is not continuous and which takes seven days. *Sehaj Path* is also not continuous, but is without time limit for the completion of reading.

While reading the *Guru Granth Sahib* the reader or another person close by will wave over it a *chaur sahib* (a whisk made of white yaks' hair). This is not intended to serve as a fly whisk or a fan, but is waved as a sign of respect for the *Guru Granth Sahib*.

Karah Prashad and Langar

Worship ends with the distribution of *Karah Prashad*. This is a sweet food made from flour, sugar, clarified butter and water which is served to every person present. *Karah Prashad* is blessed during *Ardas* at the end of worship and is therefore considered to be sanctified food. Its free distribution to every person present symbolises the central Sikh belief in the equality and unity of humankind and the repudiation of *caste* distinctions.

Langar, a communal meal, is provided free of charge to all who attend the *gurdwara*. The food provided, which has been blessed, is vegetarian and will not contain meat, fish or eggs or their by-products. Both *Karah Prashad* and *Langar* symbolise universal fraternity and equality since it is intended that all should eat together regardless of their social position.

SIKH CALENDAR AND FESTIVALS

Calendar

Most dates for Sikh festivals are calculated according to the lunar calendar and may vary from the Gregorian calendar within a period of fifteen days. A few festivals, notably *Vaisakhi*, are calculated by the *Vikrami* (North India) solar calendar, which is why the date of *Vaisakhi* remains almost constant in the *Gregorian* calendar. Sikh calendars and some Sikh authors use a dating system based on the first day of *Guru* Nanak Dev's birth. This calendar is known as *Sammat Nanak Shahi*. 2001 is the Nanak Shahi Sammat 532/533. The approximate times of the occurrence of the festivals which are cited below refer to when they take place according to the *Gregorian* calendar.

Festivals

Gurpurbs

Festivals which are celebrated by means of *Akhand Path*, *Kirtan*, prayers, religious lectures, *Karah Prasad* and *langar*. Those which specifically commemorate the birth or death of a *Guru* are known as *Gurpurbs*. The four major *Gurpurbs* which are celebrated in the UK are, in calendar order:

Guru Nanak Dev's Birth Anniversary
(November)

Martyrdom of Guru Tegh Bahadur
(November or December)

Guru Gobind Singh's Birth Anniversary
(December or January)

Martyrdom of Guru Arjan Dev (May or June)

Other Sikh festivals include:

Installation of the Guru Granth Sahib
This festival occurs in August-September. It celebrates the installation of the *Adi Granth* in Amritsar in 1604.

Vaisakhi (April)
This celebrates the day in 1699 when *Guru Gobind Singh* founded the order of the *Khalsa* by offering *amrit* to the *Panj Pare*. This is nearly always celebrated on 13th April, but very occasionally on 14th April, due to the discrepancy between the *Vikrami* and *Gregorian* solar calendars. On this day Sikhs usually replace the cover of the *Nishan Sahib* (see under section on *gurdwara* above) which flies outside the *gurdwara* with a new one, usually in the context of a *nagar kirtan* (procession) carrying the *Guru Granth Sahib* through the streets after *diwan* in the *gurdwara*.

Diwali (Oct/Nov)
For Sikhs, *Diwali* primarily commemorates *Guru* Hargobind's return from imprisonment by the Mughal Emperor, Jehangir, in Gwalior fort, together with fifty-two Hindu kings for whose freedom the *Guru* had asked. It is thus

a festival of *deliverance*, and is celebrated by the illumination of *gurdwaras*. (*Diwali* is also celebrated by Hindus, but for a different reason).

SIKH ORGANISATIONS

General Organisations

There are national, regional and local Sikh organisations. The Network of Sikh Organisations facilitates co-operation among Sikhs in the UK and is developing as a representative umbrella body. A major municipal grouping of *gurdwaras* is the Council of Sikh Gurdwaras in Birmingham. There are also Councils of Gurdwaras in a number of other towns and cities.

Sikh organisations often serve several functions including the provision of youth and women's activities and education in addition to what are often understood to be more specifically religious functions. Other groups exist which serve the diverse needs of particular sections of the Sikh population, including literary, social, cultural or professional societies and associations, for example, the World Sikh Foundation and the Sikh Missionary Society. A number of groups see themselves in relation to the political demand for an independent Sikh homeland of Khalistan.

Educational Organisations

In 1999, the Guru Nanak Primary school and Secondary school in Hayes, Middlesex, became the first state-funded Sikh schools in the UK. There are also many local supplementary schools which, outside of schools hours, teach Punjabi, as well as Sikh religion and culture. The World Sikh University, London, was established in 1998, and it offers Master's and Doctoral studies in comparative religion, specialising in Sikh studies.

Social Groupings

Sikhism teaches that there are no distinctions between people and rejects the concept of *caste* (or *Jat*), which therefore has no religious significance for Sikhs. The majority of *gurdwaras* in the world, including in the UK, follow guidance from the Shiromani Gurdwara Parbandhak Committee (SGPC), Amritsar, which is based at the *Harmandir Sahib* (Golden Temple) complex at Amritsar in the Punjab, as the highest Sikh authority.

Many *gurdwaras* are named after one of the *Gurus* or the Sri Guru Singh Sabha, which was the name of the movement which helped to found the SGPC at the end of the nineteenth century. Other terms which appear in the titles of some *gurdwaras*, such as *Ramgarhia* and *Bhatra*, are historically related to economic categories and are rooted in the history of the forebears of the families concerned. They do not necessarily define any contemporary economic or social status or who is allowed to attend a *gurdwara*, although they may in practice indicate the background of those who do actually attend.

Historically, *Bhatras* were itinerant traders. Many settled in British ports before the second World War and therefore some of the earliest *gurdwaras* were founded by *Bhatras*. They retain their own organisations in order to maintain their specific traditions and way of life.

Ramgarhias were originally a community of blacksmiths, bricklayers, carpenters, engineers and technicians. The name *Ramgarhia* derives from the name of Guru Ram Das and the fort called Ramgarh, constructed to defend the *Darbar Sahib* by the *misal* (confederation) who thus became known as *Ramgarhias*. The British encouraged groups of *Ramgarhias* to move to East Africa at the end of the nineteenth century in order to assist in the development of the transport network. As a result of the Africanisation policies of the newly independent East African states, many migrated from there to the UK or arrived as refugees.

Personnel

A Management Committee, which consists of honorary office bearers, president, secretary and treasurer, usually runs a *gurdwara*. The people who serve on such committees are usually elected by the *congregation* every two years or so. Committees usually run for two years and change on *Vaisakhi Day*. There are also a number of *gurdwaras* which are led by a *sant* (individual charismatic leader), for example, Guru Nanak Nishkam Sewak Jatha of the late Baba Puran Singh Karichowale in Birmingham.

Any adult male or female Sikh is permitted to perform religious ceremonies but many *gurdwaras* employ a *granthi*. A *granthi* is a professional reader of the *Guru Granth Sahib* and is usually also responsible for its care.

Although the word "priest" is sometimes used by people outside of Sikhism, Sikhism recognises no priesthood and all Sikhs are of equal status in religious terms. Sikh leaders may therefore be called *Bhai* (brother) or *Bhen* (sister). A *giani* is a learned and devout person who has meditated upon the *Guru Granth Sahib* and interprets its meaning to the congregation. There is often a regular group of *ragis* (singers and musicians) to help with diwan.

Other waged personnel may include a caretaker and sometimes, in the larger *gurdwaras*, a community development worker.

FURTHER READING

Babraa, D Kaur, *Visiting a Sikh Temple*, Lutterworth Educational, Guildford, 1981.

Ballard, R, "Differentiation and Disjunction Among the Sikhs", in Ballard, R (ed), *Desh Pardesh: The South Asian Presence in Britain*, Hurst, London, 1994, pp 88-116.

Ballard, R, "The Growth and Changing Character of the Sikh Presence in Britain", in Coward, H; Hinnells, J; Williams, R, *The South Asian Religious Diaspora in Britain, Canada and the United States*, State University of New York Press, New York, 2000, pp 127-144.

Ballard, R and C, "The Sikhs: The Development of South Asian Settlements in Britain", in J L Watson (ed), *Between Two Cultures*, Basil Blackwell, Oxford, 1977.

Beetham, D, *Transport and Turbans: A Comparative Study in Local Politics*, Open University Press, Milton Keynes, 1970.

Bhachu, P, *Twice Migrants: East African Sikh Settlers in Britain*, Tavistock, London, 1985.

Brown, K, *Sikh Art and Literature*, Routledge, London, 1999.

Cole, W O, *A Sikh Family in Britain*, Religious Education Press, Oxford, 1973.

Cole, W O, *The Guru in Sikhism*, Darton, Longman and Todd, London, 1982.

Cole, W O, "Sikhs in Britain", in Paul Badham (ed), *Religion, State and Society in Modern Britain*, Edwin Mellen Press, Lampeter, 1989, pp 259-276.

Cole, W O, *Teach Yourself Sikhism*, Hodder, London, 1994.

Cole, W O and Sambhi, P Singh, *Sikhism*, Ward Lock International, London, 1973.

Cole, W O and Sambhi, P Singh, *A Popular Dictionary of Sikhism*, London, 1990.

Cole, W O and Sambhi, P Singh, *The Sikhs: Their Religious Beliefs and Practices* (2nd edition), Sussex Academic Press, London, 1995.

Grewal, K S, "The Khalsa in Sikh Tradition (Part I)", in *World Faiths Encounter*, No. 23, July 1999, pp 5-16.

Grewal, K S, "The Khalsa in Sikh Tradition (Part II)", in *World Faiths Encounter*, No. 24, November 1999, pp 20-36.

Helweg, A W, *Sikhs in England: The Development of a Migrant Community*, Oxford University Press, Delhi, (2nd edition), 1986.

Henley, A, *Caring for Sikhs and Their Families: Religious Aspects of Care*, National Extension College, Cambridge, 1983.

James, A, *Sikh Children in Britain*, Oxford University Press, London, 1974.

Kalra, S S, *Daughters of Tradition: Adolescent Sikh Girls and their Accommodation to Life in British Society*, Diane Balbir Publications, Birmingham, 1990.

Kalsi, S Singh, *The Evolution of a Sikh Community in Britain*, Community Religions Project, University of Leeds, Leeds, 1992.

Kalsi, S Singh, *A Simple Guide to Sikhism*, Global Books, Folkestone, 1999.

MacLeod, W H (ed), *Textual Sources for the Study of Sikhism*, Manchester University Press, Manchester, 1984.

Madra, A S and Singh P, *Warrior Saints: Three Centuries of the Sikh Military Tradition*, Tauris and Co, London, 1999.

Nesbitt, E, *Aspects of Sikh Tradition in Nottingham*, unpublished MPhil thesis, University of Nottingham, 1980.

Nesbitt, E, *The Religious Lives of Sikh Children in Coventry*, unpublished PhD thesis, University of Warwick, 1995.

Nesbitt, E and Kaur, G, *Guru Nanak, RMEP*, London, 1999.

Shackle, C, *The Sikhs*, Minority Rights Group, London, 2nd edition, 1986.

Shiromani Gurdwara Parbandhak Committee, *Sikh Reht Maryada* (translation), Shiromani Gurdwara Parbandhak Committee, Amritsar (available through the Sikh Missionary Society, London)

Singh, G, *The Sikh Festivals*, Sikh Cultural Society of Great Britain, Edgware, 1982.

Singh, K, *The Sikhs Today*, Orient Longman Ltd, Bombay, 1976.

Singh, K, *The Sikh Symbols*, Sikh Missionary Society, London, 1970.

Singh, P, *The Sikhs*, John Murray, London, 1999.

Singh, R, *Sikhs and Sikhism in Britain: fifty years on - the Bradford perspective*, Bradford Libraries, (Bhupinder do you have date please)

deSouza, A, *The Sikhs in Britain*, Batsford, London, 1986.

Strong, S (ed), *The Arts of the Sikh Kingdoms*, V & A Publications, London, 1999.

Tatla, D Singh, "The Punjab Crisis and Sikh Mobilisation in Britain". in Barot, R (ed), *Religion and Ethnicity: Minorities and Social Change in the Metropolis*, Kok Pharos, Kampen, The Netherlands, 1993, pp 96-109.

Tatla, D Singh, *The Politics of Homeland: A Study of Ethnic Linkages and Political Mobilisation Among Sikhs in Britain and North America*, unpublished PhD Thesis, University of Warwick, Coventry, 1993.

Tatla, D Singh and Nesbitt, E, *Sikhs in Britain: An Annotated Bibliography*, University of Warwick Centre for Research in Ethnic Relations, Coventry, (revised edition) 1993.

Thomas, T, Sikhism: *The Voice of the Guru*, Open University, Cardiff, 1978.

Thomas, T, "Old Allies, New Neighbours: Sikhs in Britain", in Parsons, G (ed) *The Growth of Religious Diversity: Britain from 1945, Volume I: Traditions*, Routledge, London, 1993, pp 205-241.

Thomas, T and Ghuman, P, *A Survey of Social and Religious Attitudes Among Sikhs in Cardiff*, Open University, Cardiff, 1976.

Thompson, M, *Sikh Belief and Practice*, Edward Arnold, London, 1985.

SIKH UNITED KINGDOM ORGANISATIONS

The organisations listed in this section include both head offices of organisations with branches throughout the country and organisations which aspire to serve the Sikh community on a UK-wide basis.

3HO UK*
Kriya Centre, 25-27 Bikerton Road, Archway, London N19 5JT
Tel: (020) 7272 5811 **Fax:** (020) 7272 5811
Email: satyakaur@karamkriya.co.uk
Contact: Satya Kaur
Position: European Senator
Activities: Community centre, newsletter/journal, inter-faith
Affiliations: 3HO International
Providing activities and an environment for people who are curious about Sikhism, offering rational/scientific answers to questions. Organises Yoga classes and retreats.

Akaal Purkh Ki Fauj - UK*
PO Box 3, Brentford TW8 9XP
Tel: (020) 8568 8054 **Fax:** (020) 8568 9993
Email: info@fauj.org
Website: http://www.fauj.org/
Contact: Dr Kanwar Ranvir Singh
Contact Tel: (07956) 287602
Activities: Central body, youth, women, inter-faith
Other Languages: Punjabi
The UK branch of a world-wide Sikh Organisation with almost 3,000 members. In the UK we operate Sikh scout groups and occasional seminars and conferences.

Babe Ke*
Bericote Road, Blackdown, Leamington Spa CV32 6QW
Tel: (01926) 863131 **Fax:** (01926) 863367
Website: http://www.babeke.org/
Contact: Mr Jatinder Birdi
Position: Accountant
Contact Tel: (01926) 428738
Activities: Worship/practice/meditation, community centre, resources
Other Languages: Punjabi

Bebe Nanki Charitable Trust*
189 Rookery Road, Handsworth, Birmingham B21 9PX
Tel: (0121) 5513489 **Fax:** (0121) 5513489
Contact: Mr K S Ajimal
Position: General Secretary
Contact Tel: (0121) 5512120
Activities: Worship/practice/meditation, community centre, visits, inter-faith
Other Languages: Punjabi, Hindi
The trust provides religious services to the community and promotes relations between communities. It welcomes visits from educational

organisations and provides charitable services to the community as a whole.

British Organisation of Sikh Students*

PO Box 4350, Handsworth, Birmingham B20 2EB
Tel: (07939) 345678
Email: info@boss-uk.org
Website: http://www.boss-uk.org/
Contact: Mr Jatinder Singh
Position: Executive member
Activities: Umbrella body, youth, resources
Other Languages: Punjabi

BOSS is an independent organisation which acts as an umbrella organisation in helping to develop, assist and support Sikh youth groups/societies, especially those aged 15-30 at institutions of further and higher education.

British Sikh Education Council*

10 Featherstone Road, Southall UB2 5AA
Tel: (020) 8574 1902
Contact: Dr Kanwaljit Kaur-Singh
Position: Chairperson
Other Languages: Panjabi
Affiliations: Sikh Missionary Society; Network of Sikh Organisations

Prepares literature on Sikhism, InService training for teachers, promotion of Sikh Studies; liaison with the DFEE, SCAA, OFSTED, Shap etc on teaching of Religious Education, Collective Worship and values in state schools. Affiliated to the RE Council for England and Wales.

Guru Nanak Nishkam Sewak Jatha*

18-20 Soho Road, Handsworth, Birmingham B21 9BH
Tel: (0121) 5511125 **Fax:** (0121) 5510022
Email: enquiries@gnnsj.org
Website: http://www.gnnsj.org/
Contact: Bhai Mohinder Singh
Position: Chairman
Activities: Worship/practice/meditation, resources, visits youth, elderly, women, inter-faith
Other Languages: Punjabi

A non-political, non-profit making religious charity funded by voluntary donations dedicated to selfless service of humanity and propagation of religious belief and spirituality. All members are unpaid volunteers.

International Gatka Organisation*

18 Amberley Road, Leyton, London E10 7ER
Tel: (020) 8539 8331
Email: uptej.rattan@bt.com

Website: http://www.internationalgatka.org/
Contact: Uptej Singh
Activities: Umbrella body

Gatka is the Sikh martial art.

International Sikh Youth Federation*

Gate 2 Unit 5b, Booth Street, Warley, Birmingham B66 2PF
Tel: (07973) 439227 **Fax:** (0121) 5652550
Email: 106004.1160@compuserve.com
Contact: Sukhvinder Singh
Position: Public Relations Officer
Activities: Resource, media, umbrella body, visits, youth, elderly
Other Languages: Punjabi
Affiliations: All India Sikh Student Federation

Its purpose is to highlight human rights issues in the Punjab. It is working for an independent state there through democratic structures.

Khalsa Aid*

PO Box 1545, Slough SL1 2GS
Tel: (01895) 621313
Email: khalsaaid@yahoo.co.uk
Contact: Ravinder Singh
Contact Tel: (07748) 114030

An international disaster relief organisation.

Maharajah Duleep Singh Centenary Trust*

261 Broadway North, Walsall WS1 2PS
Tel: (01922) 613532
Email: info@mdsct.org.uk
Website: http://www.mdsct.org.uk/
Contact: H.S Rana
Position: Project Director
Contact Email: hsr@mdscet.org.uk.

National Council for Panjabi Teaching*

40 Bourne Hill, London N13 4LY
Tel: (020) 8886 5765
Contact: Mr Surinder Singh Attariwala
Position: Chair
Activities: Resources
Other Languages: Panjabi

Network of Sikh Organisations UK*

1st Floor Office Suite, 192 The Broadway, Wimbledon, London SW19 1RY
Tel: (020) 8540 3974
Email: nso@sikhisunuk.fsnet.co.uk
Contact: Indarjit Singh OBE
Position: Director
Activities: Resource, media, umbrella body, youth, elderly, women, newsletters, inter-faith

Other Languages: Punjabi
Affiliations: Inter Faith Network for the UK
The Network is a loose linking of Gurdwaras and others. It facilitates cooperation on issues of common concern, organises national celebrations of major Sikh festivals and generally advances the interests and image of the Sikh community.

Panjabi Language Development Board*

2 Saint Annes Close, Handsworth Wood,
Birmingham B20 1BS
Tel: (0121) 5515272 **Fax:** (0121) 5515272
Email: v.kalra@man.ac.uk
Contact: Mr Surjit Singh Kalra
Position: Director
Activities: Youth, newsletter/journal, books, interfaith, resources
Other Languages: Punjabi
The aim of the Board is to promote the Panjabi language and Sikh religion. Publishing material, arranging translation work in various South Asian languages and providing speakers on the Sikh faith.

Shiromani Akali Dal UK*

15 Manor Way, Southall UB2 5JJ
Tel: (020) 8571 2842
Contact: Sardar Bachittar Singh
Position: President
Activities: Worship/practice/meditation, youth, elderly, women, visits, inter-faith, resources
Other Languages: Punjabi
Affiliations: Shromani Akali Dal, Punjab, India
The organisation is religious and political and undertakes to give information on the Sikh religion. It fights against racist misunderstandings and for basic human rights. It engages in Religious Education and the singing of religious hymns.

Sikh Association of Great Britain*

18 Smestow Street, Park Village, Wolverhampton WV10 9AB
Tel: (01902) 751105
Contact: Mr Balbir S Gill
Position: Chair
Activities: Elderly
Other Languages: Punjabi

Sikh Council for Interfaith Relations UK*

1st Floor Office Suite, 192 The Broadway, London SW19 1RY
Tel: (020) 8540 3974
Contact: Mr Indarjit Singh OBE
Position: General Secretary
Affiliations: Network of Sikh Organisations

Aims to develop and focus interest on interfaith dialogue in the Sikh community and to promote a greater understanding of Sikhism among non-Sikhs producing suitable literature and disseminating information on interfaith dialogue with meetings and seminars.

Sikh Divine Fellowship*

46 Sudbury Drive, Harrow HA1 3TD
Tel: (020) 8904 9244
Email: hardip@harrow46.freeserve.co.uk
Contact: Professor Harminder Singh
Position: Secretary
Activities: Worship/practice/meditation

Sikh Education Council*

14 Brightside Road, Leicester LE5 5LD
Tel: (0116) 2737647
Contact: Mr Sarwan Singh
Position: Chairman
Activities: Youth, elderly, visits
Other Languages: Punjabi, Gurmukih

Sikh Educational and Cultural Association (UK)*

Sat Nam Kutia, 18 Farncroft, Gravesend DA11 7LT
Tel: (01474) 332356
Contact: Kartar Surinder Singh
Position: Chair and Consultant
Activities: Resource, umbrella body, youth, newsletters
Other Languages: Punjabi
Affiliations: Network of Sikh Organisations UK
Established in 1972, the association is a privately run voluntary centre whose objective is to create an awareness of the Sikh philosophy among the faith communities and to promote the understanding and practices of Sikh principles.

Sikh Educational Advisory Services*

42 Park Avenue, Leeds LS15 8EW
Tel: (0113) 2602484
Contact: Roop Singh
Position: Head of Service
Activities: Resource, visits, youth, inter-faith
Other Languages: Punjabi
Affiliations: Akal Takhat - Amritsar
Specialises in stories from the Sikh world.

Sikh Human Rights Group*

PO Box 45, Southall UB2 4SP
Tel: (020) 8840 3222 **Fax:** (020) 8579 7439
Email: shrg1@btconnect.com
Website: http://www.shrg.org/

Contact: Dr Jasdev Singh Rai
Position: Director
Contact Tel: (07974) 919655
Contact Email: jasdevsrai@hotmail.com
Activities: Resources
Other Languages: Punjabi
Human Rights organisation based on the humanitarian principles of Sikhism. It is concerned with maintaining human rights around the world, particularly in India, and producing documentation and specialist asylum reports.

Sikh Missionary Society (UK)*

10 Featherstone Road, Southall UB2 5AA
Tel: (020) 8574 1902 **Fax:** (020) 8574 1912
Contact: Kirpal Singh Rai
Position: General Secretary
Contact Tel: (020) 8845 6402
Activities: Worship/practice/meditation, youth, books, visits, resources
Other Languages: Punjabi
Affiliations: Inter Faith Network for the UK; Sri Akaal Takht Sahib Amritsar, Punjab, India

Sikh Religion and Cultural Heritage Forum*

20 Nairn Close, Stenson Fields, Derby DE24 3LU
Tel: (01332) 768972
Email: hardialsd@yahoo.co.uk
Contact: Dr Hardial Singh Dhillon
Position: Consultant
Other Languages: Punjabi
Affiliations: Guru Arjan Dev Gurdwara, Derby
To promote Sikh religion and cultural awareness and provide help and advice to schools, colleges, universities, employers, employees; to encourage use of Punjabi among youngsters and develop multi-cultural skills.

Sikh Religious Symbols Action Committee International*

11 Apollo Way, Perry Bar, Birmingham B20 3ND
Contact: Bhai Madan Singh
Position: Chief Convenor
Contact Tel: (0121) 3567070
Activities: Umbrella body, elderly, women, books, radio, inter-faith, resources
Other Languages: Punjabi, Hindi, Urdu
To promote Sikhism, particularly to schools and colleges where religious education is taught; provide advice, information and support and promote good relations between different communities.

Sikh Research Resource Centre*

1 Hanger Green, London W5 3EL
Tel: (020) 8810 6810 **Fax:** (020) 8997 6699
Email: jsclondon@aol.com
Contact: Jaswinder Singh Chadha
Activities: Books
Established to identify and rectify the gaps and inaccuracies in information relating to the Sikh religion and Sikh history. To provide advice on Sikh literature and Sikh institutions.

The Puthohar Association UK*

35 Petts Hills, Northolt UB5 4NT
Tel: (020) 8423 0515 **Fax:** (020) 8248 7468
Contact: Mr Tarlok Singh Bagga
Position: President
Activities: Community centre, youth, elderly, books
Other Languages: Punjabi, Hindu, Urdu
Sikh community organisation formed to fulfil the aspirations and requirements of Sikhs from the Puthohar region.

World Sikh Foundation (Incorporating the Sikh Cultural Society of Great Britain)*

33 Wargrave Road, South Harrow HA2 8LL
Tel: (020) 8864 9228 **Fax:** (020) 8864 9228
Contact: Mrs Harjas Bharara
Position: Circulation Manager
Activities: Newsletter/journal, inter-faith, resources
Other Languages: Punjabi
Distributes worldwide, free of charge, pamphlets in English on every aspect of the Sikh religion. Since 1960 it has also published in English the quarterly "Sikh Courier International", whose circulation is worldwide.

World Sikh University London*

10 College Road, Harrow HA1 1BE
Tel: (020) 8427 5132 **Fax:** (020) 8427 4880
Email: registrar@sikh-uni.ac.uk
Website: http://www.sikh-uni.ac.uk/
Contact: Dr Sukhbir Singh Kapoor
Position: Vice Chancellor
Activities: Resources

SIKH REGIONAL AND LOCAL ORGANISATIONS AND GURDWARAS

A variety of forms of Sikh regional and local organisations are listed in this directory. These include *gurdwaras*, associations, centres, welfare and youth organisations.

ENGLAND   566

NORTH EAST   566

YORKSHIRE AND THE HUMBER   567

NORTH WEST   569

EAST MIDLANDS   570

WEST MIDLANDS   572

EAST OF ENGLAND   578

LONDON   579

SOUTH EAST   582

SOUTH WEST   584

NORTHERN IRELAND   584

SCOTLAND   585

WALES   585

ENGLAND

NORTH EAST
City, Town or Local Bodies

Darlington Sikh Temple
Louisa Street, Darlington DL1 4ED
Tel: (01325) 461252

Gurdwara Bhatra Singh Sabha Sikh Temple*
23 Lorne Street, Middlesbrough TS1 5QY
Tel: (01642) 250125
Contact: Golab Singh
Position: Vice President
Activities: Worship, resource, visits
Other Languages: Punjabi
Affiliations: Bhatra Sikh Temple, Middlesbrough

Gurdwara Sri Guru Singh Sabha*
Tindal Close, Newcastle-upon-Tyne NE4 5SA
Tel: (0191) 2738011
Contact: S.S. Papiha
Position: General Secretary
Activities: Worship, resource, visits, youth, elderly, women
Other Languages: Punjabi

Gurdwara Khalsa Mero Roop Hai Khas*
West Way, South Shields NE33 4SR
Email: webservant@soul-stirring.com
Website: http://www.soul-stirring.com/
Contact: Gurpreet Singh
Position: Trustee
Contact Email: gurpreet.singh@sunderland.ac.uk
Activities: Worship/meditation, resources, visits, youth, books
Other Languages: Panjabi
Affiliations: Akhal Takht Sahib

Guru Nanak Gurdwara and Sikh Community Centre*
31 Allens Street, Stockton-on-Tees
Tel: (01274) 661914
Contact: Kuldip Singh
Position: Secretary
Activities: Youth, elderly, women, inter-faith
Other Languages: Punjabi

YORKSHIRE AND THE HUMBER
Regional or County Bodies

Yorkshire Sikh Forum*
130 Ashbourne Way, Kings Park, Bradford
BD2 1ER
Tel: (01274) 735918
Contact: Mr Harjap Singh Pooni
Position: Secretary
Activities: Central body
Other Languages: Punjabi

City, Town or Local Bodies

**Bradford Educational and Cultural Association
of Sikhs***
7 Clyde Street, Bingley BD16 4LE
Contact: Nirbhai Singh Bhandal
Position: Secretary
Contact Tel: (01274) 562961
Activities: Youth, women, visits, inter-faith,
resources
Other Languages: Punjabi, Hindi, Urdu
Affiliations: Yorkshire Sikh Forum

Gurdwara Amrit Parchar Dharmik Diwan*
Peckover Street, Little Germany, Bradford
BD1 5BD
Tel: (01274) 724853
Website: http://www.gurdwara-apdd.uklinux.net/
Contact: Mr Pritam Singh
Position: President
Contact Tel: (01274) 737283
Activities: Worship/practice/meditation,
community centre, central body, umbrella body,
youth, elderly, women, books, radio, visits, inter-
faith, resources
Other Languages: Punjabi, Hindi, Urdu
Affiliations: The Council of Sikh Gurdwaras,
Bradford; Gurdwara Nirmal Kutya Johal Jalandhar,
Punjab, India

Gurdwara Guru Nanak Dev Ji*
Prospect Hall, Wakefield Road, Bradford BD4 7DP
Tel: (01274) 723557
Contact: Mr Nirmal Singh
Position: Assistant secretary
Contact Tel: (01274) 788435
Activities: Worship/practice/meditation
Other Languages: Punjabi

Gurdwara Singh Sabha Bradford*
10 Grant Street, off Garnett Street, Bradford
BD3 9HF
Tel: (01274) 738834
Contact: Sardar Tarsem Singh
Position: Chair
Activities: Worship, resource, visits youth, elderly,
women, inter-faith
Other Languages: Punjabi

**Guru Gobind Singh Sikh Temple - Gobind
Marg***
Malvern/Ventnor Street, off Leeds Road, Bradford
BD3 7DG
Tel: (01274) 727928
Contact: Sarbant Singh Dosanjh
Position: Jathadar
Activities: Worship, resource, visits, inter-faith
Other Languages: Punjabi, Hindi

Ramgarhia Gurdwara*
Victoria Hall, Bolton Road, Bradford BD3 0ND
Tel: (01274) 731674
Contact: Mr Rajinder Singh Panesar
Position: General Secretary

United Sikh Association*
Gobind Marg, Off Leeds Road, Ventnor Street,
Bradford BD3 9JN
Tel: (01274) 727928
Contact: Sewa Singh Atta
Position: President
Other Languages: Punjabi

Gurdwara Sri Guru Teg Bhadar Sahib Ji*
98 Balby Road, Doncaster DN4 0JL
Fax: (01302) 390056
Contact: G S Mann
Position: General Secretary
Contact Tel: (01302) 360816
Activities: Worship, resource, youth
Other Languages: Punjabi, Hindi
Affiliations: Council of Sikh Gurdwaras,
Birmingham

Guru Kalgidhar Gurdwara Sikh Temple*
73 St James Street, Waterdale, Doncaster DN1 3AX
Tel: (01302) 369003
Contact: Mr Mehal Singh
Position: Secretary

Shri Guru Arjan Dev Gurdwara
Cherry Tree Road, Doncaster DN4 0BJ

The Sikh Religious and Education Society*
43 Nursery Lane, Ovenden, Halifax HX3 5SW
Tel: (01422) 251085
Email: singhjiuk@yahoo.com
Contact: Rajinder Singh Panesar
Activities: Resources

International Sikh Youth Federation*
1 Hayfield Avenue, Oaks, Huddersfield HD3 4FZ
Tel: (01484) 315398
Position: President
Activities: Worship/practice/meditation
Other Languages: Punjabi, Hindi, Urdu

Kirklees Sikh Doctor's Association*
37 Norwood Road, Birkby, Huddersfield
HD2 2YD
Contact: Mrs Manjeet Kaur
Position: Practice Manager
Contact Tel: (01484) 519911
Other Languages: Punjabi, Urdu

Shri Guru Singh Sabha*
34 Hillhouse Lane, Fartown, Huddersfield
HD1 6JT
Tel: (01484) 542982
Contact: Sukhdev Singh Pasla
Position: Assistant Secretary
Activities: Worship, resource
Other Languages: Punjabi
Affiliations: Network of Sikh Organisations UK

Sri Guru Nanak Sikh Sangat*
Prospect Street, Springwood, Huddersfield
HD1 2NA
Tel: (01484) 461654
Contact: Mr Jaswant Singh Sohanpal
Position: Education Administrator
Contact Tel: (01484) 461654
Contact Email: jas_ssohanpal@freeserve.co.uk
Activities: Worship/practice/meditation,
community centre, youth, elderly, women, visits,
resources
Other Languages: Punjabi, Hindi

Sri Guru Nanak Gurdwara Sikh Centre*
2a Parkfield Drive, Kingston upon Hull HU3 6TB
Tel: (01482) 505605
Contact: Mr Daljit Singh Dale
Position: Trustee
Contact Tel: (01482) 801560

Activities: Worship/practice/meditation
Other Languages: Gurmukhi, Panjabi

Gurdwara Kalgidhar Sahib*
138 Chapeltown Road, Chapeltown, Leeds
LS7 4EE
Tel: (0113) 2625425
Contact: Sher Singh
Position: Secretary
Activities: Worship/practice/meditation
Other Languages: Punjabi

*Guru Nanak Nishkam Sewak Jatha (UK-
Leeds)**
78 Ladypit Lane, Beeston, Leeds LS11 6DP
Tel: (0113) 2760261
Contact: Mr Sagoo
Position: Administrator
Activities: Worship

Ramgarhia Board Leeds*
8/10 Chapeltown Road, Sheepscar, Leeds LS7 3AL
Tel: (0113) 2625427
Contact: The President
Activities: Worship, youth, elderly, women

Sri Guru Nanak Sikh Temple*
62 Tong Road, Armley, Leeds LS12 1LZ
Contact: Mr Gurmukh Singh Bahra
Position: President
Contact Tel: (0113) 2632697
Activities: Worship/practice/meditation,
community centre, visits
Other Languages: Punjabi

Guru Nanak Sikh Temple*
41 Normandy Road, Scunthorpe DN15 6AS
Tel: (01724) 841361
Contact: Mr N S Nijjar
Position: President
Contact Tel: (01724) 357437
Contact Email: vaz.nijjar@clugust.uk
Activities: Worship/practice/meditation, elderly,
women
Other Languages: Punjabi

Guru Nanak Sikh Temple*
207/209 Frodingham Road, Crosby, Scunthorpe
DN15 7NS
Tel: (01724) 861880
Contact: Mr Daljit Singh
Position: General Secretary
Activities: Worship/practice/meditation,
community centre, youth, elderly, women, visits,

inter-faith
Other Languages: Punjabi, Hindi

Sikh Temple*
Ellesmere Road North, Sheffield S4 7DN
Tel: (0114) 2420108
Contact: Mr Jeswinder Singh
Position: President

NORTH WEST
City, Town or Local Bodies

Siri Guru Singh Sabha Gurdwara*
8 Culshaw Street, Blackburn BB2 6HD
Tel: (01254) 581965
Contact: Mr Manjit Singh Walia
Position: Secretary
Contact Tel: (07932) 638450
Contact Email: manjit_walia07@yahoo.com
Activities: Worship/practice/meditation
Other Languages: Punjabi, Hindi

Gurdwara and Sikh Community Centre*
Wellington Avenue, Liverpool LE15 0EH
Tel: (0151) 2222140

Central Gurdwara*
32 Derby Street, Manchester M8 8RY
Tel: (0161) 8322241

Gurdwara Dasmesh Sikh Temple*
98 Heywood Street, Cheetham Hill, Manchester
M8 0PD
Tel: (0161) 2055273
Contact: K Singh
Position: Secretary
Activities: Worship, youth, elderly, women, inter-faith
Other Languages: Punjabi

Gurdwara Sri Guru Harkrishan Sahib*
12 Sherborne Street, Strangeways, Manchester
M3 1FE
Tel: (0161) 8326577 **Fax:** (0161) 8352125
Email: gurmat@gurdwara12.co.uk
Contact: J S Kohli
Position: President
Contact Tel: (0161) 8317879
Activities: Worship/practice/meditation
Other Languages: Punjabi

Guru Nanak Dev Ji Gurdwara*
15 Monton Street, Moss Side, Manchester
M14 4LS
Tel: (0161) 2261131
Email: nanakdevji@hotmail.com
Contact: Manjeet Singh Rattan
Position: President
Activities: Worship, visits, youth, women, inter-faith
Other Languages: Punjabi, Hindi, Urdu
Affiliations: Siri Harmandir Sahib, Amritsar, India

Sikh Union of Manchester*
31 Burford Road, Whalley Range, Manchester
M16 8EW
Tel: (0161) 8817067 **Fax:** (0161) 8607500
Email: ujjal@hotmail.com
Contact: Mr Ujjal D Singh
Position: Honorary Secretary
Activities: Umbrella body, visits, resources
Other Languages: Punjabi

Guru Gobind Singh Sikh Temple*
1 Great Hanover Street, Preston PR1 1PY

Guru Nanak Gurdwara*
Bhatra Singh Sabha, 2 Clarendon Street,
Frenchwood, Preston PR1 3YN
Tel: (01772) 251008
Contact: Guljar Singh
Position: President
Contact Tel: (01772) 492586
Activities: Worship
Other Languages: Punjabi

Guru Nanak Gurdwara, Cultural and Recreation Centre
2-10 Tunbridge Street, Preston PR1 5YP
Tel: (01772) 798395

Preston Sikh Cultural Association
c/o 12 Holmfield Road, Preston PR2 8EP

Guru Nanak Gurdwara*
Dover Road, Latchford, Warrington WA4 1NW
Tel: (01925) 418208
Contact: Mr Hansra
Position: President
Activities: Worship/practice/meditation,
community centre, youth, elderly, women
Other Languages: Punjabi

EAST MIDLANDS
Regional or County Bodies

Federation of Sikh Organisations, Leicestershire*
106 East Park Road, Leicester LE5 4QH
Tel: (0116) 2760517 **Fax:** (0116) 2769297
Contact: S Gurbinder Singh
Position: Secretary
Activities: Worship, resource, media, umbrella body, visits youth
Other Languages: Punjabi

Shromani Akali Dal (UK) Leicestershire*
Leicester Sikh Centre, 219/227 Clarendon Park Road, Leicester LE2 3AN
Tel: (0116) 2701705
Contact: Mr Reshwel Singh
Position: Secretary
Activities: Worship, visits, youth, elderly, women
Other Languages: Punjabi
Affiliations: Network of Sikh Organisations UK

City, Town or Local Bodies

Guru Arjan Dev Gurdwara*
Stanhope Street, Pear Tree, Derby DE23 6QJ
Tel: (01332) 776872 **Fax:** (01332) 767787
Contact: Mr Jogindar Singh Johal
Position: General Secretary
Contact Tel: (01332) 760324
Contact Email: jogindar1936@hotmail.com
Activities: Worship/practice/meditation, youth, elderly, women, visits, inter-faith
Other Languages: Punjabi

Ramgarhia Sabha Sikh Temple*
14-16 St James Road, Derby DE3 8QX
Tel: (01332) 371811
Contact: Mr Mohan S Manku
Position: General Secretary
Activities: Worship, resource, visits, youth, elderly, women
Other Languages: Punjabi
Affiliations: Ramgarhia Council UK

Sikh Study Centre*
5 Lindrick Close, Mickleover, Derby DE3 5YJ
Tel: (01332) 510675 **Fax:** (01332) 510675
Contact: Mr D S Ahluwalia
Position: Chair
Activities: Youth, inter-faith, resources
Other Languages: Punjabi, Hindi

Sri Guru Singh Sabha
23-25 King Street, Kettering NN16 8QP
Tel: (01536) 511447

British Sikh Society*
230 Loughborough Road, Leicester LE4 5LG
Tel: (0116) 2661293 **Fax:** (0116) 2661293
Contact: Mr Sukhdev Singh Sangha
Position: Secretary
Contact Email:
sukhdev@s.s.sangha.freeserve.co.uk
Activities: Worship/practice/meditation, media, inter-faith
Other Languages: Punjabi
Affiliations: Leicester Sikh Centre

Guru Amar Das Gurdwara*
219-227 Clarendon Park Road, Leicester LE2 3AN
Contact: Mr Karmjit Singh Minhas
Position: Treasurer
Contact Tel: (0116) 2701705
Activities: Worship/practice/meditation, community centre, elderly, women
Other Languages: Punjabi
Affiliations: Shromani Gurudwara Prabhadank Committee, Amritsar, India

Guru Nanak Community Centre*
9 Holybones, Leicester LE1 4LJ
Tel: (0116) 2539374 **Fax:** (0116) 2539374
Contact: Avtar Kair
Position: General Secretary
Activities: Youth, elderly, women
Other Languages: Punjabi
Affiliations: Guru Nanak Gurdwara

Guru Nanak Gurdwara Library*
9 Holybones, Leicester LE1 4LJ
Tel: (0116) 2539374 **Fax:** (0116) 2628606
Contact: Harjinder Singh
Position: Librarian
Activities: Resource
Other Languages: Punjabi
Affiliations: Guru Nanak Gurdwara

Guru Nanak Gurdwara*
9 Holy Bones, Leicester LE1 4LJ
Tel: (0116) 2628606
Contact: Mr Kulwinder Singh Johal
Position: General Secretary
Activities: Worship/practice/meditation, community centre, umbrella body, youth, elderly, women, radio, television, visits, inter-faith, resources
Other Languages: Panjabi

Guru Nanak Panjabi School*
9 Holy Bones, Leicester LE1 4LJ
Tel: (0116) 2628606 **Fax:** (0116) 2628606
Email: gnps.leicester@virgin.net
Contact: Mrs Virpal Kaur
Position: Administrator
Activities: Resources
Other Languages: Punjabi, Hindi

Guru Nanak Sikh Museum*
9 Holy Bones, Leicester LE1 4LJ
Email: gnps.leicester@virgin.net
Contact: Mrs Virpal Kaur
Position: Project Co-ordinator
Contact Tel: (0116) 2628606
Activities: Visits
Other Languages: Punjabi, Hindi, Urdu
Affiliations: Guru Nanak Gurdwara

Guru Tegh Bahadur Gurdwara*
106 East Park Road, Leicester LE5 4QB
Tel: (0116) 2769297
Contact: Mr M S Sangha
Position: General Secretary
Activities: Worship, resource, youth, elderly, inter-faith
Other Languages: Punjabi
Affiliations: Federation of Sikh Organisations, Leicestershire; International Sikh Youth Federation

Leicester Sikh Centre*
219 Clarendon Park Road, Leicester LE2 3AN
Tel: (0116) 2701705
Contact: Mrs Jagdev Kaur Gill
Position: Chairperson
Activities: Worship, resource, media, visits, youth, elderly
Other Languages: Punjabi, Hindi, Hindi

Raja Sarb
208 London Road, Leicester LE2 1NE

Ramgarhia Board Gurdwara*
51 Meynell Road, Leicester LE5 3NE
Tel: (0116) 2760765
Contact: Mr Jagid-Singh Sahota
Position: General Secretary

Ramgarhia Sikh Circle*
3 Landscape Drive, Evington, Leicester LE5 6GA
Contact: Mr Joga Singh Bhamrah
Position: Secretary
Contact Tel: (0116) 2128941
Activities: Youth, elderly, women
Other Languages: Punjabi

Sikh Culture, Welfare and Religious Society
10 Edward Avenue, Braunstone, Leicester LE3 2PB
Tel: (0116) 2823544
Contact: Mr Sukhwant Singh Dhillon
Position: Secretary
Activities: Resource, youth, inter-faith
Other Languages: Punjabi, Hindi, Urdu
Affiliations: Organisation of Sikh Gurdwaras, Leicestershire

Sikh Parents' Association*
Leicester Sikh Centre, 219/227 Clarendon Park Road, Leicester LE2 3AN
Tel: (0116) 2701705
Contact: Reshwel Singh
Position: Chairman
Activities: Resource, visits
Other Languages: Punjabi, Hindi, Urdu
Affiliations: Guru Amardas Gurdwara, Leicester

Sikh Youth Missionary Project (IYSP)*
106 East Park Road, Leicester LE5 4QB
Tel: (0116) 2661712
Contact: Mr Kashmir Singh
Activities: Resource, youth
Other Languages: Punjabi
Affiliations: Guru Tegh Bahadhur Gurdwara, Leicester; International Sikh Youth Federation (UK)

Sikh Temple (Gurdwara Sahib)
33/34 Clarence Street, Loughborough LE11 1DY
Tel: (01509) 232411

Ramgarhia Board Northampton*
Sikh Gurdwara Community Centre, 2 Craven Street, Northampton NN1 3EZ
Tel: (01604) 621135
Contact: Jatinder Singh Sehmi
Position: General Secretary
Activities: Worship, resource, visits
Other Languages: Punjabi

Sikh Community Centre*
23/25 St George's Street, Northampton NN1 2TN
Tel: (01604) 639636
Contact: Mr Sukhy Chohan
Position: Development Worker
Languages: Punjabi

Sikh Temple
53 Queens Park Parade, Northampton NN2 6LP

Sikh Temple*
17-19 St George's Street, Northampton NN1 2TN
Tel: (01604) 634641
Position: General Secretary

Sri Guru Singh Sabha*
17-19 St George's Street, off Regent Square,
Northampton NN5 2TN
Tel: (01604) 634641
Contact: Mr Ranjeet Singh Grewal
Position: Secretary
Activities: Worship
Other Languages: Punjabi, Hindi

Bhatra Sikh Temple
36 Church Street, Nottingham NG7 2FF

Gurdwara Baba Budha Ji*
24 Gladstone Street, Nottingham NG4 1EL
Tel: (0115) 8448888
Contact: Sarabjit Singh Landa
Position: Liaison Officer

Guru Nanak Dev Ji Gurdwara*
36 Charter Street, Nottingham
Tel: (0115) 9700750
Contact: Mr G Singh
Position: President

Guru Nanak Sat Sang Gurdwara*
60/62 Forest Road West, Nottingham NG7 4EP
Tel: (0115) 9781394
Contact: Gurbachan Singh Paddam
Position: President
Activities: Worship

Ramgarhia Sabha*
Religious Hall, 31 Percy Street, Nottingham
NG6 0GF
Tel: (0115) 9791595
Contact: Mr T S Bhogal
Position: General Secretary
Contact Tel: (07884) 364825
Other Languages: Punjabi

Sikh Academy*
97 Ilkeston Road, Wollaton, Nottingham
NG7 3HA
Tel: (0115) 9420070 **Fax:** (0115) 9121164
Email: gurunanakgurdwara@yahoo.co.uk.
Contact: Biant Virdee
Position: Chairman
Contact Email: bsuirdee@yahoo.co.uk

Activities: Resources
Other Languages: Punjabi

Sikh Community and Youth Services
203 Ilkeston Road, Nottingham NG7 3FW
Tel: (0115) 9702003

Sikh Gurduwara*
26 Nottingham Road, Basford, Nottingham
NG7 7AE
Tel: (0115) 9622132
Contact: Mr G S Sanghera
Position: President

Sikh Temple
Bentinck Road, Hyson Green, Nottingham
NG7 4AA

Sikh Temple*
26 Nottingham Road, Basford, Nottingham
NG7 7AE
Tel: (0115) 9622132
Contact: Mr G S Sanghera
Position: Secretary
Activities: Worship

WEST MIDLANDS
Regional or County Bodies

City, Town or Local Bodies

Council of Sikh Gurdwaras in Birmingham*
627 Stratford Road, Sparkhill, Birmingham
B11 4LS
Tel: (0121) 7730399 **Fax:** (0121) 7730699
Email: csgb@sikh-council.demon.co.uk
Contact: Mr Jatinder Singh
Position: Development Officer
Contact Email: jatinder@sikh-
council.demon.co.uk
Activities: Umbrella body, youth, women, radio,
visits, inter-faith, resources
Other Languages: Punjabi

Gurdwara Bebe Naraki
189 Rookery Road, Handsworth, Birmingham
B21
Tel: (0121) 5513489

Gurdwara Nanaksar*
Old Methodist Church, Waterloo Road,
Smethwick, Birmingham B66 4JS

Tel: (0121) 5589048
Contact: Bahadar Singh
Position: Sevadar
Activities: Worship

Gurdwara Singh Sabha*
Somerset Road, Handsworth Wood, Birmingham
B20 2JB
Tel: (0121)551 1248

Gurdwara Yaadgar Baba Deep Singh Ji Shaheed
4 Holyhead Road, Handsworth, Birmingham
B21 0LT
Tel: (0121) 7530092

Guru Gobind Gurdwara Bhat Singh Sabha
221 Mary Street, Balsall Heath, Birmingham
B12 9RN

Guru Nanak Gurdwara Bhat Singh Sabha Community Centre*
Community Centre 248-250 Moseley Road,
Balsall Heath, Birmingham B12 0DG
Tel: (0121) 4402387
Contact: Sivnabh Singh
Position: President

Guru Nanak Nishkam Sewak Jatha
18-20 Soho Road, Handsworth, Birmingham
B12 9BX
Tel: (0121) 5511125

Guru Nanak Khalsa School*
145a Soho Road, Handsworth, Birmingham
B21 9ST
Tel: (0121) 5511579
Contact: Mr G S Atwall
Position: President

Guru Nanak Sikh Temple
629/631 Stratford Road, Birmingham B11 4LS

Guru Ramdas Khalsa School
495 Moseley Road, Balsall Heath, Birmingham
B12 9BX

Guru Ramdas Singh Sabha Gurdwara*
495 Moseley Road, Balsall Heath, Birmingham
B12 9BX
Tel: (0121) 4403653
Contact: Ram Singh
Position: General Secretary
Activities: Worship

Khalsa Welfare Trust*
Khalsa House, 4 Holyhead Road, Handsworth,
Birmingham B21 0LT
Tel: (0121) 5548034
Contact: Mr Charan Singh Pancchi
Position: Chairman
Activities: Worship, resource, visits, youth, women, inter-faith
Other Languages: Punjabi, Hindi, Urdu
Affiliations: Council of Sikh Gurdwaras in Birmingham; Network of Sikh Organisations;

Mahanraja Jassa Singh Ramgarhia Hall*
Newhall Hill, Birmingham B1 3JH
Fax: (0121) 2339095
Contact: Mr Ajit Singh Ubhi
Position: General Secretary
Activities: Worship/practice/meditation, community centre
Other Languages: Punjabi
Affiliations: Ramgarhia Council UK

Punjab Culture Centre*
127 Petersfield Road, Hall Green, Birmingham
B28 0BG
Contact: Mr Jagjit Singh Taunque
Position: Chairman
Contact Tel: (0121) 6247339
Activities: Community centre, youth, elderly, women, inter-faith, resources
Other Languages: Punjabi, Urdu, Gujarati

Punjabi Community Centre*
66 Gipsy Lane, Erdington, Birmingham B23 7SR
Tel: (0121) 6813625
Contact: Mr Narinder Jit Singh
Position: President
Other Languages: Punjabi
Affiliations: Council of Sikh Gurdwaras in Birmingham

Punjabi Cultural Society*
145a Soho Road, Handsworth, Birmingham
B21 9ST
Tel: (0121) 5511579
Contact: Mr Atwal

Ramgarhia Circle*
108 Gladys Road, Bearwood, Birmingham
B67 5AN
Tel: (0121) 4296823
Email: mrkalsi@hotmail.com
Contact: Prem Singh Kalsi

Position: General Secretary
Other Languages: Punjabi

Ramgarhia Gurdwara*
25-29 Waverley Road, Small Heath, Birmingham
B10 0EG
Tel: (0121) 7710680 **Fax:** (0121) 7710680
Contact: Mr H S Sokhi
Position: President
Contact Tel: (0121) 798548
Activities: Worship/practice/meditation,
community centre, youth, women, visits, resources
Other Languages: Punjabi, Hindi
Affiliations: Ramgarhia Council UK; Akal Takat,
Amritsar, India

Ramgarhia Sikh Temple*
Graham Street, Birmingham B1 3LA
Tel: (0121) 2365435
Contact: Mr G S Matharu
Position: General Secretary

Shaheed Udham Singh Welfare Centre*
346 Soho Road, Handsworth, Birmingham
B21 8EG
Contact: Mr K S Sanghera

Sikh Community and Youth Service*
348 Soho Road, Handsworth, Birmingham
B21 9QL
Tel: (0121) 5230147 **Fax:** (0121) 5154880
Contact: Mr D S Dhesy
Position: Vice Chairperson
Contact Tel: (0121) 5230147
Activities: Community centre, youth, elderly,
women, visits, inter-faith, resources
Other Languages: Punjabi

Sikh Nari Manch UK (All Sikh Women's Organisation)*
180 Plantsbrook Road, Walmley, Sutton Coldfield
Birmingham B76 1HL
Tel: (0121) 3515191 **Fax:** (0121) 3515191
Email: sikhnarimanch.uk@btinternet.com
Website: http://www.allsikhwomen.org/
Contact: Mrs Gurdev Kaur
Position: Chair Person (Founder)
Contact Email: gurdev@btinternet.com
Activities: Women
Other Languages: Punjabi, Hindi, Urdu
Affiliations: Network of Sikh Organisations.
London

Sikh Parents Association*
629/631 Stratford Road, Sparkhill, Birmingham
B11 4LS
Tel: (0121) 7710092
Contact: Mr Samra
Position: General Secretary

Sikh Sahit and Sabhyachar Kendra*
145a Soho Road, Handsworth, Birmingham
B21 9ST
Tel: (0121) 5511579
Contact: Mr Atwal

Sikh Youth Service, Khalsa House*
4 Holyhead Road, Handsworth, Birmingham
B21 0LT
Tel: (0121) 5548034
Contact: Mr C S Tanchi
Position: Chairperson

Singh Sobha Akal Darbar
521-527 Park Road, Hockley, Birmingham
B18 5TR

Singh Sabha Bhatra Gurdwara*
221 Mary Street, Balsall Heath, Birmingham
B12 9RN
Tel: (0121) 4402358
Contact: Mr N Singh
Position: Secretary

Singh Sabha Gurdwara*
Somerset Road, Handsworth, Birmingham
B20 2JB
Tel: (0121) 551 1248
Contact Tel: (0121) 5511248
Other Languages: Punjabi

Smethwick Youth and Community Centre*
126 High Street, Smethwick, Birmingham
B66 3AP
Tel: (0121) 5558844
Contact: Humraaj Singh
Activities: Youth
Other Languages: Punjabi

Sri Dashmesh Sikh Temple*
305 Wheeler Street, Lozells, Birmingham B19 2EU
Tel: (0121) 5236059
Contact: Sardar Kulbir Singh Chitti
Position: General Secretary
Activities: Worship, resource, visits, youth, elderly,
women
Other Languages: Punjabi

Affiliations: Council of Sikh Gurdwaras; World Sikh Council (Europe Zone)

Gurdwara Ajit Darbar Coventry UK*
Lockhurst Lane, Foleshill, Coventry CV6 5NQ
Tel: (024) 7666 2448
Contact: Mr S S Singh

Gurdwara Guru Hargobind Charitable Trust*
Sikh Temple, 53 Heath Road, Coventry CV2 4QB
Tel: (024) 7645 0260
Contact: Councillor Jaswant Singh Birdi
Position: Secretary General
Activities: Worship

Gurdwara Shri Guru Singh Sabha*
47-49 Cross Road, Foleshill, Coventry CV6 5GR
Tel: (024) 7668 4802 **Fax:** (024) 7668 8633
Contact: Mr Karnail Singh Mandair
Position: General Secretary
Activities: Worship/practice/meditation, youth, elderly, women, visits
Other Languages: Punjabi
Affiliations: Council of Sikh Gurdwaras in Coventry; Amritsar, Punjab

Nanak Parkash Gurdwara*
71/81 Harnall Lane West, Foleshill, Coventry CV2 2GJ
Tel: (024) 7622 0960
Contact: Mr Sadhu Singh
Position: President
Activities: Worship/practice/meditation
Other Languages: Punjabi

Nanaksar Gurdwara Gursikh Temple*
224-226 Foleshill Road, Coventry CV1 4HW
Tel: (024) 7622 0434 **Fax:** (024) 7663 3326
Contact: Bhagwant Singh Pandher
Position: Treasurer
Contact Tel: (024) 7663 3326
Activities: Worship, resource, visits, women, inter-faith
Other Languages: Punjabi, Hindi, Urdu
Affiliations: Council of Sikh Gurdwaras in Coventry; Nanaksar Gurdwara Gursikh Temple

Ramgarhia Gurdwara and Family Centre*
1103 Foleshill Road, Foleshill, Coventry CV6 6EP
Tel: (024) 7666 3048
Contact: G S Ghataurhae
Position: General Secretary
Activities: Worship, resource, visits
Other Languages: Punjabi

Affiliations: Council of Sikh Gurdwaras in Coventry, Ramgarhia UK Council

Shiromani Akali Dal*
15 Park Street, Coventry CV6 5AT
Tel: (024) 7668 4042
Contact: Mr Mohinder Pal Singh Dhillon
Position: General Secretary
Activities: Resource
Other Languages: Punjabi
Affiliations: Sharomani Akali Dal UK; Sharomani Akali Dal, Amritsar, Punjab

Sikh Mission*
Khalsa House, 19 St Luke's Road, Holbrooks, Coventry CV6 4JA
Tel: (024) 7627 1838 **Fax:** (024) 7627 1832
Email: sikhmission@khalsa.com
Website: http://www.geocities.com/sikhmissionuk
Contact: D S Kundra
Position: Organiser
Activities: Newsletter/journal, inter-faith, resources
Other Languages: Punjabi, Hinhi, Urdu

Gurdwara Guru Teg Bahadur*
7 Vicar Street, Dudley DY2 8LX
Tel: (01384) 238936
Contact: Mr A S Shergill
Activities: Worship/practice/meditation, community centre, umbrella body, youth, elderly, women, visits, inter-faith
Other Languages: Punjabi

Guru Nanak Sikh Temple
Sikh Temple, 118 Wellington Road, Dudley DY1 1UB
Tel: (01384) 253054

Gurdwara Sahib Leamington and Warwick
96-102 New Street, Leamington Spa CV31 1HL
Tel: (01926) 424297

Sikh Community Centre*
1 Mill Street, Leamington Spa CV31 1ES
Tel: (01926) 883129 **Fax:** (01926) 883129
Contact: Mr Jasvinder Singh Guru
Position: Manager
Activities: Community centre, youth, elderly, women, visits, resources
Other Languages: Punjabi, Hindi

Guru Nanak Gurdwara*
59-61 Park Avenue, Nuneaton CV11 4PQ

Tel: (024) 7638 6524
Contact: Sawadar
Position: Trustee Board
Activities: Worship, resource, visits, youth, elderly, women
Other Languages: Punjabi, Hindi, Urdu

Guru Teg Bahadar Gurdwara
Sikh Mission Centre, Marlborough Road, Nuneaton CV11

Gurdwara Guru Hargobind Sahib Ji*
Unit 1 Dudley Road West, Tividale, Oldbury B69 2PJ
Tel: (0121) 5224828 **Fax:** (0121) 5222300
Contact: Balwinder Singh
Position: Chair
Activities: Worship
Other Languages: Punjabi
Affiliations: Council of Sikh Gurdwaras, Sandwell

Sandwell Sikh Community and Youth Forum and Sikh Refuge Support Group*
74 Dudley Road West, Tividale, Oldbury B69 2HR
Tel: (0121) 5206542 **Fax:** (0121) 5209107
Email: sikhrefugee@yahoo.com
Website: http://www.sikhrefugee.freeserve.co.uk
Contact: Manjit Singh
Position: Co-ordinator
Activities: Resource, youth, elderly, women, inter-faith
Other Languages: Punjabi

Guru Nanak Gurdwara*
4 Craven Road, Rugby CV21 3HY
Tel: (01788) 333396
Contact: G S Atwal
Position: Secretary
Contact Tel: (01788) 331322
Other Languages: Punjabi

Gurdwara Baba Sang Ji
Empire Buidling, St Pauls Road, Sandwell B66

Guru Nanak Gurdwara*
65-67 Walsall Road, Willenhall, Stafford WV13 2RD
Tel: (01902) 605286
Contact: General Secretary
Activities: Worship, resource, visits, elderly, women, inter-faith
Other Languages: Punjabi

Nanaksar Gurdwara*
90 Tithe Barn Road, Stafford ST16 3PQ

Tel: (01785) 258590
Contact: Narinder Singh Mahil
Position: President
Activities: Worship, visits, inter-faith
Other Languages: Punjabi

Guru Nanak Gurdwara*
61 Liverpool Road, Stoke-on-Trent ST4 1AQ
Tel: (01782) 415670
Contact: Kewal Singh Sangha
Position: General Secretary
Activities: Worship, resource, visits, youth, elderly, women
Other Languages: Punjabi
Affiliations: Network of Sikh Organisations

Ramgarhia Sikh Temple
141 Wheldon Road, Fenton, Stoke-on-Trent ST4 4JG
Tel: (01782) 844940

Guru Nanak Sikh Temple*
19a Church Parade, Oakengates, Telford TF2 6EX
Tel: (01952) 677632
Contact: Mr Jagtar Singh Gill
Position: General Secretary
Activities: Worship, resource, umbrella body, visits, youth
Other Languages: Punjabi

Gurdwara Nanaksar
4 Wellington Street, Walsall WS2 9QR
Tel: (01922) 641040

Gurdwara Amrit Parchar Dharmik Diwan*
65 Birmingham Road, Oldbury, Warley B69 4EH
Tel: (0121) 5523778
Contact: Gian Singh Riat
Position: Secretary
Activities: Worship
Other Languages: Punjabi

Gurdwara Nanaksar*
62 Waterloo Road, Smethwick, Warley B66 4JS
Tel: (0121) 5653162
Contact: Gurdial Singh Samra
Position: President
Activities: Worship, resource, visits, youth, elderly, women
Other Languages: Punjabi, Hindi, Urdu

Guru Nanak Gurdwara*
128-130 High Street, Smethwick, Warley B66 3AP
Tel: (0121) 5555926 **Fax:** (0121) 5555926

Contact: Ravinder Singh Pouvar
Position: President
Activities: Worship, resource, umbrella body, visits, youth, elderly
Other Languages: Punjabi, Hindi, Urdu
Affiliations: Sandwell Council of Sikh Gurdwaras; Sikh Welfare Association; Khalsa Human Rights; Shiromani Gurdwar

Guru Har Rai Gurdwara*
126-128 High Street, West Bromwich B70 6JW
Tel: (0121) 5537219
Contact: Mr G S Sidhu
Position: Secretary
Activities: Worship/practice/meditation, visits
Other Languages: Punjabi
Affiliations: Sandwell Council of Sikh Gurdwaras

Sikh Community Welfare Council*
49 Springfield Crescent, West Bromwich B70 6LN
Tel: (07967) 439398
Contact: Mr Bhajan Singh
Position: Chairman
Activities: Worship/practice/meditation, umbrella body, elderly, visits

Council of Sikh Gurdwaras in Wolverhampton*
c/o Cannock Road Temple, 200-204 Cannock Road, Wolverhampton WV10 0AL
Tel: (01902) 450453
Contact: Mr Gurmit Singh
Position: Treasurer
Activities: Umbrella body

Dera Bab Gobind Dass*
95 Wellington Road, Wolverhampton WV14 6BQ
Tel: (01902) 492252
Contact: Mr Chaman Sandhu
Position: Secretary
Other Languages: Punjabi

Guru Nanak Gurdwara*
Arthur Street, Off Wellington Road, Bilston, Wolverhampton WV1 0DG
Tel: (01902) 492383
Contact: Malkiat Singh Gill
Position: President
Activities: Worship, visits
Other Languages: Punjabi
Affiliations: Council of Sikh Gurdwaras in Wolverhampton

Guru Nanak Gurdwara*
205-206 Lea Road, Penfields, Wolverhampton WV3 0LG
Tel: (01902) 710289
Contact: Mr Balbir Singh Sandhu
Position: Secretary
Contact Tel: (01902) 577656
Contact Email: balbirsandhu@talk21.com
Activities: Worship/practice/meditation, community centre
Other Languages: Punjabi

Guru Nanak Sikh Gurdwara*
Sedgeley Street, Blakenhall, Wolverhampton WV2 3JA
Tel: (01902) 459413 **Fax:** (01902) 458877
Contact: Gurdial Singh Dhaliwal
Position: General Secretary
Activities: Worship, inter-faith
Other Languages: Punjabi

Guru Nanak Sikh Gurdwara*
200-204 Cannock Road, Park Village, Wolverhampton WV10 0AL
Tel: (01902) 450453
Contact: Mr Gurmit Singh
Position: General Secretary
Activities: Worship, resource, youth, women, inter-faith
Other Languages: Punjabi, Hindi
Affiliations: Council of Sikh Gurdwaras in Wolverhampton

Guru Nanak Sikh Temple*
Baggot Street, Wolverhampton WV2 3AJ
Contact: Gurdial Singh Dhaliwal
Position: Secretary
Other Languages: Punjabi

Guru Tegbahadur Gurdwara Sikh Temple
8 Upper Villiers Street, Wolverhampton WV2 4NP

Nanaksar Thath Isher Darbar
Mander Street, Wolverhampton WV3 0JZ
Tel: (01902) 29379

Ramgarhia Sabha*
342-344 New Hampton Road East, Whitmore Reans, Wolverhampton WV1 4AD
Tel: (01902) 425156
Contact: Mr Pyara Singh Jandu
Position: Presdent
Activities: Worship, resource, visits, youth, elderly,

women
Other Languages: Punjabi
Affiliations: Wolverhampton Gurdwara Council;
Ramgarhia Council, UK; Ramgaria Educational
Council, Phagwar, Punjab

Sant Darbar Singh Ik-Onkar Trust (UK)
95 Woden Road, Wolverhampton WV10 0BB

EAST OF ENGLAND
City, Town or Local Bodies

Guru Nanak Gurdwara
72 Ford End Road, Queens Park, Bedford
MK40 4JW

Ramgarhia Sikh Society*
33-39 Ampthill Street, Bedford MK42 9BT
Tel: (01234) 342969
Contact: Mr Malkit Singh Sehmbi
Position: Vice General Secretary
Contact Tel: (01234) 309579
Contact Email: malkit_sehmbi@in-online.com
Activities: Worship/practice/meditation,
community centre, central body, youth, elderly,
women, newsletter/journal, books, newspapers,
visits, resources
Other Languages: Punjabi

Cambridge Sikh Society*
17 Woodcock Close, Impington, Cambridge
CB4 9LD
Tel: (01223) 232519
Contact: Mr Amrik Singh Sagoo
Position: Trustee
Contact Email: amrik.sagoo@talk21.com
Activities: Worship/practice/meditation,
community centre
Other Languages: Punjabi

Harlow Sikh Society*
80 Greygoose Park, Harlow CM19 4JL
Tel: (01279) 432177
Email: dsbawa@talk21.com
Contact: Mr D S Bawa
Position: Chair
Activities: Worship/practice/meditation
Other Languages: Panjabi

Guru Nanak Sikh Gurdwara
37 Wilbury Way, Hitchin SG4 0TW

Guru Singh Sabha Gurdwara*
Radcliffe Road, Hitchin SG5 1QH
Tel: (01462) 432993
Contact: Mr Ajit Singh Sarai
Position: Secretary

Ramgarhia Gurdwara Society - Hitchin
Bearton Avenue, Hitchin SG5 1NZ

Guru Nanak Gurdwara*
719 Bramford Road, Ipswich IP1 2LJ
Tel: (01473) 747195

Sikh Temple*
6 Maidstone Road, Thurrock, Grays RM17 6NF
Tel: (01375) 376086
Contact: Mr Gill Singh
Position: Secretary

Guru Nanak Gurdwara*
2a Dallow Road, Luton LU1 1LY
Tel: (01582) 721072
Contact: Ranjit Singh Ahluwalia
Position: General Secretary
Activities: Worship, visits, youth, elderly, women
Other Languages: Punjabi, Hindi, Urdu

Gurdwara Sikh Bhat Samparda*
184-186 Cromwell Road, Peterborough PE1 2EJ
Tel: (01733) 565133
Contact: BhakarKulwant Singh
Position: General Secretary
Contact Tel: (01733) 777663
Activities: Worship/practice/meditation, visits,
resources
Other Languages: Punjabi

Singh Sabha Gurdwara*
Newark Road, Fengate, Peterborough
Tel: (01733) 348842
Contact: Joga Singh
Position: President
Contact Tel: (01945) 410287
Other Languages: Punjabi

Guru Nanak Sikh Sabha*
12 Colne Way, Garston, Watford WD25 9DB
Tel: (01923) 673471 **Fax:** (01923) 663411
Contact: Mr Sachdev Singh Seyan
Position: Secretary
Contact Tel: (0850) 620285
Contact Email: sach@sseyan.freeserve.co.uk
Activities: Worship/practice/meditation, youth,
elderly, women, inter-faith, resources

Other Languages: Punjabi
Affiliations: Watford Sikh Association

Sikh Youth Association*
Gurdwara Sri Guru Singh Sabha, 48 Kings Close,
Watford WD1 8UB
Tel: (01923) 244050
Contact: Mr Harjit Singh
Position: Chair
Contact Tel: (07958) 644655
Activities: Worship, resource, visits, young, women,
inter-faith
Other Languages: Punjabi

Watford Sikh Association*
48 Kings Close, Watford WD1 8UB
Tel: (01923) 244050
Contact: Sohan Singh Ahluwalia
Position: General Secretary
Activities: Worship, resource, visits, youth, elderly,
women
Other Languages: Punjabi

LONDON
Borough or Local Bodies

BEXLEY

Guru Nanak Durbar (Erith and Belvedere)
31 Mitchell Close, Bexley DA17 6AA
Contact: Balbir Singh Khella
Position: Trustee

BRENT

Brent Sikh Centre*
241 Stag Lane, Kingsbury NW9 0EF
Tel: (020) 8206 1231
Activities: Worship

CROYDON

Nanak Community Centre*
St James Road, Croydon CR0 2RJ
Tel: (020) 8688 8155
Contact: C S Dhanjal
Position: Chairperson
Activities: Worship

EALING

Gurdwara Nanaksar*
60 Kingsbridge Crescent, Southall UB1 2DL
Tel: (020) 8571 9886
Email: info@nanaksa.co.uk

**Guru Amardas Gurmat Society and Education
Centre***
1a Clifton Road, Southall UB2 5QP
Tel: (020) 8571 1335 **Fax:** (020) 8813 9681
Contact: Daljit Singh Saggu
Activities: Worship, resource, youth, elderly,
women
Other Languages: Punjabi
Affiliations: Baba Jaswant Singh Trust

Guru Nanak Gurdwara*
67-73 King Street, Southall UB2 4DQ
Tel: (020) 8571 3265
Contact: Mr Kirat Singh Bhatra
Position: President
Contact Tel: (07957) 261422

Ramgarhia Sabha Southall
53-57 Oswald Road, Southall UB1 1HN
Tel: (020) 8571 4867

Ramgarhia Welfare Darbar
31 Hart Grove, Ealing, London W5 3NA

Sikh Arts and Cultural Association*
PO Box 90, Southall UB2 4RU
Tel: (020) 8867 9111 **Fax:** (020) 8867 9111
Email: webmaster@saca.co.uk
Website: http://www.saca.co.uk/
Contact: Harmi
Position: Media Rep
Contact Tel: (0208) 8679111
Contact Email: harmi@saca.co.uk
Activities: Youth
Other Languages: Punjabi
Affiliations: National Sikh Youth (NSY)

Sikh Religion and Cultural Centre*
253-263 The Broadway, Southall UB1 1NF
Tel: (020) 8571 3926

Sri Guru Singh Sabha Gurdwara
Havelock Road, Ealing, London UB2 4NP

Sri Guru Singh Sabha Gurdwara
2 Park Avenue, Southall UB2 4NP
Tel: (020) 8571 9687 **Fax:** (020) 8893 5094

ENFIELD

Nanak Darbar North London*
136 High Road, New Southgate, London N11 1PJ
Tel: (020) 8368 7104
Contact: Mr Sital Singh Maan
Position: President
Contact Tel: (020) 7836 9787
Activities: Worship/practice/meditation, community centre, newsletter/journal, visits, resources
Other Languages: Punjabi

Sachkand Nanak (Darshan Darbar) UK*
337 Fore Street, Edmonton, London N9 0NU
Tel: (020) 8803 6362 **Fax:** (020) 8803 8549
Contact: Gita
Position: Secretary

Sikh Nari Manch North London*
155 Conaught Gardens, Palmers Green, London N13 5BU
Tel: (020) 8292 9725
Email: satyakaur@karamkriya.co.uk
Contact: Balwant Kaur Rehal
Activities: Women

GREENWICH

Greenwich Sikh Association*
1 Calderwood Street, Woolwich, London SE18 6QW
Tel: (020) 8854 4233
Contact: S Mokha
Position: President
Activities: Worship, resource, visits, youth, elderly, women
Other Languages: Punjabi, Hindi, Urdu

Ramgarhia Gurdwara
Masons Hill, Woolwich, London SE18 6EJ
Tel: (020) 8854 1786

HARINGEY

Singh Sabha Gurdwara*
68 Gloucester Drive, London N4 2LN
Tel: (020) 8800 7233

HARROW

Academy of Punjabi Heritage*
70 Southfield Park, North Harrow HA2 6HE
Tel: (07956) 969370
Email: academy_of_punjabi_heritage@hotmail.com
Contact: Mr Paramjit Singh Kohli
Other Languages: Punjabi

HILLINGDON

Guru Nanak Sikh Secondary VA School*
Springfield Road, Hayes UB4 0LT
Tel: (020) 8573 6085 **Fax:** (020) 8561 6772
Email: rss@gurunanak.fsnet.co.uk
Contact: R.S. Sandhu
Position: Headmaster
Contact Tel: (020) 8573 6085
Activities: Resources
Other Languages: Punjabi
Affiliations: Nanaksar Trust

HOUNSLOW

Gurdwara Guru Nanak Nishkam Sewak Jatha (UK)*
142 Martindale Road, Hounslow TW4 7HQ
Tel: (020) 8570 4774
Contact: Mr Sarup Singh Mahon
Position: Trustee

Gurdwara Sri Guru Singh Sabha*
Alice Way, Hanworth Road, Hanworth Road, Hounslow TW3 3UA
Tel: (020) 8577 2793
Contact: Mohan Singh Nayyar
Position: Secretary
Activities: Worship, resource, visits, youth, elderly, women
Other Languages: Punjabi
Affiliations: Network of Sikh Organisations UK

Shiromani Akali Dal*
29 Waye Avenue, Cranford, Hounslow TW5 9SD
Tel: (020) 8897 9612
Contact: Mr S S Sandhu

Sikh Art and Culture Centre*
38 Clevedon Gardens, Cranford, Hounslow TW5 9TS
Tel: (020) 8897 0158
Contact: Mr Nirmal Singh Ahluwalia
Position: President
Activities: Resources
Other Languages: Panjabi

KENSINGTON AND CHELSEA

The Central Gurdwara (Khalsa Jatha) London*
62 Queensdale Road, Shepherds Bush, London
W11 4SG
Tel: (020) 7603 2789
Email: ksg@khalsa.com
Contact: Kuljit Singh Gulati
Position: Secretary
Contact Tel: (020) 7481 8176
Contact Email: Goraj 181@hotmail.com
Activities: Worship
Other Languages: Punjabi
Affiliations: Network of Sikh Organisations, UK

NEWHAM

Baba Namdev Community Centre*
c/o 2a Lucas Avenue, Upton Park, London
E13 0RL
Tel: (020) 8548 1546
Contact: Dr Jaswant Singh
Position: President
Contact Tel: (020) 8571 8912
Activities: Worship, elderly, women
Other Languages: Punjabi, Urdu, Hindi

Dashmesh Darbar Gurdwara*
97-101 Rosebery Avenue, Manor Park, London
E12 6PT
Tel: (020) 8471 2204 **Fax:** (020) 8470 7313
Contact: Mr Harjinder Singh
Position: President
Activities: Worship, visits, youth, elderly, women,
inter-faith
Other Languages: Punjabi

**Kshatrya Sabha London & Bhaghat Namdev
Mission**
2a Lucas Avenue, Upton Park, London E13 0RL
Tel: (020) 8548 1546
Contact: Dr Jaswant Singh
Position: President
Contact Tel: (020) 8471 8912
Activities: Worship, elderly, women
Other Languages: Punjabi, Urdu, Hindi
Affiliations: Community Belonging to Bhagat
Namdev; Sikh Organisation of Gurdwaras

Ramgarhia Education Centre*
270 Neville Road, Newham, London E7 9QN
Tel: (020) 8472 3738

Contact: Mr Hunjan Megar Singh
Position: President

Ramgarhia Sikh Gurdwara*
10-16 Neville Road, Forest Gate, London E7 9SQ
Tel: (020) 8472 3738
Contact: Maghar Singh Hunjan
Position: Honorary General Secretary
Activities: Worship, resource, media, umbrella
body, visits, youth
Other Languages: Punjabi
Affiliations: Ramgarhia Council UK

REDBRIDGE

Gurdwara Singh Sabha*
100 North Street, Barking IG11 8JD
Tel: (020) 8594 3940
Contact: G Singh Hundal
Position: Secretary
Activities: Worship, visits, youth, elderly, women,
inter-faith
Other Languages: Punjabi
Affiliations: Network of Sikh Organisations, UK;
Sri Akal Takhat Sahib, Amritsar

Redbridge Punjabi Sabhiacharik Sabha*
293-297 Ley Street, Ilford IG1 4BN
Tel: (020) 8478 4962
Contact: Mr Sansar Singh Narwal
Position: Chair Person
Contact Tel: (01708) 753649
Activities: Youth, elderly, women
Other Languages: Punjabi, Hindi, Urdu

Shiromani Akali Dal UK*
100 North Street, Barking IG1 8JD
Tel: (020) 8594 3940
Contact: Inder Singh Jamu
Position: President
Other Languages: Punjabi

SOUTHWARK

Gurdwara Baba Bhudha Sahib Ji
2 Shawbury Road, East Dulwich, London
SE22 9HD
Tel: (020) 8693 1162

Sikh Temple
1 Thorncombe Road, Camberwell, London
SE22 8PX

TOWER HAMLETS

Gurdwara Sikh Sangat
1a Campbell Road, Bow, London E3 4DS
Tel: (020) 8980 2281

Gurdwara Singh Sangat*
Harley Grove, London E3 2AT
Tel: (020) 8980 8861
Contact: Mr P Singh
Position: General Secretary
Contact Tel: (020) 8220 2333
Activities: Worship/practice/meditation
Other Languages: Punjabi

WALTHAM FOREST

Gurdwara Sikh Sangat*
71 Francis Road, Leyton, London E10 6PL
Tel: (020) 8556 4732
Contact: G S Sandhu
Position: President
Activities: Worship, umbrella body, visits, youth, elderly, women
Other Languages: Punjabi

WANDSWORTH

Khalsa Centre
95 Upper Tooting Road, London SW17 7TW
Tel: (020) 8767 3196

Sikh Gurdwara South London*
142 Merton Road, Southfields, London SW18 5SP
Tel: (020) 8870 7594 **Fax:** (020) 8874 3518
Email: gurdwara@southlondonsw18.fsnet.co.uk
Contact: Mr A S Dhanjal
Position: President
Activities: Worship/practice/meditation, community centre, youth, elderly, women, visits, inter-faith, resources
Other Languages: Punjabi, Urdu, Hindi

SOUTH EAST
City, Town or Local Bodies

Sikh Sangat Gurdwara*
Sydney Road, Chatham ME4 5BR
Tel: (01634) 815934
Contact: Kuldip Singh
Position: Chair

Activities: Worship, visits
Other Languages: Punjabi
Affiliations: Bhat Sangat

Sri Guru Singh Sabha*
27-29 Spencer Road, West Green, Crawley
RH11 7DE
Tel: (01293) 530163
Contact: Mr Manmohan Singh Majhail
Position: Trustee
Activities: Worship, visits
Other Languages: Punjabi, Urdu, Hindi, Malay and Swaheli
Affiliations: Sikh Missionary Society of Great Britain

Gurdwara Guru Hargobind Sahib*
8-10 Highfield Road, Dartford DA1 2JJ
Tel: (01322) 222951
Contact: G.S. Rai
Position: Secretary
Contact Tel: (07960) 122911
Activities: Worship, visits youth, elderly, women
Other Languages: Punjabi

Kent Ramgarhia Darbar*
63 Franklyn Road, Gillingham ME7 4DQ
Tel: (01634) 576618 **Fax:** (01634) 576618
Contact: Dr K S Jhita
Contact Tel: (07939) 554745
Contact Email: jhita54@khalsa.com
Activities: Worship/practice/meditation, community centre, visits, inter-faith
Other Languages: Panjabi
Affiliations: Sikh Educational and Cultural Association; Shiromani Gurdwara Prabandak Committee, Amritsar, India

Sri Guru Nanak Gurdwara*
Byron Road, Gillingham ME7 5XZ
Tel: (01634) 850921
Contact: Mr J S Bassie
Position: President

Guru Nanak Darbar Gurdwara*
Clarence Place, Gravesend DA12 1LD
Tel: (01474) 534121 **Fax:** (01474) 350611
Contact: Mr Gurder Singh
Position: President
Contact Tel: (07957) 124780

Guru Nanak Education Centre
Khalsa Avenue, off Trinity Road, Gravesend
DA12 1LU

Sikh Temple*
4 Milton Avenue, Gravesend DA12 1QL
Tel: (01474) 567418
Contact: G Singh
Position: Secretary
Activities: Resource, youth, books, elderly
Other Languages: Punjabi

Sikh Community Association*
58 Nutberry Avenue, Thurrock, Grays RM16 2TL
Tel: (01375) 376086
Contact: Mrs P S Gill
Position: Secretary
Contact Tel: (01375) 394353
Other Languages: Punjabi

Sikh Association*
17 Rye View, High Wycombe HP13 6HL
Contact: Mr Joginder Singh Bnasil
Position: President
Contact Tel: (01494) 446347
Activities: Community centre
Other Languages: Punjabi
Affiliations: Amrit Parchar Dhai Mak Diwan;
Singh Sabha Gurdwara, Southall; Golden Temple,
Amritsar, India

Nanaksar Sar Thath Ishar Darbar*
7 Gernon Walk, Letchworth SG6 3HW
Tel: (01462) 684153
Contact: Mr N Rana
Position: Trustee

Guru Nanak Satsang Sabha*
31 Rutland Road, Maidenhead SL6 4DL
Tel: (01628) 673329
Contact: Mr Karnail Singh Pannu
Position: President
Contact Email: karnailpannu@yahoo.co.uk
Activities: Worship/practice/meditation, inter-
faith
Other Languages: Punjabi
Affiliations: Sikh Gurdwaras UK; Shromani
Gurdwara Pabandhak Committee, Amritsar, India

Ramgarhia Sabha
Kiln Farm House, Kiln Farm, Tilers Road, Milton
Keynes MK11 3LH

Sri Gurdwara Sahib*
Phoenix Drive, Leadenhall, Milton Keynes
MK6 5LU
Tel: (01908) 231663
Position: General Secretary

Guru Nanak Sandesh Parchar Board*
12 Ranelagh Gardens, Northfleet DA11 8NT
Tel: (01474) 361834
Contact: Mr Kabul Singh Sodhi
Position: Chair
Activities: Resource
Other Languages: Punjabi

Guru Nanak Sar Gurdwara*
5 Margate Road, Southsea, Portsmouth PO5 1EY
Tel: (023) 9275 1942
Contact: Kirpal Singh Digpal
Position: President
Contact Tel: (02392) 791502
Activities: Worship, resource, umbrella body, visits
youth, elderly
Other Languages: Punjabi, Hindi, Urdu

Sri Guru Singh Sabha Gurdwara*
30a Cumberland Road, Reading RG1 3LB
Tel: (0118) 9623836
Email: ssbrar@tinyworld.co.uk
Contact: Mr S S Brar
Position: General Secretary
Contact Tel: (0118) 9618781
Activities: Worship/practice/meditation,
community centre, youth, elderly, women,
newsletter/journal, visits, inter-faith, resources
Other Languages: Punjabi

Medway Towns Gurdwara Sabha*
Cossack Street, Medway, Rochester ME1 2EF
Tel: (01634) 849782
Contact: Mr Sirjit Singh Marway
Position: Secretary
Contact Tel: (01634) 409606
Activities: Worship/practice/meditation,
community centre, visits, resources
Other Languages: Punjabi

Ramgarhia Sikh Gurdwara*
Baylis Road, Woodland Avenue, Slough SL1 3BQ
Tel: (01753) 525458

Ramgarhia Sikh Gurdwara*
Woodland Avenue, Slough SL1 3BU
Tel: (01753) 525458 **Fax:** (01753) 525458
Email: rsg_slough@hotmail.com
Contact: Secretary
Activities: Worship/practice/meditation

Sri Guru Singh Sabha Gurdwara*
Waxham Court, Sheehy Way, Slough SL2 5SS
Tel: (01753) 526828

Contact: Mr Tarbedi Singh Benipal
Position: General Secretary
Activities: Worship

Gurdwara Guru Tegh Bahadur Sahib*
7 St Mark's Road, Newtown, Southampton
SO14 0NW
Tel: (023) 8039 3440
Position: Secretary
Activities: Worship
Other Languages: Punjabi

Gurdwara Nanaksar
3 Peterborough Road, Bevois Valley, Southampton
SO14 6HY
Tel: (023) 8022 6464

Gurdwara Singh Sabha*
Cranbury Avenue, Onslow Road, Bevois Valley,
Southampton SO14 0LR
Tel: (023) 8033 3016
Contact: Mr Ramesher Singh Hayer
Position: President
Contact Tel: (023) 8057 0446
Activities: Worship, practice, meditation, resource,
visits, youth, women, inter-faith
Other Languages: Punjabi, Hindi

SOUTH WEST
City, Town or Local Bodies

Bristol Sikh Temple*
71-75 Fishponds Road, Eastville, Bristol BS5 6UK
Tel: (0117) 9020104
Contact: Mr Satnam Singh
Position: General Secretary
Contact Tel: (0117) 9029586
Activities: Worship/practice/meditation, women,
visits, inter-faith
Other Languages: Punjabi

Ramgharia Sikh Temple*
81 Chelsea Road, Easton, Bristol BS5 6AS
Tel: (0117) 9554929
Contact: Mr Balwant Singh
Position: President

Sangat Shat Singh Sabha Gurdwara*
11 Summerhill Road, St George, Bristol BS5 8HG
Tel: (0117) 9559333
Contact: Piara Singh Roud
Position: General Secretary

Contact Tel: (0117) 9512459
Activities: Worship, youth
Other Languages: Punjabi
Affiliations: Sikh Organisations UK

Sikh Resource Centre*
114 St Marks Road, Easton, Bristol B55 6JD
Tel: (0117) 9525023 **Fax:** (0117) 9525023
Contact: Narinder Vir Kaur
Position: Coordinator
Activities: Resource, media, umbrella body, visits,
youth, elderly
Other Languages: Punjabi, Hindi, Urdu
Affiliations: The Sikh Missionary Society

Singh Khalsa Heritage*
c/o 491 Stapleton Road, Bristol BS5 6PQ
Contact: Mukhtyar Singh
Contact Tel: (0117) 9393088
Other Languages: Punjabi

Siri Guru Singh Sabha*
301-303 Church Road, St George, Bristol
BS5 8AH
Contact: Mr Santokh Singh Dulai
Position: General Secretary
Contact Tel: (0117) 9650507
Activities: Worship/practice/meditation,
community centre, youth, elderly, women, visits,
inter-faith, resources
Other Languages: Punjabi
Affiliations: Golden Temple, Amritsar

Guru Arjan Niwas Sikh Temple
4b Clifton Street, Exeter EX1 2EN

Sikh Temple*
North Street, Swindon SN1 3JX
Email: mal_babbra@iee.org.uk
Contact: Mr Lamkit S Babbra

NORTHERN IRELAND

Regional or County Bodies

Northern Ireland Sikh Association*
1 Simpson's Brae, Waterside, Londonderry
BT47 1DL
Tel: (028) 7134 3935 **Fax:** (028) 7134 3935
Contact: Mr K S Panesar
Position: President
Contact Email: panesarfrcs@hotmail.com
Activities: Worship/practice/meditation,

community centre, visits, inter-faith, resources
Other Languages: Punjabi

SCOTLAND

City, Town or Local Bodies

Sri Guru Nanak Gurdwara*
1-3 Nelson Street, Dundee DD1 2PN
Tel: (01382) 223383
Email: msathwal@aol.com
Contact: Mr Athwal
Position: Vice Chair
Contact Tel: (01382) 779353
Activities: Worship/practice/meditation
Other Languages: Punjabi

Edinburgh Bhatra Sikhs*
1 Mill Lane, Sherrif Brae, Leith, Edinburgh
EH6 6TJ
Contact: Mr Baldev Singh
Position: Treasurer
Contact Tel: (0131) 2589494
Activities: Worship/practice/meditation,
community centre, visits
Other Languages: Punjabi

Central Gurdwara Singh Sabha*
138 Berkeley Street, Glasgow G3 7HY
Tel: (0141) 2216698
Contact: Partinder Singh Purba
Position: Secretary
Activities: Worship, resource, media, visits youth,
elderly, women
Other Languages: Punjabi, Hindi, Urdu

Gurdwara Guru Granth Sahib Sikh Sabha*
163 Nithsdale Road, Glasgow G41 5QS
Tel: (0141) 4238288
Contact: Daljeet Singh Dilber
Position: President
Activities: Worship, umbrella body, visits, elderly,
women, inter-faith
Other Languages: Punjabi
Affiliations: Glasgow Gurdwara Committee

Guru Nanak Sikh Temple (Ramgarhia Association)*
19-27 Otago Street, Glasgow G12 8JJ
Tel: (0141) 3349125
Contact: Sardara Singh Jandoo
Position: Secretary
Contact Tel: (0141) 7623688

Activities: Worship, resource, visits, youth
Other Languages: Punjabi

Shri Guru Tegh Bahadur Gurdwara Bhatra Sangat*
32 St Andrew's Drive, Glasgow G41 5SG
Tel: (0141) 429 3763
Contact: Granthi
Activities: Worship

WALES

City, Town or Local Bodies

Gurdwara Nanak Darbar Bhat Sikh Association*
18 Copper Street, Roath, Cardiff CF2 1LH
Tel: (01222) 450175
Contact: Mr Kaboul Singh
Position: Chair
Activities: Worship, visits
Other Languages: Punjabi

Sikh Gurdwara*
212a Pearl Street, Roath, Cardiff CF24 1RD
Tel: (029) 2046 5514
Activities: Worship/practice/meditation, visits,
inter-faith
Other Languages: Punjabi

Sri Dasmais Singh Sabha Gurdwara Bhatra Sikh Centre*
97-203 Tudor Street, Cardiff CF11 6RE
Tel: (029) 2022 4806
Contact: General Secretary
Activities: Worship

Guru Nanak Sikh Temple*
239 Peniel Green Road, Swansea SA7 9BJ
Tel: (01792) 411078

INTRODUCING ZOROASTRIANS IN THE UK

ZOROASTRIANS IN THE
UNITED KINGDOM 587

ORIGINS AND DEVELOPMENT
OF ZOROASTRIANISM 588

SOURCES OF ZOROASTRIAN
BELIEFS AND PRACTICES 589

KEY ZOROASTRIAN BELIEFS 589

ZOROASTRIAN LIFE 591

ZOROASTRIAN WORSHIP 593

ZOROASTRIAN CALENDARS
AND FESTIVALS 594

ZOROASTRIAN
ORGANISATIONS 596

FURTHER READING 596

ZOROASTRIANS IN THE UNITED KINGDOM

Origins

The first Zoroastrian known to have visited the United Kingdom came in 1723. The first Indian firm to open for business in Britain was run by a *Parsi* (see section on *Parsis* below) family called Cama and Company and began in 1855. Zoroastrians thus form a long-established community in the UK. It was from its *Parsi* members, who made up the majority of the early Zoroastrian settlers, that the first three Asian British Members of Parliament came. The first of these was the Liberal MP, Dadabhai Naoroji, elected in 1892.

Migration

The founders of the community initially settled in Britain in the nineteenth century and the first community organisation was formally established in 1861. Other *Parsis* came from India in the 1950s, immediately following Indian independence and later, prior to the introduction in the 1960s of tighter immigration controls on migration from New Commonwealth countries. There were also Indian origin *Parsis* who came from Aden and from East Africa (mainly Zanzibar, Kenya and Uganda), after the introduction in the late 1960s and early 1970s of Africanisation policies in these newly independent states. Iranian Zoroastrians came to Britain from Iran largely after the downfall of the Pahlavi dynasty in 1979.

Globally, Zoroastrians are found mainly in Iran, India (particularly Bombay and Gujarat state), Pakistan, Britain, North America, Australia and New Zealand. In the UK, there is only one Zoroastrian place of worship recorded in the directory, namely a designated room for worship within Zoroastrian House.

Languages

Zoroastrians with family roots in India, whether directly from India or via East Africa, have *Parsi* Gujarati as their tongue of daily conversation. Zoroastrians with an Iranian family background, have Persian or Farsi as a mother tongue, although very many of the young generation are fluent in English. Zoroastrian prayers are said in the ancient Iranian languages of Avestan and Pahlavi.

ORIGINS AND DEVELOPMENT OF ZOROASTRIANISM

Zarathushtra

The term Zoroastrianism comes from the Greek form (Zoroaster) of the name Zarathushtra, who was the founder of the religion. The religion is also known as *Zarathushtrianism* from the Iranian form of the founder's name, or else as *Mazdayasni Zarthushti/Zartoshti* (*Mazdayasni* meaning worshipper of God).

There is considerable debate about the precise dates of Zarathushtra's life. Some Zoroastrians argue for a date as early as 6,000BCE, while other Zoroastrians and many external academics argue for a date around 1,200BCE. Whatever his precise date of birth, it is generally agreed that Zarathushtra lived in North Eastern Iran.

Zoroastrians believe that Zarathushtra's life was threatened by evil forces from infancy onwards. At a young age he went to live a solitary life of meditation in the countryside and it is believed that his first vision came to him at the age of thirty. His personal visionary experiences inspired him to infuse the traditional Iranian religion in which he functioned as a *zaotar* or (priest), with a personal, experiential dimension.

He spent the following forty-seven years of his life spreading a *prophet's* message in which he denounced the *daevas* (the former gods of some of the Iranians, which Zarathushtra saw as demonic spirits); proclaimed the worship

of Ahura Mazda (the Wise Lord) as the source of *asha* (truth, righteousness, order, justice) and *vohu manah* (good mind); and called people to the threefold ethic of *humata* (good thoughts), *hukhta* (good words) and *hvarshta* (good deeds).

Zarathushtra's teaching was accepted by the then king Vishtaspa of the Kayanian dynasty, but he faced considerable opposition from supporters of the existing *polytheistic* religious structures.

History and Influence

Zoroastrianism eventually became the imperial religion of three successive Iranian empires. Precisely how this occurred is uncertain, although just prior to the Achaemenid period, the *Magi*, whom the historian Herodotus identifies as a *priestly* grouping of the Medes in the North West of Iran, seem to have adopted Zoroastrian beliefs and to have played a part in developing the religion's unifying role within the Empire.

In various forms of development Zoroastrianism became, successively, the religion of the Achaemenids (559-331BCE), the Parthians (mid second century BCE - 224CE) and the Sasanians (224-652CE). In various ways it is thought to have influenced post-exilic Judaism, Christianity, Islam, Greek philosophers such as Plato, Pythagoras and Aristotle and also *Mahayana* Buddhism in the East.

The Parsis in India and the Zoroastrians in Iran

In the ninth century CE some Zoroastrians from Khorasan, a province in north-eastern Iran, left Iran following the Arab conquest, seeking religious and economic freedom. They settled at Sanjan in Gujarat, North West India, in 936CE. This community became known as the *Parsis* or *Parsees*, from Pars the name of the province of north east Iran from which they had first set out. Over the next thousand years many more Zoroastrians emigrated to India due to religious persecution in Iran. Because of this, many Zoroastrians consider India as their adopted homeland, although a significant community also remained in Iran.

SOURCES OF ZOROASTRIAN BELIEFS AND PRACTICES

The Avesta

The main body of Zoroastrian scripture is known as the *Avesta*. It originally consisted of twenty-one books, the contents of which were orally transmitted for many centuries from generation to generation and then written down in the fifth or sixth century CE in a specially composed Avestan alphabet. Only about one quarter of these texts survive in their original form. In their present form, the Zoroastrian scriptures may be classified into five divisions:

Yasna and Gathas

The *Yasna* is concerned with acts of worship, praise, prayer, supplication and religious devotion. It is divided into seventy-two chapters, which include the seventeen *Gathas*. The *Gathas* are *The Divine Hymns of Zarathushtra* and are metrical compositions written in the ancient Avestan language. They are difficult to translate today since some words in the *Gathas* only appear in these sources and nowhere else. Sometimes, therefore, one can only gain an approximate sense of their meaning.

The Yashts (hymns)

The *Yashts* (*Yashti* meaning "homage" in Avestan) are prose and verse hymns addressed to individual *yazatas/yazads* (adorable beings worthy of adoration). In all, there are twenty-one *Yashts*, some of which are thought to be very ancient.

The Vendidad (or Videvdat)

The word *Vendidad* is the present form of the ancient Avestan word *Vidaeva-data*, meaning

rules and regulations to oppose *daeva* or evil. It is not read as a prayer book, but it specifies in detail the laws of purity and also contains diverse material such as the account of creation; the geography of *Airyana Vaeja* (the known limits of the Aryan world); the legend of a golden age; legal matters; and the revelation received by Zarathushtra.

Visperad

Visperad (which means "Service of all the Masters") is a collection of materials supplementary to the *Yasna*. These are never recited independently, but are usually recited at the six religious festivals known as *gahanbars* (see below) and they contain invocations and offerings of homage to "all the Lords or heavenly powers" (*Vispe Ratavo*).

Khordeh Avesta

The *Khordeh Avesta* is a short extract from the *Avesta* containing: *Nyayeshes*, which are praises to the elements – *Khorshed* (sun), *Mehr* (the heavenly light), *Mahabokhta* (the moon), *Avan* (water) and *Adar* (fire); the *Afrinagan* and *Afrins*, which are blessings; the *Gahs*, which are prayers to the five parts into which a day is divided; and the *Sirozah*, which contains twenty-two *Yashts*, invoking the *Yazatas*.

Later Texts

In addition to the *Avesta* there are many texts written in *Pazand* (a mixture of Pahlavi and Persian), mostly in the ninth century CE, which reflect the later growth of the religion and its encounter with Judaism, Christianity, Islam and Buddhism, and include some translations and summaries of otherwise lost ancient sources.

KEY ZOROASTRIAN BELIEFS

Ahura Mazda

Zarathushtra taught that Ahura Mazda (the Wise Lord or the Lord of Wisdom) is to be seen as the One Supreme, All-Powerful, All-Knowing, All-Wise, uncreated, eternally

Good and Perfect, ever-present, Creator of *Asha* and *Vohu Manah* (Good Mind). Ahura Mazda is present everywhere, and is seen as a friend to all, never to be feared by human beings. According to the teaching of Zarathushtra, Ahura Mazda alone is worthy of absolute worship.

Zoroastrians believe that Zarathushtra identified, for the first time in human history, the importance of the *Vohu Manah* (Good Mind). His ethical *monotheism* taught human beings to think and reflect with a clear, rational mind, in order to dispel ignorance and blind faith.

Spenta Mainyu (The Holy Spirit) and Angra Mainyu (The Destructive Spirit)

The classical Zoroastrian teaching is that Ahura Mazda did not create evil: a perfect, All-Wise and Good God could, by definition, not create evil. Rather, evil is seen as the work of *Angra Mainyu* (the Destructive Spirit). The characteristics of *Angra Mainyu* are anger, greed, jealousy and destruction. In this present world, the forces of evil attack and afflict Ahura Mazda's creations, adopting a kind of parasitic existence and eating away at the good creation, bringing chaos, violence and destruction in opposition to the force of *Spenta Mainyu* (the Holy Spirit). Human beings are seen as *hamkar* (fellow-workers) with Ahura Mazda in bringing about the ultimate defeat of evil.

Whilst all Zoroastrians share the conviction that evil will be overcome by Ahura Mazda, Zoroastrianism is a complex and living tradition that has evolved over the centuries. Its richness has therefore included differing emphases and accounts of how evil will be overcome. For example, in a Pahlavi text of the 9th century, the world is represented as a trap into which evil is ensnared, in order that evil may ultimately be destroyed. Some Zoroastrians, however, assign sole authority to the *Gathas* (see above) and in their interpretation of the *Gathas* emphasise the absolute power of Ahura Mazda over evil.

The Seven Good Creations and Their Guardians

The sky, waters, earth, plants, cattle, humans, and fire are the seven primary creations which make up the world. Zoroastrians believe that Ahura Mazda fashioned this world with the aid of spiritual forces which he created as guardians of the seven creations. They collectively came to be known as the *Amesha Spentas* (Bounteous Immortals). They are also believed, in their turn, to have brought forth the *yazatas* (see below) which are referred to as the "adorable ones".

Amesha Spentas

The virtues of the *Amesha Spentas* reflect the attributes of Ahura Mazda although some Zoroastrians see them more as symbolic ideals. In either case, they set the ethical framework for humankind.

Vohu Manah (Good Mind) is the guardian of cattle; Asha Vahishta (Best Order/Truth and Righteousness) is the guardian of fire; Kshathra Vairya (Divine Kingdom/Dominion) is the guardian of sky; Spenta Armaiti (Bounteous Devotion) is the guardian of earth; Haurvatat (Wholeness) is the guardian of water; Ameretat (Immortality) is the guardian of plants.

The *Amesha Spentas* all have Pahlavi names as well, where Vohu Manah is known as Bahman; Asha Vahishta as Ardibehesht; Kshathre Vairya as Shahrevar; Spenta Armaiti as Aspandarmad; Haurvatat as Khordad; and Ameretat as Amardad. Each of these forces is symbolically represented in important rituals and when invoked with devotion and purity are believed to be powerfully present.

Yazatas

Next in rank to the *Amesha Spentas* come the *Yazatas/Yazads* (or "adorable ones"). They are seen neither as gods nor angels. They came to be understood as beings which assist the *Amesha Spentas* and further the well-being of the seven good creations of Ahura Mazda. Thus, for example, Asha Vahishta, the guardian of fire, is helped by Adar Yazad who is the *Yazata* for fire and Haurvatat, the guardian of the waters, is assisted by Tir Yazad who is the *Yazata* for the rains. Each *Amesha Spenta* is assisted by three or four *Yazatas* and the *Yazatas* have a particular role in helping human beings to realise the inherent nature of Ahura Mazda and to achieve an all-embracing happiness rooted in recognising the nature of Wisdom. Many Zoroastrians say that this makes them like angels.

The Role of Humanity

In Zoroastrian teaching, the first human was the hermaphrodite, Gayomard who had both male and female offspring. Of all the beings created by Ahura Mazda, humans are the most able to come to understand the Good Mind (*Vohu Manah*). They have been given a *Fravashi* (guardian angel).

This immaterial essence and directing principle operates through wisdom, innate reason, intellect, will and conscience to enable them to make genuine choices between good and evil thoughts, words and deeds. Ahura Mazda has given humanity this freedom to choose between the forces of good and evil. Human beings, therefore, are the makers of their own destiny according to the choices they make. The *Fravashi* is believed to operate on the basis of wisdom, innate reason, intellect and will, all of which are understood to be filtered through conscience.

The Concept of Death and Afterlife

In Zoroastrianism, death is seen as the separation of body and soul. On the morning after the fourth day after death, it is believed that the *urvan* (soul) is judged at the *Chinvat Bridge (Bridge of the Separator)*. Its good thoughts, words and deeds are weighed in the balance against the evil and the *urvan* either ascends to the *House of Song* (heaven) or falls from the bridge into the abyss of the *House of Deceit* (hell) which, in Zoroastrian texts, is pictured as cold and dark.

Saoshyant, The End Time, Resurrection, Last Judgement and Frasho-keriti

There is some contemporary debate about the details of these beliefs but, in classical Zoroastrian belief, the soul was believed to continue to exist after death in heaven or hell until the end of time. It was believed that, at the end of time the forces of evil would be completely destroyed by the good and the *Saoshyant* (Saviour) would raise the dead and initiate judgement.

Everyone was believed to pass through "an ocean of molten metal" in which the good would feel the "molten metal" as "cool milk", while the imperfect would be cleansed before joining the blessed. Time would cease to exist and the world would return to its original perfect state of total goodness and harmony known to Zoroastrians as *Frasho-keriti* (Making Wonderful).

ZOROASTRIAN LIFE

Zoroastrian Ethics

Asha (truth/righteousness) is the central principle of Zoroastrian ethics. It is related to *Vohu Manah* and includes within it all virtues. Among the choices which confront human beings in the cosmic battle between good and evil are those between good thoughts, good words and good deeds and bad thoughts, bad words and bad deeds; between happiness and despair; between optimism and pessimism; between joy and misery; between moderation and deficiency or excess; between truth and falsehood; between order and chaos; between light and darkness; between charity and greed; between life and death.

Zoroastrians are urged to live life to the full and to enjoy the good creation. Zoroastrians, who believe that Ahura Mazda made the whole of the material world, including plants and animals, have always been very environmentally conscious. *Fasting* and celibacy are seen as weakening human beings and lessening their power to struggle against evil and as rejecting the divine gift of the good life. Moderation is encouraged. Zoroastrian ethics enjoin an active, industrious, honest and charitable life.

Initiation

Navjote (Gujarati for "new birth") or *Sedreh-Pushi* (Farsi for "wearing *sedreh*") are names for the initiation ceremony for the children of Zoroastrian parents. The actions of a child born of Zoroastrian parents are held to be the responsibility of its parents until the child has undergone this ceremony. Although in earlier times the ceremony took place at the age of fifteen, it now usually takes place for both males and females between the ages of seven and eleven, before puberty. Exceptionally, it can be held later on, with the permission of the officiating *priest*. Friends and relatives of the child attend the ceremony which combines prayer, ritual and celebration.

Before the ceremony the initiate is given a ritual purificatory bath and is then invested with the *sudreh* and *kushti* (see below) and recites the *Fravarane* which is a declaration of faith said daily by Zoroastrians. The *Fravarane* begins with the words: "Come to my aid, O Mazda! I profess myself a worshipper of Mazda, I am a Zoroastrian worshipper of Mazda." It praises good thoughts, good words and good deeds, and ends by ascribing all good things to Ahura Mazda.

Sudreh and Kushti/Koshti

The *sudreh* and *kushti* are meant to be worn at all times by Zoroastrians. The *sudreh* is always worn next to the skin and is seen as "the garment of *vohumanah* (good purpose)". It is a sacred shirt which is always white in order to symbolise purity, and is made of muslin or cotton cloth. At the bottom of its v-shaped neck there is a one inch square pocket which contains a slit. This pocket is known as the *gireban* or *kisseh-kerfeh* (pocket

of good deeds) and reminds Zoroastrians that they should be filling up their lives with good deeds, but also that whatever good a person does, it is only one square inch compared to Ahura Mazda's goodness. There is also a large pouch (known as a *girdo*) at the back of the *sudreh* which represents a storehouse for future good deeds.

A small vertical dart, known as a *tiri*, comes out of the hem of the *sudreh*, the significance of which has varying interpretations. There is also a small triangular patch on the opposite side of the *tiri* which symbolises the threefold Zoroastrian teaching of good thoughts, good words and good deeds.

The *sudreh* symbolises "the advantageous path" and the *kushti* indicates the proper direction for proceeding on that path. The *kushti* is a sacred cord which is worn over the *sudreh*. It is passed three times around the waist and knotted at the front and back. It is woven from seventy-two threads of fine lambs' wool which symbolise the seventy-two chapters of the *Yasna* (Act of Worship). The *kushti* is sanctified by special prayers at every stage of the weaving.

Both *sudreh* and *kushti* are seen as a protection against evil. The *sudreh-kushti* is commonly known as the armour and sword belt of the religion, worn in the battle against evil.

Gah/Geh

For devotional purposes the twenty-four hours in a day are divided into five *Gah* (times): *Havan* (from sunrise to noon); *Rapithwan* (from noon till 3.00pm); *Uziren* (from 3.00pm to sunset); *Aiwisruthrem* (from sunset to midnight); *Ushahen* (from midnight to sunrise).

To prepare for prayer Zoroastrians wash their hands, face and all uncovered parts of the body. They untie the *kushti* and stand, holding it before Ahura Mazda, focusing on the sun, fire, or artificial light if no natural light is available, as a symbol of *asha* (truth). Prayer is then offered to Ahura Mazda and the *kushti* is retied.

The *Ashem Vohu* three line prayer is the first prayer taught to all Zoroastrian children and is concerned with *asha*. It is followed by the twenty-one word *Ahunavar* or *Ahuna Vairya*, which in the Zoroastrian scriptures is said to have been recited by Ahura Mazda when He created the world. This prayer is deemed to be the most powerful instrument of prayer in warding off evil.

Death Practices

Death is seen as the work of evil. A dead body represents the apparent triumph and presence of evil and is therefore polluting. Because of this, it is believed that disposal should be carried out as quickly as possible and in a way which is least harmful to the living. Disposal into rivers or the sea is believed to pollute the water and disposal by burial could pollute the land. Therefore, in India and Pakistan, the customary system is what is argued to be the ecologically sound exposure of the body in a *dokhma*. This is a confined building, also known colloquially as the *Tower of Silence*. In this, the body is rapidly consumed by the vultures and the bones are destroyed by the action of lime in a deep pit.

In accordance with purity laws professional corpse-bearers who enter the *dokhma* must regularly undergo a ritual purification bath. Only a small number are still in use in India and Pakistan, whilst in Iran this practice has been discontinued. In the UK, when bodies are not flown back to India, they are usually buried or cremated and the ashes interred at the Zoroastrian cemetery at Brookwood in Surrey, established in 1863.

Diet

There are no dietary requirements for Zoroastrians although, from personal choice or sometimes from deference to the wider religious population of Iran and India, many abstain from pork and beef and some are vegetarian.

ZOROASTRIAN WORSHIP

Places of Worship

Traditionally, Zoroastrian places of worship are known as *Fire Temples* because a consecrated fire burns perpetually inside them. A reverence for fire is found within the broader Aryan tradition which pre-dates Zarathushtra. The use of temples was introduced into Zoroastrianism during the times of the Achaemenid kings in around the fifth century BCE.

Before entering the worship hall, Zoroastrian men and women must bathe, remove shoes, cover their heads when praying, and then perform the *kushti* ritual in the entrance to the place of worship. There is a consecrated chamber where the fire is housed and into which only *priests* may enter. *Parsi* Zoroastrian worshippers may bow before the fire and take some cold ash to place on their forehead in order to receive the divine blessing.

Fire

Fire (*Atar* or *Adur/Adar*) is used in many Zoroastrian ceremonies and many individual Zoroastrians keep an oil lamp burning in their homes. This centrality of fire in Zoroastrian worship has led some people to describe Zoroastrians as "fire worshippers". This is, however, a misunderstanding and offensive to Zoroastrians. Zoroastrians do not worship fire but worship Ahura Mazda and venerate the *Amesha Spentas* and the *Yazatas*. Fire is seen as the creation of *Asha* and is considered a sacred force because it is a source of light and warmth as well as a symbol of truth and righteousness. Fire has therefore become an icon of Zoroastrianism.

Fire energy is understood to be the source of all other energies and of life itself throughout the universe. Standing before the fire, Zoroastrians believe they are standing in the presence of Ahura Mazda. This philosophy lies behind the *Atash Nyayesh* (Litany of Fire).

ZOROASTRIAN CALENDARS AND FESTIVALS

Calendar

The Zoroastrian view of time is a linear one which has a specific end in view with the restoration of all things to a state of wholeness and perfection. The current Zoroastrian dating system began with the date of the coronation and designation of the last Zoroastrian monarch of Sasanian Iran, Yazdegird III, whose reign commenced in 631 CE. The letters "AY" (After Yazdegird) are used to denote the year, making 2001 CE the Zoroastrian year 1400 AY.

The annual calendar is composed of twelve months with thirty days in each month. The twelfth month, however, also has five additional *Gatha* days making a three hundred and sixty-five day annual calendar. Traditionally, one month was added every one hundred and twenty years in order to synchronise this calendar with the solar calendar consisting of three hundred and sixty-five and a quarter days.

In the Zoroastrian calendar, the names of the months correspond with the names of the *Amesha Spentas* and the *Yazatas*.

The *Shahenshahi* or *Yazdegerdi* calendar first adopted by the *Parsis* runs one month behind the Iranian *Kadmi* (ancient) calendar. Then the *Fasli* (solar) calendar was adopted by some *Parsis* in the diaspora. The *Fasli* calendar has dates which are fixed in alignment with the *Gregorian* calendar and is observed by the Iranian Zoroastrians.

There are therefore three calendars which might be found in use amongst Zoroastrians. The majority of Zoroastrians in the UK follow the *Shahenshahi* calendar, although it should be noted that very many Zoroastrians in the UK, and elsewhere in the world, tend to celebrate festivals such as New Year in all three calendars. The dates given below are in accordance with the solar calendar.

Festivals

Religious festivals, of which there are various kinds, play a central role in the devotional life of Zoroastrians.

Gahanbars (seasonal festivals)

These are a series of six festivals devoted to the *Amesha Spentas* and to the creation of sky, water, earth, plants, animals and people. These festivals traditionally last for five days each. They are holy days of obligation during which prayers are recited. On the final day a communal feast is held.

The first *gahanbar*, called *Maidyoizaremaya* or *Maidyu Zarem* (meaning "mid-Spring") is connected with the sky. The second, *Maidyoishema* or *Maidyu Shem* (meaning "mid-Summer") is linked with the waters. The third, *Paitishahya* or *Paiti Shahim* (meaning "bringing in the corn") is linked with the earth. The fourth, *Ayathrima* or *Ayathrem* (meaning "homecoming") is linked with plants. The fifth, *Maidhyairya* or *Maidyaryam* (meaning "mid-Winter") is linked with cattle. The sixth *gahanbar*, *Hamaspathmaedaya* or *Hamas Pathmaidyam*, also known as *Fravahrs* (meaning "*Feast of Heavenly Souls*"), is a special festival in honour of humanity's creation.

The cycle is then completed by the observance of *No-Ruz* (see below) which is the New Year festival. The dates of the *gahanbars* vary according to which calendar is used and all vary in relation to the *Gregorian* calendar. The principal observance at the *gahanbars* is the *Yasht-i-Visperad* which is a three-hours long service commencing at sunrise, giving thanks for the creations and sanctifying them with rituals and sacred words.

No-Ruz (New Year's Day - Spring Vernal Equinox) (20th/21st March)

This is one of the most important festivals signifying the imminent arrival of spring. According to popular belief, it was founded by King Jamshid of the ancient Pishdadian dynasty. It is marked by the wearing of new clothes, the holding of festivities, and the giving and receiving of presents. The *Shahenshahi No Ruz* is celebrated in August.

Khordad Sal (6th day after No-Ruz)

Celebrates the birth of the Prophet Zarathustra. Among Iranian Zoroastrians the festival is known as *Zad Rooz-e Ashoo Zartosht*.

Zarthosht no Diso (5th day, 10th month)

Marks the anniversary of Zarathushtra's death.

Muktad (25th day, 12th month)

This is the name given to the final ten days of the year observed in *Parsi* custom. Among Iranian Zoroastrians only the last five days before *No-Ruz* are observed. These days are in honour of the *Fravashis* (the heavenly selves of all people) and are usually marked by prayers and a ritual meal in honour of them. During the last five days of *Muktad*, the five *Gathas* are recited and ceremonies are performed in Zoroastrian homes and *Fire Temples*. Vases of flowers are put around homes and in *Fire Temples* to commemorate relatives who have died and prayers are recited in remembrance of them and for all human souls since it is believed that the souls of the dead pay visits at this time. The Iranian Zoroastrians also call the first five days of this period *Panje-kas* (the *Lesser Pentad*) and the last five days *Panje-mas* (the *Greater Pentad*).

Jashans

Each day and month in the Zoroastrian calendar is dedicated to an *Amesha Spenta* or *Yazata*, except for *Farvardin* which is connected with the first month and the nineteenth day, known as *Farvardingan*, observed as a day of remembrance for departed souls. In addition to the obligatory days of observance outlined above there are other festival days when the particular days and months dedicated to the *Amesha Spentas* and the *Yazatas* coincide. Marking these days

is not obligatory, but it is considered meritorious. The *Jashans* include:

Tiragan (or Tir ruz/rojand, and Tir mah) (10th day, 4th month)

A festival devoted to *Tir*, the *Yazata* of rain and fertility. The festival overlaps with the second seasonal *gahanbar* and on this day, people throw water at each other in celebration of its significance.

Mehrgan (or Meher ruz/roj, or Mehr mah) (10th day, 7th month)

An autumnal festival, dedicated to the *Yazata Mehr*, who is associated with justice and with the sun.

Ava-roj Parab (or Avaroj or Avamah) (10th day, 8th month)

Celebrated as the birthday of the waters. Special food offerings and prayers are made on this day in which Zoroastrians go to a river or to the sea-side and give thanks for its purification and pray for the nourishment of the world.

Adar-roj Parab (or Adar-roj or Adar mah) (9th day, 9th month)

Celebrated as the festival of fire on which, traditionally, food is not cooked in the house so that fire is allowed to rest whilst Zoroastrians give thanks for the warmth and light which come from it throughout the year. Special prayers are offered in the presence of the house fire.

Sadeh (10th day, 11th month)

An open air mid-winter festival celebrated with bonfires and held fifty days before *No-Ruz*. It celebrates the discovery of fire by Hoshang Shah, believed by Zoroastrians to have been an historical figure of the Pishdadian dynasty.

Jashan ceremonies include the representation of the sevenfold creation by means of the display of a variety of objects. The sky is represented by a piece of metal; water is contained in a beaker; the objects are placed on the carpeted ground of the earth; plant life is represented by flowers and fruits; animal life by milk; humanity by the officiating priests; and spiritual fire by physical fire, fed by sandalwood and incense. Each of these items is offered with specific prayers to their spiritual counterparts among the *Amesha Spentas* who are, in turn, by their powerful presence believed to bless the offerings which are then shared by those present.

ZOROASTRIAN ORGANISATIONS

Organisations

The first Zoroastrian organisation in the UK was established in 1861 and was known as the Religious Fund of the Zoroastrians of Europe. Later, it became The Incorporated Parsi Association of Europe and obtained rented premises for meetings and worship and in 1925 purchased a building. In 1969 this organisation, by then known as the Zoroastrian Association of Europe, purchased a centre in West Hampstead, London. Since 1978, the organisation has been known as The Zoroastrian Trust Funds of Europe.

Although there are small numbers of Zoroastrians elsewhere in Britain and Europe, the headquarters and centre of the Zoroastrian Trust Funds of Europe (Incorporated) in London is the focus for most Zoroastrian activity in the country. The building, known as Zoroastrian House, is used for worship and other community activities.

Personnel

A *Dastur* (high priest) or a *Mobed* (authorised priest) officiates at Zoroastrian ceremonies and may be helped by *Ervad Sahebs* (assistants to the high priest). When officiating, Zoroastrian priests are dressed in white and wear the traditional *padan* (piece of white cloth) over their mouths, in order not to pollute the fire while praying. The ceremony

for initiation into the priesthood takes over a month and there are two grades of initiation. In the UK, the *Ervads* (priests) are members of priestly families who have been initiated in India and function here as priests on a part-time basis, as required.

FURTHER READING

Azargoshasb, A, *Festivals of Ancient Iran*, Tehran, 1970.

Boyce, M, *A History of Zoroastrianism*, Volume I, E J Brill, Leiden, 1976.

Boyce, M, *A Persian Stronghold of Zoroastrianism*, Clarendon Press, Oxford 1977.

Boyce, M, *Textual Sources for the Study of Zoroastrianism*, Manchester University Press, Manchester, 1984.

Boyce, M, Zoroastrians: Their Religious Beliefs and Practices, Routledge and Kegan Paul, London, 1984.

Boyce, M, Grenet, F, and Beck, R, *A History of Zoroastrianism*, Volume III, E J Brill, Leiden, 1990.

Boyce, M, *Zoroastrianism: Its Antiquity and Constant Vigour*, 1985 Columbia University Iranian Lectures, 1992.

Clark, P, *Zoroastrianism: An Introduction to an Ancient Faith*, Brighton, 1998.

Dhalla, M N, *History of Zoroastrianism*, Ubsons, Bombay, 1985.

Dauond, P (trans), *The Holy Gathas*, D J Irani, Bombay, 1924.

Hinnells, J, *Zoroastrianism and the Parsis*, Ward Lock Educational, London, 1981.

Hinnells, J, "Parsi Zoroastrians in London", in Ballard, R (ed), *Desh Pardesh: The South Asian Presence in Britain*, Hurst and Company, London, 1994, pp 251-271.

Hinnells, J, *Zoroastrians in Britain*, Oxford University Press, Oxford, 1996.

Hinnells, J, *Zoroastrian and Parsi Studies: The Selected Works of John R. Hinnells*, Ashgate, Aldershot, 2000.

Kulke, E, *The Parsis in India: A Minority as Agent of Social Change*, Weltforum–Verlag, Munich, 1974.

Mehr, F, *The Zoroastrian Tradition: An Introduction to the Ancient Wisdom of Zarathustra*, Element Books, Dorset, 1991.

Mistree, K, *Zoroastrianism: An Ethnic Perspective*, Zoroastrian Studies, Bombay, 1982.

Modi, J J, *Religious Ceremonies and Customs of the Parsis*, Bombay, 1986.

Shahzadi, F, *The Zarathushti Religion: A Basic Text*, Chicago, 1998.

Writer, R, *Contemporary Zoroastrians: An Unstructured Nation*, University Press of America, Maryland, 1994.

Writer, R, "Parsi survival in India: the role of caste", in *World Faiths Encounter*, No 10, March 1995, pp 38-47.

Zaehner, R, *The Teachings of the Magi*, Allen and Unwin, London, 1956.

Zaehner, R, *The Dawn and Twilight of Zoroastrianism*, Weidenfeld & Nicolson, London, 1961.

ZOROASTRIAN UNITED KINGDOM ORGANISATIONS

The two Zoroastrian organisations listed in this section, whilst based in the United Kingdom and having a United Kingdom role, also have a role beyond the United Kingdom itself.

World Zoroastrian Organisation*
135 Tennison Road, South Norwood, London
SE25 5NF
Tel: (020) 8660 5048
Contact: Mr Rumi Sethna
Position: Chairman
Activities: Umbrella body, youth, elderly, newsletter/journal, books
Social Groups: Iranian Zoroastrian, Parsi
Other Languages: Gujarati, Persian
A world body set up to establish and maintain contact between Zoroastrians worldwide; advance the Zoroastrian religious faith; establish charitable homes and provide grants for further education and medical treatment.

Zoroastrian Trust Funds of Europe (Inc)*
Zoroastrian House, 88 Compayne Gardens, West Hampstead, London NW6 3RU
Tel: (020) 7328 6018 **Fax:** (020) 7625 1685
Email: library@ztfe.com
Website: http://www.ztfe.com/
Contact: Mr Malcolm M Deboo
Position: Information Officer
Activities: Worship/practice/meditation, community centre, central body, umbrella body, youth, elderly, women, newsletter/journal, visits, inter-faith, resources
Social Groups: Parsi
Other Languages: Gujarati, Parsi, Persian
Affiliations: Federation of Zoroastrian Organisations; Inter Faith Network for the UK
Established in 1861, it advances the study of the Zoroastrian faith; maintains a separate burial ground; holds religious, social and communal functions; provides a place of worship and gives assistance to Zoroastrian students.

ZOROASTRIAN REGIONAL AND LOCAL ORGANISATIONS AND COMMUNITIES

Since the Zoroastrian community in the United Kingdom is not very numerous or geographically widespread or structured into many local organisations, a range of contacts are given for each local Zoroastrian community. These are organised according to the various regions into which the local sections of the directory are divided.

With regard to the Greater London region, in this chapter only, all details are under conflated regional area, borough and local section. In the majority of cases the organisations concerned cover more than one part of London.

ENGLAND	599
NORTH EAST	599
NORTH WEST	599
EAST MIDLANDS	600
WEST MIDLANDS	600
LONDON	600
SOUTH EAST	600

ENGLAND

NORTH EAST
Regional and County Bodies

North East Zoroastrian Community*
37 Kingsley Avenue, Melton Park, Gosforth
NE3 5QN
Tel: (0191) 2367443
Contact: Kersi Fanibunda
Other Languages: Gujarati

North East Zoroastrian Community*
15 St Charles Road, Spennymoor DL16 6JY
Tel: (01388) 815983
Contact: Jeeroji Fiji Kotwall
Position: County Durham Contact
Other Languages: Gujarati

NORTH WEST
City, Town or Local Bodies

Zarthusthi-Parsi-Irani Forum*
11 Prospect Avenue, Darwen BB3 1JQ
Tel: (01254) 705306
Email: zipassociates@aol.com
Contact: Maneck Meher Mehta
Position: Director
Activities: Resource, media, youth, newsletters, books, inter-faith
Other Languages: Gujarati, Persian, Avesta

North West Zoroastrian Community
5 Craigweil Avenue, Didsbury, Manchester, Greater Manchester M20 6JQ
Tel: (0161) 4457554
Email: b.avari@mmu.ac.uk
Contact: Burjor J Mehta
Position: Chair
Activities: Youth, inter-faith
Social Groups: Parsi
Other Languages: Gujarati, Farsi
Affiliations: Zoroastrian Trust Funds of Europe

North West Zoroastrian Community*
48 Bank Road, Stalybridge SK15 2LG
Tel: (01614) 457554
Contact: Mr Avari
Position: Stalybridge Contact

North West Zoroastrian Community*
121 Wood Lane, Timperley WA15 7PG
Tel: (0161) 9801921 **Fax:** (0161) 980 1921
Email: skhambatta@aol.com
Contact: Shireen Khambatta
Position: Timperley Contact
Other Languages: Gujarati

EAST MIDLANDS
Regional and County Bodies

Zoroastrian Community of the Midlands*
Rosendale Cottage, Coventry Road, Elmdon,
Birmingham B26 3QS
Tel: (0121) 782 4371
Contact: Mini Pochkhanawala
Position: Birmingham Contact

WEST MIDLANDS
Regional or County Bodies

Zoroastrian Community of the Midlands*
Rosendale Cottage, Coventry Road, Elmdon,
Birmingham B26 3QS
Tel: (0121) 782 4371
Contact: Mini Pochkhanawala
Position: Birmingham Contact

LONDON
Regional and Area Bodies

**North London Zoroastrian Association
(NOLZA)***
1 Salisbury Mansions, St Ann's Road, London
N15 3JP
Tel: (020) 8800 3698
Contact: Faridoon Madon
Position: Founder President
Activities: Resource, youth, elderly, women, inter-faith
Social Groups: Iranian Zoroastrian, Parsi
Other Languages: Gujarati, Persian

Borough and Local Bodies

BRENT

Harrow Zoroastrian Group*
53 Norton Road, Wembley HA0 4RG
Tel: (020) 8903 7791 **Fax:** (020) 89226940
Email: rostam bhedwar@aol.com
Contact: Ervad Rustom Bhedwar
Position: Chairman/Priest
Activities: Inter-faith
Other Languages: Gujarati, Farsi, Avesta
Affiliations: Zoroastrian Trust Funds of Europe

MERTON

Zoroastrians of South London*
21 Eldertree Way, Mitcham CR4 1AJ
Tel: (020) 8648 3292
Contact: Mrs Meher Kapadia
Position: Honorary Treasurer
Activities: Elderly, newsletter, inter-faith
Social Groups: Parsi
Other Languages: Gujarati

NEWHAM

Zoroastrians of East London*
109 Chestnut Avenue, London E7 0JF
Contact: Keki Kanga
Position: Newham Contact

REDBRIDGE

Zoroastrians of East London*
104 Mortlake Road, Ilford IG1 2SY
Tel: (020) 8478 8828
Contact: Councillor Filly Maravala
Position: Secretary
Activities: Worship, resource, visits, youth, elderly, newsletters
Other Languages: Gujarati, Farsi

SOUTH EAST
City, Town or Local Bodies

Zoroastrian Community of Brighton
24 Roundway, Coldean, Brighton BN1 9AQ
Tel: (01273) 686981
Contact: Mr Tehmtan Framroze

SOME OTHER RELIGIOUS COMMUNITIES AND GROUPS

INTRODUCTION 601

BRAHMA KUMARIS 603

CHRISTIAN SCIENTISTS 605

CHURCH OF JESUS CHRIST OF LATTER-DAY SAINTS 606

JEHOVAH'S WITNESSES 608

NAMDHARI SIKH COMMUNITY 610

PAGANS 613

RASTAFARIANS 615

RAVIDASSIA 616

SANT NIRANKARIS 618

SATHYA SAI SERVICE ORGANISATION 619

VALMIKIS 620

INTRODUCTION

The directory focuses primarily on nine world religious communities. However, the present chapter offers some supplementary information about a number of other forms of religious life in the United Kingdom which are not dealt with in detail within the other chapters but have, in most cases, some historical or doctrinal relationship with the nine traditions which form the directory's major subject matter.

The precise nature of these relationships is often a disputed one, particularly from the perspective of the majority traditions covered in the earlier chapters. The directory does not attempt to adjudicate on these disputes, resulting as they do from conflicting and often mutually exclusive self-understandings (although placing these traditions in this section is an acknowledgement of the existence of the issues involved). The reader may, in other contexts, see one or more of these groups referred to as "New Religious Movements", although there are also many more groups, that are beyond the scope of this directory, which might also be described by that name. For information on these, the directory is referred to INFORM (Information Network on New Religious Movements) Houghton Street, London, WC2A 2AE, Tel: (020) 7955 7654 (see display panel at the end of this chapter).

Some of the groups included in this chapter, such as the Sant Nirankaris and the Sathya Sai Baba Organisation, understand themselves in universalistic terms as spiritual traditions which can include members of different religious traditions. Paganism understands itself as being entirely independent of the traditions covered in the earlier chapters. Some forms of Pagan organisation are relatively modern but Pagans in general understand themselves as in some way representing the older indigenous religious traditions of the UK. It therefore seemed important to include some information on Pagan traditions within the directory.

Because this chapter provides only brief overviews, generally speaking only a single contact point is provided for each community and grouping listed in this chapter. This does not, however, imply that there might not be other useful points of contact.

BRAHMA KUMARIS

The Brahma Kumaris World Spiritual University is a movement based upon the teachings given earlier this century by a Sindhi businessman of Hindu religious background. He was born as Dada Lekhraj and later became known by the spiritual name of Prajapita Brahma. It is believed that Prajapita Brahma received a vision that the transformation of the world as we know it will be followed by the establishment of an earthly paradise from which competition, hunger, the pain of death and inequalities (especially between men and women) will be abolished.

The movement believes in the soul as the eternal identity of the human being which uses the costume of the body to express itself. The human soul also goes through birth and rebirth, but always in human form. God is believed to be the Supreme of all souls, an unlimited source of light, love and peace. The movement sees the universe in a cyclical process of creation, degeneration and re-creation similar to the Hindu framework of *yugas* or ages. The recreation of a paradise at the end of each cycle comes about through understanding and imbibing fundamental spiritual truths that are universal to most faiths.

The movement's world headquarters are in Mount Abu, Rajasthan, India. There are local Brahma Kumari Centres throughout India and in sixty-five countries around the world. There are forty centres in the UK. Students at these centres practice *Raja Yoga* meditation, the experience of the consciousness of the soul and the awareness of the eternal relationship with the Supreme Soul. Courses are offered in meditation and spiritual understanding. Other courses and activities include Positive Thinking, Stress Management and workshops on Inter-Personal Skills. Workshops and classes are also held in hospitals, prisons, in businesses, and for other special interest groups.

Early morning meditation classes are held daily, on Thursday mornings. Food is offered to God which is then shared with everyone who is present. Regular students of the Brahma Kumaris are vegetarian, abstain from tobacco and alcohol and are celibate. Most centres outside India are run by people who are working and who devote their free time to teaching meditation. At larger centres, some full time teachers are required who lead a *"surrendered"* spiritual life. There is no membership, but people attend centres as regular students and also help with teaching and other duties, sometimes within a few months of studying.

The Brahma Kumaris are a Non-Governmental Organisation affiliated to the United Nations and also have consultative status with the United Nations Economic and Social Council and UNICEF. In this capacity they have organised three international projects. The Million Minutes for Peace and Global Co-operation for a Better World Projects reached 129 countries. As part of their current project "Sharing Our Values for a Better World", the publication *Living Values: A Guidebook*, is in use as an educational tool in schools and community establishments in several countries. A programme is also being developed for educators entitled "Lifelong Learning: An Education in Values for the Development of Human Potential".

Brahma Kumaris World Spiritual University
Global Co-operation House, 65 Pound Lane, London NW10 2HH
Tel: (020) 8459 1400 **Fax:** (020) 8451 6480
Contact: Sister Maureen
Position: Programme Co-ordinator
E-Mail: bk@bkwsugch.demon.co.uk

Bibliography

Babb, L A, *Redemptive Encounters: Three Modern Styles in the Hindu Traditions*, University of California Press, Berkeley, 1986, pp 93-158.

Chander, J, *A Brief Biography of Brahma Baba*, Prajapita Brahma Kumaris World Spiritual University, Mount Abu, 1984.

Chander, J and Panjabi, M, *Visions of a Better World: A United Nations Peace Messenger Publication*, Brahma Kumaris World Spiritual University, London, 1994.

Kirpalani, J and Panjabi, M, *Living Values: A Guidebook*, Brahma Kumaris World Spiritual University, London, 1995.

O'Donnell, K, *Raja Yoga, New Beginnings*, Prajapita Brahma Kumaris World Spiritual University, Mount Abu, 1987.

Waling, F, "The Brahma Kumaris", in *Journal of Contemporary Religion*, Volume X, No. 1, 1995, pp 3-28.

CHRISTIAN SCIENTISTS

The Christian Science movement was founded by Mary Baker Eddy, who was born in New Hampshire, in the United States, in 1821. The Church of Christ, Scientist, was incorporated with a charter in 1879. It sought to restore what it understood to be original Christianity and particularly the lost element of the healing ministry in contrast to reliance upon conventional medical treatment. In 1908, Mary Baker Eddy founded the daily newspaper, *The Christian Science Monitor*, which is still published today.

Christian Science understands its authority to be drawn from the *Bible*. Its complete teachings are set out in the textbook entitled *Science and Health with Key to the Scriptures* by Mary Baker Eddy. A Christian Scientist's understanding of God and of human beings is based on the first chapter of Genesis where it is recorded that God made man in "his own image". God, Spirit, is understood to be all-powerful, ever-present Mind, the source of all good. His creation is seen as spiritual, entirely good and free from sin, suffering and death.

Christian Scientists believe they find freedom and redemption from sin by acknowledging their God-given identity. They look to Jesus Christ as the *Way-shower* and *Exemplar*, and they seek to follow his teachings and example. They understand Jesus as exemplifying the *Christ*, his God-given nature. They accept Jesus' *virgin birth*, *crucifixion*, *resurrection* and *ascension*.

The Christian Science movement thus emerged from within the Christian community, and understands itself as within it, although this self-understanding would be disputed by many of the organisations listed in the chapter on "Introducing the Christian Community", particularly on the basis of differences in understanding the person and role of Jesus.

The movement is organised in branch *churches* which are each expected to maintain a *Reading Room* in which Christian Science literature may be read, borrowed or bought. On Wednesday evenings at Christian Science *churches Testimony Meetings* are held where people testify about the healings which they have experienced. The movement has *Practioners* who devote their lives full-time to practising the Church's healing methods.

Church of Christ, Scientist

Christian Science Committee on Publication, 2 Elysium Gate, 126 New Kings Road, London SW6 4LZ
Tel: (020) 7371 0060 **Fax:** (020) 7371 9204
Contact: Mr Alan Grayson
Position: District Manager for Great Britain and Ireland
Internet: http://www.tfccs.com/

Bibliography

Christian Science Publishing Society, *A Century of Christian Science Healing*, The Christian Science Publishing Society, Boston, 1966.

Eddy, Mary Baker, *Science and Health with Key to the Scriptures*, First Church of Christ, Scientist, Boston, 1994.

Peel, Robert, *Spiritual Healing in a Scientific Age*, Harper and Row, Cambridge, 1988.

CHURCH OF JESUS CHRIST OF LATTER-DAY SAINTS

The *Mormons*, as they are often popularly known, are officially named The Church of Jesus Christ of Latter-day Saints. They claim to be a Christian *Church* and assert that there are three basic Christian positions. The first is that of the *Churches* claiming an unbroken line of *Apostolic Succession*, such as the *Roman Catholic* and *Eastern Orthodox Churches*. The second is that of those *Churches* which claim a *Reformation* was necessary to restore the doctrinal integrity of the *Church*. The third is the position of The Church of Jesus Christ of Latter-day Saints which believes that apostasy has led to the need for a restoration of the true *Church*, believing that this restoration had to be divine not human.

Mormons claim that they are that *Restored Church* in these, the *Latter-days*. They use the term *saints* in the *New Testament* sense to indicate a believer (as distinct from someone who has been *canonised* as a *saint*).

Mormons differ from other Christian *Churches* in a number of other ways: they do not accept the teaching of the *Trinity* and affirm that the Godhead of Father, Son and Holy Ghost are three separate and distinct Beings. They also teach that the Father and the Son have physical bodies. They believe that their *Church President* is a *prophet* who receives continuing revelation from God.

The *Church* was founded in Fayette, New York, USA by Joseph Smith who became its first *President*. He claimed a mandate from God, through an event in 1820 that *Mormons* call the *First Vision* and which they believe consisted of the appearance of God the Father and His Son, Jesus Christ to the young Smith. In 1827, Smith published *The Book of Mormon: Another Testament of Jesus Christ*. The *Church* uses this as scripture alongside the *Bible* in its King James version. Two other works are accepted as scripture: the *Doctrine and Covenants* and the *Pearl of Great Price*.

The *Church* formally came into existence in 1830. Its first foreign mission was to Britain, in 1837, and its oldest continuous branch anywhere in the world is in Preston, Lancashire. By the year 1996, its worldwide membership was 9,500,000, with 170,000 British members.

The worldwide governing body of the *Church* is the *First Presidency* (the *President* and two *Counsellors*). They are assisted by *The Council of the Twelve Apostles* and by *The Councils of the Seventy*. Worldwide, the *Church* is organised into *stakes* (the equivalent of a *diocese*), *wards* (organised local units), and *branches* (embryonic *wards*). Government is through *priesthood*, with two orders: the *Aaronic Priesthood* (for males aged twelve and upwards and judged worthy) and the *Melchizedek Priesthood* (a higher order for men aged eighteen and over).

The *Church* is well known for its *missionary work*. Many members (usually nineteen to twenty-one year old men) dedicate two years of their lives to serve as unpaid *missionaries* wherever they are sent. Members are encouraged to live by a health code known as *The Word of Wisdom*. This encourages healthy living and discourages the use of stimulants such as alcohol, tea and coffee.

The *Church* has *chapels* for regular public worship, but its *temples* are reserved for *sacred ordinances* and are entered only by members in good standing. *Temples* exist throughout the world, of which there are two in the United Kingdom. One of these is in Lingfield, Surrey and the other is in Chorley, Lancashire.

The family is viewed as of critical importance and its ultimate expression is believed to be found in *temple ordinances* for both the living and the dead. These *ordinances* include a course of instruction on the *gospel*. This course is known as an *endowment*. It is accompanied by a rite known as *sealing*, in which husbands and wives, who will previously have been married in a civil ceremony, extend their vows beyond this life to "time and all eternity".

In a similar ceremony parents are also *sealed* to their children and any existing children would be brought in, after the *sealing* of the couple, and *sealed* to them at that point. Any future children are automatically *sealed* to their parents and do not need to be *sealed* to them by an additional ceremony as they are deemed to be born "under the *covenant*".

Mormons believe that *temple* blessings may be offered to those of their family who have died. They practice *baptism* and, following genealogical research, they extend the offer of *baptism* through what they understand as *New Testament*-style proxy *baptisms* (I Corinthians 15 v 29). Proxy *sealings* are also performed. Throughout, though, the right to choose remains. Deceased ancestors have the full right to accept or reject *ordinances* performed on their behalf. Such *baptisms* are not recorded on membership records. Mormons refer to this proxy work as a "labour of love", offered freely, without compulsion.

The *Church* believes in good inter-faith relationships and it also co-operates with other *Churches* in worthwhile social and humanitarian projects designed to relieve suffering and uphold Christian values. Because of what it perceives to be its unique position as the divinely-inspired restored *Church* it does not, however, participate in *ecumenical* councils, believing that *ecumenism* can lead to doctrinal compromise.

Church of Jesus Christ of Latter-day Saints
751 Warwick Road, Solihull B91 3DQ
Tel: (0121) 711 2244, Ext 202
Fax: (0121) 709 0180
Contact: Mr Bryan J Grant
Position: Director of Public Affairs

Bibliography

Arrington, L J and Britton D, *The Mormon Experience: A History of the Latter-day Saints*, Allen and Unwin, London, 1979.

Hinckley, G B, *Truth Restored*, The Church of Jesus Christ of Latter-day Saints, 1979.

Ludlow, D H (ed), *Encyclopaedia of Mormonism*, Macmillan, New York, 1992.

Smith, J F, *Essentials in Church History*, Deseret News Press, Salt Lake City, 1942.

JEHOVAH'S WITNESSES

The Jehovah's Witness movement was founded by Charles Taze Russell, who was born into a Presbyterian Christian family in Pennsylvania, North America, in 1852. After a period of religious scepticism, between 1870 and 1875 he became deeply engaged in the study of the *Bible* with a group of six people. He issued a pamphlet entitled *The Object and Manner of the Lord's Return*, arguing for the spiritual nature of *Christ's* second coming.

In 1879, Russell founded *Zion's Watch Tower* and *Herald of Christ's Presence*. The Zion's Watch Tower Society was established in 1881 and, in 1884, the Society was granted a legal charter for "the dissemination of *Bible* truths in various languages" by means of publications.

Russell then produced a seven volume series of doctrinal works now known as *Studies in the Scriptures*. At a convention of the Society in 1931, a motion was adopted that the Society should from then on be known as Jehovah's Witnesses. The emphasis of the movement's activity moved increasingly towards witness in the streets and on the doorsteps of people's homes. In seeking to share their faith with others, where the *New World* translation of the *Bible* is available in the language of the people concerned this is used in preference to other translations, since it is understood to be a literal translation from the original biblical languages of Hebrew, Aramaic and Greek.

The local units of the Jehovah's Witness organisation are the *congregations* which meet in what are known as *Kingdom Halls* and are organised under the direction of a body of *elders*. The *congregations* are linked together into *circuits*. These, in turn, are grouped in *districts*. Worldwide, their work is overseen by a small governing body.

Jehovah's Witnesses base their religious authority upon an appeal to the *Bible*. For Jehovah's Witnesses, Jesus is viewed as God's Son, but not as "Jehovah God". He is seen as the first creation of Jehovah. The holy spirit is seen as the active force of Jehovah and Jehovah's Witnesses therefore reject the doctrine of the *Trinity* held by the historic Christian *Churches*.

Jehovah's Witnesses view obedience to government authorities as part of their worship to God. They believe the *Bible* requires Christians to obey the law, pay taxes, show honour to government officials, and be willing to do good work in the community.

They do not dictate what stand their fellow believers or others should take on issues regarding military service, political voting, or flag saluting. Such decisions are left to each individual Witness to resolve in harmony with the *Bible* and his or her *Bible*-trained conscience. However, when Witnesses choose not to enter the armed forces, they are free to perform alternative civilian duty if this is required and if their *Bible*-trained conscience so allows them.

This position of political neutrality is rooted in the belief that the only true government is that of Jehovah who rules in heaven alongside Jesus Christ and 144,000 individuals who were once earthly humans. Jehovah's Witnesses believe that, in the near future, Jehovah will replace all human government with his own. The earth will become again like Eden and the righteous of all the ages of the earth will be resurrected to live in harmony under Jehovah's rule.

To become a Jehovah's Witness involves a period of study of the *Bible* with other Jehovah's Witnesses. Then the person dedicates himself or herself formally to witnessing to, and serving, Jehovah God and is fully immersed in *baptismal* water to mark this new life of witness. Jehovah's Witnesses see witnessing to Jehovah's work and divine purpose as essential in their faith. Door to door witnessing is part of this.

Jehovah's Witnesses
Watch Tower House, The Ridegway,
London NW7 1RN
Tel: (020) 8906 2211
Fax: (020) 8906 3938

Bibliography

Beckford, J, *The Trumpet of Prophecy: A Sociological Study of Jehovah's Witnesses,* Basil Blackwell, Oxford, 1975.

Watchtower Bible and Tract Society, *Jehovah's Witnesses, Proclaimers of God's Kingdom,* Watchtower and Bible Tract Society, 1993.

NAMDHARI SIKH COMMUNITY

All Namdhari Sikhs are *Amritdhari* (initiated) and adhere strictly to the teachings of all the Sikh *Gurus* and believe in a continuing succession of living *Gurus* starting with the founder *Satguru* Nanak Dev. They believe with equal reverence in the Sikh scriptures of the *Adi Granth Sahib* and the *Dasam Granth Sahib*.

It is their fundamental belief that the tenth Guru, *Satguru* Gobind Singh did not pass away at Nander (Maharastra) in 1708 as Sikhs generally believed, but actually lived until 1812. The Namdharis further believe that the *Guruship* still continues with the successive living *Gurus* rather than that it has been conferred on the *Adi Granth*. For Namdharis, there has been no change in the status of the *Adi Granth* since the time of the fifth *Guru*, *Satguru* Guru Arjan Dev. In the understanding of Namdhari Sikhs the institution of scripture and of *Guruship* continue side by side, and do not coincide.

The Namdhari Sikhs believe that the eleventh Namdhari *Guru*, *Satguru* Balak Singh (1785-1862), was installed to *Guruship* by *Satguru* Gobind Singh. The twelfth Namdhari *Guru*, *Satguru* Ram Singh (born 1816 and exiled to Burma in 1872) was succeeded by *Satguru* Hari Singh (1819-1906) who, in turn, passed the *Guruship* to *Satguru* Partap Singh (1890-1959). The present supreme spiritual head of over 2.5 million Namdhari Sikhs world-wide is His Divine Holiness Sri *Satguru* Jagjit Singh ji Maharaj who was born in 1920 and attained *Guruship* in 1959. It is this principle of a continuous succession and presence of a supreme spiritual authority forever in a living *Satguru* which distinguishes the Namdharis.

Satguru Ram Singh revived and reformed the Sikh principles laid down by earlier Sikh *Gurus* by challenging the distortions which many saw as having crept into the Sikh community over the years. As a sign of the restoration of the Sikh code of ethics and their social, moral, religious and political spirit, *Satguru* Ram Singh unfurled a white triangular Flag on the day of the *Baisakhi* Festival on 12 April 1857, symbolising freedom, truth, unity, love, purity, simplicity and peace. On this day the Namdhari *Panth* (*Sant Khalsa*) was inaugurated. In India's political records, Namdharis are also known as *Kukas* ("shouters", in their state of mystical ecstasy). They were pioneers in the struggle for the freedom of India from the British Raj and hold an honourable place in the history of the independence of India. Today Namdharis are pacifists.

Namdharis are initiated by their living *Satguru* (True *Guru*) with the sacred *Nam* known as *Gurmantar* (God's Holy word), whispered into their ears secretly. The practice of *Nam* was originated by the *Satguru* Nanak and is used for silent recitation with meditation for the purpose of spiritual realisation, under the direct guidance and grace of their living *Satguru*.

Namdhari Sikhs are strict vegetarians and totally abstain from all intoxicating drinks containing drugs and any foods which contain animal products. They are also widely known for their very simple mass marriage ceremonies in the presence of their *Satguru* and they have an intense love for devotional and traditional Indian classical music. Namdharis can easily be recognised from their white turbans tied horizontally across their forehead and the white woollen *mala* or rosary (made with 108 knots) used in their meditation and prayer.

Namdharis are found in many countries all over the world. Their international headquarters is at Sri Bhaini Sahib, Ludhiana District in Punjab, India. It is estimated that there are around 10,000 Namdhari Sikhs in the UK.

National Organisation

Namdhari Sangat UK (The Sant Khalsa Spiritual Institute of the Namdhari Sikh Community in the UK)

Contact: can be made through the Publicity Secretary, Mr Vasdev Singh Bhamrah, 4 Hawthorne Road, Blakenhall, Wolverhampton WV2 3EH
Tel: (01902) 332964 **Fax:** (01902) 332964

or

Contact: can also be made through the General Secretary Namdhari Sangat, Leicester Mr Ranjit Singh Flora, 60 Ring Road, Leicester LE2 3RR
Tel: (0116) 2127719 **Fax:** (0116) 2127719
Tel: (0116) 2994242 **Fax:** (0116) 2994242

Namdhari Sikh Gurdwaras and Community Centres in the UK

Gurdwara Namdhari Sangat

96 Upton Lane, Forest Gate,
London E7 9LW
Tel: (020) 8257 1460

Namdhari Sikh Community Centre

Unit 6, Balfour Buss Centre, Balfour Road,
Southall, Middlesex UB2 5BD
Tel: (020) 8893 6071

Gurdwara Namdhari Sangat and Namdhari Sikh Community Centre

1199 Coventry Road, Hay Mills,
Birmingham B25 8DF
Tel: (0121) 7530092

Gurdwara Namdhari Sangat

61 Louis Street, Leeds, West Yorkshire
LS7 4BP
Tel: (0113) 2625095

Bibliography

Achint, N D, *Sikh-Gurus Avtar*, Namdhari Darbar, Ludhiana, 1998.

Ahluwalia M M, *Kukas: The Freedom Fighters of Punjab*, Allied Publishers, New Delhi, 1965.

Bali, Y and Bali, K, *The Warriors in White: Glimpses of Kooka History*, Har Anand Publications, New Delhi, 1995.

Cole, W and Singh Sambhi, Piara, *The Sikhs: Their Religious Beliefs and Practices*, Routledge and Kegan Paul, London, 1978.

Grewel, G Singh, *Freedom Struggle of India and Sikhs in India* (2 volumes), Sant Isher Singh Rarewala Education Trust, Ludhiana, 1991.

Hanspal, H, *Namdharis Before and After Independence*, Punjabi Press, New Delhi, 1989.

Kaur, Beant, *The Namdhari Sikhs*, Namdhari Sangat, UK, London, 1999.

MacLeod, W, *Textual Sources for the Study of Sikhism*, Manchester University Press, Manchester, 1984.

Singh Bhai N and Singh Bhai K, *Rebels Against the British Rule*, Atlantic Publishers and Distributors, New Delhi, 1989.

Singh, Fauja, *Eminent Freedom Fighter of Punjab*, Punjabi University, Patiala, 1972.

Singh Gurmit, *Sant Khalsa*, Usha Institute of Religious Studies, Sirsa, 1978.

Singh, Jaswinder, *Kuka Movement*, Atlantic Publishing, New Delhi, 1985.

Singh, Khushwant, *A History of the Sikhs (Volume II)*, Oxford University Press, New Delhi, 1977.

Singh Nahar, *Guru Ram Singh & Kuka Sikhs*, R K Printings (Vol 1, 2 and 3), New Delhi, 1966.

Singh Nihal, *Enlighteners, Namdhari Sahit Parkashan*, Sri Jiwan Nagar, 1966.

Singh Sanehi, "The Nature of Guruship According to the Namdhari Tradition", in McMullen, C (ed), *The Nature of Guruship*, Christian Institute for Sikh Studies, Batala, 1976.

Suri, V, *Ludhiana District Gazette, People - Namdhari*, Government of Punjab, Chandigarh, 1970.

Wells, S and Bhamrah, V, Singh, *Meeting the Namdhari Sikhs*, Wolverhampton Inter Faith Group, Wolverhampton, 1991.

PAGANS

Paganism is not a single, structured religion. Pagans understand it to be an indigenous religious outlook which is nature-venerating and recognises many deities, both goddesses and gods. Some Pagan traditions in the UK pre-date other major religious traditions. Among contemporary Pagans there are those who believe that modern Paganism is in continuity with these pre-Christian traditions. Paganism is distinguishable from *Satanism* which can be seen either as a deliberate inversion of Christianity or else as a celebration of personal power, pride and potential.

There are a number of Pagan traditions. Some Pagans follow their own inspirations whilst others are trained in particular disciplines, including the *Craft* (or *Witchcraft* for which some prefer the name *Wicca*), *Druidry*, *Odinism* (*Asatru*), *Shamanism*, *Women's Traditions*, and *Men's Traditions*. Whilst there are significant differences between these aspects of Paganism, most Pagans share in common an ecological vision and involvement that is born of Paganism's belief in the organic vitality and spirituality of the natural world.

Some Pagans practise *Magical* techniques ranging from the folk traditions of herbalism through to the use of elaborate techniques of visualisation and high ritual drama. Such practice is understood as "the art and science of changing reality according to the Will" and may be supplemented by mystical techniques which aim at a radical transformation of consciousness.

The *Craft* or *Wicca* is an initiatory path aiming at communion with the powers of Nature and the human psyche which aims at self-transformation. Within these traditions men are initiated as *priests* and women as *priestesses*. In the UK, four main traditions of the *Craft* can be found - *Gardnerian, Alexandrian, Traditionalist* and *Hereditary. Gardnerians* claim lineage from Gerald Gardner who was central in the modern revival of the *Craft; Alexandrians* identify with Alex and Maxine Sanders who developed Gardner's ideas; *Traditionalists* claim

that their methods pre-date *Wicca's* twentieth-century revival and have been passed down to them; *Hereditaries* claim traditions passed on through relations of blood and marriage in particular families. Each *Craft* tradition is formed of many local independent groups, sometimes called *covens*, but an increasing number of people celebrate alone and are known as *solitaries*.

There are over twenty Pagan *Druid Orders* although not all *Druid Orders* are Pagan. Some of the *Druid* groups understand themselves to be Christian; some are Celtic; others are folk in character; some are committed to religious mysteries; and others are more populist in orientation. A Council of British Druids meets to discuss matters of concern to all *Druids*. Some are teaching groups based upon correspondence courses whilst others focus on particular sacred locations, such as Stonehenge or Glastonbury.

The *Hutta* tradition is found in many forms but is centred around the *Aesir*, which are culture deities and the *Vanir*, which are vitality and fertility deities. Both groups of deities are part of the pre-Christian traditions of Northern Europe. Some people within these north-west European traditions prefer the word *Asatru* (meaning "trust in deities"). Others, who have a particular affinity with the deity Odin, prefer the name *Odinist*.

Shamanism is extremely diverse. Today *Shamanism* often refers to the tradition of Pagans who do not belong to *Druid, Heathen* or *Craft* groups and who meet in relatively unstructured and very participatory gatherings without belonging to identifiable traditions or groups within Paganism. Some *Shamans* describe themselves as *Wiccan, Druidic* or as *Women's Mystery Shamans*. Others, however, underline the specifically *Shamanistic* nature of their path which emphasises the reality of the spirit world and the *Shaman's* role as an intermediary with this world or as a guide through it.

All modern Pagan traditions have been influenced in some way by feminism, with which they share many concerns. Women's spirituality is therefore respected in all Pagan traditions and Women's Spirituality groups relate to the vision of the Goddess or of Goddesses. Some Pagan women work within existing traditions whilst others have established their own traditions.

A few Men's groups have been formed to celebrate male spirituality by exploring male mysteries and initiatory cults, either ancient or modern.

Pagan Federation

BM Box 7097, London WC1N 3XX
President: Prudence Jones
Media enquiries: (01209) 831850
Fax: (01691) 671066
Email: Secretary@paganfed.org
Contact: Sally Fisher (Secretary) or Andy Norfolk (Media Officer)
Internet: http://paganfed.org
http://pagandawn.org

Bibliography

Aswynn, F, *Leaves of Yggdrasil: a Synthesis of Runes, Gods, Magic, Feminine Mysteries and Folklore*, Llewellyn, 1990.

Carr-Gomm, P and Murphy-Gibb, D, *The Druid Renaissance*, Harper Collins, London, 1996.

Crowley, V, *Wicca: The Old Religion in the New Age*, Thorsons, 1996.

Crowley, V, *Principles of Paganism*, Thorsons, 1996.

Dobson, B P (ed), *The Little Red Book: The International Guide to Pagan Resources and Events*, Oakleaf Circle, Preston, 1996.

Gadon, E, *The Once and Future Goddess*, Aquarian, Wellingborough, 1990.

Harvey, G, *Listening People, Speaking Earth: Contemporary Paganism*, Hurst & Co, London, 1997.

Harvey, G and Hardman, C, (eds), *Paganism Today*, Thorsons, 1996.

House of the Goddess (ed), *The Pagan Index*, House of the Goddess, London, 1994.

Hutton, R, *The Pagan Religions of the British Isles: Their Nature and Legacy*, Blackwell, Oxford, 1993.

Hutton, R, *The Triumph of the Moon*, Blackwell, Oxford, 1999.

Jennings, P, *Norse Tradition, A Beginner's Guide*, Hodder Headline, London, 1998.

Jones, P and Pennick, N, *A History of Pagan Europe*, Routledge, London, 1995.

MacLellan, G, *Shamanism*, Piatkus, London, 1999.

Matthews, J (ed), *Choirs of God: Revisioning Masculinity*, Mandala Books, 1991.

Pagan Federation, *Pagan Federation Information Pack*, Pagan Federation, London, (new edition), 2001 (packs are also available on *Druidry*, *Wicca*, and the *Northern Tradition*).

Pennick, N, *Practical Magic in the Northern Tradition*, Thoth, Northampton, 1994.

Starhawk, *The Spiral Dance*, Harper and Row, New York, 1989.

RASTAFARIANS

The name Rastafarian derives from *Ras* (Prince) Tafari who, in 1930, became Emperor Haile Selassie I of Ethiopia, and is seen as being the 225th descendent in direct line of succession from King Solomon, having the titles *King of Kings, Lord of Lords* and *Conquering Lion of the Tribes of Judah*.

The origins of the contemporary Rastafarian movement are to be found in the experience of the dispossessed black people of a racially stratified Jamaica in the early part of this century. In this context, a variety of movements developed which sought to emphasise the dignity and pride of the black inheritance and promised the possibility of African political and economic independence. One of those who was significant in this regard was Marcus Garvey, who prophesied the crowning of a black king. In studying the *Bible* in the light of contemporary events, groups of people came to see Haile Selassie as the *Lion of the Tribe of Judah* foretold in the *Book of Revelation* and what Rastafarians refer to as Ras Tafari Livity came into being.

The beliefs of Rastafarians can be quite varied. However, there is a general belief that, following what Rastafarians characterise as his physical "disappearance", the presence of Haile Selassie can still be accessed as *Jah*. Accordingly, Rastas use the terminology of "I and I" instead of referring to "me" or "you", and this indicates the indwelling of *Jah* within human beings. Rastas also refer to the image of *Babylon* as a symbol of the totality of the godless system of the western world which is destined to collapse. Life outside Africa is experienced in terms of exile and suffering, but with the hope of an *Exodus* - a return to Ethiopia. As a symbol of continuous independence this stands for something far more than the present geographical boundaries of the modern state of Ethiopia.

Rastafarians often have a strong emphasis on living in harmony with the natural world and, accordingly, most are vegetarians and some are vegans. Many Rastafarians abstain from alcohol and tobacco, although the use of cannabis is seen as being sanctioned by the *Bible*. The *Bible* is seen as a divine Word, interpreted by Rastafarians through collective reading, study and debate, which is known among Rastafarians as *reasoning.*

Uncut, plaited hair, known as *dreadlocks*, are found amongst most male Rastafarians. The colours of black, red, green and gold (standing, respectively, for the black race; the memory of the blood of slavery; the promised land; and a golden future) are often found in combination in the clothing of Rastafarians.

There are a whole range of Rastafarian organisations and groups in the United Kingdom. Although some Rastafarians have rejected western Christianity as a white religion, some have been baptised as members of the Ethiopian Orthodox Church. Further information and advice on Rastafarians can be obtained from:

Rastafarian Society, The
290-296 Tottenham High Road, London
N15 4AJ
Tel: (020) 8808 2185 **Fax:** (020) 8801 9815

Bibliography

Cashmore, E, *Rastaman: The Rastafarian Movement in England*, George Allen and Unwin, London, 1979.

Clarke, P, *Black Paradise: The Rastafarian Movement*, Aquarian Press, Wellingborough, 1986.

Plummer, J, *Movement of Jah People: The Growth of the Rastafarians*, Press Gang, Birmingham, 1978.

RAVIDASSIA

Ravidassia is the name of the community which takes its name from Guru Ravidass, who was born in Benares (Varanasi), the sacred city of the Hindu tradition, in northern India, in the first quarter of the fifteenth century CE. At this time, the religious situation in India was very complex and poor people felt greatly oppressed by the tyranny of high-*caste* society. Guru Ravidass was one of the prime exponents of a movement which pre-dated the emergence of Sikhism and which aimed to reform society through the preaching of *bhakti* (devotion) to God and the equality of humankind, and declared that God was accessible to all.

Against this background, Guru Ravidass struggled against the powerful in society in order to work for justice, equality and social freedom for all. Contemporary Ravidassia are inspired by his philosophy which encourages them to seek to create a classless society in which all may live with equal rights and freedom. They follow the teachings and philosophy of Guru Ravidass and worship the holy book the *Sri Guru Granth Sahib*, within which forty-one hymns composed by Guru Ravidass are included. Ravidassia believe that these hymns were presented to Guru Nanak, the founder of the Sikh religion, at Benares and were later included the *Guru Granth Sahib*. The Ravidassia community has its own identity, religious practice and symbols. They greet one another with the words "Jai Gurdev". Their *Jaikara* is "Jo Bole So Nirbhai....Guru Ravidass Maharaj Ji Ki Jai".

There are nineteen Guru Ravidass *sabhas* (associations) in the UK. Each *sabha* is a charity through its membership of the Sri Guru Ravidass Sabha UK which is registered with the Charity Commission. Each local *sabha* has its own *bhawan* (temple) but all are governed by the Supreme Council of the Sri Guru Ravidass Sabha UK, which operates from its head office at the Sri Guru Ravidass Bhawan in Handsworth, Birmingham. Also affiliated to this Supreme Council are Guru Ravidass *bhawans* in France, the USA and Canada. The identity of the Ravidassia Community is registered with relevant local authorities in the United Kingdom.

The *sabha*, a worship place for the community, also looks after its social, educational and cultural interests. The Supreme Council produces programmes to co-ordinate and organise activities which are designed to benefit the community in its leading of a peaceful and successful life in the UK.

Ravidassia celebrate Guru Ravidass's birthday as a major event and hold celebrations on the birthdays of the Sikh *Gurus* and other prominent *saints* who participated in the *Bhakti* movement to reform society. The Ravidassia are committed to peace but do not participate in any political activities.

Sri Guru Ravidass Sabha UK

Shri Guru Ravidass Sabha, Shri Guru Ravidass Bhawan, Union Row, Handsworth, Birmingham B21 9EN
Tel: (0121) 5548761 **Tel:** (07711) 701048 (mobile)
Email: brij_dhande@hotmail.com
Contact: Mr Brij Lal Dhande
Position: Assistant General Secretary

Bibliography

Cole, W O and Sambhi, P Singh, *A Popular Dictionary of Sikhism*, Curzon Press, London, 1990.

Juergensmeyer M, *Religion as Social Vision: The Movement Against Untouchability in 20th Century Punjab*, University of California Press, California, 1982.

Kalsi, S Singh, *The Evolution of a Sikh Community in Britain: Religious and Social Change Among the Sikhs of Leeds and Bradford*,

Community Religions Project Monograph Series, University of Leeds Department of Theology and Religious Studies, Leeds, 1992.

Nesbitt, E, "Pitfalls in Religious Taxonomy: Hindus and Sikhs, Valmikis and Ravidasis," in *Religion Today*, Volume VI, 1, 1990, pp 9-12.

Nesbitt, E, *My Dad's Hindu, My Mum's Side are Sikh: Issues in Religious Identity*, ACE Research and Curriculum Paper, Charlbury National Foundation for the Arts Education, Warwick, 1991.

Webster, C B, *Popular Religion in the Punjab Today*, ISPCK, Delhi, 1974.

SANT NIRANKARIS

The Sant Nirankari Mission (Universal Brotherhood) acts under the guidance of His Holiness Satguru Baba Hardev Ji with the aim of removing the barriers of difference created by ignorance. It does not profess to be a new religion, but rather a spiritual movement, the aim of which is to unite humankind. Universal brotherhood does not subscribe to any form of casteism and believes in complete equality and responsible living in society. The Mission has a high regard for all religions and spiritual movements and is based on the teaching, set out by His Holiness Satguru Baba Hardev Ji that "True religion unites, never divides".

The Mission believes that spiritually enlightened beings realise the value of human life and recognise the presence of the formless God, Nirankar, in every individual. Through such enlightenment material, social and religious divisions melt away, and are replaced by the bridges of compassion, respect, and fellow feeling. His Holiness Baba Ji does not seek to remove individuality. Rather, it is hoped that there can be unity in diversity which the movement believes is already turning into reality through devotees throughout the world who live together in peace and harmony. It is hoped that through such efforts, humankind will once again enjoy the peace and joy that it deserves.

The Mission's headquarters are based in Delhi, India, where it has its largest following, although it also has a significant presence in other parts of the world. In the United Kingdom, the Mission is a registered charity by the name of Sant Nirankari Mandal UK, under which there are currently twenty-two registered branches. It has been a leading member in promoting blood donation camps as well as having involvement in numerous charitable activities and emergency aid services.

Sant Nirankari Mandal UK
217–219 Cheshire Road, Smethwick
BS67 6DJ
Contact: The General Secretary

Bibliography

Chadha, Khem Raj, *Enlightening the World, Volumes I & II*, Sant Nirankari Mandal, Delhi, 1994.

Kalsi, S Singh, *The Evolution of a Sikh Community in Britain: Religious and Social Change Among the Sikhs of Leeds and Bradford*, Community Religions Project Monograph Series, University of Leeds Department of Theology and Religious Studies, Leeds, 1992.

Lal, Krishan, *The Mission and the Missionaries*, Sant Nirankari Mandal, Delhi, 1987.

Sargar, Kirpar, *Understanding the Sant Nirankari Mission*, Sant Nirankari Mandal, Delhi, 1994.

Satyarthi, J R D, *Gurudev Hardev*, Sant Nirankari Mandal, Delhi, 1988.

Seekree, H S, "The Sant Nirankaris", in Webster, C B, *Popular Religion in the Punjab Today*, ISPCK, Delhi, 1974, pp 26-29.

SATHYA SAI SERVICE ORGANISATION

Sai Baba was born in a tiny village called Puttaparthi in southern India in 1926 and began a mission at the age of fourteen. He teaches that basic human nature is divine and that the purpose of this life is the realisation of that divinity. He states that this will occur through leading a moral life, rendering selfless service to those in need, and developing love and respect for all life.

Sai Baba says that he has not come to disturb any religion but to confirm each in his own faith so that a Christian may become a better Christian, a Muslim a better Muslim, a Hindu a better Hindu. He teachers that love is the core of all religion and that this love crosses the boundaries of religion and embraces the whole of humanity.

Sai Baba has established elementary and secondary schools, colleges, a major university, clinics, hospitals and, more recently, a speciality hospital, all of which provide services without charge.

The Satya Sai organisation is global, being found in 137 countries. In the UK, there are over 145 centres and groups, consisting of people from all faiths and walks of life who practise Sai Baba's teachings through spiritual disciplines, education in human values and selfless service. The organisation understands itself as a spiritual organisation which embraces all faiths.

Sathya Sai Baba Organisation
9 Currie Gardens, Pasteur Close, Colindale, London
Tel: (020) 8200 3594
Contact: Mr Ishver Patel
Position: President

Bibliography

Bowen, D, *The Sathya Sai Baba Community in Bradford: Its Origin and Development, Religious Beliefs and Practices*, Community Religions Project Monograph Series, University of Leeds, Leeds, 1988.

Hislop, J S, *Conversation with Bhagawan Sn Sathya Sai Baba*, Sri Sathya Sai Books and Publications Trust, Prashanti Nilayam, India.

Kasturi, N, *Sai Baba: Sathyam Sivam Sundaram*, Sri Sathya Sai Books and Publications Trust, Prashanti Nilayam, India.

Krystal, P, *Sai Baba: The Ultimate Experience*, Aura Books, Los Angeles, Califomia.

Mason, P and Laing, R, *Sai Baba: The Embodiment of Love*, Sawbridge Enterprises, London.

Murphet, H, *Sai Baba Avatar*, Macmillan India Ud, Madras.

Sandweiss, S, *Sai Baba The Holy Man and the Psychiatrist*, Birth Day Publishing Company, San Diego, Califomia.

Sathya Sai Speaks Volumes 1 to 31, Sri Sathya Sai Books and Publications Trust, Prashanti Nilayam, India.

VALMIKIS

The Valmiki community derives its name from the *Maharishi* Valmiki, who is believed to have written the Hindu holy book, the *Ramayana*. Valmikis believe that they lived in India before the Aryan invasion and had a very rich and developed culture. The foundation of their social life was based upon the philosophy of *dharma*, *karma* and non-violence and the society was not divided into castes. Hence, Valmikis do not recognise the *caste* system as formulated in the later Hindu scriptures called the *Manusmriti*.

Valmikis focus upon the main themes of the Holy *Ramayana* as being: kingly obligations, parental authority, filial duty, wifely devotion, brotherly love, friendly loyalty, love and care for the environment and the whole creation. These are the values which are believed to reflect the spirit of the times and community to which the Holy *Ramayana* belonged. They also still form the basis of the Valmiki way of life here in the UK and all over the world.

Maharishi Valmik Sabha
2, St Luke's Road, Holbrooks, Coventry
CV6 4JA
Tel: (01203) 688744 **Tel:** (01203) 662845
Contact: Dr Davinder Prasad
Position: Vice President

Bibliography

Nesbitt, E, "Pitfalls in Religious Taxonomy: Hindus and Sikhs, Valmikis and Ravidasis," in *Religion Today*, Volume VI, 1, 1990, pp 9-12.

Nesbitt, E, "Religion and identity: The Valmiki community in Coventry", in *New Community*, Volume XVI, No. 2, pp 261-274.

For information on new religious movements

INFORM

Information Network Focus on Religious Movements

Houghton Street
London WC2A 2AE

Tel: (020) 7955 7654
Fax: (020) 7955 7679

inform@lse.ac.uk
http://www.inform.ac

Office hours: Mon-Fri
10am - 4.30pm

● INFORM is a non-sectarian charity (Reg. 801729) which was founded in 1988 to help enquirers by providing information about new religious movements ("alternative religions" or "cults") which is as objective, balanced, and up-to-date as possible.

● Enquirers can contact INFORM by telephone, letter, email or fax or by making an appointment to visit the office, based at the London School of Economics in central London.

● INFORM's research covers the collection, analysis and dissemination of information about the whereabouts and diverse beliefs, practices, and organisation of new religious movements as well as about the effects that their existence can have on both their members and the rest of society.

● INFORM's international network of contacts includes scholars and organisations engaged in research, friends and relatives of members of the movements, current members and former members of the movements, and others, such as lawyers, doctors, counsellors, and NGOs with specialist knowledge in a wide variety of areas connected directly or indirectly with the subject.

● INFORM provides speakers for schools, universities, religious and other institutions. It also organises two day-long seminars each year, focusing on a particular aspect of new religions (e.g. children, law, media, conversion, leaving, finances).

Among those who contact INFORM are the friends and relatives of people who have joined one of the movements, former members, members of traditional religions and secular agencies, educational establishments, researchers, government departments, law-enforcement agencies, the media, and members of the general public.

INFORM receives funding from a variety of sources such as the Home Office, mainstream Churches and a number of foundations including the Smith's, J.P. Getty, Nuffield, Wates and the Jerusalem Trust. INFORM has a policy of not accepting money from any of the new religious movements or any organisation that might wish to prejudice the outcome of its research.

Strict confidentiality is observed concerning individual enquirers.

FINDING OUT MORE: SOME OTHER RELEVANT PUBLICATIONS AND RESOURCES

FINDING OUT MORE   623

GENERAL TEXTS ON RELIGIONS   625

DIRECTORIES OF RELIGIOUS ORGANISATIONS   628

DIRECTORIES OF ETHNIC MINORITY ORGANISATIONS 631

SOME RELEVANT RESOURCE ORGANISATIONS   633

SOME RELEVANT PUBLICATIONS   638

FINDING OUT MORE

There are many resources available for anyone who wants to find out more about any aspect of religion. Direct contact can be made with the faith community organisations listed in this directory. Some produce literature which they will be glad to send or they may have suggestions for where to go to get further information written by members of their tradition.

In addition, as a basic strategy the following sources of information can be used:

- *Whitaker's Books in Print*, which can be consulted at most bookshops, will indicate if the books you want are in print in the UK and can be ordered.

- If you do not wish to purchase the books, your local library may have the books or should be able to obtain them for you through an inter-library loan from another library in the UK.

- Other useful resources are libraries of universities with a Department of Theology, Divinity or Religious Studies, and some university collections of materials on race and ethnic relations. (Ring to ask if you can use these for reference purposes since loans are rarely possible unless you are a student or member of staff of the institution or, in some cases, can register as an external user).

- There are also useful collections of resources in Religious Education Centres. The National Society's Religious Education Centre in London at 36, Causton Street, London, SW1P 4AU, Tel: (020) 7932 1190, can tell you if there is an RE Centre in your area. (Internet site: http://www.natsoc.org.uk/RECentre/london.html)

- Electronic subject, title and key word searches of CD-ROM and on-line book and journal bibliographies and library catalogues can give you many suggestions for further reading. Ask your local library what computer search options are available through their system (there can sometimes be a charge for printing out references).

- The Internet provides a vast and growing resource for information and discussion about religions, including home pages on particular subjects, much of which is free to the user, although some is accessible only on a subscription basis. To access the Internet one needs to be able to use a computer linked to a modem and to have an Email address and an Internet search engine.

- In using the Internet it is important to be aware that whilst there is much that will be of value, there is also a lot of material of questionable worth and also some of questionable accuracy. It is therefore a resource that should be used with discernment.

- There are electronic discussion groups on the Internet, the number and scope of which is constantly changing. A full list of such Scholarly E-Conferences is available by anonymous file transfer protocol (FTP) from Diane Kovacs at the website http://www.lovacs.com/directory.html

- You can post a query on the Internet in an electronic conference on a relevant topic.

- Complete texts are accessible on the Internet and can be downloaded to PC and disc including, for example, parallel versions of some scriptures in different languages.

- With respect to electronic resources on the Christian Churches, ChurchNet UK http://www.churchnet.org.uk/ provides a valuable electronic gateway into relevant information, and for Religious Education resources, there is RE-XS http://www.re-xs.ucsm.ac.uk (available by subscription).

- *MultiFaithNet* is a self-access Internet service, offered from the University of Derby at http://www.multifaithnet.org. It includes resources on religious traditions and communities, and on inter-faith

initiatives, together with the possibility to post questions, notices and engage in on-line dialogues. It also provides a platform for *Religions in the UK: On-Line*, the electronic version of *Religions in the UK*, which is available by subscription and includes on-line search features and Internet links to the websites and email addresses of organisations featured in the directory.

Overviews of Religions

- Look up overview articles in this book, in encyclopaedias such as the *Encyclopaedia Britannica* or one of the encyclopaedias specifically dedicated to religion such as the *Macmillan Encyclopaedia of Religion*.

- Another possibility is to consult relevant chapters in readily available general overview books on world religions (see sub-section on "World Religions: Overview" in the section on "General Texts on Religions" below). It is important to remember, however, that interpretations of a given tradition's history, beliefs and practices can vary widely, and beyond basic facts there may be many different ways of describing the tradition in question.

Special Topics

- To look at a topic across all the religions or to find out more about a particular issue in one religion, check the sub-section on "World Religions: Special Topics" in the section on "General Texts on Religions" below and the "Further Reading" sections at the end of most chapters in this directory.

- An electronic keyword search of the Internet, on CD-ROM bibliographies (such as *Religion Index I*, see below) or of library catalogues can provide a mine of information to follow up on particular topics.

- The further reading on each religious community in this directory includes some translations or interpretations of sacred texts (among Muslims, it is understood that the Qu'ran cannot be adequately "translated" from the original Arabic, but only "interpreted" into other languages). In the section on "General Texts on Religions" below, you will find suggestions of publications which bring together selections from the sacred texts of various traditions.

A Note for School Students

If working on a project, it is best to get as much help as you can directly from your teacher or your nearest RE Centre (see section on "Some Relevant Organisations" in this chapter) before contacting religious organisations or University departments. Do not be surprised if not all religious organisations answer a written enquiry. Many of them are very small and may not have the staff needed to answer all the queries which they receive, even if you have helpfully enclosed a stamped and self-addressed envelope. To increase your chance of getting an answer:

- Discuss your question with your teacher. Make sure it is not too big or too vague. Focus on a clear topic.

- Write to the organisation at least two weeks before you need the information you hope that they can send you.

- Tell the person to whom you are writing exactly what sort of information you hope they can send you.

- Enclose a large, stamped and self-addressed envelope.

- If you are sent particularly helpful information it is courteous to write back and thank the organisation – especially if someone has written you a personal letter.

GENERAL TEXTS ON RELIGIONS

This section lists a selection of the large number of useful general overviews of religious traditions which exist. Some of these provide an overview of a variety of world religious traditions. Others cover particular topics across a number of religions, such as women or prayer. Still others are bibliographical in nature. Finally, there is a section which covers books which include a variety of scriptural texts from different religions. In addition to texts on the world religious traditions, there is also a selection of texts which provide an overview of the forms of organised religious life known as "New Religious Movements".

World Religions: Overviews

Al-Faruqi, I (ed), *Historical Atlas of the Religions of the World*, Macmillan, New York, 1974.

Bishop, P (ed), *The Encyclopaedia of World Faiths*, Orbis, New York, 1987.

Bowker, J, *The Oxford Dictionary of Religions*, OUP, Oxford, 1997.

Bowker, J, *World Religions*, Dorling Kindersley, London, 1997.

Bowker, J (ed), *The Oxford Dictionary of World Religions*, Oxford University Press, Oxford, 1997.

Cole, W O and Morgan, P, *Six Religions in the Twentieth Century*, Hulton Educational, London, 1984.

Eliade, M (ed), *The Encyclopaedia of Religion* (sixteen volumes), Collier Macmillan, London, 1986.

Geaves, R, *Continuum Glossary of Religious Terms*, Pinter, London, 2000.

Hardy, F (ed), *The World's Religions: The Religions of Asia*, Routledge, London, 1988.

Harris, I, Mews, S, Morris, P and Shepherd, J, *Contemporary Religions: A World Guide*, Longman, London, 1993.

Hinnells, J (ed), *A New Dictionary of Religions*, Blackwells, Oxford, 1995.

Hinnells, J (ed), *A New Handbook of Living Religions*, 2nd edition, Blackwells, Oxford, 1996.

Lurker, M, *Dictionary of Gods and Goddesses, Devils and Demons*, Routledge and Kegan Paul, London, 1987.

Rausch, D and Voss, C, *World Religions: A Simple Guide*, SCM Press, London, 1994.

Schumacher, S and Woerner, G (eds), *The Rider Encyclopaedia of Eastern Philosophy and Religion: Buddhism, Hinduism, Taoism, Zen*, Rider, London, 1989.

Smart, N, *The World's Religions: Old Traditions and Modern Transformations*, Cambridge University Press, Cambridge, 1989.

Smith, Huston, *The World's Religions*, Harper Collins, San Francisco, 1991.

World Religions: Special Topics

Brosse, J, *Religious Leaders*, W & R Chambers, Edinburgh, 1991.

Carmody, D and J, *Prayer in World Religions*, Orbis, New York, 1990.

Cohn-Sherbok, D (ed), *World Religions and Human Liberation*, Orbis, New York, 1992.

Cooey, P, Eakin, W and McDaniel, J (eds) *After Patriarchy: Feminist Transformations of the World Religions*, Orbis, New York, 1991

Hinnells, J (ed), *Who's Who of World Religions*, Macmillan, London, 1991.

Holm, J and Bowker, J (eds), *Worship*, Pinter, London, 1994.

Holm, J and Bowker, J (eds), *Making Moral Decisions*, Pinter, London, 1994.

Holm, J and Bowker, J (eds), *Myth and History*, Pinter, London, 1994.

Holm, J and Bowker, J (eds), *Attitudes to Nature*, Pinter, London, 1994.

Holm, J and Bowker, J (eds), *Human Nature and Destiny*, Pinter, London, 1994.

Holm, J and Bowker, J (eds), *Sacred Writings*, Pinter, London, 1994.

Holm, J and Bowker, J (eds), *Picturing God*, Pinter, London, 1994.

Holm, J and Bowker, J (eds), *Rites of Passage*, Pinter, London, 1994.

Holm, J and Bowker, J (eds), *Sacred Place*, Pinter, London, 1994.

Holm, J and Bowker, J (eds), *Women in Religion*, Pinter, London, 1994.

King, U, *Women in the World's Religions*, Paragon, New York, 1987.

Magida, A, *How to be a Perfect Stranger: A Guide to Etiquette in Other People's Ceremonies*, Jewish Light Publishing, Woodstock, Vermont, 1996.

Morgan, P and Lawton, C (ed), *Ethical Issues in Six Religious Traditions*, Edinburgh University Press, Edinburgh, 1996.

Prickett, J (ed), *Living Faiths: Initiation Rites*, Lutterworth, Press, London, 1978.

Prickett, J (ed), *Living Faiths: Death*, Lutterworth Press, London, 1980.

Prickett, J (ed), *Living Faiths: Marriage and the Family*, Lutterworth Press, London, 1985.

World Religions: Bibliographical Resources

American Theological Library Association, *Index to Book Reviews in Religion: An Author, Title, Reviewer, Series and Annual Classified Index to Reviews of Books Published in and of Interest to the Field of Religion*, American Theological Library Association, Evanston, Illinois, annual (since 1989 and now available on a single Religion Index CD-Rom).

American Theological Library Association, *Religion Index One: Periodicals*, American Theological Library Association, Evanston, Illinois, semi-annual (since 1949 and now available on a single Religion Index CD-Rom).

American Theological Library Association, *Religion Index Two: Multi-Author Works*, American Theological Library Association, Evanston, Illinois, annual (since 1976 and now available on a single Religion Index CD-Rom).

Barley, L, Field, C, Kosmin, B and Nielsen, J, *Reviews of United Kingdom Statistical Sources, Volume XX, Religion: Recurrent Christian Sources, Non-Recurrent Christian Data, Judaism, Other Religions*, Pergamon Press, Oxford, 1987.

Daniels, T, *Millennialism: An International Bibliography*, New York, Garland, 1992.

Carman, J and Juergensmeyer, M (eds), *A Bibliographic Guide to the Comparative Study of Ethics*, Cambridge University Press, Cambridge, 1991.

Holm, J, *Keyguide to Information Sources on World Religions*, Mansell, London, 1991.

Lea, E and Jesson A (compilers), *A Guide to the Theological Libraries of Great Britain and Ireland*, Association of British Theological and Philosophical Libraries, London, 1986.

Whitaker, *Religious Books in Print: A Reference Catalogue*, Whitaker, London, annual (since 1984).

World Religions: Texts

Burke, T, *The Major Religions: An Introduction with Texts*, Blackwell, Oxford, 1996.

Comte, F, *Sacred Writings of World Religions*, W & R Chambers, Edinburgh, 1992.

Coward, H, *Sacred Word and Sacred Text: Scriptures in World Religions*, Orbis, New York, 1991.

Markham, I (ed), *A World Religions Reader*, Blackwell, Oxford, 1996.

Smart, N and Hecht, R (eds), *Sacred Texts of the World: A Universal Anthology*, Macmillan, London, 1982.

New Religious Movements: Bibliographical Resources

Arweck, E and Clarke P B, *New Religious Movements in Western Europe: An Annotated Bibliography*, Greenwood Press, London, 1997.

Barker, Eileen, *New Religious Movements: A Practical Introduction*, HMSO, London, 1989.

Barrett, David V, *Sects 'Cults' and Alternative Religions: A World Survey and Sourcebook*, Cassell, London, 1998.

Barrett, David V, *The New Believers: Sects, 'Cults' and Alternative Religions*, Cassell, London, 2001.

Beckford, J, *Cult Controversies: The Societal Response to the New Religious Movements*, Tavistock, London, 1985.

Beckford, J, (ed) *New Religious Movements and Rapid Social Change*, Sage, London, 1986.

Clarke, P (ed), *The New Evangelists: Recruitment, Methods and Aims of New Religious Movements*, Ethnographica, London, 1987.

Dyson, A and Barker, E (eds), *Sects and New Religious Movements*, Bulletin of the John Rylands University Library of Manchester, Manchester, 1988.

Melton, G (ed), *New Age Encyclopaedia*, Gale, Detroit, 1990.

Needleman, J and Baker, G, *Understanding the New Religions*, The Seabury Press, New York, 1978.

Wallace, R, *The Elementary Forms of New Religious Life*, Routledge and Kegan Paul, London, 1983.

Wilson, B, *The Social Dimensions of Sectarianism: Sects and New Religious Movements in Contemporary Society*, Clarendon Press, Oxford, 1990.

Special Topics: Bibliographical Resources

There is an interesting range of publications which provide details on a multi-faith basis, about particular topics or themes. An example is included below of publications on health, dying, death and disposal.

Badham, P and Badham, L (eds) *Death and Immortality in the Religions of the World*, New York, Paragon House, 1986.

Berger, A, Badham, P, Kutscher, A H, Berger, Perry, Michael and Berloff, J (eds), *Perspectives of Death and Dying: Cross Cultural and*

Multidisciplinary Viewpoints, T Charles Press Publishing, Philadelphia, 1990.

Bowker, J, *The Meanings of Death*, Cambridge University Press, Cambridge, 1991.

Cobb, M *The Dying Soul*, Open University Press, Milton Keynes, 2001.

Dickenson, D and Johnson, M (eds), *Death, Dying and Bereavement,* Sage, London, 1993.

Green, J and Green, M, *Dealing with Death: Practices and Procedures*, Chapman Hall, 1992.

Henley, A and Schott, J, *Culture Religion and Patient Care in a Multi-Ethnic Society: A Handbook for Professionals*, Age Concern, London, 1999.

Hinnells, J R and Porter, Roy, (eds) *Religion, Health and Suffering,* Kegan Paul International, London, 1999.

Irish, P D, Lundquist, K and Jenkins, V, *Ethnic Variations in Dying, Death and Grief,* Taylor and Francis, 1993.

Johnson, C J and McGee, M G, *How Different Religions View Death and Afterlife,* Charles Press Publications, Philadelphia, 1998.

Kirkwood, Neville A, *A Hospital Handbook on Multiculturalism and Religion*, Morehouse, Harrisburg, 1994.

Koenig, Harold, G. *Handbook of Religion and Mental Health,* Academic Press, London, 1998.

Mondragon, D (ed), *Religious Values of the Terminally Ill: A Handbook for Health Professionals*, University of Scranton Press, 1997.

Neuberger, J *Caring for Dying Patients of Different Faiths*, Mosby, London, 1994.

P???, D, *Death and Bereavement: The Psychological, Religious and Cultural Interface*, Wharr Publishers, London, 1997

Schott, J and Henley, A, *Culture, Religion and Childbearing in a Multiracial Society*, Butterworth-Heinemann, Oxford, 1996.

Spiro, H M, McCrea, C, Mary G, and Palmer Wandel, Lee (eds), *Facing Death*, Yale University Press, New Haven and London, 1996.

DIRECTORIES OF RELIGIOUS ORGANISATIONS

This section includes details of relevant directories and handbooks on the religions covered in the directory. Some of these give less detail on particular organisations than can be found in this directory and some give more. A number are produced annually and others every few years, some on a regular and others on an irregular basis. Some of the religious community directories are now quite old, but where they have not been superseded by later editions they are included here as an historical record of the development of these communities.

Bahá'í

There is no generally available publication giving details of Bahá'í groups in the UK. However, the Bahá'í Community of the UK (27 Rutland Gate, London, SW7 1PD, Tel: (020) 7584 2566, Internet site: http://www.bahai.org.uk) maintains up-to-date listings of all Spiritual Assemblies and Local Groups.

Buddhist

Parsons, R (ed), *The Buddhist Directory: Buddhist Groups and Centres and Related Organisations in the United Kingdom and Ireland*, 7th edition, Buddhist Society Publications, London, 2000.

Christian

Most of the Christian *Churches* and some of the organisations listed in this directory have their own national and regional level directories or handbooks. At a local level many Churches Together ecumenical bodies also produce directories of their member *Churches* and organisations. Those listed below are therefore only those directories which cover a number of *Churches* or types of Christian group:

Brierley, P (ed), *UK Christian Handbook 2000/2001*, Christian Research Association, London, 1999 (biennial).
Internet site:
http://www.christianresearch.org.uk/ukch2000.htm

Brierley, P (ed), *UK Christian Handbook Religious Trends No2 2000/2001*, Christian Research Association, London, 1999 (biennial).
Internet site:
http://www.christianresearch.org.uk/rt2000.htm

Brierley, P (ed), *The Irish Christian Handbook: Lámhleabhar Chríostaí na hEireann, 1995/96*, Christian Research Association, London, 1994.

Butt, P (ed), *The Body Book: A Directory of Christian Fellowships*, 5th edition, Team Spirit Services, Romford, 1995.

Centre for Black and White Christian Partnership, *Black Majority Churches UK: Directory 2000,* Centre for Black and White Christian Partnership, African and Caribbean Evangelical Alliance, Birmingham, 2000.
Internet site: http://www.cbwcp.com

Churches Together in England, *Register of Local Ecumenical Projects and Sponsoring Bodies*, Churches Together in England, London, 1992.
Internet site:
http://www.churches-together.org.uk

Gerloff, R, "Appendix 5:I, List of Black Independent and Related Churches (including Councils of Churches) in Britain" in, *A Plea for British Black Theologies: The Black Church Movement in Britain in its Transatlantic Cultural and Theological Interaction, Volume II*, Peter Lang, Frankfurt-am-Main, Germany, 1992, pp 863-1055.

National Association of Christian Communities and Networks, *Directory of Christian Groups*, Communities and Networks, 4th edition, NACCAN, Birmingham, 2000.

Hindu

There is no generally available Hindu publication listing Hindu religious groups nationally, although lists have appeared in some general publications, e.g. Virat Hindu Sammelan, *Virat Hindu Samaj,* Milton Keynes, 1999. The National Council of Hindu Temples and ISCKON jointly maintain a database of Hindu *mandirs* which have installed deities. There are a wide range of handbooks pertaining to specific *caste* organisations, but these are not generally publicly available.

Jain

There are no publicly available Jain directories or handbooks. However, the Institute of Jainology (Unit 18, Silicon Business Centre, 26-28 Wandsworth Road, Greenford, Middlesex, UB6 7JZ, Tel: (020) 8997 2300 maintains an up-to-date database of Jain groups.

Jewish

Many local/regional Jewish Representative Councils produce their own directories of member organisations and synagogues. These include, for example, Dorsey, Sue (ed) (2001) *Leeds Jewish Representative Council: Year Book 2000/5761~62* Leeds, as do many national umbrella organisations within the Jewish community. The most comprehensive overall Jewish directory is annual and the current edition is:

Massil, S (ed), *The Jewish Year Book*, Vallentine Mitchell, London, 2001.
Internet site:
http://www.frankcass.com/vm/yearbook.htm

Muslim

Ali, M, *The Mosques in the United Kingdom and Eire and Prayer Time Table*, Ambala Sweet Centre, London, 1991.

Darr, N (ed), *Muslim Directory UK, 2000*, Muslim Directory, London, 2001.

Internet site:
http://www.muslimdirectory.co.uk

Lancashire Council of Mosques, *Annual Report 1998-1999,* Lancashire Council of Mosques, 1999.
Internet site:
http://www.lancashiremosques.org.uk

Sikh

There is no generally available up-to-date Sikh directory or handbook.

Zoroastrian

There is no generally available Zoroastrian directory or handbook. However, the Zoroastrian Trust Funds of Europe maintains details of the Zoroastrian community in the UK.

New Religious Movements

INFORM (The Information Network on New Religious Movements, based at Houghton Street, London, WC2A 2AE, Tel: (020) 7955 7654) maintains a database of details, including contact information, on New Religious Movements in the UK.

Ward, G (series ed) Dandelion, B P (Associate editor for the UK) and Poggi, I (Associate Editor for Ireland), *Religions Directory International: A Comprehensive Guide to the World's Religions, Churches, Denominations, Temples, Synagogues, Religious Organisations and Spiritual Groups: Volume I: UK and Ireland,* Apogee Books, Detroit, Michigan, 1990.

Local Religious: General

Many local and regional directories and listings exist. Details of these can often be obtained through local Racial Equality Councils, local Councils for Voluntary Service, or local libraries (which sometimes also have computerised listings). Examples of some of those which are published in the more permanent form of booklets and pamphlets are given below:

Aston Community Involvement Unit, *Newham Directory of Religious Groups,* Third Edition 1999, Aston Community Involvement Unit, London, 1999.
Internet site:
http://www.astoncharities.org.uk

Birmingham City Council Department of Planning and Architecture, *Sacred Spaces: A Guide to Birmingham's Varied Religious Buildings,* Birmingham City Council Department of Planning and Architecture, Birmingham, nd.

Bexley Directorate of Education, Libraries and Museums, *List of Local Places of Worship, 1994/95 edition,* Bexley Directorate of Education, Libraries and Museums, 1994.

Capey, C (ed), *Faiths in Focus in Ipswich and Suffolk: A Collection to Celebrate the Centenary of the World's Parliament of Religions, held in Chicago in 1893,* Ipswich, 1993.

Cornwall County Council Education Department, *Religious Education Directory Cornwall,* Cornwall County Council Education Department, nd.

Faivre, D, *Glimpses of a Holy City: A Guide to Places of Worship in Southall,* Brother Daniel Faivre, Southall, 1992.

Gwent County Council Libraries and Information Services, *Religious Organisations in Gwent,* Gwent County Council Libraries and Information Services, Gwent, 1995.

Hertfordshire County Council Education Department, *Faith Communities Handbook (Hertfordshire),* Hertfordshire County Council Education Department, Hertfordshire, 1991.

Hillingdon Standing Advisory Committee on Religious Education, *Visiting Places of Worship: A Resource Pack,* Hillingdon Standing Advisory Committee on Religious Education, Hillingdon, nd.

Community Relations Section, *A Guide to Ethnic and Faith Organisations in the Royal Borough,* Community Relations Section, Kensington, 2000.

Internet site:
http://www.rbkc.gov.uk/communityrelations

King, T (ed), *Places of Worship in Birmingham*, City of Birmingham Education Department and the Regional R E Centre (Midlands), Birmingham, nd.

Leeds City Council Department of Education, *Directory of Faith Communities in Leeds*, Leeds City Council Department of Education, Leeds, nd.
Internet site:
http://www.leeds.gov.uk/links/comlinks.ht ml

Lewisham Education Quality Assurance and Development Team and South London Multi-Faith Religious Education Centre, *Directory of Places of Worship in the London Borough of Greenwich: For School Visits as Part of Religious Education, 2nd edition*, Lewisham Education Quality Assurance and Development Team and Southwark Standing Advisory Council on Religious Education, 1995.

London Borough of Barking and Dagenham, Places of Worship Summary found at:
Internet site:
http://www.barkingdagenham.gov.uk/ leisure/index.htm

Mason, L (ed), *Religion in Leeds*, Alan Sutton, Stroud, 1994.

Mead, J (ed), *Visiting Places of Worship in Waltham Forest*, Multi-Cultural Development Service, Waltham Forest, nd.

Merton Standing Advisory Council for Religious Education, *Directory of Places of Worship in the London Borough of Merton*, Merton, nd.

Milton Keynes Justice and Peace Centre, *Milton Keynes Directory of Faiths: A Guide to the Faith Communities of Milton Keynes*, Milton Keynes Justice and Peace Centre, 1994.

Plummer, A, *Places of Worship and Clergy or Leaders' List: Borough of Greenwich*, 3rd edition, Anthony Plummer, Plumstead, 1995.

Publicity Unit of the Chief Executive's Department of the Metropolitan Borough of Trafford, *Places of Worship in the Metropolitan Borough of Trafford*, Publicity Unit of the Chief Executive's Department of the Metropolitan Borough of Trafford, Trafford, nd.

Redbridge Standing Advisory Council on Religious Education, *Redbridge Religions Directory: Handbook for Religious Education*, London Borough of Redbridge, London, 1994.

Warwickshire County Council Education Department, *A Directory of Places of Worship and Useful Contacts and Addresses for Teachers of Religious Education in Warwickshire*, Warwickshire County Council Education Department, Warwick, nd.

Westminster Information for the Community, *Places of Worship in Westminster: Churches, Mosques, Synagogues, Temples*, Westminster Libraries and Archives, Westminster, 1999.

Westminster Interfaith Programme, *Who is My Neighbour? Other Faiths in West London: A Directory*, Westminster Interfaith Programme, Southall, 1991.

Wolverhampton Inter Faith Group and Wolverhampton Multi-Cultural Support Team, *Directory of Places of Worship in Wolverhampton*, Wolverhampton Inter Faith Group and Wolverhampton Multi-Cultural Support Team, Wolverhampton, 1989.

Wycombe District Council, *Worship in Wycombe District*, Wycombe District Council, Wycombe, 1999.
Internet site:
http://www.wycombe.gov.uk/services/ voluntary.ihtml

DIRECTORIES OF ETHNIC MINORITY ORGANISATIONS

There are a number of ethnic minority directories which are not primarily concerned to cover religious groups but do, in fact, provide useful contact information for them. At local level there are many such directories and listings, the details of which can often be obtained through bodies such as local Racial Equality Councils, (Internet site: http://www.cre.gov.uk/publs/pubslist.html) local Councils for Voluntary Service, contact NCVO, Regent's Wharf, 8 All Saints Street, London, N1 9RL, Tel: (020) 7713 6161, (Internet site: http://www.ncvo-vol.org.uk/) or local libraries. The directories listed below are restricted to some which aim to give UK-wide coverage:

Confederation of Indian Organisations (UK), *Directory of Asian Voluntary Organisations, 1994/95*, Confederation of Indian Organisations, London, 1994.

Hansib Publications, *EM: Ethnic Minorities Directory: A Commercial and Social Directory of African, Asian and Caribbean Communities in Britain*, Hansib Publishing, London, 1993.

O'Maolain, C, *Ethnic Minority and Migrant Organisations, European Directory: 1996*, Joint Council for the Welfare of Immigrants, London, with the Centre for Research in Ethnic Relations, Warwick University, Coventry, 1996.

Patel, A, *Leicester Directory of Ethnic Minority Organisations 1997/98*, Corporate Equalities Team, Leicester City Council, Leicester, 1998.

Patel, C B, *Who's Who of Asians in Britain*, New Life Publications, London, 1988.

Sachar, J S, *Asian Who's Who International: Millennium Edition*, Ilford, 2000.

SOME RELEVANT RESOURCE ORGANISATIONS

There are a wide range of organisations which can give further advice on the religious traditions and organisations covered in this volume. Those listed here are organisations which can provide information spanning two or more religious traditions. This section comprises a single list in alphabetical order, not split further down, unlike most chapters, into countries of the UK, regions, towns and cities.

In the chapters on the various religious communities there are a number of entries which relate to resource organisations operating on a UK and local basis with respect to particular, individual religious traditions.

Alliance of Religions and Conservation (ARC)*
3 Wynnstay Grove, Fallowfield, Manchester
M14 6XG
Tel: (0161) 2485731 **Fax:** (0161) 2485736
Email: arc@icorec.nwnet.co.uk
Website:
http://www.religionsandconservation.org/
Contact: Martin Palmer
Position: Secretary General
Other Languages: Italian, Chinese, French, Arabic
ARC works in over sixty countries with forty one faith traditions drawn from the eleven religions who are formally part of ARC. Our role is the promotion of practical environmental work.

Art and Spirituality Network*
11 Birch Grove, Rusholme, Manchester M14 5JX
Tel: (0161) 2244985 **Fax:** (0161) 2249533
Email: info@transcendingimages.org
Website: http://www.transcendingimages.org/
Contact: Craig Russell
Position: Co-ordinator
Activities: Inter-faith, resources
Runs education programmes, workshops and exhibitions to help share the wisdom of the faith communities through the arts. For artists and others interested in using visual imagination to explore spirituality.

Banbury Area Religious Education Centre*
The Methodist Church, Marlborough Road,
Banbury OX16 5BZ
Tel: (01295) 257193
Contact: Mrs Gillian Hunt
Position: Centre Manager
Activities: Visits, inter-faith, resources

Bharatiya Vidya Bhavan, Institute of Indian Art and Culture*
4a Castletown Road, West Kensington, London
W14 9HE
Tel: (020) 7381 3086 **Fax:** (020) 7381 8758
Email: info@bhavan.net
Website: http://www.bhavan.net/
Contact: Dr H V S Shastry
Position: Academic Director
Activities: Practice/meditation, community centre, central body, youth, elderly, women, newsletter/journal, books, visits, inter-faith, resources.
Traditions: Multi-Traditional
Other Languages: Gujarati, Hindi, Tamil, Bengali
Affiliations: Bharatiya Vidya Bhavan, India; Inter Faith Network for the UK

Promotes Indian art and culture as an integral part of the culture of the UK. The Bhavan holds classes, concerts and workshops on Indian classical music, dance and drama.

BFSS National Religious Education Centre*
Brunel University, Osterley Campus, Borough Road, Isleworth TW7 5DU
Tel: (020) 8891 8324 **Fax:** (020) 8891 8325
Email: re-centre@brunel.ac.uk
Contact: Ms Lynne Broadbent
Position: Director
Activities: Newsletter/journal, books, visits, resources
We also hold INSET Training/research.

Bradford Interfaith Education Centre*
Listerhills Road, Bradford BD7 1HD
Tel: (01274) 731674 **Fax:** (01274) 731621
Email: interfaith@bradford.gov.uk
Website:
http://www.bradford.gov.uk/education/interfaith
Contact: David Fitch
Position: Co-ordinator
Activities: Visits, resources
Other Languages: Urdu, Punjabi, Gujarati, Hindi
A unique resource centre with a multi-faith team of Faith Tutors providing training to adults as a support for RE and school collective worship. An information/advice/bookshop/reference library and a library loan service is available.

Centre for Jewish Christian Relations, The*
Wesley House, Jesus Lane, Cambridge CB5 8BJ
Tel: (01223) 741048 **Fax:** (01223) 741049
Website: http://www.cjcr.cam.ac.uk/
Contact: Ms D Patterson Jones
Contact Email: d.patterson-jones@cjcr.cam.ac.uk
Activities: Newsletter/journal, books, visits, inter-faith, resources
CJCR is an independent self-financing organisation seeking to promote religious tolerance and positive interfaith response through education and dialogue. CJCR's courses, including the MA in Jewish-Christian Relations, are offered on-site in Cambridge and by distance learning.

Centre for the Study of Islam and Christian-Muslim Relations*
Elmfield House, Bristol Road, Birmingham B29 6LQ
Tel: (0121) 4152279 **Fax:** (0121) 4152279
Email: csic@bham.ac.uk
Website: http://www.bham.ac.uk/csic

Contact: Ms Carol Bebawi
Position: Secretary
Contact Email: c.a.bebawi@bham.ac.uk
Activities: Newsletter/journal, books, inter-faith, resources
Other Languages: Arabic
Affiliations: Inter Faith Network for the UK
The Centre was established in 1976. Postgraduate courses are available in Islamic Studies and Christian-Muslim relations. Staff and Students are Muslims and Christians from many countries.

Centre for the Study of South Asian Religions and Christianity*
University of Birmingham, Elmfield House, Bristol Road, Selly Oak, Birmingham B29 6LQ
Tel: (0121) 4152413 **Fax:** (0121) 4152297
Email: d.cheetham@bham.ac.uk
Website:
http://www.artsweb.bham.ac.uk/dcheetham/centre.htm
Contact: Dr David Cheetham
Position: Director
Activities: Newsletter/journal, inter-faith, resources
Other Languages: Punjabi, Gujarati
The centre represents the collaborative efforts of the local religious communities and Birmingham University. It encourages the study of inter-religious relations in both and an academic and a practical sense, particularly between religions of South Asian origins and Christianity.

Community Religions Project*
Department of Theology and Religious Studies, University of Leeds, Leeds LS2 9JT
Tel: (0113) 2333644 **Fax:** (0113) 2333654
Email: k.knott@leeds.ac.uk
Contact: Professor Kim Knott
Position: Director
Activities: Books, resources
Affiliations: Inter Faith Network for the UK

DTF Asian Books and Musicals*
117 Soho Road, Handsworth, Birmingham B21 9ST
Tel: (0121) 5151183
Email: info@dtfasianbooks.com
Website: http://www.dtfasianbooks.com/

Edinburgh International Centre for World Spiritualities*
4 William Black Place, South Queensferry, Edinburgh EH30 9PZ

Tel: (0131) 3314469
Email: neillw@hotmail.com
Website: http://www.eicws.org.uk/
Contact: Neill James Walker
Position: Principal Founder
Activities: Newsletter/journal, inter-faith, resources

The charitable purpose of the EICWS is an educational purpose. The principal subject matter of the EICWS is world spiritualities. The EICWS is developing a spirit of synergy and collaboration.

Graduate Institute for Theology and Religion*

University of Birmingham, Elmfield House, Bristol Road, Selly Oak, Birmingham B29 6LQ

INFORM (Information Network Focus on Religious Movements)*

Houghton Street, London WC2A 2AE
Tel: (020) 7955 7654 **Fax:** (020) 7955 7679
Email: inform@lse.ac.uk
Website: http://www.inform.ac
Activities: Resources
Other Languages: French

The primary aim of INFORM is to help people by providing them with accurate, balanced and up-to-date information about New Religious Movements. The information line is open from 9am to 4.30pm Monday-Friday. Also see page 621.

Interfaith Resource Centre

91 Mantilla Drive, Styvechale, Coventry CV3 6LG
Tel: (01203) 415531
Contact: Dr C S Chan

International Institute of Peace Studies and Global Philosophy*

Camlad House, Forden, Nr Montgomery SY21 8NZ
Tel: (01938) 580319
Email: lipsq@clara.net
Website: www.macedonia.co.uk
Contact: Dr Thomas Daffen
Position: Director

International Sacred Literature Trust*

1st Floor, 341, Lower Addiscombe Road, Croydon CR9 6DA
Tel: (020 8654 4004 **Fax:** (020) 8662 0777
Email: islt@dial.pipex.com
Website: http://ds.dial.pipex.com/islt
Contact: Mr Malcolm Gerratt
Position: Director
Activities: Books

Established to publish, in contemporary and literary,

English the teachings, stories, poetry and songs from humanity's vast spiritual heritage, thereby increasing tolerance through understanding.

National Association of SACRES*

Westhill RE Centre, University of Birmingham, Selly Oak, Birmingham B29 6LL
Tel: (0121) 4152258 **Fax:** (0121) 1412969
Email: g.m.teece@bham.ac.uk
Contact: Mr Geoff Teece
Position: Secretary
Activities: Umbrella body, newsletter/journal, inter-faith
Affiliations: Inter Faith Network for the UK

National Society's Religious Education Centre*

36 Causton Street, London SW1P 4AU
Tel: (020) 7932 1190 **Fax:** (020) 7932 1199
Contact: Mrs Alison Seaman
Position: Director

Founded in 1811, we aim to support everyone involved in Christian and Religious Education by providing information and advice.

Plymouth Religious and Cultural Resource Centre*

3a Watts Road, St Judes, Plymouth PL4 8SE
Tel: (01752) 254438 **Fax:** (01752) 254438
Contact: Jonathan Marshall
Position: Co-ordinator
Activities: Youth, visits, inter-faith, resources

Our main aim is to create opportunities for dialogue and understanding.

RE Centre Southern Regional Group*

Church House, 9 The Close, Winchester SO23 9LS
Tel: (01962) 624760
Email: ian.knight@chsewinchester.clara.net
Contact: Mr Ian Knight
Position: Secretary
Activities: Umbrella body, newsletter/journal, visits, resources
Affiliations: Religious Education Council of England and Wales

Religious Education and Environment Programme

8th Floor, Rodwell House, Middlesex Street, London E1 7HJ
Tel: (020) 7377 0604 **Fax:** (020) 7247 2144
Email: reep@globalnet.co.uk
Contact: Robert Vint
Position: Programme Administrator
Activities: Newsletter/journal, books, inter-faith

REEP provides down-to-earth training for teachers

of Religious Education and for staff responsible for assemblies and the moral and spiritual development of children.

Religious Education Council for England and Wales*

RE Today, Royal Buildings, Victoria Street, Derby DE1 1GW
Tel: (01332) 296655 **Fax:** (01332) 343253
Contact: Sue Hart
Position: Secretary
Contact Tel: (01405) 869317
Activities: Umbrella body
Affiliations: Inter Faith Network for the UK
The Council is a forum for those involved in Religious Education in schools whether faith communities or professional bodies.

Religious Experience Research Centre*

Department of Theology and Religious Studies, University of Wales, Lampeter SA48 7ED
Tel: (01570) 424708 **Fax:** (01570) 423641
Contact: Peggy Morgan
Position: Director
Contact Tel: (01865) 556464
Activities: Newsletter/journal, books, inter-faith, resources
Religious experience and spirituality is a central dimension in all faiths and world views. We have a research archive of accounts of experience and are engaged in research in the area.

Religious Resource and Research Centre (RRRC)*

University of Derby, Mickleover, Derby DE3 5GX
Tel: (01332) 592131 **Fax:** (01332) 622766
Email: j.hinnells@derby.ac.uk
Contact: Professor John Hinnells
Position: Centre Director
Affiliations: Inter Faith Network for the UK
A designated research centre of the University of Derby. For further details see the display pages on the RRRC and the University on page 11.

Scottish Joint Committee for Religious and Moral Education*

c/o Department of Education, Church of Scotland, 121 George Street, Edinburgh EH2 4YN
Tel: (0131) 2255722
Contact: Revd John Stevenson
Position: Secretary

Scottish Working Party on Religions of the World in Education

Department of Social Studies Education, University of Strathclyde, 76 Southbrae Drive, Glasgow G13 1BP
Tel: (0141) 0503393
Contact: Mr Chris Foxon

Sea of Faith Network*

15 Burton Street, Loughborough LE11 2DT
Website: http://www.sofn.org.uk/
Contact: Revd Stephen J Mitchell
Position: Chair
Contact Tel: (01509) 412471
Activities: Newsletter/journal, books, inter-faith, resources
The Network exists to explore and promote religious faith as a human creation. It does this by conferences, local discussion groups, publications and study courses.

Shap Working Party on World Religions in Education*

c/o National Society RE Centre, 36 Causton Street, London SW1P 4AU
Tel: (020) 7932 1194 **Fax:** (020) 7932 1199
Contact: Mr Mike Berry
Position: Administrator
Affiliations: Inter Faith Network for the UK
Shap was set up to encourage the study and teaching of world religions. Its publications include a calendar of religious festivals and an annual journal.

Slough and District Religious Studies Resource Centre*

Lea Junior School, Grasmere Avenue, Slough SL2 5JD
Tel: (01753) 822888 **Fax:** (01753) 822888
Contact: Miss Heather Collins
Position: Warden
Activities: Visits, inter-faith, resources
Affiliations: Southern Regional Group of RE Centres
Books, videos, posters and artefacts relating to main world religions available for loan from this resource centre, an independent charity. Open Tuesday/Thursday 3.30-5.30pm, Wednesday 4.30-6.00pm.

St Mungo Museum of Religious Life and Art*

2 Castle Street, Cathedral Precinct, Glasgow G4 0RH
Tel: (0141) 5532557 **Fax:** (0141) 5524744
Website: http://www.glasgow.gov.uk/
Contact: Mr Harry Dunlop

Position: Curator
Contact Email: harry.dunlop@cls.glasgow.gov.uk
Activities: Youth, women, newsletter/journal, books, visits, inter-faith, resources
The Museum opened in 1993. It communicates the importance of religion in people's lives across the world and across time using a variety of objects. The museum is becoming a focus for inter faith debate and dialogue to promote mutual understanding.

Study Centre for Christian-Jewish Relations*
17 Chepstow Villas, London W11 3DZ
Tel: (020) 7727 3597 **Fax:** (020) 7727 3597
Email: sioncentrecjr@btinternet.com
Contact: Sister Mary Kelly
Position: Co-Director
Activities: Women, inter-faith, resources
Other Languages: French
Affiliations: Sisters of Sion; Inter Faith Network for the UK
The Centre with its library and lectures provides a place for the study of Judaism and the Jewish roots of Christianity as well as a meeting ground for Christians and Jews.

Welsh Association of SACREs
Curriculum Support Service, County Hall, Mold CH7 6ND
Tel: (01352) 704103 **Fax:** (01352) 754202
Contact: Mr Gavin Graigen
Position: Secretary
Contact Tel: (01745) 354023
Other Languages: Welsh
Forum for SACREs in Wales to discuss concerns and make representations to other bodies; facilitate the sharing of experience and expertise among SACREs; and to undertake other activities benefiting RE and collective worship in Wales.

Welsh National Centre for Religious Education*
University of Wales, Bangor Normal Site, Bangor LL57 2PX
Tel: (01248) 382956 **Fax:** (01248) 383954
Email: eds00d@bangor.ac.uk
Website: http://www.bangor.ac.uk/rs/wncre
Contact: Professor Leslie J Francis
Position: Director
Contact Tel: (01248) 382566
Contact Email: l.j.francis@bangor.ac.uk
Activities: Newsletter/journal, books, inter-faith, resources
Other Languages: Welsh

Westhill RE Centre*
University of Birmingham, Westhill, Selly Oak, Birmingham B29 6LL
Tel: (0121) 4152258 **Fax:** (0121) 4142969
Email: g.m.teece@bham.ac.uk
Website: http://www.bham.ac.uk/olrc/reresources.htm
Contact: Mr Geoff Teece
Position: Director
Activities: Books, visits, inter-faith, resources
Affiliations: Federation of RE Centres

York Religious Education Centre*
College of Ripon and York St John, Lord Mayor's Walk, York YO31 7EX
Tel: (01904) 716858 **Fax:** (01904) 612512
Email: l.alexander@ucrysj.ac.uk
Website: http://www.ucrysj.ac.uk/library/yre3.htm
Contact: Lottie Alexander
Position: Centre Librarian
Activities: Resources
Affiliations: The National Society (Church of England)
The York RE Centre provides resources and a consultancy service for students and teachers. We also serve Church ministers, youth workers and all those involved in Religious Education in their own faith community and the wider community.

SOME RELEVANT PUBLICATIONS

A number of newspapers and magazines are published in the UK which serve particular communities. In some cases these are explicitly religious. In other cases they serve a community defined by ethnic or linguistic background but carry materials relating to faith traditions represented within their readership.

Details for other media resources such as national papers and television and radio can be found in such publications as the "*The Guardian Media Guide*" (2001). This also gives details of the regulatory bodies dealing with the various media.

A useful resource for organisations wishing to get their activities covered by the media is Moi Ali's *DIY Guide to Public Relations for Charities, Voluntary Organisations and Community Groups*, Directory of Social Change, 1995.

An additional field of information other than standard ones is included in the organisations listed in this section.

Al-Sharq-al Aousat*
Arab Press House, 182-184 High Holborn, London WC1V 7AP
Tel: (020) 7831 8181 **Fax:** (020) 7831 2310
Audience: Arab
Frequency: Daily

Asian Times*
148 Cambridge Heath Road, Bethnal Green, London E1 5QJ
Tel: (020) 7702 8012
Audience: South Asian

Baptist Times, The*
PO Box 54, 129 The Broadway, Didcot, Oxford OX11 8XB
Tel: (01235) 517670
Contact: Mr John Capon
Position: Editor
Frequency: Weekly

Buddhist Quarterly, The*
58 Eccleston Square, London SW1V 1PH
Tel: (020) 7834 5858 **Fax:** (020) 7976 5238
Contact: Mr Desmond Biddhulph
Position: Editor
Frequency: Quarterly

Catholic Herald, The
Herald House, Lamb's Passage, Bunhill Road, London EC1Y 8TQ
Tel: (020) 7588 3101 **Fax:** (020) 7256 9728
Contact: Dr William Oddie
Position: Editor
Frequency: Weekly

Church of England Newspaper, The*
20-26 Brunswick Place, London N1 6DZ
Tel: (020) 7216 6400 **Fax:** (020) 7216 6410
Email: cen@parlicom.com
Website: http://www.churchnewspaper.com/
Contact: C M Blakely
Position: Editor
Contact Email: colin.blakely@parlicom.com
Activities: Newsletter/journal, newspaper
Audience: Anglican
Frequency: Weekly

Church Times, The*
33 Upper Street, London N1 0PN
Tel: (020) 7359 4570 **Fax:** (020) 7226 3073
Email: editor@churchtimes.co.uk
Website: http://www.churchtimes.co.uk/
Contact: Paul Handley

Position: Editor
Activities: Newspapers
Audience: Church of England, Anglican Communion
The Church Times is the leading Anglican weekly newspaper, based in England, covering British and international news and affairs.

Churches' Advisory Council for Local Broadcasting (CACLB)*
PO Box 124, Westcliff-on-Sea SS0 0QU
Tel: (01702) 348369 **Fax:** (01702) 305121
Email: office@caclb.org.uk
Website: http://www.caclb.org .uk/
Contact: Mr Jeff Bonser
Position: General Secretary
Contact Email: jeff@caclb.org.uk
Activities: Umbrella body, newsletter/journal
Traditions: Ecumenical/Interdenominational
Audience: Christians
CACLB helps the Churches to understand, influence and be involved in broadcasting. It organises the Association of Christians in Broadcasting and the Churches' Broadcasting Conference.

Daily Jang*
1 Sanctuary Street, London SE1 1ED
Tel: (020) 7403 5833 **Fax:** (020) 7378 1653
Email: jang@globalnet.co.uk
Website: http://www.jang.com.pk/
Contact: Zahoor Niazi
Position: Editor
Contact Email: editor@jang.globalnet.co.uk
Activities: Newsletter/journal
Other Languages: Urdu
Audience: Asians from sub-continent
Frequency: Daily

Dialogue*
Al Khoei Foundation, Stone Hall, Chevening Road, Kilburn, London NW6 6TN
Tel: (020) 7372 4049 **Fax:** (020) 7372 0694
Email: postmaster@al-khoei.demon.co.uk
Contact: Sayyed Nadeem A Kazmi
Other Languages: Arabic, French
Frequency: Monthly

English Churchman Trust Ltd*
22 Fitch Drive, Brighton BN2 4HX
Tel: (01273) 818555 **Fax:** (01273) 386362
Contact: Mr Evans
Position: Office Manager
Activities: Newspapers

Audience: Christian - Protestant
A Protestant Family Newspaper

Garavi Gujarat*
Garavi Gujarat Publications Ltd, 1 Silex Street, London SE1 0DW
Tel: (020) 7928 1234 **Fax:** (020) 7261 0055
Contact: Ramniklal Solanki OBE
Position: Editor
Other Languages: Gujarati
Audience: Hindus and Muslims
Frequency: Weekly

Gujarat Samachar *
Gujarat Samachar Publications Ltd, 8/16 Coronet Street, London N1 6HD
Tel: (020) 7729 5453 **Fax:** (020) 7739 0358
Contact: Chandrakant Babubhai Patel
Position: Editor
Other Languages: Gujarati
Audience: Hindu, Jain, Muslim, Christian
Frequency: Weekly

Hindusim Today
1b Claverton Street, London SW1V 3AY
Tel: (020) 7630 8688
Email: 100700.513@compuserve.com
Contact: Acharya Palaniswami
Position: Editor
Audience: Hindu
Frequency: Monthly

Impact International*
PO Box 2493, Suite B, 233 Seven Sisters Road, London N4 2BL
Tel: (020) 7272 1417 **Fax:** (020) 7272 8934
Email: impact@globalnet.co.uk
Contact: Mr M H Faruqj
Position: Editor
Activities: Inter-faith
Frequency: Monthly

Islamic Times, The*
Raza Academy, 138 Northgate Road, Edgeley, Stockport SK3 9NL
Tel: (0161) 4771595 **Fax:** (0161) 2911390
Contact: Mr Khetab
Position: Editor
Traditions: Sunni
Movements: Barelwi, Tasawuf
Other Languages: Urdu, Punjabi, Arabic
Audience: Muslim, any other interested
Frequency: Monthly

Jewish Chronicle*
25 Furnival Street, London EC4A 1JT
Tel: (020) 7415 1500 **Fax:** (020) 7405 9040
Email: jconline@thejc.com
Website: http://www.thejc.com/
Contact: Ned Temko
Position: Editor
Contact Email: jceditor@thejc.com
Audience: Jewish
Frequency: Weekly

Jewish Quarterly*
PO Box 2078, London W1A 1JR
Tel: (020) 8830 5367 **Fax:** (020) 7629 5110
Email: jewish.quarterly@ort.org
Contact: Matthew Reisz
Position: Editor
Contact Email: editor@jewquart.freeserve.co.uk
Audience: Jewish
Frequency: Quarterly

Lotus Realm A New Voice for Buddhist Women*
Taraloka Retreat Centre, Bethsfield, Nr Whitchurch SY13 2LD
Tel: (01984) 710646 **Fax:** (01984) 710646
Email: lotusrealm@taraloka.org.uk
Contact: Dharmacharini Kalyanaprabha
Position: Editor
Audience: Buddhist women
Frequency: Two times a year

Manna*
The Sternberg Centre for Judaism, 80 East End Road, London N3 2SY
Tel: (020) 8349 5700
Contact: Rabbi Tony Bayfield
Frequency: Quarterly

Methodist Recorder*
122 Golden Lane, London EC1Y 0TL
Tel: (020) 7251 8414 **Fax:** (020) 7608 3490
Email: editorial@methodistrecorder.co.uk
Website: http://www.methodistrecorder.co.uk/
Contact: Ms Moira R Sleight
Position: Editor
Audience: Methodists
Frequency: Weekly

Mountain of Light Productions Limited*
3 Furlong Road, London N7 8LA
Tel: (020) 7700 7586 **Fax:** (020) 7700 0425
Email: info@mountainoflight.com
Website: http://www.mountainoflight.com/
Contact: Majid Hussain

Position: Co-ordinator
Contact Email: majid@mountainoflight.com
Activities: Books, resources
Traditions: Sunni
Other Languages: Arabic, Urdu, French, German
MOL is an audio visual production company with in-house studio and creative facilities. It was formed in 1994 by Yusuf Islam, the former popstar Cat Stevens.

Muslim Directory*
65a Grosvenor Road, London W7 1HR
Tel: (020) 8799 4455 **Fax:** (020) 8799 4456
Email: info@muslimdirectory.co.uk
Website: http://www.muslimdirectory.co.uk/
Contact: Naeem Darr
Position: Editor
Contact Email: naeem@muslimdirectory.co.uk
Activities: Newsletter/journal, books, resources
Other Languages: Urdu, Punjabi, Arabic
An essential guide of services and businesses for the Muslim community, media organisations, government bodies and schools.

Muslim Magazine, The*
Dexion House, 2-4 Empire Way, Wembley HA9 0EF
Tel: (020) 8903 0819 **Fax:** (020) 8903 0820
Email: info@q-news.com
Website: http://www.q-news.com/
Contact: Mr Fuad Nahdi
Position: Publisher
Contact Email: fuad@q-news.com
Audience: Muslim
Frequency: Weekly

Muslim News*
PO Box 380, Harrow HA2 6LL
Tel: (020) 7608 2822 **Fax:** (020) 7608 1232
Email: info@muslimnews.co.uk
Website: http://www.muslimnews.co.uk/
Contact: Mr Ahmed Versi
Position: Editor
Contact Tel: (07768) 241325
Contact Email: versi@muslimnews.co.uk
Audience: Muslim
Established in 1989 this weekly publication is the largest circulation newspaper in the UK for all sectors of the Muslim Community.

Punjabi Times*
PTI Media Limited, 24 Cotton Brook Road, Sir Francis Ley Industrial Park, Derby DE23 8YJ

Tel: (01332) 372851 **Fax:** (01332) 372833
Contact: Mr R Singh Purewal
Position: Chair
Other Languages: Punjabi
Audience: Sikh, English
Frequency: Weekly

Sikh Messenger*
43 Dorset Road, Merton Park, London SW19 3EZ
Tel: (020) 8540 4148
Contact: Mr Indarjit Singh
Audience: Sikh, non-Sikh
Frequency: Quarterly

Sikh Spirit*
12 Sussex Place, London W2 2TP
Tel: (0705) 0648307 **Fax:** (0870) 0567386
Email: info@sikhspirit.com
Website: http://www.sikhspirit.com/
Contact: Mr Bhupinder Singh
Position: Managing Editor
Contact Email: bsingh@sikhspirit.com
Activities: Youth, newsletter/journal, inter-faith
Other Languages: Punjabi
Affiliations: Akaal Purkh Ki Fauj
Established in 1995 as a freely distributed newsletter.
Our major activity is the running of the Sikh Spirit
website and working with other organisations in
arranging occasional seminars.

Punjabi Guardian*
Soho News Building, 129 Soho Road,
Handsworth, Birmingham B21 9ST
Tel: (0121) 5543995 **Fax:** (0121) 5071065
Contact: Inderjit Singh Sangha
Position: Director
Audience: Sikh
Frequency: Fortnightly

Sussex Jewish News*
PO Box 2178, Hove BN3 3SZ
Tel: (01273) 330550 **Fax:** (01273) 504455
Email: doris@sjnews.fsnet.co.uk
Website:
http://www.sussexjewishnews.freeserve.co.uk/
Contact: Mrs Doris Levinson
Position: Editor
Activities: Newsletter/journal, radio, inter-faith,
resources
Traditions: Cross-community
Affiliations: Brighton and Hove Jewish
Representative Council
Many people who subscribe to SJN are not

members of synagogues. It is the "oracle" of the
community, is published monthly and keeps people
informed of local Jewish events.

Tablet, The*
1 King Street Cloisters, Clifton Walk, London
W6 0QZ
Tel: (020) 8748 8484
Contact: Mr John Wilkins
Position: Editor
Frequency: Weekly

Universe, The *
Gabriel Communications, 1st Floor, St James's
Buildings, Oxford Street, Manchester M1 6FP
Tel: (0161) 2368856
Contact: Mr Joseph Kelly
Position: Editorial Director
Frequency: Weekly

Windhorse Publications*
11 Park Road, Moseley, Birmingham B13 8AB
Tel: (0121) 4499191 **Fax:** (0121) 4499191
Email: windhorse@compuserve.com
Website: http://www.windhorsepublications.com/
Contact: Dharmachari Dharmashura
Position: Chairman
Contact Tel: (0121) 4499191
Activities: Newsletter/journal, books, resources
Traditions: Western
Movements: Friends of the Western Buddhist
Order
Affiliations: Friends of the Western Buddhist
Order

THE SHAP WORKING PARTY ON WORLD RELIGIONS IN EDUCATION

For over 30 years the **Shap Working Party** has promoted good practice in the teaching of world religions.

Shap is committed to:

- Promoting excellence in the study of religions at all levels
- Supporting those who, in their professional lives, work with different religious communities
- Providing an accurate understanding of religious beliefs and practices

Shap provides:

- **An annual Calendar of Religious Festivals** appearing each year in August, covering a period of 15 months
- **A colour coded wall chart** of the festivals
- **A laminated festivals mini-chart** to fit an A5 desk diary or personal organiser
- **An annual Journal** on a different theme each year
- **A handbook on teaching** world religions, for teachers
- A revised edition of '**Festivals in World Religions**' (RMEP, 1998);

*Further details of **Shap publications** and subscriptions to the Journal and/or the Calendar can be obtained from:

The Administrator,
The Shap Working Party,
c\o NSREC,
36 Causton Street,
London SW1P 4AU
Tel: 020 7932 1194 Fax: 020 7932 1199
Email: mike.berry@london.anglican.org

ACKNOWLEDGEMENTS

INTRODUCTION

The Multi-Faith Directory Research Project which led to this 2001 edition was funded by the University of Derby and The Inter Faith Network for the United Kingdom.

Many individuals and organisations have offered assistance to the project. Of all the acknowledgements which should be made, the most significant must be to **Mrs Eileen Fry** and to **Mrs Michele Wolfe**.

Eileen Fry built on her previous experience of working on the 1997 edition, by assuming the larger responsibility of Project Manager for the four years which lie behind the current edition. Her efficiency and dedication to the project have been the bedrock of the project and have been evidenced in her attention to detail and sensitive handling of the mechanics of consultation, information collection and retrieval. Her strong financial management has conserved and maximised the use of the project's resources. Over her years of working on the project, Eileen has built up an extensive network of relationships and trust, both with the consultants whose role within the project is so important, with the representatives of many of the organisations listed in the directory, and with a wide range of people and organisations who find the directory to be of considerable value to them.

Throughout most of the period leading to the current edition, Michele Wolfe has contributed to the project in a variety of capacities which underline the commitment that she has brought to her work on it. Initially she worked for the project on a voluntary basis. For a period she was employed as Research Assistant to the Project Director, with a proportion of her time allocated to the directory project. For the final year of the project she was fractionally employed as a Research Assistant specifically for the directory project. But during all of this time, she has continued to offer a voluntary contribution, considerably above and beyond any contractual obligations. As well as making a general contribution across the project, Michele has had special responsibility for tracking down new sources of project information, especially in respect of other directories and listings, and for updating and developing a number of aspects of the "Finding Out More" chapter of the directory.

The current edition builds upon the 1993 and 1997 editions as well as extending them. As a partnership between the University of Derby Religious Resource and Research Centre and the Inter Faith Network for the United Kingdom, special acknowledgements are also due to the staff of the Inter Faith Network for their contributions and encouragement throughout the period of the project: **Mr Brian Pearce**, the Network's Director, to **Dr Harriet Crabtree**, its Deputy Director, and to **Mr Bhupinder Singh**, its Information Officer, for their support to the project team in Derby and their attention to detail in commenting upon drafts of the entire directory. Thanks are also due to **Ms Sharon Wilson**, **Miss Beverley Maron** and **Miss Henny Rolan** for their help in the Network office in checking sections of the listings. Special thanks are due to **Ms Rukiya Khan** of the Network office for her detailed help in the last stages of proofreading.

CONSULTATION PROCESSES AND THE CONTENTS OF THE 2001 EDITION

For the 1993 and 1997 editions of the directory, panels of consultants were convened which included both individuals from within the religious traditions concerned and a number of individuals with particular academic expertise from outside of the traditions. These panels of consultants include the individuals and organisations listed below who offered their time and expertise in commenting upon and contributing to drafts of the texts for each religious community, the section on "Religious Statistics" in the "Religious Landscape of the UK" chapter; the chapter on "Inter-Faith Activity in the UK"; and the chapters on "Visiting Places of Worship and Hosting Visits" and on "Making Contact, Organising Events and Consultations." A number of these consultants also commented helpfully on the categories of "traditions", "movements", "languages": which were used in seeking information from organisations and places of worship for use in the listings sections. They also contributed to the checking of listings of national organisations within their religions.

The 1993 edition established texts which were recognised and affirmed by consultants both from within and from outside the religions covered in the directory as providing an accurate portrayal of the traditions and communities concerned. The 1997 edition updated and, where necessary, provided additional balance to the written texts so that, based upon six years of consultative and editorial processes, they could be regarded as being as reliable a portrayal as possible.

The present edition has, by and large, only carried out significant amendment of the texts of 1997 edition where this was necessary in order to be up to date and accurate. Therefore, in large measure, the textual parts of the present edition of the directory still reflect the contributions to the drafting process made by the consultants to the 1997 edition of the directory. These consultants cannot, of course, be held responsible for any errors that may be contained in the present amended texts, as they have not been consulted on these. However, since they contributed to the preparation of these texts for previous editions, it is appropriate to acknowledge again their earlier contributions as consultants to the project. Therefore, in recognition of this, they are listed at the end of this "Acknowledgements" chapter.

The most extensive changes were made to the "Religious Landscape of the UK" chapter, with considerable changes to that on "Inter Faith Activity in the UK". In both cases, the vast majority of the changes were concerned with reflecting the changes and developments that have occurred since the publication of the 1997 edition. Some amendments to improve clarity and user-friendliness were made to the chapters on "Visiting Places of Worship and Hosting Visits" and "Making Contact, Organising Events and Consultations".

CONSULTANTS TO THE 2001 EDITION

Consultants on the Introductions to Individual Religions in the UK

Special thanks are due for their comments on the revised materials for their own religion to those who were at that time members of the Executive Committee of the Inter Faith Network for the UK:

Dr Manazir Ahsan MBE (Muslim); *Dr Fatma Amer* (Muslim); *Mrs Bhupinder Kaur Bagga* (Sikh); *Rt Revd Dr Tom Butler* (Christian); *Mrs Saraswati Dave*

(Hindu); *Mr Jaswant Singh Heera* (Sikh); *Rt Revd Charles J Henderson* (Christian); *Revd Canon Dr Michael Ipgrave* (Christian); *Mrs Angela Jagger* (Christian); *Mr Ayub Laher* (Muslim); *Mrs Saroj Lal* (Hindu); *Hon Barnabas Leith* (Bahá'í); *Mr Bipin Mehta* (Jain); *Mr Neville Nagler* (Jewish); *Mr Nitin Palan* (Hindu); *Rabbi Alan Plancey* (Jewish); *Mrs Jean Potter* (Christian); *Mrs Rosalind Preston OBE* (Jewish); *Moulana M Shahid Raza* (Muslim); *Rev Simon Reynolds* (Christian); *Mr Jehangir Sarosh* (Zoroastrian); *Mr Paul Seto* (Buddhist); *Dr Natubhai K Shah* (Jain); *Mr Ramesh Shah* (Jain); *Mr Om Parkash Sharma* MBE (Hindu); *Sr Margaret Shepherd nds* (Christian); *Mr Indarjit Singh OBE* (Sikh); *Mr Jagjiwan Singh* (Sikh); *Sister Isabel Smyth* (Christian); *Rabbi Jacqueline Tabick* (Jewish); *Miss Gillian Wood* (Christian); *Most Venerable Dr Medagama Vajiragnana* (Buddhist).

The project has, however, also depended upon the voluntary contributions of a number of other individuals and organisations from within the religious communities of the UK. In relation to the directory's introductory materials on the various religions in the UK, where there was special need to check out some aspect of the chapter, consultation arrangements were established with some individuals from beyond the Officers and membership of the Network's Executive Committee. These consultants included: *Revd John C Clifford* (Unitarian and Free Christian Christian tradition); *Canon Michael Evans* (Roman Catholic Christian tradition); *Chas Raws* (Quakers/Society of Friends tradition); *Professor Jonathan Powers* (in respect of aspects of Tibetan Buddhist traditions).

Consultants on the Chapter on Visiting Places of Worship and Hosting Visits

For the chapter on "Visiting Places of Worship and Hosting Visits", the members of the Inter Faith Network Executive Committee (listed above) were consulted.

Consultants on the Chapter on Making Contact, Organising Events and Consultations

For the chapter on "Making Contact, Organising Events and Consultations", the members of the Inter Faith Network Executive Committee (listed above) were consulted.

Consultants on the Chapter on Religious Landscape of the UK

For the chapter on "The Religious Landscape of the UK", members of the Inter Faith Network Executive Committee (listed above) were consulted, as also were the following individuals with specific relevant expertise on religions in the UK:

Ms Elizabeth Arweck, King's College, University of London; *Dr Roger Ballard*, University of Manchester; *Dr Rohit Barot*, University of Bristol; *Dr Peter Brierley*, Christian Research Association; *Professor Steve Bruce*, University of Aberdeen; *Ms Mandy Clough*, Office for National Statistics; *Dr Grace Davie*, University of Exeter; *Professor Leslie Francis*, University of Wales; *Dr Sophie Gilliat-Ray*, University of Cardiff; *Revd J G Harris and Mr Hywell Evans*, Welsh National Association of Standing Advisory Councils on Religious Education; *Dr Sewa Singh Kalsi*, University of Leeds; *Professor Kim Knott*, University of Leeds; *Mr John Leigh*, Churches and Chapels Section, Office for National Statistics; *Dr Eleanor Nesbitt*, University of Warwick; *Revd Dr Stephen Orchard*, Religious Education Council; *Mr David Owen*, University of Warwick; *Dr Gerald Parsons*, Open University; *Professor Ceri Peach*, University of Oxford; *Mr David Rayner*, Inner Cities' Religious Council, Department for the Environment, Transport and the Regions; *Revd Maurice Ryan*, Stranmillis College, Belfast; *Ms Marlena Schmool*, Board of Deputies of British Jews; *Mr Greg Smith*, University of East London; *Revd John Stevenson*, Church of Scotland; *Dr Steve Vertovec*, University of Oxford.

Consultants on the Chapter on Inter-Faith Activity in the UK

For the chapter on "Inter-Faith Activity in the UK", the members of the Inter Faith Network Executive Committee (listed above) were consulted, as also were the following individuals associated with local, national and international inter-faith organisations based in the UK:

Mr Alfred Agius (Westminster Interfaith); *Mrs Gill Atkinson* (Bolton Interfaith Council); *Mrs Cynthia Bailey* (Wellingborough Multi-Faith Group); *Ms Heather Bailey* (Bedford Council of Faiths); *Revd Noel Beattie* (Medway Inter Faith Action); *Ms Carol Bebawi* (Centre for the Study of Islam and Christian-Muslim Relations); *Mrs Sandy Bharat* (International Interfaith Centre); *Mr Hugh Boulter* (Reading Inter-Faith Group); *Revd Robert Boulter* (Manchester Inter-Faith Group); *Mrs Anne Bowker* (Wycombe Sharing of Faiths); *Mr Eric Bramsted* (South London Inter Faith Group); *Revd Marcus Braybrooke* (World Congress of Faiths); *Mr Charles Bridge* (York Interfaith Group); *Mr Edward Brown* (Gateshead Interfaith Forum); *Ms Judith Bruni* (Watford Inter-Faith Association); *Mrs A Burkitt* (Frome Interfaith Group); *Mrs Cynthia Capey* (Suffolk Inter-Faith Resource); *Revd Fergus Capie* (Brent Interfaith); *Mr J B Carver* (Woking Multi-Faith Group); *Ms Elizabeth Coleman* (Newham Association of Faiths); *Revd David Cooper* (North Staffordshire Faiths in Friendship); *Revd Malcolm Cooper* (North Kent Council for Inter-faith Relations); *Revd Derek Duncanson* (Peterborough Inter-Faith Council); *Mr J A Eedle* (Beaminster One World Fellowship); *Mr John Elderton* (Wimbledon Interfaith Group); *Mrs Rosemary Eddy* (Dundee Inter-Faith Group); *Father Damian A Howard* SJ (Lambeth Multi Faith Action Group); *Mr James Fitzpatrick* (Basingstoke Association of Faiths and Cultures); *Mr Tom Flanagan* (Blackburn/Darwen Interfaith Council); *Mr Mark Fleming* (Redbridge Council of Faiths); *Mr Tony Fleming* (Taunton Inter Faith Group); *Mr Zvi Friedman* (Milton Keynes Inter Faith Forum); *Mrs Phiroza Gan* (Harrow Inter-Faith Council); *Augusta Gibrill* (Greenwich Multi-Faith Forum); *Mr Mark Graham* (Loughborough Council of Faiths); *Mrs Margaret Griffiths* (Swindon Interfaith Group); *Dr Almuth Groos* (West Somerset Inter Faith Group); *Sister Kathleen Harmon* (Nottingham Inter-Faith Council); *Mr Hiromi Hasegawa* (Norwich Inter Faith Link); *Ms Kathryn Hendry* (Aberdeen Inter Faith Group); *Mr Shanthi Hettiarachchi* (Luton Council of Faiths); *Mr Stanley Hope* (Rochdale Interfaith Action); *Rev B Hopkinson* (Cleveland Interfaith Group); *Ms Jessamine Hoskins* (Richmond Inter-Faith Group); *Revd Sandra Howes* (Sheffield Interfaith); *Ms Shelagh James* (Bath Inter-Faith Group); *Mr Bill Jones* (Kirklees and Calderdale Inter-Faith Fellowship); *Mrs Lorraine Khan* (Cardiff Interfaith Association); *Mr John Lally* (Leicester Council of Faiths); *Mrs Geraldine Layton* (Newport Inter Faith Group); *Father David Lyon* (Hyndburn Inter-Faith Forum); *Revd Jennifer Mckenzie* (Manchester Interfaith Forum); *Mr Trevor McGairl* (Swansea Inter Faith Group); *Revd Jim McManus* (Wolverhampton Inter-Faith Group); *Mr Michael*

Malik (Glasgow Sharing of Faiths Group); *Mr Jonathan Marshall* (Plymouth Interfaith Group); *Mrs Cathy Michell* (Cambridge Inter-Faith Group); *Revd Supriyo Mukherjee* (Coventry Inter Faith Group and Coventry Multi-Faith Forum); *Mr G H Musa* (Gloucestershire Inter Faith Action); *Mrs E B Noel* (of the former Worcester Inter Faith Council); *Mr Adrian Ogle* (Building Bridges, Pendle Inter Faith Group); *Mr R Parmar* (Bradford Concord Interfaith Society); *Mr David and Mrs Jean Potter* (Exeter Interfaith Group); *Mrs June Ridd* (Bristol Inter Faith Group); *Imam Dr Abduljalil Sajid, JP* (Brighton and Hove Inter Faith Contact Group); *Mr Sidney Shipton* (Three Faith Forum); *Sister Sujata* (Birmingham Council of Faiths); *Mr Hari Shukla* (Tyne and Wear Racial Equality Council); *Ms Janine Shrigley* (Derby Open Centre Multi-Faith Group); *Revd Ken Smith* (Croydon Inter Faith Group); *Revd Mark Stobert* (Dudley Council of Faiths); *Mr Kaushar Tai* (North Kirklees Interfaith Council); *Dr Elizabeth Templeton* (Edinburgh Interfaith Association); *Revd Peter Thomas* (Preston Inter-Faith Forum); *Mr S K Vadivale* (Oxford Round Table of Religions); *Mrs Phyllis Vallon* (Bury Inter-Faith Council); *Revd Michael J Walling* (Canterbury and District Inter Faith Action); *Revd Marjorie Warnes* (Leamington Spa Inter Faith Group); *Mr Frank Watkinson* (Leeds Concord, Inter-Faith Fellowship); *Revd John Whittle* (Torquay Inter Faith); *Mrs Margaret Wilkins* (Walsall Inter-Faith Group); *Revd Canon Michael Wolfe* (Merseyside Inter-Faith Group).

In addition, the following organisations were consulted:
Calamus Foundation
Council of Christians and Jews
International Association for Religious Freedom
Maimonides Foundation
Standing Conference of Jews, Christians and
  Muslims in Europe
United Religions Initiative
World Conference on Religion and Peace

Consultants on the Chapter on Some Other Religious Communities and Groups

For the chapter on "Some Other Religious Communities and Groups", the following representatives of the communities and groups that are covered were consulted:

On the Brahma Kumaris, *Sister Maureen* of the Brahma Kumaris World Spiritual University; on the Church of Christ, Scientist, *Mr Alan Grayson* of the Christian Science Committee on Publication for Great Britain and Ireland; on the Church of Jesus Christ of Latter-day Saints, *Mr Bryan Grant* of the Public Affairs Office of the Church of Jesus Christ of Latter-day Saints, Europe North area; on the Jehovah's Witnesses, the *P S Gillies* of the Public Information Desk of The Watch Tower Bible and Tract Society of Britain; on the Namdharis, *Mr Vasdev Singh Bhamrah* of the Namdhari Sangat UK; on the Sant Nirankaris, *Mr Jagjit Khambe* of the Sant Nirankari Mission; on Pagans, *Prudence Jones* of the Pagan Federation, *Dr Graham Harvey* of King Alfred's College of Higher Education, Winchester and *Dr Ronald Hutton*, University of Bristol; on the Rastafarians, *Mr Henry Nicholson* of the Rastafarian Society, London; on the Ravidassia, *Mr Brij Lal Dande* of the Sri Guru Ravidass Sabha UK; on the Sri Sathya Sai Service Organisation, *Mr Ishver Patel* of the Central Council of the United Kingdom; on the Valmikis, *Dr Davinder Prasad* of the Maharishi Valmik Sabha, Coventry.

COLLECTION AND VERIFICATION OF DIRECTORY LISTINGS

To compile the original contact lists which form the basis of the organisational listings in this directory, the project contacted all the organisations and places of worship contained in the 1997 edition. It supplemented information gained in this way with further research aimed at including organisations which were not uncovered by the research for the 1997 edition or did not yet exist at that time. For this research, the project acknowledges the co-operation and contributions of many individuals and organisations which have provided it with information and examined draft listings.

The individuals and organisations who gave substantial help throughout the project are individually named above. Gratitude for help and assistance should also be recorded to all the organisations which are affiliated to *the Inter Faith Network*; many local *Race Equality Councils*; many local *Councils for Voluntary Service*; many *Local Education Authority Religious Education Advisers*; many *Local Authority Planning Departments*; and many *Local Authority Library Services*. Not all from these organisations who assisted can be named individually here but they provided valuable information upon organisations in composing the information grid which the project used to identify organisations for possible inclusion. Together with individuals from the inter-faith organisations previously listed, and a range of national and regional faith community bodies, the following organisations specifically assisted the project in the final checking of the draft listings:

Council of Sikh Gurdwaras in Birmingham
Crawley Racial Equality Council
Edinburgh and Lothians Racial Equality Council
Essex Racial Equality Council
Greenwich Council for Racial Equality
Medway Racial Equality Council
Peterborough Racial Equality Council
Preston and Western Lancashire Racial Equality
  Council
Representative Council of North East Jewry
Royal Borough of Kensington and Chelsea
  Community Relations Section
Sussex Racial Equality Council
Swansea Bay Racial Equality Council
Wellingborough District Racial Equality Council
Wiltshire Racial Equality Council
Worcester Racial Equality Council

Acknowledgements should also be recorded to the *editors* and *publishers* of existing handbooks and directories of religious organisations and groups (which this directory is not intended to replace, but rather to complement). The project referred to these during the process of preparing to make its own direct contact with the organisations listed in this edition which had not previously been in existence or had not been uncovered by the research for the 1997 edition. Details of these handbooks and directories are to be found in the "Finding Out More: Some Other Relevant Publications and Resources" chapter of this volume.

CONSULTANTS TO THE 1997 EDITION

The chapters on different religions in the UK have not substantially altered from those included in the 1997 edition. The following is a list of those consultants to the 1997 edition who have not been consultants on the 2001 edition:

Bahá'ís in the UK

Mr Hugh Adamson, Bahá'í Community of the United Kingdom; *Dr Novin Doostar*, Bahá'í representative on the Inter Faith Network for the UK Executive Committee.

Buddhists in the UK

Mr Stephen Batchelor, Sharpham; *Mr Anil Goonewardene*, Buddhist Society; *Venerable Rathna Jothi*, East Midlands Buddhist Association; *Dharmachari Kulananda*, Friends of the Western Buddhist Order; *Mr Ron Maddox*, The Buddhist Society; *Revd Myokyo-ni*, The Zen Centre, London; *Dr Akong Tulku Rinpoche*, Kagyu Samye Ling; *Ms Dal Strutt*, The Buddhist Society; *Ms Georgina Black*, Network of Buddhist Organisations (UK) who co-ordinated wider consultation with a number of the Network of Buddhist Organisations' member organisations. Additionally consulted were *Professor Richard Gombrich*, University of Oxford; and *Dr Paul Williams*, University of Bristol. Special thanks for assistance in detailed drafting are due to *Mrs Peggy Morgan*, Westminster College, Oxford.

Christians in the UK

Most Revd Father Olu Abiola, Council of African and Afro-Caribbean Churches (UK); *Mr John Adegoke*, Centre for Black and White Christian Partnership, Birmingham; *Canon David Atkinson*, Archdeacon of Lewisham; *Father Michael Barnes*, Westminster Interfaith Programme; *Ms Vida Barnett*, Shap Working Party on World Religions in Education; *Revd Esme Beswick*, Joint Council for Anglo-Caribbean Churches; *Revd Marcus Braybrooke*, World Congress of Faiths; *Revd Eric Brown*, Afro-West Indian United Council of Churches; *Mrs Jenny Carpenter*, Churches Together in England; *Revd Canon Dr Tony Chesterman*, University of Derby, Religious Resource and Research Centre Steering Committee; *Revd Maxwell Craig*, Action of Churches Together in Scotland; *Revd Dr Colin Davey*, Council of Churches for Britain and Ireland; *Revd Noel Davies*, Churches Together in Wales; *Revd S M Douglas*, International Ministerial Council of Great Britain; *Canon Michael Evans*, Tunbridge Wells; *Venerable Ian Gatford*, University of Derby, Religious Resource and Research Centre Steering Committee; *Mrs Ivy Gutridge, MBE*,

Wolverhampton Inter-Faith Group; *Revd Basil Hazledine*, Epsom; *Revd David Heslop*, University of Derby, Religious Resource and Research Centre; *Revd Carmel Jones*, New Assembly of Churches; *Revd Canon Dr Christopher Lamb*, Churches' Commission for Inter Faith Relations, Council of Churches for Britain and Ireland; *Revd Anne McClelland*, Richmond Inter-Faith Group; *Revd Paul Quilter*, University of Derby, Religious Resource and Research Centre Steering Committee; *Revd Geoffrey Roper*, General Secretary of the Free Church Federal Council; *Revd David Staple OBE*, former General Secretary of the Free Church Federal Council; *Dr David Stevens*, Irish Council of Churches; *Rt Revd Roy Williamson*, former Church of England Bishop of Southwark.

Hindus in the UK

Mr Rameshbhai Acharya, Leicester; *Mr Vipin Aery*, National Council of Hindu Temples; *Sri Akhandadi das*, International Society for Krishna Consciousness; *Mr Raj Bali*, University of Derby, Religious Resource and Research Centre Steering Committee; *Professor Bharadwaj*, Arya Pratinidhi Sabha; *Mr A Daxini*, Shree Sanatan Mandir, Leicester; *Mr Deepak Naik*, National Council of Hindu Temples; *Dr Nandakumara*, Bharatiya Vidya Bhavan; *Mr Jitubhai Pancholi*, Swaminarayan Hindu Mission; *Mr D B Patel*, Shree Sanatan Mandir, Leicester; *Mr Navin Patel*, Swaminarayan Hindu Mission; *Rasamandala das*, ISKCON Education Service; *Dr H V Satyanarayana Shastry*, Bharatiya Vidya Bhavan; *Dr Ramanbhai Shah*, Swaminarayan Hindu Mission. Also consulted were *Dr Kim Knott*, University of Leeds; *Dr Julius Lipner*, University of Cambridge; *Dr Eleanor Nesbitt*, University of Warwick; *Dr Malory Nye*, University of Stirling. Special thanks for assistance in detailed drafting were also due to *Dr Dermot Killingley*, University of Newcastle upon Tyne.

Jains in the UK

Mr Nemu Chandaria, Institute of Jainology; *Professor Padminabh Jaini*, University of California, Berkeley, USA and Trustee of the Institute of Jainology; *Mr Vinod Kapashi*, Federation of Jain Organisations in the UK. Also consulted were: *Dr Paul Marett*, Jain Academy; *Ms Kristi Wiley*, University of California, Berkeley, USA.

Jews in the UK

Rabbi David Goldberg, London Society of Jews and Christians; *Revd Jonathan Gorsky*, Council of Christians and Jews; the late *Rabbi Hugo Gryn CBE*, West London Synagogue of British Jews; *Rabbi Dr Julian Jacobs*, Chief Rabbi's Representative on Inter-Faith Affairs; *Mr Paul Mendel*, Council of Christians and Jews; *Professor Eric Moonman OBE*, London; *Mr Robert Rabinowitz*, Jewish Continuity; *Mr Laurie Rosenberg*, Board of Deputies of British Jews; *Ms Marlena Schmool*, Board of Deputies of British Jews; *Rabbi Dr Norman Solomon*, Oxford Centre for Hebrew and Jewish Studies.

Muslims in the UK

Dr Bahadur Dalal, World Ahl ul-Bayt (AS) Islamic League; *Mr Gai Eaton*, Islamic Cultural Centre, Regent's Park Mosque, London; *Mr Mohsin Jaffer*, Islamic Education Board; *Mrs Ummul Banin S Merali*, World Ahl ul-Bayt (AS) Islamic League; *Mr Abdul Hamid Qureshi*, Lancashire Council of Mosques; *Maulana Mohammad Shahid Raza*, Imams and Mosques Council, UK; *Mr Iqbal Sacranie*, UK Action Committee on Islamic Affairs; *Mr Aslam Siddiqi*, University of Derby, Religious Resource and Research Centre Steering Committee; *Dr Ataullah Siddiqui*, Islamic Foundation; *Mr Syed Syediau*, World Islamic Mission (UK). Also consulted were *Dr Jorgen Nielsen*, Centre for the Study of Islam and Christian-Muslim Relations, Selly Oak Colleges, Birmingham and *Mr Ahmed Andrews*, University of Derby.

Sikhs in the UK

Mr Surinder Singh Attariwala, Network of Sikh Organisations (UK); *Mr Mohinder Singh Chana*, Bradford; *Dr Hardial Singh Dhillon*, University of Derby, Religious Resource and Research Centre Steering Committee; *Mr Surjit Singh Kalra*, Birmingham; *Mr Teja Singh Manget*, Sikh Missionary Society; *Mrs Satwant Kaur Rait*, Leeds; *Mr Gurpal Singh*, Bhatra Sikh Centre, Cardiff; *Dr Kartar Surinder Singh*, Sikh Council for Inter Faith Relations; *Mr Darshan Singh Tatla*, Birmingham. Also consulted were *Dr Eleanor Nesbitt*, University of Warwick and *Professor Christopher Shackle*, School of Oriental and African Studies, University of London.

Zoroastrians in the UK

Mr Malcolm Deboo, Zoroastrian House; *Mr Shahrokh Shahrokh*, London; *Dr Rashna Writer*, Birkbeck College, London. Also consulted was *Professor John Hinnells*, School of Oriental and African Studies, University of London and Professor of Comparative Religion, University of Derby.

OTHER ACKNOWLEDGEMENTS

The participation and support of the consultants to both the 1997 edition and the 2001 edition saved the project from making a number of avoidable errors and has ensured that the directory is the product of a truly co-operative process of partnership. At the same time, neither the 1997 nor the 2001 consultants are responsible for any errors which might remain through the editing process. Having acknowledged the contributions of all those above, as Editor I should, of course, state that I take responsibility for the final product of this process and that no one other than myself should bear the responsibility for any errors or imbalances which remain.

However, the collaborative nature of the project includes the contribution of others too. It is difficult individually to acknowledge all those who have contributed in so many ways and I apologise for any whose names I have left out in error.

The contributions of *Denise Benjamin*, *Famida Bhatti*, *Helen Cobb*, *Gail Haslam*, *John Pepper*, *Lydia Powell*, *Derick Thomas*, (students or former students of the University of Derby) should also be acknowledged for their voluntary services in preparing and filling the many envelopes which this project entailed. Acknowledgements are also due to *Ms Clare Chisholm*, a former General Manager of the University of Derby Student Employment Agency, for arranging the employment of *Michele Wolfe* in the earlier stages of the project and of *James Hatton* a student of the University who worked extensively on the project. *Denise Benjamin*, *Richard Fox*, *Margaret Gibson*, *Sophie Gwilliam*, *Moyra Hinojosa*, *Maria Kunica* (students or former students of the University) were employed in checking listing in the closing stages of the project.

During the project four school students worked on the project for work experience, *Kelly Gray*, *Nazia Iqbal*, *Gail Newton* and *Karan Saxena*. A number of other individuals also contributed to the project as volunteers in a variety of capacities, including *Holly Breen*, *Patricia Broad*, *Matthew Claridge*, *Andrew Fry*, *Dr Eleanor Jackson*, *Mandala Jackson*, *Sagari Rajkaruna*, *Amy Smith* and *Brian Trowbridge*.

The support of a range of past and present University of Derby staff has also been crucial to the progress of the project. For their initial support to getting the project which led to the first edition off the ground in 1990, thanks remain due to *Mr David Udall*, former Deputy Director (Academic); *Mr Trevor Easingwood*, former Deputy Director (Resources); and *Mr Michael Hall*, Deputy Vice-Chancellor, as well as to *Professor Jonathan Powers*, former Pro Vice Chancellor and now Vice Chair of the Multi Faith Centre at the University of Derby. Derby University Enterprises provided support for the development of *MultiFaithNet* which gave a platform for the electronic version of the directory, *Religions in the UK: On-Line*. *Dr Klaus Stoll* and *Mr Kay Stecher* provided the technical expertise to develop the website, *Dr Paul Trafford* who maintained and developed it and *David Craig* as Reviews Editor, as well as to *Mrs Eileen Fry* who, together with managing the Multi-Faith Directory Research Project, has also managed the *MultiFaithNet* project.

For contributions to the preparation, publication and administration of the current edition the support and contributions of the following should be acknowledged: *Ms Sue Dakin* and *Ms Fiona Wallace*, the University's Press Officers; *Helen Orchard*, *Margaret Wagstaff* and *Denise Leeson* of the Mickleover site Reception staff who process incoming and outgoing site mail and upon whose practical assistance in processing a large amount of mail, the project has depended; as well as to *Sharon Millington* in the University Finance Office, for liaison in respect of project finances. For general help and support, the contributions of *Louise Richards*, School of Education and Social Science Research Administrator, and *Sima Parmar*, secretary to the School Research Professors, should also be acknowledged.

Thanks are also due to *Paul Radcliffe* and *Dennis Parkes*, lecturers in the University's School of Mathematics and Computing, for helping to set up the organisation database. In addition, the support of the members of the University's Religious and Pastoral Services Steering Committee and of colleagues at the University of Derby within the Religious Studies subject area and the Religious Resource and Research Centre is acknowledged.

Special thanks are due to **Ms Debbie Martin, Mr David Bush** and **Mr John White** of the University Print Department; and to **Mr Neville Wells**, Head of Estates and Printing Services, for their professionalism, patience and collaborative working with project staff.

A final word of thanks is due to my wife **Greta Preisler-Weller** who, together with her patience with my commitment to this project was also a contributor to the project in her own right by designing the directory's cover used in this edition, as in the 1993 and 1997 editions; and to my parents, **Denis** and **Rhoda Weller**, for supporting me in and through the educational opportunities and professional developments which lie behind and inform my work in this project.

As with the previous two editions of the directory, for my children, **David**, **Lisa** and **Katrina Weller**, it is my hope that this new edition of the directory will make another small contribution towards the creation of a society for them to grow up in, in which prejudicial, inaccurate and unbalanced portrayals of the beliefs, values, commitments and perspectives of people of diverse religions can be overcome, and in which the distinctiveness of diverse religions can be properly understood and their communities properly valued for their contribution to the development of an equitable and religiously inclusive United Kingdom and Europe.

Paul Weller

Professor of Inter-Religious Relations

Editor, Religions in the UK and Project Director, Multi-Faith Directory Research Project

Religious Resource and Research Centre, School of Education, Human Sciences and Law, University of Derby

TOPIC INDEX

The "Topic Index" lists the page references within the general introductory chapters and the introductions to each religious community where you can find paragraphs of material on particular items. The items appearing in bold are the standard main section titles (see page 16) in the "User's Guide" which appear in the introductions to each religion. The items in normal type are the sub-sections particular to the religion concerned, and the sections in italics are more detailed and specific paragraphs within these sub-sections.

If a word which you are looking for does not appear in this index, you can also search for it in the "Significant Word Index" which gives individual page references for each word which is italicised in the text (generally, these are Romanisations of words in languages other than English, or are English language words with a specific meaning within the religion concerned: see page 17 in the "User's Guide") and also for a number of other significant words including names of religious personalities and leaders.

USER'S GUIDE

Calendars and Festivals: 16
Finding Out More: Some Other Relevant
    Publications and Resources: 21
Further Reading and Help: 21
How the Organisation Listings Were
    Compiled: 20
Apparent Omissions: 21
Level of Accuracy: 20
Indexes: 21
Introduction: 15
Introductions to the Religions in the UK: 15
    Calendar and Festivals: 16
    Further Reading: 16
    In the UK: 16
    Key Beliefs: 16
    Life: 16
    Organisation: 16
    Origins and Development: 16
    Sources of Beliefs and Practices: 16
    Traditions: 16
    Worship: 16

Map of the United Kingdom Showing
    Regions, Counties and Other Areas: 18
Religions Covered by the Directory: 15
Transliteration, Translation and Diacritical
    Markings: 16
Understanding the Organisation Listings: 19
    Activities: 20
    Address: 19
    Affiliations: 21
    Community Audience: 20
    Contact: 20
    Contact Person's Email: 20
    Contact Person's Telephone: 20
    Email: 20
    Fax: 20
    Internet: 20
    Movements: 20
    Name: 19
    Organisation Self-description: 21
    Other Languages: 19
    Position: 20
    Social Groups: 20
    Telephone: 19
    Traditions: 20
Using the Organisation Listings: 17
    Christian Listings: 17
    England: 17
    National, Regional and Local Organisations
      and Places of Worship: 17
    Northern Ireland: 17
    Scotland: 17
    UK-wide Organisations: 17
    Wales: 17

RELIGIOUS LANDSCAPE OF THE UK

"Certified" Buildings in England Wales: 35
Challenge of the Future, The: 54
Chaplaincy and Pastoral Care: 44
Collective Worship in England and Wales: 52
Further Information: 55
Further Reading: 56
Geographical Distribution of Religions: 28
Higher Education and Religious Identity: 54
Historical Development of a Religiously
    Plural Country, The: 25
Media and Advertising: 43
Nineteenth and Early Twentieth Centuries,
    The: 25
Patterns of Consultation: 43
Places of Worship: 29

Post–Second World War: 26

Recognition and the Legal Protection of
    Religious Identity: History: 46

Recognition and the Legal Protection of
    Religious Identity: The Present Position: 47

Religion and Education in Northern Ireland: 53

Religion and Education in Scotland: 52

Religion, Ethnicity and Language: 27

Religion and Human Rights New
    Developments: 49

Religion and the Law: 46

Religion, State and Society in the UK: 40
    England: 41
    Scotland: 41
    Wales: 42
    Ireland (Northern Ireland and the
    Republic of Ireland): 42
    Religions and the Legal Systems
    of the UK: 46

**Religions in Public Life: the Christian
    Inheritance: 40**

**Religions in Public Life: an Evolving
    Diversity: 42**

Religious Communities and Education: 49

Religious Discrimination: Evidence and Policy
    Options: 48

Religious Education in England and Wales: 50

Religiously Based Schools in England and
    Wales: 49

Size of the Religious Communities: 30

State Occasions and Religious Observances: 44

Statistical Problems: 30
    UK Figures in This Directory: 32
    Bahá'ís: 33
    Buddhists: 33
    Christians: 33
    Hindus: 33
    Jains: 33
    Jews: 33
    Muslims: 34
    Sikhs: 34
    Zoroastrians: 34
    Statistics for Northern Ireland: 34
    Figures for Christian Traditions
       in the UK: 34
    Some Other Widely Used UK Figures: 34
    Global Figures: 35

Statistics on Places of Worship: 35

Trends (statistics): 39

Variety of Religions, The: 23

MAKING CONTACTS, ORGANISING EVENTS AND CONSULTATIONS

Allow Plenty of Planning and Organising Time: 65

Arranging a Multi-Faith Event: 64

**Arranging Multi-Faith Consultations or
    Panels: 68**

Avoid Clashes with Religious Festivals: 64

Avoiding Stereotypes: 64

Catering for Multi-Faith Events: 66

Choose an Appropriate Venue: 65

Consider Arranging a Créche: 68

Further Help: 69

Gender Relations: 67

Introduction: 63

Introductory Materials, The Importance of the: 63

Making Contact: 63

Possible Areas of Sensitivity: 64

Producing Guidelines: 69

Producing Information Packs: 69

Religious Observance During an Event: 65

Shared Religious Observance During an Event: 66

Some Things to be Aware of When Making
    Contact: 63

What Kind of Input is Actually Wanted?: 68

What Should the Composition of a
    Panel/Consultants be?: 68

VISITING PLACES OF WORSHIP AND HOSTING VISITS

Clothing in Bahá'í Places of Worship: 72

Clothing in a Buddhist Temple: 72

Clothing in a Christian Church: 72

Clothing in a Gurdwara: 75

Clothing in a Jain Temple: 74

Clothing in a Hindu Mandir: 73

Clothing in a Mosque: 75

Clothing in a Synagogue: 74

Entering a Bahá'í Meeting: 72

Entering a Buddhist Shrine Room: 72

Entering a Church: 73

Entering a Gurdwara Prayer Hall: 76

Entering a Hindu Mandir: 73

Entering a Jain Temple Area: 74

Entering a Mosque: 75

Entering a Mosque Prayer Hall: 75

Entering a Synagogue: 74

Further Help: 77

Hosting Visits to Places of Worship: 77

Introduction: 71

Parents of Children Visiting a Mosque,
    A Note for: 75
Visiting Places of Worship: 71
Visiting a Bahá'í Place of Worship: 74
Visiting a Buddhist Temple: 72
Visiting a Christian Church: 72
Visiting a Hindu Mandir: 73
Visiting a Jain Temple: 74
Visiting a Jewish Synagogue: 74
Visiting a Muslim Mosque: 75
Visiting a Sikh Gurdwara: 75
Visiting a Zoroastrian Place of Worship: 76
Women Visiting a Hindu Mandir: A Note for: 74
Women Visiting a Jain Temple: A Note for: 74
Women Visiting a Muslim Mosque:
    A Note for: 75
Worship in a Bahá'í Place of Worship: 72
Worship in a Buddhist Temple: 72
Worship and Sacred Food in a Christian
    Church: 73
Worship and Sacred Food in a Hindu Mandir: 73
Worship in a Jain Temple: 74
Worship and Sacred Food in a Jewish Synagogue:
    74
Worship and Sacred Food in a Sikh Gurdwara: 76
Worship in a Mosque: 75

INTER-FAITH ACTIVITY IN THE UK

Bilateral Initiatives: 83
Bilateral Dialogues, Other: 84
Building Good Relations with People of Different
    Faiths and Beliefs: 91
Calamus Foundation, The: 84
Centre for the Study of Islam and Christian-
    Muslim Relations, The: 84
Christian-Jewish Initiatives, Other: 83
Council of Christians and Jews, The: 83
**Faith Communities and Inter-Faith
    Relations: 85**
Further Reading: 92
Inter Faith Network for the UK, The: 80
International Association for Religious
    Freedom: 82
International Interfaith Centre, Oxford, The: 82
International Inter-Faith Initiatives, Other: 83
Inter-Religious Social and Political
    Co-operation: 87
Introduction: 79
Local Inter-Faith Activity: 84
Maimonides Foundation, The: 83

**Millennium as a Time for Focus on Shared
    Values, The New: 89**
**Multi-Lateral Initiatives: UK and
    International: 80**
Northern Ireland, Scotland and Wales: 84
**Pattern of Involvement in Inter-Faith
    Activities: 86**
Prayer and Worship Together: 87
Prayers in the Scottish Parliament: 87
Quest for Common Values, The: 88
Special Issues: 87
Standing Conference of Jews, Christians and
    Muslims in Europe, The: 84
Three Faiths Forum, The: 84
Towards the Future: 90
Trilateral Initiatives: 94
Types of Inter-Faith Initiative: 79
United Religions Initiative: 82
World Conference on Religion and Peace: 82
World Congress of Faiths: 81

BAHÁ'ÍS IN THE UK

'Abdu'l-Bahá: 112
Báb, The: 111
Bahá'í Calendar and Festivals: 116
Bahá'í Life: 114
Bahá'í Organisations: 117
Bahá'í Scriptures: 112
Bahá'í Worship: 115
Bahá'ís in the United Kingdom: 111
Bahá'u'lláh: 112
Calendar: 116
Consultative Principle, The: 117
Daily Prayers: 115
Diet: 114
Education and Spirituality: 114
Ethics and Spirituality: 114
Festivals: 116
Firesides: 115
Further Reading: 118
History: 111
Houses of Worship: 115
International Level: 118
Joining the Community: 114
Key Bahá'í Beliefs: 113
Local Groups: 118
Local Spiritual Assemblies: 117
National Spiritual Assemblies: 118
Nature and Goal of Human Life: 113
Oneness of Humankind: 113
Origins: 113

Origins and Development of the Bahá'í Faith: 111
Personnel: 118
Progressive Revelation: 113
Recent Decades: 112
Regional Level: 118
Regular Worship: 115
Shoghi Effendi: 112
Sources of Bahá'í Beliefs and Practices: 112
Summary, A: 113
Teaching and Pioneering: 114
Traditions in the Bahá'í Faith: 115
Universal House of Justice: 112
Voluntary Sharing: 114
Women and Men: 114

BUDDHISTS IN THE UK

Beginnings in the UK: 139
Bodhi: 144
Buddha: 141
Buddha, The: 141
Buddhist Calendar and Festivals: 151
Buddhist Life: 148
Buddhist Link Organisations: 152
Buddhist Organisations: 152
Buddhist Worship: 150
Buddhists in the United Kingdom: 139
Buildings for Devotional Practice: 150
Calendar: 151
Ch'an (Chinese) and Zen (Japanese) Buddhism: 147
Dependent Origination: 144
Dharma: 142
Duhkha (Unsatisfactoriness): 139
Ethnic Chinese: 140
Festivals: 151
Five Precepts, The: 148
Four Noble Truths: 143
Friends of the Western Buddhist Order: 154
Further Reading: 156
Gautama Buddha/Gotama Buddha: 140
Jataka Stories: 143
Karma and Vipata: 144
Key Buddhist Beliefs: 143
Mahayana: 145
Mahayana Buddhist Organisations: 153
Marga (the Way): 144
Meditation: 149
Migration: 140
Nichiren Buddhism: 148
Nirodha (Cessation of Duhkha): 143

Noble Eightfold Path: 148
Northern Canon, The: 142
Origins and Development of Buddhism: 140
Paramitas: 149
Personnel: 154
Pure Land Buddhism: 148
Pure Land Buddhist Organisations: 153
Right Action: 149
Right Concentration: 149
Right Effort: 149
Right Intention: 148
Right Livelihood: 149
Right Mindfulness: 149
Right Speech: 148
Right Understanding: 148
Samgha: 142
Samsara: 144
Samudaya (Origin of Unsatisfactoriness): 143
Shingon Mahayana Buddhism: 154
Shrines and Buddharupas: 150
Shunyata/Sunnata: 144
Social Action Groups: 154
Some Other Japanese Buddhist Groups: 154
Sources of Buddhist Beliefs and Practices: 141
Southern Canon, The: 142
Three Refuges, The: 141
Theravada: 145
Theravada Organisations: 152
Tibetan Buddhism: 146
Tibetan Buddhist Organisations: 153
Traditions in Buddhism: 145
Transmission: 141
Vegetarianism: 150
Zen Buddhist Organisations: 153

CHRISTIANS IN THE UK

Anglican: 213
Anglican Churches: 226
Anglo-Catholic: 214
Baptism: 215
Baptist Movement: 228
Beginnings in the United Kingdom: 203
Black-Majority Churches: 230
Brethren: 230
Charismatic: 214
Christian Calendar, The: 221
Christian Calendar and Festivals: 221
Christian Life: 215
Christian Organisations: 224
Christian Witness: 216

Christian Worship: 218
Christians in the United Kingdom: 203
Church, The: 207
Church Buildings: 219
Churches in the UK: 225
Church Year and Festivals, The: 221
Churchmanship: 214
Confirmation and Membership: 216
Congregationalism: 229
Creeds, The: 207
Denominational and Ethnic Diversity: 204
Dietary Issues: 217
Early Years: 205
Eastern and Western Christendom and Protestant
    Reformation: 205
Ecumenical Movement, The: 215
Ecumenical Structures: 231
England and Wales: 225
Ethics and Discipleship: 217
Evangelical: 214
Further Reading: 234
God, Incarnation and Revelation: 208
Holy Communion: 218
Holy Trinity, The: 210
House Churches: 230
Jesus: 208
Judgement and Eternal Life: 210
Key Christian Beliefs: 208
Liberal: 214
Local Leadership: 232
Lutheran: 229
Methodism: 228
Monks, Nuns and Religious: 217
Moravian: 230
Numbers and Geography: 204
Ordained Leadership: 232
Origins and Development of
    Christianity: 205
Orthodox: 212
Orthodox Churches: 227
Other Christian Organisations: 232
Other Interdenominational Networks: 232
Pastoral Care: 233
Pentecostal: 213
Pentecostal Churches: 230
Personnel: 232
Prayer: 219
Preaching: 219
Protestant: 212
Protestant Churches: 228
Protestant Reformation: 204

Protestant Reformation and the Missionary
    Movement: 206
Quakers: 231
Quakers and Unitarians: 214
Reason, Conscience and Experience: 207
Reformed Churches: 228
Regional, National and International Leadership: 233
Restorationist and House Church
    Movements: 213
Roman Catholic: 211
Roman Catholic Church: 227
Saints, The: 211
Salvation: 209
Salvation Army: 229
Scotland: 226
Scriptures: 206
Sin and Grace: 215
Sources of Christian Beliefs and
    Practices: 206
Sunday: 221
Tradition: 207
Traditions in Christianity: 211
Unitarian and Free Christian Churches: 231
Virgin Mary, The: 210

HINDUS IN THE UK

Achintya-Bhedha-Abheda: 304
Advaita Vedanta: 304
Advaita: 303
Arya Samajis: 313
Ashramas: 307
Atman: 302
Brahmins: 306
Calendar: 310
Dharma: 302
Dvaita: 303
Dvaita-Advaita: 304
Educational Organisations: 313
Ethnic Composition: 297
Fasting: 308
Features and Activities, Other: 309
Festivals: 310
Four Aims, The: 305
Four Varnas, The: 306
Four Vedas, The: 299
Further Reading: 314
Gender Roles: 307
Guru-Disciple Relationship: 307
Hindu Calendar and Festivals: 310
Hindu Life: 305
Hindu Organisations: 311

Hindu Related Groups: 313
Hindu Worship: 308
Hindus in The United Kingdom: 297
Jati: 306
Jati (Community) Associations: 311
Karma: 302
Key Hindu Beliefs: 301
Krishna Consciousness: 312
Kshatriyas: 306
Languages: 298
Mahabharata: 300
Mandirs: 308
Maya: 302
Migration: 297
Moksha: 302
Murtis: 309
Navya Vishishta-Advaita: 304
One and Many: 301
Oral Tradition: 299
Origins: 298
Origins and Development of the Hindu
      Tradition: 298
Other Features and Activities: 309
Other Texts: 301
Personnel: 313
Pilgrimages: 311
Puranas: 300
Pushtimargis: 312
Ramakrishna Mission: 313
Ramayana: 300
Regional/Linguistic Groups: 313
Representative Groups: 313
Sampradaya: 304
Shaiva Siddhanta: 304
Shruti: 299
Shuddha-Advaita: 304
Shuddha-Dvaita: 304
Six Darshanas, The: 303
Smriti: 300
Sources of Hindu Beliefs and Practices: 299
Spiritual Movements: 312
Sudras: 306
Swaminaryans: 312
Traditions in Hinduism: 303
Vaishnavas, Shaivas and Shaktas: 305
Vaishyas: 306
Values: 305
Variety: 298
Varnas, The Four: 306
Varnashrama Dharma: 305
Vedanta: Dvaita and Advaita: 303

Vegetarianism: 308
Vishishta-Advaita: 304
Yuga: 302

JAINS IN THE UK

Ahimsa: 359
Angabahya: 359
Angas: 358
Anuvratas: 362
Calendar: 363
Digambara: 361
Distribution: 357
Festivals: 363
Further Reading: 364
Jain Calendar and Festivals: 363
Jain Life: 362
Jain Organisations: 364
Jain Worship: 362
Jainism in India: 358
Jains in the United Kingdom: 357
Karma: 360
Key Jain Beliefs: 359
Mahavira: 358
Mahavratas: 362
Mandirs: 363
Migration: 357
Origins and Development of Jainism: 357
Other Texts: 359
Path To Moksha: 360
Personal Puja: 362
Personnel: 364
Purvas: 358
Reality in Jain Perspective: 359
Scriptures: 358
Sentient Beings: 359
Shvetambara: 361
Sources of Jain Beliefs and Practices: 358
Tirthankaras, The: 357
Traditions in Jainism: 361

JEWS IN THE UK

Barmitzvah and Batmitzvah: 381
Calendar: 385
Circumcision: 381
Clothing and Prayer: 385
Diaspora, Holocaust and Israel: 377
Eretz Yisrael, Zionism and Attitudes Towards
      Israel: 379
Festivals: 385

Further Reading: 389
General Organisations: 387
Geographical Spread: 375
Halakhah: 378
Haredim: 380
Hasidic: 380
Humanity: 379
Independent Synagogues: 389
Israel: 382
Jewish Calendar and Festivals: 385
Jewish Life: 391
Jewish Organisations: 387
Jewish Worship: 383
Jews in the United Kingdom: 375
Kashrut: 382
Key Jewish Beliefs: 378
Kingdom of God: 379
Kingdoms and Exile: 377
Languages: 376
Masorti: 389
Masorti (Conservative): 380
Midrash: 378
Minor Festivals and Additional Fast Days: 387
Moses and the Israelites: 376
Origins and Development of Judaism: 376
Orthodox: 380
Orthodox Organisations: 388
Other Communal Worship: 384
Patriarchs: 376
Personnel: 389
Progressive: 380
Reform and Liberal Organisations: 388
Sephardi and Ashkenazi: 375
Shabbat: 381
Shabbat Worship: 383
Shalosh Regalim, The: 386
Shema: 378
Sources of Jewish Beliefs and Practices: 377
Synagogue: 384
Talmud: 377
Tenakh: 377
Torah and Mitzvot: 378
Traditions in Judaism: 380
Women: 383
Yamim Noraim, The: 386

MUSLIMS IN THE UK

Ahl-e-Hadith: 438, 444
Barelwis: 438, 444
Becoming a Muslim: 439
Calendar: 442

Caliphate and Imamate: 434
Community Groups: 446
Dawah: 445
Deobandis: 438, 444
Development and Diversity: 435
Educational Organisations: 445
Ethnic Backgrounds and Languages: 434
Further Reading: 446
Gender and Family: 440
Goal and Purpose of Human Life: 437
Halal: 440
Hajj: 437
Jamaat-i-Islami: 438, 444
Jihad: 440
Key Beliefs and Five Pillars of Islam: The: 437
Key Muslim Beliefs: 437
Migration and Patterns of Settlement: 433
Monotheism: 437
Mosques: 441
Muslim Calendar and Festivals: 442
Muslim Life: 439
Muslim Organisations: 444
Muslim Worship: 441
Muslims in the United Kingdom: 433
Origins and Development of Islam: 434
Other National and Regional Organisations: 444
Personnel: 446
Prophet Muhammad and the 'Ummah: 434
Qur'an: 435
Ramadan: 437
Revelation: 434
Salat: 437, 441
Schools: 436
Shahadah: 437
Shi'a: 439
Shari'ah: 436, 439
Sources of Muslim Beliefs and Practices: 435
Sufi Orders: 444
Sunni: 437
Tablighi Jamaat: 438, 444
Tasawwuf: 439
Traditions in Islam: 437
Twelvers and Seveners: 439
Women: 446
Youth: 445
Zakat: 437

SIKHS IN THE UK

Amrit Pahul: 555
Beginnings in the UK: 549
Birth, Marriage and Death: 554
Calendar: 558
Community Languages: 550
Daily Prayers: 557
Dasam Granth: 551
Definitions: 552
Diet: 556
Educational Organisations: 559
Equality: 555
Ethics: 554
Festivals: 558
Five Ks: 555
Further Reading: 560
General Organisations: 559
Goal of Life: 553
God: 552
Gurdwara: 556
Guru Granth Sahib, The: 551
History: 551
Kachhera: 556
Kangha: 556
Kara: 556
Karah Prashad and Langar: 558
Kesh (Uncut Hair): 555
Key Sikh Beliefs: 552
Khalsa Panth: 553
Kirpan: 556
Nam Japna: 554
Origins and Development of Sikhism: 550
Path: 557
Personnel: 560
Pilgrimage: 556
Rahit Maryada: 552
Rahit Nama: 551
Sadh Sangat: 557
Sikh Calendar and Festivals: 558
Sikh Life: 554
Sikh Organisations: 559
Sikh Worship: 556
Sadh Sangat: 557
Sikhs in the United Kingdom: 549
Singh and Kaur: 556
Social Groupings: 559
Sources of Sikh Beliefs and Practices: 551
Ten Gurus, The: 550
Traditions in Sikhism: 553
Works of Bhai Gurdas and Bhai Nandlal: 552

ZOROASTRIANS IN THE UK

Ahura Mazda: 589
Amesha Spentas: 590
Avesta, The: 589
Calendar: 594
Concept of Death and Afterlife, The: 591
Death Practices: 593
Diet: 593
Festivals: 594
Fire: 593
Further Reading: 596
Gah/Geh: 592
History and Influence: 588
Initiation: 592
Key Zoroastrian Beliefs: 589
Khordeh Avesta: 589
Languages: 588
Later Texts: 589
Migration: 587
Organisations: 596
Origins: 587
Origins and Development of Zoroastrianism: 588
Parsis in India and the Zoroastrians in Iran, The: 588
Personnel: 596
Places of Worship: 593
Role of Humanity, The: 591
Saoshyant, The End Time, Resurrection, Last Judgement and Frasho-Keriti: 591
Seven Good Creations and their Guardians: 590
Sources of Zoroastrian Beliefs and Practices: 589
Spenta Mainyu (The Holy Spirit) and Angra Mainyu (The Destructive Spirit), The: 590
Sudreh and Kushti/Koshti: 592
Vendidad (or Videvdat): 589
Visperad: 589
Yashts: 589
Yasna and Gathas: 589
Yazatas: 590
Zarathushtra: 588
Zoroastrian Calendars and Festivals: 594
Zoroastrian Ethics: 591
Zoroastrian Life: 591
Zoroastrian Worship: 593
Zoroastrians in the United Kingdom: 587
Zoroastrian Organisations: 596

SOME OTHER RELIGIOUS COMMUNITIES AND GROUPS

Brahma Kumaris: 603
Christian Scientists: 605
Church of Jesus Christ of Latter-day Saints: 606
Introduction: 601
Jehovah's Witnesses: 608
Namdhari Sikh Community: 610
Pagans: 613
Rastafarians: 615
Ravidassia: 616
Sant Nirankaris: 618
Sathya Sai Baba Organisation: 619
Valmikis: 620

FINDING OUT MORE: SOME OTHER RELEVANT PUBLICATIONS AND RESOURCES

Directories of Religious Organisations: 628
 Bahá'í Directories: 628
 Buddhist Directories: 628
 Christian Directories: 628
 Hindu Directories: 629
 Jain Directories: 629
 Jewish Directories: 629
 Local Religious General Directories: 630
 Muslim Directories: 629
 New Religious Movements Directories: 630
 Sikh Directories: 630
 Zoroastrian Directories: 630
 Some Relevant Resource
  Organisations: 633
 Some Relevant Publications: 638
Directories of Ethnic Minority Organisations: 631
Finding Out More: 623
General Texts on Religions: 625
 New Religious Movements: 627
 Special Topics: 624
 World Religions: Bibliographical
  Resources: 626
 World Religions: Overviews: 625
 World Religions: Special Topics: 626
 World Religions: Texts: 627
Overviews of Religions: 624
School Students, A Note for: 625
Bibliographical Resources: 627

ACKNOWLEDGEMENTS

Introduction: 643
Collection and Verification of Directory Listings: 646
Consultation processes and the contents of the 2001 edition: 643
Consultants to the 2001 edition: 644
Consultants on the Introductions to Individual Religions in the UK: 644
Consultants on the Chapter on Visiting Places of Worship and Hosting Visits: 644
Consultants on the Chapter on Making Contact, Organising Events and Consultations: 644
Consultants on the Chapter on Religious Landscape of the UK: 645
Consultants on the Chapter on Inter-Faith Activity in the UK: 645
Consultants on the Chapter on Some Other Religious Communities and Groups: 646
Consultants to the 1997 Edition: 647
Other Acknowledgements: 648

SIGNIFICANT WORD INDEX

This index lists all the significant words appearing in the directory's textual materials, but not in the listings. These significant words include all the words appearing within the text in italics (generally, these are Romanisations of words in languages other than English, or are English language words with a specific meaning within the religion concerned: see pages 16–17 in the "User's Guide"). But a number of other significant words are also given, including names of various scriptures, religious personalities and leaders, as well as the names of continents, countries, regions and significant cities or places in various religions.

Whilst an attempt has been made to be consistent within the directory's textual materials, words that appear in other than English and non-European languages can be found in English in a variety of Romanisations, so it is always worth checking the index for other possible renderings of the word which you want to find. Therefore once you have looked up a word initially, if other renderings are noted, it would also be worth checking if there are references for these within this index.

The singular form of English words in the index covers page references for both the singular and plural forms of the word. Not every single instance of a word within the directory is given, but a range are included that will help users to unlock the meaning of the word or to set it in a wider context.

General thematic references are not included in this index. For these, such as worship, festivals etc in the various religions, the reader should consult the directory's Topic Index which sets out the pages on which these topics are dealt with in respect of each religion, and also more general topics such as religious education, religion and the law.

A

'Abdu'l-Bahá, 111–117
Aaronic Priesthood, 606
Abbasid, 435
Abbot, 153
Abdul'Baha, 26
Abhidhamma-pitaka, 142
Abi Talib, 435
Abraham, 376, 381, 434, 437, 444
Abu Bakr, 434–435
Abul A'la Mawdudi, 438, 444
Achaemenid, 588, 593
Acharanga Sutra, 358
Acharya Tejendraprasad Pande, 312
Acharya Umasvati, 359
Acharyas, 362
Achintya-Bhedha-Abheda, 304
Acts of the Apostles, 208, 213
Ad, 551
Adam, 209
Adar Yazad, 591
Adar, 589, 591, 593, 595
Aden, 587
Adharma, 359
Adi Granth, 551–552, 558, 610
Administrative Order, 114

Adur, 593
Advaita, 301–305, 311, 313
Advaitins, 303
Advent, 221–222
Aesir, 613
Afghanistan, 298
Africa, 204–206, 232, 434–435, 437
African, 230, 232, 297, 433
African Churches, 230, 232
African-Caribbean, 204
Africanisation, 297, 433, 559, 587
Afrinagan, 589
Afrins, 589
Afro-Caribbean Churches, 230
Afterlife, 591
Aga Khan, 439
Agama, 142, 358
Agape, 209, 215
Agencies, 231
Aggadah, 378
Agha Khanis, 440
Ahimsa, 73, 305, 308, 359, 362
Ahl-e-Hadith, 439, 445
Ahuna Vairya, 593
Ahunavar, 593
Ahura Mazda, 590, 592
Airyana Vaeja, 589

Aiwisruthrem, 592
Ajiva, 359
Akal Purakh, 552
Akal Takhat, 551
Akasha, 359
Akhand Path, 554, 557–558
Akka, 112, 115–116
Akong Rinpoche, 153
Akshardham, 311
Akshaya-tiritiya, 363
Al Hijrah, 443
Al Muhajiroun, 445
Alá, 116
Alcohol, 440
Alexandrian, 613
Ali, 434, 435, 439–440
Al-khulafa ar-rashidun, 434
Ali-Muhammad, 112
Allah, 434, 437
Altar, 73, 220, 223
Amardad, 590
Ambaji, 302
Ambedkarite, 140–141, 152
Ameretat, 590
Amesha Spentas, 590, 591, 593–596
Amida Buddha, 148
Amitabha, 148

Amrit, 550, 552-553, 555, 558
Amritdhari, 67, 555, 610
Amritsar, 551-552, 558-559
Amsterdam Treaty, 47, 54-55
Anand Karaj, 554
Anand, 554-555, 557
Ananda Metteyya, 139, 153
Ananda, 155
Anandpur, 553, 555-556
Anatman, 143-144
Anavil, 306, 312
Anekantavada, 359
Angabahya, 358-359
Angas, 358-359
Angel Gabriel, 222
Angel Jibreel, 434
Anglican, 39, 41, 49-50, 205,
    207, 210-211, 213-216, 218-
    226, 232-233
Anglicanism, 213
Anglo-Catholic, 210, 213-214,
    218-220, 223
Angra Mainyu, 590
Anitya, 143
Annakuta, 311
Anno Domini, 221
Anointed One, 208, 379
Anuvratas, 362
Aparigracha, 362
Apia, 115
Apocrypha, 206
Apostles, 207-208, 211, 213, 232
Apostolic Church, 230
Apostolic succession, 606
Apostolicity, 211-212
Aql, 436
Arab, 375, 436, 588
Arabia, 435
Arabian, 434
Arabic, 111-112, 376
Arahat, 145
Aramaic, 378
Aranyakas, 300
Aravot, 386
Arba Kanfot, 385
Archangel Michael, 224
Archbishop, 40, 203, 212, 213,
    227, 233
Ardas, 554, 557-558
Ardhamagadhi, 358
Ardibehesht, 590
Arhat, 361-362
Aristotle, 588
Ariya Atthangika Magga, 144

Arjuna, 300
Armenian, 227
Aron Kodesh, 384
Aroras, 307
Artha, 305
Artharva Veda, 300
Arthaveda, 300
Arti, 73, 310
Arya Ashtangika Marga, 144
Arya Astangika Marga, 148
Aryan, 589, 593
Asa, 557
Asalaam-u-'alaikum, 75
Asalha, 152
Asatru, 613
Ascended, 208
Ascension, 116-117, 221, 223,
    602
Ascetic, 141, 358, 362, 439
Ash Wednesday, 67, 222
Asha Vahishta, 590-591
Asha, 588, 590-593
Asher, 376
Asherites, 439-440
Ashkenazi, 375-376, 384, 388
Ashrama, 305-307
Asia, 204
Aspandarmad, 590
Asr, 441
Assam, 550
Assembly, 114, 117-119, 221,
    229, 231, 234
Associations, 224, 229-230
Assumption, 221, 224
Asteya, 362
Atar, 593
Atash Nyayesh, 593
Atharva Veda, 299
Atheistic, 303
Atisha, 147
Atman, 302-304
Atmas, 359
Atoned, 209
Atonement, 219
Augustine, 203
AUM, 309
Australia, 115, 587
Autocephalous, 212
Auxiliary Boards, 118
Avalokiteshvara, 145-146
Avamah, 595
Avan, 589
Avaroj, 595
Avatamsaka Sutra, 142

Avatar, 310
Avataras, 303
Avesta, 589
Avestan, 588-589
Ayodhya, 310-311
Ayurveda, 299
Ayyam-i-Ha, 117

B

Baal Shem Tov, 380
Báb, 111-112, 116
Baba Puran Singh Karichowale,
    560
Baba, 554, 560
Bábis, 112
Babylon, 377, 615
Babylonia, 377
Babylonian, 377
Badrinath, 311
Baghdad, 116
Bahá'í Centres, 115
Bahá'í Councils, 118
Bahá'í International
    Community, 119
Bahá'u'lláh, 111,112, 116-118
Bahá'u'lláh's Declaration, 116
Bahá'u'lláh's Hidden Words, 112
Bahá'u'lláh's Will, 112
Bahji, 112, 115
Bahman, 590
Bahudaanya, 310
Baidyas, 307
Baisakhi, 610
Balkans, 435
Bandha, 360
Bangladesh, 141, 435, 438, 444
Bangladeshi, 444
Bani, 554
Baptism, 213-216, 222-224,
    228-229,607
Baptism in the Spirit, 213, 214
Baptismal, 215, 608
Baptist, 205, 216, 220, 225, 228-
    229, 233-234
Baptizo, 215
Bardo Retreat, 146
Bareilly, 438
Barelwi, 438, 443-444
Barmitzvah, 381
Barnabas, 207, 211
Basket, 142
Bat Hayil, 381
Batmitzvah, 381

Beatitudes, 217
Beatles, 312
Being, 113-114, 116-117, 143-145, 147, 149-150, 155-156
Benares, 141, 152, 311
Benedictines, 218
Bengal, 297, 312
Bengali, 298, 313, 434, 444
Bennett, Alan, 139
Beth Din, 378, 382, 388-389
Bethlehem, 208
Bhagat Bani, 551
Bhagavad Gita, 300, 306
Bhagavata Purana, 299, 301
Bhagavati Sutra, 358
Bhai Gurdas, 552
Bhai Kanhaya, 553
Bhai Mani Singh, 551
Bhai Nandlal, 552
Bhai, 551-554, 560
Bhajan, 309-311
Bhakti, 305, 616
Bhakti yoga, 303
Bhaktivedanta Swami Prabhupada, 304, 312
Bharat, 300
Bhatra, 559
Bhen, 560
Bhikkhu Asoka, 139
Bhikshuni, 155
Bible, 206, 212, 217, 225, 376, 378, 380, 602, 608, 615
Biblical, 209-210, 221, 223, 377, 379, 382
Bihar, 358
Birh, 551
Birth, 116-117, 143-145, 152, 552-554, 558
Bishop, 40, 203, 205-217, 219, 226-227, 233-234
BKagyur, 142
Black-Majority Churches, 230
Blasphemous Libel, 47
Blasphemy, 47
Blessed Lord, 300
Blessed Virgin Mary, 221-222, 224
Blessing, 73
Bo Tree, 140
Bodh Gaya, 140, 152
Bodhi, 140-141, 144, 152
Bodhi Tree, 140-141, 152
Bodhidhamma, 147

Bodhisattva, 72, 145-146, 149, 152, 155
Bodhisattva Way, 145, 155
Bodhisattvayana, 145
Bodhissatas, 145
Book of Genesis, 381
Book of Revelation, 207, 210, 615
Book of Ruth, 386
Book of the Acts of the Apostles, 208
Book of the Esther, 387
Booth, William, 229
Bosnia, 433
Bounteous Devotion, 590
Bounteous Immortals, 590
Brahma Samaj, 312
Brahma, 300-301, 304, 309, 312
Brahmacharin, 307
Brahmacharya, 362
Brahman, 301-305
Brahmanas, 300
Brahmin, 306-307, 312-313
Breaking of Bread, 218
Brethren, 230, 233
Bridge of the Separator, 591
Brihaspati Agam, 298
Brit, 376, 381
Britain, 139-140, 153-154, 156, 203, 215, 227-231, 234, 297, 388-389, 434, 437, 445-446, 549, 587, 596
British Indian, 549
British Isles, 118, 203, 228, 230
British Raj, 551
British, 203, 228, 230-231, 433, 435, 439, 549, 551, 559
Britons, 434
Broad Church, 21
BsTangyur, 142
Buddha, 72, 113, 140-146, 148-152, 155, 298
Buddhahood, 144
Buddha-nature, 142
Budh, 141
Buddharupa, 150
Buddhism, 139-150, 152-155, 588-589
Buddhist, 139-145, 147-156, 158-202
Burma, 139-141, 145, 152

C

Cairo, 435
Calcutta, 312
Caliph, 435, 438
Caliph Yazid, 435
Caliphate, 434-435
Calvin, John, 204
Calvinism, 226
Calvinist, 204, 226
Cambodia, 141, 145
Canaan, 376, 386
Canon, 142
Canonical, 551
Canterbury, 203, 213, 226, 233
Cantor, 389
Cardinals, 234
Caribbean, 230, 232, 297, 434
Carmelites, 218
Carthage, 206
Caste, 553-554, 556, 559, 616
Castilian Spanish, 376
Cathedra, 220
Cathedral, 44, 66, 220
Catholic, 25, 72-73, 203-207, 210-214, 215-227, 231-234
Catholicity, 211
Cattari Ariyasaccani, 143
Catur Aryasatya, 143
CEC, 215
Celtic, 203-204
Central America, 115
Central Asia, 141
Ch'an, 140, 146-147, 154
Ch'an-na, 147
Chaitanya, 298, 304, 312
Chandas, 301
Chandra, 301
Chapel, 219
Charismatic, 213-214
Charnamrita, 310
Chasidic, 67
Chaupai, 555
Chaur Sahib, 558
Cheder, 376
Chenrezig, 145
Chicago, 115
Chief Rabbi, 388
Chief Stewards of the Faith, 112
China, 141, 145-146, 148, 206
Chinese, 140, 142, 147, 150, 152-154
Chinese Buddhists, 140
Chinese Ch'an, 147, 154

Chinese Christians, 204
Chinese Zen, 150
Chinvat Bridge, 591
Chishti, 439
Chogyam Trungpa, 153
Choirs, 220
Christ, 113, 208, 211-212, 214, 219, 221, 223, 228-229, 233, 602
Christening, 216
Christian Brethren, 34, 230, 233
Christian Church, 203-204, 206, 214-217, 219, 224, 231-233, 377
Christlike, 212
Christological, 231
Christos, 208
Church, 18-19, 26, 28-29, 39-44, 69, 72-73, 65-66, 203-207, 210, 212-234, 442, 602, 606, 608
Church Buildings, 210-211, 215, 219-220
Church Council, 206
Church Fathers, 207
Church Government, 204, 212, 226, 230
Churchmanship, 214, 232
Church-sponsored, 224
Circumcise, 381, 387
Circumcision, 381
Clean Monday, 222
Clergy, 226, 68-69
Code of Discipline, 551
Colombo, 139
Commandments, 381
Commissions, 231
Common Era, 203, 221
Communal, 375, 377, 381, 383-388
Communio, 217
Communion, 73, 211-212, 216, 218-220, 223-224, 233
Confirmation, 216
Confucian, 140
Congregation, 217-220, 225, 229, 233
Congregational, 221, 225, 228-229, 384
Congregationalism, 229
Congregationalist, 34, 225, 226, 229
Congregations, 217, 225, 228-232, 381, 383, 388-389, 608

Conquering Lion of the Tribes of Judah, 615
Conscience, 207, 217, 233
Consciousness, 359-360
Consecrated, 219-220
Conservative Judaism, 380
Continental Boards of Counsellors, 118
Coptic, 227
Corps, 229
Corpus Christi, 221, 224
Council, 206, 209, 211-212, 215, 227, 229-231
Council of the Seventy, 606
Council of the Twelve Apostles, 606
Counsellors, 606
Covenant, 115, 117
Covenantal, 376
Covenant-breakers (Bahá'í), 115
Covens, 613
Craft, 613
Creator, 209-210, 552-553
Credal, 207, 209, 214
Credo, 207, 212, 231
Cross, 208, 223
Crucifixion, 208, 223, 602
Cyprus, 227, 434
Czech Republic, 230

D

Dadabhai Naoroji, 587
Daevas, 588
Daily Prayers, 557
Dalai Lama, 140, 147, 153
Dalit, 307
Damdama Birh, 551
Damdama Sahib, 551
Dan, 376
Daral'ulum, 438
Darbar Sahib, 551, 556, 559
Darshan, 310
Darshanas, 303
Dar-ul-Uloom, 444
Dasam Granth, 551-552, 610
Dasha-lakshana-parva, 364
David, 377, 379, 384
Dawah, 445
Dawat-ul-Islam, 444
Dawning Place of God's Praise, 116
Day of Judgement, 437
Day of the Covenant, 117

Daya Ram, 553
Dayan, 389
Dayanim, 389
Deacons, 211, 219, 224
Deaneries, 226
Death, 207-209, 219, 221, 223, 552-554, 558, 591, 593, 595
Decalogue, 217
Dechen, 154
Declaration, 111, 116
Deepawali, 311
Deer Park, 141, 152
Defender of the Faith, 41
Deities, 300, 303, 308-311
Deliverance, 559
Denomination, 213, 219
Denominational, 204
Deoband, 439
Deobandi, 438-439, 444
Dependent Origination, 144
Destructive Spirit, 590
Deuteronomy, 377-378, 385
Dev Vak, 299
Devas, 301
Devi, 301-302
Devotees, 305, 310-312
Devotion, 363
Devotional, 115, 117
Dhanurveda, 300
Dharam Das, 553
Dharam Khand, 553
Dharamsala, 151
Dharma Protectors, 146
Dharma Shastra, 300-301
Dharma, 141-142, 146-148, 150, 152, 155, 298, 300-307, 311, 359, 620
Dharmachakra, 152
Dharmacharinis, 156
Dharmacharis, 156
Dhatu, 310
Dhr, 302
Dhu'l Hijjah, 443
Diaconate, 233
Diakonos, 233
Diamond Peak, 154
Diamond Vehicle, 146
Diaspora, 376-377, 379, 386
Diet, 114, 217, 556, 593
Differing, 212
Digambara, 358, 361-364
Diksha, 362, 364
Diocesan, 226
Diocese, 220, 226-227, 233

Diocletian, 205
Dipas, 311
Disciples, 142, 145-146, 216, 550
Discipleship, 217
Disestablished, 42
Disestablishment, 226
District Chairman, 233
Districts, 228-230, 608
Divas, 311
Divine, 300-301, 303-305, 307-309, 313, 379, 550-553, 557
Divine Essence, 113
Divine Hymns of Zarathushtra, 589
Divine Kingdom, 590
Divine Light, 438
Divine Liturgy, 218
Divine Manifestation, 113
Divine Reality, 437
Divisions, 215, 229
Diwali, 311, 364, 558-559
Diwan, 557-558, 560
Doctrine of the Covenants, 606
Dokhma, 593
Dominicans, 218
Dominion, 590
Dorje Shugden, 147
Dormition, 224
Dosen Risshi, 148
Douglas, Gordon, 139
Dr Ambedkar, 141, 152
Dravya, 359
Drolma Lhakhang Monastery, 153
Druid, 613
Druidry, 613
Dualistic, 303
Duhkha, 143-144, 148-149, 302
Durga, 301-302, 305, 311
Dussehra, 311
Dvaita, 301-305
Dvaita-Advaita, 304
Dvaitins, 303
Dwarka, 311

E

East Africa, 434, 549, 559, 587-588
East African, 357, 559
East European, 375-376
East Punjab, 549
Eastern Buddhism, 143, 145, 154
Eastern Europe, 112, 212, 380
Eastern Orthodox, 204-205

Ecclesia, 224
Ecclesiastical, 41, 224
Ecumenical, 30, 44, 206, 211-212, 215, 217-218, 231-232
Ecumenical Council, 211-212
Ecumenical instruments, 17, 19
Ecumenical Movement, 206, 215, 217
Ecumenical Partnerships, 231
Ecumenical Patriarch, 212
Ecumenical Structures, 231-232
Ecumenism, 607
Education Act, 49-50, 52-53
Education Reform Act, 50, 52-53
Egypt, 376, 386, 437
Eid, 443
Eid-al-Adha, 75
Eid-al-Fitr, 75
Eightfold Path, 144, 148-149
Ekklesia, 207
Elders, 145, 228, 608
Elveden Estate, 549
Emperor Ashoka, 358
Emperor Aurangzeb, 552
Emperors Decius, 205
Employment Act, 46
Emptiness, 144
Encyclicals, 217
Endowment, 606
England, 111, 118, 203-205, 213, 218-221, 225-233, 357, 375-376, 388, 433-434, 550
English Civil War, 375
English, 111, 116, 139-140, 153-154, 204, 207-210, 222-223, 225, 227, 298, 301-302, 306, 314, 375-376, 383-384, 386, 434, 436, 442, 447, 550, 588
Enjoyment Body, 146
Enlightened, 141, 144
Enlightenment, 140, 142, 144, 146, 151-152
Eostre, 223
Ephraim, 376
Epiphany, 221-222
Episcopal, 42, 213, 216, 226
Episcopalian, 226
Epistles, 206-208
Eretz Yisrael, 379
Ervad Sahebs, 596
Established, 39-41, 52, 204, 225-226, 379-380, 384, 388, 433-435, 439, 442, 445-446
Established Churches, 43

Establishment, 43
Esther, 377, 387
Eternal Life, 210, 212
Ethics, 114, 217
Ethiopian Orthodox Church, 227
Etrog, 386
Eucharist, 73, 212, 218-221, 224, 229, 233
Eucharistic, 219
Europe, 203, 206, 212, 229, 308,
European Buddhists, 153
European Convention on Human Rights, 49
European, 204, 206, 213, 215, 375-377, 388
Evangelical, 204, 210, 213-214, 219, 228-230, 232
Evangelical Alliance, 232
Evangelical Christian, 140, 210, 214, 229, 232
Evangelical Revival, 219, 228
Euangelion, 214
Evangelism, 214
Eve, 209
Exclusive Brethren, 230
Exemplar, 605
Exile, 377, 379
Exodus, 377, 386, 615
Ezekiel, 377

F

Faith, 206, 208-213, 215-216, 219, 228, 232
Fajr, 441
Family, 439-441, 443
Far East, 142
Far Eastern Mahayana Buddhists, 152
Farsi, 434, 588, 592
Farvardin, 595
Farvardingan, 595
Fasli, 594
Fast, 116-117, 217, 308
Fasting, 222, 308, 310-311, 363, 437, 443, 592
Father, 208-210, 212, 224, 234
Fatiha, 436
Fatima, 439
Fatimid, 435
Fiji, 297
Filioque, 212
Fire Temples, 37, 593, 595
Firesides, 115

First Communion, 219
First Presidency, 606
First Temple, 387
First World War, 433
Fish, 382, 440
Five Great Vows, 364
Five Ks, 555-556
Five Pillars of Islam, 437
Five Precepts, 148-149, 154
Flower Ornament, 142
Font, 215
Food, 308-311, 382, 440
Foot washing, 223
Ford-Makers, 358
Four Noble Truths, 142-143,
    149
Four Sakyampa, 153
Fourth Caliph, 435
Fox, George, 231
Franciscans, 218
Frankfurt, 115
Frasho-keriti, 591
Fravarane, 592
Fravashi, 591, 595
Free Christians, 34
Free Church, 205, 219, 228,
    230-231
Free Churches, 28, 40, 205, 212,
    214, 219, 225, 231
French Reformed Huguenots,
    204
French, 204, 222
Fuqaha, 446

G

Gabriel, 434
Gad, 376
Gah, 592
Gahanbars, 589, 594
Gahs, 589
Galilee, 208, 377
Gampopa, 146
Ganadharas, 358
Ganden, 147
Gandharvaveda, 299
Gandhi, 307
Gandhinagar, 311
Ganesha, 301, 309
Ganges, 311, 358
Garbha-griha, 309
Gardnerian, 613
Gate, 112
Gatha, 589-590, 594-595

Gautama, 140-142, 144, 149,
    151, 155
Gayomard, 591
Geh, 592
Gelugpa, 153
Geluk, 147
Gemara, 378
Gender, 301, 307, 437, 440
General Assembly, 41, 231, 234
General Secretary, 234
General Synod, 226
Genesis, 377, 381
Gentiles, 205, 222
German, 230
Germany, 375, 380
Geshe Kelsang Gyatso, 153
Ghar mandir, 308
Ghayr muqallidun, 438
Gian Khand, 553
Giani, 560
Girdo, 592
Gireban, 592
Glory, 112, 116
Glossolalia, 213
Goal, 438
Gobind, 550-553, 555-556, 558
God, 112-114, 116, 299, 301-
    305, 307, 309, 376, 378-381,
    383-384, 386, 550, 552-553,
    555, 557, 550, 552-553, 554,
    557, 588, 590
God-bearer, 210
Goddess, 301-302, 305, 311
Goddess Lakshmi, 301, 311
Godhead, 212
Godparents, 216
Godspell, 207
Gohonzon, 154
Golden Temple, 551, 559
Gonchok Gyelpo, 147
Good Friday, 223
Good Mind, 588, 590
Good News, 207, 214, 216
Gopi, 309
Gospel, 206-209, 216, 220, 222-
    223, 228, 434, 438, 606
Gospels, 206-209, 219
Gotama Buddha, 140
Grace, 209, 211,215, 305, 552-
    555
Granth, 550-552, 554-555, 557-
    558, 560
Granthi, 69, 551, 554-555,
    560

Great Britain, 227-230, 234
Great Fast, 222
Great Hero, 358
Great Scripture Store, 142
Great Soul, 307
Great Vehicle, 145
Greater One, 112
Greater Pentad, 595
Greek, 204, 206-212, 214-216,
    218, 222, 224, 226-228, 232-
    233, 588
Grihastha, 307
Grihya Sutra, 300
Guardian of the Faith, 112
Gudi Parva, 310
Guided One, 439
Gujarat, 311-313, 357-358, 587-
    588
Gujarati, 297-298, 312, 313,
    434, 588, 592
Gunas, 302
Gurbani, 552, 554, 557
Gurdwara, 27, 29, 39, 65, 76, 49,
    549-550, 552, 554-560
Gurdwara Reform Movement,
    552
Gurmantar, 610
Gurmat, 550, 554
Gurmikh, 554
Gurmukhi, 550-551
Gurpurbs, 558
Gurshabad, 552
Guru Amar Das, 550
Guru Angad Dev, 550
Guru Arjan Dev, 550-552, 558
Guru Gobind Singh, 555-556,
    558
Guru Granth Sahib, 76, 550-
    552, 554, 557
Guru Har Krishan, 550
Guru Har Rai, 550
Guru Hargobind, 550-551, 558
Guru Nanak Dev, 550, 554-557
Guru Ram Das, 550, 559
Guru Rinpoche, 146
Guru Shishya Sambandh, 307
Guru Tegh Bahadur, 550-551,
    558
Guru, 305, 307, 308, 314, 550-
    551, 554, 556-557, 610, 616
Gwalior, 558

H

Hadith, 436, 438
Haftarah, 383
Haggadah, 386
Haifa, 112, 118
Hajj, 437, 443
Halachah, 383
Halachically, 383
Halakhah, 378, 381
Halal, 67, 440, 556
Haldi, 309
Haman, 387
Hametz, 386
Hamkar, 590
Hanafi, 436, 438
Hanbali, 436
Hands of the Cause of God, 112
Hankar, 553
Hanukah, 387
Hanukiah, 387
Hanukiyyot, 387
Hanuman, 301
Haram, 67, 440
Haredim, 376, 379-380
Hari Jayanti, 310
Hari, 552
Harijans, 307
Harmandir Sahib, 559
Harrison, George, 312
Harvest, 224, 386-387
Hasan, 435
Hasid, 380
Hasidic, 380, 388-389
Hatha Yoga, 313
Hau mai, 553
Haumai, 553-554
Haurvatat, 590-591
Hausa, 434
Havan, 308-309, 592
Havdalah, 381
HazIratul-Quds, 118
Hazzan, 389
Hazzanim, 389
Heathen, 613
Heaven, 114
Hebrew, 376-378, 381-384, 386, 388
Hebrew Bible, 376
Hebrew Scriptures, 206
Hechsher, 67
Heder, 384
Hellenists, 387
Herald of Christ's Presence, 608

Hereditaries, 613
Herodotus, 588
Herzl, Theodor, 379
High Church, 213
High Holy Days, 379, 384
High Priest, 387
Hijab, 441
Hijra, 442
Himmat Rai, 553
Hinayana, 145
Hindi, 298, 364, 550
Hindu-related, 313
Hindusthan, 298
Hizb-ut-Tahrir, 445
Holi, 310
Holiness Churches, 204, 230
Holocaust Remembrance Day, 387
Holocaust, 377, 387-388
Holy Ark, 384
Holy Communion, 216, 218-220, 223-224
Holy Father, 234
Holy Land, 111
Holy Roman Emperor, 205
Holy Saturday, 221, 223
Holy Spirit, 208, 210, 212, 214-216, 224, 231, 590
Holy Trinity, 209-210, 212, 215
Holy Week, 221, 223
Hong Kong Chinese, 140
Hoshang Shah, 595
House Church Movement, 204, 213, 220, 232
House of Deceit, 591
House of God, 437
House of Song, 591
Houses of Worship, 37, 115
Huguenots, 204
Hujjah, 439
Hukam, 553
Hukhta, 588
Hutta, 613
Human Rights Act, 49
Humash, 377, 380
Humata, 588
Humphreys, Christmas, 139-140
Husayn Ali, 112
Husayn, 435, 439, 442
Hvarshta, 588
Hypostases, 210

I

Ibadah, 441
Iconographic, 220
Iconostasis, 220
Icons, 220
Ijma, 436, 438
Ijtihad, 436
Imam, 65, 69, 439-440, 445-446
Imam Ali, 439
Imam Husayn, 439, 443
Imamate, 434-435, 440
Immaculate Conception, 211, 222
Immortal Third, 363
Immortality, 590
Incarnation, 208-210, 221
Independent, 40
India, 112, 115, 140-141, 145, 147, 151-154, 297-298, 300, 305-308, 310-312, 314, 357-358, 361-363, 435, 437-439, 549, 556, 558
Indian, 140-141, 146-148, 155, 204, 227, 298, 307, 313, 364, 433, 435, 438-439, 549-550, 587
Indians, 153
Indonesia, 435, 437
Indo-Pakistani, 433-434
Indra, 301
Indus, 298
Initiation, 592, 596
Injil, 434, 437
Intercalary Days, 117
Inter-Church Process, 231
Interdenominational, 232
Intermediate Bodies, 232
International Counsellors, 118
Interpreter of Scripture, 112
Iona, 218
Iran, 111, 434, 587-589, 593-594
Iranian, 587-588, 594-595
Iranian Revolution, 111
Iraq, 377
Ireland, 111, 118, 139, 203-205, 215, 219, 226-231, 233
Irish Republic, 226
Isaac, 376, 381
Isaiah, 377
Isha, 442
Ishmael, 381, 443
Ishta-devata, 305
Ishvara, 310

Ishwara, 304
Ismail, 439
Ismailis, 439-440
Israel, 112, 115, 118, 375-377, 379-380, 382, 385-387
Israeli, 375, 382, 387
Israeli Independence, 387
Israelites, 376, 386
Issachar, 376
Italy, 227
Itihasa, 300

J

Jaap, 557
Jacob, 376-377
Ja'fari, 436
Jah, 615
Jaimini, 299
Jakata, 145
Jamaat Ahl-e-Sunnat, 444
Jamaat-i-Islami, 438, 444
Jamgon Kongtrul, 147
Jami, 441
Janmashtami, 311
Jap, 555, 557
Japa, 309
Japan, 141-143, 145-146, 148, 151-152, 206
Japanese, 140, 142, 147-148, 150, 153-154, 156
Japanese Government, 156
Japanese Zen, 147, 150, 154
Japji, 555, 557
Japji Sahib, 557
Jashan, 595-596
Jashan, 76
Jat, 559
Jataka Stories, 143
Jati, 306, 311-313
Je Tsong Khapa Losang Drakpa, 147
Jehangir, 558
Jeremiah, 377
Jerusalem, 222-223, 377, 379, 384, 386-387
Jesuits, 218
Jesus, 205-224, 434, 438
Jew, 208-209, 221, 375-390
Jewish, 205-206, 208-209, 221, 224, 435, 441
Jewish Representative Councils, 387
Jewish Tanakh, 206

Jhatka, 556
Jihad, 440
Jina, 357, 360-361, 363
Jina Rishabha, 363
Jirik, 148
Jiva, 359
Jnana, 360
Jnana yoga, 303
Jnana-pancami, 363
Jodo Shinshu, 148
Jodo Shu, 148
Joshua, 376-377
JPIC, 217
Judaea, 208
Judaeo-Arabic, 376
Judaeo-German, 376
Judah, 376-377
Judgement, 210, 217
Judges, 377
Julian, 221
Justice, 217, 231, 378-380
Jyotisha, 301

K

Ka'bah, 437
Kabbalah, 380
Kabbalat Shabbat, 383
Kabbalat Torah, 381
Kabbalistic, 380
Kachhera, 556
Kadampa, 147, 153
Kadmi, 594
Kagyu, 146
Kagyupa, 153
Kala, 359
Kalasha, 309
Kali, 300, 302-303, 306, 311
Kali Yuga, 299, 300, 302-303, 306, 311
Kalpa, 301
Kalpa Sutra, 359, 364
Kam, 553
Kama, 305
Kamma, 144
Kammic, 144
Kampala, 115
Kangha, 556
Kangyur, 142
Kapilavatthu, 140
Kara, 556
Karah Prashad, 76, 557-558
Karam Khand, 553
Karbala, 435, 439

Karma, 144, 146-147, 299, 302-303, 360, 360-361, 620
Karma Kagyu, 147
Karma Lingpa, 146
Karma vipata, 144
Karma yoga, 303
Karmapa, 146-147
Karmic, 144, 360-361
Karmically, 144
Karnataka, 358
Karodh, 553
Kartarpur, 550-551
Kartarpuri Birh, 551
Karttika-purnima, 364
Karuna, 144
Kashered, 382
Kashi, 311
Kashmir, 311
Kashrut, 382
Kathina Day, 152
Kaur, 556
Kayanian, 588
Kedaranath, 311
Kegon, 146
Kensho, 147
Kenya, 297, 357, 433, 587, 555
Keshdhari, 555
Ketuvim, 377
Kevala jnana, 357-358
Kevalin, 361
Khalifa, 434
Khalistan, 559
Khalsa, 550-551, 553, 555, 557-558
Khanda, 555, 557
Khande, 555
Khandhas, 143
Khattris, 306
Khorasan, 588
Khordad Sal, 595
Khordeh Avesta, 589
Khorshed, 589
Kiddush, 75, 381, 383
King David, 377, 379
King Edward VI, 225
King Henry VIII, 204, 225, 227
King Jamshid, 594
King of Kings, 615
King Rama, 300
King Solomon, 377, 379
Kingdom Halls, 608
Kippah, 383
Kirk, 41
Kirpan, 556

Kirtan, 309, 554, 557-558
Kirtan Sohila, 554, 557
Kisseh-kerfeh, 592
Kitáb-i-Aqdas, (Most Holy Book) 112
Kitáb-i-Iqán, (Book of Certitude) 112
Knowledge-Fifth, 363
Kodashim, 378
Kongocho, 154
Korea, 141, 145, 204
Korean Son, 153
Kosher, 66, 74, 382-383, 440
Koshti, 592
Krishna, 113, 298, 300-302, 304-305, 309-312
Krishna Consciousness, 312
Krishna-Janmashtami, 312
Kshathra Vairya, 590
Kshatriya, 306-307, 358
Kshetra, 359
Kumkum, 309
Kuriakon, 207
Kurukshetra, 298, 300
Kushinagara, 141, 151
Kushti, 592-593
Kutch, 297, 312

L

Ladino, 376
Lailat, 443
Laity, 68, 226, 232
Lakshmi, 301, 311
Lam Rim, 153
Lama, 142, 147, 153-154, 155
Lama Thubten Yeshe, 153
Langar, 76, 554, 556-558
Laos, 141, 145
Last Judgement, 210, 217, 591
Last Supper, 218, 223
Latin America, 204, 206
Latin, 204, 206-207, 209, 211, 218, 221, 223, 225
Latter-days, 606
Lav, 554
Lavan, 554
Laws of Manu, 301, 307
Lay minister, 147
Lent, 67, 217, 222-223
Lesser Pentad, 595
Leva Patel, 312
Leviticus, 377
Lhasa, 153

Liberal, 75, 213-214, 376, 380-381, 388-389
Liberation, 553
Lilas, 300
Limbs, 358
Lineages, 146
Linga, 310
Little Vehicle, 145
Liturgical, 213, 221
Liturgy, 212, 218
Lobh, 553
Local Assembly, 72
Local Churches, 203, 220, 229-231, 233
Local Preachers, 228
Local Spiritual Assembly, 114, 116-119
Lohana, 306, 312
Loka, 359
Lord, 207-208, 218-219, 221, 300, 304, 310-312, 309, 378
Lord Krishna, 311
Lord of Lords, 615
Lord Rama, 310
Lord Shiva, 310
Lord Swaminarayan, 311
Lotus, 142, 146, 148, 154
Lotus Sutra, 148, 154
Lotus-Born, 146
Low Church, 213
Lubavitch, 388
Luke, 207
Lulav, 386
Lumbini, 140
Lutheran, 34, 229-230, 234

M

Maariv, 383-384
Maccabees, 387
Madhahib, 436
Madhhabs, 436
Madhva, 298, 304
Madina, 434, 443, 550
Madrassahs, 445
Magen David, 384
Maghadha, 358
Maghrib, 441
Magi, 222, 588
Maha, 145
Mahabharata, 298-300, 303
Maha-Bodhisattvas, 146
Mahabokhta, 589
Mahamudra, 147

Mahara, 313
Maharaja Dalip Singh, 549
Maharaja Ranjit Singh, 549, 551
Maharashtra, 358
Maharishi, 620
Mahashivaratri, 310
Mahatma, 307
Mahatma Gandhi, 363
Mahavairocara, 154
Mahavira, 358-359, 363-364
Mahavira Jayanti, 363
Mahavratas, 362, 364
Mahayana, 140-146, 149, 152-156
Mahayana Buddhism, 144, 153-154, 588
Mahayana Buddhist, 141-143, 152-153
Mahayana Parinirvana Sutra, 142
Mahdi, 439
Mahzorim, 384
Making Wonderful, 591
Makka, 434, 437, 442-445, 550
Malawi, 297
Malay, 434
Malaysia, 434-435, 437
Maliki, 436
Mandal, 364
Mandalas, 149
Mandatum, 223
Mandir, 27, 65, 73-74, 308-310, 363-364
Manifestations, 113
Manjushri, 145-146
Mantras, 149-150, 299
Manusmriti, 301, 307, 620
Mardi Gras, 222
Marga, 143-144, 148
Marpa, 146
Marriage, 554
Martin Luther, 204, 230
Martyrdom, 116
Mary, 210-211, 220-222, 224-225
Mashiach, 208, 379
Mashriqu'l-Adhkar, 116
Masjid, 441
Masorti, 74, 376, 380-381, 389
Mass, 73, 212, 218-219, 221
Mataji, 302
Mathura, 311, 358
Matthew, 207
Matzah, 386
Maulana Ahmad Raza Khan, 438
Maulana Muhammad Ilyas, 438
Maulana Muhammad Qasim, 438

Mauryan, 358
Mawdudi, 439, 444
Maya, 302, 304, 553-554
Mazda, 588-594
Mazdayasni, 588
Meat, 556, 558
Mecca, 443
Medes, 588
Meditation, 140, 142, 147-150
Mediterranean, 38, 208, 212
Meeting houses, 219
Meetings, 204, 231
Meher, 595
Mehr, 589, 595
Mehrgan, 595
Meiji Restoration, 155
Melchizedek Priesthood, 606
Men, 441-443, 550, 555-557
Men's traditions, 613
Menasseh, 375-376
Mendicant, 140, 154, 358-359,
   361-362
Menorah, 384, 387
Menstruating, 441, 443
Messenger, 112-114, 437, 439
Messiah, 208, 379
Messianic, 379
Methodism, 212, 228
Methodist, 50, 53, 207, 220,
   225, 228, 233-234
Methodist Conference, 228, 234
Mezuzot, 389
Micchami, 364
Michaelmas, 224
Middle Ages, 205, 224
Middle East, 205, 212, 375,
   433-434, 550
Middle English, 222
Middle Way, 144
Midrash, 378
Midrashic, 386
Mihrab, 441, 442
Mikveh, 383
Milad, 438, 442
Milarepa, 146
Millennium, 221
Mimamsa, 303
Minbar, 442
Mindfulness, 67
Minhah, 384
Ministers, 155
Ministry, 233
Minor, 377, 386-387
Minster, 220

Minyan, 383, 384
Mishnah, 377-378
Missionary, 203, 206, 606
Mitzvot, 378, 381
Mobed, 596
Mochis, 306, 312
Moderator, 229, 233-234
Moghul, 435
Moh, 553
Mohan, 552
Mohel, 381
Mohinder Singh, 556
Mohkam Chand, 553
Moksha, 302-303, 305, 358,
   360-361, 364
Monarchy, 225-226, 229
Monastery, 140, 151, 153, 155
Monastic, 142, 151, 154-155
Mongol Emperor Altan Khan,
   147
Monists, 301
Monks, 42, 72, 140, 142, 150-
   153, 155-156, 217-218, 233,
   361-363
Monogamy, 440
Monotheism, 437, 590
Monotheistic, 437, 552
Monotheists, 208, 301
Moravian, 34, 230
Mormons, 606
Moses, 113, 376-378, 434
Moses Maimonides, 378
Mosque, 27, 29, 39, 65, 75, 441-
   442, 445-446
Most Holy Book, 112
Mother Church, 222
Mother of Jesus, 210
Mother Temple, 116
Motor Cycle Helmet Act, 46
Mount Govardhan, 311
Mount Sinai, 376-377, 386
Mudras, 149
Mufti, 438
Mughal Court, 552
Mughal Emperor, 552, 558
Mughal Empire, 551
Muhammad, 112-113
Muhammad Al-Muntazar, 439
Muharram, 442
Mukti, 553-554
Mul Mantar, 552
Mulla Husayn, 116
Murti, 308-309, 313
Murugan, 301

Musaf, 383
Music, 115, 443
Musta'lian Ismailis, 439
Mystery, 210, 224

N

Nagar kirtan, 558
Najaf, 439
Nam, 552
Nam Japna, 552, 554
Namaz, 75, 441
Namdhari Sikhs, 551
Nam-myoho-renge-kyo, 154
Namu, 148
Namu-Amida-butsu, 148
Namu-myoho-renge-kyo, 154
Nanak Shahi Sammat, 558
Nandi, 301, 309
Nankana Sahib, 550, 556
Naphtali, 376
Naqshbandi, 439
Narasimha, 310
Narasingha, 310
Naropa, 146
Nashim, 378
Nathdwar, 311
National Spiritual Assembly,
   118-119
Nature, 113, 116
Navaratri, 311
Navjote, 592
Navnat, 364
Navya Vishishta-Advaita, 304
Naya, 359
Nazareth, 205, 208-209
Nazi, 309, 363, 375, 377
Nazism, 309
Nembutsu, 148
Nepal, 140
Networks, 231-232
Nevi'im, 377, 383
New Church, 204, 230
New Delhi, 115
New Kadampa, 147, 153
New Testament, 204, 206-208,
   219, 230, 606
New World, 206, 608
New York, 119
New Zealand, 587
Nezikin, 378
Nibbana, 141
Nicene Creed, 207
Nichidatsu Fuji, 154

Nichiren, 148, 154
Nichiren Buddhism, 148
Nimbarka, 298, 304
Nineteen-Day Feasts, 115-117
Nirankar, 552
Nirgun, 552
Nirjara, 361
Nirodha, 143
Nirukti, 301
Nirvana, 143-144, 146, 358
Nishan Sahib, 557-558
Nizaris, 439
Noble Eightfold Path, 144, 148-149
Noble Truths, 142-144, 148-149
Noncomformist, 25, 42, 204, 219, 226
North Africa, 205-206
North America, 206, 230-231, 587
North Eastern Iran, 588
North India, 140, 298, 558
North West India, 588
Northern Buddhism, 155
Northern Ireland, 118, 203-205, 226-227
Northern Kutch, 297
Northern Silk Road, 146
Northern Transmission, 141, 145, 152
Numbers, 377
Nuns, 142, 150-156, 217-218, 361-364
Nutan Varsh, 311
Nyakpa Jampa Thaye, 153
Nyaya, 303
Nyayeshes, 589
Nyingmapa Tibetan Buddhists, 152

O

Odinism, 613
Oikumene, 215
Old School, 146
Old Testament, 206, 217, 377
OM, 309
One Greater, 112
One Supreme, 301
Oral Tradition, 299
Ordained, 115, 118, 155, 213, 219, 228-229, 231-233
Order, 142, 144-145, 149, 152-156, 206, 208, 212-215, 217-218, 221-222, 225, 232-233, 440, 445, 447

Ordinances, 607
Ordination, 154-155
Organs, 220
Oriental Orthodox, 227
Original Sin, 209, 211, 222
Orthodox Beth Din, 389
Orthodox Christianity, 205, 211-212, 227
Orthodox Christians, 204, 218
Orthodox Church, 207, 212, 220, 225, 227
Orthodox Churches, 205, 207, 212, 215-216, 218-222, 224-225, 227, 232-234
Orthodox Dioceses, 220
Orthodox Jews, 378, 380, 382, 385, 388
Orthodox Judaism, 380-381, 383, 388
Oshwal, 357, 363-364
Ottoman Empire, 435, 436
Ottoman Turkish, 112
Outcastes, 307

P

Pacific, 112
Padmasambhava, 146, 152
Pahlavi, 587-590
Pahul, 550, 552-553, 555
Paila, 299
Pakistan, 435, 438, 444, 446, 549-550, 556, 587, 593
Palestine, 112, 377, 379
Pali, 139-140, 142, 145
Palm Sunday, 223
Panama City, 115
Panca Silani, 148
Pancami, 363
Panca-namaskara-mantra, 362
Panchen Lama, 147
Pandit, 313
Panj Pyare, 553, 555, 558
Panje-kas, 595
Panje-mas, 595
Panth, 550-551, 553, 555
Papacy, 204
Papal, 206, 227
Parabrahman, 304
Paramitas, 149
Paramjit Kaur, 556
Parashah, 383
Parinirvana, 141-142, 151
Parish, 213, 219, 226

Parochet, 384
Pars, 588
Parsi, 25, 587-588, 594-596
Parsi Gujarati, 588
Parsi Zoroastrian, 593
Parthians, 588
Parvati, 301-302, 305
Parve, 382
Paryayas, 359
Paryushana-parva, 363
Paschal, 223
Passion, 223
Passover, 67, 386
Pastoral Care, 228, 233
Path, 144-145, 148-149, 553-554, 557-558
Patidar, 306-312
Patriarch, 212, 234, 376
Patristic, 207
Paul, 209, 211, 221
Pavapuri, 358
Pazand, 589
Peace Pagodas, 150, 154
Peace, 217, 231
Pearl of Great Price, 606
Peking, 143
Pentecost, 221, 223-224, 386
Pentecostal, 204-205, 211, 213-214, 216, 220, 225, 230, 233
Pentecostalism, 213
Pentecostalist, 40, 230, 213
Perfected Being, 361-362
Persia, 111-112, 116-117
Persian, 111-112, 298, 387, 447, 552, 588-589
Personalist monotheism, 303
Persons, 210
Pesach, 67, 386
Peter, 211, 221
Petertide, 224
Pews, 73
Pharaohs, 376
Philippines, 435, 437
Pigs, 382, 440
Pilgrim, 311
Pilgrim Festivals, 384
Pilgrimage, 311, 437, 439, 556
Pioneering, 114
Pirs, 438-439, 446
Pishdadian, 595
Plato, 588
Plymouth Brethren, 230
Poland, 380
Polyandry, 440

Polygamy, 440-441
Polytheistic, 301, 588
Pope, 203-205, 211-212, 217, 234
Pope Gregory, 203
Portugal, 375
Portuguese Sephardi, 388
Poson, 152
Postulants, 155
Prahlada, 310
Prajna-paramita, 142
Prakriti, 303-304
Pramukh Swami, 312
Prasad, 310
Prasadam, 310
Prasthana Vakya, 300
Pratikramana, 362-363
Pravachan, 309
Prayer, 206, 212, 215-219, 225-226, 229, 376, 378-379, 383-386, 436-437, 439-443, 445, 447, 589, 592-593, 299, 310-311
Preacher, 220
Preaching, 212, 219, 233
Presbyterian, 28, 41-42, 53, 204-205, 225-226, 228-229
Presbyterianism, 204, 226, 228
Presbyterians, 226
Presbytery, 41, 226
President, 140, 228, 234
Prevention of Incitement to Hatred Act, 47
Priest, 211, 219, 224-225, 232-233, 306-307, 310, 313-314
Priesthood, 155, 606
Priestly, 588
Primordial Buddha, 146
Prince Arjuna, 300
Progressive, 376, 379-383, 385, 388-389
Progressive Jews, 379-380, 382-383, 385, 388
Progressive Judaism, 380-381, 383, 388
Progressive Revelation, 113
Progressive Synagogues, 380, 383, 388-389
Prophet, 75, 112-113, 434-436, 438-440, 442-443
Prophet Muhammad, 112, 434-435, 438, 440, 442-443
Protectorate, 229

Protestant, 28, 42, 204-206, 210-221, 225-226, 228, 232-234
Protestant Christian, 206, 212, 226
Protestant Christianity, 204, 214, 219
Protestant Churches, 72, 205-206, 210, 212, 215, 218-221, 225, 228, 232-234
Protestant Reformation, 204-206
Protestantism, 213
Province, 226-227, 229-230
Provincial Moderator, 229, 233
Psalms, 377, 381
Pudgalas, 359
Puja, 72, 150, 152, 309-311, 313, 362
Pujaris, 364
Pulpit, 220, 442
Punjab Province, 549
Punjabi, 297-298, 312-313, 434, 549-550, 555-556, 559
Purana, 299-301, 313
Purdah, 441
Pure Land Buddhism, 148, 154
Pure Land Buddhists, 148
Pure Land School, 148, 154, 156
Pure Land, 146, 148, 154, 156
Purgatory, 210
Purim, 387
Puritan Separatists, 229
Purohit, 313
Purusha Sukta, 306
Purva Mimamsa, 303
Purvas, 358
Pushtimarg, 312
Pushto, 434
Pythagoras, 588

Q

Qadiri, 438-439
Qatar, 436
Qibla, 75
Qiblah, 441
Qiyas, 436, 438
Quaker, 34, 214, 218-219, 225, 231
Queen Mary, 225
Qur'an, 67
Qur'anic, 445

R

Rabbinate, 388
Rabbinic, 377-378, 387, 389
Rabbi, 377-378, 383, 388-389
Rabi, 443
Race Relations Act, 48
Radha, 309
Ragis, 560
Rahit Maryada, 552
Rahit Nama, 551-552
Rains Retreat, 152
Raja Yoga, 303, 313, 602
Rajas, 302
Rajasthan, 357-358
Rakhi, 306
Rakshabandhan, 306
Ram, 298, 550, 552-553, 559
Rama Navami, 310
Rama Rajya, 300
Rama, 298, 300-301, 310-311
Ramadan, 67, 437, 444
Ramakrishna, 313
Ramanuja, 298, 304
Ramayana, 299-300, 311, 620
Ramgarh, 559
Ramgarhia, 559
Rapithwan, 592
Rarhi Brahmins, 307
Ravana, 300-301
Ravidasis, 307
Readers, 232-233
Reading room, 602
Reality, 359-360, 552-553
Reason, 207, 213, 220, 225
Reasoning, 615
Rebbe, 389
Rebecoming, 144
Rebirth, 143, 144, 146, 304, 553
Recitation, 148, 154
Redeemer, 209-210
Reform Beth Din, 389
Reform Jews, 380, 388
Reform Judaism, 381, 388
Reform, 67, 74, 376, 380-381, 383, 388-389
Reformation, 41, 52, 204-206, 211-214, 219-220, 225, 229, 606
Reformed Churches, 216, 221, 225, 228, 233-234
Reformed, 204, 211-213, 215-216, 221, 225-226, 228-229, 233-234

Regional Bahá'í Councils, 118
Rehras, 557
Reincarnation, 144, 147
Reiyukai, 154
Religious Brothers, 217
Religious Discrimination, 47-49
Religious Education and
  Collective Worship, 52
Religious, 203-208, 214, 217-218,
  220, 225, 228, 231-232
Religious Orders, 232
Restoration, 209, 226, 229
Restorationist, 213, 220, 232
Restored Church, 606
Resurrected, 208-209
Resurrection, 208, 591, 602
Reuben, 376
Revd Master Ptnh Jiy-Kensett,
  154
Revd Nikkyo Niwano, 154
Revelation, 207-210, 213, 377-
  378, 380, 387, 434, 438-439
Reverence, 435
Rig Veda, 299, 306
Right Action, 148-149
Right Concentration, 149
Right Effort, 149
Right Intention, 148-149
Right Livelihood, 149-150
Right Mindfulness, 149
Right Speech, 149
Right Understanding, 148-149
Righteousness, 588, 590-591, 593
Rimé, 147
Rinzai, 148, 154, 156
Risen Christ, 223
Rissho Kosei-Kai, 154
Ritual, 437, 439-443
River Ganga, 311
Road Traffic Act, 46
Roman Catholic, 25, 34, 42, 50,
  52, 204-207, 210-212, 215-227,
  231-234
Roman Catholic Church, 28, 205,
  210-212, 216, 218-223, 225,
  227, 231, 233-234
Rome, 203, 205, 211, 225, 234
Rosh Hashanah, 385-386
Royal Family, 383
Rumalas, 557
Rupas, 142, 149
Russian, 204, 207, 227
Russian Empire, 375

Russian Orthodox Church, 207
Ruth, 377, 387

S

Sabbatarian, 221, 230
Sabbath, 74, 378, 381
Sabha, 616
Sach Khand, 553
Sacrament, 218-219, 229
Sacred Fold, 118
Sacred ordinances, 606
Sadaqa, 437
Saddharma-pundarika, 142
Sadh Sangat, 554, 557
Sadhu, 362, 358, 362, 364
Sadhvi, 358, 362, 364
Sahajananda, 298, 304, 312
Sahajananda Swami, 312
Sahajdhari, 555
Sahib Chand, 553
Sahib, 550-560
Saints, 207, 211, 220-221, 224, 616
Sakya, 142, 147
Sakyamuni, 141
Salat, 75, 436-437, 441-442
Salman Rushdie, 445
Saltva, 302
Salvation, 209, 212, 215-216, 218-
  219, 223, 229, 234
Salvation Army, 216, 218, 229, 234
Salvationists, 34
Salvific, 209
Sama Veda, 299-300
Samaj, 364
Samanis, 361
Samaria, 208
Samgha Day, 152
Samgha, 141-142, 150, 152, 155
Samhitas, 300
Samjna, 143
Samkhya, 303
Sammat Nanak Shahi, 558
Sampradaya, 304-305, 312
Samsara, 144, 149, 302
Samudaya, 143
Samuel, 377
Samvatsari-pratikramana, 364
Samyagajiva, 149
Samyagdrishti, 148
Samyagvac, 149
Samyagvayama, 149
Samyak-caritra, 361
Samyak-darshana, 360

Samyakkarmanta, 148-149
Samyaksamadhi, 149
Samyaksamkalpa, 148
Samyaksmriti, 149
Sanatana Dharma, 38, 298, 302,
  305, 311
Sanctification, 75
Sangh, 364
Sanjan, 588
Sanna, 143
Sannyasa, 307
Sannyasin, 307, 313
Sanskrit, 140, 142, 147, 298-299,
  301-302, 359
Sant, 549, 554, 560
Sant Khalsa, 610
Sant Teja Singh, 549
Santokh, 553
Saoshyant, 591
Saptah Path, 557
Saram Khand, 553
Sarasvati, 301, 311
Saraswati, 301, 313
Sargun, 552
Sasanian Iran, 594
Sasanians, 588
Sat, 552
Satan, 224
Satanic Verses, 47, 445
Satanism, 613
Satguru, 610
Satnam, 552
Satori, 147
Satya, 362
Saudi Arabia, 436
Saviour, 208, 591
Sawm, 437
Sayyed Qassim Al-Jalali, 447
Sayyid Abul A', 439
Scandinavian, 230
Scheduled castes, 141, 307
Schism, 205
School Standards and Framework
  Act, 50
Scotland, 111, 118, 150, 154, 203-
  205, 212, 218-219, 221, 225-
  229, 231, 233-234, 433
Scottish Parliament, 118
Scripture, 204, 206-208, 211-215,
  217, 219, 223, 225, 358-359,
  362-363
Sealed, 607
Sealing, 606

Second Coming, 210, 222
Second Review of the Race Relations Act, 48
Second Temple, 377, 387
Second World War, 111, 227, 433, 549, 559
Secretaries, 389
Sedarim, 378
Seder, 386
Sedreh, 592
Sedreh-Pushi, 592
Sefer Torah, 384-385
Sehaj Path, 554, 557
Sentient Beings, 359, 362
Separate, 382
Sephardi, 375-376, 388
Serbs, 227
Serene Reflection Meditation, 148
Sermon, 209, 217
Servant, 112
Setayeshgah, 76
Seveners, 439-440
Seventh Day, 221, 229
Sewa Panthis, 553
Sewa, 553-554
Shabads, 551
Shabbat, 378-385
Shafi'i, 436
Shahadah, 437
Shaharit, 383-384
Shahenshahi, 594-595
Shahrevar, 590
Shaiva Siddhanta, 304
Shaivas, 305
Shaktas, 305
Shakti, 301, 305
Shakya, 142
Shakyamuni, 141, 146
Shakyamuni Buddha, 146
Shalosh Regalim, 386
Shamanism, 613
Shamatha, 149
Shankara, 298, 304
Shari'ah, 67, 436-437, 439-441
Sharmanera, 154
Shat Khanda-Agama, 358
Shavuot, 386-387
Shawwal, 444
Shaykhs, 439
Shechita, 382, 388, 440
Sheitel, 383
Shema, 378, 385

Shi'a, 111, 435, 438-441, 443-445, 438
Shi'ite, 435
Shikantaza, 148
Shiksa, 301
Shilpaveda, 300
Shin, 148, 153, 154
Shingon, 146, 154
Shiraz, 112, 116
Shiromani Gurdwara Parbandhak Committee, 559
Shiv, 298
Shiva, 300-302, 304-305, 309-311
Shivah, 384
Shivaratri, 310
Shobo-an, 154
Shochet, 382
Shoghi Effendi, 111-112, 117
Shravakayana, 145
Shrimad Bhagavatam, 299
Shrimad Rajachandra, 363
Shrine, 72, 150-151
Shriven, 222
Shromani Gurdwara Parbandhak Committee, 552
Shrove Tuesday, 222
Shruta, 358
Shruta-pancami, 363
Shruti, 299
Shtetls, 380
Shuddha-Advaita, 304
Shuddha-Dvaita, 304
Shudgen, 147
Shul, 384
Shunyata, 144-145
Shvetambara, 358-359, 361, 363-364
Sicily, 435
Siddha, 361
Siddhanta, 358
Siddhartha Gautama, 140-141
Siddhas, 362
Sidrah, 383
Sikh, 551
Silsilahs, 439
Simchat Torah, 385-386
Simeon, 376
Sin, 209, 211, 215, 222, 379
Sinai, 376-378, 386
Sindhu, 298
Singh, 549-553, 555-556, 558-560

Sinhalese Anagarika Dharmapala, 140
Sinhalese, 140
Sino-Japanese, 154
Sirozah, 589
Sita, 300, 311
Sitting Shivah, 384
Siva, 298
Six Parts, 358
Skandhas, 143
Slavic, 376
Smriti, 299-300
Sodar Rehras, 557
Sofer, 389
Sohila, 554, 557
Solitaries, 613
Solomon, 377, 379
Somalia, 433
Son of God, 208
Son of Man, 208
Son, 208-210, 212, 222, 224
Song of Songs, 377
Song of the Blessed Lord, 300
Soto Zen, 148, 154
Soul, 360-361, 554
South America, 112
South Asian, 145, 152, 438
South East Asia, 145
Southern Canon, 140, 142
Southern Iraq, 439
Southern Transmission, 142, 145
Spain, 375, 380, 435
Spanish, 376, 388
Speaking with tongues, 214
Spenta Armaiti, 590
Spenta Mainyu, 590
Spirit, 207-208, 210, 212-216, 218-219, 224, 231
Spiritual Assemblies, 111, 116-119
Spiritual Churches, 204, 206
Spiritual Movements, 304-305, 312
Spiritual Victors, 357
Splendour, 116
Sri Guru Granth Sahib, 616
Sri Guru Singh Sabha, 559
Sri Lanka, 139-141, 145, 152-153, 297, 439, 550
Sri Lankan Buddhism, 152-153
Sri Lankan, 140, 152-153
Srinathji, 312
St Benedict, 218

St Dominic, 218
St Michael, 224
St Paul, 209
Sthanakvasi, 361, 363
Strict Baptists, 229
Subsidiary Canon, 358-359
Sudras, 306-307
Sudreh, 592
Suf, 439
Sufi, 438-440, 444, 446
Sufism, 437, 440
Suhrawardi, 440
Sukha, 360
Sukkot, 386
Sumantu, 299
Sunday, 205, 221-224
Sunna, 435-438
Sunnata, 144
Sunni, 434, 437-439, 441, 443, 447
Superintendent Minister, 228
Supper, 218, 223
Supreme Godhead, 304
Supreme Governor, 41, 225
Supreme Lord, 312
Supreme Person, 301
Supreme Spirit, 302
Surah, 436
Surmang, 153
Surrendered, 602
Surya, 301
Susami, 313
Sustainer, 209
Sutra, 142, 148, 154
Sutta-pitaka, 142
Svadharma, 305
Swami Dayananda Saraswati, 313
Swami Vivekananda, 313
Swaminarayan, 304, 308, 311-313
Swamis, 309, 314
Swastika, 309, 363
Swayas, 555, 557
Syadvada, 359
Syat, 359
Sydney, 115
Synagogal, 383
Synagogue, 29, 39-40, 74, 375-376, 380-389
Synod, 203, 226, 230
Syria, 435
Syrian Orthodox, 227

T

Tabernacle, 220
Tabernacles, 386
Tablets, 112
Tablighi Jamaat, 438, 444
Taizokyo, 142
Tallis, 385
Tallit, 385
Tallitot, 385
Talmud, 377-378, 380
Talmudic, 388
Talwandi, 550
Tamil, 298
Tanha, 143
Tantras, 301, 313
Tantric, 146
Tanzania, 297, 357
Taoist, 140
Tapas, 361
Tasawwuf, 439
Ta-ts'ang-ching, 142
Teacher's Fifth, 363
Teaching Lineage, 146
Temple, 377-379, 384, 386-387, 606
Ten Commandments, 217
Ten Precepts, 155-156
Ten Virtues, 364
Tenakh, 376-377
Tendai, 146
Tengyur, 143
Tenzin Gyatso, 147
Tephilin, 385, 389
Terapanthi, 361, 363
Terephah, 382
Test Acts, 46
Testimony Meeting, 602
Thai New Year, 152
Thai, 150, 152-153, 155
Thailand, 140-141, 145, 153
Thang-ka, 149
Theists, 66
Theosophical Society, 139
Theotokos, 210
Theravada, 140-143, 145, 149-150, 152-153, 155-156
Theravadins, 152
Three Baskets, 142
Three Jewels, 141, 155, 361
Three Signs of Being, 143, 149
Tibet, 140-141, 145-147, 153-154
Tibetan, 140, 142, 145-147, 149-151, 153-156

Tibetan Book of the Dead, 146
Tibetan Buddhism, 145-147, 150, 155
Tibetan Buddhist, 142, 147, 149, 150-151,153-154
Tibetan Lamas, 153
Tibetan Lunar, 153
Tibetan Medical Centre, 151
Tibetan Schools, 146
Tilopa, 146
Tipitaka, 142
Tir Yazad, 591
Tir, 591, 595
Tiratana, 141
Tirthankara, 357-359, 363
Tirupathi, 311
Tishah Be-Av, 387
Tohorot, 378
Torah, 377-381, 383-387, 389, 434, 438
Tower of Silence, 593
Transcendental Meditation, 313
Transfiguration, 224
Transmigration, 144
Transmission, 141-142, 145, 152, 155
Treif, 382
Trimurti, 301
Trinidad, 297
Trinitarian, 39, 40, 212, 231
Trinity, 209-210, 212, 215, 224, 608
Triratna, 141
Trishna, 143
Trishul, 309
Trisong Detsen, 146
Tritheism, 210
True Dharma, 142
True Pure Land, 148
Truth, 552, 588, 590-591, 593
Turbans, 555
Turkish, 434
Turning the Wheel of the Law, 152
Twelvers, 436, 439
Tzitzit, 385

U

Udasis, 550
Uganda, 115, 297, 357, 433, 587
UK, 357-365
Ulama, 447

Ultra-Orthodox, 379-380
Umayyad, 435
UN, 119
UNICEF, 119
Unificationists, 27
Unitarian, 34, 207, 214, 225, 231
Unitarian Churches, 214, 225, 231
United Kingdom, 111, 118, 120-125, 203, 230, 237-250, 297, 317-323, 357, 366-368, 375, 391-401, 433, 449-466, 587, 598
United Nations, 119
United States, 380-381
Unity, 112-113, 115
Unity Feast, 72
Universal House of Justice, 112, 115, 118
Universalist, 231
Unsatisfactoriness, 143
Untouchability, 307
Untouchables, 141, 307
Upadhyayas, 362
Upanishads, 300, 303
Upavedas, 299
Urdu, 434, 442-443
USA, 115, 380
Ushahen, 592
Uttar Pradesh, 297, 438
Uttara Mimamsa, 303
Uziren, 592

V

Vahana, 309
Vaisakha Puja, 152
Vaisakhi, 558, 560
Vaisesika, 303
Vaishampayana, 299
Vaisheshika, 303
Vaishnava, 299, 305, 311-312
Vaishnodevi, 311
Vaishyas, 306-307
Vajradhara, 146
Vajrayana, 145-146
Vak, 554
Vallabha, 298, 304, 312
Valmiki, 300
Vanaprastha, 307
Vand Chkakna, 554
Vanir, 613
Var, 557

Varanasi, 311
Vardhamana, 358
Varna, 305
Varnashrama Dharma, 305
Vases, 595
Vassa, 152
Vatican II, 211
Veda, 299-300
Vedana, 143
Vedanga, 300, 301
Vedanta, 303-304, 313
Vedanta-Sutras, 301
Vedas, 298-301, 303, 313
Vedic, 298, 300-301, 306, 313
Vegetarianism, 150
Vehicle, 145
Vendidad, 589
Venerable Mahinda, 152
Venerable Myokyo-ni, 153
Venerable Sangharakshita, 154
Venerable Sumedho, 153
Veneration, 148
Vicar, 69
Vice-President (Christian), 228
Vidaeva-data, 589
Videvdat, 589
Vietnam, 141, 145
Vietnamese Buddhist, 140
Vigil Sunday Mass, 221
Vihara, 29, 37, 72, 139
Vijayadashami, 311
Vijnana, 143
Vikramasamvat, 363
Vikrami, 558
Vinaya, 155
Vinaya-pitaka, 142
Vinnana, 143
Vipassana, 149
Vipata, 144
Vira-Nirvana, 364
Vira-nirvana-samvat, 363
Virgin birth, 602
Virgin Mary, 210, 220-222, 224
Virupa, 147
Vishishta-Advaita, 304
Vishnu, 300-301, 304-305, 309-310
Vishnuswami, 304
Vishtaspa, 588
Vishwa Hindu Parishad, 313
Vispe Ratavo, 589
Visperad, 589
Visualisation, 146

Vohu Manah, 588, 590-591
Vohumanah, 592
Voidness, 144
Vrats, 308
Vrindavan, 311
Vyakarana, 301
Vyasasangs, 309

W

Wa 'alaikum-us-salaam, 75
Waheguru, 552
Wales, 111, 118, 154, 203-205, 213, 219, 221, 225-231, 233, 376, 433-434, 447, 550
Way, 139, 141, 143-145, 148, 150-151, 156
Way-shower, 602
WCC, 215
Welsh Assembly, 118
Welsh, 225, 229
Wesak, 152
Wesley, Charles, 228
Wesley, John, 228
West Africa, 437
West Bengal, 297
West Punjab, 549
Western Buddhists, 152
Western Christendom, 203-205, 212
Western Christian, 205, 222-223
Western Christianity, 204-205, 210, 218
Western Church, 224
Western Samoa, 115
Wheel, 144, 152
White Sunday, 224
Whitsun, 224
Wholeness, 590, 594
Wicca, 613
Wills, 115
Wilmette, 115-116
Wisdom, 589, 591
Wise Lord, 588-589
Wise Men, 222
Witchcraft, 613
Witness, 216-217
Women, 113-114, 117-119, 208, 211, 217, 233, 378, 381, 383-385, 387, 441-444, 446-447, 550, 555-557
Women's traditions, 613
Wonderful Lord, 552

Word, 207-210, 212, 214-216,
218-219, 222, 224, 228, 232-
233, 550, 552, 554-555, 557, 560
Word of God, 208
World War, 549, 559
Worshippers, 557
Wrathful deities, 146
Writings, 112, 117-118
Wudu, 75, 441

Y

Yad, 385
Yajrayana, 145-146
Yajur Veda, 299-300
Yama, 301
Yamim Noraim, 385-386
Yamuna River, 358
Yana, 145
Yarmulkah, 383
Yashti, 589
Yasht-i-Visperad, 594
Yashts, 589
Yasna, 589, 592
Yavneh, 377
Yazads, 589-590
Yazata, 589-591, 593-595, 589-
591, 593-595
Yazata Mehr, 595
Yazdegird III, 594
Yearly Meeting, 231
Yemeni Muslims, 433, 441
Yeshiva, 388
Yeshivot, 388
Yiddish, 376, 383-384
Yoga, 303, 313
Yom Haatzma'ut, 387
Yom Hashoa, 387
Yom Kippur, 386
York, 226, 233
Youth, 445-447
Yuga, 298-300, 302-303, 306, 311
Yugadi, 310
Yugas, 302, 603

Z

Zakat, 437, 442
Zambia, 297
Zanzibar, 587
Zaotar, 588
Zarathushtra, 588-590, 593, 595
Zarathushtrianism, 588
Zartoshti, 588

Zazen, 147-148
Zebulun, 376
Zen, 146-148, 150-152, 154
Zen Buddhist Organisations, 153
Zen Master, 148
Zenna, 147
Zeraim, 378
Zion, 379
Zion's Watch Tower, 608
Zionism, 379
Zionist, 379, 388
Zohar, 380
Zoroaster, 113, 588
Zuhr, 441

UK AND NATIONAL ORGANISATION INDEX

This index includes all UK and national level organisations of the religious traditions included in the directory, together with UK and national inter-faith organisations and resource organisations, listed in alphabetical order of organisation name (with organisations having a Welsh name listed under both their English and Welsh names). In each case the religion or type of organisation indexed is indicated by a code preceding the page references. This will be particularly helpful in cases where only the name of the organisation and not its religion is known to a directory user, as there are organisations of different religions but with similar names. The codes are as follows:

Ba: Bahá'í   Je: Jewish
Bu: Buddhist   M: Muslim
C: Christian   R: Resource
H: Hindu   S: Sikh
IF: Inter-Faith   So: Some other
Ja: Jain   Z: Zoroastrian

3HO UK, S: 562
45 Aid Society Holocaust Survivors, Je: 391

A

Action by Christians Against Torture, C: 245
Action of Churches Together in Scotland, C: 283
Aden Vanik Association of UK, Ja: 366
Afro-West Indian United Council of Churches, C: 238
Agudath Hashochtim V'Hashomrim of Great Britain (Cattle Section), Je: 391
Agudath Hashochtim V'Hashomrim of Great Britain (Poultry Section), Je: 391
Ahimsa for Quality of Life, Ja: 366
Akaal Purkh Ki Fauj – UK, S: 562
Al Khoei Foundation, M: 449
Al Muntada Al Islami Trust, M: 449
Aladura International Church (UK and Overseas), C: 241
Al-Furqan Charity Trust, M: 449
Al-Hoda Limited, M: 449

Al-Hurau Schools Trust, M: 450
Al-Muhajiroun, M: 450
Al-Muttaqiin, M: 450
Al-Sharq-al Aousat, R: 638
Alliance of Religions and Conservation, IF: 95, R: 633
AMANA, M: 450
Ambedkar International Mission, Bu: 158
Amida Trust, Bu: 158
Amnesty International Religious Liaison Panel, IF: 95
Anglo-Jewish Association, Je: 391
Apostolic Church, The, C: 241
Armenian Orthodox Church in Great Britain, C:241
Art and Spirituality Network, R: 633
Arthur Rank Centre, The, C: 245
Arya Pratinidhi Sabha (UK), H: 317
Asaholah (Ministries of God), IF: 95
Asian Times, R: 638
Assemblies of God, C: 241
Assemblies of God in Great Britain and Ireland, Ireland Regional Council, C: 279
Assemblies of God Scottish Regional Council, C:283
Assembly of Masorti Synagogues, Je: 391
Assembly of Rabbis, Je: 391
Association of Bahá'í Studies - English speaking Europe, Ba: 120
Association of Bahá'í Women – Northern Ireland, Ba:136
Association of Bahá'í Women – Scotland, Ba: 136
Association of Bahá'í Women – Wales, Ba: 137
Association of Baptist Churches in Ireland, C:279
Association of Interchurch Families, C: 245
Association of Jewish Ex-Berliners, Je: 392
Association of Jewish Ex-Servicemen and Women, Je: 392
Association of Jewish Friendship Clubs, Je: 392
Association of Jewish Refugees in GB (AJR Charitable Trust), Je: 392
Association of Jewish Sixth Formers, Je: 392
Association of Jewish Teachers, Je: 392
Association of Jewish Women's Organisations in the UK, Je: 392
Association of Ministers (Chazanim) of Great Britain, Je: 392
Association of Muslim Lawyers, M: 450
Association of Muslim Professionals, M: 450
Association of Muslim Researchers, M: 451
Association of Muslim Scholars of Islamics in Britain, M: 451

Association of Muslim Schools of UK and Eire (AMS), M: 451

Association of Orthodox Jewish Professionals of GB, Je: 393

Association of Reform and Liberal Mohelim, Je:393

Association of United Synagogue Women, Je: 393

Association for British Muslims, M: 450

Association for Pastoral and Spiritual Care and Counselling (APSCC), IF: 95

Assyrian Church of the East, C: 241

Astana Aliya Naqeebiya, M: 451

Aukana Trust, Bu: 158

Azeemia Foundation (UK), M: 451

B

B'nai B'rith Hillel Foundation, Je: 393

B'nai B'rith Youth Organisation, Je: 393

Babe Ke, S: 562

Bahá'í Academy for the Arts, Ba: 120

Bahá'í Council for Northern Ireland, Ba: 136

Bahá'í Council for Scotland, Ba: 136

Bahá'í Council for Wales, Ba: 137

Bahá'í Office of Religious and Educational Affairs, Ba: 120

Bahá'í Publishing Trust, Ba: 120

Bahá'í Service for the Visually Impaired, Ba: 120

Banbury Area Religious Education Centre, R:633

Baptist Times, The, R: 638

Baptist Union of Great Britain, C: 242

Baptist Union of Wales, C: 291

Barn, The, Bu: 159

Basava International Foundation, H: 317

Bebe Nanki Charitable Trust, S: 562

BFSS National Religious Education Centre, R:634

Bharatiya Vidya Bhavan, Institute of Indian Art and Culture, R: 633

Bible Society, C: 245

Board of Deputies of British Jews, Je: 393

Bochasanwasi Shri Akshar Purushottamni Sansatha, The Swaminarayan Hindu Mission, H:317

Bradford Interfaith Education Centre, R: 634

Brahma Kumaris World Spiritual University, So:603

Brahmrishi Mission, H: 317

Britain Burma Trust, Bu: 159

British Buddhist Association, Bu: 159

British Organisation of Sikh Students, S: 563

British Shingon Buddhist Association, Bu: 159

British Sikh Education Council, S: 563

Buddha Dharma Association, Bu: 159

Buddhapadipa Temple, Bu: 159

Buddhavihara Temple, Bu: 159

Buddhism Psychology and Psychiatry Group, Bu:160

Buddhist Christian Network, IF: 95

Buddhist Co-operative, Bu: 160

Buddhist Hospice Trust, Bu: 160

Buddhist Interhelp, Bu: 160

Buddhist Publishing Group, Bu: 160

Buddhist Quarterly, The, R: 638

Buddhist Society, The, Bu: 160

Bulgarian Orthodox Church, C: 242

Byelorussian Autocephalic Orthodox Church, C:242

C

CAFOD (Catholic Fund for Overseas Development), C: 245

CAFOD Wales, C: 295

Calamus Foundation, The, IF: 96

Campaign for the Protection of Shechita, Je: 393

Canon Law Society of Great Britain and Ireland, C: 246

Catholic Association for Racial Justice (CARJ), C: 246

Catholic Education Service, C: 246

Catholic Herald, The, R: 638

Central Jamiat Ulama, UK M: 451

Central Moonsighting Committee of Great Britain, M: 451

Central Scotland Islamic Centre, M: 542

Centre for Black and White Christian Partnership, C: 246

Centre for Jewish Christian Relations, The, R: 634

Centre for Jewish Education, Je: 393

Centre for the Study of Islam and Christian-Muslim Relations, R: 634

Centre for the Study of South Asian Religions and Christianity, R: 634

CEWERN (Churches' East-West European Relations Network), C: 246

Chai-Lifeline (Cancer Care), Je: 393

Cherubim and Seraphim Council of Churches UK, C: 238

Children's Educational Service, Ba: 120

Christian Aid, C: 246

Christian Education, C: 246

Christianity and the Future of Europe, C: 246

Christians Abroad, C: 246

Christians Against Torture, C: 295

Christians Aware, C: 247

Church Action On Poverty, C: 247

Church and Peace (Britain and Ireland), C: 247

Church in Wales, C: 291

Church of England General Synod, C: 252

Church of England Newspaper, The, R: 638

Church of Ireland, C: 279

Church of Jesus Christ of Latter-day Saints, So:607

Church of Scotland England Presbytery, C: 252

Church of Scotland, C: 283

Church of the Holy Protection, C: 291

Church Times, The, R: 638

Churches Together in Britain and Ireland, C: 237

Churches Together in England North and Midlands Office, C: 251

Churches Together in England, C: 251

Churches' Advisory Council for Local Broadcasting (CACLB), R: 639

Churches' Agency for Inter-Faith Relations in Scotland (CAIRS), C: 289

Churches' Commission for Inter-Faith Relations, C: 247, IF:96

Churches' Commission for International Students (CCIS), C: 247

Churches' Commission for Racial Justice (CCRJ), C:247

Churches' Commission on Mission, C: 247

Churches' Committee for Hospital Chaplaincy, C: 247

Churches' Community Work Alliance, C: 247

Churches' Joint Education Policy Committee, C:248

Churches' Stewardship Network, C: 248

Clear Vision Trust, The, Bu: 160

Commonwealth Jewish Council and Trust, Je:393

Community of Interbeing, Bu: 161

Community Religions Project, R: 634

Confederation of Indian Organisations, H: 317

Conference of Religious in England and Wales (CMRS), C: 248

Congregational Federation, C: 252

Congregational Federation in Wales, C: 291

Congregational Union of Ireland, C: 279

Coptic Orthodox Church, C: 242

Council of African and African-Caribbean Churches (UK), C: 238

Council of Christians and Jews, IF: 96

Council of European Jamaats, M: 451

Council of Oriental Orthodox Churches UK, C:239

Council of Reform and Liberal Rabbis, Je: 394

Countess of Huntingdon's Connexion, C: 242

Covenanted Baptist Churches in Wales, C: 291

Cymdeithas Y Cymod Yng Nghymru, C: 295

Cyngor Eglwysi Rhyddion Cymru, C: 290

CYTUN: Churches Together in Wales, C: 290

D

Daily Jang, R: 639

Dar al-Hekma Trust, M: 451

Dar al-Islam Foundation, M: 452

Darul Uloom Muslim Training College, M: 452

Dar-ul-Ehsan Publications, M: 452

Dawatul Islam UK and Eire, M: 452

Dawatul Islam Youth Group, M: 452

Department of International Affairs, Catholic Bishops' Conference, C:248

Dhanakosa Buddhist Retreat Centre, Bu: 161

Dharma School, Bu: 161

Dharmachakra, Bu: 161

Dialogue, R: 639

Digambar Jain Visa Mewada Association of UK, Ja: 366

Discover Islam Centre, M: 452

Dr Ambedkar Memorial Committee of Great Britain, Bu: 161

DTF Asian Books and Musicals, R: 634

Dzogchen Community UK, Bu: 161

E

Ecumenical Patriarchate Archdiocese of Thyateira and Great Britain, C: 242

Edhi International Foundation UK, M: 452

Edinburgh International Centre for World Spiritualities, R: 634

Eglwys Bresbyteraidd Cymru, C: 292

Eglwys Yng Nghymru, C: 291

Eglwysi Cyfamodol Yng Nghymru, C: 290

Eglwysi Ynghyd Yng Nghymru, C: 290

ENFYS – Covenanted Churches in Wales, C: 290

English Churchman Trust Ltd, R: 639

Eritrean Orthodox Church, C: 242

Ethiopian Orthodox Church, C: 242

European Islamic Mission, M: 452

Evangelical Alliance, Scotland, C: 289

Evangelical Alliance, Northern Ireland, C: 282

Evangelical Alliance, Wales, C: 295

Evangelical Alliance, UK, C: 239

F

Fa Yue Buddhist Monastery, Bu: 161
Federation of Ambedkarite and Buddhist
  Organisations UK, Bu: 162
Federation of Brahmin Associations UK, H: 318
Federation of Islamic Organisations in Europe
  (FIOE), M: 452
Federation of Patidar Associations, H: 318
Federation of Students Islamic Societies of the
  UK and Eire (FOSIS), M: 452
Federation of Synagogues, Je: 394
Feed the Minds, C: 248
Fellowship of Churches of Christ, C: 242
Fellowship of Reconciliation, England, C: 248
Fellowship of Reconciliation, Scotland, C: 289
Fellowship of Reconciliation, Wales, C: 195
Fellowship of St Alban and St Sergius, C: 248
Focolare Movement, C: 248
Free Church Council for Wales, C: 290
Free Church of England, C: 252
Free Churches Group, C: 240
Friends of the Western Buddhist Order, Bu: 162
Friends of the Western Buddhist Order
  (Communications), Bu: 162
Friends of the Western Buddhist Order Study
  Centre, Bu: 162
Friends of the Western Buddhist Order Taraloka,
  Bu: 162

G

Garavi Gujarat, R: 639
Gaudiya Mission (Vasudev Gaudiya Math), H:318
General Assembly of Unitarian and Free
  Christian Churches, Wales, C: 291
GET (Religious Divorce) Advisory Service,
  Je:394
Graduate Institute for Theology and Religion,
  R:635
Guild of Jewish Journalists, Je: 394
Gujarat Samachar, R: 639
Gujarati Arya Kashktriya Mahasubha (UK),
  H:318
Gujarati Association of Scotland, H: 355
Guru Nanak Nishkam Sewak Jatha, S: 563
Guyana United Sad'r Islamic Anjuman, M: 452
Gynghrair Gynulleidfaol, C: 291

H

Halal Food Authority, The, M: 453
Hijaz College, M: 453
Hindu Centre London, H: 318

Hindu College London, H: 318
Hindu Council (UK), H: 318
Hindu Cultural Trust Centre, H: 318
Hindu Marathon, H: 318
Hindu Resource Centre, H: 319
Hindu Swayamsevak Sangh (UK), H: 319
Hindusim Today, R: 639
Holocaust Educational Trust, Je: 394
Holy Island Project, IF: 96

I

Idara Isha'at al Islam (Masjid-e-Imdadia), M: 453
Imams and Mosques Council, M: 453
Impact International, R: 639
Indian Buddhist Society UK, Bu: 162
Indian Muslim Federation (UK), M: 453
INFORM (Information Network Focus on
  Religious Movements), R: 635
Initiation Society, Je: 394
Inner Cities Religious Council, IF: 96
Inspire: The Spirit of Regeneration, IF: 96
Institute for Jewish Policy Research, Je: 394
Institute of Higher Rabbinical Studies, Je: 394
Institute of Islamic Banking and Insurance,
  M:453
Institute of Islamic Studies, M: 453
Institute of Jainology, Ja: 366
Institute of Jewish Studies, Je: 394
Institute of Muslim Minority Affairs, M: 454
Institute of Oriental Philosophy European
  Centre, Bu: 163
Inter Faith Network for the UK, The, IF: 96
Interfaith Centre, IF: 97
Interfaith Foundation, The, IF: 97
Interfaith Resource Centre, R: 635
International Ambedkar Institute UK, Bu: 163
International Association for Religious Freedom
  (British Chapter), IF: 97
International Association for Religious Freedom
  (International Secretariat), IF: 97
International Buddhist Progress Society, UK,
  Bu:163
International College of Islamic Sciences (ICIS),
  M: 454
International Council for Islamic Information,
  M: 454
International Gatka Organisation, S: 563
International Institute of Peace Studies and
  Global Philosophy, R: 635
International Interfaith Centre, IF: 97
International Jewish Vegetarian Society, Je: 395

International Mahavir Jain Mission, Ja: 366
International Ministerial Council of Great
  Britain, C: 240
International Sacred Literature Trust, R: 635
International Sikh Youth Federation, S: 563
International Society for Krishna Consciousness
  (ISKCON), H: 319
International Thinkers Forum, M: 454
International Zen Association, UK Bu: 163
Iona Community, C: 289
IQRA Trust, M: 454
Irish Catholic Bishops' Conference, C: 279
Irish Council of Churches, C: 278
Irish Fellowship of Reconciliation, C: 282
Irish Inter-Church Meeting, C: 279
Irish School of Ecumenics (Trinity College
  Dublin), C: 282
ISKCON Communications, H: 319
ISKCON Educational Services, H: 319
ISKCON Scotland, H: 355
Islamia Girls High School, M: 454
Islamia Schools Trust, M: 454
Islamic Academy, The, M: 454
Islamic Book Club (UK), M: 454
Islamic Book Service, M: 455
Islamic Centre of England, M: 455
Islamic College London, M: 455
Islamic Council on Palestine, M: 455
Islamic Education and Training Centre, M: 455
Islamic Education Board, M: 455
Islamic Educational Trust, M: 455
Islamic Forum Europe, M: 455
Islamic Foundation, M: 455
Islamic Foundation for Ecology and
  Environmental Sciences (IFEES), M: 456
Islamic Human Rights Commission, M: 456
Islamic Information Centre (London), M: 456
Islamic Jihad of Europe, M: 456
Islamic Men and Women's Association, M: 456
Islamic Museum in London and Cultural Centre,
  M: 456
Islamic Prayer Group (IPG), M: 456
Islamic Propagation Centre International, M: 456
Islamic Relief UK/World-Wide (National
  Office), M: 456
Islamic Relief World-Wide (International Office),
  M:457
Islamic Research Academy (IRAP), M: 457
Islamic Research Institute of GB, M: 457
Islamic Rights Movement, M: 457
Islamic Sharia Council of UK and Eire, M: 457
Islamic Society of Britain, M: 457

Islamic Society for the Promotion of Religious
  Tolerance in the UK, M: 457
Islamic Texts Society, M: 458
Islamic Times, The, R: 639
Islamic Vision Limited, M: 457
Ismaili Centre, M: 458
Iyengar Yoga Institute, H: 320

J

Jain Association of UK, Ja: 367
Jain Centre, Ja: 367
Jain Samaj Europe, Ja: 367
Jain Sangha of Europe, Ja: 367
Jain-Christian Association, IF: 97
Jain-Jewish Association, IF: 97
Jama't Ahl-e-Sunnat UK (Association of Sunni
  Muslims, UK), M: 458
Jameah Islameah, M: 458
Jamiat-e-Ulama of Britain, M: 458
Jehovah's Witness, So: 609
Jewish Aids Trust, Je: 395
Jewish Association for the Mentally Ill (JAMI),
  Je:395
Jewish Blind and Disabled, Je: 395
Jewish Blind Society (Scotland), Je: 430
Jewish Book Council, Je: 395
Jewish Care, Je: 395
Jewish Care Scotland, Je: 430
Jewish Chronicle, R: 640
Jewish Committee for H M Forces, Je: 395
Jewish Council for Racial Equality, Je: 395
Jewish Crisis Helpline (Miyad), Je: 396
Jewish Deaf Association, Je: 396
Jewish Education Bureau, Je: 396
Jewish Guide Advisory Council, Je: 396
Jewish Lads' and Girls' Brigade, Je: 396
Jewish Lesbian and Gay Helpline, Je: 396
Jewish Marriage Council, Je: 396
Jewish Memorial Council, Je: 396
Jewish Museum, The, Je: 397
Jewish Museum, The – Camden Town, Je: 396
Jewish Quarterly, R: 640
Jewish Refugees Committee, World Jewish
  Relief, Je: 397
Jewish Scout Advisory Council (JSAC), Je: 397
Jewish Woman's Network, Je: 397
Jewish Womens' Aid, Je: 397
Jignyasu Satsang Seva Trust, H: 320
Jodo Shu Foundation of Great Britain, Bu: 163
Joint Council for Anglo-Caribbean Churches,
  C:240

K

Kafel Fund International, M: 458
Kagyu Samye Ling, Bu: 163
Karuna Trust, Bu: 163
Keston Institute, C: 249
Khalsa Aid, S: 563
Khaniqahi Nimatullahi, M: 458
Khilafah Movement, M: 458
Kokani Muslim World Foundation, M: 459

L

Lam Rim Buddhist Centre, Bu: 164
League of British Muslims UK, M: 459
League of Jewish Women, Je: 397
Leo Baeck College, Je: 397
Lights In The Sky, Bu: 164
Linh-Son Buddhist Association in the UK, Bu:164
Living Spirituality Network, C: 249
Living Stones, C: 249
Lohana Community of the UK, H: 320
London Beth Din, Je: 397
London Buddhist Vihara, Bu: 164
London Central Mosque and Islamic Cultural Centre, The, M: 459
London Jewish Cultural Centre, Je: 398
London School of Jewish Studies, Je: 398
Longchen Foundation, Bu: 164
Lotus Realm A New Voice for Buddhist Women, R: 640
Lubavitch Foundation, Je: 398
Lumbini Nepalese Buddha Dharma Society UK, Bu: 164
Lutheran Church in Ireland, C: 279
Lutheran Church Wales, C: 291
Lutheran Council of Great Britain, C: 243

M

Madrasah-e-Darul Qirat Majidiah (UK), M: 459
Maharajah Duleep Singh Centenary Trust, S: 563
Maharishi Valmik Sata, So: 620
Mahavir Jain Temple, Ja: 367
Maimonides Foundation, IF: 97
Makor – AJY, Je: 398
MAKOR (Formally JPMP), Je: 398
Malaysian Islamic Study Group - UK and Eire, M: 459
Manna, R: 640
Manor House Centre for Psychotherapy and Counselling, The, Je: 398
Markazi Jamiat Ahl-e-Hadith (UK), M: 459

Mazal Tov: The Progressive Jewish Marriage Bureau, Je: 398
Medical Aid for Palestinians, M: 459
Medina Islamic Mission, M: 459
Memon Association UK, M: 460
Methodist Church, C: 243
Methodist Church in Ireland, C: 279
Methodist Church in Scotland, C: 283
Methodist Church, Wales, C: 291
Methodist Recorder, R: 640
Moravian Church in Great Britain and Ireland, C: 243
Moravian Church (Irish District), C: 279
Mountain of Light Productions Limited, R: 640
Muhammadi Trust, M: 460
Multi Faith Nonviolence Group (International Fellowship of Reconciliation), IF: 98
Multifaith and Multicultural Mediation Services, IF: 98
Muslim Advisory and Community Welfare Council, M: 460
Muslim Aid, M: 460
Muslim Association of Nigeria (UK), M: 460
Muslim College, M: 460
Muslim Community Studies Institute, M: 460
Muslim Council of Britain, M: 460
Muslim Directory, R: 640
Muslim Education Consultative Committee, M:461
Muslim Education Forum, M: 461
Muslim Educational Co-ordinating Council (UK), M: 461
Muslim Educational Trust, M: 461
Muslim Food Board, M: 461
Muslim Hands, M: 461
Muslim Information Centre, M: 461
Muslim Institute for Research and Planning, M:461
Muslim Ladies Hostel (FOSIS), M: 462
Muslim Law (Shariah) Council, M: 462
Muslim Magazine, The, R: 640
Muslim Men's Hostel (FOSIS), M: 462
Muslim News, R: 640
Muslim Parliament of Britain (Head Office), M:462
Muslim Parliament of Great Britain, M: 462
Muslim Scholars Movement of Europe, M: 462
Muslim Ummah Solidarity Movement, M: 462
Muslim Welfare House, M: 462
Muslim Women's Helpline, M: 462
Muslim World League, M: 462

N

Namdhari Sangat UK, So: 611

Naqshbandi Haqqani Trust, M: 463

National Association of Christian Communities and Networks (NACCAN), The, C: 249

National Association of Patidar Samaj, H: 320

National Association of SACRES, R: 635

National Council of Hindu Temples (UK), H:320

National Council of Shechita Boards, Je: 399

National Council of Vanik Associations, H: 320

National Council of Vanik Organisations (UK), Ja: 367

National Council of YMCAs of Ireland Limited, C: 282

National Council for Panjabi Teaching, S: 563

National Hindu Students Forum (UK), H: 320

National Muslim Education Council of UK, M:463

National Network of Jewish Social Housing, Je:399

National Society's Religious Education Centre, R: 635

National Spritiual Assembly of the Bahá'ís of the United Kingdom, Ba: 120

Navnat Vanik Association of the UK, Ja: 367

Network of Buddhist Organisations UK, Bu: 164

Network of Engaged Buddhists (UK), Bu: 165

Network of Sikh Organisations UK, S: 563

New Assembly of Churches, C: 240

New Kadampa Tradition, Bu: 165

New Testament Assembly, C: 243

New Testament Church of God, C: 243

Nipponzan Myohoji (Peace Pagoda), Bu: 165

Nipponzan Myohoji, Bu: 165

Noam Masorti Youth, Je: 399

Non-Subscribing Presbyterian Church of Ireland, C: 279

O

Office for the Advancement of Bahá'í Women, Ba: 121

Office of the Chief Rabbi, Je: 399

Office of Tibet, Bu: 165

Old Baptist Union, C: 243

One World Week, C: 249

Operation Judaism, Je: 399

Organisation of British Muslims, M: 463

Orthodox Church of Antioch, The, C: 243

Oshwal Association of the UK, Ja: 367

P

Padmaloka Retreat Centre, Bu: 165

Pagan Federation, So: 614

Pakistan Muslim League UK, M: 463

Pancholi Samaj, H: 320

Panjabi Language Development Board, S: 564

Pashtoon Association UK, M: 463

Pioneer (Charismatic Evangelical), C: 243

Plymouth Religious and Cultural Resource Centre, R: 635

Presbyterian Church in Ireland, C: 279

Presbyterian Church of Wales, C: 292

Punjabi Guardian, R: 641

Punjabi Times, R: 640

Pure Land Buddhist Fellowship, Bu: 165

Q

Quranic Mission UK, M: 463

R

Rabbinical Commission for the Licensing of Shochetim, Je: 399

Rabbinical Council of the United Synagogue, Je:399

Rastafarian Society, The, So: 615

Raza Academy, M: 463

RE Centre Southern Regional Group, R: 635

Reform Synagogues of Great Britain Youth and Students Division, Je: 399

Reform Synagogues of Great Britain, Je: 400

Reiyukai, Bu: 166

Religious Advisory Committee of the United Nations Association – UK, IF: 98

Religious Education and Environment Programme, R: 635

Religious Education Council for England and Wales, R: 636

Religious Experience Research Centre, R: 636

Religious Resource and Research Centre (RRRC), R: 636

Religious Society of Friends (Quakers), C: 244

Religious Society of Friends in Ireland, C: 280

RIGPA Fellowship, Bu: 166

Rissho Kosei-Kai of the UK, Bu: 166

Rivendell Buddhist Retreat Centre, Bu: 166

Roman Catholic Church in England and Wales, C: 244

Roman Catholic Church in Scotland, C: 283

Romanian Orthodox Church in London, C: 244

RSGB/ULPS Social Action, Je: 400

Rushi Panchang, H: 321

Russian Orthodox Church, C: 244

S

S I Education Society, M: 464

Samatha Trust, Bu: 166

Sang-ngak-cho-dzong, Bu: 166

Sant Nirankari Mandal UK, So: 618

Satya Sai Baba Organisation, So: 619

Sayagyi U Ba Khin Memorial Trust, Bu: 166

Scottish Council of Synagogues, Je: 430

Scottish Episcopal Church, C: 283

Scottish Jewish Archives Centre, Je: 430

Scottish Joint Committee for Religious and
  Moral Education, R: 636

Scottish Unitarian Association, C: 283

Scottish Working Party on Religions of the
  World in Education, R: 636

Sea of Faith Network, R: 636

Seerah Foundation, M: 464

Serbian Orthodox Church, C: 244

Seventh Day Adventist Church, C: 244

Seventh Day Adventist Church, Ireland, C: 280

Seventh Day Adventist Church, Scotland, C: 283

Seventh Day Adventists Church (Welsh Mission),
  C: 292

Shambhala Meditation Centre, Bu: 167

Shap Working Party on World Religions in
  Education, R: 636

Sharpham College For Buddhist Studies And
  Contemporary Enquiry, Bu: 167

Shiromani Akali Dal UK, S: 564

Shree Mirzapur Association (UK), H: 321

Shree Swaminarayan Mandir, H: 321

Shri Vallabh Nidhi UK, H: 321

Sikh Association of Great Britain, S: 564

Sikh Council for Interfaith Relations UK, S: 564,
  IF: 98

Sikh Divine Fellowship, S: 564

Sikh Education Council, S: 564

Sikh Educational Advisory Services, S: 564

Sikh Educational and Cultural Association (UK),
  S: 564

Sikh Human Rights Group, S: 564

Sikh Messenger, R: 641

Sikh Missionary Society (UK), S: 565

Sikh Religion and Cultural Heritage Forum,
  S:565

Sikh Religious Symbols Action Committee
  International, S: 565

Sikh Research Resource Centre, S: 565

Sikh Spirit, R: 641

Sivananda Yoga Vedanta Centre, H: 321

Slough and District Religious Studies Resource
  Centre, R: 636

Society for Jewish Study, Je: 400

Society for the Advancement of Buddhist
  Understanding, Bu: 167

Society of Muslim Lawyers, M: 464

Soka Gakkai International UK, Bu: 167

Sri Guru Ravidass Sabha UK, So: 616

Sri Lanka Islamic Association/Sri Lanka Islamic
  Cultural Home (UK), M: 464

Sri Lanka Islamic UK Association, M: 464

Sri Lanka Muslim Refugee Assistance (UK),
  M:464

Sri Lankan Sangha Sabha UK, Bu: 167

Sri Saddhatissa International Buddhist Centre,
  Bu: 167

St James Mar Thoma Church UK, C: 244

St Mungo Museum of Religious Life and Art,
  R:636

Sternberg Centre for Judaism, Je: 400

Study Centre for Christian-Jewish Relations,
  R:637

Sussex Jewish News, R: 641

Swaminarayan Satsang Organisation, H: 321

Swaminarayan Temple, H: 321

Syrian Orthodox Church of Antioch, C: 244

Syrian Orthodox Churches Council (UK), C:241

T

Ta Ha Publishers Ltd, M: 464

Tablet, The, R: 641

Tay-Sachs Screening Centre, Clinical Genetics,
  Je:400

The Puthohar Association UK, S: 565

Three Faiths Forum, IF: 98

Throssel Hole Buddhist Abbey, Bu: 167

Tiratanaloka Women's Retreat Centre, Bu: 168

Tzedek, Je: 400

U

UK Action Committee on Islamic Affairs, M: 465

UK Islamic Mission, M: 465

UK Turkish Islamic Cultural Centre and
  Suleymaniye Mosque, M: 465

Ukranian Autocephalous Orthodox Church, C:
  245

Undeb Bedyddwr Cymru, C: 291

Undeb yr Annibynwyr Cymraeg, C: 292

Union of Jewish Students, Je: 400

Union of Liberal and Progressive Synagogues,
  Je:400

Union of Maccabi Associations, Je: 400

Union of Muslim Families (UK), M: 465

Union of Muslim Organisations of UK and Eire (UMO), M: 465

Union of Orthodox Hebrew Congregations, Je:400

Union of Welsh Independents, C: 292

Unitarian and Free Christian Churches, General Assembly of, C: 242

United Free Church of Scotland, C: 284

United Muslim Organisations of Scotland, M:542

United Reformed Church, C: 245

United Reformed Church National Synod of Wales, C: 292

United Reformed Church Synod of Scotland, C: 284

United Religions Initiative (Britain and Ireland), IF: 98

United Synagogue, Je: 401

United Synagogue Agency for Jewish Education, Je: 401

Universal Sufism – Sufi Movement, M: 465

Universe, The, R: 641

V

Vajrasana Retreat Centre, Suffolk, Bu: 168

Vanik Association of the United Kingdom, H:322

Vedanta Movement, H: 322

Veerashaiva Samaja United Kingdom (VSUK), H:322

Vishwa Hindu Parishad (UK), H: 322

Vivekananda Centre, H: 322

W

WAQF Al-Birr Educational Trust, M: 465

Week of Prayer for World Peace, IF: 98

Welsh Association of SACREs, R: 637

Welsh National Centre for Religious Education, R: 637

Wesleyan Holiness Church, C: 245

Wesleyan Reform Union of Churches, C: 245

Western Ch'an Fellowship, Bu: 168

Westhill RE Centre, R: 637

White Plum Zen Sangha, Bu: 168

William Temple Foundation, C: 249

Windhorse Publications, R: 641

Women's Co-ordinating Group for Churches Together in England, C: 250

World Ahl Ul-Bayt Islamic League, M: 465

World Assembly of Muslim Youth (WAMY) Western Europe Office, M: 466

World Conference on Religion and Peace (UK Chapter), IF: 98

World Congress of Faiths, IF: 99

World Council of Jain Academies, Ja: 368

World Federation of Khoja Shia Ithna-Asheri Muslim Communities, M: 466

World Islamic Mission (UK), M: 466

World Islamic Propagation Establishment (UK), M: 466

World of Islam Trust (ALTAJLR), M: 466

World Sikh Foundation (Incorporating the Sikh Cultural Society of Great Britain), S: 565

World Sikh University London, S: 565

World Zoroastrian Organisation, Z: 598

Wyndham Place Trust, IF: 99

Y

Yakar Educational Foundation, Je: 401

York Religious Education Centre, R: 637

Young Indian Vegetarians, Ja: 368

Young Jains, Ja: 368

Young Men's Christian Association, C: 250

Young Muslim Organisation UK, M: 466

Young Women's Christian Association, C: 250

Youth Muslim Organisation, M: 466

Yr Eglwys Liwtheraidd, C: 291

Yr Eglwysi Bedyddiedig Cyfamodol Yng Nghymru, C: 291

Z

Zoroastrian Trust Funds of Europe (Inc), Z: 598

LOCAL GUIDE INDEX

The local guide index enables directory users to find the entry for an organisation without consulting the regional lists in each individual chapter. It gives references for the pages on which all local (or regional, in the case of Christian organisations) religious and inter-faith organisations in a given place can be found. In each case the religion or type of organisation indexed is indicated by means of a code preceding the page references, as follows:

Ba: Bahá'í
Bu: Buddhist
C: Christian
H: Hindu
IF: Inter-Faith

Ja: Jain
Je: Jewish
M: Muslim
S: Sikh
Z: Zoroastrian

A

Aberdeen, Ba:137 Bu:199 C:284, 288-289 IF:108 M: 542
Abergele, Bu:200
Aberystwyth, Bu:201 M:545
Abingdon, Ba:133
Accrington, IF:102 M:482-483
Alperton, Bu:187,192
Amersham, Je:425
Ashford, C:272
Ashton-under-Lyne, H:326 M:483
Aylesbury, Bu:192 C:271

B

Bakewell, Bu:178
Banbury, C:266, 272 M:534
Bangor, Bu:201 C:280-281, 293 M:545
Barking, M:518 S:581
Barry, Bu:194, 201 C:273 M:545
Basildon, Je:412 M:514
Basingstoke, Ba:133 IF:106 M:534
Bath, Ba:135 C:266, 276-277, 285 IF:107 M:539
Bathgate, C:287
Batley, M:469-470
Batley Carr, M:470
Battle, H:353
Beaminster, IF:107
Bedford, Ba:133 Bu:183 C:271 H: 340, 353 IF:105 M:514 S:578
Belfast, Ba:136 Bu:198 C:278-282, 288 H:355 IF:108

Belvedere, S:582
Beverley, Bu:171 C:283
Bexhill-on-Sea, H:353 Je:425
Bexley, S:582
Billinge, Bu:174
Bingley, S:567
Birkenhead, C:259
Birmingham, Bu:180, 182 C:263-265, 278 H:336-338 IF:104 Ja:370 Je:411-412 M:501-508 S:572-574, 576
Blackburn Bu:173-174 C:257, 260 H:326 IF:102 M:483-485 S:569
Blackpool, Je:406
Bognor Regis, Je:425
Bolton, C:258, 260 H:326-327 IF:102 M:485-487
Borehamwood, Ba: 135 C:278 Je: 426 M:540
Bradford, Ba:126 Bu:171 C:254, 256 H:324-325 IF:101 Je:403 M: 470-475 S:567
Bradford-on-Avon, Bu:181
Brighton, Ba:133 Bu:192-193 C:251, 262, 271, 274 H:353 IF:106-107 Ja: 373 M:534-535 Z: 600
Bristol, Ba:135 Bu:196-198, 201 C:275-278 H:354 IF:107-108 Je:429 M:540-541 S:584
Bromley, Ba:130 C:273-274 Je:417
Bromsgrove, Bu:181
Burnley, Ba:127 M:487
Burton-on-Trent, M:509
Bury, Bu:174, 183 M:469, 487-488, 490
Bury St Edmunds: Bu:183
Bushey, H:340 Je:412, 428

C

Camberley, M: 534
Cambridge, Ba:129 Bu:183-184, 193 C:253, 266, 268-269 H:341 IF:105 Je:412-413 M:515 S:578
Canning Town, M:527
Canterbury, Bu:192-193 C:272 IF:107 M:535
Cardiff, Ba:137 Bu:201 C:291-295 H:356 IF:109 Je:431 M:545-547 S:585
Carlisle, Bu:174,190 C:257
Carnalea, Ba:136
Carshalton, M:530
Chatham, H:353 IF:107 M:534 S:582
Cheadle, Bu:174 Ja:369-370 Je: 406
Chelmsford, M:515
Cheltenham, C:278 H:355 Je:426 M:540-541
Chesham, Je:425 M:534
Chester, Ba: 127 Bu:173-174 C:257-258 M:469, 484, 488
Chesterfield, Ba:128 M:496

Chichester, Bu:193, 195 C: 272
Chigwell, Ba:132 H:341
Chorley, M:488
Clitheroe, IF:102
Colchester, Ba:30 Bu:184 Je:412 M:515
Coleraine, Ba:136
Colne, Bu:174 M:487
Colwyn Bay, Ba:137 Bu:201
Corwen, Bu:201
Coventry, Ba:129 C:263-265 H:337-338 IF:
   104 Ja:370 Je:422 M:502-503 S:575
Crawley, H:353 Je:426 M:534 S:582
Crewe, Bu:173-174, 179 C:256 M:488
Croydon, Ba: 31 Bu:187 C:274 H:345-346
   M:520 S:579
Cwmbran, Bu:201 C:292

D

Dagenham, Ba:130 Je:414
Darlaston, H:338
Darlington, Bu:169 C:253 Je:402 S:566
Dartford, S:582
Darwen, M:488 Z:599
Derby, Ba:128 C:261-262 H:329-330 IF:103
   S:569-570
Dereham, Ba: 184
Dewsbury, C:255 IF:102 M:474-475
Dingwall, Bu:199
Doncaster, Ba:126 H:325 M:475 S:567-568
Douglas, Bu:174 C:257-258, 284, 288
Dudley, Bu:173, 180-181 C:265 H:339 IF:104
   M:510 S:575-576
Dumfries, Bu:199 C:284
Dundee, Ba:137 C:285, 288 H:355 M:542, 545
   S:585
Dunfermline, C:285 M:542
Dunstable, M:515
Durham, Ba:126 Bu:169-170 Bu:170 C:252
   M:467

E

East Barnet, Je:412
Eastbourne, Ba:133 Je:426 M:534
Edgware, Ja:370, 372 Je:414 M:518
Edinburgh, Ba:137 Bu:198-199 C:253, 274,
   283, 285, 287-288 H:355 IF:108 Je:430
   M:542-543 S:585
Elstree, Je:426
Enfield, Ba:131 Je:418
Epsom, Ba:133
Etwall, Bu:178, 180
Exeter, Ba:135 C:275-277 IF:108 Je:429
   M:541 S:584

F

Falkirk, C:283, 285 M:543
Fareham, C:274
Fareham, M:535
Folkestone, M:535
Formby, Bu:175
Frome, IF:108

G

Gateshead, Bu:170 IF:101 Je:403
Gillingham, Ba:134 H:353 M:535 S:582
Glasgow, Ba:137 Bu:199 C:284-285, 287, 289
   H:355 IF:109 Je:430-431 M:542-545 S:585
Glenrothes, M:544
Gloucester, C:268, 275-276 H:355 IF:108
   M:541
Gosforth, Je:402
Gravesend, Ba:134 M:535 S:582
Grays, S:578, S:583
Greenhithe Quay, IF:107
Greenford, H:346 M:520
Grimsby, C:255 Je:403 M:475
Guildford, C:272

H

Halifax, M:475-477 S:568
Harlow, Bu:171,184 S:578
Harpenden, C:267
Harrogate, Bu:171 C:255 Je:403-405
Harrow, Bu:188 H:348 Ja:372 Je:417, 420
   M:524 S:580
Harrow-on-Hill, H:348
Haslingden, M:488
Hastings, Ba:134 Bu:193 C:272 M:471
Hatfield, C:268 Je:413 M:517
Haverfordwest, C:291, 294
Hayes, H:348 IF:107 M:524-525 S:580
Hemel Hempstead, Je:413 M:515
Hendon, M:519
Hereford, Ba:129 C:263-264 M:547
Hexham, Bu:170 C:253
High Wycombe, Ba:134 IF:107 M:535 S:583
Hinckley, M:497
Hitchin, C:272 IF:107 M:535 S:578
Hounslow, Ba:132 Ja:373 Je:421 M:525 S:580
Hove, C:272, 274 H:353 Je:426-427 M:536
Huddersfield, Ba:127 H:325 M:475-477 S:568
Hull, Bu:171-172 C:254-256, 274 Je:403-404
   M:478
Huntingdon, M:515
Hyde, M:475, 488

I

Ilford, C:273 H:351 Ja:373 Je:413, 422-423
M: 528-529 S:581 Z:600
Ilkeston, M:501
Inverness, Ba:137 Bu:200 C:289
Ipswich, Ba:130 Bu:184 C:266 H:341 IF:105
M:515 S:578
Isle of Skye, Ba:137
Isleworth, M:525

J

Jersey, C:275 Je:429

K

Keighley, M:478
Kendal, Bu:175 M:484
Kennington, C:269
Kenton, Ja:372
Keswick, Bu:175
Kettering, Ba:128 Bu:178 S:570
Kidderminster, C:278
Kings Lynn, M:515
Kingsbury, S:579
Kingston-upon-Hull, S:568
Kingston-upon-Thames, H:349 Je:421 M:526
Kirkcaldy, M:545

L

Lampeter, M:547
Lancaster, Bu:175 C:259 H:327 IF:102
M:488-489
Langholm, Bu:177, 200
Leamington Spa, Ba:129 Bu:182 H:339 M:510
S:575
Leeds, Ba:127 Bu:172 C:254-256 H:325-326
IF:102 Ja: 369 Je:403-405 M:478-479 S:568
Leicester, Ba:128 Bu:178-179,181 C:261, 273
H:329-334 IF:103 Ja: 370 Je:409-410 M:496-
499 S:570-571
Leigh-on-Sea, H:353
Leighton Buzzard, Je:427
Letchworth, S:583
Letterstone, Bu:202
Leyburn, Bu:172
Lichfield, C:264
Lincoln, Ba:128 C:255, 260-261 IF:104 Je:413
M:499
Liss Forest, Je:427
Liverpool, Ba:127 Bu:175 C:257-260 H:327
IF:103 Je:406-407 M:489-490 S:569, 576
Livingstone, M:545
Llandrindod Wells, Bu:202
Llangollen, C:291

Llanwrda, Bu:202
London (for organisations operating within
specific London boroughs, see also the entry
below on London Boroughs for all except
Christian entries and some Jain entries. These
are not organised by London borough since
they operate across a wider area than a single
borough), Ba:130-133 Bu:158, 192, 196
C:251-252, 259, 266-270, 273-274, 280 H:343-
353, IF:105-106 Ja: 370-373 Je:413-425, 428-
429 M:517-534 S:566, 571, 574, 579-582
Z:600
London Boroughs (organisations operating
within specific London boroughs – with the
exception of Christian and some Jain
organisations - see also London above)
Barking and Dagenham, Ba:130 Je:414 M:518
Barnet, Ba:130 Bu:186 H:343 Ja:371-372 Je:
414-416 M:518-519
Bexley, S:579
Brent, Ba:130 Bu:187 H:343-345 IF:105
Ja:372 Je:416-417 M:519 S:579 Z:600
Bromley, Ba:130 Je:417 M:519
Camden, Ba:130 Bu:187 H:345 Je:417-418
M:520
City of London, Ja: 372 Je:418
Croydon, Ba:131 Bu:187 H:345-346 IF:105
Ja:372 M:520 S:579
Ealing, Ba:131 Bu:187 H:346 Je:418 M:520-
521 S:579
Enfield, Ba:131 Bu:188 H:346 Je:418 M:521
S:580
Greenwich, Ba:131 Bu:188 H:347 IF:106
M:521 S:580
Hackney, Ba:131 H:347 Je:418-419 M:521-
522
Hammersmith and Fulham, Ba:131 H:347
Je:419 M:523
Haringey, Ba:131 H:348 Je:420 M:523-524
S:580
Harrow, Ba:131 Bu:188 H:348 IF: 105
Ja:372-373 Je:420 M:524 S:580
Havering, Ba:131 Je:420 M:524
Hillingdon, Ba:131 Bu:188 H:348 Je:421-421
M:524-525 S:580
Hounslow, Ba:132 Bu:188 H:348-349 Ja:373
Je:421 M:525 S:580
Islington, Ba:132 Bu:188-189 M:525
Kensington and Chelsea, Ba:132 Bu: 89 H:349
Je:421 M:525 S:581
Kingston-Upon-Thames, Ba:132 H:349 Je:421
M:526

Lambeth, Ba:132 Bu:189–190 H:349 IF:106
Ja:373 Je:421 M:526
Lewisham, Ba:132 M:526
Merton, Ba:132 Bu:190 H:350 Je:422
M:526–527 Z:600
Newham, Ba:132 H:350–351 IF:106 Je:422
M:527–528 S:581 S:600
Redbridge, Ba:132 H:351 IF:105 Ja:373
Je:422–423 M:528–529 S:581 Z:600
Richmond Upon Thames, Ba:132 Bu:190
IF:106
Southwark, Ba:133 Bu:190 H:351 M:529–530
S:581
Sutton, Ba:133 M:530
Tower Hamlets, Bu:191 H:351 Je:423
M:530–531 S:582
Waltham Forest, H:351–352 Je:423–424
M:531–532 S:582
Wandsworth, Ba:133 Bu:191 H:352 Je:424
M:532–533 S:582
Westminster, City of, Ba:133 Bu:191 H:352
IF:105 Je:424–425 M:533
Londonderry, C:280–281 Ba:136 S:584
Long Ditton, Je:427
Longton, M:510
Loughborough, Ba:128 H:334 IF:104 M:498–
500 S:570–571
Luton, Ba:130 C:271 H:353 IF:105 Ja:370
Je:413 M:515–516

M

Maidenhead, Je:427 M:536 S:583
Maidstone, Bu:191, 193 C:274 M:536 S:578
Manchester Ba:127 Bu:173 C:251, 257–260
H:327–329 IF:103 Je:406–410 M: 489–492
S:569 Z:599
Margate, Ba:134 Je:427–428 M:536
Matlock, C:260
Melton Mowbray, C:260
Middlesbrough, C:252–253 IF:101 H:323
M:467 S:566
Milton Keynes, Ba:134 C:271 H:353 IF:107
Ja:373 M:536 S:583
Mirfield, IF:102
Mitcham, H:345, 350 M:518, 526 Z:600
Morecombe, C:258
Mossley, M:489, 492

N

Neasden, H:344–345
Nelson, C:279, 281 IF:102 M:492–493
New Brighton, Bu:176
New Malden, M:526

Newcastle-upon-Tyne, Bu:170 H:323 IF:101
Je:402 M:468
Newport, Ba:137 C:293 H:356 IF:109 M:547
Newry, C:280, 282
Newtownabbey, Ba:136
Newtownards, Ba:136
North Harrow, S:580
Northampton, Ba:128 C:260–262 H:334 Ja:
370 Je:410 M:500 S:571–572
Northfleet, Ba:134 S:583
Northholt, H:348 M:520
Northwich, Bu:177
Northwood, Je:421
Norwich, Ba:128–129 Bu:184–185 C:266–268
IF:105 Je:413 M:516
Nottingham, Ba:130 Bu:178–179, 183 C:252,
261–263 H: 335 IF:104 Je:410–411 M:500–
501 S:572
Nuneaton, Ba:129 C:263 H:339 M:510 S:575–
576

O

Okehampton, C:275
Oldbury, S:576
Oldham, Bu:177 C:258 H:328 M:493–494,
520
Orkney, Ba:137 C:286, 288
Oxford, Ba:134 Bu:193–194 C:257, 271, 273
IF:107 Je:402 Je:427 M:492, 537

P

Peebles, C:286
Perth, C:286, 288
Peterborough, C:266–269, 273 H: 341 Je:413
M:516 S:578, 584
Peterchurch, Bu:182
Petersfield, Bu:194 C:273
Pinner, Ba:131 Je:420–421
Plymouth, Ba:135 C:277 IF:108 Je:429
Pocklington, Bu:173
Poole, Ba:136 H:355
Portslade by Sea, H:353
Portsmouth, Ba:134 C:273–274 M:537 S:583
Poynton, Ba:127 Bu:177
Preston, Bu:173, 177, 192 C:258 IF:103 Je:410,
417 M:494–495 S:569

R

Radcliffe, M:495
Radlett, Je:427
Ramsgate, Je:428
Rayleigh, C:274

Reading, Ba:134 Bu:194-195 C:271-272
  H:353-354 IF:107 Je:428 M:537-538 S:583
Redbridge, Ba:132 Je:422-423 M:528-529
Redditch, M:510
Redhill, Ba:134 M:538
Retford, M:501
Richmond, Bu:170,173,190 C:292, 295 Je:428
  M:483, 533
Rochdale, Bu:177 C:258 IF:103 M:495-496
Rochester, C:273 S:583
Romford, Ba:131 Ja:373 Je:421, 428 M:524
Romsey, Bu:194
Rotherham, C:254 M:469, 479-481
Rugby, H:337 S:576
Ruislip, Bu:188 H:348
Ruislip Manor, Je:421
Ryde, Ba:135

S

Saffron Walden, Bu:194
Saintfield, Bu:198
Sale, Ba:128
Salford, C:259 Je:409
Salisbury, C:276
Sandhurst, Ba:135
Sandwell, M:509-511
Scunthorpe, Bu:172 M:480 S:568
Selsdon, Bu:186-187
Selsey, Bu:194
Sevenoaks, C:271
Sheffield, Ba:127 Bu:171-173,178 C:254-256
  IF:102 Je:405-406 M:480-482 S:569
Shetland, Ba:137 C:287
Shrewsbury, C:259, 264-265, 281
Skipton, Ba:127 C:255 M:482
Slough, Ba:135 H:354 M:538 S:583
Solihull, Ba:129
South Harrow, M:524
South Petherton, Bu:197
South Shields, M:468 S:566
Southall, Bu:187 H:346, 354 M:520 S:579, 583
Southampton, Bu:192, 195 C:272, 274, 277
  H:354 IF:107 Je: 428 M: 538 S:584
Southend-on-Sea, M:517
Southport, Ba:128 C:258 Je:409 M:496
Southwick, Ba:199
St Albans, C:267 Je:413 M:517
St Annes-on-Sea, Je:410
St Leonards-on-Sea, M:538
Stafford, S:576
Staines, Je:421, 428
Stalybridge, Z:599
Stamford, IF:104 M:522

Stanmore, Je:420 M:524
Stevenage, Ba:135
Steyning, Bu:195
Stockport, Ba:128 C:258
Stockton-on-Tees, M:468-469 S:566
Stoke-on-Trent, Je:412 M:510-511 S:576
Stoneleigh, H:354
Stourbridge, M:511
Sunderland, M:469
Surbiton, Ba:132
Sutton, Ba:129,133 M:530
Sutton Coldfield, Ba:129
Swansea, Ba:137 Bu:202 C:290-292, 294,
  H:356 Je:431 M:547 S:585
Swindon, Ba:136 C:275 H:355 IF:108 M:541

T

Tallybony-on-Usk, Ba:202
Taunton, C:278 IF:108
Tayside, M:545
Telford, Ba:129 Bu:182 C:263 M:511 S:576
Timperley, Z:600
Tipton, M:511
Todmorden, M:496
Torbay, IF:108
Torquay, C:278 M:542
Totnes, IF:108
Tunbridge Wells, M:539
Twickenham, Ba:132 Bu:190

U

Ulverston, Bu:174, 177
Uxbridge, C:270

W

Wakefield, Ba:127 Bu:173 C:255 M:473, 482
Wallasey, Ba:128
Walsall, C:263 H:339 IF:104 M:511-512
Warley, M:512-513 S:576
Warrington, C:257, 268 H:329 M:496 S:570
Warwick, Bu:182
Watchet, IF:108
Watford, Ba:130 C:268 H:341 IF:105 M:517
  S:578-579
Wednesbury, H:339 M:511-513
Wellingborough, H:335 IF:104
Welwyn Garden City, Ba:135
Wembley, Ba:130 C:265, 270 H:342-345
  Ja:370, 372 Je:417 Z:600
Wembley Park, H:343, 345
West Bromwich, H:339 S:577
West Ealing, Je:418
Westcliff-on-Sea, Je:428-429 M:539

Weybridge, Je:429
Whitchurch, Ba:182
Whitehaven, M:496
Whitehead, Ba:136 C:280
Whitfield, Ba:126
Wickford, C:266
Wigan, M:496
Wilmslow, H:329
Winchester, Ba:135 C:271, 273
Windsor, C:272
Woking, Ba:135 Bu:195 IF:107 M:539
Wolverhampton, Bu:182 C:265-266 H:340
 IF: 104 M: 513-514 S:577-578
Worcester, C:264 M:514
Worcester Park, H:349
Worthing, Ba135 M:539
Wrexham, C:290, 294 M:547

Y

Yeading, Ba:131
Yeovil, M:542
York, Ba:127 Bu:170, 173, 179, 198 C:254-255,
 265, 282 IF:102 M:482, 509-510, 541